Logical Foundations of Probability

RUDOLF CARNAP

Logical Foundations of Probability

THE UNIVERSITY OF CHICAGO PRESS
ROUTLEDGE & KEGAN PAUL

THE UNIVERSITY OF CHICAGO PRESS 60637
Routledge & Kegan Paul, London, E.C. 4
The University of Toronto Press, Toronto 5, Canada

Third Impression 1967
Printed in the United States of America

PREFACE

The purpose of this work. This book presents a new approach to the old problem of induction and probability. The theory here developed is characterized by the following *basic conceptions:* (1) all inductive reasoning, in the wide sense of nondeductive or nondemonstrative reasoning, is reasoning in terms of probability; (2) hence inductive logic, the theory of the principles of inductive reasoning, is the same as probability logic; (3) the concept of probability on which inductive logic is to be based is a logical relation between two statements or propositions; it is the degree of confirmation of a hypothesis (or conclusion) on the basis of some given evidence (or premises); (4) the so-called frequency concept of probability, as used in statistical investigations, is an important scientific concept in its own right, but it is not suitable as the basic concept of inductive logic; (5) all principles and theorems of inductive logic are analytic; (6) hence the validity of inductive reasoning is not dependent upon any synthetic presuppositions like the much debated principle of the uniformity of the world. One of the tasks of this book is the discussion of the general philosophical problems concerning the nature of probability and inductive reasoning, which will lead to the conceptions just mentioned. However, the major aim of the book extends beyond this. It is the actual construction of a system of inductive logic, a theory based on the conceptions indicated but supplying proofs for many theorems concerning such concepts as the quantitative concept of degree of confirmation, relevance and irrelevance, the (comparative) concept of stronger confirmation, and a general method of estimation. This system will be constructed with the help of the methods of symbolic logic and semantics. (However, previous knowledge of these fields is not necessarily required; all symbols and technical terms used will be explained in this book.) In this way it will for the first time be possible to construct a system of inductive logic that can take its rightful place beside the modern, exact systems of deductive logic. The system to be constructed here is not yet applicable to the entire language of science with its quantitative magnitudes like mass, temperature, etc., but only to a language system that is much simpler (corresponding to what is known technically as lower functional logic including relations and identity) though more comprehensive than the language to which deductive logic was restricted for more than two thousand years, from Aristotle to Boole.

Since this book seeks to combine various purposes, it contains material of various kinds. In preparation for the construction of a new system of inductive logic, general discussions of a philosophical or methodological nature are given (in chaps. i, ii, and iv); their purpose is argument and clarification; they are intended to lead to an understanding of the basic conception of the nature of probability and induction which is here accepted as a foundation for the construction of the system. The second part of the book (chaps. v–ix) carries out the construction of the system. This part contains less argumentation; it proceeds *more geometrico*, by the technical steps of definitions and proofs for theorems. One purpose of this part is to show by example what kinds of problems can be dealt with and solved in these fundamental parts of inductive logic. The other purpose lies in the results themselves. Many of the theorems (especially in chaps. v and viii) are known from the classical theory of probability; the purpose of restating them here lies in their more exact formulation and interpretation and in their proofs within the new framework. Many other theorems are stated and proved here for the first time (especially in chaps. vi, vii, and ix). Many of the theorems (both of deductive logic in chap. iii and of inductive logic in later chapters) are listed chiefly for reference purposes; they are not meant to be read through all at once. The reader will easily find those items that are of interest to him. To aid him, each chapter and each section is preceded by a summary (I often wonder why many of the books I have to read do not help me in the same way; could it be that the authors wish to compel me to read every word they have written?); the most important definitions and theorems are marked by '+'; many theorems are accompanied by brief remarks in nontechnical language indicating their contents and functions. Material not absolutely necessary for an understanding of the main text is printed in small type, e.g., digressions into more technical problems, examples, proofs, references to other authors, etc. A glossary is given near the end of the book, providing informal explanations for the technical terms most frequently used. (The theorems and definitions in this book are labeled for reference purposes in the following manner. Each theorem carries a mark like 'T20-5', meaning 'theorem No. 5 in § 20'; a theorem often contains parts marked by letters 'a', 'b', etc. Definitions are labeled in a similar way with 'D' instead of 'T'. A reference 'T5c' occurring in § 20 is meant to refer to T20-5, part c. The numbers assigned to the sections are not always consecutive; sometimes a number has been omitted in order to make possible later insertions; the same holds for the numbers of theorems within a section, and for the letters assigned to parts within a theorem.)

A reader who is chiefly interested in general philosophical problems and less in technical developments might first read chapters i, ii, and iv and then the following sections in other chapters: §§ 14–20 on the form and semantics of our language systems; §§ 79–81 on the comparative concept of confirmation; §§ 86–88 on the concept of confirming evidence; §§ 98–100 on estimation. The reader who is familiar with the classical theory of probability or with a modern theory based on the classical conception, and who wants to find out the relation between our theory and the classical one, is referred to chapters ii, iv, and viii. An adherent of the frequency conception of probability in the form of either R. von Mises or H. Reichenbach might be interested in chapters ii and iv (esp. §§ 41–44). If a reader acquainted with the methods of modern mathematical statistics, e.g., of the school of R. A. Fisher or of that of J. Neyman, E. S. Pearson, and A. Wald, is looking for a logical foundation of statistical inference, testing of hypotheses, and estimation, he might read chapters ii (esp. §§ 9 and 10), iv (esp. §§ 41–44, 50, 51), viii (§§ 94–96), and, above all, ix (esp. §§ 98–100). If somebody is interested, from the point of view either of applied ethics or of mathematical economics, in the problem as to how a rational agent should determine his practical decisions and what function inductive logic has in this context, he is referred to §§ 50 and 51.

The present volume is the first in a projected two-volume work, *Probability and Induction*. It begins with a brief introductory chapter which does not deal with probability but with the general problem of explication, that is, the task of finding an exactly defined concept, an "explicatum", to take the place of a given concept, the "explicandum", which is in practical use but not yet defined exactly. One of the main tasks of any new theory of probability is to supply adequate explicata for the concept of probability and for the methods of inductive reasoning which are at present applied in science and statistics. However, there does not seem to be sufficient clarity and agreement concerning the requirements that an adequate explicatum for any explicandum must fulfil. Therefore it seemed advisable to include a chapter on explication in this book, although this topic should be dealt with more appropriately in a book on concept formation in science. Chapter iii lies likewise outside the field of probability. It gives a survey of those parts of deductive logic which are needed as a basis for our construction of inductive logic. But the particular form of deductive logic here chosen may also be of interest in its own right. The system here constructed does not have the customary form of a logical calculus, based on primitive sentences and rules of inference; it takes the form of an interpreted system. Therefore the theory of the system does not belong to the field known as logical syntax but to that of semantics. The basic concepts of deductive logic, e.g., logical truth and logical implication, are here explicated as semantical concepts, defined with the help of state-descriptions, i.e., sentences describing possible worlds, and the concept of the range of a sentence, i.e., the class of those state-descriptions in which the sentence holds. Chapter iii serves as an introduction to this new semantical method of dealing with deductive logic, and, furthermore, it provides a comprehensive collection of theorems for the purpose of reference in later proofs of theorems in inductive logic.

Chapters ii and iv contain detailed general discussions on probability and induction. It is shown in chapter ii that the term 'probability' as used by scientists covers two quite different explicanda, called here 'probability$_1$' and 'probability$_2$'. The former characterizes the status of any scientific hypothesis, e.g., a prediction or a law, with respect to given evidence; this concept is explicated by the concept of degree of confirmation, which will serve as the basic concept of inductive logic. The concept of probability$_2$ means the relative frequency of a kind of event in a long sequence of events. This concept is used in science and statistics for the description and statistical analysis of mass phenomena. Since both concepts are useful and practically indispensable for science, it is important that explications be given and theories developed for both of them. Therefore it seems to me that the long and violent controversy between the "frequency school" and the "logical school" of probability over the question as to which of the two camps is in possession of "the right conception of probability" does not serve any useful purpose. Chapter iv discusses further the nature and meaning of the logical concept of probability$_1$ and the problems and difficulties involved in finding a concept of degree of confirmation as a quantitative explicatum for probability$_1$. Assuming that it were possible to find an explicatum of this kind and to construct a system of inductive logic on its basis, the questions of the usefulness of such a system both for the theoretical purposes of science and for the practical purposes of determining the best decisions for action in given situations are discussed. In the latter context, the utilization of estimates of unknown values of magnitudes is analyzed and, in particular, the rule of maximizing the estimated utility resulting from a chosen course of action. This discussion intends to clarify a problem that is of much concern in contemporary mathematical economics.

The second part of this book, consisting of chapters v–ix, contains a technical construction of the fundamental parts of inductive logic based on the general conceptions developed in the first part. First, the concept of a confirmation function, '𝔠-function' for short, is introduced. This is a numerical function which assigns a real number between 0 and 1 to any pair of sentences. If 𝔠 is a function of this kind, '$\mathfrak{c}(h,e) = r$' means: 'the degree of confirmation of the hypothesis *h*, on the basis of the evidence *e*, is *r*'. The class of regular 𝔠-functions is defined as an infinite, very comprehensive class of functions of the kind described. The most fundamental part of inductive logic consists of those theorems which hold for all regular 𝔠-functions (chap. v); among them is the famous and much debated theorem of Bayes. Later (in chap. viii), theorems for a narrower class of functions are proved, the so-called symmetrical 𝔠-functions. Among the latter theorems are two of the most important results of the classical theory of probability, viz., the binomial law and Bernoulli's theorem; but in the context of our theory the interpretation of these theorems is modified. If a new item of information is added to the available body of evidence, then the degree of confirmation for a given hypothesis either increases, or decreases, or remains unchanged. The new information is then called positively relevant for the hypothesis, or negatively relevant, or irrelevant, respectively. Theorems are developed concerning these relevance concepts, and also concerning a quantitative measure of relevance which represents the amount of positive or negative relevance (chap. vi).

Some students of probability believe that the logical concept of probability$_1$ cannot be explicated by a quantitative concept of degree of confirmation, i.e., one with numerical values. The best we can hope for, they think, is to find an explicatum of comparative form, e.g., 'the hypothesis *h* is more strongly confirmed by the evidence *e* than *h'* is by *e'*'. Although I do not share this skeptical view, I think that a comparative concept of confirmation is of interest. A definition for a concept of this kind is given which does not involve any quantitative concepts, and a system of comparative inductive logic is constructed on the basis of this definition (chap. vii). The final chapter of this volume (chap. ix) investigates the problem of estimation. This problem belongs to the most important problems connected with inductive reasoning. The investigations of contemporary statisticians concerning sampling and estimation have led to many interesting and fruitful results. However, there is no agreement among them concerning the logical nature of estimation and the validity of particular methods of estimation. A new approach to the problem is here proposed within the framework of our system of inductive logic. A general estimate-function is defined with the help of the concept of degree of confirmation. This procedure supplies the needed logical foundation for a general theory of estimation. Then, in particular, the application of the general estimate-function for the estimation of frequencies is investigated.

Some new books discussing the problems of probability and induction were published in recent years, after the writing of the manuscript of the present volume was finished. They are therefore not discussed here, or only briefly. The most important ones are those by William Kneale, C. I. Lewis, and Bertrand Russell (see Bibliography). I am especially gratified by the great similarity between the conceptions of the nature of the logical concept of probability which were developed independently by Lewis and myself. Lewis does not try to construct a technical explication of probability; but he gives a detailed and thoroughgoing analysis of the role of probability in the whole system of our empirical knowledge and, in particular, in the interpretation and confirmation of statements about the world of things in terms of expectations concerning future observations. This analysis, which connects probability and epistemology more intimately than has been done so far by philosophers, is a very valuable help in the clarification of contemporary discussions in both fields.

The second volume, now in preparation, will have chiefly two tasks. The first will be to continue the construction of inductive logic begun in this volume. While the theorems here developed refer to general classes of c-functions, in the second volume one particular c-function, symbolized by 'c*', will be selected as our quantitative explicatum for probability$_1$, our representative of the concept of degree of confirmation. The theorems in the present volume can only be of conditional form (e.g., the special addition principle: "*if* a c-function has the values r_1 and r_2, respectively, for two incompatible hypotheses h_1 and h_2 on the basis of the evidence e, then it has the value $r_1 + r_2$ for the disjunction $h_1 \vee h_2$ on the same evidence"). On the other hand, it will be possible to state theorems concerning the function c*, proved on the basis of its definition, which enable us actually to compute the value of this function for any two given sentences (within our simple language systems). A brief summary of the theory of c*, stating the definition and some of the theorems, is given in the Appendix to the present volume, § 110. It is not claimed that c* is necessarily the best explicatum possible. The theory of this function will be developed chiefly for the purpose of presenting a concrete example of a quantitative system of inductive logic which is complete (with respect to the simple language systems chosen). Furthermore, the results found for c* give occasion for discussions of general problems concerning inductive logic. Thus, for example, the problem of the confirmation of a universal law on the basis of a finite number of observational results will be discussed in detail in this context; and also the question whether a scientific, inductive procedure leading to a prediction of a single event must necessarily involve universal laws, as is usually assumed.

The second main task of the second volume will be to develop general procedures for comparing the goodness of inductive methods. The procedures are general in the sense of being applicable not only to certain methods that have actually been proposed (among them we shall discuss, e.g., Laplace's rule of succession, R. A. Fisher's maximum likelihood method of estimation, Reichenbach's rule of induction, our system of c*, and others) but also to any other inductive methods that might be proposed or considered. The comparisons will be made not with respect to the reasons offered for the choice of an inductive method by its author but rather with respect to the results to which the methods lead; more specifically, we shall examine in this context not the philosophical soundness of the basic conceptions underlying any given inductive method but rather the successful application of the given method in competition with another method. We might, for example, consider a possible universe with a given structure, represented by a state-description; we imagine that two men as representatives of two different given inductive methods make a comprehensive system of wagers. Each of these wagers is based on the common knowledge of some part of the assumed world and refers to a hypothesis concerning an unknown individual; and each wager is made in such a way that it is judged by each of the two men as favorable to himself from the point of view of his inductive method. On the basis of the given state-description we can determine for each wager who of the two men wins; hence we can calculate the over-all balance for the total system of wagers, by which all parts of the world are covered in turn. Carrying out this procedure for all possible worlds, i.e., state-descriptions, we shall determine in which of them the one inductive method is more successful and in which the other. We shall find that for any two given inductive methods, no matter how inadequate the first may appear to us in comparison with the second, there are always some state-descriptions in which the first wins out against the second. Hence we can never say of one method that it is absolutely inferior to another method in the sense of being inferior in every conceivable world. Nevertheless, the result of a comparison of two inductive methods in the manner indicated may practically influence our preference. Suppose, for example, that in comparing two given inductive methods we find that the number of those state-descriptions in which the second method is more successful is a million times as large as the number of those in which the first method is more successful. Then it may well be that this result would influence us against regarding the first method as more adequate than the second and against choosing the first in preference to the second for determining our practical decisions in the actual world, whose total structure is not known to us and for which we therefore cannot know which of the two inductive methods would be more successful in the long run.

The discussion of procedures for comparing the success of given inductive methods will naturally lead to the question whether an investigation of this kind must necessarily be restricted to the few known inductive methods or whether it can be generalized. The known methods are, so to speak, arbitrarily selected by historical accident from the totality of possible inductive methods. This totality is not a system of discrete entities but a continuum. If we could characterize each method by a few, say n, characteristic numbers or parameters, then each method would be represented by a point in an n-dimensional continuous space. This would enable us to develop a general theory of inductive methods in a simple form. We might then, for example, investigate the changes which a given inductive method would undergo if we changed its parameter values in a certain way. A system of this kind will be developed. It will contain, though not all conceivable inductive methods, still a very comprehensive infinite class of them, including all known inductive methods (among them those mentioned above) and all those others which are even remotely similar in their general structure to those known. It will turn out, surprisingly, that this can be done with the help of only two parameters; with respect to any given fixed language system, one parameter is sufficient. This parameter will be denoted by 'λ'; and the system of inductive methods will be called the λ-system. If a language system $\mathfrak{L}$ is given, then any inductive method for $\mathfrak{L}$ is completely characterized by its λ-value in the following sense: the one number λ determines uniquely the degree of confirmation of any hypothesis with respect to any evidence expressible in $\mathfrak{L}$ and the estimate for the relative frequency of a property in a class of individuals on the basis of any evidence expressible in $\mathfrak{L}$; in other words, two inductive methods have the same λ only if they always lead to the same numerical results of the kinds just described. The λ-system will enable us to analyze in a relatively simple way various inductive methods which we want to consider. Furthermore, it becomes possible to solve problems of a new kind, viz., to construct inductive methods which are most suitable for given purposes. For example, suppose that a description of a possible world representing a certain structure is given; suppose further that we choose some procedure for measuring the successfulness of inductive methods within possible worlds (e.g., by the over-all balance of a system of wagers covering the whole world, as previously indicated, or by determining the errors of estimations of relative frequency in many classes covering again the whole world). The measure of over-all success S for the given world will depend upon the inductive method applied. Since now each inductive method is completely characterized by its λ, we can represent S as a function of λ alone: $S(\lambda)$. Then it is easily possible to determine that value of λ for which $S(\lambda)$ has its maximum; in other words, to construct that particular inductive method which is most successful for the given world. The surprising fact that this and similar problems can now be solved in this simple way is a consequence of the application of the λ-system, in which the various inductive methods are no longer regarded as separate entities with incomparable features but as elements in a continuum that is numerically controlled.

The second volume will also contain investigations of various other problems, especially those connected with the task of extending our system of inductive logic to richer language systems and finally to the whole quantitative language of science. For most of these problems no complete solutions will be offered. A tentative solution will be proposed for the first step in the extension, viz., a language system in which the individuals belong to a discrete linear order, which may be regarded as a temporal sequence of events (cf. § 15B). In a system of this kind new inductive problems arise because regularities of temporal succession become relevant for the degree of confirmation. The concept of random order for a system of this kind will be defined, or rather the quantitative concept of the degree of randomness of a given order, and its opposite, the degree of uniformity. This will lead to a new definition of degree of confirmation suitable for the extended system. With the help of these concepts it will be possible to formulate and discuss the problem of the assumption of the uniformity of the world and its alleged necessity for the validity of inductive reasoning in a more exact way than in the present volume (§ 41F).

Acknowledgments. Most of the features of the theory of inductive logic presented in this volume, as well as many results concerning the function c*, were developed in the period 1942–44 during a leave of absence granted by the University of Chicago and financed by the Rockefeller Foundation. To both institutions I wish to express my gratitude for their help. In many discussions with numerous friends and colleagues I gained stimulation for the development and clarification of my conceptions and their formulations in this book. I am especially indebted to Professors Herbert Feigl, Carl G. Hempel, W. V. Quine, and Gerhard Tintner, who read an earlier version of the manuscript and made many helpful critical comments. I wish to express my thanks to Mr. Herbert G. Bohnert for his help in the preparation of the manuscript.

The editors of *Philosophy of Science*, *Philosophy and Phenomenological Research*, and *Journal of Philosophy* I wish to thank for permission to use material from my papers published in these periodicals in 1945–48 (see Bibliography).

RUDOLF CARNAP

UNIVERSITY OF CHICAGO

PREFACE TO THE SECOND EDITION

The first edition of this book has been out of print for some time. In this second edition the original text is reprinted without changes, except for a number of small corrections.[1] I have added a Supplementary Bibliography, listing the more important publications in the field which have appeared since 1950.

The purpose of this new preface is, first, to give some brief indications of the development of the field of inductive logic during the last decade and of the present situation as it appears to me. Second, I shall specify some particular points in which my views have changed since I wrote this book. But the major features of my theory, as explained in this book, are still maintained today. This holds for both the basic philosophical conception of the nature of logical probability, explained in the first half of the book, and the formal system constructed in the second half.

Only a small part of the results of the work I have done in the meantime, in collaboration with my friends, especially John G. Kemeny and Richard C. Jeffrey, has been published so far. I have abandoned my original plan of writing a companion volume to this book, as announced in the Preface to the first edition. There is now such a rapid development and change in this field that a comprehensive book, trying to describe the present situation, would probably be outdated before its appearance. Therefore we are planning instead the publication of a series of small volumes with the tentative title "Studies in Probability and Inductive Logic", each volume containing several articles, some expository, others in the nature of technical research reports.

Among the future topics announced in the original Preface was the construction of a parametric system of inductive methods, i.e., $\mathfrak{c}$-functions and corresponding estimate functions, called the lambda-system. I gave an exposition of this system in [Continuum] (see the Supplementary Bibliography). This monograph contains also a discussion of estimate functions for relative frequency, points out some serious disadvantages of certain

[1] I give here a list of those places where actual errors or serious misprints have been corrected. References in parentheses refer to corrections which were already made in the second impression (1951) and in the British edition: 12/$\bar{5}$ (i.e., page 12, line 5 from bottom); (66/6 f.); (77/20); (81, T6/1) (i.e., page 81, Theorem T19-6, line 1); 99, T90/1; (99, T11g); (101, T2a); (124/10); 158/6–8 and 15–18; 166/1f.; 229/$\overline{11}$; 312/15; (318/10); 321, T5a/2; 325, T6j/1; (334, T1d/7); 361/$\overline{13}$; 362, T1/1; 409/5; (441/11); 507/$\bar{4}$; 533/3f.; 542/11; 543/$\bar{2}$; 544/24.

estimate functions widely used in mathematical statistics, and proposes new functions avoiding these disadvantages.

The axiom system of inductive logic given in [Continuum] has since been further developed. A more comprehensive form of it was published in [Replies] § 26 and in Carnap-Stegmüller [Wahrsch.], Anhang B. The system is still in the process of change and growth.

My conception of logical probability (called 'probability$_1$' in this book) has some basic features in common with those of other authors, e.g., John Maynard Keynes, Frank P. Ramsey, Harold Jeffreys, Bruno De Finetti, B. O. Koopman, Georg Henrik von Wright, I. J. Good, and Leonard J. Savage, to mention only the names more widely known. All these conceptions share the following features. They are different from the frequency conception ('probability$_2$' in this book). They emphasize the relativity of probability with respect to the evidence. (For this reason, some of the authors call their conception 'subjective'; however, this term does not seem quite appropriate for logical probability [see pp. 43–44, 239–40].) Further, the numerical probability of an unknown possible event can be regarded as a fair betting quotient. And, finally, if logical relations (e.g., logical implication or incompatibility) hold between given propositions, then their probabilities must, according to these conceptions, satisfy certain conditions (usually laid down by axioms) in order to assure the rationality of the beliefs and the actions, e.g., bets, based upon these probabilities. I have the impression that the number of those who think and work in the direction indicated is increasing. This is certainly the case among philosophers. But it seems that also among those who work in mathematical statistics more and more begin to regard the customary exclusive use of the frequency concept of probability as unsatisfactory and are searching for another concept.

Almost every author in this field, including myself, worked at the beginning practically alone, following his own particular line. But by now there is more mutual influence. Certainly I and my friends have learned much from other authors, both in the purely mathematical theory of probability and in the methodology of its application. Often a certain approach to a problem seemed to us the best or at least acceptable at a certain time, but a few years later we saw that it had to be abandoned or modified. The change required was sometimes brought about by a clarification of the basic ideas, sometimes by the discovery of a new approach to a particular problem, sometimes by newly proved concrete mathematical results. Thus there is rapid change, and, we hope, progress, in this field.

I hold the view, in common with some, but not all, of the authors mentioned, that the concept of logical probability may serve as the basis for the construction of a system of inductive logic, understood as the logical theory of all inductive reasoning. Moreover, in contrast to the customary view that the outcome of a process of inductive reasoning about a hypothesis *h* on the basis of given evidence *e* consists in the acceptance (or the rejection, or the temporary suspension) of *h*, I believe that the outcome should rather be the finding of the numerical value of the probability of *h* on *e*. Although a judgment about *h* (e.g., a possible result of a planned experiment) is usually not formulated explicitly as a probability statement, I think a statement of this kind is implicitly involved. This means that a rational reconstruction of the thoughts and decisions of an investigator could best be made in the framework of a probability logic. It seems to me, furthermore, that the indicated conception of the form of inductive reasoning makes it possible to give a satisfactory answer to Hume's objection.[2]

In the following I shall explain some special points in which my views have changed since the time when I wrote this book.

A. The meaning of logical probability (probability$_1$) was informally explained in § 41 in several ways: (a) as the degree to which a hypothesis *h* is confirmed or supported by the evidence *e;* (b) as a fair betting quotient; and (c) as an estimate of relative frequency. Even at that time I regarded (a) as less satisfactory than (b) or (c); today I would avoid formulations of the kind (a) because of their ambiguity (see Points B and C below). Although the concept of logical probability in the sense here intended is a purely logical concept, I think that the meaning of statements like 'the probability of *h* with respect to *e* is 2/3' can best be characterized by explaining their use, in combination with the concept of utility, in the rule for the determination of rational decisions (§ 51A, rule R_5). The explanation of probability as a betting quotient is a simplified special case of this rule.

B. Two triples of concepts. In this book I distinguished three kinds of scientific concepts (§ 4): classificatory, comparative, and quantitative concepts; e.g., (1) 'x is warm', (2) 'x is warmer than y', (3) 'the temperature of x is u' ('$T(x) = u$'). If the quantitative concept T is available, (1) and (2) may be formulated as follows: (1) '$T(x) > b$', where b is a fixed number chosen as the lower boundary for 'warm'; (2) '$T(x) > T(y)$'.

But I specified only one triple of concepts connected with probability$_1$ (§ 8). At present it seems to me more appropriate to set up two triples of concepts, I and II. The concepts of I are concerned with the question

[2] I have explained this view in the last paragraphs of [Aim].

how probable the hypothesis h is on the basis of the evidence e. The concepts of II relate to the question as to whether and how much the probability of h is *increased* when new evidence i is acquired (in addition to the prior evidence which, for simplicity, we shall take here as tautological). Let us say (for the present discussion only) 'h is firm' for 'h is probable', and 'h is made firmer' for 'h is made more probable'; then we may call the concepts of I 'concepts of *firmness*', and those of II 'concepts of the *increase in firmness*'. I shall now specify, in each of the triples I and II, (1) the classificatory concept, (2) (a) the general comparative concept, and (3) the quantitative concept; under (2) I add two special cases, because they are used more frequently than the general concept, viz., (b) the comparison of two additional evidences i and i' for the same hypothesis h, and (c) the comparison of two hypotheses h and h' with respect to the same evidence i. For each of these concepts a formulation in terms of $\mathfrak{c}$ is given in the last column; $\mathfrak{c}$ is to be understood as probability$_1$ in the sense explained above under A. Thus these formulas will indicate clearly what is meant by each of the listed concepts.

I. THE THREE CONCEPTS OF FIRMNESS

I 1. h is *firm* on (the basis of) e.	$\mathfrak{c}(h, e) > b$, where b is a fixed number.
I 2. (a) h on e is *firmer* than h' on e'.	$c(h, e) > c(h', e')$.
(b) h is firmer on e than on e'.	$\mathfrak{c}(h, e) > \mathfrak{c}(h, e')$.
(c) h is firmer than h', on e.	$\mathfrak{c}(h, e) > \mathfrak{c}(h', e)$.
I 3. The (degree of) *firmness* of h on e is u.	$\mathfrak{c}(h, e) = u$.

II. THE THREE CONCEPTS OF INCREASE IN FIRMNESS

For the sake of simplicity, we shall consider here only the *initial* increase in firmness, i.e., the case that the prior evidence is tautological. The exact interpretation of these concepts depends upon the way in which we measure the increase in firmness, i.e., the increase of $\mathfrak{c}$. This can be done by different functions (compare the different relevance functions discussed in chap. vii). For the present survey let us take the simplest function of this kind, the difference; we define: $D(h, i) =_{\mathrm{Df}} \mathfrak{c}\,(h, i) - \mathfrak{c}\,(h, t)$.

II 1. h is *made firmer* by i.	$D(h, e) > 0$; hence: $\mathfrak{c}(h, i) > \mathfrak{c}\,(h, t)$.
II 2. (a) h is *made firmer* by i *more* than h' by i'.	$D(h, i) > D(h', i')$.
(b) h is made firmer by i more than by i'.	$D(h, i) > D(h, i')$; hence: $\mathfrak{c}(h, i) > \mathfrak{c}(h, i')$.
(c) h is made firmer by i more than h'.	$D(h, i) > D(h', i)$.
II 3. The (amount of) *increase in firmness* of h by i is u.	$D(h, i) = u$.

Since we took t as the prior evidence, these are concepts of *initial* increase in firmness. We see that the classificatory concept II 1 is the same as initial positive relevance (D65-2a). (The general concepts of relevance would be relative to a variable prior evidence e. In this case the concept II 1 would mean '$\mathfrak{c}(h, e \,.\, i) > \mathfrak{c}(h, e)$' and thus be the same as the general concept of positive relevance, D65-1a.)

[Note, incidentally, that for the special case 2b of the comparative concept with one hypothesis, the concept II 2b coincides with I 2b (this holds likewise if we take a variable prior evidence e instead of t). But this result depends upon the choice of the function by which we measure the amount of increase in firmness; it holds also for the quotient, but not generally for other functions.]

The triple of concepts (1), (2a), and (3), both under I and under II, are analogous to the triple Warm, Warmer, and Temperature. We see this easily when we compare the formulas with 'T' given for the latter concepts at the beginning of B, with the formulas given here under I and II, respectively.

I gave a detailed discussion of the classificatory concept in § 86, and of the comparative concept in the first sections of chapter vii. (Later, under D and E, I shall return to the problems discussed in these sections.) If we wish to ascertain what I actually meant by these concepts, we should look, not at the paraphrases in words (which were sometimes misleading, as we shall presently find, under C), but rather at the given corresponding formulas with '$\mathfrak{c}$' (which was always meant in the sense of probability$_1$). Thus we find (by formula (4), p. 464) that the classificatory concept was meant in the sense of II 1; and similarly (by formula (2), p. 431) that the comparative concept was meant in the sense of I 2a. (In formula (2) I took '$\geqq$' rather than '$>$' for reasons of technical convenience; this difference is irrelevant for our present discussion.) Since the quantitative concept was always meant as I 3, my triple of concepts consisted of II 1, I 2, and I 3. Thus my three concepts, though each of them is an interesting concept, did not fit together in the way I had intended, i.e., as analogues to Warm, Warmer, and Temperature, respectively. If I 1 is taken instead of II 1, we have a fitting triple of the kind I. It is curious to see that in my discussion of Hempel's investigations I considered I 1 as an alternative form of the classificatory concept, but explained my reasons for preferring II 1 (see under D below), which is indeed the more interesting concept of the two.

C. Terminological questions. When I examine today, from the point view of the distinction between concepts of firmness and concepts of increase in firmness, the paraphrases and informal explanations I gave in the book for various concepts, I realize that they are often ambiguous and may sometimes even be misleading. For example, the comparative concept was meant (as I mentioned above) in the sense of I 2, thus as a comparison of firmness. However, my formulations "... more strongly confirmed (or supported, ..., corroborated, etc.) ..." (p. 22, (ii)(a)) may rather suggest a comparison of increase in firmness in the sense of II 2.

In view of the fact that the verb 'to confirm' is ambiguous and has perhaps the connotation of 'making firmer' even more often than that of 'making firm', it may seem advisable to use expressions of the form '*e* is confirming evidence for *h*' or '*h* is confirmed by *e*', if at all, only in the sense of II 1 (as I did in § 86), and not in that of I 1.

I am in doubt what to propose for the concept I 3. It seems to me feasible, in spite of the ambiguity of 'to confirm', to keep the term 'degree of confirmation' as a technical term for I 3, as I did throughout this book. If we do, we have to keep in mind that 'degree of confirmation' means, not the amount of increase in firmness, but the degree of firmness that the hypothesis has on its present basis (after being made either firmer or less firm by the additional confirming or disconfirming evidence).[3]

Another possibility would be to take the good old term 'probability' also as a technical term (not only, in the form of 'probability$_1$', as a non-technical term for the explicandum, as in the book). I would certainly have liked from the beginning to follow Keynes and Jeffreys in using this term also as a technical term for the explicatum. But I decided with regret not to do so, because in the literature of mathematical statistics, which had grown in the last decades to enormous size, the term 'probability' is almost exclusively used in the different sense of probability$_2$, the frequency concept. Although I regarded this use as an illegitimate usurpation, since I believe the classical authors meant mostly not probability$_2$,

[3] I used the term 'degree of confirmation' first for a pragmatical concept referring to a person at a given time ([Testability] 1936, § 3; [Analysis] 1939), and later for the corresponding semantical concept. It seems clear from the informal explanations that, even at that time, the concept was intended as a measure of certainty, not of the increase in certainty; thus I said ([Analysis], p. 222): "The outcome of such a procedure of testing an hypothesis is either a confirmation or an infirmation of that hypothesis, or, rather, either an increase or a decrease of its *degree of confirmation.*" The term 'degree of confirmation' was perhaps first suggested to me by Karl Popper's term 'Bewährungsgrad' ([Logik] 1935, §§ 81–82). But it seems that at that time I was not quite clear about the sense of Popper's concept, nor about that of my own. I gave the first clear exposition of my concept in 1945 ([Inductive] and [Concepts]). I explained the distinction between probability$_1$ and probability$_2$—as in this book—and I said that I mean by the term 'degree of confirmation' the logical concept of probability$_1$, thus the concept I 3 in the above schema. Popper's later publications showed that what he had in mind was not I 3, nor II 3 either, but still another concept. Nowadays Popper uses for this concept the term 'degree of corroboration' instead of 'degree of confirmation'. Thus there is no longer a collision between our terms.

but something like probability$_1$ (§ 12B), it seemed to me then inadvisable to use the term 'probability' in a sense deviating from that prevalent in statistics. Today the situation looks different. As mentioned at the beginning of this preface, there are now a number of authors whose concepts of probability are similar to probability$_1$. They usually emphasize at the beginning the difference between their concept of probability and the frequency concept, sometimes by adjoining to the word 'probability' a qualifying adjective like 'subjective', 'personal', or 'intuitive'. But then they use in the body of their work mostly the simple term 'probability'. I think I would prefer to do the same if I should decide to give up the term 'degree of confirmation'.

Under B above, I explained that my three concepts did not form a triple of the kind intended; here, under C, I pointed out that my informal explanations in words were often not appropriate. I wish to emphasize that these two points do not touch the content of my system itself, consisting of the formal definitions and theorems.[4]

D. The classificatory concept of confirmation was discussed in § 86. There I paraphrased this concept thus: "*i* is confirming evidence for *h*" (p. 463, the second form). In this case the formulation is appropriate, because I had in mind, not I 1, but II 1; accordingly, I gave as the corresponding formula with '𝔠': '$\mathfrak{c}(h, i) > \mathfrak{c}(h, t)$' (p. 464, formula (4)), as in II 1 above. Later, in my discussion of Hempel's investigation, I surmised (p. 475) that his original explicandum was the same as mine (i.e., II 1), e.g., when he referred to "data favorable for *h*" or said that *i* "is strengthening *h*". But then I pointed out that at some other places the kind of arguments he gave made it likely that he had inadvertently shifted to another explicandum, viz., "the degree of confirmation of *h* on *i* is greater than *r*, where *r* is a fixed value, perhaps 0 or 1/2" (p. 475), which is I 1. Thus, if my assumption about Hempel's two explicanda is correct, there was a lack of distinction between I and II, possibly influenced, as in my own case, by the ambiguity of the word 'confirmation'.

The special aim of my investigation of the classificatory concept in § 86

[4] Popper was the first to criticize the two points mentioned. However, he combined these correct observations with a number of other comments based upon misunderstandings and mistakes; he even asserted that my system itself contained a contradiction. Bar-Hillel, Kemeny, and Jeffrey stated their agreement with Popper's criticism in the two points, but rejected his assertion of a contradiction. Bar-Hillel pointed out Popper's mistakes clearly and in detail. [See a series of discussion notes by Popper (partly reprinted in his [Logic] 1959) and Bar-Hillel in *Brit. J. Phil. Sc.*, 5 (1954), 6 (1955), and 7 (1956), and a brief note of mine (*ibid.*, 7 (1956), 243 f.); further reviews by Kemeny (*J. Symb. Logic*, 20 (1955), 304) and Jeffrey (*Econometrica*, 28 (1960), 925). Compare also my [Replies] § 31.] My agreement with Popper's criticism in the two points does, of course, in no way affect my views on the nature and function of inductive logic.

was to find a definition using no quantitative concepts like $\mathfrak{c}$, but only L-concepts. I gave a definition of this kind for a concept $\mathfrak{C}'$ (p. 465, formula (8)). However, I did not accept $\mathfrak{C}'$ as an explicatum, because I found that this concept was too narrow; I showed this by two counterexamples (p. 466). I am today still of the opinion (expressed in the last paragraph of § 86) that to find a non-quantitative explicatum is chiefly of interest for those who are skeptical about the possibility of a quantitative explicatum of probability$_1$. Within quantitative inductive logic, we have a detailed theory of relevance (chap. vi), which contains the concept II 1 as positive relevance, defined quantitatively. As to the concept I 1, it may be useful for everyday communication, e.g., 'it is probable that it will rain tomorrow', but its usefulness for scientific work is hardly higher than that of the concept Warm in physics.

E. The comparative concept, understood in the sense of I 2, was investigated in chapter vii. In this case likewise I searched for an explication in non-quantitative terms. I proposed a definition of this kind (D81-1). But Bar-Hillel showed (Note 1953) that my explicatum was too narrow. He used the same two counterexamples which I had used in § 86 against $\mathfrak{C}'$. To my earlier remark (p. 467) that it seemed doubtful whether a simple definition based upon L-terms could be found for the *classificatory* concept, I added later ([Comparative], p. 318) that in the case of the *comparative* concept the reasons for doubt are even stronger. At any rate, such a definition would have to go far beyond simple L-relations among the four sentences involved and refer also to the internal structure of the sentences. A definition of this kind would presumably not be simple. The task of finding such a definition does not seem very important today, when we recognize that a quantitative theory can be developed.

Aside from the question of an explicit, non-quantitative definition, the comparative concept may be of interest as a primitive concept in an axiom system. Many authors on probability (in a non-frequency sense) begin with a system of comparative axioms. This procedure has advantages in view of the fact that on the basis of our intuitions we often find it easier to make a comparative judgment than a quantitative one. I have proposed to add to the usual comparative axioms some new ones, among them the axiom of symmetry with respect to individual constants and the axiom of instantial relevance ([Comparative], p. 316).

F. The requirement of logical independence (§ 18B) has been abolished. Kemeny (1951) and Bar-Hillel (1951) pointed out, independently of each other, that this requirement would exclude any primitive two-place predicate that, in virtue of its meaning, possesses some structural property. For example, if the primitive predicate '*W*' designates the relation Warmer and thus is asymmetric by its meaning, then the atomic sentences '*Wab*' and '*Wba*' are incompatible, and hence any state-description containing both would not represent a possible case. However, we can admit as primitive predicates those of the kind just indicated and also one-place predicates with meaning relations holding among them (e.g., predicates designating different colors and hence being incompatible), if we apply the following procedure, which was first proposed by Kemeny. We require that all such meaning relations and structural properties are expressed by special postulates, which I call meaning postulates or A-postulates ([Postulates]; cf. Kemeny, Extension 1952, Measure function 1953). Then we define as admissible state-descriptions those in which all A-postulates hold. The analytic (or A-true) sentences, i.e., those which are true in virtue of meanings alone, are defined as those holding in all admissible state-descriptions. In inductive logic we take into account only the admissible state-descriptions. We assign the $\mathfrak{m}$-value 1 not only to all L-true sentences (T57-1d) but to all A-true sentences.

G. The requirement of completeness for the set of primitive predicates (§ 18B) has been abolished. Special axioms are adopted which assure the invariance of $\mathfrak{c}$-values with respect to an extension of the language by the addition of either new individual constants or new families of primitive predicates.

Invariance with respect to an addition of a new family did not hold in my original system. But this invariance becomes possible by a modification of the treatment of the primitive predicates. I shall now indicate this modification; for the sake of simplicity I shall refer to one-place predicates only.

The primitive predicates are classified into families (this procedure was indicated in § 18C, but not applied in the book). For example, there may be a family of colors, another family of shapes, and the like. We make sure, either by A-postulates or by a suitable special form of the state-descriptions, that in any admissible state-description, for each individual, one and only one of the predicates of any given family holds. Then the following changes have to be made. The chapters iv through ix remain essentially unchanged, except for a few places (mostly in § 107A) where the language systems $\mathfrak{L}^{\pi}$ are dealt with. The explanations and results at those places, and furthermore in the Appendix concerning the function $\mathfrak{c}^*$ and in the monograph [Continuum] concerning the lambda-system, are now to be understood as restricted to cases involving predicates of any one family only. The number π of independent primitive predicates is to be disregarded, and the number κ of Q-predicates is to be understood as the number of predicates of the family in question.

As an example, consider any formula containing 'π' or 'κ' or both, e.g., a formula in § 110 of this book about c*, say (6) or (7), or a formula in [Continuum] about a c-function of the lambda-system, e.g., (11–4). Let us apply this formula to the case $\pi = 3$, hence $\kappa = 8$. The result was originally interpreted as referring to the following situation: we have three independent primitive predicates, way 'P_1', 'P_2', and 'P_3', and hence eight *Q*-predicates (or, in the terminology of § 18C, which I now prefer: we have three families containing two predicates each; the first family contains 'P_1' and its negation; the second and third are analogous). Today I would interpret the formula differently. It is applicable to the described situation as an approximation only (since it neglects the analogy influence); but it holds exactly for another situation, viz., one family of eight primitive predicates, e.g., for eight different colors exhausting the color universe. In order to obtain exact c-values for the former situation, we need a method for three families, a method different from all those discussed in this book or in [Continuum]. Together with Kemeny I have developed a general method for an arbitrary number n of families $F^1, \ldots, F^n$, where the family $F^m (m = 1, \ldots, n)$ contains any number k_m of primitive predicates. The formula for two families is given and explained in Carnap-Stegmüller [Wahrsch.], Anhang B VIII.

RUDOLF CARNAP

UNIVERSITY OF CALIFORNIA AT LOS ANGELES

NOTE

In some formulas, where summation is expressed in a form like '$\sum_{p=1}^{n}$', the sign of equality is blurred so that the subscript looks like '$p - 1$' instead of '$p = 1$'. The same is the case at other places with the sign of product '$\prod$'.

CONTENTS

CHAPTER I

ON EXPLICATION

After a brief indication of the problems to be dealt with in this book—the problems of degree of confirmation, induction, and probability (§ 1)—the remainder of this chapter contains a discussion of some general questions of a methodological nature. By an explication we understand the transformation of an inexact, prescientific concept, the explicandum, into an exact concept, the explicatum (§ 2). The explicatum must fulfil the requirements of similarity to the explicandum, exactness, fruitfulness, and simplicity (§ 3). Three kinds of concepts are distinguished: classificatory (e.g., Warm), comparative (e.g., Warmer), and quantitative concepts (e.g., Temperature) (§ 4). The role of comparative and quantitative concepts as explicata is discussed (§ 5). The axiomatic method is briefly characterized, and the distinction between its two phases, formalization and interpretation, is especially emphasized (§ 6). In this chapter the methodological questions are discussed in a general way, without reference to the specific problems of this book. Only in later chapters will the results of these preliminary explanations be applied in the discussions concerning confirmation and probability.

§ 1. Introduction: Our Problems

A brief, preliminary indication is given of the tasks which this book will try to solve: a clarification of (1) degree of confirmation, (2) induction, (3) probability.

The chief tasks of this book will be:

1) a clarification and, if possible, a definition of the concept of *degree of confirmation;*
2) a clarification of the logical nature of *induction* and, if possible, a construction of a system of *inductive logic;*
3) a clarification of the concept of *probability.*

At the present only a few preliminary explanations of these problems will be given.

1. When scientists speak about a scientific law or a theory, or also a singular statement, for example, a prediction, on the one hand, and certain observational data or experimental results, on the other, they often state a relation between those items in forms like these:

a. 'This experiment again confirms the theory T' (or: '. . . supplies new evidence for . . .').

b. 'The quantum theory is confirmed to a considerably higher degree by the experimental data known today than by those available twenty years ago' (or: '. . . is supported more strongly by . . .').

The concepts of confirming evidence or degree of confirmation used in statements of this kind are usually sufficiently well understood for simple, practical purposes, but they are hardly ever precisely explained. It will be one of the chief tasks of this book to make concepts of this kind precise and to furnish a theory of the logical relations between any hypothesis and any piece of knowledge that might be regarded as confirming evidence for the hypothesis.

2. The problem of induction in the widest sense—concerning a hypothesis of any, not necessarily universal form—is essentially the same as the problem of the logical relation between a hypothesis and some confirming evidence for it. Thus, by laying down a definition for the concept of degree of confirmation and constructing a logical theory based upon this concept, we shall furnish a system of inductive logic. While deductive logic may be regarded as the theory based upon the concept of logical consequence or deducibility, inductive logic is the theory based upon what might be called the degree of inducibility, that is, the degree of confirmation.

3. The problem of probability is likewise closely related to that of induction. This has often been observed, at least with respect to one of the various conceptions of probability which we find in the historical development (sometimes called inductive probability). We shall try to show that we have to distinguish chiefly two concepts of probability; the one is defined in terms of frequency and is applied empirically, the other is a logical concept and is the same as degree of confirmation. It will be shown that both are important for the method of science, and thus the controversy between the two "conceptions" of probability will be dissolved.

Thus we see that one or several of the problems which we intend to approach have the following character. There is a certain term ('confirming evidence', 'degree of confirmation', 'probability') which is used in everyday language and by scientists without being exactly defined, and we try to make the use of these terms more precise or, as we shall say, to give an *explication* for them. The task of explication is of very general importance for the construction of concepts. Therefore we shall devote the remainder of this chapter (§§ 2–6) to a discussion of the general nature of the method of explication and only in the next chapter (§ 8) return to our specific problems of confirmation and probability.

§ 2. On the Clarification of an Explicandum

By the procedure of *explication* we mean the transformation of an inexact, prescientific concept, the *explicandum*, into a new exact concept, the *explicatum*. Although the explicandum cannot be given in exact terms, it should be made as clear as possible by informal explanations and examples.

The task of ***explication*** consists in transforming a given more or less inexact concept into an exact one or, rather, in replacing the first by the second. We call the given concept (or the term used for it) the ***explicandum***, and the exact concept proposed to take the place of the first (or the term proposed for it) the ***explicatum***. The explicandum may belong to everyday language or to a previous stage in the development of scientific language. The explicatum must be given by explicit rules for its use, for example, by a definition which incorporates it into a well-constructed system of scientific either logicomathematical or empirical concepts.

The term 'explicatum' has been suggested by the following two usages. Kant calls a judgment explicative if the predicate is obtained by analysis of the subject. Husserl, in speaking about the synthesis of identification between a confused, nonarticulated sense and a subsequently intended distinct, articulated sense, calls the latter the 'Explikat' of the former. (For both uses see *Dictionary of philosophy* [1942], ed. D. Runes, p. 105). What I mean by 'explicandum' and 'explicatum' is to some extent similar to what C. H. Langford calls 'analysandum' and 'analysans': "the analysis then states an appropriate relation of equivalence between the analysandum and the analysans" ("The notion of analysis in Moore's philosophy", in *The philosophy of G. E. Moore* [1943], ed. P. A. Schilpp, pp. 321–42; see p. 323); he says that the motive of an analysis "is usually that of supplanting a relatively vague idea by a more precise one" (*ibid.*, p. 329).

(Perhaps the form 'explicans' might be considered instead of 'explicatum'; however, I think that the analogy with the terms 'definiendum' and 'definiens' would not be useful because, if the explication consists in giving an explicit definition, then both the definiens and the definiendum in this definition express the explicatum, while the explicandum does not occur.) The procedure of explication is here understood in a wider sense than the procedures of analysis and clarification which Kant, Husserl, and Langford have in mind. The explicatum (in my sense) is in many cases the result of an analysis of the explicandum (and this has motivated my choice of the terms); in other cases, however, it deviates deliberately from the explicandum but still takes its place in some way; this will become clear by the subsequent examples.

A problem of explication is characteristically different from ordinary scientific (logical or empirical) problems, where both the datum and the solution are, under favorable conditions, formulated in exact terms (for example, 'What is the product of 3 and 5?', 'What happens when an electric current goes through water?'). In a problem of explication the datum, viz., the explicandum, is not given in exact terms; if it were, no explication would be necessary. Since the datum is inexact, the problem itself is not stated in exact terms; and yet we are asked to give an exact solution. This is one of the puzzling peculiarities of explication. It follows that, if a solution for a problem of explication is proposed, we cannot decide in an exact way whether it is right or wrong. Strictly speaking, the question whether the solution is right or wrong makes no good sense because there is no clear-cut answer. The question should rather be whether the proposed solution is satisfactory, whether it is more satisfactory than another one, and the like. What is meant by these questions will soon be made clearer.

Before we turn to the chief question, viz., what are the requirements for a satisfactory solution of a problem of explication, that is to say, for a satisfactory explicatum, let us look somewhat more at the way in which the problem is to be stated, that is, how the explicandum is to be given. There is a temptation to think that, since the explicandum cannot be given in exact terms anyway, it does not matter much how we formulate the problem. But this would be quite wrong. On the contrary, since even in the best case we cannot reach full exactness, we must, in order to prevent the discussion of the problem from becoming entirely futile, do all we can to make at least practically clear what is meant as the explicandum. What *X* means by a certain term in contexts of a certain kind is at least practically clear to *Y* if *Y* is able to predict correctly *X*'s interpretation for most of the simple, ordinary cases of the use of the term in those contexts. It seems to me that, in raising problems of analysis or explication, philosophers very frequently violate this requirement. They ask questions like: 'What is causality?', 'What is life?', 'What is mind?', 'What is justice?', etc. Then they often immediately start to look for an answer without first examining the tacit assumption that the terms of the question are at least practically clear enough to serve as a basis for an investigation, for an analysis or explication. Even though the terms in question are unsystematic, inexact terms, there are means for reaching a relatively good mutual understanding as to their intended meaning. An indication of the meaning with the help of some examples for its intended use and other examples for uses not now intended can help the understanding. An informal explanation in general terms may be added. All explanations of this kind serve only to make clear what is meant as the explicandum; they do not yet supply an explication, say, a definition of the explicatum; they belong still to the formulation of the problem, not yet to the construction of an answer. (Examples. 1. I might say, for example: "I mean by the explicandum 'salt', not its wide sense which it has in chemistry but its narrow sense in which it is used in the household language". This explanation is not yet an explication; the latter may be given, for instance, by the compound expression 'sodium chloride' or the synonymous symbol 'NaCl' of the language of chemistry. 2. "I am looking for an explication of the term 'true', not as used in phrases like 'a true democracy', 'a true friend', etc., but as used in everyday life, in legal proceedings, in logic, and in science, in about the sense of 'correct', 'accurate', 'veridical', 'not false', 'neither error nor lie', as applied to statements, assertions, reports, stories, etc." This explanation is not yet an explication; an explication may be given by a definition within the framework of semantical concepts, for example, by Tarski's definition of 'true' in [Wahrheitsbegriff] (for abbreviated titles in square brackets see the Bibliography at the end of this volume), or by D17-1 below. By explanations of this kind the reader may obtain step by step a clearer picture of what is intended to be included and what is intended to be excluded; thus he may reach an understanding of the meaning intended which is far from perfect theoretically but may be sufficient for the practical purposes of a discussion of possible explications.

§ 3. Requirements for an Explicatum

A concept must fulfil the following requirements in order to be an adequate explicatum for a given explicandum: (1) similarity to the explicandum, (2) exactness, (3) fruitfulness, (4) simplicity.

Suppose we wish to explicate a certain prescientific concept, which has been sufficiently clarified by examples and explanations as just discussed. What is the explication of this concept intended to achieve? To say that the given prescientific concept is to be transformed into an exact one means, of course, that an exact concept corresponding to the given concept is to be introduced. What kind of correspondence is required here between the first concept, the explicandum, and the second, the explicatum?

Since the explicandum is more or less vague and certainly more so than the explicatum, it is obvious that we cannot require the correspondence between the two concepts to be a complete coincidence. But one might perhaps think that the explicatum should be as close to or as similar with the explicandum as the latter's vagueness permits. However, it is easily seen that this requirement would be too strong, that the actual procedure of scientists is often not in agreement with it, and for good reasons. Let us consider as an example the prescientific term 'fish'. In the construction of a systematic language of zoölogy, the concept Fish designated by this term has been replaced by a scientific concept designated by the same term 'fish'; let us use for the latter concept the term 'piscis' in order to avoid confusion. When we compare the explicandum Fish with the explicatum Piscis, we see that they do not even approximately coincide. The latter is much narrower than the former; many kinds of animals which were subsumed under the concept Fish, for instance, whales and seals, are excluded from the concept Piscis. [The situation is not adequately described by the statement: 'The previous belief that whales (in German even called 'Walfische') are also fish is refuted by zoölogy'. The prescientific term 'fish' was meant in about the sense of 'animal living in water'; therefore its application to whales, etc., was entirely correct. The change which zoologists brought about in this point was not a correction in the field of factual knowledge but a change in the rules of the language; this change, it is true, was motivated by factual discoveries.] That the explicandum Fish has been replaced by the explicatum Piscis does not mean that the former term can always be replaced by the latter; because of the difference in meaning just mentioned, this is obviously not the case. The former concept has been succeeded by the latter in this sense: the former is no longer necessary in scientific talk; most of what previously was said with the former can now be said with the help of the latter (though often in a different form, not by simple replacement). It is important to recognize both the conventional and the factual components in the procedure of the zoölogists. The conventional component consists in the fact that they could have proceeded in a different way. Instead of the concept Piscis they could have chosen another concept—let us use for it the term 'piscis*'—which would likewise be exactly defined but which would be much more similar to the prescientific concept Fish by not excluding whales, seals, etc. What was their motive for not even considering a wider concept like Piscis* and instead artificially constructing the new concept Piscis far remote from any concept in the prescientific language? The reason was that they realized the fact that the concept Piscis promised to be much more fruitful than any concept more similar to Fish. A scientific concept is the more fruitful the more it can be brought into connection with other concepts on the basis of observed facts; in other words, the more it can be used for the formulation of laws. The zoölogists found that the animals to which the concept Fish applies, that is, those living in water, have by far not as many other properties in common as the animals which live in water, are cold-blooded vertebrates, and have gills throughout life. Hence the concept Piscis defined by these latter properties allows more general statements than any concept defined so as to be more similar to Fish; and this is what makes the concept Piscis more fruitful.

In addition to fruitfulness, scientists appreciate simplicity in their concepts. The simplicity of a concept may be measured, in the first place, by the simplicity of the form of its definition and, second, by the simplicity of the forms of the laws connecting it with other concepts. This property, however, is only of secondary importance. Many complicated concepts are introduced by scientists and turn out to be very useful. In general, simplicity comes into consideration only in a case where there is a question of choice among several concepts which achieve about the same and seem to be equally fruitful; if these concepts show a marked difference in the degree of simplicity, the scientist will, as a rule, prefer the simplest of them.

According to these considerations, the task of explication may be characterized as follows. If a concept is given as explicandum, the task consists in finding another concept as its explicatum which fulfils the following requirements to a sufficient degree.

1. The explicatum is to be *similar to the explicandum* in such a way that, in most cases in which the explicandum has so far been used, the explicatum can be used; however, close similarity is not required, and considerable differences are permitted.

2. The characterization of the explicatum, that is, the rules of its use (for instance, in the form of a definition), is to be given in an *exact* form, so as to introduce the explicatum into a well-connected system of scientific concepts.

3. The explicatum is to be a *fruitful* concept, that is, useful for the formulation of many universal statements (empirical laws in the case of a nonlogical concept, logical theorems in the case of a logical concept).

4. The explicatum should be as *simple* as possible; this means as simple as the more important requirements (1), (2), and (3) permit.

Philosophers, scientists, and mathematicians make explications very frequently. But they do not often discuss explicitly the general rules which they follow implicitly. A good explicit formulation is given by Karl Menger in connection with his explication of the concept of dimension ("What is dimension?" *Amer. Math. Monthly*, 50 [1943], 2–7; see p. 5: § 3 "Criteria for a satisfactory definition" [explication, in our terminology]). He states the following requirements. The explicatum "must include all entities which are always denoted and must exclude all entities which are never denoted" by the explicandum. The explication "should extend the use of the word by dealing with objects not known or not dealt with in ordinary language. With regard to such entities, a definition [explication] cannot help being arbitrary." The explication "must yield many consequences," theorems possessing "generality and simplicity" and connecting the explicatum with concepts of other theories. See also the discussions by C. H. Langford, referred to in § 2.

Terminological remarks. 1. The word '*concept*' is used in this book as a convenient common designation for properties, relations, and functions. [Note that (*a*) it does not refer to terms, i.e., words or phrases, but to their meanings, and (*b*) it does not refer to mental occurrences of conceiving but to something objective.] For more detailed explanations see [Semantics], p. 230; [Meaning], p. 21. 2. If I speak about an expression (e.g., a word, a phrase, a sentence, etc.) in distinction to what is meant or designated by it, I include it in *quotation marks*. That this distinction is necessary in order to avoid confusion has become more and more clear in the recent development of logic and analysis of language. 3. If I want to speak about a concept (property, relation, or function) designated by a word, I sometimes use the device of *capitalizing* the word, especially if it is not a noun (compare [Meaning], p. 17 n.). For example, I might write 'the relation Warmer'; to write instead 'the relation warmer' would look strange and be contrary to English grammar; to write 'the relation of *x* being warmer than *y*' would be inconvenient because of its length; the customary way of writing 'the relation 'warmer' ' would not be quite correct, because 'warmer' is not a relation but a word designating a relation. Similarly, I shall sometimes write: 'the property (or concept) Fish' (instead of 'the property of being a fish'); 'the property (or concept) Red' (instead of 'the property of being red' or 'the property of redness'), and the like.

Arne Naess defines and uses a concept which seems related to our concept Explicatum ("Interpretation and preciseness. I. Survey of basic concepts" [Oslo Universitetets Studentkontor, 1947] [mimeographed]; this is the first chapter of a forthcoming book). Naess defines 'the formulation *U* is more precise than *T* (in the sense that *U* may with profit be substituted for *T*)' by 'there are interpretations of *T* which are not interpretations of *U*, but there are no interpretations of *U* which are not also interpretations of *T*' (*ibid*., p. 38). This comparative concept enables Naess to deal with a series of consecutive "precisations" of a given concept. Naess announces that a later chapter (iii) of the book will be "devoted to the question of how to measure degrees of ambiguity, vagueness, and similar properties". The comparative concept mentioned and these quantitative concepts may prove to be effective tools for a more penetrating analysis of explication.

§ 4. Classificatory, Comparative, and Quantitative Concepts

A *classificatory* concept (e.g., Warm) serves for classifying things into two kinds. A *comparative* concept is a relation based on a comparison, with the sense of 'more (in a certain respect)' (e.g., Warmer) or 'more or equal'. A *quantitative* concept serves to describe something with the help of numerical values (e.g., temperature).

Among the kinds of concept used in science, three are of special importance. We call them classificatory, comparative, and quantitative concepts. We shall make use of this distinction in our later discussion of confirmation and probability. In prescientific thinking classificatory concepts are used most frequently. In the course of the development of science they are replaced in scientific formulations more and more by concepts of the two other kinds, although they remain always useful for the formulation of observational results. *Classificatory concepts* are those which serve for the classification of things or cases into two or a few mutually exclusive kinds. They are used, for example, when substances are divided into metals and nonmetals, and again the metals into iron, copper, silver, etc.; likewise, when animals and plants are divided into classes and further divided into orders, families, genera, and, finally, species; when the things surrounding us are described as warm or cold, big or small, hard or soft, etc., or when they are classified as houses, stones, tables, men, etc. In these examples the classificatory concepts are properties. In other cases they are relations, for example, those designated by the phrases 'x is close to y' and 'the person x is acquainted with the field of science y'. (A relation may be regarded as a property of ordered pairs.) *Quantitative concepts* (also called metrical or numerical concepts or numerical functions) are those which serve for characterizing things or events or certain of their features by the ascription of numerical values; these values are found either directly by measurement or indirectly by calculation from other values of the same or other concepts. Examples of quantitative concepts are length, length of time, velocity, volume, mass, force, temperature, electric charge, price, I.Q., infantile mortality, etc. In many cases a quantitative concept corresponds to a classificatory concept. Thus temperature corresponds to the property Warm; and the concept of a distance of less than five miles corresponds to the relation of proximity. The method of quantitative concepts and hence of measurement was first used only for physical events but later more and more in other fields also, especially in economics and psychology. Quantitative concepts are no doubt the most effective instruments in the scientific arsenal. Sometimes scientists, especially in the fields of social science and psychology, hold the view that, in cases where no way is discovered for the introduction of a quantitative concept, nothing remains but to use concepts of the simplest kind, that is, classificatory ones. Here, however, they overlook the possibility and usefulness of *comparative concepts*, which, in a sense, stand between the two other kinds. Comparative concepts (sometimes called topological or order concepts) serve for the formulation of the result of a comparison in the form of a more-less-statement without the use of numerical values. Before the scientific, quantitative concept of temperature was introduced, everyday language contained comparative concepts. Instead of merely classifying things into a few kinds with the help of terms like 'hot', 'warm', 'luke-warm', 'cold', a more effective characterization was possible by saying that x is warmer than y (or colder, or equally warm, as the case may be).

A comparative concept is always a relation. If the underlying classificatory concept is a property (e.g., Warm), the comparative concept is a dyadic relation, that is, one with two arguments (e.g., Warmer). If the classificatory concept is a dyadic relation (e.g., the relation of x being acquainted with (the field) y), the comparative concept has, in general, four arguments (e.g., the relation of x being better acquainted with y than u with v). It is sometimes useful to regard the tetradic relation as a dyadic relation between two pairs. (We might say, for example: 'the relation of being acquainted holds for the pair x, y to a higher degree than for the pair u, v'.) Sometimes the introduction of a triadic relation is preferred to that of a tetradic relation. If we do not know how to compare the degree of Peter's knowledge in physics with Jack's knowledge in history, we might perhaps be content to use either or both of the two triadic relations expressed by the following phrases: 'x is better acquainted with (the field) y than with v', 'x is better acquainted with y than u'. The first of these two relations requires that we are able to compare the degree of Peter's knowledge in physics with that in history, which might seem problematical. The second relation involves the comparison of Peter's knowledge in physics with that of Jack; here it seems easier to invent suitable tests.

Each of the comparative concepts given above as an example has the meaning of 'more' or 'to a higher degree' with respect to a given classificatory concept. To any of those classificatory concepts (e.g., Warm), we can likewise construct a comparative concept meaning 'less' or 'to a lower degree' (e.g., Less-warm; in other words, Colder); this is the converse of the first comparative concept. In either case the comparative concept, regarded as a dyadic relation (of simple entities, pairs, etc.), has obviously the following relational properties: it is irreflexive, transitive, and (hence) asymmetric. (For definitions of these and other terms of the theory of relations see D25-2.)

In addition to the form of comparative concepts just mentioned, there is another form, less customary but often more useful. A concept of this second kind does not mean 'more' but 'more or equal' with respect to the underlying classificatory concept, in other words, 'to at least the same degree', that is, 'to the same or a higher degree' (e.g., the relation of x being at least as warm as y). Or it may mean 'less or equal' (e.g., the relation of x being less warm than y or equally as warm as y; in other words, of x being at most as warm as y). It is easily seen that a comparative concept of this second kind, regarded as a dyadic relation, is reflexive and transitive but neither symmetric nor asymmetric. A comparative relation is sometimes of such a kind that, for any x and y, it holds either between x and y or between y and x (or both). In this case the relation (for example, Warmer-Or-Equally-Warm) orders its members in a kind of linear order. If, however, the condition is not fulfilled, then there are incomparable cases. Thus it might perhaps be that we find it possible to compare the scientific achievements of two persons if both work in the same field, while we do not know a way of comparing a physicist with a historian.

In everyday language the first form of comparative concept is much more customary than the second. There are many single words for those of the first form, for instance, 'above', 'beyond', 'after', etc., and especially the comparatives, for instance, 'more', 'warmer', etc., while there are hardly any single words for those of the second form. On the other hand, there is a general trend in the development of the language of science toward concepts which are wider than corresponding concepts of prescientific language by including extreme cases, especially cases of zero value or of identity or equality; for example, the term 'number' is now taken as including 0, 'class' as including the null class, 'velocity' as including the case of rest regarded as velocity 0, etc. With respect to comparative concepts, this trend means a development from those of the first kind to those of the second, because the latter include the boundary case of equality. One advantage of those of the second kind consists in the fact that on the basis of 'more or equal' we can define both 'equal' and 'more' ('$x = y$' can be defined by '$x \geqq y$ and $y \geqq x$'; '$x > y$' by '$x \geqq y$ and not $y \geqq x$'), while on the basis of 'more' we cannot define either 'equal' or 'more or equal'. For these reasons, when we come to a discussion of a comparative concept of confirmation (§ 8), we shall take one of the second form, as expressed by: 'h is confirmed by e to the same or a higher degree than h' by e''.

For an analysis of comparative and quantitative concepts and an explanation of the steps to be taken in the construction of concepts of these kinds see Carnap, *Physikalische Begriffsbildung* (Karlsruhe, 1926). C. G. Hempel and P. Oppenheim have developed and improved the characterizations of the two kinds of concept and illustrated their roles in various fields of science in their book *Der Typusbegriff im Lichte der neuen Logik: Wissenschaftstheoretische Untersuchungen zur Konstitutionsforschung und Psychologie* (Leiden, 1936).

§ 5. Comparative and Quantitative Concepts as Explicata

The role of comparative and quantitative concepts as explicata is discussed in preparation for a later discussion of comparative and quantitative concepts of confirmation.

Classificatory concepts are the simplest and least effective kind of concept. Comparative concepts are more powerful, and quantitative concepts still more; that is to say, they enable us to give a more precise description of a concrete situation and, more important, to formulate more comprehensive general laws. Therefore, the historical development of the language is often as follows: a certain feature of events observed in nature is first described with the help of a classificatory concept; later a comparative concept is used instead of or in addition to the classificatory concept; and, still later, a quantitative concept is introduced. (These three stages of development do, of course, not always occur in this temporal order.)

The situation may be illustrated with the help of the example of those concepts which have led to the quantitative concept of temperature. The state of bodies with respect to heat can be described in the simplest and crudest way with the help of classificatory concepts like Hot, Warm, and Cold (and perhaps a few more). We may imagine an early, not recorded stage of the development of our language where only these classificatory terms were available. Later, an essential refinement of language took place by the introduction of a comparative term like 'warmer'. In the case of this example, as in many others, this second step was already made in the prescientific language. Finally, the corresponding quantitative concept, that of temperature, was introduced in the construction of the scientific language.

The concept Temperature may be regarded as an explicatum for the comparative concept Warmer. The first of the requirements for explicata discussed in § 3, that of similarity or correspondence to the explicandum, means in the present case the following: The concept Temperature is to be such that, in most cases, if x is warmer than y (in the prescientific sense, based on the heat sensations of the skin), then the temperature of x is higher than that of y. Here a few remarks may be made.

(i) The requirement refers to most cases, not to all cases. It is easily seen that the requirement is fulfilled only in this restricted sense. Suppose I enter a moderately heated room twice, first coming from an overheated room and at a later time coming from the cold outside. Then it may happen that I declare the room, on the basis of my sensations, to be warmer the second time than the first, while the thermometer shows at the second time the same temperature as at the first (or even a slightly lower one). Experiences of this kind do not at all lead us to the conclusion that the concept Temperature defined with reference to the thermometer is inadequate as an explicatum for the concept Warmer. On the contrary, we have become accustomed to let the scientific concept overrule the prescientific one in all cases of disagreement. In other words, the term 'warmer' has undergone a change of meaning. Its meaning was originally based directly on a comparison of heat sensations, but, after the acceptance of the scientific concept Temperature into our everyday language, the word 'warmer' is used in the sense of 'having a higher temperature'. Thus the experience described above is now formulated as follows: "I believed that the room was at the second time warmer than at the first, but this was an error; the room was actually not warmer; I found this out with the help of the thermometer". For this second, scientific meaning of 'warmer' we shall use in the following discussion the term 'warmer*'.

(ii) The converse of the requirement mentioned above would be this: the concept Temperature is to be such that, if x is not warmer than y (in the prescientific sense), then the temperature of x is not higher than that of y. It is important to realize that this is not required, not even "in most cases". When the difference between the temperatures of x and y is small, then, as a rule, we notice no difference in our heat sensations. This again is not taken as a reason for rejecting the concept Temperature. On the contrary, here again we have become accustomed to the new, scientific concept Warmer*, and thus we say: "x is actually warmer* than y, although we cannot feel the difference".

(iii) Thus, we have two scientific concepts corresponding to the prescientific concept Warmer. The one is the comparative concept Warmer*, the other the quantitative concept Temperature. Either of them may be regarded as an explicatum of Warmer. Both are defined with reference to the thermometer. Since the thermometer has a higher discriminating power than our heat sensations, both scientific concepts are superior to the prescientific one in allowing more precise descriptions. The procedure leading from the explicandum to either of the two explicata is as follows. At first the prescientific concept is guiding us in our choice of an explicatum (with possible exceptions, as discussed earlier). Once an explicatum is defined in a relatively simple way, we follow its guidance in cases where the prescientific concept is not sufficiently discriminative. It would be possible but highly inadvisable to define a concept Temperature in such a way that x and y are said to have the same temperature whenever our sensations do not show a difference. This concept would be in closer agreement with the explicandum than the concept Temperature actually used. But the latter has the advantage of much greater simplicity both in its definition—in other words its method of measurement—and in the laws formulated with its help.

(iv) Of the two scientific terms 'warmer*' and 'temperature', the latter is the one important for science; the former serves merely as a convenient abbreviation for 'having a higher temperature'. The quantitative concept Temperature has proved its great fruitfulness by the fact that it occurs in many important laws. This is not always the case with quantitative concepts in science, even if they are well defined by exact rules of measurement. For instance, it has sometimes occurred in psychology that a quantitative concept was defined by an exact description of tests but that the expectation of finding laws connecting the values thus measured with values of other concepts was not fulfilled; then the concept was finally discarded as not fruitful. If it is a question of an explication of a prescientific concept, then a situation of the kind described, where we do not succeed in finding an adequate quantitative explicatum, ought not to discourage us altogether from trying an explication. It may be possible to find an adequate comparative explicatum. Let us show this by a fictitious example. The experience leading to the concept Temperature was first a comparative one; it was found that, if x is warmer than y (in the prescientific sense) and we bring a body of mercury first in contact with x and later with y, then it has at the first occasion a greater volume than at the second. By a certain device it was made possible to measure the small differences in the volume of the mercury; and that was taken as basis for the quantitative concept Temperature. Now let us assume fictitiously that we did not find technical means for measuring the differences in the volume of the mercury, although we were able to observe whether the mercury expands or contracts. In this case we should have no basis for a quantitative concept Temperature, but it would still be possible to define the comparative concept Warmer* with reference to an expansion of the mercury. This scientific concept Warmer* could then be taken as explicatum for the prescientific concept Warmer. Here, in the fictitious case, the concept Warmer* would be of greater importance than it is in actual physics, because it would be the only explicatum. Note that Warmer* here is essentially the same concept as Warmer* in the earlier discussion but that there is a difference in the form of the two definitions. In the former case we defined Warmer* in terms of higher temperature, hence with the help of a quantitative concept; here, in the fictitious case, it is defined with reference to the comparative concept of the expansion of mercury without the use of quantitative concepts. The distinction between these two ways of defining a comparative concept, the quantitative way and the purely comparative, that is, nonquantitative, way, will be of importance later when we discuss the comparative concept of confirmation.

To make a weaker fictitious assumption, suppose that the volume differences could be measured and hence the quantitative concept Temperature could be defined but that—this is the fictitious feature—no important laws containing this concept had been found. In this case the concept would be discarded as not fruitful. And hence in this case likewise the comparative concept Warmer* would be taken as the only explicatum for Warmer.

Later, when we discuss the problem of explication for the concept of confirmation, we shall distinguish three concepts, the classificatory, the comparative, and the quantitative concept of confirmation. They are analogous to the concepts Warm, Warmer, and Temperature; thus the results of the present discussion will then be utilized.

§ 6. Formalization and Interpretation

The axiomatic method consists of two phases, formalization and interpretation. The formalization of a theory consists in the construction of an axiom system. This is a semiformal system; the axiomatic terms are left uninterpreted, while some logical terms are taken with their customary meanings. The interpretation of an axiom system is given by rules which determine the meanings of the axiomatic terms. As an illustration for the distinction between the two phases, the difference between Peano's axiom system of arithmetic and the Frege-Russell system of arithmetic, which gives an interpretation, is explained.

The introduction of new concepts into the language of science—whether as explicata for prescientific concepts or independently—is sometimes done in two separate steps, formalization and interpretation. The procedure of separating these steps has steadily grown in importance during the last half-century. The two steps are the two phases of what is known as the axiomatic (or postulational) method in its modern form (as distinguished from its traditional form dating from Euclid). Frequently, the first step alone is already very useful, and sometimes considerable time passes until it is followed by the second step.

The formalization (or axiomatization) of a theory or of the concepts of a theory is here understood in the sense of the construction of a formal system, an *axiom system* (or postulate system) for that theory.

We are not speaking here of a formal system in the strict sense, sometimes called a calculus (in the strict sense) or a syntactical system; in a system of this kind all rules are purely syntactical and all signs occurring are left entirely uninterpreted (see [Semantics] § 24). On the other hand, we are not speaking of axiom systems of the traditional kind, which are entirely interpreted. In the discussions of this book we are rather thinking of those semiformal, semi-interpreted systems which are constructed by contemporary authors, especially mathematicians, under the title of axiom systems (or postulate systems). In a system of this kind the axiomatic terms (for instance, in Hilbert's axiom system of geometry the terms 'point', 'line', 'incidence', 'between', and others) remain uninterpreted, while for all or some of the logical terms occurring (e.g., 'not', 'or', 'every') and sometimes for certain arithmetical terms (e.g., 'one', 'two') their customary interpretation is—in most cases tacitly—presupposed. (For an explanation of the semiformal character of axiom systems see [Foundations] § 16.)

The *interpretation* of an axiom system consists in the interpretation of its primitive axiomatic terms. This interpretation is given by rules specifying the meanings which we intend to give to these terms; hence the rules are of a semantical nature. (They are sometimes called correlative definitions (Reichenbach's "Zuordnungsdefinitionen") or epistemic correlations (Northrop).) Sometimes the interpretation of a term can be given in the simple form of an explicit definition; this definition may be regarded as a semantical rule which states that the term in question is to have the same meaning as a certain compound expression consisting of terms whose meanings are presupposed as known.

For our later discussions on probability it will be of great importance to recognize clearly the character of the axiomatic method and especially the distinction between formalization and interpretation. Some authors believe they have given a solution of the problem of probability, in our terminology, an explication for probability, by merely constructing an axiom system for probability without giving an interpretation; for a genuine explication, however, an interpretation is essential. We shall now illustrate the axiomatic method and the distinction between its two phases by taking as an example the arithmetic of natural numbers. The prescientific terms of this field are the numerals 'one', 'two', etc. (or the corresponding figures) and terms for arithmetical operations like 'plus' (previously 'and'), 'times', etc., as they are used in everyday language for counting things and for calculating with numbers applied to things. Preliminary steps toward a systematization of the theory and an explication of the terms have been made for several thousand years in the form of rules of calculation. The first axiom system for arithmetic which satisfies modern requirements as to the exactness of formulation is the famous axiom system of *G. Peano*. This system takes as primitive axiomatic terms '0', 'number', and 'successor'. It consists of five axioms, among them: '0 is a number' and 'the successor of a number is a number'. On the basis of the primitive terms mentioned, terms for the ordinary arithmetical operations can be introduced by recursive definitions. On the basis of the axioms and the recursive definitions, the ordinary theorems of elementary arithmetic can be proved. In this procedure the primitive terms mentioned and the terms introduced on their basis remain uninterpreted. It is only for didactic, psychological reasons that not arbitrarily chosen symbols are taken as primitive terms but customary signs or words. Their well-known meanings facilitate the manipulations of the signs in the deductions, but these deductions are formal in the sense that they do not make use of the meanings of the axiomatic terms at any point.

Peano's axiom system, by furnishing the customary formulas of arithmetic, achieves in this field all that is to be required from the point of view of formal mathematics. However, it does not yet achieve an explication of the arithmetical terms 'one', 'two', 'plus', etc. In order to do this, an interpretation must be given for the semiformal axiom system. There is an infinite number of true interpretations for this system, that is, of sets of entities fulfilling the axioms, or, as one usually says, of models for the system. One of them is the set of natural numbers as we use them in everyday life. But it can be shown that all sets of any entities exhibiting the same structure as the set of natural numbers in their order of magnitude—in Russell's terminology, all progressions—are likewise models of Peano's system. From the point of view of the formal system, no distinction is made between these infinitely many models. However, in order to state the one interpretation we are aiming at, we have to give an explication for the terms 'one', 'two', etc., as they are meant when we apply them in everyday life.

The first exact explications for the ordinary arithmetical terms have been given by G. Frege and later in a similar way by Bertrand Russell. Both Frege and Russell give explicata for the arithmetical concepts by explicit definitions on the basis of a purely logical system whose primitive terms are presupposed as interpreted. On the basis of this interpretation of the arithmetical terms, Peano's axioms become provable theorems in logic. It is a historically and psychologically surprising fact that this explication was such a difficult task and was achieved so late, although the explicanda, the elementary concepts of arithmetic, are understood and correctly applied by every child and have been successfully applied and to some extent also systematized for thousands of years.

It is important to see clearly the difference between Peano's and Frege's systems of arithmetic. Peano's system, as mentioned, does not go beyond the boundaries of formal mathematics. Only Frege's system enables us to apply the arithmetical concepts in the description of facts; it enables us to transform a sentence like 'the number of fingers on my right hand is 5' into a form which does not contain any arithmetical terms. Peano's system contains likewise the term '5', but only as an uninterpreted symbol. It enables us to derive formulas like '$3 + 2 = 5$', but it does not tell us how to understand the term '5' when it occurs in a factual sentence like that about the fingers. Only Frege's system enables us to understand sentences of this kind, that is to say, to know what we have to do in order to find out whether the sentence is true or not.

The result of this discussion is, in general terms, the following. As soon as we go over from the field of formal mathematics to that of knowledge about the facts of nature, in other words, to empirical science, which includes applied mathematics, we need more than a mere calculus or axiom system; an interpretation must be added to the system.

Concerning the arithmetical systems of Peano, Frege, and Russell: G. Peano, *Arithmetices principia* (1889); G. Frege, *Grundlagen der Arithmetik* (1884); *Grundgesetze der Arithmetik* (2 vols.; 1893, 1903); Bertrand Russell, *The principles of mathematics* (1903); with A. N. Whitehead, [Princ. Math.]. For a discussion of the distinction between Peano's arithmetic and that of Frege and Russell see Russell, *Introduction to mathematical philosophy* (1918), chaps. 1 and 2; and Carnap [Foundations] §§ 17 ff.

CHAPTER II

THE TWO CONCEPTS OF PROBABILITY

The various theories of probability are attempts at an explication of what is regarded as the prescientific concept of probability. In fact, however, there are two fundamentally different concepts for which the term 'probability' is in general use. The two concepts are as follows, here distinguished by subscripts.

(i) Probability$_1$ is the degree of confirmation of a hypothesis *h* with respect to an evidence statement *e*, e.g., an observational report. This is a logical, semantical concept. A sentence about this concept is based, not on observation of facts, but on logical analysis; if it is true, it is L-true (analytic).

(ii) Probability$_2$ is the relative frequency (in the long run) of one property of events or things with respect to another. A sentence about this concept is factual, empirical.

Both concepts are important for science. Many authors who take one of the two concepts as explicandum are not aware of the importance or even of the existence of the other concept. This has led to futile controversy.

Probability$_2$ is obviously an objective concept. It is important to recognize that probability$_1$ is likewise objective. It seems to me that most of those authors from classical to present times who do not accept a frequency interpretation of probability mean something like probability$_1$ as their explicandum and that their systems themselves are objectivistic. The latter fact is often veiled by the use of misleading subjectivistic formulations, mostly in preliminary explanations, e.g., in terms of degree of actual or reasonable belief. This psychologism in inductive logic, i.e., in the theory of probability$_1$, is quite analogous to the well-known psychologism in deductive logic, which is more and more eliminated in modern logic.

§ 8. The Semantical Concepts of Confirmation

The concepts of confirmation to be dealt with in this book are semantical, i.e., based upon meaning, and logical, i.e., independent of facts. They belong, not to deductive, but to inductive logic. We distinguish three semantical concepts of confirmation: (i) the *classificatory* concept of confirmation ('the hypothesis *h* is confirmed by the evidence *e*', in symbols '$\mathfrak{C}(h,e)$'); (ii) the *comparative* concept of confirmation ('*h* is confirmed by *e* at least as highly as *h'* by *e''*, '$\mathfrak{MC}(h,e,h',e')$'); (iii) the *quantitative* concept of confirmation, the concept of *degree of confirmation* ('*h* is confirmed by *e* to the degree *q*', '$\mathfrak{c}(h,e) = q$').

One of the chief tasks of this book will be the explication of certain concepts which are connected with the scientific procedure of confirming or disconfirming hypotheses with the help of observations and which we therefore will briefly call *concepts of confirmation*. We leave for later chapters the task of laying down definitions of explicata; at present we are concerned only with an explanation of the explicanda—in other words, with the formulation of our problem, not yet with its solution.

The procedure of confirmation is a complex procedure consisting of components of different kinds. In this book we are concerned only with what may be called the logical aspect of confirmation, namely, with certain logical relations between sentences (or propositions expressed by these sentences). Within the practice of the procedure of confirmation, these relations are of interest to the scientist, for instance, in the following situation. He intends to examine a certain hypothesis *h;* he makes many observations of particular events which he regards as relevant for judging the hypothesis *h;* he formulates the results of all observations made or as much of them as are relevant in a report *e*, which is a long sentence. Then he tries to determine whether and to what degree the hypothesis *h* is confirmed by the observational evidence *e*. This last question alone is what we shall be concerned with. We call it a logical question because, once a hypothesis is formulated by *h* and any possible evidence by *e* (it need not be the evidence actually observed), the problem whether and how much *h* is confirmed by *e* is to be answered merely by a logical analysis of *h* and *e* and their relations. This question is not a question of facts in the sense that factual knowledge is required to find the answer. The sentences *h* and *e*, which are studied, do themselves certainly refer to facts. But, once *h* and *e* are given, the question mentioned requires only that we be able to understand them, that is, to grasp their meanings, and to establish certain relations which are based upon their meanings. Since we take semantics as the theory of the meanings of expressions in language and especially of sentences (this will be explained later), the relations betwen *h* and *e* to be studied may be characterized as semantical; therefore we call them *semantical concepts of confirmation*.

The question of confirmation in which we are here interested has been characterized above as a logical question. In order to avoid misunderstandings, a qualification should here be made. The question mentioned does not belong to deductive logic but to inductive logic. The similarities and differences between these two branches of logic will later be discussed in detail (§ 43B). Both branches have in common that the solution of their problems does not require factual knowledge but only analysis of meaning; therefore both parts of logic belong to semantics. This similarity makes it possible to explain the logical character of the relations of confirmation by an analogy with a more familiar relation in deductive logic, viz., the relation of *h* being a logical consequence of *e*, in our terminology, the relation of L-implication (i.e., logical implication or entailment, in distinction to material implication) between *e* and *h*. Let *e* be the sentence 'all men are mortal, and Socrates is a man', and *h* the sentence 'Socrates is mortal'. Both *e* and *h* have factual content. But, in order to answer the question whether *e* L-implies *h*, we need no factual knowledge, we need not know whether *e* is true or false, whether *h* is true or false, whether anybody believes in *e* and, if so, on what basis. All that is required is a logical analysis of the meanings of the two sentences. Analogously, to answer the question how much a hypothesis *h* is confirmed by an observational report *e*—a question in logic, but here in inductive, not in deductive, logic—we need not know whether *e* is true or false, whether *h* is true or false, whether anybody believes in *e* and, if so, on the basis of observations or just by imagination or in whatever way else. All we need is a logical analysis of the meanings of the two sentences. That is the reason why we call our problem the logical or semantical problem of confirmation, in distinction to what might be called methodological problems of confirmation (§ 44A), e.g., how best to construct an apparatus and to arrange it for certain experiments, how to carry out the experiments, how to observe the results, etc., all this for the purpose of an experimental examination of a given hypothesis.

In this book we shall deal with *three semantical concepts of confirmation*. Although in the application outlined above, the evidence is usually an observational report and the hypothesis a law or a prediction, we shall not restrict our concepts of confirmation to any particular contents or forms of the two sentences. The three semantical concepts of confirmation belong to the three levels of concepts earlier explained (§ 4).

(i) ***The classificatory concept of confirmation*** is that relation between two sentences *h* and *e* which is usually expressed by sentences of the following forms:

'*h* is confirmed by *e*.'
'*h* is supported by *e*.'
'*e* gives some (positive) evidence for *h*.'
'*e* is evidence substantiating (or corroborating) the assumption of *h*.'

Here *e* is ordinarily, as in the previous example, an observational report, but it may also refer to particular states of affairs not yet known but merely assumed and may even include assumed laws; *h* is usually a statement about an unknown state of affairs, e.g., a prediction, or it may be a law or any other hypothesis. It is clear that this concept of confirmation is a relation between two sentences, not a property of one of them. Thus it is analogous to the examples with 'close' or 'acquainted' for classificatory concepts in § 4 rather than to those of properties. Customary formulations which mention only the hypothesis are obviously elliptical; the evidence is tacitly understood. For instance, when a physicist says, 'This hypothesis is well confirmed,' he means '. . . on the evidence of the observational results known today to physicists.' (On the disadvantages of these elliptical formulations see below, §§ 10A and 42A.) In the discussion of explicata for the classificatory concept of confirmation we shall use the symbol '𝔈' (§ 86); thus '𝔈(h,e)' will correspond to the formulations mentioned above.

(ii) ***The comparative concept of confirmation*** is usually expressed in sentences of the following or similar forms:

a. 'h is more strongly confirmed (or supported, substantiated, corroborated, etc.) by e than h' by e''.

Here we have a tetradic relation between four sentences. It may also be regarded as a dyadic relation between two pairs of sentences, h,e and h',e'. In general, the two hypotheses h and h' are different from one another, and likewise the two bodies of evidence e and e'. Some scientists will perhaps doubt whether a comparison of this most general form is possible and may, perhaps, restrict the application of the comparative concept to those situations where two bodies of evidence are compared with respect to the same hypothesis (example (b)), or where two hypotheses are examined with respect to one evidence (example (c)). In either case the comparative concept is a triadic relation between three sentences.

b. 'The general theory of relativity is more strongly confirmed by the results of laboratory experiments and astronomical observations known today than by those known in 1905.'

c. 'The optical phenomena available to physicists in the nineteenth century were more adequately explained by the wave theory of light than by the corpuscular theory; in other words, they gave stronger support to the former theory than to the latter.'

The forms (a), (b), and (c) use that kind of comparative concept which means 'more (in a certain respect)'. We have seen earlier (§ 4) that there is a second kind which means 'more or equal' and which, although less customary, is sometimes more useful. This is the case also with the concepts of confirmation. Therefore, when we later approach the problem of explication for a comparative concept of confirmation (chap. vii), we shall take as explicandum the relation usually expressed in sentences of the following or a similar form:

d. 'h is confirmed by e at least as strongly (i.e., either more strongly or equally) as h' by e''.

We shall then use '𝔐𝔈' as a symbol for an explicatum to be discussed. Thus '𝔐𝔈(h,e,h',e')' corresponds to the customary formulation (d).

(iii) ***The quantitative (or metrical) concept of confirmation***, the concept of ***degree of confirmation.*** Opinion seems divided as to whether or not a concept of this kind ever occurs in the customary talk of scientists, that is to say, whether they ever assign a numerical value to the degree to which a hypothesis is supported by given observational material or whether they use only classificatory and comparative concepts of confirmation. For the present discussion we leave this question open; even if the latter were the case, an attempt to find a quantitative explicatum for the comparative explicandum would be worth while. (This would be analogous to the example discussed earlier (§ 5): for the comparative explicandum Warmer, not only a comparative explicatum Warmer* but also an adequate quantitative explicatum Temperature has been found.) Again opinion today is divided as to whether there is a good prospect for finding a satisfactory quantitative concept of confirmation. We shall discuss this problem in detail. In our general discussions of possible solutions the symbol '𝔠' will be used for the degree of confirmation (following Hosiasson). Thus '$\mathfrak{c}(h,e) = q$' will be written for 'the degree of confirmation of h with respect to e is q'; here, h and e are sentences and q is a real number of the interval 0–1. In Volume II we shall define a specific concept of this kind and propose it as explicatum; for it the symbol '$\mathfrak{c}^*$' will be used. On the basis of this concept a system of inductive logic will be constructed.

§ 9. The Two Concepts of Probability

The various theories of probability offer many different explicata. They are sometimes classified in three groups: (i) the classical conception, (ii) the logical conception, (iii) the frequency conception. However, it is found that the various theories are not answers to the same problem, i.e., explications of the same explicandum. There are two principal explicanda, two fundamentally different meanings of the word 'probability' in presystematic use: (i) *probability*$_1$ = degree of confirmation and (ii) *probability*$_2$ = relative frequency. The controversy between the frequency conception and the theories on the other side is seen as futile, caused chiefly by the fact that most authors on either side do not realize that those on the other side start from a different explicandum whose explication is likewise of great importance for science. A few explanations on probability$_2$ are given.

The history of the theory of probability is the history of attempts to find an explication for the prescientific concept of probability. The number of solutions which have been proposed for this problem in the course of its historical development is rather large. The differences, though sometimes slight, are in many cases considerable. To bring some order into the bewildering multiplicity, several attempts have been made to arrange the many solutions into a few groups. The following is a simple and plausible classification of the various conceptions of probability into three groups (proposed by Nagel [Principles]): (i) the classical conception, originated by Jacob Bernoulli, systematically developed by Laplace, and represented by their followers in various forms; here, probability is defined as the ratio of the number of favorable cases to the number of all possible cases; (ii) the conception of probability as a certain objective logical relation between propositions (or sentences); the chief representatives of this concept are John M. Keynes and Harold Jeffreys; (iii) the conception of probability as relative frequency, developed most completely in the theories of Richard von Mises, Hans Reichenbach, and those of modern mathematical statistics.

At the present we shall not enter a discussion of these various conceptions. While the main point of interest both for the authors and for the readers of the various theories of probability is normally the solutions proposed in those theories, we shall inspect the theories from a different point of view. We shall not ask what solutions the authors offer but rather which problems the solutions are intended to solve; in other words, we shall not ask what explicata are proposed but rather which concepts are taken as explicanda.

This question may appear superfluous, and the fact obvious, that the explicandum for every theory of probability is the prescientific concept of probability, i.e., the meaning in which the word 'probability' is used in the prescientific language. Is the assumption correct, however, that there is only one meaning connected with the word 'probability' in its customary use or, at the least, that only one meaning has been chosen by the authors as their explicandum? When we look at the formulations which the authors themselves offer in order to make clear which meanings of 'probability' they intend to take as their explicanda, we find phrases as different as 'degree of belief', 'credibility', 'degree of reasonable expectation', 'degree of possibility', 'degree of proximity to certainty', 'degree of partial truth', 'relative frequency', and many others. This multiplicity of phrases shows that any assumption of a unique explicandum common to all authors is untenable. We might even be tempted to go to the opposite extreme and to conclude that the authors are dealing not with one but with a dozen or more different concepts. However, I believe that this multiplicity is misleading. It seems to me that the number of explicanda in all the various theories of probability is neither just one nor about a dozen, but in all essential respects—leaving aside slight variations—very few and chiefly two. In the following discussions we shall use subscripts in order to distinguish these two principal meanings of the term 'probability' from which most of the various theories of probability start; we are, of course, distinguishing between two explicanda and not between the various explicata offered by these theories, whose number is much greater. The two concepts are (i) ***probability***$_1$ = degree of confirmation; (ii) ***probability***$_2$ = relative frequency in the long run. Strictly speaking, there are two groups of concepts, since, both for (i) and for (ii), there is a classificatory, a comparative, and a quantitative concept; however, at the present moment, we may leave aside these distinctions.

Let me emphasize again that the distinction made here refers to two explicanda, not to two explicata. That there is more than one explicatum is obvious; and, indeed, their number is much larger than two. But most investigators in the field of probability apparently believe that all the various theories of probability are intended to solve the same problem and hence that any two theories which differ fundamentally from each other are incompatible. Consequently, we find that most representatives of the frequency conception of probability reject all other theories and, vice versa, that the frequency conception is rejected by most of the authors of other theories. This whole controversy seems futile and unnecessary.

A few examples may show how much of the futile controversy between representatives of different conceptions of probability is due to the lack of awareness, on both sides, of the existence and importance of the probability concept of the other side. We take as examples a prominent contemporary representative of each conception: Mises, who constructed the first complete theory based on the frequency conception, and Jeffreys, who constructed the most advanced theory based on probability$_1$. Mises seems to believe that probability$_2$ is the only basis of the Calculus of Probability ([Probab.], first lecture). To speak of the probability of the death of a certain individual seems to him meaningless. Any use of the term 'probability' in everyday life other than in the statistical sense of probability$_2$ has in his view nothing to do with the Calculus of Probability and cannot take numerical values. That he regards Keynes's conception of probability as thoroughly subjectivistic indicates clearly his misunderstanding (see below, § 12A).

On the other hand, Jeffreys lays down certain requirements which every theory of probability (and that means for him probability$_1$) should fulfil and then rejects all frequency theories, that is, theories of probability$_2$, because they do not fulfil his requirements. Thus he says: "No 'objective' definition of probability in terms of actual or possible observations . . . is admissible" ([Probab.], p. 11), because the results of observations are initially unknown, and, consequently, we could not know the fundamental principles of the theory and would have no starting point. He even goes so far as to say that, "in practice, no statistician ever uses a frequency definition, but that all use the notion of degree of reasonable belief, usually without ever noticing that they are using it" (p. 300). While Mises' concern with explicating the empirical concept of probability$_2$ by the limit of relative frequency in an infinite sequence has led him to apply the term 'probability' only in cases where such a limit exists, Jeffreys misunderstands his procedure completely and accuses the empiricist Mises of apriorism: "The existence of the limit is taken as a postulate by Mises. . . . The postulate is an *a priori* statement about possible experiments and is in itself objectionable" (p. 304). Thus we find this situation: Mises and Jeffreys both assert that there is only one concept of probability that is of scientific importance and that can be taken as the basis of the Calculus of Probability. The first maintains that this concept is probability$_2$ and certainly not anything like probability$_1$; the second puts it just the other way round.

It has repeatedly occurred in the history of science that a vehement but futile controversy arose between the proponents of two or more explicata who shared the erroneous belief that they had the same explicandum; when finally it became clear that they meant different explicanda, unfortunately designated by the same term, and that the different explicata were hence compatible and moreover were found to be equally fruitful scientific concepts, the controversy evaporated into nothing.

One of the outstanding examples is the controversy between the followers of Descartes and those of Leibniz concerning the concept of living force ('vis viva', also called 'quantity of motion'). Both sides believed that it was practically clear enough what was meant by the 'living force' of a moving body; both agreed that this magnitude increases with the mass and the velocity of the body. But they disagreed in their explications for this supposedly one explicandum. The first group proposed as explicatum mv, the product of mass and velocity; the second rejected this and proposed instead mv^2. It took a long time until it became clear that the two assertions of the disputants were not two incompatible answers to the same problem but two correct answers to two different problems. Both concepts were recognized as fruitful and necessary for mechanics; the first is the magnitude now called momentum, the second (with the factor $\frac{1}{2}$ attached to it) is now called kinetic energy. To the physicist of our time, familiar with both concepts, the historic dispute about the question which of the two concepts is "the right one" seems somewhat strange. As soon as we recognize the distinction between probability$_1$ and probability$_2$, the contemporary controversy about probability will appear just as strange and futile.

The distinction between the two concepts which serve as explicanda is often overlooked on both sides. This is primarily due to the unfortunate fact that both concepts are designated by the same familiar but ambiguous word 'probability'. Although many languages contain two words (e.g., English 'probable' and 'likely', Latin '*probabilis*' and '*verisimilis*', French '*probable*' and '*vraisemblable*'), these words seem in most cases to be used in about the same way or at any rate not to correspond to the two concepts we have distinguished. Some authors (e.g., C. S. Peirce, R. A. Fisher, and Jeffreys) have suggested utilizing the plurality of available words for the distinction of certain concepts. We shall later (§ 60) use the term 'likelihood' in a certain special sense for which it was proposed by Jeffreys. For the two concepts probability$_1$ and probability$_2$, however, we shall simply make the distinction with the help of the subscripts. The terms 'probability$_1$' and 'probability$_2$' will chiefly be used in our discussions of explicanda, especially when we analyze customary formulations in prescientific language and the formulations of other authors. On the other hand, in the discussion of possible explicata we shall mostly use the terms '(degree of) confirmation' and 'relative frequency'.

Probability$_1$, the logical concept of probability as explicandum, has been explained in the preceding section and will later be analyzed in greater detail (§ 41). A few explanations may here be given for *probability*$_2$, just to make clear its distinction from probability$_1$. The theory of probability$_2$ itself lies outside the program of this book, which deals with inductive logic and therefore with probability$_1$. A typical example of the use of the term 'probability' in the sense of probability$_2$ is the following statement:

'The probability of casting an ace with this die is 1/6.'

Statements of this form refer to two properties (or classes) of events: (i) the reference class K, here the class of the throws of this die; and (ii) the specific property M, here the property of being a throw with any die resulting in an ace. The statement says that the probability$_2$ of M with respect to K is 1/6. The statement is tested by statistical investigations. A sufficiently long series of, say, n throws of the die in question is made, and the number m of these throws which yield an ace is counted. If the relative frequency m/n of aces in this series is sufficiently close to 1/6, the statement is regarded as confirmed. Thus, the other way round, the statement is understood as predicting that the relative frequency of aces thrown with this die in a sufficiently long series will be about 1/6. This formulation is admittedly inexact; but it is only intended to indicate the meaning of 'probability$_2$' as an explicandum. To make this concept exact is the task of the explication.

There are two schools of thought which take the frequency concept, probability$_2$, as explicandum. The first, usually referred to as that of the frequency theory of probability, takes as explicatum for this explicandum the limit of the relative frequency of *M* within an infinite sequence; in our example and similar ones, this sequence may consist of the events of the class *K*, here assumed to be infinite, in their temporal order. This explication was first proposed by Venn ([Logic] (2d ed., 1876), chap. v, secs. 36, 37; (3d ed., 1888), chap. vi, secs. 36, 37). It was systematically developed by Mises and Reichenbach. Mises' definition requires that the reference sequence exhibit a random order. This concept of randomness involves certain difficulties. It was originally defined in too strong a form which was found to lead to contradictions. A suitable redefinition avoiding the contradiction was proposed by Wald [Kollektiv]. The problems here involved are still under discussion. The second school is that of modern mathematical statistics as developed by R. A. Fisher, J. Neyman, E. S. Pearson, and others in the course of the last decades. (For the publications of the authors mentioned see the Bibliography; for technical systematic expositions of the whole theory see Wilks [Statistics] and Cramér [Statistics]; Wald [Principles] gives a clear survey of the basic ideas and methods.) Here, 'probability' is taken as an undefined term in an axiomatic system. The reference class *K*, called the population, is not required to be denumerable as in the first school but may be a continuum; therefore the limit concept is not directly applicable. However, both the formulation of the axioms and the nonformal explanations of the term 'probability' make it clear that it is meant in the sense of relative frequency (see, e.g., Fisher [Foundations], p. 312; Wilks [Statistics], pp. 3–6; Cramér [Statistics], pp. 148–51). [Some further remarks concerning the limit concept in connection with probability$_2$ will be made later, in § 106B.]

It is clear that the concept of probability$_2$ involves statistics of mass phenomena and their frequencies. However, this is not a distinguishing characteristic of this concept. The same also frequently holds for probability$_1$ in the sense that the evidence referred to in a probability$_1$ statement is, as we shall see (§ 44B), often of a statistical nature specifying, for instance, the frequency of a property in a given population or in a given sample taken from a population.

We shall later (§ 42) come back to the discussion of the distinction between probability$_1$ and probability$_2$ and, in particular, the problem of how the word 'probability', which originally meant only probability$_1$, came to be used also in the sense of probability$_2$.

§ 10. The Logical Nature of the Two Probability Concepts

Both probability$_1$ and probability$_2$, taken as quantitative concepts, are functions of two arguments, whose values are real numbers of the interval 0–1. *A*. The arguments of probability$_1$ are sentences (or propositions expressed by them). Probability$_1$ has *two* arguments, the hypothesis and the evidence. A reference to the latter is often omitted; but this omission leads sometimes to a neglect of the relativity of probability$_1$ and thereby to misconceptions. An elementary statement of probability$_1$ is not factual but L-determinate. *B*. The arguments of probability$_2$ are properties; its elementary statements are factual, empirical. However, the theorems of the theory of probability$_2$ state, not values of this function, but general relations between such values, and are L-true. Those authors who support a frequency theory of probability have clearly probability$_2$ as their explicandum. I believe that the explicandum of most of the others is probability$_1$, in spite of the variety of their explanations.

On the basis of the preceding explanations, let us now characterize the two probability concepts not with respect to what they mean but merely with respect to their logical nature, more specifically, with respect to the kind of entities to which they are applied and the logical nature of the simplest sentences in which they are used. [Since the prescientific use of the two concepts is often too vague and incomplete, e.g., because of the omission of the second argument (viz., the evidence or the reference class), we take here into consideration the more careful use by authors on probability. However, we shall be more concerned with their general discussions than with the details of their constructed systems.] For the sake of simplicity, let us consider the two concepts in their quantitative forms only. They may be taken also in their comparative and in their classificatory forms (as explained for probability$_1$, i.e., confirmation, in § 8), and these other forms would show analogous differences. Probability$_1$ and probability$_2$, taken as quantitative concepts, have the following characteristics in common: each of them is a function of two arguments; their values are real numbers belonging to the interval 0–1. Their characteristic differences will now be explained.

A. *Probability$_1$, Degree of Confirmation*

1. The *two arguments* are variously described as events (in the literal sense, see below), states of affairs, circumstances, and the like. Therefore each argument is expressible by a sentence and, hence, is, in our terminology, a proposition. Another alternative consists in taking as arguments the sentences expressing the propositions, describing the events, etc. We shall choose this alternative and hence take probability$_1$ as a semantical concept (as in § 8). (Fundamentally it makes no great difference whether propositions or sentences are taken as arguments; but the second method has certain technical advantages which will be explained later, in § 52.)

2. An *elementary statement* of probability$_1$, i.e., one which attributes to two given arguments a particular number as value of probability$_1$, is either L-true (i.e., logically true, analytic) or L-false (i.e., logically false, logically self-contradictory), hence in any case L-determinate, not factual (synthetic). (For an explanation of the L-terms see § 20.) Therefore, a statement of this kind is to be established by logical (semantical) analysis alone, as has been explained earlier (§ 8). It is independent of the contingency of facts because it does not say anything about facts (although the two arguments do in general refer to facts).

Many empiricist authors have rejected the logical concept of probability$_1$ as distinguished from probability$_2$ because they believe that its use violates the principle of empiricism and that, therefore, probability$_2$ is the only concept admissible for empiricism and hence for science. One of the reasons given for this view is as follows. The concept of probability$_1$ is applied also in cases in which the hypothesis h is a prediction concerning a particular event, e.g., the prediction that it will rain tomorrow or that the next throw of this die will yield an ace. Some philosophers believe that an application of this kind violates the principle of verifiability (or confirmability). They might say, for example: "How can the statement 'the probability of rain tomorrow on the evidence of the given meteorological observations is one-fifth' be verified? We shall observe either rain or not-rain tomorrow, but we shall not observe anything that can verify the value one-fifth." This objection, however, is based on a misconception concerning the nature of the probability$_1$ statement. This statement does not ascribe the probability$_1$ value $1/5$ to tomorrow's rain but rather to a certain logical relation between the prediction of rain and the meteorological report. Since the relation is logical, the statement is, if true, L-true; therefore it is not in need of verification by observation of tomorrow's weather or of any other facts. The situation may be clarified by a comparison with deductive logic. Let h be the sentence 'there will be rain tomorrow' and j the sentence 'there will be rain and wind tomorrow'. Suppose somebody makes the statement in deductive logic: 'h follows logically from j.' Certainly nobody will accuse him of apriorism either for making the statement or for claiming that for its verification no factual knowledge is required. The statement 'the probability$_1$ of h on the evidence e is $1/5$' has the same general character as the former statement; therefore it cannot violate empiricism any more than the first. Both statements express a purely logical relation between two sentences. The difference between the two statements is merely this: while the first states a complete logical implication, the second states only, so to speak, a partial logical implication; hence, while the first belongs to deductive logic, the second belongs to inductive logic. Generally speaking, the assertion of purely logical sentences, whether in deductive or in inductive logic, can never violate empiricism; if they are false, they violate the rules of logic. The principle of empiricism can be violated only by the assertion of a factual (synthetic) sentence without a sufficient empirical foundation or by the thesis of apriorism when it contends that for knowledge with respect to certain factual sentences no empirical foundation is required.

The fact that *probability$_1$ is relative to given evidence* and that therefore a complete statement of probability$_1$ must contain a reference to the evidence is very important. Keynes was the first to emphasize this relativity ([Probab.], pp. 6 f.). The omission of any reference to evidence is often harmless if the elliptical nature of the statement is clearly recognized. However, this omission was the general custom with earlier authors, and it often caused lack of clarity. It had sometimes the effect that the authors overlooked the relativity of probability$_1$ and thus came to the belief that probability$_1$ was dependent upon our knowledge and that hence the validity of a statement on probability$_1$ was merely subjective. At other times it led to the belief that this validity was dependent upon certain physical facts. I think that a certain fundamental discrepancy in Kries's conception of probability is perhaps to be explained by his neglect of the evidence as an essential argument to the concept of probability. On the one hand, he speaks of the probability of assumptions or expectations; he refers to "logical connections which, when some things are regarded as certain, constitute for other things a more or less great probability" (of a comparative, not a quantitative, nature) ([Prinzipien], p. 26); this shows that he means probability$_1$, not probability$_2$ (which he rejects explicitly, pp. 18 ff.). On the other hand, he says that the probability sentences have an empirical content (e.g., p. 170). It seems to me that his neglect of the relativity with respect to the evidence has led him to the mistake of ascribing the factual content of our knowledge, e.g., concerning the physical conditions of the way in which a die is thrown or a roulette is played, to the probability sentence itself instead of to the evidence. Reichenbach's views that even those probability statements which concern what he calls "weight" or "the logical concept of probability" are of an empirical nature ([Experience] §§ 32–34; cf. our discussion below, in § 41E) is perhaps to be explained in a similar way. He feels correctly that the statement 'the weight (or predictional value) of the prediction that it will rain tomorrow is 3/4' must somehow be based upon our empirical knowledge, in particular, our observation of the present weather situation and statistical results concerning past weather observations, especially the relative frequency with which rain has been observed to follow upon weather situations similar to that of today. This leads him to the conception that the statement about the weight 3/4 must itself be interpreted as a statement concerning the observed relative frequency 3/4 and hence as being itself a factual, empirical statement. Our conception agrees with Reichenbach's with respect to the point that the value of the weight, our probability$_1$, is based on the observed relative frequency; but we regard the weight statement as elliptical. The relevant empirical knowledge, including the observation of the present state of the weather and the past results, especially the observed relative frequency, is to be expressed in the evidence *e;* and the complete formulation of the weight statement is a statement on probability$_1$ which does not contain *e* and is not derived from *e* but instead contains a reference to *e*. Thus our empirical knowledge does not constitute a part of the content of the probability$_1$ statement (which would make this statement empirical) but rather of the sentence *e* which is dealt with in the probability$_1$ statement. Thus the latter, although referring to empirical knowledge, remains itself purely logical.

Many writers on probability formulate a reference to the evidence in the form of a conditional clause, for example:

(1) 'If an urn contains a hundred balls, of which seventy are white and and thirty black, then the probability that the next ball drawn from this urn will be white is 0.7'.

This formulation is preferable to the elliptical one because the danger of overlooking the evidence is here avoided. But it is not quite correct. In a genuine conditional sentence of the form 'If *A*, then *B*', for example:

(2) 'If it rains, Jack will not come',

the main clause *B* is a meaningful sentence, complete in itself (if we leave aside cases involving pronouns). On the other hand, the main clause in the probability statement (1) 'the probability that the next ball drawn from this urn will be white is 0.7' is incomplete because a reference to evidence is lacking. Many authors, even among the best contemporary writers on probability$_1$, have sometimes used the conditional formulation of probability statements. In some cases they have been misled by this form to the view that the evidence expressed in the conditional clause, if known, provides a ground or premise from which the probability expressed in the main clause can be *inferred.* This view is based on a false analogy due to the incorrect conditional formulation. If a genuine conditional statement 'If A, then B' is known and 'A' is supplied as additional information, 'B' can indeed be inferred. Thus there is the temptation to proceed analogously with (1). Suppose that (1) is known as an instance of a general theorem on probability and that we are given the information that this particular urn contains seventy white and thirty black balls; then we might be inclined to say that we can *infer* from this information that the probability of drawing a white ball is 0.7. However, this alleged conclusion is incomplete and hence, strictly speaking, meaningless. If we wish to use the word 'inference', as is customary, in a wider sense than it has in deductive logic so that we can speak of 'nondeductive' or 'nondemonstrative inference' or positively of 'probability inference' or 'inductive inference' (§ 44B), we may say that the hypothesis h is inductively inferred from the evidence e. But in this case we must be careful not to overlook the fact that the probability value characterizes not the hypothesis ('the next ball will be white') but rather the inference from the evidence to the hypothesis or, more correctly speaking, the logical relation holding between the evidence and the hypothesis.

Thus we see that from the evidence e together with the statement 'the probability of h with respect to e is $1/5$' we can infer (in the strict sense of this word) neither h itself, which may be false, nor a statement of the probability of h, which would be meaningless. In fact, nothing can be inferred from those two premises (except, trivially, for those conclusions which follow from e alone). This negative answer to an often discussed problem will become clear in the course of the later development of our theory.

B. *Probability$_2$, Relative Frequency*

1. The *two arguments* are properties, kinds, classes, usually of events or things. [As an alternative, the predicate expressions designating the properties might be taken as arguments. In the present case, however, in distinction to (1), there does not seem to be any advantage in this method; cf. § 52.]

2. An *elementary statement* of probability$_2$ is factual and empirical; it says something about the facts of nature and hence must be based upon empirical procedure, the observation of relevant facts. From these elementary statements the theorems of a mathematical theory of probability$_2$ must be clearly distinguished. The latter do not state a particular value of probability$_2$ but say something about connections between probability$_2$ values in a general way, usually in a conditional form, for example: 'if the values of such and such probabilities$_2$ are q_1 and q_2, then the value of a probability$_2$ related to the original ones in a certain way is such and such a function, say, product or sum, of q_1 and q_2.' These theorems are not factual but L-true (analytic). Thus a theory of probability$_2$, e.g., the system constructed by Mises or that by Reichenbach is not of an empirical but of a logicomathematical nature; it is a branch of mathematics, fundamentally different from any branch of empirical science, e.g., physics.

Mises has repeatedly stated (e.g., [Comments 1], p. 45) that his theory of probability is empirical, is a branch of the natural sciences like physics. However, his theorems, although referring to mass phenomena, are quite obviously purely analytic; the proofs of these theorems (in distinction to examples of application) make use only of logicomathematical methods, in addition to his definition of 'probability', and not of any observational results concerning mass phenomena. Therefore his theory belongs to pure mathematics, not to physics. This point has been discussed in detail and completely clarified by F. Waismann [Wahrsch.], pp. 239 f.

We shall sometimes call probability$_2$, in distinction to probability$_1$, an empirical concept. This is not to be understood as saying that its definition refers to nonlogical concepts, which is obviously not the case, but merely as saying that its ordinary application, that is, its application to factual properties as arguments, is to be formulated in factual, empirical statements; in other words, the determination of its values in ordinary cases is an empirical procedure. Probability$_2$ is in this respect similar to the concept of the cardinal number of a property. The definition of the latter concept is likewise purely logical; nevertheless, its application to factual properties leads to factual, empirical statements, and its values in these cases are found by the empirical procedure of counting.

In spite of the fundamental difference between the concepts of probability$_1$ and probability$_2$, many theorems concerning these concepts show a striking analogy. Later discussions will throw some light from various angles on the basis of this analogy. We shall see that in certain cases probability$_1$ may be interpreted as an estimate of relative frequency or probability$_2$ (§ 41D). Later, on the basis of an analysis of sentences with the help of their ranges, it will be seen that probability$_1$ can likewise be regarded as a ratio of the measures of two classes (see § 55B); but there remains the important difference that in this case the ratio is determined in a purely logical way, while in the case of probability$_2$ it is determined empirically.

A terminological remark concerning the *word 'event'* seems required in view of (A1) and (B1). It is very important to distinguish clearly between *kinds of events* (war, birth, death, throw of a die, throw of this die, throw of this die yielding an ace, etc.) and *events* (Caesar's death, the throw of this die made yesterday at 10:00 A.M., the series of all throws of this die past and future). This distinction is particularly important for discussions on probability, because one of the characteristic differences between the two probability concepts is this: the first concept refers sometimes to two events, the second to two kinds of events (see A1 and B1). Many authors of probability use the word 'event' (or the corresponding words 'Ereignis' and 'événement') when they mean to speak, not about events, but about kinds of events. This usage is of long standing in the literature on probability, but it is very unfortunate. It has only served to reinforce the customary neglect of the fundamental difference between the two probability concepts, which arose originally out of the ambiguous use of the word 'probability', and thereby to increase the general confusion in discussions on probability. The authors who use the term 'event' when they mean kinds of events get into trouble, of course, whenever they want to speak about specific events. The traditional solution is to say 'the happenings (or occurrences) of a certain event' instead of 'the events of a certain kind'; sometimes the events are referred to by the term 'single event'. But this phrase is rather misleading; the important difference between events and kinds of events is not the same as the inessential difference between single events (the first throw made today with this die) and multiple or compound events (the series of all throws made with this die). Keynes, if I interpret him correctly, has noticed the ambiguity of the term 'event'. He says ([Probab.], p. 5) that the customary use of phrases like 'the happening of events' is "vague and unambiguous", which I suppose to be a misprint for "vague and ambiguous"; but he does not specify the ambiguity. He proposes to dispense altogether with the term 'event' and to use instead the term 'proposition'. Subsequent authors dealing with probability$_1$, like Jeffreys, for example, have followed him in this use.

Many authors have made a distinction between two (or sometimes more) kinds of probability. Some of these distinctions are quite different from the distinction made here between probability$_1$ and probability$_2$. For instance, a distinction is sometimes made between mathematical probability and philosophical probability; their characteristic difference appears to be that the first has numerical values, the second not. However, this difference seems hardly essential; we find both a concept with numerical values and one without, in other words, both a quantitative and a comparative concept on either side of our distinction between the two fundamentally different meanings of 'probability'. Another distinction has been made between subjective and objective probability. However, I believe that practically all authors really have an objective concept of probability in mind and that the appearance of subjectivist conceptions is in most cases caused only by occasional unfortunate formulations; this will be discussed soon (§ 12).

Other distinctions which have been made are more or less similar to our distinction between probability_1 and probability_2. For instance, F. P. Ramsey ([Foundations] (1926), p. 157) says: ". . . the general difference of opinion between statisticians who for the most part adopt the frequency theory of probability and logicians who mostly reject it renders it likely that the two schools are really discussing different things, and that the word 'probability' is used by logicians in one sense and by statisticians in another".

It seems to me that practically all authors on probability have meant either probability_1 or probability_2 as their explicandum, despite the fact that their various explanations appear to refer to a number of quite different concepts.

For one group of authors, the question of their explicandum is easily answered. In the case of all those who support a frequency theory of probability, i.e., who define their explicata in terms of relative frequency (e.g. as a limit or in some other way), there can be no doubt that their explicandum is probability_2. Their formulations are, in general, presented in clear and unambiguous terms. Often they state explicitly that their explicandum is relative frequency. And even in the cases where this is not done, the discussion of their explicata leaves no doubt as to what is meant as explicandum.

This, however, covers only one of the various conceptions, i.e., explicata proposed, and only one of the many different explanations of explicanda which have been given and of which some examples were mentioned earlier. It seems clear that the other explanations do not refer to the statistical, empirical concept of relative frequency, and I believe that practically all of them, in spite of their apparent dissimilarity, are intended to refer to probability_1. Unfortunately, many of the phrases used are more misleading than helpful in our efforts to find out what their authors actually meant as explicandum. There is, in particular, one point on which many authors in discussions on probability_1, or on logical problems in general, commit a certain typical confusion or adopt incautiously other authors' formulations which are infected by this confusion. I am referring to what is sometimes called psychologism in logic. This will be discussed in the next two sections.

§ 11. Psychologism in Deductive Logic

Logical relations, e.g., logical consequence, are (i) logical, i.e., nonfactual, based merely upon meanings, (ii) objective, i.e., not dependent upon anybody's thinking about them. Most logicians treat them within their systems as objective relations, but, in spite of this, many characterize them in their general preliminary remarks in subjectivistic terms, e.g., with reference to actual thinking or believing. We call this discrepancy primitive psychologism in (deductive) logic. A qualified psychologism refers, not to actual, but to correct or rational thinking. This is usually meant in an objectivistic sense; in this case, the reference to thinking is gratuitous.

Those who work in the history of science or the methodology of science are familiar with the fact that there is frequently a discrepancy between what an author actually does and what he says he does; in particular, between the sense in which he actually uses a term or a sentence and the sense which he explicitly attributes to it. This holds especially for abstract terms and general principles. Consequently, in order to find out which sense a certain term has for the author, it is often not sufficient to look at his explicit explanations. We should also examine how he uses the term and, especially, how he argues pro or con statements in which the term occurs. And if these two tests are not in good agreement, the latter is more reliable than the first; it gives a better indication of the actual sense of the term for the author, that is, his general habit of using it. Suppose, for instance, we wish to know what a certain historian or political scientist means by 'democracy'. The best way is to observe under what conditions he applies this term and, still more important, what reasons he gives for these applications; we can accelerate the procedure by asking him questions as to whether and why he would apply the term to a country whose form of government was such and such. Of course, the direct way of asking: "What do you mean by 'democracy'?" is much simpler and quicker, and in many cases it will do. But there is always the danger that, instead of defining his actual meaning, he will give a definition which he has read in a theoretical book by a political scientist or even by a philosopher.

The discrepancy here discussed is likewise found in exact fields. Frege has repeatedly shown (especially in his *Über die Zahlen des Herrn H. Schubert* [Jena, 1899]) that the definitions of 'number' given by some mathematicians are deplorably inadequate and would lead to absurd and never intended applications, while the actual use of the term in the construction of a theory of numbers is quite correct.

The discrepancy discussed takes a special form in the case of logic. Before we approach the logical concept of probability$_1$, which is one of the fundamental concepts of inductive logic, let us look at the older and more familiar field of deductive logic, logic in the narrower sense. The task of logic (in this sense) has been the same for Aristotle as for modern (symbolic) logic, although the form of the systems constructed for the solution of this task has undergone considerable change in the course of the development. The task is the establishment of certain relations between sentences (or the propositions expressed by the sentences) usually called logical relations, among them, as one of the fundamental concepts of logic, the relation of logical consequence or deducibility. We cannot give here a full and exact characterization of these relations but will only indicate some of their characteristics. (i) They are independent of the contingency of the facts of nature, hence formal (in the traditional, not the syntactical, sense; see [Semantics], p. 232, meaning II); consequently, for ascertaining one of these relations in a concrete case, we need only know the meanings of the sentences involved, not their truth-values. (ii) The relations are objective, not subjective, in this sense: whether one of these relations does or does not hold in a concrete case is not dependent upon whether or what any person may happen to imagine, think, believe, or know about these sentences. As an example, let i be the sentence 'all swans are white', and j be 'all nonwhite things are nonswans', and suppose we have come to an agreement as to the meaning of all terms occurring. Suppose that a person X believes at the present time that j is a logical consequence of i, while at an earlier time he believed that this was not the case. That the relation is objective is meant in this sense: the change in X's belief about the relation has no effect upon the status of the relation itself; if his present belief is right (as I think it is), then his former belief was wrong; and, if his former belief was right, his present belief is wrong. It does not even make sense to assume that each of the two beliefs was right at its time, i.e., that the relation of logical consequence holds now between the two sentences but did not hold at the former time; this relation is timeless, i.e., it has no time value as argument. I hope that nobody will misinterpret my statement of the objectivity of logical relations as a metaphysical statement of the "subsistence" of these relations in a Platonic heaven (as earlier statements of mine have been misinterpreted). The statement is intended merely to point out the following character which logical concepts share with physical concepts—from which they are fundamentally different in other respects: a sentence which ascribes one of these concepts in a concrete case (e.g., 'j is a consequence of i', like 'this stone is heavier than that') is complete without any reference to the properties or the behavior of any person. (This is not in contradiction to the obvious fact that the *recognition* of a logical or a physical or any other kind of relation involves a person.) In distinction to logical and physical concepts, certain other concepts are subjective in this sense: their application requires a reference to a person or a kind of person; e.g., 'known', 'familiar', 'pleasant', 'confirmed' (in the pragmatical sense as distinguished from the semantical sense, in which we take the term in our discussions here, see § 8). For example, 'this pattern is familiar' is not a complete sentence; it must be supplemented by something like 'to me', 'to Mr. *X*', 'to the persons of such and such a class'.

This objectivist conception of logic (in this section always understood in the sense of deductive logic), the view that the concepts of logic and hence the principles and theorems of logic which employ these concepts are objective, is certainly not new. On the contrary, it characterizes the work of practically all logicians. When they lay down their principles and rules or, on this basis, solve a logical problem, they do so in objectivist formulations, from Aristotle on through the Aristotelian tradition, up to modern logic. They say, for instance, 'from premises of the form so and so, a conclusion of the form so and so follows', or '. . . is deducible', or 'the deduction (inference) of . . . from . . . is valid', or the like. Here, for the work within their systems, they would hardly ever use subjectivist formulations, that is, those referring to persons, for instance, 'such and such an inference is valid for me now', or '. . . valid for persons of an introverted type'. And, in order to find out whether a certain conclusion follows from given premises, they do not in fact make psychological experiments about the thinking habits of people but rather analyze the given sentences and show their conceptual relations. However, if we examine not their actual procedure in solving logical problems but their general remarks concerning the task and nature of logic, chiefly in the introductory sections of their books, we often find something entirely different. Here, logic is often characterized as the art of thinking, and the principles of logic are called principles or laws of thought. These and similar formulations refer to thinking and hence are of a subjectivist nature. These references to thinking are in most cases entirely out of tune with what the same author does in the body of his work. Thus we have here a special case of the discrepancy discussed in the beginning of this section. A discrepancy of this kind, where the problems themselves are of an objective nature but the descriptions by which the author intends to give a general characterization of the problems are framed in subjectivist, psychological terms (like 'thinking'), is often called *psychologism*. Thus formulations of the kind mentioned above, frequently occurring in books on logic, are instances of *psychologism in deductive logic*. In some cases we find a situation still worse than that just described. It happens sometimes that the author does not only mislead the readers by his psychologistic general remarks but misleads himself; in this case, we find traces of subjectivism in the logical system itself, in the discussion of the logical problems, mixed with objective logical components; the result is inevitably rather confusing. [The situation is entirely different in cases where not only the general characterization but also the discussion of the problems themselves is consistently subjectivistic. A procedure of this kind, even if its author applies to it the title 'Logic', cannot be criticized as psychologism, because there is no mixture of heterogeneous components; there is merely a terminological difference in the use of the term 'logic'. It seems to me that John Dewey's *Logic, the theory of inquiry* (New York, 1938) is an instance of this kind. This book deals with that kind of behavior which is appropriate to problematic situations and leads to their "solutions"; it does not deal with logic in our sense (except in a few sections which seem somewhat out of place and have little connection with the remainder of the book). The fact that many logicians, that is, men who work in the field of logic in our sense, have erroneously characterized this field as the art of thinking has caused Dewey, who actually works on the art of thinking, that is, the theory and technology of procedures for overcoming problematic situations, to choose the title 'Logic'.]

We find psychologism in deductive logic not only in the literature of traditional logic but also in that of modern logic. A conspicuous example is the title of the book which may be regarded as marking the beginning of modern symbolic logic, Boole's *Laws of thought.* But one of the important achievements in the development of modern logic has been the gradual elimination of psychologism and the gradual clarification of the nature of logic. It seems that the great majority of contemporary writers in modern logic—though not those in logic of the traditional style—are free of psychologism. This is chiefly due to the efforts of the mathematician, Gottlob Frege, and the philosopher, Edmund Husserl, who emphasized the necessity of a clear distinction between empirical psychological problems and nonempirical logical problems and pointed out the confusion caused by psychologism. In this respect, they have also influenced indirectly the attitude of many logicians who have never read their works.

For Frege's emphasis on the objectivity of logic and arithmetic and his rejection of psychologism see his *Grundlagen der Arithmetik* (1884), §§ 26, 27, and *Grundgesetze der Arithmetik*, Vol. I (1893), Preface, pp. xiv ff. Husserl's own position was originally psychologistic (*Philosophie der Arithmetik* [1891]); but later, under the influence of Frege, he became one of the prominent opponents of psychologism (*Logische Untersuchungen*, Vol. I [1900], Preface and chaps. 3–11). Concerning this development of Husserl's views cf. Marvin Farber, *The foundation of phenomenology* (1943).

A primitive psychologistic explanation of the relation of logical consequence would perhaps be somewhat like this. That *j* is a logical consequence of *i* means that, if somebody believes in *i*, he cannot help believing also in *j*. Now, in fact, a psychologistic explanation will hardly ever be given in this crude form, because its inadequacy is too obvious. Taken literally, the explanation given would require us to investigate the statistical results of series of psychological experiments. There are not many logicians who would regard this procedure as appropriate.

A nice illustration, though not meant quite seriously, of primitive psychologism in arithmetic—which is part of deductive logic—is the following passage by P. E. B. Jourdain (*The philosophy of Mr. B*rtr*nd R*ss*ll* [1918], p. 88, quoted by Jeffreys [Probab.], p. 37): "I sometimes feel inclined to apply the historical method to the multiplication table. I should make a statistical inquiry among school children, before their pristine wisdom had been biased by teachers. I should put down their answers as to what 6 times 9 amounts to, I should work out the average of their answers to six places of decimals, and should then decide that, at the present stage of human development, this average is the value of 6 times 9."

Many logicians prefer formulations which may be regarded as a kind of *qualified psychologism*. They admit that logic is not concerned with the actual processes of believing, thinking, inferring, because then it would become a part of psychology. But, still clinging to the belief that there must somehow be a close relation between logic and thinking, they say that logic is concerned with correct or rational thinking. Thus they might explain the relation of logical consequence as meaning: 'if somebody has sufficient reasons to believe in the premise *i*, then the same reasons justify likewise his belief in the conclusion *j*'. It seems to me that psychologism thus diluted has virtually lost its content; the word 'thinking' or 'believing' is still there, but its use seems gratuitous. The explanation of logical consequence just mentioned does not say more than a formulation in nonpsychologistic, objectivist terms, for instance: 'any evidence for *i* is also evidence for *j*'; or: 'if *i* is true, then *j* is necessarily also true' (where 'necessarily' means not more than 'in any possible case, no matter what the facts happen to be'); indeed, we might say that the formulation in terms of justified belief is derivable from this one. Hence that formulation is not wrong. The characterization of logic in terms of correct or rational or justified belief is just as right but not more enlightening than to say that mineralogy tells us how to think correctly about minerals. The reference to thinking may just as well be dropped in both cases. Then we say simply: mineralogy makes statements about minerals, and logic makes statements about logical relations. The activity in any field of knowledge involves, of course, thinking. But this does not mean that thinking belongs to the subject matter of all fields. It belongs to the subject matter of psychology but not to that of logic any more than to that of mineralogy.

Because of the frequent discrepancy between introductory general remarks and the actual working theory of an author, we ought to be cautious in judging the latter on the basis of the former. The fact that an author uses occasionally some psychologistic formulations in general remarks about the task of logic, or in preliminary explanations of the meaning of some fundamental terms in logic, is not a sufficient reason for assuming that he has a subjectivistic conception of logic. If those explanations are in terms of correct or rational or justified thinking rather than of actual thinking, then in most cases they are not even subjectivistic. The reference to correctness or justification is presumably meant in the sense of 'in accordance with the rules of logic'; and these rules are regarded as objective by most logicians. The decisive point to examine is the way in which an author solves his logical problems, demonstrates logical theorems. If here his procedure is objectivistic, that is, free from references to the features of actual processes of thinking, then we have to regard his logic as objectivistic. This holds even if we find in his general remarks formulations not only of qualified but of primitive psychologism. If his working procedure is objectivistic, his occasional psychologistic formulations should be regarded as inessential relics from a traditional way of speech rather than as characteristics of his system of logic.

This view concerning the interpretation of psychologistic formulations in deductive logic, where the situation is relatively simple, will help us in understanding the analogous situation in the field of inductive logic, where the situation is at the present time much less clear.

§ 12. Psychologism in Inductive Logic

The situation with respect to psychologism in inductive logic, i.e., in the theory of probability$_1$, is analogous to that in deductive logic. We analyze here the formulations of some authors in two groups. *A*. Those who characterize *probability as a logical relation* similar to logical consequence (e.g., Keynes, Jeffreys). Here we find the systems themselves thoroughly objectivistic, but some general remarks show qualified psychologism, e.g., explanations of probability as degree of reasonable or justified belief; the concept meant is clearly probability$_1$. *B*. Authors of *the classical theory of probability* (e.g., Bernoulli, Laplace). Here, we find, in addition, formulations of primitive psychologism, e.g., explanations of probability as degree of belief or expectation. Nevertheless, it seems to me that their theories themselves were objectivistic; and, further, that they meant in most cases probability$_1$, not probability$_2$.

A. *Probability as a Logical Relation*

Deductive logic may be regarded as the theory of the relation of logical consequence, and inductive logic as the theory of another concept which is likewise objective and logical, viz., probability$_1$ or degree of confirmation. That probability$_1$ is an objective concept means this: if a certain probability$_1$ value holds for a certain hypothesis with respect to a certain evidence, then this value is entirely independent of what any person may happen to think about these sentences, just as the relation of logical consequence is independent in this respect. Consequently, a definition of an explicatum for probability$_1$ must not refer to any person and his beliefs but only to the two sentences and their logical properties within a given language system.

Now we shall show that the situation with respect to psychologism in inductive logic is in all essential respects analogous to that in deductive logic as discussed in the preceding section.

We have previously (§ 9) classified the theories of probability in three groups. In one of these groups the frequency conception of probability is adopted; here, the explicandum is obviously probability$_2$. The other two conceptions are the classical one (Bernoulli, Laplace) and the conception of probability as a logical concept related to deducibility (Keynes, Jeffreys).

Our problem is to discover what is the explicandum for the various authors of these two remaining groups. Let us begin with the last-mentioned group. Here, it will be easy to see that the explicandum is the objective, logical concept of probability$_1$. But even here we shall find psychologistic formulations. This fact will help us later in the analysis of classical authors to look through the deceiving shell of psychologistic formulations to the objectivistic core of their conception.

Keynes makes it quite clear that he regards probability as an objective, logical concept: "In the sense important to logic, probability is not subjective. It is not, that is to say, subject to human caprice. A proposition is not probable because we think so. When once the facts are given which determine our knowledge, what is probable or improbable in these circumstances has been fixed objectively, and is independent of our opinion. The Theory of Probability is logical, therefore" ([Probab.], p. 4). Keynes admits that probability may also be called subjective in another sense; it seems to me that here the term 'relative', in the sense of 'relating to a second proposition as evidence', would be more appropriate. He says (p. 4, in a passage immediately preceding the above quotation): "A proposition is capable at the same time of varying degrees of this relationship [of probability], depending upon the knowledge to which it is related, so that it is without significance to call a proposition probable unless we specify the knowledge to which we are relating it. To this extent, therefore, probability may be called subjective. But in the sense . . .". Then the preceding quotation follows, which makes it clear that Keynes's concept is in no respect meant as subjective in the sense opposite to objective.

Now it is interesting to see that Keynes, immediately following the passage quoted above in which he explicitly emphasizes the objective, logical nature of his concept, uses formulations of the kind which we have previously called qualified psychologism. He says: "The Theory of Probability is logical, therefore, because it is concerned with the degree of belief which it is *rational* to entertain in given conditions, and not merely with the actual beliefs of particular individuals, which may or may not be rational" (p. 4, italics in the original). His explicit contrasting of rational versus actual degree of belief and the use of 'because' show clearly that the reference to beliefs is not intended to modify in any way the characterization of the concept as a logical one or to bring in a subjective component. This will make us hesitant to interpret similar formulations of other authors as genuine symptoms of a subjectivistic conception. The situation here is analogous to that in deductive logic. Suppose that the hypothesis h has the probability$_1$ q with respect to the evidence e. Then, indeed, it follows that if somebody knows e and nothing else, he is justified in believing in h to the degree q and likewise justified in acting accordingly, e.g., in betting on h with q against $1 - q$. But this reference to belief should be avoided in a characterization of probability$_1$, because it blurs the important boundary line between logical and psychological concepts. Of course, in incidental informal explanations of probability$_1$, references to believing and betting will often facilitate the understanding—as in analogous cases in deductive logic and mathematics—but care should be taken that these references to something extra-logical do not obscure the nature of probability$_1$ as a purely logical concept.

That the objective logical concept meant by Keynes is the same as what we call probability$_1$, i.e., the logical concept of confirmation, becomes quite clear both by numerous preliminary explanations and by his reasonings in the construction of his system. He says, for instance: ". . . a logical connection between one set of propositions which we call our evidence and which we suppose ourselves to know, and another set which we call our conclusions, and to which we attach more or less weight according to the grounds supplied by the first" (p. 5 f.). Keynes takes the concept in general as nonquantitative, similar to our comparative concept of confirmation; only in special cases does his theory allow the attribution of numerical values like our quantitative concept of degree of confirmation.

It is true, some statements of Keynes concerning his concept of probability are not in agreement with our conception of probability$_1$. He says, for example: "A definition of probability is not possible. . . . We cannot analyze the probability-relation in terms of simpler ideas" (p. 8); later he speaks of "a faculty of direct recognition of many relations of probability" (p. 53) by a kind of "logical intuition" (p. 52). But I do not think that this is evidence against our interpretation of his concept in the sense of our probability$_1$. It is one question whether two persons mean the same by certain terms and quite another question whether or not they agree in their opinions concerning the thing meant.

With other representatives of this group the situation is on the whole similar. We see easily from their systematic constructions and often also from explicit explanations that their explicandum is an objective, logical concept and, more specifically, that it is probability$_1$. Often, but not always, we find also psychologistic formulations, mostly of the qualified form. For the reasons earlier discussed, we do not regard these formulations as symptoms of a genuinely subjectivist conception but merely as vestiges of an old tradition that has been overcome in substance but still lingers on in some forms of speech.

The general remarks just made may be illustrated by some brief references to some authors of this group.

That *Jeffreys* understands 'probability' in the sense of probability$_1$ becomes abundantly clear through his whole theory. The very first sentence of the preface of his chief work ([Probab.], p. v) describes his aim "to provide a method of drawing inferences from observational data". He begins with a comparative concept with three arguments ("on data p, q is more probable than r", p. 15), from which he develops a quantitative concept by suitable conventions (p. 19). The whole conception is thoroughly objectivistic but accompanied by occasional formulations of qualified psychologism, e.g., "The probability, strictly, is the reasonable degree of confidence" (p. 20), "reasonable degree of belief" (p. 31).

F. P. Ramsey's conception of probability seems at first inspection more psychological and subjectivistic than the conception of most of the other authors ([Truth] and [Considerations], both published in [Foundations];

my references are to the latter book). He says that the theory of probability is "the logic of partial belief" (pp. 159, 166); "we must therefore try to develop a purely psychological method of measuring belief" (p. 166); "I propose to take as a basis a general psychological theory" (p. 173). Thus it is not surprising that many authors have judged Ramsey's conception as a particularly clear case of subjectivism. However, it seems to me that a closer examination is apt to evoke serious doubts about this judgment. It is true that the psychological method of measuring the actual degree of belief of a person in a proposition plays a central role in Ramsey's discussion. But he does not define probability as or identify it with actual degree of belief. He says: "It is not enough to measure probability; in order *to apportion correctly our belief* to the probability we must also be able to measure our belief"; "if the phrase 'a belief two-thirds of certainty' is meaningless, a calculus [viz., the theory of probability] whose sole object is *to enjoin such beliefs* will be meaningless also" (both on p. 166; the italics are mine). Thus, he regards the theory of probability not as a part of psychology describing the actually occurring degrees of belief but rather as a part of logic giving standards or norms which tell us which degrees of belief we should entertain if we want to be rational and consistent in our beliefs. This interpretation seems confirmed by his statement that "the laws of probability are laws of consistency, an extension to partial beliefs of formal logic, the logic of consistency" (p. 182); "having degrees of belief obeying the laws of probability implies a further measure of consistency, namely such a consistency between the odds acceptable on different propositions as shall prevent a book being made against you". This shows that the standard imposed upon our beliefs by the theory of probability is regarded as an objective one, viz., avoiding certain unfavorable results in betting. Later (p. 191) he characterizes logic "as the science of rational thought. We found", he continues, "that the most generally accepted parts of logic, namely, formal logic, mathematics, and the calculus of probabilities, are all concerned simply to ensure that our beliefs are not self-contradictory". This conception of the nature of logic as normative for, rather than descriptive of, beliefs is clearly expressed in the following words: "Logic, we may agree, is concerned not with what men actually believe, but what they ought to believe, or what it would be reasonable to believe" (p. 193). This formulation must clearly be judged as qualified rather than primitive psychologism. Therefore our previous consideration that the step from primitive to qualified psychologism shows an underlying objectivist conception applies also to Ramsey. This judgment seems confirmed by Ramsey's own later remark (written in 1929) concerning his earlier paper ([Truth], written in 1926): "The defect of my paper on probability was that it took partial belief as a psychological phenomenon to be defined and measured by a psychologist" (p. 256).

One of the rare cases in which primitive psychologism with respect to probability is meant literally is to be found in *James Jeans's* discussion of the probability waves in quantum mechanics (*Physics and philosophy* [New York, 1943]). We may leave aside here the question as to whether the concept of probability used in quantum theory is to be understood in the sense of probability$_1$ or of probability$_2$; maybe formulations of both kinds are possible. At any rate, both concepts are objective; the application of the one is a matter of logic, that of the other a matter of physics; neither of them is a psychological concept. Jeans, however, believes that probability in quantum theory is something of a mental nature. Hence he comes to the conclusion that Dirac's waves of probability are waves of knowledge; "the final picture consists wholly of waves, and its ingredients are wholly mental constructs". Consequently, he sees in this development of physics "a pronounced step in the direction of mentalism".

B. *The Classical Theory of Probability*

Now let us see to what extent psychologism is to be found in the so-called classical conception of probability, as originated by Jacob Bernoulli and Laplace. This conception shows itself in the definition of probability and in the way in which this definition is used; in other words, in the explicatum of these authors and their followers. Here, however, we shall not discuss their explicatum but their explicandum. We find many psychologistic formulations; probability is explained, for instance, as degree of belief, degree of certainty, and the like. Therefore, many later writers have characterized the classical conception as subjectivistic. If those formulations were taken literally, the theorems on probability would be statements of psychological laws; most of them would be obviously false just as are theorems of deductive logic interpreted as psychological laws, because our beliefs are often influenced by irrational factors. Thus it is understandable that many adherents of the classical conception seem not to feel quite satisfied with these formulations and use, either in addition or instead, those of qualified psychologism, for instance, 'rational degree of belief', and the like. As we have seen earlier, formulations of this kind may be regarded as a step toward the elimination of psychologism and are indeed no longer subjectivistic because they presuppose—in most cases tacitly—objective standards. Therefore, the occurrence of these formulations suggests that perhaps the use of primitive psychologistic formulations is likewise not a proof of a genuinely subjectivist conception but merely a customary, though not quite adequate, way of dealing with concepts which are meant as logical, not psychological.

Jacob Bernoulli makes some general explanatory remarks about the nature and application of probability in the beginning of Part Four of his *Ars conjectandi*, a work that marks the beginning of the systematic study of probability. He declares that "probability is the degree of certainty and differs from it as a part from the whole" (p. 211). The highest certainty is attributed by him to those things which we know by revelation, reasoning, or sensory perception; all other things have a less perfect measure of certainty. All this has a psychologistic sound. It becomes, however, quite clear that Bernoulli's theory of probability which he calls the art of conjecture ("ars conjectandi sive stochastice", p. 213) is not meant as a description of actual processes of reasoning but rather as a guide to correct and useful reasoning. He defines this art as "the art of measuring the probabilities of things as exactly as possible, so that we can always select and heed in our judgments and actions that which appears to us as better, more suitable, more certain or advisable" (p. 213).

Similarly *Laplace* understands 'probability' not in a psychological, subjective sense but in an objective sense. This is clearly shown by some passages near the end of his philosophical work ([Essai]; our quotations are from the edition of 1921). Here he says that the theory of probability makes exact what we feel by a kind of instinct; that it leaves nothing arbitrary in the choice of our opinions, since, with its help, the most advantageous choice can be determined; further, that the theory guides our judgments and protects us from illusions (II, 105 f.).

If the explicandum which the classical authors had in mind was not a subjective concept, which objective concept was it? The logical concept of probability$_1$ and the empirical concept of probability$_2$ are both objective. I am inclined to assume that on most occasions, though perhaps with a few exceptions, they meant something like probability$_1$, that is to say, not an empirical but a logical concept, which characterizes the strength given to a certain hypothesis by some amount of evidence.

Laplace ([Essai], I, 7) discusses an example of three urns—A, B, C. We know that one of them contains only black balls, but we do not know which of the three it is; we know further that the two other urns contain only white balls. Laplace raises the question as to what is the probability that a ball which will be drawn from the urn C will turn out to be black. From our present point of view, the essential fact is that Laplace states different values of the probability: first one on the basis of the knowledge mentioned; then another value which the probability takes on when we learn that the urn *A* contains only white balls; and, finally, a third value when we learn, in addition, that *B* likewise contains only white balls. This shows that Laplace is not speaking about probability$_2$ or any other physical property of the urns, because these properties do not change when we learn more about the urns. What he means must be something that is dependent upon the state of our knowledge; hence it seems likely that he means something like the weight of evidence that our knowledge gives to a certain hypothesis, in other words, something like probability$_1$.

The formulations by which the classical authors intend to explain what they mean by 'probability' vary a good deal, even with the same author, and are often not as clear as we might wish. Thus we must base our interpretation also on the way in which they reason about probability in their theories. Often when we try to interpret an ambiguous term used by an author of another period, in another language or in an unfamiliar terminology, we proceed in the following way. Suppose the author in question is known for many valuable results he has found in the same or a related field; suppose further that he uses the term in question at certain places not in a casual way but in the formulation of theorems which are clearly important to him; suppose, finally, that among the meanings of the term which come into consideration there is one for which these theorems would hold, while they would be false for the other meanings. Then there is some reason to regard these facts as supporting the assumption that the meaning of the term which makes the theorems true is the one intended by the author. Certainly, this method must be used with caution; otherwise it would lead to rather arbitrary interpretations and, in the extreme, to the absurd result that all assertions of all authors seem to agree with our opinions. But as an auxiliary procedure, in combination with a consideration of the author's own explanations of the term, it may sometimes be helpful. Let us apply this to our case. The classical theory of probability contains certain theorems of the following kind. If interpreted in the sense of probability$_2$, these theorems are obviously false (even after certain modifications which seem necessary for any interpretation, e.g., the addition of a second argument of the probability function). Therefore the representatives of the frequency conception have rejected these theorems and have even expressed their amazement that any sensible man should assume such absurdities. These theorems are, of course, also false if interpreted in the sense of the psychological concept of degree of belief, as are practically all theorems. On the other hand, these theorems are true or at least not quite implausible if interpreted in the sense of probability$_1$. (Examples are certain specializations of the controversial principle of indifference; this principle itself in the customary form, however, is too general and leads to contradictions.) It seems to me that this fact lends additional support to our assumption that the explicandum which the classical authors had in mind during most of their discussions is probability$_1$ or something similar to it. I formulate this assumption with these cautious restrictions because it seems to me that there is no one meaning of the term 'probability' which is applied with perfect consistency throughout his work by any of the classical authors. There are some places where, I think, the interpretation as probability$_1$ makes no good sense while the interpretation as probability$_2$ does. (Examples are the references to "unknown probabilities"; see below, § 41D.)

Our interpretation of the classical theory in terms of probability$_1$ is in agreement with the view of Jeffreys, who offers forceful arguments in favor of this interpretation as against one in terms of frequency; one strong argument is simply the characteristic title *Ars conjectandi* of Bernoulli's book. Jeffreys comes to the following conclusion: "I maintain that the work of the pioneers [Bernoulli, Bayes, and Laplace] shows quite clearly that they were concerned with the construction of a consistent theory of reasonable degrees of belief, and in the cases of Bayes and Laplace, with the foundations of common sense or inductive inference" ([Probab.], p. 335).

With respect to those later writers who follow the classical tradition the situation is quite similar. In spite of psychologistic formulations, it is usually quite clear that they have an objectivist conception. We may perhaps have some doubt in this respect in the case of *De Morgan* because of his persistent formulations in terms of primitive psychologism. But even here we find that finally the author not only takes the saving step from primitive to qualified psychologism but regards this step merely as a transition from a natural, though not quite adequate, formulation to a more correct one rather than as a change in the conception itself: " 'It is more probable than improbable' means . . . 'I believe that it will happen more than I believe that it will not happen'. Or rather, 'I *ought* to believe, etc.' " ([Logic], pp. 172 f.). [Incidentally, a formulation like 'It is more probable than improbable that it will rain', used by some authors, seems a somewhat jumbled way of saying 'It is more probable that it will rain than that it will not rain'; it is like saying: 'I believe that it will rain more than I disbelieve that it will rain'.]

It seems to me that, on the basis of the discussions of this section, it is plausible to assume that for most, perhaps for practically all, of those authors on probability who do not accept a frequency conception the following holds. (i) Their theories of probability are objectivistic; the frequent formulations of psychologism, qualified or even primitive, are usually only preliminary remarks not affecting their actual working method. (ii) The objective concept which they mean, clearly or vaguely, as their explicandum is something similar to probability$_1$; in the classical period the explicandum is often not yet quite clear; but it seems that in the course of the historical development the concept of probability$_1$ emerges more and more clearly.

It cannot, of course, be denied that there is also a subjective, psychological concept for which the term 'probability' may be used and sometimes is used. This is the concept of the degree of actual, as distinguished from rational, belief: 'the person X at the time t believes in h to the degree r'. This concept is of importance for the theory of human behavior, hence for psychology, sociology, economics, etc. But it cannot serve as a basis for inductive logic or a calculus of probability applicable as a general tool of science.

CHAPTER III

DEDUCTIVE LOGIC

In this chapter (§§ 14–40) the language systems $\mathfrak{L}$ are constructed, to which our theory of inductive logic will later be applied; and as much of the deductive logic with respect to these language systems is outlined as is necessary as a basis for the later construction of inductive logic.

The first part of this chapter (§§ 14–20) gives the semantical foundations of deductive logic. The knowledge of this part is presupposed already in the next chapter, while the study of the other parts may be postponed until their material is used in later chapters. The *language systems* $\mathfrak{L}$ are constructed as systems of *semantical rules*. There is one system $\mathfrak{L}_\infty$ with an infinite number of individuals, and other systems $\mathfrak{L}_N$ with a finite number N of individuals. The rules of formation determine the ways in which the signs of the systems $\mathfrak{L}$ (§ 15) may be combined into sentences (§ 16). We use individual variables as the only variables (hence our systems correspond to what is known in symbolic logic as the lower functional logic). The rules of truth give sufficient and necessary conditions for the truth of the sentences (§ 17). Certain sentences which completely describe all individuals with respect to all properties and relations expressible in the system are called *state-descriptions* ($\mathfrak{Z}$) (D18-1); they represent all possible states of affairs for the whole domain of individuals. The *rules of ranges* determine for every sentence i in which of the state-descriptions it holds (D18-4); the class of these state-descriptions is called the *range* of i ($\mathfrak{R}_i$, D18-6a). In this way the rules give an interpretation of the language system, i.e., they determine the meaning of every sentence; for to know the meaning of a sentence is to know in which of all possible cases it would be true. The rules, by determining the ranges, serve also as a basis for what we call the *L-concepts* (§ 20). For instance, a sentence is said to be L-true (logically true, analytic) if it holds in all possible cases, hence if its range comprises all state-descriptions (D20-1a); other L-concepts, e.g., L-falsity, L-implication, L-equivalence, are likewise defined on the basis of the concept of range (D20-1). Deductive logic may be regarded as the theory of the L-concepts; hence, in our method, it is based on the concept of range. In a later chapter we shall define functions representing the degree of confirmation likewise with the help of the concept of range; thus, inductive logic will likewise be based on the concept of range.

The second part of this chapter (§§ 21–24) lists theorems of deductive logic for later reference, most of them well known. They deal with the connectives of *propositional logic* (§ 21), *general sentences* (§ 22), replacements (§ 23), and identity (§ 24).

The third and largest part (§§ 25–38) deals with special topics of deductive logic, selected because of their importance for inductive logic. Concepts applied to predicates, or to the properties and relations designated by them, are defined (§ 25). Isomorphism of sentences is defined (D26-3a). This concept, especially in its application to state-descriptions, will later be of great importance in inductive logic. If two *state-descriptions* are *isomorphic* (§ 27), they may be said to attribute to the realm of individuals the same structure. Certain sentences, which describe the possible structures, are called *structure-descriptions* ($\mathfrak{Str}$, D27-1). The most important special kind of our language systems $\mathfrak{L}$ comprises those whose primitive predicates designate only properties, not relations; they are called the systems $\mathfrak{L}^\pi$ (§ 31). These systems are dealt with in detail (§§ 31–38). Predicates of a special kind, 'Q_1', 'Q_2', etc., are introduced (§ 31). The *Q-properties* designated by these *Q-predicates* are the strongest properties expressible in the system. If a state-description is given, then we call the cardinal numbers of the *Q*-properties the *Q-numbers* of that state-description (§ 34). Isomorphic state-descriptions have the same *Q*-numbers, and any structure is completely characterized by its *Q*-numbers. In a later chapter the *Q*-numbers will be used for determining the degree of confirmation. Some deductive properties of *universal laws* are discussed (§ 37), in particular of laws of conditional form (§ 38).

In the last section of this chapter (§ 40) some mathematical definitions and theorems are listed for reference in this and later chapters.

§ 14. Preliminary Explanations

The importance of an exact description of the object languages for inductive logic is emphasized. As metalanguage, English will be used, supplemented by German letters and other special signs.

The present chapter does not deal with probability or inductive logic but supplies the necessary foundations for our later discussions of these topics. Here, we shall describe certain language systems $\mathfrak{L}$, and we shall outline a deductive logic for these systems. In later chapters, possibilities of inductive logic, that is, a theory of probability$_1$ (degree of confirmation), will be discussed in application to these language systems $\mathfrak{L}$ and based upon the deductive logic to be outlined here.

This chapter consists of three parts, only the first of which is presupposed in the next chapter. (i) The first sections (§§ 14–20) describe the systems $\mathfrak{L}$ and explain some semantical concepts in application to these systems. These concepts will be used continually in the later chapters. Therefore it seems advisable for the reader to become acquainted with them and their chief characteristics; but it is not necessary to study now all theorems given for them; the most important definitions and theorems are marked by '+'. (ii) Some subsequent sections (§§ 21–24) contain chiefly well-known material of deductive logic. They are written in the first place for purposes of later reference, not so much for reading. Of the same nature is the last section in this chapter (§ 40); it lists some mathematical definitions and theorems. (iii) The remaining sections (§§ 25–38) deal with special topics in deductive logic which are needed for certain later chapters. The reader who is impatient to come to inductive logic as soon as possible may skip them at present, to return to the one or the other of them only later when the need arises and indications are given. (The material of §§ 25–27 will be needed in chap. viii; that of §§ 31 and 32 in § 107.)

When we come to inductive logic, we shall see that it is even more necessary there than in deductive logic to describe the whole structure of the language to which it is to be applied; that is to say, the value of the degree of confirmation for two given sentences is dependent not only upon the two sentences but also upon the particular features of the language to which the sentences belong. Although many contemporary authors have used symbolic logic in their discussions on probability$_1$ (for instance, Keynes, Jeffreys, Mazurkiewicz, Hosiasson), none of them, let alone earlier authors, has paid sufficient attention to the language structure. In my view, this is a serious defect of most theories from the classical period up to our time; it is responsible for certain difficulties and even for contradictions resulting from certain principles in their customary form. Therefore it is essential that we specify our language systems in detail before applying inductive logic to them.

For the language systems to be constructed here we choose a relatively simple structure, with individual variables as the only variables. [This structure corresponds approximately to what is known as the lower functional logic with only individual variables, or (in the terminology of Alonzo Church, [Dictionary], p. 174) a simple applied functional calculus of first order.] The actual language of science and even that of elementary physics has, of course, a much more complex structure; space-time points are represented by their coordinates, and hence real number variables are required; events are described in a quantitative way, with the help of physical functions with numerical values. However, it seems advisable not to try the construction of an inductive logic immediately for a language of this complex form but to begin with simpler structures. Deductive logic, which is more than two thousand years older than inductive logic, was likewise first applied to simple language forms. Aristotle's logic, the traditional logic based upon it, and even the first systems which used the exact, symbolic methods of modern logic (constructed by Boole and his followers) deal only with sentence forms which constitute a small fraction of those in the systems to be here constructed. Frege was the first (in *Begriffsschrift* [1879]) to construct a system of deductive logic for a language form which reaches the complexity of the one we shall use here and even goes far beyond it. Later, some indications will be made concerning possible ways for solving the problems of extending our system of inductive logic to more comprehensive languages. These problems concern especially languages containing a basic order of the individuals (§ 15) and those containing quantitative physical concepts.

Since we intend to construct inductive logic as a theory of degree of confirmation, based upon the meanings of the sentences involved—in contradistinction to a mere calculus—we shall construct the language systems $\mathfrak{L}$ with an interpretation, hence as systems of semantical rules, not as uninterpreted syntactical systems. The systems $\mathfrak{L}$, our object languages, are symbolic systems, containing customary symbols of symbolic logic and some letters as nonlogical constants. This book presupposes some knowledge of the simplest elements of symbolic logic; but it does not presuppose acquaintance with the semantical method as developed in [Semantics]. The semantical concepts here used will be explained to the extent necessary for the purposes of this book.

Those readers who wish to obtain a fuller understanding of the semantical method, and especially the semantical L-concepts, may be referred to the more detailed discussions in [Semantics] and [Meaning]. The broader field of semiotic, the general theory of signs, of which semantics forms a part, is briefly sketched in Charles Morris' *Foundations of the theory of signs* (= "Encyclopedia of unified science," Vol. I, No. 2 [1938]), and surveyed in greater detail in his *Signs, language, and behavior* (1946).

As metalanguage in which we describe the systems $\mathfrak{L}$ and formulate theorems of deductive logic concerning these systems and later the theorems of inductive logic, we use the English language supplemented by some technical signs, especially *German letters*, as follows:

'$\mathfrak{in}$' refers to the individual constants (of the systems $\mathfrak{L}$ in general or of the one under discussion),

'$\mathfrak{i}$' to the individual variables,

'$\mathfrak{pr}$' to the primitive predicates,

'$\mathfrak{A}$' refers to any expressions (that is, single signs or finite sequences of signs),

'$\mathfrak{S}$' to the sentences,

'$\mathfrak{M}$' to (sentential) ***matrices*** (that is, either sentences or expressions of analogous forms but with free variables, e.g., 'Px'),

'$\mathfrak{K}$' to classes of sentences (sometimes also to classes of other expressions);

further (see later explanations): '$\mathfrak{Z}$' refers to state-descriptions, '$\mathfrak{R}$' to ranges (§ 18), and '$\mathfrak{Str}$' to structure-descriptions (§ 27).

We adopt the *term 'matrix'* from Quine, because the more customary terms 'propositional function' or 'sentential function' are misleading (see [Semantics], pp. 232 f.). Following the usage of most mathematicians, the *term 'function'* is applied in this book only to certain concepts (e.g., 'c-functions'), but not to linguistic expressions.

These German letters will be used in two ways. (i) A German letter *without subscript* will sometimes be used as a convenient abbreviation for the corresponding English noun or phrase (or its plural form); for example, we shall sometimes write 'all $\mathfrak{Z}$ are . . .' as short for 'all state-descriptions are . . .', 'this system contains three $\mathfrak{pr}$' for '. . . three primitive predicates', 'this sentence contains no $\mathfrak{in}$' for '. . . no individual constant', etc. (ii) A German letter *with one of the subscripts* '*i*', '*j*', etc., serves as a variable of the metalanguage for reference to the kind of signs or expressions of the systems $\mathfrak{L}$ indicated above. (Less frequently, a German letter with one of the subscripts '1', '2', etc., is used as a constant of the same kind.) For instance, a formulation like: 'If $\mathfrak{S}_i$ L-implies $\mathfrak{S}_j$, then the negation of $\mathfrak{S}_j$ L-implies the negation of $\mathfrak{S}_i$' is to be understood as saying: 'If a first sentence L-implies a second sentence (which is not necessarily different from the first), then the negation of the second L-implies the negation of the first". Since the arguments of degree of confirmation are sentences, our discussions and theorems will contain very many references to sentences; therefore it is convenient to have simpler signs for these references. For this reason, we shall, instead of '$\mathfrak{S}_i$', '$\mathfrak{S}_j$', '$\mathfrak{S}_k$', '$\mathfrak{S}_l$', usually write simply '*i*', '*j*', '*k*', '*l*'; '*e*' and '*h*' are used in the same way. Note that these letters, although italics, belong, not to the symbolic systems $\mathfrak{L}$, but to the metalanguage, that is, they are used, like German letters, in the English context.

Some other German letters are used in the metalanguage, not as designations for expressions of the object languages, but for certain semantical concepts of inductive logic; these are chiefly the functors '$\mathfrak{m}$' (measure function, § 55A) and '$\mathfrak{c}$' (degree of confirmation, § 55A); furthermore, in some special chapters, the functors '$\mathfrak{r}$' (relevance measure, § 67) and '$\mathfrak{e}$' (estimate, § 99) and the predicates '$\mathfrak{MC}$' (the comparative concept of confirmation, § 79), '$\mathfrak{C}$' (the classificatory concept of confirmation, § 86), and others. '$\mathfrak{L}$' is used for the semantical systems to be constructed here.

In connection with the use of German letters, we lay down two conventions. The first one is customary.

Convention 14-1. A name in the metalanguage for a compound expression of the object language is formed by simple juxtaposition of the names (or variables) for the signs of which the compound expression consists.

For example, if '$\mathfrak{pr}_i$' refers to '*R*', '$\mathfrak{in}_j$' to '*a*', and '$\mathfrak{in}_k$' to '*b*', then '$\mathfrak{pr}_i\mathfrak{in}_j\mathfrak{in}_k$' refers to '*Rab*'. Further, for the sake of simplifying the symbolic notation in the metalanguage, we shall permit the use of symbols of the object languages as names of themselves, provided the occurrence of a symbol of the metalanguage, e.g., a German letter, makes it clear that the whole expression belongs to the metalanguage. Because of this restricting condition, no ambiguity can arise. Hence we lay down the following convention:

Convention 14-2. If a compound symbolic expression contains a German letter (or one of the letters 'e', 'h', . . . , 'l', which are equivalent to German letters) or '⊦' (see below), then the whole expression is to be understood as an expression of the metalanguage, and any symbol of the object language occurring in it is to be understood as a name of itself, that is, as if it were included in quotation marks or replaced by a corresponding German letter.

We shall, however, make use of the notation allowed by this convention only in the following two ways:

(*a*) In order to form the name of an expression (according to Convention 1), we very often take as names of symbols of the object language (usually nonletter symbols or 't') these symbols themselves, as is customary. (For example, if 'i' refers to 'Pa', and 'j' to 'Qb', then '$(\sim i) \vee j$' refers to '$(\sim Pa) \vee Qb$'; hence the connectives and parentheses are used here as names of themselves.)

(*b*) We write occasionally (not frequently) an expression of the object language instead of its name when it occurs as an argument expression following either a German letter functor (e.g., '$\mathfrak{m}$', '$\mathfrak{c}$') or a German letter predicate (e.g., '$\mathfrak{MC}$') of the metalanguage. (For example, we might write '$\mathfrak{c}(Pb, e)$' instead of '$\mathfrak{c}$('Pb', e)' or '$\mathfrak{c}(\mathfrak{pr}_1\mathfrak{in}_2, e)$'.)

Some other special signs are used in the metalanguage in combination with German letters. We take '⊦' for 'L-true' (to be explained later, § 20); thus we write '$\vdash i$' as short for 'i is L-true (in the system in question)'. Hence (according to later explanations) '$\vdash i \supset j$' means the same as 'i L-implies j (in the system in question)' (thus the earlier example will be written like this: 'If $\vdash i \supset j$ then $\vdash \sim j \supset \sim i$'). The following signs are used in combinations with class expressions in the metalanguage. '$\mathfrak{K}_i \subset \mathfrak{K}_j$' is written as short for '$\mathfrak{K}_i$ is a subclass of $\mathfrak{K}_j$'; '. . . $\epsilon \mathfrak{K}_j$' for '. . . belongs to (is an element of) $\mathfrak{K}_j$'; '$\mathfrak{K}_i \cup \mathfrak{K}_j$' for 'the class-sum of $\mathfrak{K}_i$ and $\mathfrak{K}_j$'; '$\mathfrak{K}_i \cap \mathfrak{K}_j$' for 'the class-product of $\mathfrak{K}_i$ and $\mathfrak{K}_j$'; '$-\mathfrak{K}_i$' for 'the complement-class of $\mathfrak{K}_i$' (i.e., 'the class of all sentences not belonging to $\mathfrak{K}_i$'); '$\mathfrak{K}_j - \mathfrak{K}_i$' for '$\mathfrak{K}_j \cap (-\mathfrak{K}_i)$'. '$\{i\}$' designates the class whose only element is i; '$\{j_1, j_2, \ldots, j_n\}$' the class whose only elements are $j_1, j_2, \ldots, j_n$. '$=_{\mathrm{Df}}$' is used as sign of definition in the metalanguage. '$(\ )(\mathfrak{M}_k)$' is short for '$(\mathfrak{i}_{k1})(\mathfrak{i}_{k2}) \ldots (\mathfrak{i}_{kn})(\mathfrak{M}_k)$', where $\mathfrak{i}_{k1}, \mathfrak{i}_{k2}, \ldots, \mathfrak{i}_{kn}$ are the variables occuring freely in $\mathfrak{M}_k$, in the order of increasing subscripts.

This book makes use of *symbolic logic* and presupposes some elementary knowledge in this field. All the symbols used will be explained in the next section. Elementary introductions to symbolic logic: Alfred Tarski, *Introduction to logic* (New York, 1941), John Cooley, *A primer of formal logic* (New York, 1942), Hans Reichenbach, *Elements of symbolic logic* (New York, 1947). Systematic works on a higher technical level: Whitehead and Russell [Princ. Math.], which is the great standard work in the field, and Quine [Math. Logic], which constructs a system of a new form.

§ 15. The Signs of the Systems $\mathfrak{L}$

A. The infinite system $\mathfrak{L}_\infty$ contains an infinite sequence of individual constants (in): 'a_1', 'a_2', etc. Any finite system $\mathfrak{L}_N$ contains only the first N of them. All other signs are the same in all systems. There is a finite number of primitive predicates (pr) of any degrees. There is an infinite sequence of individual variables (i): 'x_1', 'x_2', etc.; they are the only variables. There are universal quantifiers, and the customary symbols for identity, negation, disjunction, and conjunction. The customary symbols for existence, conditional, biconditional, and nonidentity are introduced as unofficial abbreviations (A1). *B*. Some indications are made concerning possibilities for the construction of a more comprehensive language system describing a basic order of the individuals and for a method of inductive logic suitable to that system.

A. *The Signs Occuring in Our Systems*

Our language systems $\mathfrak{L}$ comprise one ***infinite system*** $\mathfrak{L}_\infty$ and the ***finite systems*** $\mathfrak{L}_N$; the latter form an infinite sequence of systems with N running through all positive integers: $\mathfrak{L}_1$, $\mathfrak{L}_2$, $\mathfrak{L}_3$, etc.

The system $\mathfrak{L}_\infty$ contains an infinite sequence of ***individual constants*** (in): 'a_1', 'a_2', 'a_3', etc. (in examples we shall sometimes use 'a', 'b', 'c', etc.); they refer to all the ***individuals*** in the domain of individuals (universe of discourse) of $\mathfrak{L}_\infty$. These individuals may be things, events, positions, or the like. Further, $\mathfrak{L}_\infty$ contains a finite number of ***primitive predicates*** (pr) of any degree (i.e., number of arguments). Those of degree one, for example, 'P_1', 'P_2', etc., designate *properties* of individuals; those of degree two, for example, 'R_1', 'R_2', etc., designate dyadic *relations* between individuals; and so on. Properties and relations together will be called ***attributes***. We do not specify the number of pr beforehand; sometimes we shall do so in order to make the description of $\mathfrak{L}_\infty$ and the other systems more specific. Further, we do not lay down an interpretation for the pr or the in because the choice of a particular interpretation is irrelevant for both deductive and inductive logic. Thus, what we shall actually construct is, strictly speaking, not a semantical system but, so to speak, a skeleton of a semantical system. We assume that for any concrete application of deductive or inductive logic the systems are supplemented in the following way: (i) a finite number of $\mathfrak{pr}$ is chosen and their degrees are specified; (ii) an interpretation for these $\mathfrak{pr}$ is given by rules of designation, that is, semantical rules of a form like this: '$\mathfrak{pr}_1$ designates the property Blue'; (iii) the $\mathfrak{in}$ are interpreted by a general rule of designation of the following form: 'With respect to such and such an infinite sequence of entities, the *n*th individual constant (i.e., 'a_n') designates the *n*th entity in the sequence'; this rule is assumed to be such that we can see from it alone without the use of factual knowledge that any two different individual constants designate different entities. (The interpretations of the $\mathfrak{pr}$ and the $\mathfrak{in}$ must fulfil a requirement of logical independence to be explained later, § 18B.) We shall speak of a *class of individuals* usually only in case the individuals are given by an enumeration with the help of individual constants, but not in case they are characterized by a common property. Thus, for example, we shall say 'the class of the individuals *a, b, c*' or 'the class of the individuals referred to in the sentence *e*' (meaning 'the class of the individuals whose $\mathfrak{in}$ occur in *e*'); but we shall not say 'the class of those individuals which are P_1' or 'the class Blue', but rather 'the property (of being) P_1' or 'the property Blue'.

If we were only concerned with deductive logic, there would not be much reason to construct finite systems in addition to $\mathfrak{L}_\infty$. However, we shall see that the construction of an inductive logic is made technically simpler if we apply it, not immediately to $\mathfrak{L}_\infty$, but first to finite systems and then with their help to $\mathfrak{L}_\infty$. $\mathfrak{L}_N$ contains only the *N* first individual constants of $\mathfrak{L}_\infty$; hence $\mathfrak{L}_1$ contains only 'a_1'; $\mathfrak{L}_2$ contains 'a_1' and 'a_2'; etc. The $\mathfrak{in}$ in $\mathfrak{L}_N$ designate the same individuals as in $\mathfrak{L}_\infty$; thus the individual domain of each finite system is a part of that of $\mathfrak{L}_\infty$. It is clear that every individual constant of $\mathfrak{L}_\infty$ occurs also in some finite systems, and indeed in infinitely many such systems; for a given *n*, 'a_n' occurs in every $\mathfrak{L}_N$ with $N \geqq n$. Since all the other signs are the same in all systems, every sentence of $\mathfrak{L}_\infty$ occurs in infinitely many finite systems; if 'a_n' is the individual constant with the highest subscript occurring in the sentence ***i*** of $\mathfrak{L}_\infty$, then ***i*** occurs also in every $\mathfrak{L}_N$ with $N \geqq n$.

Every system $\mathfrak{L}$, finite or infinite, contains an infinite number of ***individual variables*** ($\mathfrak{i}$): 'x_1', 'x_2', 'x_3', etc. (or '*x*', '*y*', '*z*', etc.). The individual constants and individual variables are together called ***individual signs***. The values of these variables in a given system are the individuals of that system, that is, the individuals designated by the $\mathfrak{in}$ of that system.

Every system contains universal quantifiers with individual variables; '$(x)(Px)$' means 'for every individual x (of the domain of individuals of the system in question), x is P'. The existential quantifiers (e.g., '$(\exists x)$', 'there is an individual x (of the system in question)') do not occur in the systems themselves; but we shall introduce them by the customary definition for the purpose of convenient, inofficial abbreviations (A1c). According to the given explanation, the sentence '$(x)(Px)$' in $\mathfrak{L}_N$ means the same as the conjunction '$Pa_1 \,.\, Pa_2 \,.\, \ldots \,.\, Pa_N$' with N components; and we shall lay down the semantical rules in such a way that these two sentences are L-equivalent. Thus, in different finite systems, the universal sentence '$(x)(Px)$' has different meanings. And in $\mathfrak{L}_\infty$ the same sentence has again a different meaning because it says something about the infinitely many individuals. In $\mathfrak{L}_\infty$ the *scope* 'Px' has an infinite number of *instances* 'Pa_1', 'Pa_2', etc.; therefore we cannot form a conjunction out of them; but the universal sentence is L-equivalent to the infinite class of these instances.

It is important to realize clearly the fact that the same sentence may have different meanings in different systems and hence also different properties both in deductive and in inductive logic. Perhaps a reader might think that, although we have the same string of marks in different systems, we cannot properly speak here of the same sentence if the meanings are different. However, we have decided to understand by the term 'sentence' just the string of marks (more exactly speaking, a sentence-design is a finite sequence of sign-designs, see [Semantics] §§ 2, 3). If somebody prefers to use the phrase 'the same sentence' only if both the signs and the meanings are identical, there is no objection; however, in this case we should have to look for another term to take the place of our term 'sentence'. The relationship between '$(x)(Px)$' as an item occurring in the system $\mathfrak{L}_1$, and the same string of marks in $\mathfrak{L}_5$, and the same in $\mathfrak{L}_\infty$, is not a mere typographical accident (as is the case, for example, with '$\sim$' in Russell's and in Hilbert's notations, where there is no connection of meanings). The meanings, although different, stand in a close relationship to each other. The meanings of '$(x)(Px)$' in the systems $\mathfrak{L}_N$ with increasing N converge, so to speak, toward its meaning in $\mathfrak{L}_\infty$; this fact will later be of great importance in inductive logic for the definition of degree of confirmation with respect to sentences in $\mathfrak{L}_\infty$ (§ 56). For this reason, our way of speaking of 'the same sentence' will be very convenient.

The sentences in our systems contain no free variables. These systems contain only individual variables, no attribute variables. (This is that form of the lower functional logic which has been applied more frequently in recent years and has been shown to be a good working basis for logic.)

All signs except the individual constants occur in all systems 𝔏 alike. All signs except the individual variables have the same meanings wherever they occur; hence every sentence without variables has the same meaning in all systems in which it occurs. Thus the following explanations of the remaining signs apply to all systems.

The systems contain '=' as the customary sign of ***identity*** for individuals; this sign is not regarded as a predicate and hence not counted among the primitive predicates (𝔭𝔯). As mentioned earlier, it is presupposed that different individual constants designate different individuals; that is to say, we shall construct the semantical rules in such a way that a full sentence of '=' with two different in (e.g., '$a_1 = a_3$') becomes L-false (for explanation of the terms with 'L-', see § 20). Further, we shall of course make the rules such that an =-sentence with two occurrences of the same in will be L-true. Hence all =-sentences will be L-determinate. '≠' will be defined as sign for nonidentity (A1d).

The systems 𝔏 contain '*t*' as a *tautological sentence*. It would, of course, be possible to define '*t*' as abbreviation for some tautological sentence (e.g., for '$P_1a_1 \vee \sim P_1a_1$'). However, we prefer to take it as a primitive sign belonging to the systems themselves; this seems convenient for the construction of normal forms.

Of the customary ***connectives***, only the signs of negation ('∼', meaning 'not'), disjunction ('∨', 'or' in the nonexclusive sense), and conjunction ('.', 'and') occur in the systems themselves. The signs of the conditional ('⊃', meaning 'if—then') and of the biconditional ('≡', 'if and only if') will be introduced by their customary definitions (A1a and b). Following Quine, we regard these and all other defined signs not as belonging to the systems themselves; an expression containing a defined sign serves, so to speak, as shorthand for the corresponding expanded expression in primitive notation. (Concerning a later deviation from this procedure see remark preceding D33-1.)

The definitions introducing abbreviations for expressions of the object languages, i.e., the systems 𝔏, are marked by 'A'; the much more frequent definitions introducing words, phrases, or signs (e.g., German letters) into the metalanguage are marked by 'D', theorems by 'T', etc.; each of these letters 'A', 'D', 'T', etc., is followed by two numerals (e.g., 'A15-1'); the first gives the number of the section, the second that of the particular item. For references within the same section the first numeral is omitted (for example, a reference 'A1a' in this section refers to A15-1a). The more important definitions, theorems, etc., are marked by '+' (e.g., D18-1).

A15-1. Expressions containing the signs '$\supset$', '$\equiv$', '$\exists$', and '$\neq$' will be used as unofficial abbreviations in the following way.

a. $\mathfrak{M}_i \supset \mathfrak{M}_j$ for $(\sim\mathfrak{M}_i) \vee \mathfrak{M}_j$.

b. $\mathfrak{M}_i \equiv \mathfrak{M}_j$ for $(\mathfrak{M}_i \supset \mathfrak{M}_j) \,.\, (\mathfrak{M}_j \supset \mathfrak{M}_i)$.

c. $(\exists\mathfrak{i}_k)(\mathfrak{M}_j)$ for $\sim(\mathfrak{i}_k)(\sim\mathfrak{M}_j)$.

d. $\mathfrak{A}_i \neq \mathfrak{A}_j$ for $\sim(\mathfrak{A}_i = \mathfrak{A}_j)$.

For example, according to A1a, we shall write a partial expression '$P_1x \supset P_2y$' within a sentence as shorthand for '$(\sim P_1x) \vee P_2y$'.

B. *On the Possibility of an Ordered System*

Some brief remarks may be made concerning possibilities of a future development. If *inductive logic* is to be *extended* so as to apply to language systems more comprehensive than our system $\mathfrak{L}$ (for infinitely many individuals, that is, $\mathfrak{L}_\infty$), it might be useful to construct a stronger system $\mathfrak{L}'$ possessing the following features. First, $\mathfrak{L}'$ refers to a universe whose individuals exhibit a fixed basic order of the structure of a progression (i.e., a linear, discrete order with one initial and no terminal member). For this purpose $\mathfrak{L}'$ contains a symbol (functor) for the concept of immediate successor in the basic order (for instance, 'a'' is written for 'the successor of a'). This order may be interpreted as a kind of temporal order of events, and hence the individuals as temporal positions (in this simplified universe there is only one event at any time-point). Furthermore, it seems desirable to have in $\mathfrak{L}'$ variables and constants for natural numbers; arithmetical functions (e.g., sum, product, etc.) can then be introduced by recursive definitions; thus the arithmetic of natural numbers can be formulated in $\mathfrak{L}'$. The frequency of a property within a given class of individuals can then be expressed in a simple way. A system $\mathfrak{L}'$ possessing the features described can be constructed by the following convenient and simple procedure without the need for a second kind of variable. Instead of 'a', 'a'', 'a''', etc., we write '0', '0′', '0″', etc. These expressions are primarily interpreted as expressions for the natural numbers 0, 1, 2, etc. To each position in the basic linear order a natural number is assigned as its coordinate: the number 0 to the initial position, the number 1 to the next following position, etc. An atomic sentence, say, 'P(0′)', may then say, for example, that the position with the coordinate 1 is blue. Strictly speaking, 'P' stands here for 'the position with the coordinate . . . is blue' and '0′' stands merely for '(the number) 1'. But it will then be convenient to allow, for practical purposes, a slightly changed interpretation to the effect that '*P*' stands for '. . . . is blue', and '0′' for 'the position with the coordinate 1'. Thus the individual expressions, which were primarily interpreted as expressions for numbers, are regarded in the secondary interpretation as expressions for positions. This involves no actual ambiguity, because theoretically the primary interpretation is the only one; the secondary interpretation constitutes merely a convenient mode of speech in the metalanguage. In accordance with the secondary interpretation, we may then allow ourselves to say that the positions are the individuals of the universe of this system. The essential point is that in this system the positions as individuals are referred to not by names (like '*a*', '*b*', etc.) but by coordinate expressions. (For a description of a coordinate language of the structure here indicated see [Syntax] § 3; for a general discussion of the semantical character of coordinate languages see [Meaning], chap. ii.) Consequently, the individual variables '*x*', '*y*', etc., which in 𝔏′ likewise are the only variables, are interpreted primarily as variables for the natural numbers and secondarily as variables for the positions. The extension of 𝔏 to 𝔏′ may appear to be only slight, but in fact the logical character of the new system 𝔏′ is quite different from that of 𝔏, even in deductive logic. [For instance, since 𝔏′ contains arithmetic, according to Goedel's result it is impossible to construct one calculus in which all L-true sentences of 𝔏′ are provable.] For the extension of inductive logic to the new system 𝔏′ there are two possible forms which could be constructed in two successive steps; we call them forms I and II.

Form I of inductive logic. The old definitions of degree of confirmation constructed in this book for the system 𝔏 (in particular, the definitions of regular 𝔪- and 𝔠-functions (§§ 55, 56), symmetrical 𝔪- and 𝔠-functions (§§ 90, 91), and 𝔠* (§ 110A)) are simply transferred to the system 𝔏′. [This is possible because the state-descriptions and therefore also the rules of ranges (§ 18D) remain in 𝔏′ essentially the same.] The main task is merely to develop, on the basis of those definitions, theorems of inductive logic which cover also the new sentences of 𝔏′. It seems that this can be done without great difficulties. The structure of form I of inductive logic as just described for 𝔏′ is fundamentally the same as that developed in this book for 𝔏. Although the basic order of the individuals is expressible in 𝔏′, it is not regarded, in form I, as influencing the degree of confirmation 𝔠. Suppose that the evidence *e* says that of three observed individuals two had the property *M* and one $\sim M$, and the hypothesis *h* says that a certain unobserved individual is *M*. Then, in form I, the value of $\mathfrak{c}(h, e)$ is the same no matter whether the individual with $\sim M$ is the first, the second, or the third among the three observed individuals in their basic order and how the unobserved individual is located in relation to them. To disregard thus the temporal order of the events is customary in the traditional theory of probability and even in most parts of modern mathematical statistics, although in everyday life and in science regular temporal patterns which we have observed among past events often have a decisive influence upon our expectations for the future.

Form II of inductive logic. The second step consists in constructing new definitions for the concepts of degree of confirmation so as to take into account not only the observed or expected frequencies of the properties in question but also the order in which these properties occur.

In modern mathematical statistics, in distinction to the traditional theory of probability, temporal sequences are studied (e.g., in the analysis of time-series (see Wold [Time Series] and Kendall [Statistics], Vol. II, chaps. 29 and 30) and the sequential analysis (see Wald [Sequential])). However, these investigations do not show a way for constructing an adequate explicatum $\mathfrak{c}$ of the kind described. A preliminary study which I have made seems to show that it is not too difficult to construct a fairly adequate definition. However, the application of this definition to cases which involve many individuals, and the development of general theorems based on the definition seem to become rather complicated. Here arise new and very interesting problems; it remains for future investigations to discover whether satisfactory solutions can be found.

If we wish to express the temporal order of events and have it influence the degree of confirmation as in the form II just explained, there is an alternative method which can even be applied in our present system $\mathfrak{L}$ on the basis of the present definitions of degree of confirmation. This method consists in designating the relation of temporal priority by a primitive predicate (whereupon immediate priority can be defined). If this method is chosen, then the order of events is taken into account even by the form of inductive logic developed in this book. Here, the temporal order ('x is earlier than y') is not expressed as a basic positional relation but in analogy to an empirical, qualitative relation (e.g., 'x is warmer than y'). Consequently, such fundamental characters of the temporal order as asymmetry and transitivity are represented in this method as contingent features. As an example consider the following prediction concerning balls drawn from an urn: 'the first red ball which will appear will come earlier than the first blue ball; and this blue ball will appear earlier than the red one'. This hypothesis must be regarded, on the basis of the method under discussion, not as impossible, but at worst as improbable. Its degree of confirmation on any finite evidence will not be 0 but will have a positive value. It seems, however, rather doubtful whether this sentence could be regarded as expressing a possible outcome of observations. For this and other reasons I have some doubt concerning the adequacy of this method. I believe that the temporal order and, more generally, the spatiotemporal order is to be regarded as a basic positional order rather than a qualitative order; in other words, that it is more adequate to represent the spatiotemporal order by the form of the individual expressions (coordinate expressions) rather than by primitive predicates. At any rate, further clarification of this problem is required. At the present time not even the nature of the problem itself is clear. Should it be regarded as a question concerning the "true nature" of space and time, to be answered by ontological or phenomenological methods? I think a more fruitful approach would be to construct language systems of both forms—the first expressing spatiotemporal relations by primitive predicates, the second by the form of coordinate expressions for the positions—and develop inductive logic for both of them. Preference will then be given to that language system for which a more adequate or more convenient inductive method can be developed.

§ 16. The Rules of Formation

Rules of formation are laid down. They determine the customary forms of (sentential) matrices, which include sentences (D2). A sentence is defined as a matrix without free variables (D4). Some kinds of matrices (D3) and sentences (D6) are defined: atomic, basic (atomic or negation), molecular (without quantifier or sign of identity), general (with quantifier).

On the basis of the informal explanations in the preceding section, we shall now begin the construction of the systems $\mathfrak{L}$ by laying down their semantical rules. In this section we give the first kind of these rules, the *rules of formation;* they state, in the form of definitions, which kinds of signs belong to the systems $\mathfrak{L}$ and how sentences are formed out of these signs.

D16-1. $\mathfrak{A}_i$ is a ***sign*** in $\mathfrak{L}$ $=_{Df}$ $\mathfrak{A}_i$ belongs to one of the following kinds:

a. *Individual constants* ($\mathfrak{in}$). In $\mathfrak{L}_\infty$, an infinite number: 'a_1', 'a_2', 'a_3', etc. (Instead of 'a_1', . . . , 'a_5', we write sometimes 'a', 'b', 'c', 'd', 'e'.) In $\mathfrak{L}_N$, a finite number N: 'a_1', 'a_2', . . . , 'a_N'.

b. A finite number of ***primitive predicates*** ($\mathfrak{pr}$) of any degrees: 'P_1', 'P_2', etc.; 'R_1', etc.

c. An infinite number of ***individual variables*** ($\mathfrak{i}$): 'x_1', 'x_2', etc. (Instead of 'x_1', 'x_2', 'x_3', we write sometimes 'x', 'y', 'z'.)

d. Seven single signs: '$\sim$', '$\vee$', '$\cdot$', '$=$', 'ι', '(', ')'.

An ***expression*** in $\mathfrak{L}$ is a finite sequence of signs in $\mathfrak{L}$.

D16-2. $\mathfrak{A}_i$ is a (sentential) ***matrix*** ($\mathfrak{M}$) in $\mathfrak{L} =_{\text{Df}} \mathfrak{A}_i$ consists of signs of $\mathfrak{L}$ and has one of the following forms.

a. $\mathfrak{pr}_i\mathfrak{A}_{j_1}\mathfrak{A}_{j_2} \ldots \mathfrak{A}_{j_n}$, where $\mathfrak{pr}_i$ is of degree *n* and each of the *n* argument expressions is an individual sign, i.e., an $\mathfrak{in}$ or an $\mathfrak{i}$.

b. $\mathfrak{A}_k = \mathfrak{A}_j$, where $\mathfrak{A}_k$ and $\mathfrak{A}_j$ are individual signs.

c. '*t*'.

d. $\sim(\mathfrak{M}_i)$.

e. $(\mathfrak{M}_i) \vee (\mathfrak{M}_j)$.

f. $(\mathfrak{M}_i) \,.\, (\mathfrak{M}_j)$.

g. $(\mathfrak{i}_k)(\mathfrak{M}_j)$.

In the actual writing of symbolic formulas or of their descriptions in the metalanguage, we shall usually omit the parentheses including a component in the forms D2d, e, f or a scope in the form D2g under the customary conditions: we take the universal and existential quantifiers and '$\sim$' as of greatest strength (hence, if one of these is not followed by an expression included in parentheses, its scope is the smallest matrix immediately following), then come '$\vee$' and '.', and finally '$\supset$' and '$\equiv$'. (Thus, for example, '$\sim t \vee P_1 a \supset (x)P_2 x \,.\, P_3 b$' is short for '$[(\sim t) \vee P_1 a] \supset [(x)(P_2 x) \,.\, P_3 b]$'.) Further, we shall speak in the customary way of disjunctions and conjunctions with *n* components for any $n \geqq 1$ (for $n = 1$, the sentence or matrix itself is its only disjunctive or conjunctive component; for example, if we say: 'let *i* be the disjunction of those sentences which fulfil such and such a condition' and it turns out that only *j* fulfils that condition, then this is meant to say that *i* is the sentence *j* itself).

In D3 some particular kinds of matrices are defined.

D16-3. Let $\mathfrak{M}_i$ be a matrix in $\mathfrak{L}$.

a. $\mathfrak{M}_i$ is a matrix of ***degree n*** (for any $n \geqq 0$) $=_{\text{Df}} \mathfrak{M}_i$ contains *n* different free variables.

b. $\mathfrak{M}_i$ is an *atomic matrix* $=_{\text{Df}} \mathfrak{M}_i$ has the form D2a. (Note that the forms D2b and c are not counted as atomic.)

c. $\mathfrak{M}_i$ is a *basic matrix* $=_{\text{Df}} \mathfrak{M}_i$ is either an atomic matrix or the negation of one.

d. $\mathfrak{M}_i$ is an *identity matrix* ($=$-matrix, $=$-$\mathfrak{M}$) $=_{\text{Df}} \mathfrak{M}_i$ has the form D2b.

e. $\mathfrak{M}_i$ is a *molecular matrix* $=_{\text{Df}} \mathfrak{M}_i$ is either atomic or constructed out of one or more atomic matrices with the help of connectives. (Hence, quantifiers, '$=$', and '*t*' do not occur in $\mathfrak{M}_i$.)

f. $\mathfrak{M}_i$ is a *general matrix* $=_{\text{Df}}$ $\mathfrak{M}_i$ contains at least one quantifier.

g. $\mathfrak{M}_i$ is a *nongeneral matrix* $=_{\text{Df}}$ $\mathfrak{M}_i$ contains no quantifier. (Hence, $\mathfrak{M}_i$ has either one of the forms D2a, b, c or is constructed out of these forms with the help of connectives.)

h. $\mathfrak{M}_i$ is a *purely general matrix* $=_{\text{Df}}$ $\mathfrak{M}_i$ is general and contains no $\mathfrak{in}$.

D16-4. $\mathfrak{A}_i$ is a ***sentence*** ($\mathfrak{S}$) in $\mathfrak{L}$ $=_{\text{Df}}$ $\mathfrak{A}_i$ is a matrix of degree 0 (that is, without free variables).

D16-5. i is an ***instance*** of $\mathfrak{M}_j$ (in $\mathfrak{L}$) $=_{\text{Df}}$ i is a sentence (in $\mathfrak{L}$) constructed out of $\mathfrak{M}_j$ by the substitution of individual constants (of $\mathfrak{L}$) for all free variables.

D6 defines some particular kinds of sentence in analogy to D3.

D16-6. Let i be a sentence in $\mathfrak{L}$.

a. i is an ***atomic sentence*** $=_{\text{Df}}$ i has the form D2a.

b. i is a ***basic sentence*** $=_{\text{Df}}$ i is an atomic sentence or the negation of one.

c. $\mathfrak{K}_i$ is a ***basic pair*** $=_{\text{Df}}$ $\mathfrak{K}_i$ is a class of two sentences, one being an atomic sentence and the other its negation.

d. i is an ***identity sentence*** $=_{\text{Df}}$ i has the form D2b.

e. i is a ***molecular sentence*** $=_{\text{Df}}$ i is either atomic or constructed out of one or more atomic sentences with the help of connectives. (Hence, variables, '=', and 't' do not occur in i.)

f. i is a ***general sentence*** $=_{\text{Df}}$ i contains at least one variable, and hence a quantifier.

g. i is a ***nongeneral sentence*** $=_{\text{Df}}$ i contains no quantifier (and hence no variable).

h. i is a ***purely general sentence*** $=_{\text{Df}}$ i is general and contains no $\mathfrak{in}$.

i. i is a ***singular sentence*** $=_{\text{Df}}$ i is a molecular sentence containing occurrences of only one individual constant.

We presuppose that an *alphabetical order* for all primitive signs has been established. (Which particular order is chosen is of course arbitrary and unimportant. A simple way would be this: we take first the $\mathfrak{pr}$ (whose number is finite even in $\mathfrak{L}_\infty$) ordered according to increasing degrees and within each degree according to increasing subscripts; then the seven signs of D1d in the order there given; finally, the $\mathfrak{in}$ and $\mathfrak{i}$ in this order: $\mathfrak{in}_1$, $\mathfrak{i}_1$, $\mathfrak{in}_2$, $\mathfrak{i}_2$, $\mathfrak{in}_3$, $\mathfrak{i}_3$, etc.) On the basis of the alphabetical order of the signs a *lexicographical order* of all expressions is defined (D8).

D16-8. $\mathfrak{A}_i$ precedes $\mathfrak{A}_j$ in the *lexicographical order* $=_{\text{Df}}$ either (a) the first sign in $\mathfrak{A}_i$ which differs from the corresponding sign in $\mathfrak{A}_j$ precedes the latter alphabetically; or (*b*) $\mathfrak{A}_i$ is an initial proper part of $\mathfrak{A}_j$.

The alphabetical order applies only to primitive signs, and hence the lexicographical order only to expressions consisting of primitive signs. When we speak of the lexicographical order of expressions which contain defined signs, we mean the order of their expansions in primitive signs.

§ 17. Rules of Truth

Rules of truth are laid down in the form of a recursive definition of 'true in $\mathfrak{L}$' for sentences (D1) and classes of sentences (D2). Thereby, a sufficient and necessary condition for the truth of any sentence is determined (T1). This constitutes an interpretation for the systems $\mathfrak{L}$.

The rules of formation determine only the forms of sentences but not their interpretation. Now we have to lay down semantical rules of a more important kind, those which interpret the systems $\mathfrak{L}$, that is, which determine the meanings of all sentences of these systems. The first, simple step toward this aim consists in laying down rules of designation for the nonlogical constants, viz., the $\mathfrak{pr}$ and the $\mathfrak{in}$. These rules determine which attributes (properties or relations) are designated by the $\mathfrak{pr}$ and which individuals by the $\mathfrak{in}$. We shall not actually lay down these rules because we want to keep our deductive and inductive logic general, that is, applicable to any particular language systems of the structures here described that anybody may choose; we presuppose that these rules have been chosen in some way or other as indicated in § 15A. Now our problem is how to lay down further rules which serve best for the purpose for which we intend to use these systems. For this purpose, the rules must determine the meanings of the sentences in such a way that we can define with their help the following concepts: (i) truth and falsity; (ii) the L-concepts, especially L-truth and L-implication, which are the basis of deductive logic; (iii) the concept of degree of confirmation, which is the basis of inductive logic.

We begin by laying down *rules of truth*. Their purpose is to state for every sentence and every class of sentences in any system $\mathfrak{L}$ a sufficient and necessary condition for its truth. This is done by first laying down direct rules of truth for simple sentences (D1a, b, c), and then indirect rules for compound sentences (D1d, e, f, g) and classes of sentences (D2); the rules of the latter kind are indirect inasmuch as they refer to the truth of components, instances, or elements, respectively. The rules of truth together form a recursive definition of 'true in $\mathfrak{L}$'. If any sentence *i* is given, then this definition tells us under what condition *i* is true; however, in general, the definition alone cannot tell us whether or not the condition is fulfilled, in other words, whether or not i is true. In order to find out whether this is the case, we need, in general, knowledge about the relevant facts in addition to the truth-rules.

The semantical concept of truth defined by D1 is such that the statement 'the sentence i is true in $\mathfrak{L}$' in the metalanguage conveys the same factual information as the sentence i itself, which belongs to the object language. (For more detailed discussions of this concept see Tarski [Wahrheitsbegriff] and "The semantic conception of truth", *Philosophy and Phenom. Research*, 4 [1944], reprinted in Feigl [Readings]; Carnap [Truth].)

+**D17-1.** Let i be a sentence in a system $\mathfrak{L}$. i is ***true*** in $\mathfrak{L}$ $=_{\mathrm{Df}}$ i fulfils one of the following conditions (a) to (g).

a. i is an atomic sentence $\mathfrak{pr}_k\mathfrak{in}_{j1}\mathfrak{in}_{j2} \ldots \mathfrak{in}_{jn}$, and the attribute designated by $\mathfrak{pr}_k$ holds for the individuals designated by $\mathfrak{in}_{j1}$, $\mathfrak{in}_{j2}$, . . . , $\mathfrak{in}_{jn}$. (For $n = 1$, this means that the individual designated by $\mathfrak{in}_{j1}$ has the property designated by $\mathfrak{pr}_k$).

b. i has the form $\mathfrak{in}_j = \mathfrak{in}_j$.

c. i is 't'.

d. i is $\sim j$, and j is not true.

e. i is $j \vee k$, and at least one of the two components is true.

f. i is $j \,.\, k$, and both components are true.

g. i is $(\mathfrak{i}_k)(\mathfrak{M}_j)$, and all instances of $\mathfrak{M}_j$ are true.

D1 leads immediately to the following theorem, which states, for every sentence in $\mathfrak{L}$, either directly its truth or nontruth (in (c), (d), (e)), or a sufficient and necessary condition for its truth.

+**T17-1.** *Theorem of truth-conditions.*

a. An atomic sentence of the form $\mathfrak{pr}_k\mathfrak{in}_j$ is true if and only if the individual designated by $\mathfrak{in}_j$ has the property designated by $\mathfrak{pr}_k$.

b. An atomic sentence of the form $\mathfrak{pr}_k\mathfrak{in}_{j1}\mathfrak{in}_{j2} \ldots \mathfrak{in}_{jn}$ for $n > 1$ is true if and only if the relation designated by $\mathfrak{pr}_k$ holds for the individuals designated by $\mathfrak{in}_{j1}$, $\mathfrak{in}_{j2}$, . . . $\mathfrak{in}_{jn}$.

c. $\mathfrak{in}_j = \mathfrak{in}_j$ is true.

d. $\mathfrak{in}_j = \mathfrak{in}_k$, with two different $\mathfrak{in}$, is not true.

e. 't' is true.

f. A sentence $\sim j$ is true if and only if j is not true.

g. A sentence $j \vee k$ is true if and only if at least one of the two components is true.

h. A sentence $j \,.\, k$ is true if and only if both components are true.
i. A sentence $(\mathrm{i}_k)(\mathfrak{M}_j)$ is true if and only if all instances of $\mathfrak{M}_j$ are true.

T1f, g, h are clearly in accordance with the customary meanings of the connectives, as they are usually stated with the help of truth-tables. T1c, d, e, i are in accordance with our earlier explanations of the meanings of the sign of identity, '*t*', and the universal quantifier in our systems $\mathfrak{L}$. Thus T1 shows that the interpretation given by the rules of truth D1 is the one intended.

We construe, as is customary, a class of sentences as meaning the same as a joint assertion of its sentences. Hence D2.

D17-2. $\mathfrak{K}_i$ is *true* in $\mathfrak{L}$ $=_{\mathrm{Df}}$ every element of $\mathfrak{K}_i$ is a true sentence in $\mathfrak{L}$.

D17-3.
a. i is *false* in $\mathfrak{L}$ $=_{\mathrm{Df}}$ i is a sentence in $\mathfrak{L}$ and not true in $\mathfrak{L}$.
b. $\mathfrak{K}_i$ is *false* in $\mathfrak{L}$ $=_{\mathrm{Df}}$ $\mathfrak{K}_i$ is a class of sentences in $\mathfrak{L}$ and not true in $\mathfrak{L}$.

T17-2. $\mathfrak{K}_i$ is false in $\mathfrak{L}$ if and only if $\mathfrak{K}_i$ is a class of sentences in $\mathfrak{L}$ and at least one sentence of $\mathfrak{K}_i$ is false. (From D3b, D2.)

§ 18. State-Descriptions ($\mathfrak{Z}$) and Ranges ($\mathfrak{R}$)

A. A class of sentences which for every atomic sentence i in a system $\mathfrak{L}$ contains either i or $\sim i$ but not both describes completely a possible state of the domain of individuals of $\mathfrak{L}$ with respect to all attributes (properties and relations) designated by primitive predicates in $\mathfrak{L}$. As *state-descriptions* ($\mathfrak{Z}$), we take in $\mathfrak{L}_\infty$ the classes of this kind, and in $\mathfrak{L}_N$ the corresponding conjunctions. *B*. In order to insure that the state-descriptions describe possible states, the interpretation of the individual constants and the primitive predicates must fulfil the *requirement of logical independence*. For the purpose of inductive logic, every system $\mathfrak{L}$ must furthermore fulfil the *requirement of completeness*, that is, it must be sufficient for expressing all qualitative attributes occurring in the given universe. *C*. The possibility of families with more than two related properties (e.g., colors) is discussed. *D*. A method for interpreting all sentences in a system $\mathfrak{L}$ is applied, which is different from but analogous to the method in § 17. It consists in laying down rules which determine, for every sentence i, in which state-descriptions it holds and in which not (D4); in other words, in which possible cases i would be true and in which not. Thus the rules determine for every sentence i its *range* (designated by '$\mathfrak{R}(i)$' or '$\mathfrak{R}_i$'), that is, the class of those $\mathfrak{Z}$ in which i holds (D6); therefore, we call them rules of ranges. The concept of range will be fundamental in our construction both of deductive and of inductive logic.

A. *State-Descriptions*

In addition to the rules of truth, we need other semantical rules to serve as a basis for the L-concepts and the concept of degree of confirmation, in other words, for deductive and inductive logic. The method which we shall apply for these purposes is characterized by the use of the two concepts of state-description and range. We are led to the first by the problem of an explication of the concept of possible cases or states-of-affairs. Our first step in making this vague concept more precise and specific consists in realizing that it must be taken as relative to a language system. Thus we come, with respect to any of our systems $\mathfrak{L}$, to the concept of a logically possible state of the domain of individuals of $\mathfrak{L}$ with respect to all attributes (properties and relations) designated by the $\mathfrak{pr}$ of $\mathfrak{L}$. A possible state in this sense belongs to that type of entities which may be expressed by sentences, hence to the type of propositions. We shall soon have to deal with certain classes of possible states; hence this would lead us to classes of propositions. Now I personally believe that there is no danger in speaking of propositions and classes of propositions provided it is done in a cautious way, that is to say, in a way which carefully abstains from any reification or hypostatization of propositions, in other words, from the attribution to propositions of anything that can correctly be attributed only to things. However, there are advantages in avoiding propositions altogether and speaking instead about the sentences or classes of sentences expressing them, whenever this is possible. In our present case this is possible, and we shall do so. We shall see that, with respect to any of our systems $\mathfrak{L}$—in distinction to more complex language systems, for instance, those containing real number variables—every possible state can be expressed by a sentence or a class of sentences in the system, by a ***state-description***, as we shall call it. There are chiefly two advantages in this method. First, we avoid a discussion of the controversial question whether the use of the concept of proposition would involve us in a kind of Platonic metaphysics and would violate the principles of empiricism. Second, there is the technical advantage that for this method a metalanguage of simpler structure suffices. (To give only a brief indication: this method, in distinction to that using propositions, can be applied in an extensional (truth-functional) metalanguage; for more detailed explanations see [Semantics] §§ 18, 19 and [Meaning] §§ 2 and 38.)

A state-description for a system $\mathfrak{L}$ in the sense indicated must state for every individual of $\mathfrak{L}$ and for every property designated by a primitive predicate of $\mathfrak{L}$ whether or not this individual has this property; and analogously for relations. In other words, if i is any atomic sentence in $\mathfrak{L}$, a state-description for $\mathfrak{L}$ must either affirm or deny i, hence it must affirm exactly one sentence of the basic pair $\{i, \sim i\}$. Every possible state can be described by a class of sentences in $\mathfrak{L}$ which contains exactly one sentence from every basic pair in $\mathfrak{L}$. As state-descriptions for $\mathfrak{L}_\infty$ we shall actually take the classes described (D1b). In a finite system $\mathfrak{L}_N$, every class of the kind described is finite (for example, {'*Pa*', '$\sim$*Pb*', '*Pc*'} in a system with three in and one pr of degree one). Therefore, in $\mathfrak{L}_N$, we can take as state-descriptions instead of those classes the corresponding conjunctions (in the example mentioned, '*Pa* . $\sim$*Pb* . *Pc*'); in order to have only one state-description for every possible state, we add a requirement which uniquely determines the order of the conjunctive components (D1a). For the state-descriptions in $\mathfrak{L}_N$ we use in the metalanguage the sign '${}_N\mathfrak{Z}$', and for those in $\mathfrak{L}_\infty$ '${}_\infty\mathfrak{Z}$'; however, we shall usually write simply '$\mathfrak{Z}$' if the context of the discussion makes it sufficiently clear which system or systems are concerned. ['$\mathfrak{Z}$' is taken from the German 'Zustand'.]

+D18-1.

a. *i* is a ***state-description*** in $\mathfrak{L}_N$ ('${}_N\mathfrak{Z}$' or briefly '$\mathfrak{Z}$') $=_{\text{Df}}$ *i* is a conjunction which contains as components exactly one sentence from every basic pair in $\mathfrak{L}_N$ and no other sentences, these components being arranged in their lexicographical order (D16-8).

b. $\mathfrak{K}_i$ is a ***state-description*** in $\mathfrak{L}_\infty$ ('${}_\infty\mathfrak{Z}$' or briefly '$\mathfrak{Z}$') $=_{\text{Df}}$ $\mathfrak{K}_i$ contains exactly one sentence from every basic pair in $\mathfrak{L}_\infty$ and no other elements.

B. *The Requirement of Logical Independence and Completeness*

If the conjunctions and classes in a system $\mathfrak{L}$ which we call state-descriptions are to fulfil their purpose of describing possible states of the universe of $\mathfrak{L}$, the interpretation of $\mathfrak{L}$ must fulfil the following ***requirement of logical independence***, here formulated in three parts; parts II and III follow from I.

I. The interpretation of $\mathfrak{L}$ must be such that the *atomic sentences* are logically independent of each other; that is to say, it must never occur that a class containing some atomic sentences and the negations of other atomic sentences logically entails (contains in its meaning) another atomic sentence or its negation. If this requirement is not fulfilled, then some state-description will be self-contradictory and hence not describe a possible state. (This holds for any state-description containing the class specified and, in addition, the negation of the other atomic sentence or this sentence itself, respectively.) Suppose, for example, that *i* and *j* were atomic sentences in $\mathfrak{L}$ such that *i* entailed *j*. [The term 'entailment' is here used not as an exact, systematic term but as a common term whose meaning may be roughly indicated by saying that the content of *i* is the same as that of *i* . *j*, that is, the joint assertion of *i* and *j*. A corresponding exact concept, an explicatum for the concept of entailment as explicandum, will be introduced later (D20-1c) under the term 'L-implication'. An analogous remark holds for the term 'self-contradictory'.] Then any state-description containing both *i* and $\sim j$ would be self-contradictory because it would assert both *j* and $\sim j$. In order to fulfil this requirement for the atomic sentences, the $\mathfrak{in}$ and $\mathfrak{pr}$ must fulfil the following requirements II and III.

II. The *individual constants* in $\mathfrak{L}$ must be interpreted in such a manner that they designate different and separate individuals. If, for instance, '*a*' and '*b*' designated the same individual, '*Pa*' would entail '*Pb*', and '$Pa \,.\, \sim Pb$' would be self-contradictory. If the individual *a* were a spatio-temporal part of *b* and if '*P*' designated the property of being hot throughout, then '$Pb \,.\, \sim Pa$' would be self-contradictory.

III. The *primitive predicates* in $\mathfrak{L}$ must be interpreted in such a manner that they designate attributes (properties or relations) which are logically independent of each other. For instance, if the properties Raven and Black are understood in such a way that the first entails the second (logically, not merely by a law of nature) and if they were designated by two $\mathfrak{pr}$ in $\mathfrak{L}$, say, 'P_1' and 'P_2', then '$P_1a \,.\, \sim P_2a$' would be self-contradictory. If the property Warm and the relation Warmer were designated by two $\mathfrak{pr}$, say, '*P*' and '*R*', then '$Pa \,.\, \sim Pb \,.\, Rba$' would be self-contradictory.

The requirement of independence concerns only the *interpretation* of the nonlogical signs ($\mathfrak{in}$ and $\mathfrak{pr}$) of our language-systems $\mathfrak{L}$. For the purely logical work both in deductive logic (in this chapter) and in inductive logic (in the remainder of this book), we need not consider any particular interpretation of the nonlogical signs. If, however, it is desired to give a specific interpretation in order to see how deductive and inductive logic work in application to a particular universe, real or imaginary, then care must be taken that the interpretation chosen fulfil the requirement of independence. (This requirement belongs, not to deductive or inductive logic proper, but to the methodology of logic [see § 44A]; the same holds for the requirement of completeness to be discussed soon.) If an interpretation is given, it may not always be easy to determine whether the requirement is fulfilled. But it is not difficult to choose an interpretation for which we can be practically certain that the requirement is fulfilled. It seems perhaps best to imagine as individuals in a system $\mathfrak{L}$, not extended regions like the physical bodies or events in our actual world, but rather positions like the space-time points in our actual world, hence unextended, indivisible entities. Since, however, the number of individuals in a system $\mathfrak{L}$ is either finite or denumerably infinite, they cannot form a continuum, as the space-time points of the world described in physics do, but must instead be imagined as isolated positions in a discrete (i.e., non-continuous) universe. Since this is a simplified universe, the qualities and relations with which we are acquainted in our actual world cannot, strictly speaking, be applied. For instance, a color occurs in the actual world only as property of an extended, continuous area. Nevertheless, in order to visualize the simplified universe to which a system $\mathfrak{L}$ refers, we may imagine as attributes designated by the $\mathfrak{pr}$ in $\mathfrak{L}$ something similar to the directly observable qualities and relations which we perceive in our world, e.g., something like Blue, Hot, Hard, Darker, and the like, but now attributed to the isolated positions which we take as individuals in $\mathfrak{L}$. If one wants to study an inductive problem involving a complex property *W*, it is advisable to take '*W*' not as a $\mathfrak{pr}$ but rather as a predicate defined on the basis of suitable $\mathfrak{pr}$ which designate simpler concepts. It was explained earlier (§ 15B) that it is advisable to express positional attributes of individuals, corresponding to spatiotemporal attributes in our actual world, not with the help of primitive predicates but by the form of coordinate expressions used as individual expressions in an extended form of the systems $\mathfrak{L}$ (coordinate languages). Consequently, it seems best to choose as designata for the $\mathfrak{pr}$ only attributes of a purely qualitative nature rather than those which are either positional or mixed, that is, containing both qualitative and positional components (for example, the property expressed by '*x* is red or identical with *b*' or the relation expressed by '*x* is darker and earlier than *y*').

In distinction to the requirement of independence, which seems essential both for deductive and for inductive logic, I regard the requirement now to be introduced as necessary for inductive logic, although it is not necessary for deductive logic and therefore has so far not been discussed by logicians, it seems. This is the ***requirement of completeness:*** the set of the $\mathfrak{pr}$ in a system $\mathfrak{L}$ must be sufficient for expressing every qualitative attribute of the individuals in the universe of $\mathfrak{L}$, that is, every respect in which two positions in this universe may be found by observation to differ qualitatively. This requirement can be divided into the following two parts I and II.

I. It is assumed that any two individuals differ only in a finite number of respects. This assumption seems related to Keynes's principle of limited variety: "We seem to need some such assumption as that the amount of variety in the universe is limited in such a way that there is no one object so complex that its qualities fall into an infinite number of independent groups" ([Probab.], p. 258). This assumption, if applied to our actual world, may at first appear as rather doubtful in view of the fact that it seems impossible to give an exhaustive description of any physical body. However, this is a different question; a physical body is a continuum (a nondenumerable set) of space-time positions, while our assumption refers only to *one* individual (or to *n* individuals in the case of an *n*-adic relation). If we think of the world of things with perceptible qualities, then it is not implausible to assume that the number of perceptible qualities, say, shades of color, sounds, smells, etc., is finite though rather large. And if, on the other hand, we think of the world as conceived in theoretical physics, then we find a finite and, indeed, a very small number of fundamental magnitudes to which, according to the assumption of physicists, the great variety of phenomena is ultimately reducible. Thus in either case the assumption I is not as implausible as it may appear at first.

II. If a language system $\mathfrak{L}$ is to be constructed for the purpose of applying inductive logic to a given universe, it is required that a system of $\mathfrak{pr}$ be taken which is sufficiently comprehensive for expressing all qualitative attributes exhibited by the individuals in the given universe. For the purposes of inductive logic we may leave aside the epistemological question as to how we are able to know whether this requirement is fulfilled by a given system $\mathfrak{L}$ for a universe with which we are confronted, just as both deductive and inductive logic leave it to epistemology or methodology of empirical knowledge to answer the question as to the procedure by which we acquire knowledge of the premises or evidence. The requirement may also be formulated conversely: if a system $\mathfrak{L}$ is given and a universe, real or imaginary, is to be chosen as an illustration or model for $\mathfrak{L}$ for the purposes of inductive logic, then this universe must be neither richer nor poorer in qualitative attributes than $\mathfrak{L}$ indicates. For example, let $\mathfrak{L}$ contain only two $\mathfrak{pr}$, both of degree one, say 'P_1' and 'P_2'. Suppose that we decide to interpret them as designating the properties Bright and Hot, respectively. Then we must imagine a universe whose positions differ only with respect to Bright and Not-Bright and with respect to Hot and Not-Hot. A richer universe in which furthermore the distinction between Hard and Not-Hard can be made, is not a fitting interpretation for $\mathfrak{L}$ for the purpose of inductive logic, although in deductive logic $\mathfrak{L}$ could, of course, be used for this universe.

At the present stage of research concerning inductive logic and the conditions of its applicability, it is not yet quite clear whether the requirement of completeness in its full strength is necessary or whether a modified and weaker form of it might be sufficient. At the present moment we need not go further into a discussion of the problems connected with this requirement. The requirement is, it seems, not necessary for those parts of inductive logic which will be developed in the present volume. We shall resume the discussion of these problems in the second volume, in connection with our system of quantitative inductive logic. Then the function of the requirement within the procedures of inductive logic will become clearer. (For a discussion of a special problem connected with the requirement of completeness see [Application] § 5, third paragraph.)

It might seem plausible to apply the requirement of completeness not only to the 𝔭𝔯 but also to the 𝔦𝔫 in 𝔏. This would mean that 𝔏, in order to be adequate for a given universe, must either (*a*) contain 𝔦𝔫 for all individuals of the given universe (which, of course, is possible only if the number of individuals is not more than denumerable) or (*b*) at least contain individual variables whose domain of values comprehends all individuals of the given universe. However, for our system of inductive logic it is not necessary to lay down this requirement because, as we shall see (in Vol. II), the degree of confirmation of *h* on *e* is not changed by the existence of individuals not referred to in *h* and *e*. In other words, if *h* and *e* contain no variables, the degree of confirmation of *h* on *e* is the same for all systems 𝔏 in which *h* and *e* occur, provided these systems contain the same 𝔭𝔯 and differ only in the number of 𝔦𝔫.

We shall later (§ 45A) discuss the problem of how a system of inductive logic pertaining to simplified universes can nevertheless be applied, under certain conditions, to the actual world. There we shall also lay down a further requirement, that of total evidence; it does not concern the interpretation of the systems, as the two requirements just discussed do, but is essential for the application of results of inductive logic to given knowledge situations.

C. *Families of Related Properties*

Suppose that two or more properties are related to each other in the following way: every individual must necessarily have one and only one of these properties; and this is a matter of logical necessity. That is, it follows from the meanings alone; it is not merely a contingent law of nature for which the occurrence of counterinstances remains always possible. We speak in this case of a ***family of related properties.*** Analogously, we speak of related relations. If a system 𝔏 contains 𝔭𝔯 designating related attributes, we call them a *family of related primitive predicates.* For instance, the properties Cold, Luke-Warm, Medium-Warm, Hot may constitute a family in a certain universe and may then be designated by four related 𝔭𝔯; likewise the properties Blue, Green, Yellow, Red in a universe where these are the only possible colors and no individual can be colorless (otherwise we should have to add Colorless and thus form a five-member-family). If 'P' is a pr belonging to a family of n pr, '$\sim P$' is logically equivalent to the disjunction of the other $n - 1$ pr. Hence in a two-member-family consisting of 'P_1' and 'P_2', '$\sim P_1$' is logically equivalent to 'P_2', and '$\sim P_2$' to 'P_1'. Thus in this case we do not actually need both pr; we can express the two properties either by 'P_1' and '$\sim P_1$' or by '$\sim P_2$' and 'P_2', and it does not matter which of these two ways we choose. (Similarly, we can express n related properties by $n - 1$ pr and the negation of the disjunction of these pr.) For the sake of simplicity, we shall always presuppose that our systems $\mathfrak{L}$ contain only two-member-families; one attribute in each family is then designated by a pr and the other by its negation. By this restriction we avoid some complications in certain definitions and theorems. If, however, someone wishes to apply our theory to systems with larger families of pr, it is easy to make the necessary modifications.

The chief modifications are as follows. Let a system $\mathfrak{L}'$ containing φ families of basic attributes be given. Let the pth family ($p = 1, 2, \ldots, \varphi$) contain n_p attributes of degree d_p. For the sake of uniformity let us assume that in $\mathfrak{L}$ *all* these basic attributes, even those belonging to a two-member-family, are designated by pr. Then the basic matrices (D16-3c) and sentences (D16-6b) coincide with the atomic ones; they do not contain the sign of negation. A class of n_p atomic sentences formed with the n_p pr of the pth family and containing the same in (or d_p-tuple of in) is called a family of (related) atomic sentences. A state-description (D18-1) is defined as a conjunction or class containing exactly one atomic sentence from each family. (The requirement of independence applies here only to atomic sentences and *primitive* predicates of *different* families.) The definitions of range (D18-6) and of the L-concepts (§ 20) remain the same. It follows that the pr of each family form a division (D25-4). The concept of a correlation of basic matrices (§ 28) is replaced by the simpler concept of a correlation of the pr, defined analogously. A pr of the pth family has the degree d_p; therefore an argument expression fitting to it in an atomic sentence is an ordered d_p-tuple of in. The number of such d_p-tuples in $\mathfrak{L}'_N$ is N^{d_p}. This is likewise the number of atomic sentences with a given pr of the pth family. Therefore the number of all atomic sentences with pr of the pth family in $\mathfrak{L}'_N$ is $n_p N^{d_p}$; and the number of all atomic sentences in $\mathfrak{L}'_N$ is $\sum_p [n_p N^{d_p}]$. A state-description contains for every d_p-tuple of in exactly one of the n_p atomic sentences with the n_p pr of the pth family. Thus there are $n_p^{N^{d_p}}$ possibilities for those sub-conjunctions of state-descriptions which contain only pr of the pth family. Hence the number of state-descriptions in $\mathfrak{L}'_N$ (T29-1a) is $\zeta = \prod_p [n_p^{N^{d_p}}]$.

Now let us consider the case in which all pr in $\mathfrak{L}'_N$ are of degree one, hence designate properties, not relations (§ 31). A Q-predicate-expression (D31-1a) is here a conjunction of pr containing exactly one pr from each family. Therefore the number of Q's (T31-1) is $\kappa = \prod_p n_p$. The definitions of width and relative width (D32-1) remain unchanged. But the relative width of a pr of the pth family is not necessarily $1/2$ (T33-1b) but $1/n_p$. The relative width of a conjunction of several nonrelated pr is the product of their separate relative widths.

If expressed in terms of κ, certain important values are the same as before. This holds, in particular, for the number of $\mathfrak{Z}$ ($\zeta = \kappa^N$, T35-1b), the number of $\mathfrak{Str}$ (τ, T35-1d), and the number of those $\mathfrak{Z}$ which have a given set of Q-numbers (ζ_i, T35-4). The latter two numbers will later be taken as the basis for the determination of the measure-function $\mathfrak{m}^*$ and the degree of confirmation $\mathfrak{c}^*$ (§ 110, (2)).

D. *The Range of a Sentence*

We write '$V\mathfrak{Z}$' for the class of all state-descriptions in a given system (the universal range) and '$\Lambda\mathfrak{Z}$' for the null class of state-descriptions (the null range). When necessary, a left-hand subscript 'N' or '∞' is added.

D18-2.
a. ${}_N V\mathfrak{Z}$ (or simply $V\mathfrak{Z}$) $=_{\mathrm{Df}}$ the class of all $\mathfrak{Z}$ in $\mathfrak{L}_N$.
b. ${}_\infty V\mathfrak{Z}$ (or $V\mathfrak{Z}$) $=_{\mathrm{Df}}$ the class of all $\mathfrak{Z}$ in $\mathfrak{L}_\infty$.
c. ${}_N\Lambda\mathfrak{Z}$ (or $\Lambda\mathfrak{Z}$) $=_{\mathrm{Df}}$ the null class of $\mathfrak{Z}$ in $\mathfrak{L}_N$.
d. ${}_\infty\Lambda\mathfrak{Z}$ (or $\Lambda\mathfrak{Z}$) $=_{\mathrm{Df}}$ the null class of $\mathfrak{Z}$ in $\mathfrak{L}_\infty$.

If we understand the meaning of a sentence, then we know in which of the possible cases it would hold and in which not. And if we wish to give an interpretation to a sentence, in other words, to state its meaning, then one possible method for doing so consists just in saying in which of the possible cases it holds and in which not. Speaking in terms of state-descriptions instead of the possible cases which they describe, we can give an interpretation to a sentence by saying in which state-descriptions it holds and in which not. We shall do this now by rules which state the conditions for 'i holds in $\mathfrak{Z}_h$' for all sentences in a system $\mathfrak{L}$. This concept has a certain analogy to that of truth, it is, so to speak, conditional truth because it means: 'i would be true *if* the possible case described by $\mathfrak{Z}_h$ were the real case'; in other words, 'i would be true *if* the individuals had just those properties and relations which are attributed to them by $\mathfrak{Z}_h$'. Therefore, D4 is quite analogous to the earlier definition of truth (D17-1); and we can easily see that D4 is in accordance with the interpretation intended just as the earlier definition was.

D3 serves merely for the introduction of a convenient abbreviating phrase.

D18-3. Let i be a sentence in a system $\mathfrak{L}$ and $\mathfrak{Z}_h$ a state-description in $\mathfrak{L}$. *i belongs to* $\mathfrak{Z}_h$ $=_{\mathrm{Df}}$ i is a basic sentence in $\mathfrak{L}$ and occurs in $\mathfrak{Z}_h$ either as a conjunctive component (if $\mathfrak{L}$ is finite) or as an element (if $\mathfrak{L}$ is infinite).

+**D18-4.** Let i be a sentence in a system $\mathfrak{L}$, and $\mathfrak{Z}_h$ a state-description in $\mathfrak{L}$. *i holds in* $\mathfrak{Z}_h$ $=_{\mathrm{Df}}$ one of the following conditions (a) to (g) is fulfilled.
a. i is an atomic sentence and belongs to $\mathfrak{Z}_h$ (D3).

b. i has the form $\mathfrak{in}_j = \mathfrak{in}_j$.
c. i is 't'.
d. i is $\sim j$, and j does not hold in $\mathfrak{Z}_h$.
e. i is $j \vee k$, and at least one of the two components holds in $\mathfrak{Z}_h$.
f. i is $j \,.\, k$, and both components hold in $\mathfrak{Z}_h$.
g. i is $(\mathfrak{i}_k)(\mathfrak{M}_j)$, and all instances of $\mathfrak{M}_j$ hold in $\mathfrak{Z}_h$.

D18-5. Let $\mathfrak{K}_i$ be a class of sentences in $\mathfrak{L}$. $\mathfrak{K}_i$ ***holds in*** $\mathfrak{Z}_h =_{\text{Df}}$ every sentence of $\mathfrak{K}_i$ holds in $\mathfrak{Z}_h$.

According to our previous explanation, the meaning of a sentence i is determined by the class of those $\mathfrak{Z}$ in which i holds. We call this class the L-range or, briefly, the ***range*** of i (D6); for this, we write in signs '$\mathfrak{R}(i)$' or simply '$\mathfrak{R}_i$'; and for the range of $\mathfrak{K}_i$, '$\mathfrak{R}(\mathfrak{K}_i)$' (here no shorter form).

+**D18-6.** Let i be a sentence in a system $\mathfrak{L}$ and $\mathfrak{K}_i$ a class of sentences in $\mathfrak{L}$.

a. The ***range*** of i in $\mathfrak{L}$ ('$\mathfrak{R}(i)$', '$\mathfrak{R}_i$') $=_{\text{Df}}$ the class of those $\mathfrak{Z}$ in $\mathfrak{L}$ in which i holds.
b. The ***range*** of $\mathfrak{K}_i$ in $\mathfrak{L}$ ('$\mathfrak{R}(\mathfrak{K}_i)$') $=_{\text{Df}}$ the class of those $\mathfrak{Z}$ in $\mathfrak{L}$ in which $\mathfrak{K}_i$ holds.

On the basis of this definition D6 and the rules constituting D4 and D5, we easily see that the ranges for all forms of sentences and for $\mathfrak{K}_i$ are determined by the following theorem.

+**T18-1.** ***Theorem of ranges.*** Let i be a sentence and $\mathfrak{K}_i$ a class of sentences (in a system $\mathfrak{L}$).

a. If i is an atomic sentence, $\mathfrak{R}_i$ is the class of those $\mathfrak{Z}$ to which i belongs.
b. If i is $\mathfrak{in}_j = \mathfrak{in}_j$, $\mathfrak{R}_i$ is $V_{\mathfrak{Z}}$.
c. If i is $\mathfrak{in}_j = \mathfrak{in}_k$ with two different $\mathfrak{in}$, $\mathfrak{R}_i$ is $\Lambda_{\mathfrak{Z}}$.
d. If i is 't', $\mathfrak{R}_i$ is $V_{\mathfrak{Z}}$.
e. If i is $\sim j$, $\mathfrak{R}_i$ is $V_{\mathfrak{Z}} - \mathfrak{R}_j$.
f. If i is $j \vee k$, $\mathfrak{R}_i$ is $\mathfrak{R}_j \cup \mathfrak{R}_k$.
g. If i is $j \,.\, k$, $\mathfrak{R}_i$ is $\mathfrak{R}_j \cap \mathfrak{R}_k$.
h. If i is $(\mathfrak{i}_k)(\mathfrak{M}_j)$, $\mathfrak{R}_i$ is the class-product of the ranges of the instances of $\mathfrak{M}_j$.
i. If $\mathfrak{K}_i$ is non-empty, $\mathfrak{R}(\mathfrak{K}_i)$ is the class-product of the ranges of the sentences of $\mathfrak{K}_i$.
j. If $\mathfrak{K}_i$ is empty, $\mathfrak{R}(\mathfrak{K}_i)$ is $V_{\mathfrak{Z}}$.

T1 shows that the rules of D4 and D5 determine indirectly the ranges of all sentences and classes of sentences in $\mathfrak{L}$. Therefore we may call these rules *rules of ranges* (instead of 'rules of holding in a state-description'). We could, of course, formulate the rules just as well directly for ranges, in a way similar to T1; we have chosen the other way merely to facilitate the understanding.

The rules of ranges are the fundamental semantical rules for our systems $\mathfrak{L}$. The concept of range, which is determined by these rules, will, in our construction, be the cornerstone both for deductive and for inductive logic, since we shall define with its help both the L-concepts and the concept of degree of confirmation.

We have twice given an interpretation for the sentences in $\mathfrak{L}$, first by the rules of truth (D17-1), then again by the rules of ranges (D18-4). We have done so only in order to make the definition of truth more easily understandable. In fact, truth could be defined, instead of by D17-1, on the basis of D18-4 in the following way. 'True atomic sentence' would be defined in a way similar to D17-1a. Then the true state-description $\mathfrak{Z}_T$ would be defined as that state-description to which all true atomic sentences and the negations of the other atomic sentences belong. Finally, we define: *i* is true if it holds in $\mathfrak{Z}_T$.

§ 19. Theorems on State-Descriptions and Ranges

Some theorems concerning $\mathfrak{Z}$ and $\mathfrak{R}$ are stated, as lemmas for later theorems in deductive and inductive logic.

We state here some theorems on $\mathfrak{Z}$ and $\mathfrak{R}$. They are not of much interest in themselves but serve as lemmas for later theorems on L-concepts and on confirmation. These theorems hold, if not indicated otherwise, with respect to any finite or infinite system $\mathfrak{L}$ for the sentences and the $\mathfrak{Z}$ of that system.

T19-1. For every atomic sentence *i* and every $\mathfrak{Z}_j$, either *i* or $\sim i$ belongs to $\mathfrak{Z}_j$, but not both. (From D18-1, D18-3.)

+T19-2. For every sentence *i* (of any form, not only atomic) and every $\mathfrak{Z}_j$, either *i* or $\sim i$ holds in $\mathfrak{Z}_j$, but not both. (From D18-4d.)

T19-3. If *i* is a basic sentence, $\mathfrak{R}_i$ is the class of those $\mathfrak{Z}$ to which *i* belongs.

Proof. 1. For an atomic *i*, from T18-1a. 2. Let *i* be $\sim j$. Then *j* is atomic, and $\mathfrak{R}_j$ is the class of those $\mathfrak{Z}$ to which *j* belongs (1). $\mathfrak{R}_i$ is the class of the remaining $\mathfrak{Z}$ (T18-1e), hence of those $\mathfrak{Z}$ to which *j* does not belong. This is the class of those $\mathfrak{Z}$ to which $\sim j$ belongs, which is *i*.

As mentioned earlier (§ 16), we speak generally of conjunctions with *n* components, for any finite $n > 0$; if *i* has not the form $j \,.\, k$, we regard *i* as a conjunction with one component, which is *i* itself.

D19-1. j is a *subconjunction* of $i =_{\text{Df}}$ every conjunctive component of j is also a conjunctive component of i.

T19-4.

a. For $\mathfrak{L}_N$. If $\mathfrak{Z}_j$ is a subconjunction of $\mathfrak{Z}_i$, then it is the same as $\mathfrak{Z}_i$.

b. For $\mathfrak{L}_\infty$. If $\mathfrak{Z}_j$ is a subclass of $\mathfrak{Z}_i$, then it is the same as $\mathfrak{Z}_i$.

T19-5.

a. For $\mathfrak{L}_\infty$. Let $\mathfrak{K}_i$ be a class of basic sentences not containing any basic pair. Then $\mathfrak{R}(\mathfrak{K}_i)$ is the class of those $\mathfrak{Z}$ of which $\mathfrak{K}_i$ is a subclass.

Proof. We suppose that $\mathfrak{K}_i$ is non-empty; otherwise, the theorem follows from T18-1j. Then $\mathfrak{R}(\mathfrak{K}_i)$ is the class-product of the ranges of the sentences of $\mathfrak{K}_i$ (T18-1i). 1. Let j be any sentence of $\mathfrak{K}_i$ and $\mathfrak{Z}_i$ any $\mathfrak{Z}$ of which $\mathfrak{K}_i$ is a subclass. Hence $j \epsilon \mathfrak{Z}_i$. Since j is a basic sentence, $\mathfrak{R}_j$ is the class of those $\mathfrak{Z}$ to which j belongs (T3). Hence $\mathfrak{Z}_i \epsilon \mathfrak{R}_j$. Since this holds for every sentence j of $\mathfrak{K}_i$, $\mathfrak{Z}_i$ belongs to the class-product of the ranges of the sentences of $\mathfrak{K}_i$, hence to $\mathfrak{R}(\mathfrak{K}_i)$. 2. Let $\mathfrak{Z}_k$ be any $\mathfrak{Z}$ of which $\mathfrak{K}_i$ is not a subclass. Then there is a basic sentence i belonging to $\mathfrak{K}_i$ but not to $\mathfrak{Z}_k$. Let k be the other sentence of the basic pair of i. Then k belongs to $\mathfrak{Z}_k$ (D18-1b) but not to $\mathfrak{K}_i$. i belongs to every $\mathfrak{Z}$ in $\mathfrak{R}_i$ (T3); hence $\mathfrak{Z}_k$ is not an element of $\mathfrak{R}_i$. Therefore, since $i \epsilon \mathfrak{K}_i$, $\mathfrak{Z}_k$ cannot belong to the class-product of the ranges of the sentences of $\mathfrak{K}_i$, that is, to $\mathfrak{R}(\mathfrak{K}_i)$.

b. For $\mathfrak{L}_N$. Let i be a conjunction of n basic sentences ($n \geqq 1$) among which there is no atomic sentence together with its negation. Then $\mathfrak{R}_i$ is the class of those $\mathfrak{Z}$ of which i is a subconjunction (D1).

Proof analogous to (a), with T18-1g instead of T18-1i.

T19-6. For every $\mathfrak{Z}_i$, $\mathfrak{R}(\mathfrak{Z}_i)$ is $\{\mathfrak{Z}_i\}$ (that is to say, the range of $\mathfrak{Z}_i$ contains only $\mathfrak{Z}_i$ itself).

Proof. 1. For $\mathfrak{L}_N$, from T5b, T4a. 2. For $\mathfrak{L}_\infty$, from T5a, T4b.

The following theorem T8 deals with two consecutive systems in the sequence of finite systems, viz., with $\mathfrak{L}_N$ and $\mathfrak{L}_{N+1}$. There is just one individual constant 'a_{N+1}' which is new in $\mathfrak{L}_{N+1}$, that is, not already occurring in $\mathfrak{L}_N$. Hence the atomic sentences which are new in $\mathfrak{L}_{N+1}$ are just those which contain 'a_{N+1}'. Let their number be m, and let n be 2^m. Then there are n selections of new basic sentences (T40-31g), that is, classes containing exactly one sentence from each new basic pair and no other elements. Let us use here (for T8 only) '$\mathfrak{Z}$' and '$\mathfrak{R}$' for the state-descriptions and ranges of $\mathfrak{L}_N$, but '$\mathfrak{Z}'$' and '$\mathfrak{R}'$' for those of $\mathfrak{L}_{N+1}$. For every $\mathfrak{Z}'_j$, there is exactly one $\mathfrak{Z}_i$ which is a subconjunction (D1) of it, namely, that which contains all its old basic sentences. And the new basic sentences in $\mathfrak{Z}'_j$ form one of the n selections mentioned above. In this way, n $\mathfrak{Z}'$ grow out of $\mathfrak{Z}_i$ by the adjunction of one of the n selections each; hence $\mathfrak{Z}_i$ is a subconjunction of all of them. This situation must be kept in mind for the following theorem and its proof.

T19-8. Let i be any nongeneral sentence in $\mathfrak{L}_N$, and hence in $\mathfrak{L}_{N+1}$. Then $\mathfrak{R}'_i$ is the class of those $\mathfrak{Z}'$ which contain the sentences in $\mathfrak{R}_i$ as subconjunctions.

Proof. Since i is nongeneral (D16-6g), it is constructed out of simple sentences of the forms mentioned in T18-1a, b, c, d by a finite number n ($\geqq 0$) of applications of the connectives mentioned in T18-1e, f, g. Let $\mathfrak{R}^*_i$ be the class of those $\mathfrak{Z}'$ which contain the $\mathfrak{Z}$ in $\mathfrak{R}_i$ as subconjunctions. Then the theorem says that $\mathfrak{R}'_i$ is the same as $\mathfrak{R}^*_i$. We shall show first that this holds for those four simple forms (a), (b), (c), (d); and, then, that it holds for any sentence of one of the compound forms (e), (f), (g), provided it holds for the components occurring. Then the general theorem follows by mathematical induction with respect to n. — a. Let i be atomic. Then $\mathfrak{R}_i$ is the class of those $\mathfrak{Z}$ to which i belongs (T18-1a). Likewise, $\mathfrak{R}'_i$ is the class of those $\mathfrak{Z}'$ to which i belongs, hence the same as $\mathfrak{R}^*_i$. — b. Let i be $\mathfrak{in}_j = \mathfrak{in}_j$. Then $\mathfrak{R}_i$ is the class of all $\mathfrak{Z}$ (T18-1b). Therefore, $\mathfrak{R}^*_i$ is the class of all $\mathfrak{Z}'$, hence the same as $\mathfrak{R}'_i$. — c. Let i be $\mathfrak{in}_j = \mathfrak{in}_k$ with two different $\mathfrak{in}$. Then $\mathfrak{R}_i$ is the null class (T18-1c). Therefore, $\mathfrak{R}^*_i$ is the null class, hence the same as $\mathfrak{R}'_i$. — d. Let i be 't'. This case is like (b) (T18-1d). — e. Let i be $\sim j$. Suppose the theorem holds for j, i.e., $\mathfrak{R}'_j$ is the same as $\mathfrak{R}^*_j$. Then we shall show that it holds likewise for i. $\mathfrak{R}_i$ is the class of those $\mathfrak{Z}$ which do not belong to $\mathfrak{R}_j$ (T18-1e). Likewise, $\mathfrak{R}'_i$ is the class of those $\mathfrak{Z}'$ which do not belong to $\mathfrak{R}'_j$, which is the same as $\mathfrak{R}^*_j$. Hence $\mathfrak{R}'_i$ is the class of those $\mathfrak{Z}'$ which contain none of the sentences of $\mathfrak{R}_j$ as subconjunctions, and hence contain the sentences of $\mathfrak{R}_i$ as subconjunctions; this is the class $\mathfrak{R}^*_i$. — f. Let i be $j \vee k$. Suppose the theorem holds for j and for k; i.e., $\mathfrak{R}'_j$ is the same as $\mathfrak{R}^*_j$, and $\mathfrak{R}'_k$ is the same as $\mathfrak{R}^*_k$. We shall show that it holds likewise for i. $\mathfrak{R}_i$ is $\mathfrak{R}_j \cup \mathfrak{R}_k$ (T18-1f). Likewise, $\mathfrak{R}'_i$ is $\mathfrak{R}'_j \cup \mathfrak{R}'_k$, and hence $\mathfrak{R}^*_j \cup \mathfrak{R}^*_k$. This is the class of those $\mathfrak{Z}'$ which contain as subconjunctions the sentences in $\mathfrak{R}_j$ and in $\mathfrak{R}_k$, hence the sentences in $\mathfrak{R}_i$; thus it is the class $\mathfrak{R}^*_i$. — g. Let i be $j \,.\, k$. The proof is analogous to that of (f), using T18-1g.

The following theorem T9 is analogous to T8 but deals with $\mathfrak{L}_N$ and $\mathfrak{L}_\infty$.

T19-9. Let i be any nongeneral sentence in $\mathfrak{L}_N$, and hence in $\mathfrak{L}_\infty$. Then $\mathfrak{R}_i$ in $\mathfrak{L}_\infty$ is the class of those $\mathfrak{Z}_j$ in $\mathfrak{L}_\infty$ for which there is a $\mathfrak{Z}_i$ in $\mathfrak{R}_i$ in $\mathfrak{L}_N$ such that the conjunctive components of $\mathfrak{Z}_i$ belong to $\mathfrak{Z}_j$.

Proof analogous to that of T8.

§ 20. L-Concepts

A sentence (or proposition) is usually regarded as logically (necessarily, analytically) true if it holds in any possible case. Therefore we define the explicatum for this vague, traditional concept in this way: i is L-true (in signs, '$\vdash i$') if i holds in every $\mathfrak{Z}$, hence, if $\mathfrak{R}_i$ is the universal range (D1a). We define analogously: i is L-false if i holds in no $\mathfrak{Z}$, hence, if $\mathfrak{R}_i$ is the null range (D1b); this is the case if $\vdash \sim i$ (T1a). As an explicatum for what is known as logical or necessary implication or entailment, we define: i L-implies j if j holds in every $\mathfrak{Z}$ in which i holds, hence, if $\mathfrak{R}_i$ is a subclass of $\mathfrak{R}_j$ (D1c); this is the case if $\vdash i \supset j$ (T1b). As explicatum for logical or necessary equivalence, we define: i and j are L-equivalent if they have the same range (D1d); this is the case if $\vdash i \equiv j$ (T1c).

Further, 'L-disjunct' and 'L-exclusive' are defined (D1e, f). If a sentence is either L-true or L-false, it is called L-determinate (D3); otherwise it is called factual (D4), because its truth-value is dependent upon facts. If a sentence is true but not L-true, it is called F-true (D5a), because it is true by virtue of facts. The terms 'F-false', 'F-implies', 'F-equivalent' are defined analogously (D5b, c, d). Some theorems concerning the concepts defined are given.

We shall now introduce the L-concepts. They constitute the basis of deductive logic. Our method of defining these concepts bases them on the concept of range and hence on that of state-description. We can give here only short explanations. [For a more detailed discussion of the L-concepts see [Semantics], §§ 14 ff., 20, and [Meaning], § 2; the method is developed from an idea of Wittgenstein ([Tractatus], 4.463), see [Semantics], p. 107.]

The concept of ***L-truth*** is meant as an explicatum for that concept, frequently used but seldom exactly defined, which is variously characterized as analytical truth (Kant), necessary truth, logical truth, truth based on logical grounds, as distinguished from contingent, factual truth. It seems that we are sufficiently in agreement with at least some conceptions of this explicandum if we try to make it more explicit in this way: a sentence (or proposition) has this kind of truth if it would be true under any conceivable circumstances, in other words, in any possible case. Since we have constructed the state-descriptions $\mathfrak{Z}$ in such a way that they represent the possible cases, it seems natural to define the explicatum 'L-true' in this way: i is L-true if it holds in every $\mathfrak{Z}$, in other words, if $\mathfrak{R}_i$ is the universal range (D1a). We write '$\vdash i$' as short for 'i is L-true'; the scope of '$\vdash$' is always the whole immediately following meta-expression for a sentence (for example, '$\vdash i \vee j$' is meant as '$\vdash (i \vee j)$', hence as 'the sentence $i \vee j$ is L-true').

The concept of ***L-falsity*** is introduced as an explicatum for logical impossibility, self-contradiction, falsity based on logical grounds, as distinguished from contingent, factual falsity. A sentence has this kind of falsity if it holds in no possible case. Therefore, we define the explicatum in this way: i is L-false if i does not hold in any $\mathfrak{Z}$, in other words, if $\mathfrak{R}_i$ is the null range (D1b).

The concept of ***L-implication*** is meant as an explicatum for necessary implication, logical implication, entailment, the converse of logical consequence or logical deducibility. It seems that this explicandum is meant as that relation which connects i and j (or the corresponding propositions) if it is impossible that i is true but j is not, in other words, if j holds in every possible case in which i holds. Therefore, we define the explicatum in this way: i L-implies j if j holds in every $\mathfrak{Z}$ in which i holds, in other words, if $\mathfrak{R}_i$ is a subclass of $\mathfrak{R}_j$ (D1c).

The concept of ***L-equivalence*** is intended as an explicatum for necessary equivalence, mutual entailment, mutual logical deducibility. Therefore we define it by the identity of ranges (D1d). Then it is the same as mutual L-implication (T2i).

The concept of ***L-disjunctness*** is meant as an explicatum for that relation which holds between two or more sentences (or propositions) j_1, j_2, . . . , j_n ($n \geqq 2$), if by logical necessity at least one of them is true, in other words, if in any possible case at least one of them holds. Therefore, we take as definiens for the explicatum this condition: in every $\mathfrak{Z}$ at least one of the sentences holds, in other words, the class-sum of the ranges of the sentences is the universal range (D1e). This means the same as that the disjunction of the sentences is L-true (T1d).

The concept of ***L-exclusion*** is meant as an explicatum for logical incompatibility, logical impossibility of joint truth. This explicandum is that relation which connects the sentences i and j (or the corresponding propositions) if there is no possible case in which both of them hold. Therefore, we take as definiens for the explicatum this condition: there is no $\mathfrak{Z}$ in which both sentences hold, in other words, the class-product of their ranges is null (D1f). This means the same as that the conjunction of the sentences is L-false (T1e).

+**D20-1.** Let i and j be sentences in a system $\mathfrak{L}$. The terms here defined will be applied to classes of sentences (on the basis of D18-6b) in the same way as to sentences.

a. i is ***L-true*** ('$\vdash i$') (in $\mathfrak{L}$) $=_{\text{Df}}$ $\mathfrak{R}_i$ is $V_{\mathfrak{Z}}$.

b. i is ***L-false*** (in $\mathfrak{L}$) $=_{\text{Df}}$ $\mathfrak{R}_i$ is $\Lambda_{\mathfrak{Z}}$.

c. i ***L-implies*** j (j is an *L-implicate* of i) (in $\mathfrak{L}$) $=_{\text{Df}}$ $\mathfrak{R}_i \subset \mathfrak{R}_j$.

d. i is ***L-equivalent*** to j (in $\mathfrak{L}$) $=_{\text{Df}}$ $\mathfrak{R}_i$ is the same as $\mathfrak{R}_j$.

e. j_1, j_2, . . . , j_n ($n \geqq 2$) are ***L-disjunct*** with one another (in $\mathfrak{L}$) $=_{\text{Df}}$ $\mathfrak{R}(j_1) \cup \mathfrak{R}(j_2) \cup \ldots \cup \mathfrak{R}(j_n)$ is $V_{\mathfrak{Z}}$.

f. i is ***L-exclusive*** of j (in $\mathfrak{L}$) $=_{\text{Df}}$ $\mathfrak{R}_i \cap \mathfrak{R}_j$ is $\Lambda_{\mathfrak{Z}}$.

g. The class of sentences $\mathfrak{K}_i$ is (or, the sentences of $\mathfrak{K}_i$ are) ***L-exclusive in pairs*** (in $\mathfrak{L}$) $=_{\text{Df}}$ every sentence of $\mathfrak{K}_i$ is L-exclusive of every other sentence of $\mathfrak{K}_i$.

The following theorem T1 is based on D1. It states sufficient and necessary conditions for the L-concepts just defined, except L-truth, in terms of the L-truth of certain sentences. Often these conditions are more convenient than those in D1 in terms of ranges. Therefore we shall often make use of this theorem (usually without explicit reference). We shall often write '$\vdash i \supset j$' as a convenient abbreviation for 'i L-implies j'; likewise '$\vdash i \equiv j$' for 'i is L-equivalent to j'. In this and many of the subsequent theorems, we omit for brevity the reference 'in the system $\mathfrak{L}$'; it is understood that any L-term or F-term used is meant with respect to any finite or infinite system $\mathfrak{L}$, unless otherwise indicated.

+**T20-1.** ***Theorem of the L-concepts,*** with respect to sentences.

a. i is *L-false* if and only if $\vdash \sim i$.

b. i *L-implies* j if and only if $\vdash i \supset j$.

c. i is *L-equivalent* to j if and only if $\vdash i \equiv j$.

d. $j_1, j_2, \ldots, j_n$ ($n \geqq 2$) are *L-disjunct* with one another if and only if $\vdash j_1 \vee j_2 \vee \ldots \vee j_n$.

e. i is *L-exclusive* of j if and only if $\vdash \sim(i \,.\, j)$, hence if and only if $\vdash i \supset \sim j$, hence if and only if $\vdash j \supset \sim i$.

T1 states *characteristic sentences* for the L-concepts (compare [Semantics] § 22), that is to say, sentences whose L-truth is a sufficient and necessary condition for the corresponding L-concepts. Now we shall often find situations (especially in the theory of the degree of confirmation on a given evidence e) where one of these characteristic sentences is not L-true but is L-implied by a given sentence e. In these cases we shall often use the L-term in question in a relative way with respect to e. The following definition introduces the *relative L-terms* corresponding to T1c, d, e.

D20-2. Let e, i, and j be sentences in $\mathfrak{L}$.

a. i and j are L-equivalent (to one another) *with respect to* e (in $\mathfrak{L}$) $=_{\text{Df}}$ $\vdash e \supset (i \equiv j)$.

b. $j_1, j_2, \ldots, j_n$ ($n \geqq 2$) are L-disjunct (with one another) with respect to e (in $\mathfrak{L}$) $=_{\text{Df}} \vdash e \supset j_1 \vee j_2 \vee \ldots \vee j_n$.

c. i and j are L-exclusive (of one another) with respect to e (in $\mathfrak{L}$) $=_{\text{Df}}$ $\vdash e \supset \sim(i \,.\, j)$ (hence $\vdash e \supset \sim i \vee \sim j$, $\vdash e \,.\, i \supset \sim j$, $e \,.\, i \,.\, j$ is L-false).

d. The class of sentences $\mathfrak{K}_i$ is (or, the sentences of $\mathfrak{K}_i$ are) L-exclusive in pairs with respect to e (in $\mathfrak{L}$) $=_{\text{Df}}$ every sentence in $\mathfrak{K}_i$ is L-exclusive with respect to e of every other sentence in $\mathfrak{K}_i$.

In T2, some elementary theorems concerning L-concepts are listed, which hold in any finite or infinite system $\mathfrak{L}$. (For proofs of these and related theorems see [Semantics] §§ 20 and 14.)

T20-2.

a. $\mathfrak{K}_i$ is L-true if and only if every sentence of $\mathfrak{K}_i$ is L-true.

b. If $\vdash i \supset j$ and $\vdash j \supset k$, then $\vdash i \supset k$. Analogously for classes of sentences.

c. If $\vdash i \supset j$ and $\vdash i$, then $\vdash j$.

d. If $j \epsilon \mathfrak{K}_i$, then $\mathfrak{K}_i$ L-implies j.

e. If $\mathfrak{K}_j \subset \mathfrak{K}_i$, then $\mathfrak{K}_i$ L-implies $\mathfrak{K}_j$.

f. i (or $\mathfrak{K}_i$) L-implies $\mathfrak{K}_j$ if and only if i (or $\mathfrak{K}_i$, respectively) L-implies every sentence of $\mathfrak{K}_j$.

g. If $\vdash j$, then for every i, $\vdash i \supset j$.

h. If $\vdash \sim i$, then for every j, $\vdash i \supset j$.

i. $\vdash i \equiv j$ if and only if $\vdash i \supset j$ and $\vdash j \supset i$.

j. The null class of sentences is L-true.

k. If i is a conjunction with n components ($n \geqq 1$) and $\mathfrak{K}_i$ is the class of these n components, then i and $\mathfrak{K}_i$ are L-equivalent. (From T18-1g and i.)

l. $\vdash i \supset j$ if and only if $\vdash i \,.\, j \equiv i$.

m. If $\vdash i \vee j$ (hence, i and j are L-disjunct) and $\vdash \sim(i \,.\, j)$ (hence, i and j are L-exclusive), then $\vdash i \equiv \sim j$ and $\vdash \sim i \equiv j$.

o. $\{i \supset j, i\}$ L-implies j.

p. A conjunction with n components ($n \geqq 1$) is L-true if and only if every component of it is L-true.

q. A disjunction with n components ($n \geqq 1$) is L-false if and only if every component of it is L-false.

s. If a subclass of $\mathfrak{K}_i$ is L-false, then $\mathfrak{K}_i$ is L-false.

t. Let $\mathfrak{Z}_i$ be a $\mathfrak{Z}$ in $\mathfrak{L}$. j holds in $\mathfrak{Z}_i$ (or, in other words, $\mathfrak{Z}_i \epsilon \mathfrak{R}_j$) if and only if $\mathfrak{Z}_i$ L-implies j in $\mathfrak{L}$.

Proof. j holds in $\mathfrak{Z}_i$ if and only if $\mathfrak{Z}_i \epsilon \mathfrak{R}_j$; hence if and only if $\mathfrak{R}(\mathfrak{Z}_i) \subset \mathfrak{R}_j$ (T19-6), hence if and only if $\mathfrak{Z}_i$ L-implies j in $\mathfrak{L}$ (D1c).

If i is either L-true or L-false, we can determine its truth-value by logical, that is, semantical, analysis on the basis of the rules of ranges. Therefore, we call i in this case ***L-determinate*** (D3). Otherwise, i.e., if i is neither L-true nor L-false, we call it ***factual*** (D4), because in this case we need knowledge of the relevant facts, in addition to the interpretation of the sentence, in order to find its truth-value. If i is true but not L-true, in other words, if i is true and factual, we call it ***F-true*** (for 'factually true') (D5a). Other F-terms are defined analogously (D5b, c, d); they will be used only rarely. All these terms are applied to classes of sentences in the same way as here defined for sentences.

+D20-3. i is ***L-determinate*** (in $\mathfrak{L}$) $=_{\text{Df}}$ i is either L-true or L-false.

+D20-4. i is ***factual*** in $\mathfrak{L}$ $=_{\text{Df}}$ i is a sentence in $\mathfrak{L}$ and not L-determinate.

D20-5.

a. i is ***F-true*** (in $\mathfrak{L}$) $=_{\text{Df}}$ i is true but not L-true.

b. i is ***F-false*** (in $\mathfrak{L}$) $=_{\text{Df}}$ i is false but not L-false.

c. i ***F-implies*** j (in $\mathfrak{L}$) $=_{\mathrm{Df}}$ the sentence $i \supset j$ is F-true.
d. i is ***F-equivalent*** to j (in $\mathfrak{L}$) $=_{\mathrm{Df}}$ the sentence $i \equiv j$ is F-true.

Some theorems on factuality follow.

T20-4. i (or $\mathfrak{K}_i$) is factual if and only if $\mathfrak{R}_i$ (or $\mathfrak{R}(\mathfrak{K}_i)$, respectively) is neither $V\mathfrak{Z}$ nor $\Lambda\mathfrak{Z}$.

T20-5. If i or $\mathfrak{K}_i$ fulfils one of the following conditions (a) to (g), it is factual.

a. i is a basic sentence. (From T19-3, T4.)
b. i is a $\mathfrak{Z}$ in $\mathfrak{L}_N$. (From T19-6, T4.)
c. $\mathfrak{K}_i$ is a $\mathfrak{Z}$ in $\mathfrak{L}_\infty$. (Like (b).)
d. $\mathfrak{K}_i$ is a non-empty subclass of any $\mathfrak{Z}_j$ in $\mathfrak{L}_\infty$.

Proof. $\mathfrak{K}_i$ is not L-true (T2a, (a)) and not L-false (T2s, (c)).

e. i is a subconjunction with n components ($n \geqq 1$) of any $\mathfrak{Z}_j$ in $\mathfrak{L}_N$. (Analogous to (d), from (a), (b), T2k).
f. $\mathfrak{K}_i$ is a non-empty class of basic sentences which does not contain a basic pair. (From (d), (e), T2k.)
g. i is a conjunction of n basic sentences ($n \geqq 1$) not including any atomic sentence together with its negation. (From (d), (e), T2k.)

T20-6. i is factual if and only if $\sim i$ is factual. (From T1a.)

The following theorems T8–T11 speak about L-concepts with respect to sentences in different systems.

T20-8. Let i and j be any *nongeneral* sentences (D16-6g) in $\mathfrak{L}_N$, and hence also in $\mathfrak{L}_{N+m}$ for any m.

a. i is L-true in $\mathfrak{L}_{N+m}$ if and only if it is L-true in $\mathfrak{L}_N$. (From T19-8, by mathematical induction with respect to m.)
b. i is L-false in $\mathfrak{L}_{N+m}$ if and only if it is L-false in $\mathfrak{L}_N$. (From (a).)
c. Each of the relations of L-implication, L-equivalence, L-disjunctness, L-exclusion holds for the pair i,i in $\mathfrak{L}_{N+m}$ if and only if it does in $\mathfrak{L}_N$. (From (a).)
d. i is factual in $\mathfrak{L}_{N+m}$ if and only if it is factual in $\mathfrak{L}_N$. (From (a), (b).)

T20-9. Let i and j be any *nongeneral* sentences in $\mathfrak{L}_N$, and hence also in $\mathfrak{L}_\infty$.

a. i is L-true in $\mathfrak{L}_\infty$ if and only if it is L-true in $\mathfrak{L}_N$. (From T19–9.)
b. i is L-false in $\mathfrak{L}_\infty$ if and only if it is L-false in $\mathfrak{L}_N$. (From (a).)
c. Each of the relations of L-implication, L-equivalence, L-disjunctness, L-exclusion holds for the pair i,j in $\mathfrak{L}_\infty$ if and only if it does in $\mathfrak{L}_N$. (From (a).)
d. i is factual in $\mathfrak{L}_\infty$ if and only if it is factual in $\mathfrak{L}_N$. (From (a), (b).)

T20-10. Let i and j be any *nongeneral* sentences in any finite or infinite system $\mathfrak{L}$.

a. If i is L-true in any system, then it is L-true in every system in which it occurs. (From T8a, T9a.)

b. If i is L-false (or L-determinate or factual, respectively) in any system, then it is likewise in every system in which it occurs. (From (a).)

c. If L-implication (or L-equivalence, L-disjunctness, L-exclusion) holds for the pair i,j in any system, then likewise in every system in which i and j occur. (From (a).)

T10 does not hold for all sentences. Counterexamples can easily be found among general sentences containing '='. For instance, let i be '$(x)(y)(z)(x = y \vee x = z \vee y = z)$', and j '$(\exists x)(\exists y)(x \neq y)$'; i says that there are at most two individuals, and j says that there are at least two individuals. Since both sentences do not contain any in, they occur in all systems. However, i is L-true in $\mathfrak{L}_1$ and $\mathfrak{L}_2$ only, but L-false in all other systems. j is L-false in $\mathfrak{L}_1$ only, but L-true in all other systems. Hence their conjunction $i \centerdot j$ is L-true in $\mathfrak{L}_2$ only, but L-false in all other systems. There are sentences which, if we run through the sequence of systems $\mathfrak{L}_1$, $\mathfrak{L}_2$, etc., are first L-true in some systems, then not L-true in some following systems, then again L-true in some systems, and so on in a never ending oscillation. (Examples will be given in Vol. II, in connection with $\mathfrak{m}^*$ for $\mathfrak{L}_\infty$; likewise counterexamples for the converse of T11.) A sentence of this kind cannot be L-true in $\mathfrak{L}_\infty$; this is stated by T11. (On 'final segment' see D40-5.)

T20-11.

a. If i is L-true in $\mathfrak{L}_\infty$, then i is L-true in a final segment of the sequence of the systems $\mathfrak{L}_N$ (in other words, there is an m such that i is L-true in every system $\mathfrak{L}_N$ with $N \geqq m$).

b. Analogues to (a) hold for the concepts mentioned in T10b and c with respect to i or the pair i,j, respectively.

The converse of T11 does not hold generally.

It may be remarked incidentally that T11 holds for the systems $\mathfrak{L}$ only because these do not contain attribute variables. Let j be the sentence

'$\sim(x)(Px) \centerdot (x)[Px \supset (\exists y)(z)(Rxz \equiv (z = y))] \centerdot (y)(\exists x)[Px \centerdot (z)(Rzy \equiv (z = x))]$'.

This sentence says that not all individuals are P, and R is a one-to-one correspondence between those individuals which are P and all individuals; in other words, R maps the whole universe of individuals on a proper part of it. This is possible, of course, only for the infinite universe. Therefore j is factual in $\mathfrak{L}_\infty$ but L-false in any finite system $\mathfrak{L}_N$. In systems $\mathfrak{L}'$ with attribute variables in quantifiers, a sentence j' can be constructed which follows from j by existential generalization ('there is a property F and a relation H such that . . .'). This sentence j' is, like j, L-false in every $\mathfrak{L}'_N$; but it is, in distinction to j, L-true in $\mathfrak{L}'_\infty$. Hence, T11a does not hold for the systems $\mathfrak{L}'$. Since j' is L-true only in $\mathfrak{L}'_\infty$ and otherwise L-false, it may be taken as a formulation of the infinity condition for the domain of individuals. For a discussion of infinity conditions see Hilbert and Bernays [Grundlagen], I, 213 and 209 ff. Each infinity condition corresponds to the satisfiability ("Erfüllbarkeit", cf. [Formalization], p. xi) of a matrix with free attribute variables, and hence it can be formulated by a sentence only with the help of quantifiers with attribute variables. Therefore, sentences of this kind cannot occur in our systems $\mathfrak{L}$.

This ends the first part of this chapter, which alone is a prerequisite for the next chapter (see § 14).

§ 21. Theorems of Propositional Logic

A. Some elementary theorems of propositional logic are listed for later reference. Most of them are well known. *B*. On the basis of the theorems under (A) some theorems on *truth-tables* (T7) and *state-descriptions* (T8) are proved. *C*. The disjunctive and the conjunctive *normal forms* of sentences are defined, and theorems for them are given.

In §§ 21–24 theorems on L-concepts are listed for later use. They are based on the definitions and theorems of §§ 18–20. Most of them are well-known theorems of propositional and lower functional logic. In most cases it seems unnecessary to give proofs or back references.

A. *Elementary Theorems of Propositional Logic*

The theorems of this section are theorems of *propositional logic;* this means that they apply L-concepts to sentences on the basis of the way in which these sentences are constructed with the help of connectives. Any sentence asserted to be L-true in these theorems from T3 on can easily be shown to be tautologous on the basis of the ordinary truth-tables, and is therefore L-true in $\mathfrak{L}$ (T1).

D21-1. Let i be a sentence in a system $\mathfrak{L}$. i is *tautologous* $=_{Df}$ i is constructed out of components $j_1, j_2, \ldots, j_n$ ($n \geqq 1$) with the help of connectives such that the following two conditions (a) and (b) are fulfilled.

a. Every j-component is not a negation, disjunction, or conjunction of other sentences but may have any other form whatever, including the universal form.

b. For every possible distribution of the truth-values T and F among the components, where 't' always has the value T, the truth-value of i determined on the basis of the ordinary truth-tables for the connectives is always T.

T21-1. Every tautologous sentence in $\mathfrak{L}$ is L-true in $\mathfrak{L}$.

Proof. The rules for the connectives in $\mathfrak{L}$ are in accordance with the ordinary truth-tables, see D18-4d, e, f, and, based upon it, T18-1e, f, g. (This holds likewise for our definitions A15-1a, b for '$\supset$' and '$\equiv$'; therefore, if a sentence containing these signs is given, we need not eliminate them before applying T1 but may instead use the ordinary truth-tables for these signs.)

T21-3. L-true sentences in $\mathfrak{L}$.

a. $\vdash t$.

b. $\vdash i \vee \sim i$.

c. $\vdash i \supset i$, i.e. $\vdash \sim i \vee i$.

d. $\vdash \sim (i \,.\, \sim i)$.

T21-4. L-true sentences with '$\supset$' in $\mathfrak{L}$. Each of the following items (a) to (s) states three theorems:

A. Any sentence of the form described is L-true (as indicated by '$\vdash$') (T1).

B. The antecedent of the main connective '$\supset$' L-implies the consequent (T20-1b) (for example, in (a): i L-implies $i \vee j$).

C. Let the matrix $\mathfrak{M}_k$ be constructed from a sentence here described by replacing the components i, j, etc., by any matrices. Then $\vdash (\,)(\mathfrak{M}_k)$ (T22-4). (For example, from (a): $\vdash (x)(P_1x \supset P_1x \vee P_2x)$.)

a. $\vdash i \supset i \vee j$.

b. $\vdash i \,.\, j \supset i$.

c. $\vdash (i \supset j) \,.\, (j \supset k) \supset (i \supset k)$.

d. $\vdash (i \equiv j) \,.\, (j \equiv k) \supset (i \equiv k)$.

e. $\vdash (i \supset j) \supset (i \vee k \supset j \vee k)$.

f. $\vdash (i \supset j) \supset (i \,.\, k \supset j \,.\, k)$.

g. $\vdash (i \supset j) \,.\, i \supset j$.

h. $\vdash (i \supset j) \,.\, \sim j \supset \sim i$.

i. $\vdash (i \equiv j) \,.\, i \supset j$.

j. $\vdash (i \equiv j) \,.\, \sim i \supset \sim j$.

k. $\vdash (i \equiv j) \supset (i \supset j)$.

l. $\vdash (i \equiv j) \supset (j \supset i)$.

m. $\vdash (i \vee j) \,.\, \sim i \supset j$.

n. $\vdash (i \supset j) \,.\, (k \supset l) \supset (i \vee k \supset j \vee l)$.

r. $\vdash i \supset t$.

s. $\vdash \sim t \supset i$.

T21-5. Sentences with '$\equiv$'. Each of the following items (a) to (u) (2) states five theorems:

A. Any sentence of the form described is L-true (as indicated by '$\vdash$').

B. The two components of the main connective '$\equiv$' are L-equivalent (T20-1c) (for example, in (e)(1): $i \vee j$ is L-equivalent to $j \vee i$).

C. The two components are L-interchangeable (T23-1b).

D. Let $\mathfrak{M}_k \equiv \mathfrak{M}_l$ be constructed from any sentence here described by putting any matrices in the place of the components i, j, etc. Then $\vdash (\,)(\mathfrak{M}_k \equiv \mathfrak{M}_l)$ (T22-4).

E. $\mathfrak{M}_k$ and $\mathfrak{M}_l$ are L-interchangeable. (T23-2c).

a. $\vdash i \equiv i$.

b. $\vdash i \equiv \sim\sim i$.

c. $\vdash i \equiv i \vee i$.

d. $\vdash i \equiv i \,.\, i$.

e. Principles of commutation.

(1) $\vdash i \vee j \equiv j \vee i$.
(2) $\vdash i \,.\, j \equiv j \,.\, i$.
(3) $\vdash (i \equiv j) \equiv (j \equiv i)$.

f. Principles of duality.

(1) $\vdash \sim (i \vee j) \equiv \sim i \,.\, \sim j$.
(2) $\vdash \sim (i_1 \vee i_2 \vee \ldots \vee i_n) \equiv \sim i_1 \,.\, \sim i_2 \,.\, \ldots \,.\, \sim i_n$.
(3) $\vdash \sim (i \,.\, j) \equiv \sim i \vee \sim j$.
(4) $\vdash \sim (i_1 \,.\, i_2 \,.\, \ldots \,.\, i_n) \equiv \sim i_1 \vee \sim i_2 \vee \ldots \vee \sim i_n$.

g. Principles of negation.

(1) $\vdash \sim (i \,.\, \sim j) \equiv (i \supset j)$.
(2) $\vdash \sim (i \supset j) \equiv i \,.\, \sim j$.
(3) $\vdash \sim (i \equiv j) \equiv (i \equiv \sim j)$.
(4) $\vdash \sim (i \equiv j) \equiv (i \,.\, \sim j) \vee (\sim i \,.\, j)$.

h. Principles of transposition.

(1) $\vdash (i \supset j) \equiv (\sim j \supset \sim i)$.
(2) $\vdash (\sim i \supset j) \equiv (\sim j \supset i)$.
(3) $\vdash (i \supset \sim j) \equiv (j \supset \sim i)$.
(4) $\vdash (i \equiv j) \equiv (\sim i \equiv \sim j)$.
(5) $\vdash (i \equiv \sim j) \equiv (\sim i \equiv j)$.
(6) $\vdash (i \,.\, j \supset k) \equiv (i \,.\, \sim k \supset \sim j)$.
(7) $\vdash (i \supset j \vee k) \equiv (i \,.\, \sim j \supset k)$.
(8) $\vdash (i \supset \sim j \vee k) \equiv (i \,.\, j \supset k)$.

i. (1) $\vdash (i \supset j) \equiv (i \equiv i \,.\, j)$.
(2) $\vdash (i \supset j) \equiv (i \supset i \,.\, j)$.
(3) $\vdash (i \supset j) \equiv (j \equiv i \vee j)$.
(4) $\vdash (i \supset j) \equiv (i \vee j \supset j)$.

j. (1) $\vdash i \equiv (i \vee j) \,.\, (i \vee \sim j)$.
(2) $\vdash i \equiv (i \,.\, j) \vee (i \,.\, \sim j)$.

k. (1) $\vdash (i \supset (j \supset k)) \equiv (i \,.\, j \supset k)$.
(2) $\vdash (i \supset (j \supset k)) \equiv (j \supset (i \supset k))$.

l. Principles of association.
(1) $\vdash (i \vee j) \vee k \equiv i \vee (j \vee k)$.
(2) $\vdash (i \cdot j) \cdot k \equiv i \cdot (j \cdot k)$.

m. Principles of distribution.
(1) $\vdash i \cdot (j \vee k) \equiv (i \cdot j) \vee (i \cdot k)$.
(2) $\vdash i \cdot (j_1 \vee j_2 \vee \ldots \vee j_n) \equiv (i \cdot j_1) \vee (i \cdot j_2) \vee \ldots \vee (i \cdot j_n)$.
(3) $\vdash (i_1 \vee i_2 \vee \ldots \vee i_m) \cdot (j_1 \vee j_2 \vee \ldots \vee j_n) \equiv (i_1 \cdot j_1) \vee (i_1 \cdot j_2) \vee \ldots \vee (i_1 \cdot j_n) \vee (i_2 \cdot j_1) \vee \ldots \vee (i_m \cdot j_1) \vee (i_m \cdot j_2) \vee \ldots \vee (i_m \cdot j_n)$, where at the right-hand side conjunctions for all pairs of an i-sentence and a j-sentence occur.
(4) $\vdash i \vee (j \cdot k) \equiv (i \vee j) \cdot (i \vee k)$.
(5) $\vdash i \vee (j_1 \cdot j_2 \cdot \ldots \cdot j_n) \equiv (i \vee j_1) \cdot (i \vee j_2) \cdot \ldots \cdot (i \vee j_n)$.
(6) $\vdash (i_1 \cdot i_2 \cdot \ldots \cdot i_m) \vee (j_1 \cdot j_2 \cdot \ldots \cdot j_n) \equiv (i_1 \vee j_1) \cdot (i_1 \vee j_2) \cdot \ldots \cdot (i_1 \vee j_n) \cdot (i_2 \vee j_1) \cdot \ldots \cdot (i_m \vee j_1) \cdot (i_m \vee j_2) \cdot \ldots \cdot (i_m \vee j_n)$, analogous to (3).
(7) $\vdash i \vee (j \equiv k) \equiv (i \vee j \equiv i \vee k)$.
(8) $\vdash i \supset j \cdot k \equiv (i \supset j) \cdot (i \supset k)$.
(9) $\vdash i \supset j_1 \cdot j_2 \cdot \ldots \cdot j_n \equiv (i \supset j_1) \cdot (i \supset j_2) \cdot \ldots \cdot (i \supset j_n)$.
(10) $\vdash i \supset j \vee k \equiv (i \supset j) \vee (i \supset k)$.
(11) $\vdash i \supset j_1 \vee j_2 \vee \ldots \vee j_n \equiv (i \supset j_1) \vee (i \supset j_2) \vee \ldots \vee (i \supset j_n)$.
(12) $\vdash i \supset (j \supset k) \equiv (i \supset j) \supset (i \supset k)$.
(13) $\vdash i \supset (j \equiv k) \equiv [(i \supset j) \equiv (i \supset k)]$.

n. (1) $\vdash (i \cdot j \supset k) \equiv (i \supset k) \vee (j \supset k)$.
(2) $\vdash (i_1 \cdot i_2 \cdot \ldots \cdot i_n \supset k) \equiv (i_1 \supset k) \vee (i_2 \supset k) \vee \ldots \vee (i_n \supset k)$.
(3) $\vdash (i \vee j \supset k) \equiv (i \supset k) \cdot (j \supset k)$.
(4) $\vdash (i_1 \vee i_2 \vee \ldots \vee i_n \supset k) \equiv (i_1 \supset k) \cdot (i_2 \supset k) \cdot \ldots \cdot (i_n \supset k)$.

o. $\vdash (i \supset (j \equiv k)) \equiv (i \cdot j \equiv i \cdot k)$.

p. (1) $\vdash i \equiv i \vee (i \cdot j)$.
(2) $\vdash i \equiv i \cdot (i \vee j)$.
(3) $\vdash i \vee j \equiv i \vee (j \cdot \sim i)$.
(4) $\vdash i \cdot j \equiv i \cdot (j \vee \sim i)$.
(5) $\vdash i \cdot j \equiv i \cdot (i \supset j)$.

r. Disjunctions with 't'.
(1) $\vdash i \vee t \equiv t$.
(2) $\vdash i \vee \sim t \equiv i$.

s. Conjunctions with 't'.
(1) $\vdash i \cdot t \equiv i$.
(2) $\vdash i \cdot \sim t \equiv \sim t$.

t. Conditionals with 't'.
(1) $\vdash (t \supset i) \equiv i$.

(2) $\vdash (\sim t \supset i) \equiv t$.
(3) $\vdash (i \supset t) \equiv t$.
(4) $\vdash (i \supset \sim t) \equiv \sim i$.

u. Biconditionals with 't'.
(1) $\vdash (i \equiv t) \equiv i$.
(2) $\vdash (i \equiv \sim t) \equiv \sim i$.

B. *Theorems on Truth-Tables*

The truth-table for n sentences $i_1, \ldots, i_n$ has 2^n lines (T40-31f). Each line may be represented by a conjunction of n components. Let these conjunctions be $k_1, \ldots, k_m$ ($m = 2^n$). k_1 is $i_1 \cdot i_2 \cdot \ldots \cdot i_n$; every other conjunction is formed from k_1 by replacing some components with their negations. For any sentence j constructed out of some of the i-sentences with the help of connectives, its truth-table can be constructed in the customary way; it states one of the truth values T or F for each of the m lines. The following diagram shows an example for $n = 3$, $m = 8$. If j has the value F for every line, it is L-false; otherwise j is L-equivalent to the disjunction of those k-sentences for which it has the value T. (In the example given in the last column of the accompanying table, j is L-equivalent to $k_1 \vee k_3 \vee k_7$.)

Truth-table for three components

i_1	i_2	i_3	Conjunctions	j: $(i_1 \vee \sim i_2) \cdot i_3$
T	T	T	$k_1 : i_1 \cdot i_2 \cdot i_3$	T
T	T	F	$k_2 : i_1 \cdot i_2 \cdot \sim i_3$	F
T	F	T	$k_3 : i_1 \cdot \sim i_2 \cdot i_3$	T
T	F	F	$k_4 : i_1 \cdot \sim i_2 \cdot \sim i_3$	F
F	T	T	$k_5 : \sim i_1 \cdot i_2 \cdot i_3$	F
F	T	F	$k_6 : \sim i_1 \cdot i_2 \cdot \sim i_3$	F
F	F	T	$k_7 : \sim i_1 \cdot \sim i_2 \cdot i_3$	T
F	F	F	$k_8 : \sim i_1 \cdot \sim i_2 \cdot \sim i_3$	F

The assertions of the following theorem T7 are well known. They follow from the earlier mentioned theorems of propositional logic.

T21-7. Let $i_1, i_2, \ldots, i_n$ be any sentences. Let k_1 be their conjunction $i_1 \cdot i_2 \cdot \ldots \cdot i_n$. Let $k_2, \ldots, k_m$ ($m = 2^n$) be formed from k_1 by replacing one or more of the components with their negations. Let j be any sentence constructed out of i-sentences with the help of connectives. Let $\mathfrak{K}_j$ be the class of those k-sentences which correspond to the lines of the *truth-table* for which j has the value T. Then the following holds.

a. The m k-sentences are L-exclusive in pairs.

b. The m k-sentences are L-disjunct, that is, $\vdash k_1 \vee k_2 \vee \ldots \vee k_m$.

c. If $\mathfrak{K}_j$ is empty, j is L-false.

d. If $\mathfrak{K}_j$ is not empty, j is L-equivalent to the disjunction of the sentences of $\mathfrak{K}_j$.

e. If $\mathfrak{K}_j$ contains all k-sentences, j is L-true.

f. If $\mathfrak{K}_i$ is any non-empty class of k-sentences and h is a disjunction of the sentences in $\mathfrak{K}_i$, then the truth-table for h has the value T on just those lines which correspond to the k-sentences in $\mathfrak{K}_i$.

g. If $\mathfrak{K}_j$ does not contain all the k-sentences, then j is L-equivalent to the conjunction of the negations of those k-sentences which do not belong to $\mathfrak{K}_j$.

If we take as the i-sentences all the atomic sentences in $\mathfrak{L}_N$, then the k-sentences become (by rearranging their conjunctive components in the lexicographical order) the *state-descriptions* ($\mathfrak{Z}$) in $\mathfrak{L}_N$; and, in the same way, $\mathfrak{K}_j$ becomes $\mathfrak{R}_j$. Thus we obtain the following theorems about $\mathfrak{Z}$.

+T21-8. For $\mathfrak{L}_N$.

a. Any two distinct $\mathfrak{Z}$ are L-exclusive. (From T7a.)

b. All the $\mathfrak{Z}$ in $\mathfrak{L}_N$ are L-disjunct, that is, their disjunction is L-true. (From T7b.)

c. If j is not L-false, then j is L-equivalent to the disjunction of the $\mathfrak{Z}$ in $\mathfrak{R}_j$. (From T7d.)

d. If $\mathfrak{K}_i$ is any non-empty class of $\mathfrak{Z}$, and h is a disjunction of the $\mathfrak{Z}$ in $\mathfrak{K}_i$, then $\mathfrak{R}_h$ is the same as $\mathfrak{K}_i$. (From T7f.)

e. For every class $\mathfrak{K}_k$, finite or infinite, of sentences in $\mathfrak{L}_N$, there is a sentence h L-equivalent to $\mathfrak{K}_k$.

Proof. The number of atomic sentences, and hence that of all $\mathfrak{Z}$ in $\mathfrak{L}_N$, is finite. Therefore, $\mathfrak{R}(\mathfrak{K}_k)$ is finite even if $\mathfrak{K}_k$ is infinite. We take $\mathfrak{R}(\mathfrak{K}_k)$ to be non-empty; otherwise $\mathfrak{K}_k$ is L-false and hence '$\sim t$' is L-equivalent to it. Let h be a disjunction of the $\mathfrak{Z}$ in $\mathfrak{R}(\mathfrak{K}_k)$. Then $\mathfrak{R}_h$ is the same as $\mathfrak{R}(\mathfrak{K}_k)$ (d). Hence h is L-equivalent to $\mathfrak{K}_k$.

f. If j is not L-true, then j is L-equivalent to the conjunction of the negations of those $\mathfrak{Z}$ which do not belong to $\mathfrak{R}_j$, in other words, those $\mathfrak{Z}$ which belong to $\mathfrak{R}(\sim j)$. (From T7g.)

g. The negations of any two distinct $\mathfrak{Z}$ are L-disjunct.

Proof. $\vdash \sim(\mathfrak{Z}_i \,.\, \mathfrak{Z}_j)$ (a). Hence $\vdash \sim\mathfrak{Z}_i \vee \sim\mathfrak{Z}_j$.

C. *Normal Forms*

D21-2. Let i be any sentence in $\mathfrak{L}_N$ or any nongeneral sentence in $\mathfrak{L}_\infty$. j is *a sentence of* ***disjunctive normal form*** *corresponding to* $i =_{\mathrm{Df}} j$ is formed from i by applying the following rules (a) to (p), until none of them is applicable any more; at any time the first of the rules which is applicable is to be applied; the rules apply to any part of the sentence in question (for example, (c) applies to any part which has the form of an identity sentence with two occurrences of the same $\mathfrak{in}$).

a. (For $\mathfrak{L}_N$ only.) The first quantifier together with its scope $\mathfrak{M}_i$ is replaced (1) if the quantifier is universal, by the conjunction of the N instances of $\mathfrak{M}_i$, (2) if the quantifier is existential, by the disjunction of the instances.

b. The sentence is expanded into primitive notation (that is, every defined expression occurring is eliminated with the help of its definition).

c. $\mathfrak{in}_i = \mathfrak{in}_i$ is replaced by 't'.

d. $\mathfrak{in}_i = \mathfrak{in}_j$ with two different $\mathfrak{in}$ is replaced by '$\sim t$'.

e. $\sim\sim k$ is replaced by k.

f. If the same sentence occurs more than once as a component in a conjunction or in a disjunction, then all occurrences except the last one are omitted.

g. A disjunction containing a sentence and its negation as components is replaced by 't'.

h. A conjunction containing a sentence and its negation as components is replaced by '$\sim t$'.

i. If a disjunction contains 't' as a component, then the whole disjunction is replaced by 't'.

j. If a disjunction contains '$\sim t$' as a component, then this component is omitted.

k. If a conjunction contains 't' as a component, then this component is omitted.

l. If a conjunction contains '$\sim t$' as a component, then the whole conjunction is replaced by '$\sim t$'.

m. $\sim(k_1 \vee k_2 \vee \ldots \vee k_n)$ $(n \geqq 2)$ is replaced by $\sim k_1 \,.\, \sim k_2 \,.\, \ldots \,.\, \sim k_n$.

n. $\sim(k_1 \,.\, k_2 \,.\, \ldots \,.\, k_n)$ $(n \geqq 2)$ is replaced by $\sim k_1 \vee \sim k_2 \vee \ldots \vee \sim k_n$.

o. If a disjunction contains k_1 and k_2 as components and k_1 is a subconjunction of k_2 (D19-1), then k_2 is omitted.

p. A disjunction occurring as a component in a conjunction is distributed (that is to say, $h \,.\, (k_1 \vee k_2 \vee \ldots \vee k_n) \,.\, l$ with $n \geqq 2$ is replaced by $(h \,.\, k_1 \,.\, l) \vee (h \,.\, k_2 \,.\, l) \vee \ldots \vee (h \,.\, k_n \,.\, l)$).

For the transformation into the *conjunctive normal form*, the rules (a) to (n) remain unchanged, but instead of (o) and (p) analogous rules are taken which refer to the dual forms.

T21-10. *On normal forms.* Let i be any sentence in $\mathfrak{L}_N$ or any nongeneral sentence in $\mathfrak{L}_\infty$; let j be a sentence of disjunctive normal form corresponding to i, and k a sentence of conjunctive normal form corresponding to i.

a. i, j, and k are L-equivalent to each other.

b. If i is nongeneral, then j does not contain any $\mathfrak{pr}$ or $\mathfrak{in}$ not occurring in i; likewise k.

c. j has one of the following forms: (1) 't'; (2) '$\sim t$'; (3) a basic sentence; (4) a conjunction of two or more basic sentences, in which no atomic sentence occurs together with its negation; (5) a disjunction of two or more components of the forms (3) or (4).

d. k has one of the following forms: (1) 't'; (2) '$\sim t$'; (3) a basic sentence; (4) a disjunction of two or more basic sentences, in which no atomic sentence occurs together with its negation; (5) a conjunction of two or more components of the forms (3) or (4).

T21-11. Let i and j be any factual nongeneral sentences (in a system $\mathfrak{L}$) which have no $\mathfrak{in}$ in common. Then the following holds.

a. $i \,.\, j$ is factual.

Proof. 1. Let $i_1 \vee i_2 \vee \ldots \vee i_m$ ($m \geqq 1$) be a sentence of disjunctive normal form corresponding to i; analogously, $j_1 \vee j_2 \vee \ldots \vee j_n$ ($n \geqq 1$) for j. $i \,.\, j$ is L-equivalent to $(i_1 \vee \ldots \vee i_m) \,.\, (j_1 \vee \ldots \vee j_n)$ (T10a), hence, by distribution (T5m(3)), to $(i_1 \,.\, j_1) \vee (i_1 \,.\, j_2) \vee \ldots \vee (i_m \,.\, j_n)$ with conjunctions for all pairs of an i-sentence and a j-sentence. Let $i' \,.\, j'$ be an arbitrary one of these conjunctions. i' is a basic sentence or a conjunction of basic sentences (T10c); likewise j'; neither i' nor j' contains any atomic sentence together with its negation (T10c), and they have no $\mathfrak{in}$ in common (T10b). Therefore, $i' \,.\, j'$ is a conjunction of basic sentences which does not contain any atomic sentence together with its negation. Hence, it is not L-false (T20-4g). Since this holds for every component of the disjunction, the whole disjunction is not L-false (T20-2q), and hence $i \,.\, j$ is not L-false. 2. Since neither i nor j is L-true, $i \,.\, j$ is not L-true (T20-2p). Hence, $i \,.\, j$ is factual.

b. $i \vee j$ is factual.

Proof. $\sim i$ and $\sim j$ are factual (T20-6a); hence likewise $\sim i \,.\, \sim j$ (a), hence $\sim(\sim i \,.\, \sim j)$ (T20-6a), hence $i \vee j$.

c. j is not L-dependent upon i, that is, i L-implies neither j nor $\sim j$.

Proof. $\sim i$ is factual (T20-6a). Therefore not $\vdash i \supset j$, since $\sim i \vee j$ is factual (b). Likewise with $\sim j$, since this is factual too (T20-6a).

§ 22. Theorems on General Sentences

Some theorems concerning general sentences (sentences with universal or existential quantifiers) are listed for later reference.

The theorems in this section apply the L-concepts to *general sentences;* hence they belong to that part of deductive logic which is sometimes called *lower functional logic* or *logic of quantification.*

T22-1. Let i be a *universal sentence* $(\mathfrak{i}_k)(\mathfrak{M}_j)$, and $\mathfrak{K}_i$ the class of the instances of $\mathfrak{M}_j$.

a. i and $\mathfrak{K}_i$ are L-equivalent. (From T18-1h and i.)

b. i is L-true if and only if $\mathfrak{K}_i$ is L-true. (From (a).)

c. i is L-true if and only if every instance of $\mathfrak{M}_j$ is L-true. (From (b), T20-2a.)

T22-2. Let i be the sentence $(\mathfrak{i}_{k1})(\mathfrak{i}_{k2}) \ldots (\mathfrak{i}_{kn})(\mathfrak{M}_j)$ (hence all variables occurring freely in $\mathfrak{M}_j$ are among the variables $\mathfrak{i}_{k1}, \ldots, \mathfrak{i}_{kn}$), and $\mathfrak{K}_i$ be the class of the instances of $\mathfrak{M}_j$.

a. i and $\mathfrak{K}_i$ are L-equivalent. (From T1a, by mathematical induction with respect to n.)

b. i is L-true if and only if $\mathfrak{K}_i$ is L-true. (From (a).)

c. i is L-true if and only if every instance of $\mathfrak{M}_j$ is L-true. (From (b), T20-2a.)

T22-3. For $\mathfrak{L}_N$.

a. $(\mathfrak{i}_k)(\mathfrak{M}_j)$ is L-equivalent in $\mathfrak{L}_N$ to any conjunction of the N instances of $\mathfrak{M}_j$ (in any order). (From T18-1g and h.)

b. $(\mathfrak{i}_{k1})(\mathfrak{i}_{k2}) \ldots (\mathfrak{i}_{kn})(\mathfrak{M}_j)$ is L-equivalent in $\mathfrak{L}_N$ to any conjunction of the instances of $\mathfrak{M}_j$ (in any order). (From (a), by mathematical induction with respect to n.)

c. $(\exists \mathfrak{i}_k)(\mathfrak{M}_j)$ is L-equivalent in $\mathfrak{L}_N$ to any disjunction of the N instances of $\mathfrak{M}_j$ (in any order). (From (a).)

d. $(\exists \mathfrak{i}_{k1})(\exists \mathfrak{i}_{k2}) \ldots (\exists \mathfrak{i}_{kn})(\mathfrak{M}_j)$ is L-equivalent in $\mathfrak{L}_N$ to any disjunction of the instances of $\mathfrak{M}_j$ (in any order). (From (c), by mathematical induction with respect to n.)

T3 shows that any variable can be eliminated, and hence any general sentence transformed into a nongeneral one. However, the result of the transformation is different in different systems (see § 15A).

T22-4. Let i be tautologous (D21-1) with respect to the components $j_1, j_2, \ldots, j_n$, and $\mathfrak{M}_j$ be formed from i by replacing the j-components with any matrices (all occurrences of a component to be replaced by occurrences of the same matrix). Then $\vdash ()(\mathfrak{M}_j)$. ['( )' stands for a series of universal quantifiers with all variables occurring freely in $\mathfrak{M}_j$; see § 14.]

Proof. Every instance of $\mathfrak{M}_j$ is tautologous and hence L-true (T21-1). Therefore $\vdash ()(\mathfrak{M}_j)$ (T2c).

T22-5. Let $\mathfrak{M}_l$ be $(\mathfrak{i}_i)(\mathfrak{i}_j)(\mathfrak{M}_k) \supset (\mathfrak{i}_j)(\mathfrak{i}_i)(\mathfrak{M}_k)$. Then $\vdash ()(\mathfrak{M}_l)$.

Proof. Let $\mathfrak{Z}_i$ be an arbitrary $\mathfrak{Z}$ in $\mathfrak{L}$. We shall show that $()(\mathfrak{M}_l)$ holds in $\mathfrak{Z}_i$; hence it holds in every $\mathfrak{Z}$ and is therefore L-true. Let $\mathfrak{M}'_k$ be formed from $\mathfrak{M}_k$ by substituting any individual constants for all those variables other than $\mathfrak{i}_i$ and $\mathfrak{i}_j$ which may occur freely in $\mathfrak{M}_k$. 1. Suppose that every instance of $\mathfrak{M}'_k$ holds in $\mathfrak{Z}_i$. Then $(\mathfrak{i}_j)(\mathfrak{i}_i)(\mathfrak{M}'_k)$ holds in $\mathfrak{Z}_i$ (D18-4g twice), hence also $(\mathfrak{i}_i)(\mathfrak{i}_j)(\mathfrak{M}'_k) \supset (\mathfrak{i}_j)(\mathfrak{i}_i)(\mathfrak{M}'_k)$; let this sentence be *l*. 2. Suppose that the condition (1) is not fulfilled. Then there is an instance of $\mathfrak{M}'_k$ which does not hold in $\mathfrak{Z}_i$. Hence $(\mathfrak{i}_i)(\mathfrak{i}_j)(\mathfrak{M}'_k)$ does not hold in $\mathfrak{Z}_i$. Therefore the negation of this sentence holds in $\mathfrak{Z}_i$ (T19-2), and hence *l* too. Thus, in any case, *l* holds in $\mathfrak{Z}_i$, and likewise any other instance of $\mathfrak{M}_l$, and hence also $()(\mathfrak{M}_l)$.

T22-6. Let $\mathfrak{M}_l$ be $(\mathfrak{i}_i)(\mathfrak{M}_j \supset \mathfrak{M}_k) \supset [(\mathfrak{i}_i)(\mathfrak{M}_j) \supset (\mathfrak{i}_i)(\mathfrak{M}_k)]$. Then $\vdash ()(\mathfrak{M}_l)$.

Proof. We prove the theorem (as in T5) by showing that for any $\mathfrak{Z}_i$, $()(\mathfrak{M}_l)$ holds in $\mathfrak{Z}_i$. Let *l* be an arbitrary instance of $\mathfrak{M}_l$; thus *l* has the form $(\mathfrak{i}_i)(\mathfrak{M}'_j \supset \mathfrak{M}'_k) \supset [(\mathfrak{i}_i)(\mathfrak{M}'_j) \supset (\mathfrak{i}_i)(\mathfrak{M}'_k)]$, where $\mathfrak{M}'_j$ and $\mathfrak{M}'_k$ are formed from $\mathfrak{M}_j$ and $\mathfrak{M}_k$, respectively, by the same substitutions for all free variables except $\mathfrak{i}_i$. 1. Suppose that, for every instance of $\mathfrak{M}'_j$ which holds in $\mathfrak{Z}_i$, the corresponding instance (that with the same in substituted for $\mathfrak{i}_i$) of $\mathfrak{M}'_k$ holds likewise in $\mathfrak{Z}_i$. *A*. Suppose further that every instance of $\mathfrak{M}'_j$ holds in $\mathfrak{Z}_i$. Then every instance of $\mathfrak{M}'_k$ holds likewise in $\mathfrak{Z}_i$, hence also $(\mathfrak{i}_i)(\mathfrak{M}'_k)$, hence also $(\mathfrak{i}_i)(\mathfrak{M}'_j) \supset (\mathfrak{i}_i)(\mathfrak{M}'_k)$, hence also *l*. *B*. Suppose the condition (A) is not fulfilled. Then there is an instance of $\mathfrak{M}'_j$ which does not hold in $\mathfrak{Z}_i$. Hence, $(\mathfrak{i}_i)(\mathfrak{M}'_j)$ does not hold in $\mathfrak{Z}_i$. Therefore, the negation of this sentence holds in $\mathfrak{Z}_i$ (T19-2), hence also $(\mathfrak{i}_i)(\mathfrak{M}'_j) \supset (\mathfrak{i}_i)(\mathfrak{M}'_k)$, hence also *l*. 2. Suppose the condition (1) is not fulfilled. Then there is an instance of $\mathfrak{M}'_j$ such that it holds in $\mathfrak{Z}_i$ while the corresponding instance of $\mathfrak{M}'_k$ does not. Therefore, the corresponding instance of $\mathfrak{M}'_j \supset \mathfrak{M}'_k$ does not hold in $\mathfrak{Z}_i$, and hence neither does $(\mathfrak{i}_i)(\mathfrak{M}'_j \supset \mathfrak{M}'_k)$. Therefore, the negation of the latter sentence holds in $\mathfrak{Z}_i$, and hence *l* too. Thus, *l* holds in $\mathfrak{Z}_i$ in any case, and likewise any other instance of $\mathfrak{M}_l$, and hence $()(\mathfrak{M}_l)$.

We omit proofs for the following theorems. Those for T7 and T8 can easily be constructed in a way similar to those given for T5 and T6. Our theorems T4, T5, T6, T7, and T8a, when applied to purely general sentences (that is, without in), correspond to Quine's axioms of quantification ([Math. Logic], p. 88, *100–*104). As the only rule of inference, he uses the *modus ponens* (*ibid.*, *105); to this rule, our T20-2 o and c correspond. Therefore, every sentence provable ('theorem') in Quine's system of quantification is L-true in our systems $\mathfrak{L}$. In this way we obtain all items of T9 and T11 if applied to purely general sentences (Quine [Math. Logic] §§ 17, 19, 20, 21). T8b and the other theorems applied to sentences with in are then obtained with the help of T1c.

T22-7. $\vdash ()[\mathfrak{M}_k \supset (\mathfrak{i}_i)(\mathfrak{M}_k)]$, where $\mathfrak{i}_i$ does not occur freely in $\mathfrak{M}_k$.

T22-8. $\vdash (\,)[(\mathfrak{i}_i)(\mathfrak{M}_k) \supset \mathfrak{M}'_k]$, where $\mathfrak{M}'_k$ is formed from $\mathfrak{M}_k$ by substituting for $\mathfrak{i}_i$ either (a) another $\mathfrak{i}$, or (b) an $\mathfrak{in}$.

T22-9.

a. $\vdash (\,)[(\mathfrak{i}_i)(\mathfrak{M}_k) \supset \mathfrak{M}_k]$.

b. If $\vdash (\,)(\mathfrak{M}_k \supset \mathfrak{M}_l)$ and $\vdash (\,)(\mathfrak{M}_k)$, then $\vdash (\,)(\mathfrak{M}_l)$.

c. If $\vdash (\,)(\mathfrak{M}_k)$, then $\vdash (\,)(\mathfrak{i}_i)(\mathfrak{M}_k)$.

d. If $\vdash (\,)(\mathfrak{M}_{k1} \supset \mathfrak{M}_{k2})$, $\vdash (\,)(\mathfrak{M}_{k2} \supset \mathfrak{M}_{k3})$, . . . and $\vdash (\,)(\mathfrak{M}_{k,n-1} \supset \mathfrak{M}_{kn})$, then $\vdash (\,)(\mathfrak{M}_{k1} \supset \mathfrak{M}_{kn})$.

e. If $\vdash (\,)(\mathfrak{M}_{k1} \equiv \mathfrak{M}_{k2})$, $\vdash (\,)(\mathfrak{M}_{k2} \equiv \mathfrak{M}_{k3})$, . . . and $\vdash (\,)(\mathfrak{M}_{k,n-1} \equiv \mathfrak{M}_{kn})$, then $\vdash (\,)(\mathfrak{M}_{k1} \equiv \mathfrak{M}_{kn})$.

f. $\vdash (\,)[(\mathfrak{i}_i)(\mathfrak{M}_k \equiv \mathfrak{M}_l) \supset ((\mathfrak{i}_i)(\mathfrak{M}_k) \equiv (\mathfrak{i}_i)(\mathfrak{M}_l))]$.

g. $\vdash (\,)[(\mathfrak{i}_{i1})(\mathfrak{i}_{i2}) \ldots (\mathfrak{i}_{in})(\mathfrak{M}_k) \supset \mathfrak{M}_k]$.

h. If $\vdash (\,)[\mathfrak{M}_k \supset \mathfrak{M}_l]$ and none of the variables $\mathfrak{i}_{i1}, \ldots, \mathfrak{i}_{in}$ occurs freely in $\mathfrak{M}_k$, then $\vdash (\,)[\mathfrak{M}_k \supset (\mathfrak{i}_{i1})(\mathfrak{i}_{i2}) \ldots (\mathfrak{i}_{in})(\mathfrak{M}_l)]$.

i. If $\mathfrak{i}_i$ does not occur freely in $\mathfrak{M}_k$, $\vdash (\,)[\mathfrak{M}_k \equiv (\mathfrak{i}_i)(\mathfrak{M}_k)]$.

j. $\vdash (\,)[(\mathfrak{i}_i)(\mathfrak{i}_j)(\mathfrak{M}_k) \equiv (\mathfrak{i}_j)(\mathfrak{i}_i)(\mathfrak{M}_k)]$.

k. $\vdash (\,)[(\mathfrak{i}_i)(\mathfrak{M}_k \,.\, \mathfrak{M}_l) \equiv (\mathfrak{i}_i)(\mathfrak{M}_k) \,.\, (\mathfrak{i}_i)(\mathfrak{M}_l)]$.

l. $\vdash (\,)[(\mathfrak{i}_i)(\mathfrak{M}_k) \vee (\mathfrak{i}_i)(\mathfrak{M}_l) \supset (\mathfrak{i}_i)(\mathfrak{M}_k \vee \mathfrak{M}_l)]$.

m. If $\mathfrak{i}_i$ does not occur freely in $\mathfrak{M}_k$,
$\vdash (\,)[(\mathfrak{i}_i)(\mathfrak{M}_k \,.\, \mathfrak{M}_l) \equiv \mathfrak{M}_k \,.\, (\mathfrak{i}_k)(\mathfrak{M}_l)]$.

n. If $\mathfrak{i}_i$ does not occur freely in $\mathfrak{M}_k$,
$\vdash (\,)[(\mathfrak{i}_i)(\mathfrak{M}_k \vee \mathfrak{M}_l) \equiv \mathfrak{M}_k \vee (\mathfrak{i}_i)(\mathfrak{M}_l)]$.

o. If $\mathfrak{i}_j$ does not occur freely in $\mathfrak{M}_i$ and $\mathfrak{M}_j$ is formed from $\mathfrak{M}_i$ by substituting $\mathfrak{i}_j$ for $\mathfrak{i}_i$,

$\vdash (\,)[(\mathfrak{i}_i)(\mathfrak{M}_i) \equiv (\mathfrak{i}_j)(\mathfrak{M}_j)]$.

T11 deals with sentences written with the existential quantifier (A15-1c).

T22-11.

a. $\vdash (\,)[\sim(\mathfrak{i}_i)(\mathfrak{M}_k) \equiv (\exists\mathfrak{i}_i)(\sim\mathfrak{M}_k)]$.

b. $\vdash (\,)[\sim(\exists\mathfrak{i}_i)(\mathfrak{M}_k) \equiv (\mathfrak{i}_i)(\sim\mathfrak{M}_k)]$.

c. $\vdash (\,)[\sim(\mathfrak{i}_{i1}) \ldots (\mathfrak{i}_{in})(\mathfrak{M}_k) \equiv (\exists\mathfrak{i}_{i1}) \ldots (\exists\mathfrak{i}_{in})(\sim\mathfrak{M}_k)]$.

d. $\vdash (\,)[\sim(\exists\mathfrak{i}_{i1}) \ldots (\exists\mathfrak{i}_{in})(\mathfrak{M}_k) \equiv (\mathfrak{i}_{i1}) \ldots (\mathfrak{i}_{in})(\sim\mathfrak{M}_k)]$.

e. $\vdash (\,)[\mathfrak{M}'_k \supset (\exists\mathfrak{i}_i)(\mathfrak{M}_k)]$, where $\mathfrak{M}'_k$ is formed from $\mathfrak{M}_k$ by substituting for $\mathfrak{i}_i$ either (1) another $\mathfrak{i}$, or (2) an $\mathfrak{in}$.

f. $\vdash (\,)[\mathfrak{M}_k \supset (\exists\mathfrak{i}_i)(\mathfrak{M}_k)]$.

g. $\vdash (\,)[(\mathfrak{i}_i)(\mathfrak{M}_k) \supset (\exists\mathfrak{i}_i)(\mathfrak{M}_k)]$.

h. If $\mathfrak{i}_i$ does not occur freely in $\mathfrak{M}_k$, $\vdash (\,)[\mathfrak{M}_k \equiv (\exists\mathfrak{i}_i)(\mathfrak{M}_k)]$.

i. $\vdash (\,)[(\exists\mathfrak{i}_i)(\exists\mathfrak{i}_j)(\mathfrak{M}_k) \equiv (\exists\mathfrak{i}_j)(\exists\mathfrak{i}_i)(\mathfrak{M}_k)]$.

j. $\vdash (\,)[(\exists\mathfrak{i}_i)(\mathfrak{i}_j)(\mathfrak{M}_k) \supset (\mathfrak{i}_j)(\exists\mathfrak{i}_i)(\mathfrak{M}_k)]$.

k. $\vdash (\,)[(\exists\mathfrak{i}_i)(\mathfrak{M}_k \vee \mathfrak{M}_l) \equiv (\exists\mathfrak{i}_i)(\mathfrak{M}_k) \vee (\exists\mathfrak{i}_i)(\mathfrak{M}_l)]$.

l. $\vdash (\,)[(\mathfrak{i}_i)(\mathfrak{M}_k \vee \mathfrak{M}_l) \supset (\exists \mathfrak{i}_i)(\mathfrak{M}_k) \vee (\mathfrak{i}_i)(\mathfrak{M}_l)]$.

m. $\vdash (\,)[(\mathfrak{i}_i)(\mathfrak{M}_k \supset \mathfrak{M}_l) \supset ((\exists \mathfrak{i}_i)(\mathfrak{M}_k) \supset (\exists \mathfrak{i}_i)(\mathfrak{M}_l))]$.

n. $\vdash (\,)[(\mathfrak{i}_i)(\mathfrak{M}_k) \,.\, (\exists \mathfrak{i}_i)(\mathfrak{M}_l) \supset (\exists \mathfrak{i}_i)(\mathfrak{M}_k \,.\, \mathfrak{M}_l)]$.

o. $\vdash (\,)[(\exists \mathfrak{i}_i)(\mathfrak{M}_k \,.\, \mathfrak{M}_l) \supset (\exists \mathfrak{i}_i)(\mathfrak{M}_k) \,.\, (\exists \mathfrak{i}_i)(\mathfrak{M}_l)]$.

§ 23. Theorems on Replacements

Two expressions are called L-interchangeable if the replacement of the one by the other in any sentence i transforms i into an L-equivalent sentence (D1). Some theorems on replacements and L-interchangeability are listed for later use. The one most frequently used is this: L-equivalent sentences (or matrices, or predicate expressions) are L-interchangeable (T1b, T2c).

We use the term 'replacement' in the widest sense, for the procedure of deleting one expression and putting another one in its place. Hence, if we speak of the replacement of some occurrences of an expression $\mathfrak{A}_i$ in a sentence j, we mean the replacement of one or several such occurrences and not necessarily of all occurrences of $\mathfrak{A}_i$ in j. (On the other hand, the term 'substitution' is always used in the following special sense: a variable, hence here in the systems $\mathfrak{L}$ an $\mathfrak{i}$, is replaced at all places where it occurs freely within the context in question by the same expression, here an $\mathfrak{i}$ or an $\mathfrak{in}$.) Two expressions which can always be replaced by each other without thereby changing the logical content or meaning of the sentence (in other words, the proposition expressed by it) are called L-interchangeable (D1).

D23-1. $\mathfrak{A}_i$ is ***L-interchangeable*** with $\mathfrak{A}_j$ in $\mathfrak{L}$ $=_{\text{Df}}$ if i and j are any sentences in $\mathfrak{L}$ such that j is formed from i by replacing one occurrence of $\mathfrak{A}_i$ with $\mathfrak{A}_j$ or vice versa, then $\vdash i \equiv j$; and there is at least one pair of sentences i, j of this kind.

The theorems T1 and T2 are important and well-known theorems concerning the L-interchangeability of sentences and matrices, respectively. (For proofs see, for instance, Quine [Math. Logic] § 18.)

+**T23-1.** Let j and j' be any sentences in $\mathfrak{L}$, and i' be formed from i by replacing some occurrences of j with j', then the following holds.

a. $\vdash (j \equiv j') \supset (i \equiv i')$.

b. If $\vdash j \equiv j'$, then $\vdash i \equiv i'$; in other words, L-equivalent sentences are L-interchangeable.

T1b has been utilized in T21-5C.

T2 is analogous to T1 but more general, concerning any matrices.

+**T23-2.** Let $\mathfrak{M}_j$ and $\mathfrak{M}'_j$ be any matrices in $\mathfrak{L}$. Let $\mathfrak{M}'_i$ be formed from

$\mathfrak{M}_i$ by replacing some occurrences of $\mathfrak{M}_j$ with $\mathfrak{M}'_j$, and i' from i in the same way. Then the following holds.

a. $\vdash ()[()(\mathfrak{M}_j \equiv \mathfrak{M}'_j) \supset (\mathfrak{M}_i \equiv \mathfrak{M}'_i)]$.

b. $\vdash ()(\mathfrak{M}_j \equiv \mathfrak{M}'_j) \supset (i \equiv i')$.

c. If $\vdash ()(\mathfrak{M}_j \equiv \mathfrak{M}'_j)$, then $\vdash i \equiv i'$; in other words, if two matrices (or predicate expressions) are L-equivalent (D25-1g), then they are L-interchangeable.

T2c has been utilized in T21-5E.

The following theorems are consequences of T1 and T2. They concern replacements by 't' and '$\sim t$'. T4 is useful in deductive logic for the simplification of sentences and, in particular, for the transformation into a normal form (see, for instance, D21-2). T5 and T6, together with T4, will be used in inductive logic; there, not only L-true sentences but others similar to them, which we shall call almost L-true, will be replaced by 't' for certain purposes.

T23-4.

a. If $\vdash i$, i is L-interchangeable with 't'.

Proof. If $\vdash i$, then $\vdash i \equiv t$ (T21-5u(1)). Hence theorem from T1b.

b. If $\vdash \sim i$, i is L-interchangeable with '$\sim t$'. (From T21-5u(2), like (a).)

c. If $\vdash ()(\mathfrak{M}_i)$, $\mathfrak{M}_i$ is L-interchangeable with 't'.

Proof. $\vdash ()[(\mathfrak{M}_i \equiv t) \equiv \mathfrak{M}_i]$ (T21-5u(1)D). Hence $\vdash ()(\mathfrak{M}_i \equiv t) \equiv ()(\mathfrak{M}_i)$ (T22-9f). Therefore, if $\vdash ()(\mathfrak{M}_i)$, then $\vdash ()(\mathfrak{M}_i \equiv t)$. Hence theorem from T2c.

d. If $\vdash ()(\sim\mathfrak{M}_i)$, $\mathfrak{M}_i$ is L-interchangeable with '$\sim t$'. (From T21-5u(2), like (c).)

T23-5. Let j be any sentence in $\mathfrak{L}$, and i' be formed from i by replacing some occurrences of j with 't'. Then $\vdash j \supset (i \equiv i')$. (From T1a, T21-5u(1).)

T23-6. Let j be any sentence in $\mathfrak{L}$, and i' be formed from i by replacing some occurrences of j with '$\sim t$'. Then the following holds.

a. $\vdash j \vee (i \equiv i')$. (From T1a, T21-5u(2).)

b. $\vdash j \vee i \equiv j \vee i'$. (From (a), T21-5m(7).)

§ 24. Theorems on Identity

Some theorems on identity are listed for later reference. '$a = a$' is L-true (T1a), as customary; in our systems, '$a = b$' is L-false (T1b).

This section contains theorems on identity. They are chiefly based on T18-1b, c, which in turn is based on D18-4. We remember that these rules have been laid down in such a way that '$a = a$' is L-true, while '$a = b$' is L-false.

+T24-1.

a. $\vdash \mathfrak{in}_i = \mathfrak{in}_i$. (From T18-1b.)

b. $\vdash \mathfrak{in}_i \neq \mathfrak{in}_j$, where $\mathfrak{in}_i$ and $\mathfrak{in}_j$ are two distinct $\mathfrak{in}$. (From T18-1c.)

T24-2.

a. $\vdash (\mathfrak{i}_k)(\mathfrak{i}_k = \mathfrak{i}_k)$. (From T22-1c, T1a.)

b. $\vdash (\exists \mathfrak{i}_k)(\mathfrak{i}_k = \mathfrak{in}_j)$, that is, $\vdash \sim (\mathfrak{i}_k)[\sim(\mathfrak{i}_k = \mathfrak{in}_j)]$. (From T1a, T22-1e.)

c. $\vdash (\mathfrak{i}_j)(\exists \mathfrak{i}_k)(\mathfrak{i}_k = \mathfrak{i}_j)$, that is, $\vdash (\mathfrak{i}_j) \sim (\mathfrak{i}_k)[\sim (\mathfrak{i}_k = \mathfrak{i}_j)]$. (From (b), T22-1c.)

T24-3. Let $\mathfrak{M}_k$ be $\mathfrak{i}_i = \mathfrak{i}_j \supset (\mathfrak{M}_i \supset \mathfrak{M}_j)$ where $\mathfrak{M}_j$ is formed from $\mathfrak{M}_i$ by substituting $\mathfrak{i}_j$ for $\mathfrak{i}_i$. Then $\vdash (\ )(\mathfrak{M}_k)$.

Proof. Let k be any instance of $\mathfrak{M}_k$. Then k has the form $\mathfrak{in}_i = \mathfrak{in}_j \supset (i \supset j)$, where j differs from i, if at all, by containing $\mathfrak{in}_j$ at some places where i has $\mathfrak{in}_i$. 1. If $\mathfrak{in}_i$ is the same as $\mathfrak{in}_j$, then i is the same as j, hence $\vdash i \supset j$ (T21-3c), hence $\vdash k$ (T20-2g). 2. If $\mathfrak{in}_i$ is not the same as $\mathfrak{in}_j$, $\vdash \sim (\mathfrak{in}_i = \mathfrak{in}_j)$ (T1b), and hence $\vdash k$ (T20-2h). Thus $\vdash k$ in any case. Since this holds for every instance of $\mathfrak{M}_k$, $\vdash (\ )(\mathfrak{M}_k)$ (T22-2c).

The following theorem T4 differs from the other theorems by holding only for certain systems.

T24-4. Let $\mathfrak{i}_k, \mathfrak{i}_{j1}, \mathfrak{i}_{j2}, \ldots, \mathfrak{i}_{jm}$ be $m + 1$ different $\mathfrak{i}$.

a. For $m \geqq 1$, the following holds for $\mathfrak{L}_\infty$ and for every $\mathfrak{L}_N$ with $N > m$: $\vdash (\ )(\exists \mathfrak{i}_k)[\mathfrak{i}_k \neq \mathfrak{i}_{j1} \,.\, \mathfrak{i}_k \neq \mathfrak{i}_{j2} \,.\, \ldots \,.\, \mathfrak{i}_k \neq \mathfrak{i}_{jm}]$, that is, $\vdash (\ ) \sim (\mathfrak{i}_k)[\mathfrak{i}_k = \mathfrak{i}_{j1} \vee \mathfrak{i}_k = \mathfrak{i}_{j2} \vee \ldots \vee \mathfrak{i}_k = \mathfrak{i}_{jm}]$.

Proof. Let j be an instance of $(\exists \mathfrak{i}_k)[\ \ldots\ ]$. Then j contains at most m $\mathfrak{in}$. Therefore, in any of the systems mentioned, there is an $\mathfrak{in}_k$ which is different from all $\mathfrak{in}$ in j. Hence, if k is constructed from the scope in j by substituting $\mathfrak{in}_k$ for $\mathfrak{i}_k$, every conjunctive component in k is L-true (T1b), and hence $\vdash k$, and hence $\vdash j$. Therefore the sentence described is L-true (T22-2c).

b. For $m \geqq 0$, $n \geqq 0$, $m + n \geqq 1$, the following holds for $\mathfrak{L}_\infty$ and for every $\mathfrak{L}_N$ with $N > m + n$. Let $\mathfrak{in}_{i1}, \mathfrak{in}_{i2}, \ldots, \mathfrak{in}_{in}$ be some $\mathfrak{in}$ (not necessarily distinct) in the system in question. $\vdash (\ )(\exists \mathfrak{i}_k)[\mathfrak{i}_k \neq \mathfrak{i}_{j1} \,.\, \mathfrak{i}_k \neq \mathfrak{i}_{j2} \,.\, \ldots \,.\, \mathfrak{i}_k \neq \mathfrak{i}_{jm} \,.\, \mathfrak{i}_k \neq \mathfrak{in}_{i1} \,.\, \mathfrak{i}_k \neq \mathfrak{in}_{i2} \,.\, \ldots \,.\, \mathfrak{i}_k \neq \mathfrak{in}_{in}]$, that is, $\vdash (\ ) \sim(\mathfrak{i}_k)[\mathfrak{i}_k = \mathfrak{i}_{j1} \vee \ldots \vee \mathfrak{i}_k = \mathfrak{i}_{jm} \vee \mathfrak{i}_k = \mathfrak{in}_{i1} \vee \ldots \vee \mathfrak{i}_k = \mathfrak{in}_{in}]$. (From (a).)

The theorems T4a and b can easily be made plausible, since the sentence described in (a) (or in (b)) says that the number of individuals in the domain in question (in (b): except those designated by the $\mathfrak{in}$ occurring) is greater than m.

T2a and T3 correspond to the axioms of identity in the system of Hilbert and Bernays ([Grundlagen], I, 165, formulas (J_1) and (J_2); these formulas contain free variables, our theorems refer to the corresponding closed forms). Therefore, the sentences corresponding to the formulas proved by these authors on the basis of the two axioms are L-true in our systems $\mathfrak{L}$. This yields the following theorems T6, T7a, and T8a (see Hilbert and Bernays, *op. cit.*, formulas 1, 2, 3, 4, 5, 6a, 10a).

T24-6.

a. $\vdash (\ )[\mathfrak{i}_i = \mathfrak{i}_j \supset (\mathfrak{i}_i = \mathfrak{i}_k \supset \mathfrak{i}_j = \mathfrak{i}_k)]$.

b. $\vdash (\ )[\mathfrak{i}_i = \mathfrak{i}_j \supset \mathfrak{i}_j = \mathfrak{i}_i]$.

c. $\vdash (\ )[\mathfrak{i}_i = \mathfrak{i}_j \supset (\mathfrak{i}_j = \mathfrak{i}_k \supset \mathfrak{i}_i = \mathfrak{i}_k)]$.

d. $\vdash (\ )[\mathfrak{i}_i = \mathfrak{i}_k \supset (\mathfrak{i}_j = \mathfrak{i}_k \supset \mathfrak{i}_i = \mathfrak{i}_j)]$.

e. $\vdash (\ )[\mathfrak{i}_i \neq \mathfrak{i}_j \supset \mathfrak{i}_i \neq \mathfrak{i}_k \vee \mathfrak{i}_j \neq \mathfrak{i}_k]$.

T24-7. Let $\mathfrak{M}_k$ and $\mathfrak{M}'_k$ be formed from $\mathfrak{M}_i$ by substituting $\mathfrak{i}_k$ and $\mathfrak{in}_k$, respectively, for $\mathfrak{i}_i$.

a. $\vdash (\ )[(\mathfrak{i}_i)(\mathfrak{i}_i \neq \mathfrak{i}_k \vee \mathfrak{M}_i) \equiv \mathfrak{M}_k]$.

b. $\vdash (\ )[(\mathfrak{i}_i)(\mathfrak{i}_i \neq \mathfrak{in}_k \vee \mathfrak{M}_i) \equiv \mathfrak{M}'_k]$. (From (a).)

The following is a rather special and complicated theorem that we shall need later (in Vol. II) for an important theorem in inductive logic.

T24-8. Let $\mathfrak{M}_l$ be a molecular matrix (D16-3e) without $\mathfrak{in}$ and with $\mathfrak{i}_k$ as the only free variable, such that all instances of it are factual. Let $\mathfrak{i}_k$, $\mathfrak{i}_{k1}, \mathfrak{i}_{k2}, \ldots, \mathfrak{i}_{kn}$ be $n + 1$ distinct variables ($n \geqq 1$). Let $\mathfrak{M}_i$ be $(\mathfrak{i}_k)[\mathfrak{i}_k = \mathfrak{i}_{k1} \vee \mathfrak{i}_k = \mathfrak{i}_{k2} \vee \ldots \vee \mathfrak{i}_k = \mathfrak{i}_{kn} \vee \mathfrak{M}_l]$. Let $\mathfrak{M}_h$ be the disjunction $\mathfrak{M}_{h1} \vee \mathfrak{M}_{h2} \vee \ldots \vee \mathfrak{M}_{h,n+1}$, whose $n + 1$ components are as follows. $\mathfrak{M}_{h1}$ is the sentence $(\mathfrak{i}_k)(\mathfrak{M}_l)$. For every m from 2 to $n + 1$, $\mathfrak{M}_{hm}$ is $(\ )[\mathfrak{i}_{j1} = \mathfrak{i}_{j2} \vee \mathfrak{i}_{j1} = \mathfrak{i}_{j3} \vee \ldots \vee \mathfrak{i}_{j,m-1} = \mathfrak{i}_{jm} \vee \mathfrak{M}_{l1} \vee \mathfrak{M}_{l2} \vee \ldots \vee \mathfrak{M}_{lm}] \centerdot [\sim\mathfrak{M}^*_{m1} \vee \ldots \vee \sim\mathfrak{M}^*_{ms}]$. Here $\mathfrak{i}_{j1}, \mathfrak{i}_{j2}, \ldots, \mathfrak{i}_{jm}$ are m distinct variables, and the scope described contains for any two distinct ones of these variables the identity matrix as a disjunctive component, and further the matrices $\mathfrak{M}_{l1}, \ldots, \mathfrak{M}_{lm}$, which are formed from $\mathfrak{M}_l$ by substituting for $\mathfrak{i}_k$ one of the variables $\mathfrak{i}_{j1}, \ldots, \mathfrak{i}_{jm}$ in turn. The matrices $\mathfrak{M}^*_{m1}$, etc., are formed as follows. They correspond to the s subclasses containing $m - 1$ of the n variables $\mathfrak{i}_{k1}, \ldots, \mathfrak{i}_{kn}$ mentioned before. [The number of these subclasses is $\binom{n}{m-1}$ (T40-32d); hence this is also the number s of the matrices $\mathfrak{M}^*_{m1}$, etc., to be described.] For $m = 2$ there are n subclasses containing one each of the n variables mentioned; here, the n matrices are formed from $\mathfrak{M}_l$ by substituting for $\mathfrak{i}_k$ one of the variables in turn. For $m > 2$ the matrix $\mathfrak{M}^*_{mp}$

(for $p = 1$ to s) is a conjunction containing as components the matrices formed from $\mathfrak{M}_l$ by substituting for $\mathfrak{i}_k$ one of the variables of the pth subclass in turn and furthermore the negations of the identity matrices for any two distinct variables of the pth subclass. For $m = n + 1$ the one subclass is the class of all those variables itself; here we have only one matrix, namely, $\mathfrak{M}^*_{m1}$, formed as just described but for all variables.

a. $\vdash (\,)(\mathfrak{M}_i \equiv \mathfrak{M}_h)$.

For a *proof* see Hilbert and Bernays, *op. cit.*, p. 175, formula 10a. The theorem can be made *plausible* as follows. $\mathfrak{M}_i$ says: 'For every x, if $x \neq z_1$ and $x \neq z_2$ and . . . and $x \neq z_n$, then Mx'. $\mathfrak{M}_h$ says: 'Either (1) all x are M, or (2) all x with at most one exception are M, and z_1 or z_2 or . . . or z_n is not M, or (3) all x with at most two exceptions are M and either (a) z_1 and z_2 are not M and are distinct from each other or (b) z_1 and z_3 are . . . or (c) . . . or (.) z_{n-1} and z_n are not M and are distinct from each other, or (4) . . . , or ($n + 1$) all x with at most n exceptions are M, and z_1 and z_2 and . . . and z_n are not M and are distinct from one another'. It is easily seen that $\mathfrak{M}_h$ says the same as $\mathfrak{M}_i$.

b. Let $\mathfrak{M}'_i$ be formed from $\mathfrak{M}_i$ by substituting n' distinct in for n' out of the n free variables $\mathfrak{i}_{k1}, \ldots, \mathfrak{i}_{kn}$ ($n' \leq n$). Let $\mathfrak{M}'_h$ be formed from $\mathfrak{M}_h$ by the same substitutions. Then $\vdash (\,)(\mathfrak{M}'_i \equiv \mathfrak{M}'_h)$. (From (a).)

§ 25. On Predicate Expressions and Divisions

We admit as abbreviations molecular predicate expressions constructed from predicates with the help of connectives (A1) and, further, molecular predicates as abbreviations for such expressions. Among others, the following terms are defined as applied to matrices or predicate expressions or the corresponding attributes (properties or relations): 'universal' and 'L-universal', '(L-)empty', 'factual', 'L-implication', 'L-equivalence' (D1); further, from the theory of relations, '(L-)reflexive', '(L-)symmetric', etc. (D2). A set of molecular predicates is called a division if they divide all individuals without overlapping (D4).

The third and largest part of this chapter (§§ 25–38) deals with some selected topics of deductive logic. Most of the definitions and theorems in this part are new. A number of them, although of interest for deductive logic, have not found sufficient attention so far. However, our chief reason for developing these special parts of deductive logic here is their usefulness for our theory of inductive logic. Whenever any section of this part becomes relevant in later chapters, it will be indicated there.

It will be convenient to permit as abbreviations compound predicate expressions, constructed from predicates with the help of connectives. We call them, together with the primitive predicates, *molecular predicate expressions*.

A25-1. We shall use ***molecular predicate expressions*** as unofficial abbreviations in the following way. At the place of a $\mathfrak{pr}$ as a component, any molecular predicate expression is likewise allowed. $\mathfrak{A}_i$ is any suitable argument expression consisting of one or more individual signs (for example, '*axb*' for a predicate expression of degree three).

a. $(\sim\mathfrak{pr}_j)\mathfrak{A}_i$ for $\sim(\mathfrak{pr}_j\mathfrak{A}_i)$.

b. $(\mathfrak{pr}_j \lor \mathfrak{pr}_k)\mathfrak{A}_i$ for $\mathfrak{pr}_j\mathfrak{A}_i \lor \mathfrak{pr}_k\mathfrak{A}_i$.

c. $(\mathfrak{pr}_j \centerdot \mathfrak{pr}_k)\mathfrak{A}_i$ for $\mathfrak{pr}_j\mathfrak{A}_i \centerdot \mathfrak{pr}_k\mathfrak{A}_i$.

d. $(\mathfrak{pr}_j \supset \mathfrak{pr}_k)\mathfrak{A}_i$ for $\mathfrak{pr}_j\mathfrak{A}_i \supset \mathfrak{pr}_k\mathfrak{A}_i$.

e. $(\mathfrak{pr}_j \equiv \mathfrak{pr}_k)\mathfrak{A}_i$ for $\mathfrak{pr}_j\mathfrak{A}_i \equiv \mathfrak{pr}_k\mathfrak{A}_i$.

Thus, for example, '$(P_1 \lor P_2)x$' is short for '$P_1x \lor P_2x$'; '$[(P_1 \centerdot \sim P_2) \lor \sim(P_3 \centerdot P_4)]a$' is short for '$(P_1a \centerdot \sim P_2a) \lor \sim(P_3a \centerdot P_4a)$'. Note that a molecular matrix can be abbreviated in this way only if all atomic matrices occurring in it have the same argument expression; thus, for example, '$P_1a \lor P_2b$' cannot be abbreviated.

By a ***molecular predicate*** we mean a predicate that either is primitive or is introduced as an abbreviation for a molecular predicate expression. We shall usually take '*M*', '*M'*', etc., 'M_1', 'M_2', etc., as molecular predicates to be defined from case to case, or also used without specifying their definitions; further, 'Q_1', 'Q_2', etc., for certain molecular predicates of a special kind to be defined later (§ 31). [For instance, 'M_1' may be defined by '$P_1 \centerdot \sim P_2$'; then, 'M_1a' would be short for '$(P_1 \centerdot \sim P_2)a$', hence for '$P_1a \centerdot \sim P_2a$'.] By a *molecular attribute* (property or relation) with respect to a system $\mathfrak{L}$ we mean an attribute designated by a molecular predicate expression (and hence designatable by a molecular predicate if we care to introduce one).

By a *full matrix* of a predicate expression $\mathfrak{A}_i$ (which may be a primitive or defined predicate or a compound molecular predicate expression) of degree *n* we mean a matrix of the form $\mathfrak{A}_i\mathfrak{A}_{j1}\mathfrak{A}_{j2} \ldots \mathfrak{A}_{jn}$, where the $\mathfrak{A}_{j1}$, etc., are individual signs; if all of the latter are individual constants, and hence the whole is a sentence, we call it a ***full sentence*** of $\mathfrak{A}_i$.

Each of the items D1a, b, d, e and D2a, b, c, d, e, f, g is a condensed formulation of two definitions, one to be read without the two prefixes 'L-' included in square brackets, the other to be read with both of them; thus, for instance, D1a says (1) $\mathfrak{M}_i$ is universal $=_{\text{Df}}$ $(\ )(\mathfrak{M}_i)$ is true, and (2) $\mathfrak{M}_i$ is L-universal $=_{\text{Df}}$ $(\ )(\mathfrak{M}_i)$ is L-true.

+D25-1.

a. $\mathfrak{M}_i$ is [*L-*]*universal* $=_{\text{Df}}$ the sentence $(\ )(\mathfrak{M}_i)$ is [L-]true.

b. $\mathfrak{M}_i$ is [*L-*]*empty* $=_{\text{Df}}$ $(\ )(\sim\mathfrak{M}_i)$ is [L-]true.

c. $\mathfrak{M}_i$ is *factual* $=_{\text{Df}}$ $\mathfrak{M}_i$ is neither L-universal nor L-empty.

d. $\mathfrak{M}_i$ and $\mathfrak{M}_j$ are [*L-*]*exclusive* $=_{\text{Df}}$ $(\ )[\sim(\mathfrak{M}_i \,.\, \mathfrak{M}_j)]$ is [L-]true.
e. $\mathfrak{M}_{i1}, \mathfrak{M}_{i2}, \ldots, \mathfrak{M}_{in}$ are [*L-*]*disjunct* $=_{\text{Df}}$ $(\ )[\mathfrak{M}_{i1} \vee \mathfrak{M}_{i2} \vee \ldots \vee \mathfrak{M}_{in}]$ is [L-]true.
f. $\mathfrak{M}_i$ *L-implies* $\mathfrak{M}_j$ $=_{\text{Df}} \vdash (\ )(\mathfrak{M}_i \supset \mathfrak{M}_j)$.
g. $\mathfrak{M}_i$ is *L-equivalent* to $\mathfrak{M}_j$ $=_{\text{Df}} \vdash (\ )(\mathfrak{M}_i \equiv \mathfrak{M}_j)$.

In D2 some of the customary concepts in the theory of relations are defined, together with the corresponding semantical L-concepts.

D25-2. Let $\mathfrak{M}_{ij}$ be a matrix with $\mathfrak{i}_i$ and $\mathfrak{i}_j$ as the only free variables. Let $\mathfrak{M}_{ii}$ be formed from $\mathfrak{M}_{ij}$ by substituting $\mathfrak{i}_i$ for $\mathfrak{i}_j$, and $\mathfrak{M}_{ik}$ by substituting $\mathfrak{i}_k$ for $\mathfrak{i}_j$. Let $\mathfrak{M}_{ji}$ be formed from $\mathfrak{M}_{ij}$ by simultaneous substitutions of $\mathfrak{i}_j$ for $\mathfrak{i}_i$ and $\mathfrak{i}_i$ for $\mathfrak{i}_j$; likewise $\mathfrak{M}_{jk}$ by simultaneous substitutions of $\mathfrak{i}_j$ for $\mathfrak{i}_i$ and $\mathfrak{i}_k$ for $\mathfrak{i}_j$.
a. $\mathfrak{M}_{ij}$ is [*L-*]*reflexive* $=_{\text{Df}}$ the sentence $(\mathfrak{i}_i)(\mathfrak{M}_{ii})$ is [L-]true.
b. $\mathfrak{M}_{ij}$ is [*L-*]*irreflexive* $=_{\text{Df}}$ $(\mathfrak{i}_i)(\sim\mathfrak{M}_{ii})$ is [L-]true.
c. $\mathfrak{M}_{ij}$ is [*L-*]*symmetric* $=_{\text{Df}}$ $(\ )(\mathfrak{M}_{ij} \supset \mathfrak{M}_{ji})$ is [L-]true.
d. $\mathfrak{M}_{ij}$ is [*L-*]*asymmetric* $=_{\text{Df}}$ $(\ )(\mathfrak{M}_{ij} \supset \sim\mathfrak{M}_{ji})$ is [L-]true.
e. $\mathfrak{M}_{ij}$ is [*L-*]*transitive* $=_{\text{Df}}$ $(\ )(\mathfrak{M}_{ij} \,.\, \mathfrak{M}_{jk} \supset \mathfrak{M}_{ik})$ is [L-]true.
f. $\mathfrak{M}_{ij}$ is [*L-*]*intransitive* $=_{\text{Df}}$ $(\ )(\mathfrak{M}_{ij} \,.\, \mathfrak{M}_{jk} \supset \sim\mathfrak{M}_{ik})$ is [L-]true.
g. $\mathfrak{M}_{ij}$ is [*L-*]*one-one* $=_{\text{Df}}$ the sentence $(\ )(\mathfrak{M}_{ij} \,.\, \mathfrak{M}_{ik} \supset \mathfrak{i}_j = \mathfrak{i}_k) \,.\, (\ )(\mathfrak{M}_{ik} \,.\, \mathfrak{M}_{jk} \supset \mathfrak{i}_i = \mathfrak{i}_j)$ is [L-]true.

All the terms defined in D1 and D2 will be used in the following three ways. Each of these terms may be applied
(A) to a matrix, as formulated in the definition;
(B) to a predicate expression $\mathfrak{A}_i$ (that is, to a primitive or defined predicate or a molecular predicate expression (A1)) of degree *n*, if the term applies, according to the definition, to the matrix $\mathfrak{A}_i \mathfrak{i}_1 \mathfrak{i}_2 \ldots \mathfrak{i}_n$ formed with the alphabetically first *n* variables in the alphabetical order;
(C) to the corresponding attribute (namely, the one designated by the predicate expression in (B) and hence expressed by the matrix in (A)).

For example, if '*M*' is defined by '$P_1 \,.\, \sim P_2$' and '$(x)(\sim Mx)$' is true, then we shall say of each of the following entities that it is empty: (A) the matrix '*Mx*' and its expansion '$P_1x \,.\, \sim P_2x$', (B) the molecular predicate '*M*' and the molecular predicate expression '$P_1 \,.\, \sim P_2$', and (C) the molecular property *M*, that is, the property of being P_1 but not P_2.

The definitions of the L-terms in D1 and D2 state characteristic sentences for each case in such a way that the L-term holds in the case in question if and only if the characteristic sentence is L-true. Now D3 says that for any sentence e (usually a non-L-false sentence serving as evidence for a degree of confirmation), the L-term with the addition 'with respect to e' holds if and only if the characteristic sentence j is L-implied by e, hence if and only if $\vdash e \supset j$. (This is analogous to D20-2.)

D25-3.

a. $\mathfrak{M}_i$ is L-universal *with respect to e* $=_{\mathrm{Df}} \vdash e \supset ()(\mathfrak{M}_i)$.

b. Analogously for the L-terms defined in D1b, d, e, f, g, and D2a, b, c, d, e, f, g.

T25-1. Let $\mathfrak{A}_i$ and $\mathfrak{A}'_i$ be two molecular predicate expressions of degree one and $\mathfrak{A}_j$ and $\mathfrak{A}'_j$ molecular predicates defined by $\mathfrak{A}_i$ and $\mathfrak{A}'_i$, respectively. Let i, i', j, and j' be the full sentences with $\mathfrak{in}_k$ of $\mathfrak{A}_i$, $\mathfrak{A}'_i$, $\mathfrak{A}_j$, and $\mathfrak{A}'_j$, respectively.

a. $\mathfrak{A}_i$, and hence $\mathfrak{A}_j$, is L-universal if and only if i, and hence j, is L-true.

Proof. 1. Suppose $\mathfrak{A}_i$ is L-universal. Then $\vdash (\mathfrak{i}_k)(\mathfrak{A}_i\mathfrak{i}_k)$ (D1a). Therefore, $\vdash i$ (T22-1c). 2. Suppose $\vdash i$, i.e., $\vdash \mathfrak{A}_i\mathfrak{in}_k$. Then, for every $\mathfrak{in}_h$, $\vdash \mathfrak{A}_i\mathfrak{in}_h$ because $\mathfrak{A}_i$ does not contain any $\mathfrak{in}$ (this follows from a well-known theorem which will be stated in the next section; see T26-2b). Therefore, $\vdash (\mathfrak{i}_k)(\mathfrak{A}_i\mathfrak{i}_k)$ (T22-1c). Hence, $\mathfrak{A}_i$ is L-universal (D1a).

b. $\mathfrak{A}_i$, and hence $\mathfrak{A}_j$, is L-empty if and only if i, and hence j, is L-false. (Analogous to (a).)

c. $\mathfrak{A}_i$, and hence $\mathfrak{A}_j$, is factual if and only if i, and hence j, is factual. (From (a), (b).)

d. $\mathfrak{A}_i$ and $\mathfrak{A}'_i$ are L-exclusive of each other (and hence likewise $\mathfrak{A}_j$ and $\mathfrak{A}'_j$) if and only if i and i' are L-exclusive (and hence likewise j and j'). (Analogous to (a).)

e. $\mathfrak{A}_i$ L-implies $\mathfrak{A}'_i$ (and hence $\mathfrak{A}_j$ L-implies $\mathfrak{A}'_j$) if and only if $\vdash i \supset i'$ (and hence $\vdash j \supset j'$). (Analogous to (a).)

f. $\mathfrak{A}_i$ and $\mathfrak{A}'_i$ are L-equivalent to each other (and hence likewise $\mathfrak{A}_j$ and $\mathfrak{A}'_j$) if and only if $\vdash i \equiv i'$ (and hence $\vdash j \equiv j'$). (Analogous to (a).)

The following definition is, for the sake of simplicity, formulated with respect to molecular predicates. However, it may as well be applied to the corresponding molecular predicate expressions, matrices in primitive notation, and properties designated, hence in all the ways (A), (B), and (C) explained above.

+D25-4. Let 'M_1', 'M_2', . . . , 'M_p' be p molecular predicates of degree one ($p \geqq 2$). These predicates (or the properties designated by them) form a ***division*** $=_{\mathrm{Df}}$ the following three conditions are fulfilled.

a. The predicates are L-disjunct (D1e), that is, $\vdash (x)(M_1x \vee M_2x \vee \ldots \vee M_px)$.

b. Any two distinct predicates are L-exclusive (D1d); that is, if 'M_m' and 'M_n' are distinct, $\vdash (x) \sim (M_m x \cdot M_n x)$.

c. None of the predicates is L-empty (D1b), that is, for no m, $\vdash (x) \sim M_m x$.

Hence a division divides all individuals of the system in question into p kinds or properties which are (a) exhaustive and (b) nonoverlapping. Consequently, every one of these individuals must belong to exactly one of the p kinds. Condition (c) says that none of the properties is impossible; this does, however, not exclude the case that some of them happen to be empty.

T25-2. Every predicate in a division is factual; hence any full sentence of such a predicate is factual (T1c).

T25-3. *Dichotomous division.* If 'M_1' and 'M_2' form a division, 'M_2' is L-equivalent to '$\sim M_1$'. (From D4a, b, T20-2m.)

Thus, in this case, the individuals are simply divided into those which are M_1 and the rest.

T25-4. With respect to a given division consisting of p predicates ($p > 2$), let 'M' be defined by a disjunction of n of those predicates ($1 \leqq n \leqq p - 1$), and 'M'' be defined by the disjunction of the remaining $p - n$ predicates. Then the following holds.

a. 'M' and 'M'' form a division.

b. 'M'' is L-equivalent to '$\sim M$'. (From (a), T3.)

§ 26. Isomorphic Sentences; Individual and Statistical Distributions

A. A one-one correlation among the in of a system $\mathfrak{L}$ is called an in-*correlation* (D1). If a sentence i is transformed into j by replacing all in with their correlates with respect to any in-correlation, i and j are called *isomorphic* (D3a). Although isomorphic sentences are in general not L-equivalent, nevertheless they share the L-properties (T2); e.g., if one is L-true, the other is likewise. *B.* An *individual distribution* (D6a) is a conjunction of full sentences of predicates of a division with different in. A *statistical distribution* (D6c) is a disjunction of individual distributions which are mutually isomorphic and hence assign to the kinds the same numbers of individuals.

A. *Individual Correlations and Isomorphism*

In this section we shall deal with correlations among individual constants and with transformations of sentences with the help of these correlations. (The term 'correlation' is here used, as is customary in logic, in the sense of 'correspondence' or 'one-one relation', not in its statistical sense.) These transformations will be of fundamental importance in our system of inductive logic. They are also important for deductive logic, as is shown by the fact that the L-concepts are invariant with respect to these transformations (T2). These invariances in deductive logic have so far been studied only rarely (cf. A. Lindenbaum and A. Tarski, "Ueber die Beschränktheit der Ausdrucksmittel deduktiver Theorien", *Ergebnisse eines mathematischen Kolloquiums*, Heft 7 [1936], pp. 15–23, and F. I. Mautner, "An Extension of Klein's Erlanger Program: Logic as Invariant-Theory", *Amer. Journal of Math.*, 68 [1946], 345–84).

+**D26-1.** C is (a correlation of the $\mathfrak{in}$, or briefly) an $\mathfrak{in}$-***correlation*** in $\mathfrak{L}$ $=_{\mathrm{Df}}$ C is a one-one relation whose domain as well as its converse domain is the class of all $\mathfrak{in}$ in $\mathfrak{L}$.

In the following definition D2, (b) will mostly be applied to sentences, and (c) to classes of sentences. The same holds for the later D3a and b, respectively.

D26-2. Let C be an $\mathfrak{in}$-correlation in $\mathfrak{L}$.

a. $\mathfrak{in}_i$ is the *C-correlate* of $\mathfrak{in}_j$ (in signs of the metalanguage: $\mathfrak{in}_i$ is $C(\mathfrak{in}_j)$) $=_{\mathrm{Df}}$ $\mathfrak{in}_i$ is that individual constant which is correlated with $\mathfrak{in}_j$ by C.

b. The expression $\mathfrak{A}_i$ is the *C-correlate* of the expression $\mathfrak{A}_j$ ($\mathfrak{A}_i$ is $C(\mathfrak{A}_j)$) $=_{\mathrm{Df}}$ $\mathfrak{A}_j$ is an expression in $\mathfrak{L}$, and $\mathfrak{A}_i$ is formed from $\mathfrak{A}_j$ by replacing every $\mathfrak{in}$ occurring in $\mathfrak{A}_j$ with its C-correlate (in the sense (a)).

c. The class of expressions $\mathfrak{K}_i$ is the *C-correlate* of the class of expressions $\mathfrak{K}_j$ ($\mathfrak{K}_i$ is $C(\mathfrak{K}_j)$) $=_{\mathrm{Df}}$ $\mathfrak{K}_j$ is a class of expressions in $\mathfrak{L}$, and $\mathfrak{K}_i$ is the class of the C-correlates (in the sense (b)) of the expressions belonging to $\mathfrak{K}_j$.

In order to discuss examples, we sometimes describe an $\mathfrak{in}$-correlation in a form like '$\binom{abc}{cba}$'; we write on the upper line all $\mathfrak{in}$ of the system in question (in the example, of $\mathfrak{L}_3$) and underneath each $\mathfrak{in}$ we write its correlate.

T26-1. The number of different $\mathfrak{in}$-correlations in $\mathfrak{L}_N$ is $N!$. (From T40-29b.)

+**D26-3.**

a. Let $\mathfrak{A}_i$ and $\mathfrak{A}_j$ be expressions in $\mathfrak{L}$. $\mathfrak{A}_i$ is ($\mathfrak{in}$-isomorphic, or briefly) ***isomorphic*** to $\mathfrak{A}_j$ $=_{\mathrm{Df}}$ there is an $\mathfrak{in}$-correlation C such that either $\mathfrak{A}_i$ is $C(\mathfrak{A}_j)$ or, if $\mathfrak{A}_j$ is a conjunction, $\mathfrak{A}_i$ differs from $C(\mathfrak{A}_j)$ at most in the order of the conjunctive components.

b. Let $\mathfrak{K}_i$ and $\mathfrak{K}_j$ be classes of expressions in $\mathfrak{L}$. $\mathfrak{K}_i$ is ($\mathfrak{in}$-isomorphic, or briefly) *isomorphic* to $\mathfrak{K}_j =_{\text{Df}}$ there is an in-correlation C such that $\mathfrak{K}_i$ is $C(\mathfrak{K}_j)$.

Isomorphism is obviously reflexive, symmetric, and transitive (D25-2). In D3a we admit a change in the order of conjunctive components for the following reason. We shall often apply the concept of isomorphism to $\mathfrak{Z}$. $\mathfrak{Z}_i$ in $\mathfrak{L}_N$ is a conjunction. $C(\mathfrak{Z}_i)$ is in general not a $\mathfrak{Z}$; we have required for the $\mathfrak{Z}$ the lexicographical order of the conjunctive components (D18-1a), and this order is in general disturbed by the application of C. If we rearrange the components in $C(\mathfrak{Z}_i)$ in their lexicographical order, we obtain again a $\mathfrak{Z}$, say, $\mathfrak{Z}_j$; this suggests the subsequent definition D4b. Then, according to D3a, $\mathfrak{Z}_i$ and $\mathfrak{Z}_j$ are isomorphic.

D26-4. Let C be an in-correlation in $\mathfrak{L}$. $\mathfrak{Z}_j$ is *constructed from* $\mathfrak{Z}_i$ *by* $C =_{\text{Df}}$

(**a**) (in $\mathfrak{L}_\infty$) $\mathfrak{Z}_j$ is $C(\mathfrak{Z}_i)$;

(**b**) (in $\mathfrak{L}_N$) $\mathfrak{Z}_j$ is formed from $C(\mathfrak{Z}_i)$ by arranging the conjunctive components in lexicographical order.

+T26-2. ***Invariance of L-concepts*** with respect to in-correlations. Let C be an in-correlation in $\mathfrak{L}$, i and j be sentences in $\mathfrak{L}$, i' be $C(i)$, and j' be $C(j)$.

a. $\mathfrak{R}(i')$ is the class of those $\mathfrak{Z}$ which are constructed from the $\mathfrak{Z}$ in $\mathfrak{R}_i$ by C (D4).

Proof. 1. If i is an atomic sentence, an identity sentence, or 't', the assertion follows from T18-1a, b, c, d. 2. If the assertion holds for j and for k, it holds likewise for $\sim j$, $j \vee k$, and $j \,.\, k$ (T18-1e, f, g). 3. Let i be $(\mathfrak{i}_k)(\mathfrak{M}_j)$. If the assertion holds for every instance of $\mathfrak{M}_j$, it holds also for i (T18-1h). 4. Every sentence can be constructed from sentences (whose number may be infinite) of the forms mentioned in (1) by a finite number n of steps of the four kinds mentioned in (2) and (3). Hence the assertion follows by mathematical induction with respect to n.

b. $\vdash i$ if and only if $\vdash i'$. (From D20-1a, (a).)

c. i is L-false if and only if i' is L-false. (From T20-1a, (b).)

d. L-implication (or L-equivalence, L-disjunctness, L-exclusion, respectively) holds for i and j if and only if the same relation holds for i' and j'. (From T20-1b, c, d, e, (b).)

e. i is factual if and only if i' is factual. (From (b), (c).)

Note that T2b does not assert that i and i', i.e., $C(i)$, are L-equivalent. If i is L-true, i' is likewise L-true, and hence, in this case, i and i' are L-equivalent. However, if i is factual, i' is, in general, not L-equivalent to i. [For example, let C be $\binom{ab}{ba}$. 'Pa' is of course not L-equivalent to

'Pb'. On the other hand, since '$Pa \vee \sim Pa$' is L-true, so is '$Pb \vee \sim Pb$'.]

The following is a corollary of T2b.

T26-3. Let l be a purely general sentence (D16-6h) in $\mathfrak{L}$.

a. If i and j are isomorphic sentences and $\vdash i \supset l$, then $\vdash j \supset l$.

Proof. Let the conditions be fulfilled. Then there is an in-correlation C such that j differs from $C(i)$ at most in the order of conjunctive components and hence is L-equivalent to $C(i)$. Since l does not contain an in (D16-6h), $C(l)$ is l. Therefore, $C(i \supset l)$ is $C(i) \supset l$, and thus is L-equivalent to $j \supset l$. Hence theorem from T2b.

b. If $\mathfrak{Z}_i$ and $\mathfrak{Z}_j$ are isomorphic $\mathfrak{Z}$ in $\mathfrak{L}$ and l holds in $\mathfrak{Z}_i$, then l holds likewise in $\mathfrak{Z}_j$. (From T20-2t, (a).)

B. *Individual and Statistical Distributions*

Many of the most important inductive inferences which we shall discuss later are statistical inferences, that is, some of the sentences involved speak about frequencies. Therefore we shall often make use of the concepts of individual and statistical distributions now to be defined.

+**D26-6.** Let p molecular predicates 'M_m' ($m = 1$ to p) be given which form a division in $\mathfrak{L}$ (D25-4), and n in in $\mathfrak{L}$ (n finite $\geqq 1$).

a. i is (an individually specified description of a distribution, or briefly) an ***individual distribution*** for the n given in with respect to the given division (in $\mathfrak{L}$) $=_{\text{Df}}$ i is a conjunction of n full sentences of predicates of the given division with one each of the n given in, these n conjunctive components being arranged in lexicographical order.

b. j is *the statistical distribution corresponding to i* (in $\mathfrak{L}$) $=_{\text{Df}}$ i is an individual distribution for the n given in with respect to the given division, and j is the disjunction of all those individual distributions for the same in with respect to the same division which are isomorphic to i (including i itself), the disjunctive components being arranged in lexicographical order.

c. j is (a statistical description of a distribution, or briefly) a ***statistical distribution*** for the n given in with respect to the given division (in $\mathfrak{L}$) $=_{\text{Df}}$ there is an individual distribution i for the given in with respect to the given division, and j is the statistical distribution corresponding to i (in the sense (b)).

According to our earlier explanation of conjunctions and disjunctions with n components (§ 16), an individual distribution for one in is a full sentence with that in. And analogously, if there is no other individual distribution isomorphic to i, the statistical distribution corresponding to i is i itself.

The requirement of the lexicographical order in D6a has merely the purpose to make the form of an individual distribution unique, that is to say, to make sure that there cannot be two distinct L-equivalent individual distributions. In other words, every possibility for distributing the given n individuals among the m properties of the given division is represented by one and only one of those sentences which we call individual distributions. The reason for the requirement of the lexicographical order in D6b is analogous.

The meanings of the terms defined in D6 will become clearer by some examples. Suppose that 'M_1', 'M_2', 'M_3', 'M_4' are defined as molecular predicates which constitute a division; that the order in which they have just been given is the lexicographical order of their expansions and hence also of their full sentences with any in. Let i_1 be '$M_3a \cdot M_3c \cdot M_4b$'. Then, according to D6a, i_1 is called an individual distribution for 'a', 'b', 'c' with respect to the given division. The term seems natural because i_1 specifies for each of the three individuals a, b, c, to which of the four kinds in the division it belongs. Let C' be the in-correlation $\binom{abc}{bac}$ in $\mathfrak{L}_3$ (or, in a larger system, any in-correlation beginning in this way). $C'(i_1)$ is '$M_3b \cdot M_3c \cdot M_4a$'; let us call this sentence i_2. Hence i_2 is isomorphic to i_1. On the other hand, let C be the in-correlation $\binom{abc}{cba}$. $C(i_1)$ is '$M_3c \cdot M_3a \cdot M_4b$'. Thus, this sentence is likewise isomorphic to i_1. However, it is not an individual distribution. In order to transform it into one, we have to rearrange the components in lexicographical order. Then we obtain '$M_3a \cdot M_3c \cdot M_4b$'; but this is i_1 itself. This shows that sometimes the application of an in-correlation, although it is not the identity-correlation, does not yield a new individual distribution. There are only three individual distributions isomorphic to i_1: (1) i_1; (2) i_2; (3) '$M_3a \cdot M_3b \cdot M_4c$', which we call i_3. Each of these three sentences has first two full sentences of 'M_3' and then one of 'M_4'; hence they agree in the numbers of individuals assigned to the four kinds and differ only with respect to the individuals themselves.

Let j_1 be the disjunction of the three sentences in lexicographical order, that is, '$i_3 \vee i_1 \vee i_2$'. Then, according to D6b, j_1 is the statistical distribution corresponding to the individual distribution i_1, and also that corresponding to i_2 and that corresponding to i_3. i_1, i_2, and i_3 represent the three possibilities for distributing the individuals a, b, c in such a way among the four kinds in the given division that two individuals belong to M_3 and one to M_4 and none to the other kinds. Therefore, what is expressed by the disjunction j_1 is neither more nor less than the way of distribution just described; hence j_1 says that, of the individuals a, b, c, two belong to M_3 and one to M_4 and hence none to M_1 and M_2. Thus j_1, in distinction to i_1 or i_2 or i_3, does not specify *which* individuals among a, b, c belong to each of the four kinds, but only *how many* of them do; it states that the numbers of the given individuals belonging to the four kinds are 0, 0, 2, 1, respectively. This is the reason why we call j_1 a *statistical* distribution, in distinction to the *individual* distributions i_1, i_2, i_3.

Suppose that i is an individual distribution containing n_1 full sentences of 'M_1', n_2 of 'M_2', . . . , n_p of 'M_p', and j is the statistical distribution corresponding to i. Then we shall sometimes say that i is an individual distribution and j a statistical distribution with respect to 'M_1', . . . , 'M_p' *with the cardinal numbers* n_1, . . . , n_p.

T26-5. For a given division and for n given in, let i and k be individual distributions and j the statistical distribution corresponding to i.

a. k is factual.

Proof. The full sentences of the molecular predicates in k are not L-true (T25-2). No two of them have an in in common. Therefore, k is factual (from T21-11a by mathematical induction with respect to n).

b. If i and k are distinct (i.e., not the same sentence) then they are L-exclusive, hence $\vdash k \supset \sim i$.

Proof. If i and k contained the same conjunctive components, they would be the same sentence because of the requirement of lexicographical order in D6a. Therefore, there must be at least one in which occurs in i in a full sentence of a molecular predicate different from that with which it occurs in k. These two full sentences are L-exclusive (D25-4b), and hence likewise i and k.

c. $\vdash i \supset j$. (From D6b.)

d. If j is not the statistical distribution corresponding to k, then $\vdash k \supset \sim j$.

Proof. Let the condition be fulfilled. Then k must be distinct from i, and hence $\vdash k \supset \sim i$ (b), and likewise with any other individual distribution to which j corresponds, say, i', i'', etc. Therefore, $\vdash k \supset \sim i \,.\, \sim i' \,.\, \sim i'' \,.\, \ldots$ (T21-5m(9)); hence $\vdash k \supset \sim (i \lor i' \lor i'' \lor \ldots)$ (T21-5f(2)), hence $\vdash k \supset \sim j$.

e. If $\vdash k \supset j$, then j is the statistical distribution corresponding to k.

Proof. Suppose $\vdash k \supset j$. Then not $\vdash k \supset \sim j$, because otherwise $\vdash k \supset j \,.\, \sim j$ (T21-5m(8)) and hence $\vdash \sim k$, which is not the case (a). Therefore, j is the statistical distribution corresponding to k (d).

f. The following three conditions are logically equivalent to one another (i.e., if one of them holds, the others hold also):

(1) *j* is the statistical distribution corresponding to *k*,
(2) *k* is isomorphic to *i*,
(3) *k* L-implies *j*.
(From D6a, (c), (e).)

It is easily seen that any statistical distribution for all the N $\mathfrak{in}$ in $\mathfrak{L}_N$ can be transformed into an L-equivalent, purely general sentence. The transformation is analogous to that of a structure-description which will be explained in the next section.

§ 27. Structure-Descriptions ($\mathfrak{Str}$)

All those $\mathfrak{Z}$ which are isomorphic to $\mathfrak{Z}_i$ in $\mathfrak{L}_N$ ascribe the same structural features to the primitive attributes of $\mathfrak{L}_N$. Therefore, we call the disjunction of these $\mathfrak{Z}$ (in a certain order) a *structure-description* ($\mathfrak{Str}$) (D1). This concept will play an important role in the later definition of degree of confirmation.

The most important use of the concept of ismorphism among sentences is its application to the $\mathfrak{Z}$ in finite systems $\mathfrak{L}_N$. Let us consider an example in a system $\mathfrak{L}_3$ with the three $\mathfrak{in}$ '*a*', '*b*', '*c*', and with only two primitive predicates, '*P*' of degree one and '*R*' of degree two. This system contains twelve atomic sentences, three with '*P*' and nine with '*R*'. The following conjunction of twelve basic sentences is an example of a state-description, which we will call $\mathfrak{Z}_1$: '*Pa* . *Pc* . *Rab* . *Rbc* . *Rcb* . ~*Pb* . ~*Raa* . ~*Rac* . ~*Rba* . ~*Rbb* . ~*Rca* . ~*Rcc*'. As an example of an $\mathfrak{in}$-correlation in $\mathfrak{L}_3$ let us take C: $\binom{abc}{bca}$. Then $C(\mathfrak{Z}_1)$ (D26-2b) is '*Pb* . *Pa* . *Rbc* . *Rca* . *Rac* . ~*Pc* . ~*Rbb* . ~*Rba* . ~*Rcb* . ~*Rcc* . ~*Rab* . ~*Raa*'. This, however, is not a $\mathfrak{Z}$; we obtain a $\mathfrak{Z}$, which we will call $\mathfrak{Z}_2$, by rearranging the components in lexicographical order: '*Pa* . *Pb* . *Rac* . *Rbc* . *Rca* . ~*Pc* . ~*Raa* . ~*Rab* . ~*Rba* . ~*Rbb* . ~*Rcb* . ~*Rcc*'. Thus $\mathfrak{Z}_2$ is constructed from $\mathfrak{Z}_1$ by C (D26-4) and hence is isomorphic to $\mathfrak{Z}_1$ (D26-3a).

If two $\mathfrak{Z}$ are isomorphic, we shall sometimes also say that they represent or have *the same structure*, thus extending the use of this term which is ordinarily applied to single relations (Russell's term 'relation-number') or their predicates.

The $\mathfrak{Z}$ are in certain respects similar to individual distributions. [We shall see later that in systems which contain only $\mathfrak{pr}$ of degree one, any $\mathfrak{Z}$ can even be transformed into an L-equivalent individual distribution for all $\mathfrak{in}$ (T34-1).] For a given $\mathfrak{Z}_i$ and an $\mathfrak{in}$-correlation C, even if C is not identity, sometimes the $\mathfrak{Z}$ constructed from $\mathfrak{Z}_i$ by C is $\mathfrak{Z}_i$ itself; this is analogous to an example with individual distributions considered in the preceding section. For a given $\mathfrak{Z}_i$ in $\mathfrak{L}_N$, the number of $\mathfrak{Z}$ isomorphic to it is at most $N!$, because this is the number of $\mathfrak{in}$-correlations in $\mathfrak{L}_N$

(T26-1); but for the reason just mentioned, it is often smaller and sometimes as small as 1. As an example for the latter case, take that $\mathfrak{Z}_j$ in $\mathfrak{L}_N$ whose components are the atomic sentences of $\mathfrak{L}_N$; here, obviously, any $\mathfrak{Z}$ constructed from $\mathfrak{Z}_j$ by any in-correlation is $\mathfrak{Z}_j$ itself; in other words, there is no other $\mathfrak{Z}$ isomorphic to $\mathfrak{Z}_j$. [For those systems which contain only pr of degree one, we shall later give a theorem stating the number of those $\mathfrak{Z}$ which are isomorphic to any given $\mathfrak{Z}_i$ (T35-4).]

Let us go back to the example of $\mathfrak{Z}_1$ and $\mathfrak{Z}_2$ in $\mathfrak{L}_3$. The number of in-correlations for $\mathfrak{L}_3$ is $3! = 6$ (T26-1). If we construct a $\mathfrak{Z}$ from $\mathfrak{Z}_1$ by each of these six correlations, it turns out that in this particular case all correlations, except of course the identity $\binom{abc}{abc}$, lead to $\mathfrak{Z}$ which are distinct from $\mathfrak{Z}_1$. Hence here we have six $\mathfrak{Z}$ isomorphic to $\mathfrak{Z}_1$. Among them are $\mathfrak{Z}_1$ itself and $\mathfrak{Z}_2$; the others, which we will not actually construct here, may be called $\mathfrak{Z}_3$, $\mathfrak{Z}_4$, $\mathfrak{Z}_5$, and $\mathfrak{Z}_6$. Let j be the disjunction $\mathfrak{Z}_1 \vee \mathfrak{Z}_2 \vee \mathfrak{Z}_3 \vee \mathfrak{Z}_4 \vee \mathfrak{Z}_5 \vee \mathfrak{Z}_6$. Since the $\mathfrak{Z}$ are similar to individual distributions, j is similar to a statistical distribution. We can easily see that j is L-equivalent (in $\mathfrak{L}_3$) to the following sentence h, which is purely general, that is, does not contain any in: '$(\exists x)(\exists y)(\exists z)[x \neq y \,.\, x \neq z \,.\, y \neq z \,.\, Px \,.\, Pz \,.\, Rxy \,.\, Ryz \,.\, Rzy \,.\, \sim Py \,.\, \sim Rxx \,.\, \sim Rxz \,.\, \sim Ryx \,.\, \sim Ryy \,.\, \sim Rzx \,.\, \sim Rzz]$'.

Proof. h is L-equivalent to a disjunction of all instances of the matrix included in square brackets (T22-3d). If the same in is substituted for two or three of the variables, then at least one of the $\neq$-sentences is L-false and hence the whole conjunction likewise; therefore, an instance of this kind may be dropped as a component of the disjunction. In this way only those six instances remain in which three distinct in are substituted for the variables. Here, all $\neq$-sentences are L-true and hence may be dropped as conjunctive components. Thus, the instance resulting from the substitution of 'a', 'b', 'c' for 'x', 'y', 'z', respectively, is transformed into $\mathfrak{Z}_1$. And the transformation of the whole leads to a sentence which differs from j at most in the order of conjunctive or disjunctive components.

$\mathfrak{Z}_1$, and likewise any other $\mathfrak{Z}$, states for every individual in $\mathfrak{L}_3$, whether or not it has the property P, and for every ordered pair of individuals, whether or not the relation R holds for them. The sentence j, on the other hand, does not give specific information about the particular individuals; however, it still says something about the three individuals of $\mathfrak{L}_3$, though only in a general way. Among other things, j says for instance the following, as can easily be seen by an inspection of h: (1) there are just two of the three individuals possessing the property P; (2) none of the individuals bears the relation R to itself, in other words, R is irreflexive; (3) R is not symmetric; (4) R is not asymmetric; (5) if x and y are P, R does not hold between x and y. Those features of properties and relations which can be expressed in a purely general way, that is, without the use of $\mathfrak{in}$, are called *structural* features (as examples, see the concepts defined in D25-1a, b, d, e and D25-2a to g without the prefix 'L-'). We see that j describes structural features of P (e.g., (1)), of R (e.g., (2), (3), (4)), and of P and R together (e.g., (5)). And, moreover, j does not leave open any question with respect to structural features of P and R; any such feature which is expressible in $\mathfrak{L}$ is either affirmed or denied by j, because for any purely general sentence l either $\vdash j \supset l$ or $\vdash j \supset \sim l$, as we shall see (T3b).

Thus we see that j describes those structural features of the $\mathfrak{pr}$ of $\mathfrak{L}_3$ which are expressed by $\mathfrak{Z}_1$, and likewise by each of those $\mathfrak{Z}$ which are isomorphic to $\mathfrak{Z}_1$. We might call the totality of these structural features the ***structure*** of $\mathfrak{Z}_1$, which is the same as the structure of each of the $\mathfrak{Z}$ isomorphic to $\mathfrak{Z}_1$. Each of these $\mathfrak{Z}$ describes this structure but, in addition, gives specific information about the individuals. On the other hand, j describes just this structure and does not say anything more. The same holds of course for any sentence L-equivalent to j, for instance, h. However, we shall apply the term '***structure-description***' and the synonymous sign '$\mathfrak{Str}$' to only one of the sentences L-equivalent to j, viz., the disjunction formed from j by arranging the disjunctive components in lexicographical order (D1). The reason is the same as in the analogous case of statistical distributions: on the basis of our definition there is exactly one structure-description for every structure of the universe of a given system. We shall define the term 'structure-description' only for finite systems $\mathfrak{L}_N$, because it is only in these systems that the $\mathfrak{Z}$ are sentences and hence a disjunction of them can be formed. [While the term 'structure-description' is a well-defined technical term of our theory both in deductive and in inductive logic, we use the term 'structure' only in informal explanations like those just given.]

+D27-1.

a. j is *the structure-description corresponding to* $\mathfrak{Z}_i$ (or, $\mathfrak{Z}_i$ *belongs to the structure-description* j) in $\mathfrak{L}_N =_{\mathrm{Df}}$ $\mathfrak{Z}_i$ is a $\mathfrak{Z}$ in $\mathfrak{L}_N$, and j is the disjunction of all $\mathfrak{Z}$ which are isomorphic to $\mathfrak{Z}_i$, arranged in lexicographical order.

b. j is a ***structure-description*** ($\mathfrak{Str}$) in $\mathfrak{L}_N =_{\mathrm{Df}}$ there is a $\mathfrak{Z}_i$ in $\mathfrak{L}_N$ such that j is the structure-description corresponding to $\mathfrak{Z}_i$ (in the sense (a)).

D1a and b are analogous to D26-6b and c for 'statistical distribution'; thus the remarks following D26-6 hold here in an analogous way. In particular, if there is no other $\mathfrak{Z}$ isomorphic to $\mathfrak{Z}_i$, then the structure-description corresponding to $\mathfrak{Z}_i$ is $\mathfrak{Z}_i$ itself.

In the beginning of this section we have given two examples of $\mathfrak{Z}$ in a system $\mathfrak{L}_3$ with only two $\mathfrak{pr}$. The corresponding $\mathfrak{Str}$ is a disjunction of six such $\mathfrak{Z}$. This shows that even in very poor systems the $\mathfrak{Str}$ are sometimes rather long sentences. If we had actually to write down some $\mathfrak{Str}$, the long form would be rather awkward, and it would be more convenient to choose the much shorter general form (for example, the sentence *h* with three existential quantifiers in the earlier example) as the standard form for $\mathfrak{Str}$. However, we shall hardly ever have to write down a $\mathfrak{Str}$ in the course of our discussions. It is true, the concept of $\mathfrak{Str}$ will play a fundamental role in our system of inductive logic, and we shall not only state general theorems but also often deal with concrete examples, for instance, carry out numerical computations for the degree of confirmation for given sentences. In a case of this kind, we may actually write down the sentences in question; we shall then have to speak about the $\mathfrak{Z}$ in which they hold and the $\mathfrak{Str}$ corresponding to these $\mathfrak{Z}$, and we shall have to calculate the number of $\mathfrak{Z}$ belonging to a $\mathfrak{Str}$. But even in such cases it will not be necessary to write down the $\mathfrak{Z}$—although we shall occasionally do so, as in this section—and we shall not write down any $\mathfrak{Str}$. Therefore there is no inconvenience in choosing the disjunctive form for the $\mathfrak{Str}$. And it seems that this form shows the logical relations between the $\mathfrak{Z}$ and the $\mathfrak{Str}$ in a simpler way. We imagine—without actually carrying it out—classifying all $\mathfrak{Z}$ in a given system $\mathfrak{L}_N$ with respect to their structure, that is, dividing them in classes of mutually isomorphic $\mathfrak{Z}$; and then we imagine constructing the $\mathfrak{Str}$ simply as the disjunctions of the $\mathfrak{Z}$ in each class.

The following theorem is analogous to a previous theorem on statistical distributions (T2a, b, c, f (1, 2, 3) correspond to T26-5c, d, e, f, respectively).

T27-2. Let $\mathfrak{Z}_i$ and $\mathfrak{Z}_k$ be any $\mathfrak{Z}$ in $\mathfrak{L}_N$, and $\mathfrak{Str}_j$ be the structure-description corresponding to $\mathfrak{Z}_i$.

a. $\vdash \mathfrak{Z}_i \supset \mathfrak{Str}_j$. (From D1a.)

b. If $\mathfrak{Z}_k$ does not belong to $\mathfrak{Str}_j$, then $\vdash \mathfrak{Z}_k \supset \sim\mathfrak{Str}_j$. (From T21-8a, in analogy to T26-5d.)

c. If $\vdash \mathfrak{Z}_k \supset \mathfrak{Str}_j$, then $\mathfrak{Z}_k$ belongs to $\mathfrak{Str}_j$. (From T20-5b, (b), in analogy to T26-5e.)

d. $\mathfrak{Str}_j$ holds in $\mathfrak{Z}_i$. (From (a), T20-2t.)

e. If $\mathfrak{Str}_j$ holds in $\mathfrak{Z}_k$, then $\mathfrak{Z}_k$ belongs to $\mathfrak{Str}_j$. (From T20-2t, (c).)

f. The following four conditions are logically equivalent to each other (i.e., if one of them holds, the others hold also):

(1) $\mathfrak{Z}_k$ belongs to $\mathfrak{Str}_j$,
(2) $\mathfrak{Z}_k$ is isomorphic to $\mathfrak{Z}_i$,
(3) $\mathfrak{Z}_k$ L-implies $\mathfrak{Str}_j$,
(4) $\mathfrak{Str}_j$ holds in $\mathfrak{Z}_k$.
(From D1a, (a), (c,) (d), (e).)

The following theorem T3 shows that the relation between purely general sentences (D16-6h) and $\mathfrak{Str}$ is similar to the relation between sentences of any form and $\mathfrak{Z}$. In particular, we found earlier that any not L-false sentence in $\mathfrak{L}_N$ is L-equivalent to a disjunction of $\mathfrak{Z}$ (T21-8c). Analogously, we find now that any not L-false, purely general sentence in $\mathfrak{L}_N$ is L-equivalent to a disjunction of $\mathfrak{Str}$ (T3c).

T27-3. Let l be a purely general sentence in $\mathfrak{L}_N$.

a. If l holds in $\mathfrak{Z}_i$, and $\mathfrak{Str}_k$ is the $\mathfrak{Str}$ corresponding to $\mathfrak{Z}_i$, then $\vdash \mathfrak{Str}_k \supset l$.

Proof. Let $\mathfrak{Z}_i$, $\mathfrak{Z}_i'$, $\mathfrak{Z}_i''$, etc., be the $\mathfrak{Z}$ isomorphic to $\mathfrak{Z}_i$. Then $\mathfrak{Str}_k$ differs from $\mathfrak{Z}_i \vee \mathfrak{Z}_i' \vee \mathfrak{Z}_i'' \vee \ldots$ at most in the order of disjunctive components and hence is L-equivalent to this disjunction. If l holds in $\mathfrak{Z}_i$, $\vdash \mathfrak{Z}_i \supset l$ (T20-2t), and hence $\vdash \mathfrak{Z}_i' \supset l$, $\vdash \mathfrak{Z}_i'' \supset l$, etc. (T26-3a), hence $\vdash (\mathfrak{Z}_i \supset l) \centerdot (\mathfrak{Z}_i' \supset l) \centerdot \ldots$ (T20-2p), hence $\vdash \mathfrak{Z}_i \vee \mathfrak{Z}_i' \vee \ldots \supset l$ (T21-5n(4)), hence $\vdash \mathfrak{Str}_k \supset l$.

b. For any $\mathfrak{Str}_j$ in $\mathfrak{L}$, either $\vdash \mathfrak{Str}_j \supset l$ or $\vdash \mathfrak{Str}_j \supset \sim l$.

Proof. Let $\mathfrak{Z}_j$ be one of the $\mathfrak{Z}$ belonging to $\mathfrak{Str}_j$. Then either l or $\sim l$ holds in $\mathfrak{Z}_j$ (T19-2). Hence theorem from (a).

c. If l is not L-false, l is L-equivalent to a disjunction of n $\mathfrak{Str}$ in $\mathfrak{L}_N$ ($n \geqq 1$).

Proof. If l is not L-false, $\mathfrak{R}_l$ is not empty. Let h be a disjunction of all $\mathfrak{Z}$ in $\mathfrak{R}_l$ such that mutually isomorphic $\mathfrak{Z}$ stand together as a subdisjunction of h and are arranged within this subdisjunction in lexicographical order. Then l is L-equivalent to h (T21-8c). Each of the subdisjunctions contains all $\mathfrak{Z}$ which are isomorphic to any $\mathfrak{Z}$ occurring in it (T26-3b) and hence is a $\mathfrak{Str}$. Thus, h is a disjunction of $\mathfrak{Str}$.

§ 28. Correlations for Basic Matrices

Correlations among basic matrices are defined (D1). They are analogous to in-correlations (§ 26A); they are, however, less important and will seldom be used. L-concepts are invariant with respect to transformations by these correlations (T2).

The concepts introduced and discussed in this section will not often be used, and then chiefly in Volume II.

The correlations defined by D1 have a certain similarity to the in-correlations (D26-1); they are somewhat more complicated but less important.

D28-1. C is a *correlation of the basic matrices* or an $\mathfrak{M}$*-correlation* in $\mathfrak{L}$ $=_{\text{Df}}$ C is a one-one relation between expressions in $\mathfrak{L}$ satisfying the following conditions.

a. To every atomic matrix $\mathfrak{M}_i$ (D16-3b) of the form $\mathfrak{pr}_i\mathfrak{i}_1\mathfrak{i}_2 \ldots \mathfrak{i}_n$ (containing $\mathfrak{pr}_i$ of the degree n and the n alphabetically first $\mathfrak{i}$ in their alphabetical order) exactly one expression is correlated by C; we call it the C-correlate of $\mathfrak{M}_i$ or, in signs, $C(\mathfrak{M}_i)$.

b. If $\mathfrak{M}_i$ has the form described in (a), then $C(\mathfrak{M}_i)$ is a basic $\mathfrak{M}$ (D16-3c) with a $\mathfrak{pr}$ of the same degree n as $\mathfrak{pr}_i$ (it may be $\mathfrak{pr}_i$ itself) and the same variables as in $\mathfrak{M}_i$ in any order. (Thus $C(\mathfrak{M}_i)$ may be $\mathfrak{M}_i$ itself.)

c. If both $\mathfrak{M}_i$ and $\mathfrak{M}_j$ have the form described in (a) but with two distinct $\mathfrak{pr}$, then $C(\mathfrak{M}_i)$ and $C(\mathfrak{M}_j)$ contain two $\mathfrak{pr}$ which are likewise distinct from one another (but, as mentioned in (b), not necessarily distinct from the two $\mathfrak{pr}$ occurring in $\mathfrak{M}_i$ and $\mathfrak{M}_j$).

The following definition has a certain analogy to D26-2, but is somewhat more complicated. The use of '$C(\mathfrak{M}_i)$', as defined in D1, is hereby extended to new cases.

D28-2. Let C be an $\mathfrak{M}$-correlation in $\mathfrak{L}$.

a. Let $\mathfrak{M}_j$ be an atomic matrix of a form different from that described in D1a. Let $\mathfrak{M}_i$ be that atomic matrix of the form described in D1a which contains the same $\mathfrak{pr}$ as $\mathfrak{M}_j$; hence $\mathfrak{M}_j$ can be formed from $\mathfrak{M}_i$ by certain substitutions for the variables. $C(\mathfrak{M}_j)$ $=_{\text{Df}}$ the expression (a basic matrix) formed from $C(\mathfrak{M}_i)$ by those same substitutions.

b. Let $\mathfrak{M}_j$ be atomic. (1) If $C(\mathfrak{M}_j)$ is atomic, $C(\sim\mathfrak{M}_j)$ $=_{\text{Df}}$ $\sim C(\mathfrak{M}_j)$. (2) If $C(\mathfrak{M}_j)$ is not atomic and hence of the form $\sim\mathfrak{M}_l$, $C(\sim\mathfrak{M}_j)$ $=_{\text{Df}}$ $\mathfrak{M}_l$.

c. Let $\mathfrak{M}_h$ be a nonbasic matrix in $\mathfrak{L}$. $C(\mathfrak{M}_h)$ $=_{\text{Df}}$ the expression (matrix) formed from $\mathfrak{M}_h$ by replacing every occurrence of any basic $\mathfrak{M}_k$ with $C(\mathfrak{M}_k)$ (as determined by D1 or (a) or (b)). (If $\sim\mathfrak{M}_j$ occurs with an atomic $\mathfrak{M}_j$, then $\sim\mathfrak{M}_j$ is to be replaced by its correlate (determined by (b).)

d. Let $\mathfrak{K}_i$ be a class of matrices (which may be sentences) in $\mathfrak{L}$. $C(\mathfrak{K}_i)$ $=_{\text{Df}}$ the class of the C-correlates of the elements of $\mathfrak{K}_i$.

Example. 'Rxy' has the form described in D1a. According to D1, we may choose as its C-correlate any basic matrix of degree two with the variables 'x' and 'y' in any order. Suppose we choose '$\sim Syx$'. Then the C-correlate of all other basic matrices containing 'R' is determined by D2. Thus, according to D2a, C('Ryx') is '$\sim Sxy$'; C('Rac') is '$\sim Sca$'; further, according to D2b(2), C('$\sim Rac$') is 'Sca'. Then, we can find the C-correlate of any matrix containing no other pr than 'R' with the help of D2c; thus, C('$\sim Rac \vee (x)(\exists y)Ryx$') is '$Sca \vee (x)(\exists y) \sim Sxy$'.

D3 is analogous to D26-4.

D28-3. Let C be an 𝔐-correlation in 𝔏. $\mathfrak{Z}_j$ is *constructed from* $\mathfrak{Z}_i$ by $C =_{\mathrm{Df}}$

(**a**) (in $\mathfrak{L}_\infty$) $\mathfrak{Z}_j$ is $C(\mathfrak{Z}_i)$ (in the sense of D2d),

(**b**) (in $\mathfrak{L}_N$) $\mathfrak{Z}_j$ is formed from $C(\mathfrak{Z}_i)$ by arranging the conjunctive components in their lexicographical order.

T2 is analogous to T26-2.

T28-2. *Invariance of L-concepts* with respect to 𝔐-correlations. Let C be an 𝔐-correlation in 𝔏, i and j be sentences in 𝔏, i' be $C(i)$, and j' be $C(j)$.

a. $\mathfrak{R}(i')$ is the class of those $\mathfrak{Z}$ which are constructed from the $\mathfrak{Z}$ in $\mathfrak{R}_i$ by C (D3). (Proof analogous to T26-2a.)

b. $\vdash i$ if and only if $\vdash i'$. (From D20-1a, (a).)

c. i is L-false if and only if i' is L-false. (From T20-1a, (b).)

d. L-implication (or L-equivalence, L-disjunctness, L-exclusion, respectively) holds for i and j if and only if the same relation holds for i' and j'. (From T20-1b, c, d, e, (b).)

e. i is factual if and only if i' is factual. (From (b), (c).)

Example. Since '$(x)[\sim Rax \supset (\exists y) \sim Ryx]$' is L-true, '$(x)[Sxa \supset (\exists y) Sxy]$' is likewise L-true.

T28-3. Let C be an 𝔐-correlation and C' an in-correlation in 𝔏.

a. For any i in 𝔏, $C(C'(i))$ is the same as $C'(C(i))$.

Proof. The transformation by C' concerns only the in. The transformation by C may change three things: (1) a sign of negation may be added or removed, (2) a pr may be replaced by another one, (3) the order of the argument signs may be changed. Thus the two transformations are independent of each other, and hence the order in which they are carried out is irrelevant for the final result.

b. For any $\mathfrak{Z}_i$ in 𝔏, the one $\mathfrak{Z}$ constructed by C (D3) from the one $\mathfrak{Z}$ constructed by C' (D26-4) from $\mathfrak{Z}_i$ is the same as the one $\mathfrak{Z}$ constructed by C' from the one $\mathfrak{Z}$ constructed by C from $\mathfrak{Z}_i$. (Proof analogous to (a).)

§ 29. Some Numbers Connected with the Systems $\mathfrak{L}$

Some numbers which are characteristic for any system $\mathfrak{L}$, especially for any finite system $\mathfrak{L}_N$, are defined. τ is the number of the $\mathfrak{Str}$ (D1a), ζ the number of the $\mathfrak{Z}$ (D2b) in $\mathfrak{L}_N$.

In this section we introduce into the metalanguage some symbols for certain numbers with respect to any given system $\mathfrak{L}$. [Strictly speaking, these symbols designate numerical functions whose arguments are the systems $\mathfrak{L}$; hence, in a complete notation we ought to write, for instance, '$\zeta(\mathfrak{L})$' for 'the number of $\mathfrak{Z}$ in the system $\mathfrak{L}$'; however, since the context will usually make clear which system is meant, we shall simply write 'ζ' instead.]

We intend to define 'τ' in such a way that it designates the number of structures in the system in question. (We do not take 'σ' for this purpose because it is the customary symbol for the standard deviation.) However, the definition of 'τ' will not contain the term 'structure', because we use this term only in an informal way and have not given a technical definition for it. Instead, the definition will refer to something within the language system that represents the structures. In $\mathfrak{L}_N$, we take, of course, the $\mathfrak{Str}$ for this purpose (D1b); in $\mathfrak{L}_\infty$, we may take the classes of isomorphic $\mathfrak{Z}$ (D2), in accordance with an earlier remark.

D29-1.

a. For $\mathfrak{L}_N$. $\tau =_{\text{Df}}$ the number of $\mathfrak{Str}$ in $\mathfrak{L}_N$.

b. For $\mathfrak{L}_\infty$. $\tau =_{\text{Df}}$ the number of those classes of $\mathfrak{Z}$ in $\mathfrak{L}_\infty$ which contain, for some $\mathfrak{Z}_i$, exactly those $\mathfrak{Z}$ which are isomorphic to $\mathfrak{Z}_i$.

D29-2. For any finite or infinite system $\mathfrak{L}$.

a. $\beta =_{\text{Df}}$ the number of atomic sentences (and hence of basic pairs) in $\mathfrak{L}$.

b. $\zeta =_{\text{Df}}$ the number of $\mathfrak{Z}$ in $\mathfrak{L}$.

c. $\rho =_{\text{Df}}$ the number of ranges (that is, of all classes of $\mathfrak{Z}$) in $\mathfrak{L}$.

T29-1. The following holds for any finite or infinite system $\mathfrak{L}$.

a. $\zeta = 2^\beta$. (From T40-31g.)

b. $\rho = 2^\zeta$. (From T40-31h.)

T29-2. In any finite system $\mathfrak{L}_N$, the number of largest classes of mutually L-equivalent sentences is ρ, hence 2^ζ (T1b).

Proof. Sentences are L-equivalent if and only if they have the same range (D20-1d). Furthermore, for every class $\mathfrak{K}_i$ of $\mathfrak{Z}$ in $\mathfrak{L}_N$, there is a sentence h whose range is $\mathfrak{K}_i$; if $\mathfrak{K}_i$ is non-empty, we take as h a disjunction of the $\mathfrak{Z}$ in $\mathfrak{K}_i$ (T21-8d); if $\mathfrak{K}_i$ is empty, we take '$\sim t$'.

We use the term '*proposition*' in such a sense that two sentences are said to express the same proposition if and only if they are L-equivalent

([Semantics], p. 92; [Meaning], p. 27). Hence $\rho = 2^{\zeta}$ is likewise the number of propositions expressible by sentences in $\mathfrak{L}_N$, and also the number of propositions expressible by classes of sentences (T21-8e). Thus we see that the number of propositions expressible in $\mathfrak{L}_N$ is finite (but, as we shall find later, this number is enormously large, even for rather narrow systems; see § 35), although the number of sentences and still more the number of classes of sentences in $\mathfrak{L}_N$ is infinite (the first is denumerable, the second nondenumerable).

The following theorem speaks about infinite cardinal numbers (for 'α_0', etc., see D40-8); it is merely intended to give some additional information about the logicomathematical nature of certain classes of expressions in $\mathfrak{L}_\infty$, but it will not be used for the later construction of our system of inductive logic.

T29-4. The following holds for $\mathfrak{L}_\infty$.

a. The following classes of expressions in $\mathfrak{L}_\infty$ are denumerable, hence their cardinal number is α_0: (1) the in; (2) the atomic sentences and hence the basic pairs (β); (3) the sentences; (4) the expressions.

b. The number of classes of sentences is α_1. (From (a) (3), T40-31h.)

c. $\zeta = \alpha_1$. (From T1a, (a)(2).)

d. $\rho = \alpha_2$. (From T1b, (b).)

e. The number of propositions expressible by sentences is α_0.

Proof. 1. This number cannot be larger than α_0 (a)(3). 2. The atomic sentences of the infinite sequence 'Pa_1', 'Pa_2', etc., express different propositions because no two of them are L-equivalent. Their number is α_0. Therefore the whole number of propositions cannot be smaller than α_0.

f. The number of propositions expressible by classes of sentences is α_1.

Proof. 1. This number cannot be larger than α_1 (b). 2. The subclasses of the sequence of atomic sentences mentioned in the proof of (e) express different propositions because no two of them are L-equivalent. Their number is α_1 (T40-31h). Therefore the number sought for cannot be smaller than α_1.

T4e and f show that in $\mathfrak{L}_\infty$, in distinction to $\mathfrak{L}_N$ (T2), the number of propositions expressed by sentences and that of propositions expressed by classes of sentences are different and are both smaller than ρ.

§ 31. The Systems $\mathfrak{L}^\pi$; the Q-Predicates

§§ 31–38 deal only with properties, not relations. If a system $\mathfrak{L}$ has primitive predicates for properties only, we designate the number of these predicates by 'π' and the system by '$\mathfrak{L}^\pi$'. We define the molecular predicates 'Q_1', 'Q_2', etc., by conjunctions in which every primitive predicate or its negation occurs

(A1). Thus these Q-predicates (D1) designate the strongest factual properties expressible in the system. Every factual molecular property expressible in the system is expressible by a disjunction of some of the Q-predicates (T2f). These predicates constitute a division (T2d). Their number is κ (D2), $= 2^\pi$ (T1).

The following part of this chapter (§§ 31–38) deals with that part of the deductive logic of attributes which is most important both for deductive and for inductive logic, viz., the logic of properties in distinction to the logic of relations. Although our procedure here is, of course, based upon the customary method used in the logic of attributes (the so-called lower functional logic; see §§ 22–26), many features of our procedure and most of the concepts here introduced are new. Some of these concepts (especially those of §§ 31, 32, and 34) will be continually used later in our theory of inductive logic (in Vol. II); the concepts of this part will not be used before §107.

Since in what follows we restrict ourselves to properties, we shall speak not of all systems $\mathfrak{L}$ but only of those whose primitive predicates are all of degree one. We shall designate the (finite) number of these predicates in a system of this kind with 'π'. (This use has of course nothing to do with the use of the same Greek letter for the number 3.14 . . . in analysis.) We call these systems the systems $\mathfrak{L}^\pi$. $\mathfrak{L}^\pi_N$ is a finite system of this kind; for instance, $\mathfrak{L}^3_{100}$ is the system which contains one hundred $\mathfrak{in}$ and three $\mathfrak{pr}$ of degree one and no $\mathfrak{pr}$ of higher degrees. $\mathfrak{L}^\pi_\infty$ is an infinite system of this kind, for instance, $\mathfrak{L}^5_\infty$ is that system which contains the infinite sequence of $\mathfrak{in}$ and five $\mathfrak{pr}$ of degree one.

In our theory of inductive logic to be constructed later, the definitions of the fundamental concepts, e.g., the concept of degree of confirmation and related ones, and some theorems will be formulated in a general way, with respect to any system $\mathfrak{L}$. However, most of the theorems, especially those which deal with the various kinds of inductive inferences and which state methods for the computation of the degree of confirmation for sentences of certain forms, will apply to the systems $\mathfrak{L}^\pi$ only (see § 110). In other words, the bulk of our inductive logic will deal only with properties of individuals, not with relations between individuals, except for those relations which are defined on the basis of properties. At the present time this restriction seems natural and well justified, in view of the fact that deductive logic took more than two thousand years from its start with Aristotle to the first logic of relations (De Morgan, 1860). Inductive logic, that is, the theory of probability$_1$, is only a few hundred years old. Therefore, it is not surprising to see that so far nobody has made an attempt to apply it to relations. (Incidentally, the same holds for the theory of probability$_2$, i.e., relative frequency.) The inclusion of relations in deductive logic causes obviously a certain increase in complexity. The corresponding increase in complexity for inductive logic is very much greater. One of the points where the great and so far unsurmounted difficulties in connection with relations in inductive logic arise is the following one. For the determination of $\mathfrak{m}^*$, the number τ of the $\mathfrak{Str}$ in any finite system is required (see (2) in § 110A). A general formula for τ in the systems $\mathfrak{L}_N^\pi$ can easily be given (T35-1d). However, for systems with $\mathfrak{pr}$ of higher degrees, no analogous theorem is known, not even for the simplest case of systems $\mathfrak{L}_N$ with a $\mathfrak{pr}$ of degree two as the only $\mathfrak{pr}$. In other words, the deductive logic of relations, although widely developed in other respects, is today unable to give us a general formula stating the number of structures of one dyadic relation for finite N, let alone the same for several relations.

A solution of the problem just mentioned would be of importance not only for deductive and inductive logic but also for certain branches of science. Preliminary work for the solution of the simplest case, that of one dyadic relation, has been done in that branch of combinatory topology which is known as the theory of graphs. For a survey of this theory see Denes König, *Theorie der endlichen und unendlichen Graphen: Kombinatorische Topologie der Streckenkomplexe* ("Mathematik und ihre Anwendungen," ed. Artin, Vol. 16 [Leipzig, 1936]). König discusses (in § 5) the problem of the numbers of graphs of various kinds and refers to the original investigations by C. Jordan ("Sur les assemblages de lignes", *Journal f. reine u. angew. Math.*, 70 [1869], 185–90) and A. Cayley ("On the analytical forms called trees, with application to the theory of chemical combinations", *Report British Assoc. Advanc. Science*, 1875, pp. 257–305, reprinted in *Mathem. Papers*, IX, 427–60). The graphs correspond to the structures of symmetric relations (D25-2c). For the solution of the simplest case of our problem, the results found by the authors just mentioned must be generalized so as to cover also the nonsymmetric relations.

As primitive predicates $\mathfrak{pr}_1, \mathfrak{pr}_2, \ldots, \mathfrak{pr}_\pi$ in any system $\mathfrak{L}^\pi$ we take 'P_1', 'P_2', ..., 'P_π'. If we consider a sequence of systems $\mathfrak{L}_N^\pi$ with increasing N, we shall usually take the $\mathfrak{pr}$ and hence their number π as unchanged; for example, in the sequence $\mathfrak{L}_1^3$, $\mathfrak{L}_2^3$, ... each system contains the same three $\mathfrak{pr}$ 'P_1', 'P_2', 'P_3', and so does the system $\mathfrak{L}_\infty^3$, which is the infinite system corresponding to the mentioned sequence of finite systems.

We shall now explain a procedure for defining, on the basis of the $\mathfrak{pr}$ in a system $\mathfrak{L}^\pi$, molecular predicates of a particular kind (see the terms explained at the beginning of § 25), the ***Q-predicates*** 'Q_1', 'Q_2', etc. The properties designated by these predicates will be called ***Q-properties.*** Let us illustrate the procedure for $\pi = 3$, hence for a system $\mathfrak{L}^3$. The number of $\mathfrak{in}$ is irrelevant for this procedure. Hence the following construction is the same for every system $\mathfrak{L}^3$, including $\mathfrak{L}^3_\infty$. The subsequent table A1 contains three argument columns for 'P_1', 'P_2', and 'P_3'; the lines show the eight possible distributions of two values, affirmation and negation, designated by '+' and '−', respectively, among the three $\mathfrak{pr}$. Thus this table is analogous to the truth-table for three sentences constructed in § 21B. In analogy to the k-sentences there (T21-7), we have here the molecular predicate expressions listed in the second column; we call them Q-predicate-expressions. They are conjunctions of basic predicate expressions, that is, of $\mathfrak{pr}$ or their negations. In the third column the Q-predicates are introduced as abbreviations for the Q-predicate-expressions. (A1 introduces the examples 'Q_1', etc., in the object language $\mathfrak{L}^3$; D1 introduces the terms 'Q-predicate-expression', etc., in the metalanguage.)

+A31-1. ***Table for the Q-predicates in*** $\mathfrak{L}^3$

'P_1'	'P_2'	'P_3'	Q-predicate-expressions	Q-predicates
+	+	+	$P_1 \cdot P_2 \cdot P_3$	Q_1
+	+	−	$P_1 \cdot P_2 \cdot \sim P_3$	Q_2
+	−	+	$P_1 \cdot \sim P_2 \cdot P_3$	Q_3
+	−	−	$P_1 \cdot \sim P_2 \cdot \sim P_3$	Q_4
−	+	+	$\sim P_1 \cdot P_2 \cdot P_3$	Q_5
−	+	−	$\sim P_1 \cdot P_2 \cdot \sim P_3$	Q_6
−	−	+	$\sim P_1 \cdot \sim P_2 \cdot P_3$	Q_7
−	−	−	$\sim P_1 \cdot \sim P_2 \cdot \sim P_3$	Q_8

D31-1. For any system $\mathfrak{L}^{\pi}$.

a. $\mathfrak{A}_i$ is a *Q-predicate-expression* $=_{Df}$ $\mathfrak{A}_i$ is either the conjunctive predicate expression containing all $\mathfrak{pr}$ in their alphabetical order ('$P_1 \cdot P_2 \cdot \ldots \cdot P_\pi$') or is formed from this expression by replacing some of the $\mathfrak{pr}$ with their negations.

+b. $\mathfrak{A}_i$ is a ***Q-predicate*** $=_{Df}$ $\mathfrak{A}_i$ is a predicate defined as abbreviation for a Q-predicate-expression. 'Q_m' is taken as abbreviation for the mth of the Q-predicate-expressions in their lexicographical order.

c. $\mathfrak{M}_i$ is a *Q-matrix* $=_{Df}$ $\mathfrak{M}_i$ is a full matrix of a Q-predicate.

d. i is a *Q-sentence* $=_{Df}$ i is a full sentence of a Q-predicate.

+D31-2. For $\mathfrak{L}^{\pi}$. $\kappa =_{Df}$ the number of the Q-predicates.

+T31-1. For any system $\mathfrak{L}^{\pi}$, $\kappa = 2^{\pi}$. (From T40-31f.)

If we take in the table A1, instead of the three $\mathfrak{pr}$, full sentences of them with the same $\mathfrak{in}$, for example, 'P_1a', 'P_2a', 'P_3a', then the table becomes an ordinary truth-table, as in § 21B. For instance, the k-sentence '$P_1a \cdot \sim P_2a \cdot P_3a$' corresponds to the third line. This sentence can be abbreviated by '$(P_1 \cdot \sim P_2 \cdot P_3)a$' (A25-1) and hence now, with the help of A1, by 'Q_3a'.

A look at the table A1 shows that every individual must have one and only one of the Q-properties. Hence they form a division (T2d). This *Q-division* is the strongest division possible in $\mathfrak{L}^\pi$; that is to say, no factual property stronger than a Q-property can be defined in $\mathfrak{L}^\pi$; in other words, a Q-property cannot be subdivided into several factual properties by means of the pr in $\mathfrak{L}^\pi$. In the terminology of Aristotelian logic, the Q-properties are the *infimae species*.

T31-2. For any system $\mathfrak{L}^\pi$.

+**a.** Any two distinct Q-predicates are L-exclusive. Hence a conjunction of two Q-sentences with two distinct Q-predicates and the same in is L-false. (From T21-7a, T25-1d.)

b. The Q-predicates are L-disjunct. Hence a disjunction of full sentences of all Q-predicates with the same in is L-true. (From T21-7b, D25-1e.)

c. Every Q-predicate is factual. Hence every Q-sentence is factual. (From T20-5g, D25-1c, T25-1c.)

+**d.** The Q-predicates form a division. (From (a), (b), (c), D25-4.)

e. Let 'M' be a molecular predicate L-equivalent to a disjunction of n Q-predicates ($1 \leqq n \leqq \kappa - 1$). Then the disjunction of the remaining $\kappa - n$ Q-predicates is L-equivalent to '$\sim M$'. (From (d), T25-4b.)

+**f.** Every molecular predicate expression and hence every molecular predicate is either L-empty or L-equivalent to a disjunction of n Q-predicates ($1 \leqq n \leqq \kappa$). (From T21-7d.)

g. Any disjunction of n Q-sentences ($n \geqq 1$) is not L-false. (From (c), T20-2q.)

§ 32. Logical Width

The concept of the logical width of a molecular predicate expression $\mathfrak{A}_i$ is defined in the following way (D1). If $\mathfrak{A}_i$ is L-empty, we ascribe to it the width 0. Otherwise, $\mathfrak{A}_i$ is L-equivalent to a disjunction of Q-predicates; in this case, we take the number of these Q-predicates as the width of $\mathfrak{A}_i$.

Let P_1 and P_2 be two properties which are logically independent of each other, for example, Small and Black. Then the property $P_1 \cdot P_2$ (Small-and-Black) is in a certain sense stronger or narrower than P_1; P_1 is weaker or wider. And $P_1 \vee P_2$ (Small-or-Black) is in this sense still wider than P_1. By 'wider' we do not mean here 'having a greater extension'. The extension of the property $P_1 \vee P_2$, that is, the class of individuals possessing this property, may be greater than that of P_1 or it may be the same.

The latter would be the case if all black things in the world happened to be small. Whether or not this is the case is a factual question. What we mean by 'wider' is not a factual but a logical relation. The property $P_1 \vee P_2$ is wider than P_1 by admitting more possibilities; for instance, the possible, that means, not L-empty, property $\sim P_1 . P_2$ is admitted by the first but excluded by the second.

The method just described for comparing the widths of two properties is applicable only in the special case where one of the properties L-implies the other. If P_1, P_2, P_3, P_4 are four properties all logically independent of one another, then this method does not enable us to compare $P_1 \vee P_2$ with $P_3 \vee P_4$. If we wish to make possible a comparison of widths in all cases, we need additional conventions. Now, any language system $\mathfrak{L}$ furnishes a natural basis for these conventions with respect to the properties expressible in the system by its selection of primitive properties. For the sake of simplicity, we restrict the discussion to molecular properties and the predicate expressions or predicates designating them in a system $\mathfrak{L}^\pi$. In a system $\mathfrak{L}^\pi$, the Q-properties are the narrowest non-L-empty properties. Thus it seems natural to assign to each of them the smallest positive width, say, 1. To the L-empty property we assign the width 0. Every non-L-empty property which is not a Q-property is a disjunction of two or more Q-properties (T31-2f); it seems natural to take the number of these Q-properties as its width. Thus we are led to the following definition (D1).

+**D32-1.** Let $\mathfrak{M}_i$ be a matrix of degree one in $\mathfrak{L}^\pi$, with $\mathfrak{i}_i$ as the only free variable.

a. $\mathfrak{M}_i$ has (the logical width or briefly) the ***width*** $w =_{\mathrm{Df}}$
either (1) $\mathfrak{M}_i$ is L-empty and $w = 0$;
or (2) $\mathfrak{M}_i$ is L-equivalent to a Q-matrix with $\mathfrak{i}_i$ and $w = 1$;
or (3) $\mathfrak{M}_i$ is L-equivalent to a disjunction of w distinct Q-matrices with $\mathfrak{i}_i$ ($w > 1$).

b. $\mathfrak{M}_i$ has (the relative logical width or briefly) the ***relative width*** $q =_{\mathrm{Df}}$ $\mathfrak{M}_i$ has the width w, and $q = w/\kappa$.

In analogy to D25-1 and 2, we shall use the terms 'width' and 'relative width' in the following three ways. Each of these terms is applied (A) to a matrix (of degree one), (B) to a corresponding predicate expression, for instance, a molecular predicate, (C) to the corresponding property.

The concept of logical width is very important for inductive logic. One of the decisive defects of the classical theory of probability is the failure to take into consideration the width of the properties involved. Some of the fundamental principles and theorems of the classical theory lead to contradictions because they are formulated in a too general way for all properties. One of the modifications by which we shall eliminate these contradictions will consist in making the degree of confirmation dependent, among other things, upon the widths of the properties involved.

+**T32-1.** Let $\mathfrak{A}_i$ be a molecular predicate expression in $\mathfrak{L}^\pi$, $\mathfrak{A}_j$ a molecular predicate abbreviating $\mathfrak{A}_i$, and $\mathfrak{M}_i$ a molecular matrix which is the expansion of a full matrix of $\mathfrak{A}_i$ and hence of $\mathfrak{A}_j$.

a. There is one and only one integer w which is the width of $\mathfrak{M}_i$, and hence of $\mathfrak{A}_i$ and $\mathfrak{A}_j$, and $0 \leqq w \leqq \kappa$. (From T31-2f.)

b. There is one and only one (rational) real number q which is the relative width of $\mathfrak{M}_i$, and hence of $\mathfrak{A}_i$ and $\mathfrak{A}_j$, and $0 \leqq q \leqq 1$. (From (a).)

+**T32-2.** Let $\mathfrak{A}_i$ be a molecular predicate expression or a molecular predicate in $\mathfrak{L}^\pi$ with the width w and hence the relative width $q = w/\kappa$.

a. $\mathfrak{A}_i$ is L-empty, and hence every full sentence L-false, if and only if $w = 0$ and hence $q = 0$. (From T25-1b.)

b. $\mathfrak{A}_i$ is L-universal, and hence every full sentence L-true, if and only if $w = \kappa$ and hence $q = 1$. (From T31-2b, T25-1a.)

c. $\mathfrak{A}_i$ is factual, and hence every full sentence factual, if and only if $0 < w < \kappa$ and hence $0 < q < 1$. (From (a), (b).)

d. $\sim\mathfrak{A}_i$ has the width $\kappa - w$, and hence the relative width $1 - q$. (From T31-2e.)

T32-3. Let k be a conjunction of π basic sentences in $\mathfrak{L}^\pi$ with distinct $\mathfrak{pr}$ but the same $\mathfrak{in}_i$. Hence k may be abbreviated by $(\mathfrak{A}_i)\mathfrak{in}_i$, where $\mathfrak{A}_i$ is a molecular predicate expression of conjunctive form with π components, each of them being a $\mathfrak{pr}$ or its negation, every $\mathfrak{pr}$ occurring exactly once.

a. $\mathfrak{A}_i$ is L-equivalent to a Q-predicate-expression and hence to a Q-predicate, and thus has the width 1. (From D31-1a.)

b. k is L-equivalent to a Q-sentence with $\mathfrak{in}_i$. (From (a).)

T32-4. Let k be a conjunction of n basic sentences in $\mathfrak{L}^\pi$ $(1 \leqq n < \pi)$ with n distinct $\mathfrak{pr}$ but the same $\mathfrak{in}_i$. Hence k may be abbreviated by $(\mathfrak{A}_i)\mathfrak{in}_i$, where $\mathfrak{A}_i$ is a molecular predicate expression of conjunctive form with n components, each of them being a $\mathfrak{pr}$ or its negation, no $\mathfrak{pr}$ occurring more than once.

a. (1) k is L-equivalent to a disjunction of $2^{\pi-n}$ distinct Q-sentences with $\mathfrak{in}_i$; hence

(2) $\mathfrak{A}_i$ has the width $2^{\pi-n}$.

Proof. The number m of those $\mathfrak{pr}$ which do not occur in k is $\pi - n$. We construct first the conjunction of the atomic sentences with these m $\mathfrak{pr}$ and with $\mathfrak{in}_i$, in their lexicographical order, and furthermore all those other conjunctions which are formed from the first one by replacing some atomic sentences with their negations. The number of all these conjunctions, including the first, is 2^m (T40-31g). Let these conjunctions be $h_1, h_2, \ldots$. Let h be their disjunction; then $\vdash h$ (T21-7b). Therefore, k is L-equivalent to $k \cdot h$, that is, $k \cdot (h_1 \vee h_2 \vee \ldots)$, hence, by distribution, to $(k \cdot h_1) \vee (k \cdot h_2) \vee \ldots$. For any p from 1 to 2^m, $k \cdot h_p$ is a conjunction of π basic sentences with π distinct $\mathfrak{pr}$ and the same $\mathfrak{in}_i$ and hence is L-equivalent to a Q-sentence with $\mathfrak{in}_i$ (T3b). If h_i and h_j are any two distinct h-sentences, then they are L-exclusive (T21-7a), and hence $k \cdot h_i$ and $k \cdot h_j$ are L-exclusive; therefore the corresponding Q-sentences are distinct. Thus the 2^m sentences of the form $k \cdot h_p$ correspond to 2^m distinct Q-sentences with $\mathfrak{in}_i$. 1. k is L-equivalent to their disjunction. 2. Therefore, $\mathfrak{A}_i$ is L-equivalent to the disjunction of the 2^m distinct Q-predicates, and hence has the width 2^m.

b. The relative width of $\mathfrak{A}_i$ is $1/2^n$; hence it is independent of π.

Proof. The relative width is $2^{\pi-n}/\kappa$ (a), $= 2^{\pi-n}/2^\pi$ (T31-1), $= 1/2^n$.

c. Corollary. A primitive predicate has the width $\kappa/2$ and the relative width $1/2$. (From (b), for $n = 1$.)

T32-5. Let p predicates be given which form a division (D25-4) in $\mathfrak{L}^\pi$.

a. The sum of the widths of the given predicates is κ.

Proof. Let w_m be the width of the mth predicate ($m = 1$ to p). Since the predicates are factual (T25-2), $0 < w_m < \kappa$ (T2c). The mth predicate is L-equivalent to a disjunction of w_m Q-predicates (D1a(3)). If we form these disjunctions for the p predicates, then every Q-predicate occurs in one and only one of them, because the predicates are L-disjunctive and L-exclusive in pairs (D25-4a, b). Hence the assertion.

b. The sum of the relative widths of the given predicates is 1. (From (a).)

T32-6.

a. '$(Q_1 \vee Q_2 \vee Q_3) \cdot (Q_2 \vee Q_3 \vee Q_4)$' is L-equivalent to '$Q_2 \vee Q_3$', and hence has the width 2.

Proof. By multiple distribution (T21-5m(3)), the given conjunction is L-equivalent to a disjunction of nine components, every component being a conjunction of one Q-predicate from the first parenthesis and one from the second. Of these nine conjunctions, seven contain two distinct Q-predicates and hence are L-empty (T31–2a) and hence may be dropped as components of the disjunction. What remains is '$(Q_2 \cdot Q_2) \vee (Q_3 \cdot Q_3)$', hence '$Q_2 \vee Q_3$'.

b. '$(Q_1 \vee Q_2) \cdot (Q_2 \vee Q_4)$' is L-equivalent to '$Q_2$', and hence has the width 1. (Analogous to (a).)

c. Let $\mathfrak{A}_i$ and $\mathfrak{A}_j$ be molecular predicate expressions or molecular predicates, $\mathfrak{A}_i$ being L-equivalent to a disjunction of m Q-predicates and

$\mathfrak{A}_j$ to a disjunction of n Q-predicates ($m \geqq 1$, $n \geqq 1$). Let p be the number of those Q-predicates which occur in both disjunctions.
(1) If $p = 0$, then $\mathfrak{A}_i \,.\, \mathfrak{A}_j$ is L-empty.
(2) If $p = 1$, then $\mathfrak{A}_i \,.\, \mathfrak{A}_j$ is L-equivalent to the common Q-predicate.
(3) If $p > 1$, then $\mathfrak{A}_i \,.\, \mathfrak{A}_j$ is L-equivalent to the disjunction of the p common Q-predicates.
Hence, in any case, the width of $\mathfrak{A}_i \,.\, \mathfrak{A}_j$ is p. (Analogous to (a).)

The following theorem facilitates the computation of the width of a molecular predicate expression in which not all $\mathfrak{pr}$ occur.

T32-7. Let i be a molecular sentence in $\mathfrak{L}^\pi$ all of whose ultimate components are atomic sentences with $\mathfrak{in}_i$; let the number of different $\mathfrak{pr}$ occurring in i be n, where $n < \pi$. Let the truth-table for i with respect to the n occurring atomic sentences have the value T on exactly m of the 2^n lines. Obviously, i can be abbreviated by $(\mathfrak{A}_i)\mathfrak{in}_i$, where $\mathfrak{A}_i$ is a molecular predicate expression constructed out of the n $\mathfrak{pr}$. Let i not be L-false; hence $m > 0$, and $\mathfrak{A}_i$ is not L-empty.

a. Let $w = m \times 2^{\pi-n}$, $= \frac{m}{2^n}\kappa$. Then i is L-equivalent to a disjunction of w distinct Q-sentences with $\mathfrak{in}_i$; hence, $\mathfrak{A}_i$ has the width w.

Proof. i is L-equivalent to a disjunction of m conjunctions (T21-7d). Each of these conjunctions has as components n basic sentences with the n $\mathfrak{pr}$ and with $\mathfrak{in}_i$, and is hence L-equivalent to a disjunction of $2^{\pi-n}$ distinct Q-sentences with $\mathfrak{in}_i$ (T4a). If k and k' are any two distinct ones of these conjunctions, then they are L-exclusive (T21-7a), hence $k \,.\, k'$ is L-false. Therefore, no Q-predicate can occur in both k and k'; because otherwise $k \,.\, k'$ would be L-equivalent to a disjunction of p Q-sentences with $\mathfrak{in}_i$ ($p \geqq 1$) (T6c) and would hence not be L-false (T31-2g). Thus i is L-equivalent to a disjunction of $m \times 2^{\pi-n}$ Q-sentences with $\mathfrak{in}_i$.

b. The relative width of $\mathfrak{A}_i$ is $m/2^n$; hence it is independent of π. (From (a).)

§ 33. The Q-Normal Form

It is shown how a given sentence with primitive predicates can be transformed into a sentence with Q-predicates and, in particular, into a Q-normal form (D1). The latter will be used in inductive logic.

In this section we shall show how sentences of $\mathfrak{L}^\pi$, written in primitive notation, can be transformed into L-equivalent sentences with Q-predicates, and finally into a particular form, called the Q-normal form, similar to the disjunctive normal form. Later, in inductive logic, we shall make use of the Q-normal form for the computation of the degree of confirmation.

T33-1. Let $\mathfrak{pr}_i$ be any $\mathfrak{pr}$ in $\mathfrak{L}^\pi$.

a. $\mathfrak{pr}_i$ is L-equivalent to the disjunction of those Q-predicate-expressions in which it occurs unnegated, and hence to the disjunction of the corresponding Q-predicates. (These Q-predicates correspond to those lines in the table of Q-predicates (see A31-1) where $\mathfrak{pr}_i$ has the value $+$.) (From T21-7d.)

b. $\mathfrak{pr}_i$ has the width $\kappa/2$, and hence the relative width $1/2$. (From (a).)

c. $\sim\mathfrak{pr}_i$ is L-equivalent to the disjunction of those Q-predicate-expressions in which $\sim\mathfrak{pr}_i$ occurs, and hence to the disjunction of the corresponding Q-predicates. (These Q-predicates correspond to those lines in the table of Q-predicates where $\mathfrak{pr}_i$ has the value $-$.) (From (a), T31-2e.)

d. $\sim\mathfrak{pr}_i$ has the width $\kappa/2$, and hence the relative width $1/2$. (From (c).)

e. Every basic sentence with $\mathfrak{in}_i$ is L-equivalent to a disjunction of Q-sentences with $\mathfrak{in}_i$, whose number is $\kappa/2$. (The transformation of any given basic sentence into this disjunction can be carried out according to either (a) or (c).)

T33-2. Let k be a conjunction of n basic sentences ($n \geqq 2$) with the same $\mathfrak{in}_i$. Hence, k can be abbreviated by $(\mathfrak{A}_i)\mathfrak{in}_i$, where $\mathfrak{A}_i$ is a molecular predicate expression in the form of a conjunction with n components, each being a $\mathfrak{pr}$ or a negation of a $\mathfrak{pr}$. For every conjunctive component in k (or in $\mathfrak{A}_i$), let the class of the corresponding Q-predicates be determined according to T1a or c; let $\mathfrak{K}_i$ be the class product of all these classes. Then the following holds.

a. If $\mathfrak{K}_i$ is empty, then $\mathfrak{A}_i$ is L-empty and k is L-false. (This is the case if and only if a $\mathfrak{pr}$ occurs both unnegated and negated.) (From T32-6c(1).)

b. If $\mathfrak{K}_i$ contains only one Q-predicate, then $\mathfrak{A}_i$ is L-equivalent to it and k is L-equivalent to its full sentence with $\mathfrak{in}_i$. (From T32-6c(2).)

c. If $\mathfrak{K}_i$ contains two or more Q-predicates, then $\mathfrak{A}_i$ is L-equivalent to their disjunction and k is L-equivalent to the disjunction of their full sentences with $\mathfrak{in}_i$. (From T32-6c(3).)

d. The width of $\mathfrak{A}_i$ is the number of Q-predicates in $\mathfrak{K}_i$. (From (a), (b), (c).)

Examples for the transformation of basic sentences or conjunctions of them into formulations with Q-predicates. We take the system $\mathfrak{L}^3$; hence we can use A31-1. (1) and (3) follow from T1a, (2) and (4) from T1c, (5) from T2b (or directly from A31-1), (6), (7), and (8) from T2c.

1. 'P_1a' is L-equivalent to '$Q_1a \vee Q_2a \vee Q_3a \vee Q_4a$'.
2. '$\sim P_1a$' is L-equivalent to '$Q_5a \vee Q_6a \vee Q_7a \vee Q_8a$'.
3. 'P_3a' is L-equivalent to '$Q_1a \vee Q_3a \vee Q_5a \vee Q_7a$'.

4. '$\sim P_3a$' is L-equivalent to '$Q_2a \vee Q_4a \vee Q_6a \vee Q_8a$'.
5. '$\sim P_1b \,.\, \sim P_2b \,.\, P_3b$' is L-equivalent to '$Q_7b$'.
6. '$\sim P_1b \,.\, P_3b$' is L-equivalent to '$Q_5b \vee Q_7b$'.
7. '$\sim P_1a \,.\, P_2a$' is L-equivalent to '$Q_5a \vee Q_6a$'.
8. '$P_2a \,.\, \sim P_3a$' is L-equivalent to '$Q_2a \vee Q_6a$'.

The following definition (D1) gives the *rules for transformation into a Q-normal form.* Sentences of this form, as referred to in D1 and T4, belong, strictly speaking, to enlarged systems containing the *Q*-predicates.

D1 and T4 refer to sentences in which the *Q*-predicates ('Q_1', etc.) actually occur, not only to the expansions of such sentences in primitive notation. Thus, strictly speaking, these sentences do not belong to our systems $\mathfrak{L}^\pi$ but to enlarged systems $*\mathfrak{L}^\pi$. For instance, the system $*\mathfrak{L}^3$ is constructed from $\mathfrak{L}^3$ by the addition of the eight *Q*-predicates (A31-1). In this system, a rule is laid down to the effect that the range of a *Q*-sentence is the same as that of the corresponding sentence with $\mathfrak{pr}$ (e.g., the range of 'Q_7b' is the same as that of '$\sim P_1b \,.\, \sim P_2b \,.\, P_3b$', see example (5) above). In virtue of this additional rule of ranges for any system $*\mathfrak{L}^\pi$, there is a close relationship between $*\mathfrak{L}^\pi$ and $\mathfrak{L}^\pi$ of the following kind. If *i* is any sentence in $*\mathfrak{L}^\pi$ containing one or more *Q*-predicates and *j* is the sentence formed from *i* by the elimination of all *Q*-predicates on the basis of the additional rule of ranges (e.g., in $*\mathfrak{L}^3$, on the basis of the table A31-1), then *i* and *j* are L-equivalent in $*\mathfrak{L}^\pi$. Furthermore, *j* has the same range in $*\mathfrak{L}^\pi$ as in $\mathfrak{L}^\pi$; therefore, it has the same logical properties in both systems (e.g., L-truth, L-implying a certain other sentence, etc.). Because of this relationship between the enlarged systems $*\mathfrak{L}^\pi$ and the original systems $\mathfrak{L}^\pi$ we may interpret the theorems concerning sentences with *Q*-predicates (from T31-2 on, and including those we shall state later) in the following three ways. Any such theorem holds (i) for the sentence in question with *Q*-predicates in $*\mathfrak{L}^\pi$, (ii) for the corresponding sentence without *Q*-predicates in $*\mathfrak{L}^\pi$, (iii) for this same sentence in $\mathfrak{L}^\pi$. Our previous explanations concerning references to defined signs (§ 15A) admitted only the interpretation (iii). But it seems often convenient to read a theorem in the sense (i), that is, to think of sentences actually containing *Q*-predicates and not merely of their expansions; this is correct if we place the sentence not in the original system but in the enlarged system. However, in order to avoid unnecessary complications in the formulation of our theorems, definitions, etc., we shall omit references to the enlarged systems and continue to refer simply to the systems $\mathfrak{L}^\pi$.

D33-1. Let *i* be any sentence in $\mathfrak{L}_N^\pi$ or any nongeneral sentence in $\mathfrak{L}_\infty^\pi$. *j* is *a sentence of* **Q-normal form** *corresponding to* $i =_{Df}$ *j* is formed from *i* by applying the following rules until none of them is applicable any more. (See explanations in D21-2.)

a. As D21-2a.

b. Every defined expression occurring, except the *Q*-predicates, is eliminated.

c to **p**. As D21-2c to p.

q. Every basic sentence *k* is replaced by a disjunction *h* of *Q*-sentences with the same in as in *k*; if *k* is atomic, *h* is constructed according to T1a; if *k* is the negation of an atomic sentence, *h* is constructed according to T1c.

r. A conjunction containing as components two *Q*-sentences with the same in but two distinct *Q*-predicates is replaced by '$\sim t$'.

In practice, we can shorten the transformation considerably by proceeding in the following way instead of applying (q) and (r): we rearrange a conjunction of basic sentences by grouping together the components with the same in; then we replace a subconjunction of basic sentences with the same in by a *Q*-sentence or a disjunction of such according to T2b or c. (See examples below.)

T33-4. Let *i* be a sentence in $\mathfrak{L}_N^\pi$ or a nongeneral sentence in $\mathfrak{L}_\infty^\pi$. Let *j* be a sentence of *Q-normal form* corresponding to *i*.

a. *i* and *j* are L-equivalent. (From T21-10a, T1a, T1c, T31-2a.)

b. *j* does not contain '$\sim$', unless *j* is '$\sim t$'.

Proof. After the application of the rules D1a to p, '$\sim$' occurs only in basic sentences, unless the whole sentence is '$\sim t$' (T21-10c). '$\sim$' in basic sentences disappears by D1q. If '$\sim t$' is introduced by D1r, either it disappears by D1j and l (i.e., D21-2j and l) or the whole becomes '$\sim t$'.

c. *j* has one of the following forms: (1) 't'; (2) '$\sim t$'; (3) a *Q*-sentence; (4) a conjunction of *n* *Q*-sentences ($n \geqq 2$) with *n* distinct in; (5) a disjunction of two or more components of the forms (3) or (4). (From T21-10c, (b).)

Example for a transformation into *Q-normal form*. Suppose the following sentence is given:

'$P_2a \,.\, \sim P_1b \,.\, P_3b \,.\, [P_1a \vee P_2b \supset \sim P_3a]$'.

Application of rules (b), (m), and (p) in D1 (i.e., in D21-2) yields:

'$[P_2a \,.\, \sim P_1b \,.\, P_3b \,.\, \sim P_1a \,.\, \sim P_2b] \vee [P_2a \,.\, \sim P_1b \,.\, P_3b \,.\, \sim P_3a]$'.

This is a disjunctive normal form. According to the shorter procedure mentioned, we group the basic sentences in subconjunctions with the same in:

'$[(P_2a \,.\, \sim P_1a) \,.\, (\sim P_1b \,.\, P_3b \,.\, \sim P_2b)] \vee [(P_2a \,.\, \sim P_3a) \,.\, (\sim P_1b \,.\, P_3b)]$'.

Each subconjunction is now replaced according to T2 (see the examples (7), (5), (8), (6) following T2):

'$[(Q_5a \vee Q_6a) \,.\, Q_7b] \vee [(Q_2a \vee Q_6a) \,.\, (Q_5b \vee Q_7b)]$'.

Now rule (p) (distribution of a disjunction) is applied three times:

'$[Q_5a \,.\, Q_7b] \vee [Q_6a \,.\, Q_7b] \vee [Q_2a \,.\, Q_5b] \vee [Q_2a \,.\, Q_7b] \vee [Q_6a \,.\, Q_5b] \vee [Q_6a \,.\, Q_7b]$'.

According to rule (f), the second component of the disjunction is omitted because it is the same as the last:

'$[Q_5a \,.\, Q_7b] \vee [Q_2a \,.\, Q_5b] \vee [Q_2a \,.\, Q_7b] \vee [Q_6a \,.\, Q_5b] \vee [Q_6a \,.\, Q_7b]$'.

This is a *Q*-normal form.

§ 34. The Q-Numbers

Any $\mathfrak{Z}_i$ in $\mathfrak{L}_N^\pi$ can be transformed into a conjunction of N full sentences of Q-predicates, one for each $\mathfrak{in}$. Thus, $\mathfrak{Z}_i$ is L-equivalent to an individual distribution for all $\mathfrak{in}$ with respect to the Q-division (T1). The number of full sentences of 'Q_m' in the conjunction mentioned, in other words, the number of those individuals which in $\mathfrak{Z}_i$ have the property Q_m, is called the *m*th *Q-number* in $\mathfrak{Z}_i$. Thus, $\mathfrak{Z}_i$ determines a sequence of κ Q-numbers, whose sum is N. Two $\mathfrak{Z}$ are isomorphic if and only if they have the same Q-numbers (T3). Therefore, any $\mathfrak{Str}$, and the structure described by it, is completely characterized by the κ Q-numbers. Thus, any $\mathfrak{Str}$ is L-equivalent to a statistical distribution for all $\mathfrak{in}$ with respect to the Q-division (T6). The Q-numbers will later be used for the computation of degrees of confirmation.

We shall now see how the $\mathfrak{Z}$ in $\mathfrak{L}_N^\pi$ can be transformed into sentences with Q-predicates. Any given $\mathfrak{Z}_i$ is a conjunction which contains exactly one sentence from every basic pair (D18-1a). Let us transform $\mathfrak{Z}_i$ into an L-equivalent sentence k by rearranging the conjunctive components in the following way. First, we place the components with $\mathfrak{in}_1$, i.e., 'a_1', then those with $\mathfrak{in}_2$, and so forth, finally those with $\mathfrak{in}_N$. For any $\mathfrak{in}_i$, there are π basic sentences as components, one for each of the π $\mathfrak{pr}$; we arrange these components according to increasing subscripts of the $\mathfrak{pr}$. Thus, k has the form $k_1 \cdot k_2 \cdot \ldots \cdot k_N$, where k_n (n = 1 to N) is the subconjunction with $\mathfrak{in}_n$. The first component in k_n is either $\mathfrak{pr}_1\mathfrak{in}_n$ or its negation, the second either $\mathfrak{pr}_2\mathfrak{in}_n$ or its negation, and so on. Hence, k_n can be abbreviated by a Q-sentence with $\mathfrak{in}_n$ (T32-3b). Thus k is transformed into a conjunction h of N Q-sentences, one for each of the N $\mathfrak{in}$ in $\mathfrak{L}_N^\pi$. We call h the *Q-form* of $\mathfrak{Z}_i$ (D1a). In this form, any $\mathfrak{in}_i$ occurs only once; but a Q-predicate may have any number m of occurrences ($0 \leqq m \leqq N$).

In L_∞^π, we can transform the $\mathfrak{Z}$ in a similar way; but here the Q-form is not as important as in $\mathfrak{L}_N^\pi$. In $\mathfrak{L}_\infty^\pi$, any $\mathfrak{Z}_j$ is not a conjunction but an infinite class of basic sentences, one from each basic pair (D18-1b). Let $\mathfrak{K}_n$ be the subclass of $\mathfrak{Z}_j$ containing the basic sentences with $\mathfrak{in}_n$. Then $\mathfrak{K}_n$ is finite; it contains π sentences, one for each of the π $\mathfrak{pr}$. It contains either $\mathfrak{pr}_1\mathfrak{in}_n$ or its negation, either $\mathfrak{pr}_2\mathfrak{in}_n$ or its negation, etc., finally either $\mathfrak{pr}_\pi\mathfrak{in}_n$ or its negation. Thus $\mathfrak{K}_n$ is L-equivalent to a conjunction k_n of its elements, arranged in the order of increasing subscripts of the $\mathfrak{pr}$. Hence, k_n can be abbreviated by a Q-sentence with $\mathfrak{in}_n$. Thus, $\mathfrak{Z}_j$ is L-equivalent to an infinite class of Q-sentences, one for each $\mathfrak{in}$ of the infinite sequence of $\mathfrak{in}$ in $\mathfrak{L}_\infty^\pi$. We call this class of Q-sentences the *Q-form* of $\mathfrak{Z}_j$ in $\mathfrak{L}_\infty^\pi$ (D1b).

[The Q-forms of $\mathfrak{Z}$ both in finite and in infinite systems belong, strictly speaking, to enlarged systems containing the Q-predicates; see the remarks preceding D33-1.]

D34-1.

+a. The *Q-form* of $\mathfrak{Z}_i$ in $\mathfrak{L}_N^\pi =_{\mathrm{Df}}$ that conjunction of N Q-sentences, one for each $\mathfrak{in}$ in $\mathfrak{L}_N^\pi$, arranged in the order of increasing subscripts of the $\mathfrak{in}$, which is L-equivalent to $\mathfrak{Z}_i$.

b. The *Q-form* of $\mathfrak{Z}_j$ in $\mathfrak{L}_\infty^\pi =_{\mathrm{Df}}$ that class of Q-sentences, one for each $\mathfrak{in}$ in $\mathfrak{L}_\infty^\pi$, which is L-equivalent to $\mathfrak{Z}_j$.

We have seen earlier that the Q-predicates constitute a division (T31-2d). Any $\mathfrak{Z}_i$ in $\mathfrak{L}_N^\pi$, as we see from its Q-form, specifies for every individual which of the Q-properties it has. Hence, $\mathfrak{Z}_i$ is L-equivalent to an individual distribution for all $\mathfrak{in}$ (T1); its Q-form differs from an individual distribution at most in the order of components.

+T34-1. Any $\mathfrak{Z}_i$ in $\mathfrak{L}_N^\pi$ is L-equivalent to an individual distribution for all $\mathfrak{in}$ in $\mathfrak{L}_N^\pi$ with respect to the Q-division. (From D1a, D26-6a, T31-2d.)

+D34-2. The *m*th ***Q-number*** in $\mathfrak{Z}_i$ in $\mathfrak{L}^\pi =_{\mathrm{Df}}$ the number of full sentences of 'Q_m' in the Q-form of $\mathfrak{Z}_i$. ('Q_m' is that Q-predicate which corresponds to the *m*th Q-predicate-expression in their lexicographical order; see D31-1a and the examples A31-1 for $\mathfrak{L}^3$.)

In other words, the *m*th Q-number in $\mathfrak{Z}_i$ is the number of those individuals which in $\mathfrak{Z}_i$ have the property Q_m. Since there are κ Q-properties, any $\mathfrak{Z}_i$ determines κ Q-numbers. In $\mathfrak{Z}_i$ in $\mathfrak{L}_N^\pi$, these Q-numbers, say, $N_1, N_2, \ldots, N_\kappa$, are finite; their sum is N. In $\mathfrak{Z}_j$ in $\mathfrak{L}_\infty^\pi$, a Q-number is finite or infinite; their sum is α_0 (denumerably infinite, D40-8a); hence at least one of them is α_0.

We shall now show that isomorphism of $\mathfrak{Z}$ means the same as identity of the Q-numbers, both in finite systems (T3) and in the infinite system (T4).

+T34-3. Let $\mathfrak{Z}_i$ and $\mathfrak{Z}_i'$ be two $\mathfrak{Z}$ in $\mathfrak{L}_N^\pi$. Let the Q-numbers of $\mathfrak{Z}_i$ be $N_1, N_2, \ldots, N_\kappa$, and those of $\mathfrak{Z}_i'$ $N_1', N_2', \ldots, N_\kappa'$. $\mathfrak{Z}_i$ and $\mathfrak{Z}_i'$ are isomorphic if and only if they have the same Q-numbers (i.e., for every m from 1 to κ, $N_m = N_m'$).

Proof. Let i and i' be the Q-forms of $\mathfrak{Z}_i$ and $\mathfrak{Z}_i'$, respectively. 1. Let $\mathfrak{Z}_i$ and $\mathfrak{Z}_i'$ be isomorphic. Then there is an $\mathfrak{in}$-correlation C in $\mathfrak{L}_N^\pi$ such that $\mathfrak{Z}_i'$ is constructed from $\mathfrak{Z}_i$ by C (D26-3a, D26-4b), and analogously i' from i. For every m from 1 to κ, the N_m full sentences of 'Q_m' in i contain N_m different $\mathfrak{in}$, and the full sentences of 'Q_m' in i' contain the C-correlates of those $\mathfrak{in}$. Their number must likewise be N_m, since C is one-one. On the other hand, the number of the latter full sentences is N_m'. Therefore, $N_m = N_m'$. 2. For every m from 1 to κ, let $N_m = N_m'$. Now we construct a correlation C in the following way. For every m, we correlate the N_m $\mathfrak{in}$ which occur with 'Q_m' in i in an arbitrary way with the N_m' $\mathfrak{in}$ which occur with 'Q_m' in i'. This is possible because $N_m = N_m'$. Since no $\mathfrak{in}$ occurs with more than one Q-predicate in i, and likewise in i', C is one-one. Since every $\mathfrak{in}$ of $\mathfrak{L}_N^\pi$ occurs in i and likewise in i', C is an $\mathfrak{in}$-correlation for $\mathfrak{L}_N^\pi$. i' differs from $C(i)$ at most in the order of the components. Hence, $\mathfrak{Z}_i'$ is constructed from $\mathfrak{Z}_i$ by C. Therefore, $\mathfrak{Z}_i'$ and $\mathfrak{Z}_i$ are isomorphic.

T34-4. Let $\mathfrak{Z}_i$ and $\mathfrak{Z}_i'$ be two $\mathfrak{Z}$ in $\mathfrak{L}_\infty^\pi$. Let the Q-numbers of $\mathfrak{Z}_i$ be u_1, u_2, . . . , u_κ, and those of $\mathfrak{Z}_i'$ u_1', u_2', . . . , u_κ'. $\mathfrak{Z}_i$ and $\mathfrak{Z}_i'$ are isomorphic if and only if they have the same Q-numbers (i.e., for every m from 1 to κ, $u_m = u_m'$).

The *proof* is analogous to that of T3 and even simpler, because here $\mathfrak{Z}_i$ and $\mathfrak{Z}_i'$ are classes and hence no analogue of the complication connected with the order of conjunctive components occurs.

D34-4. The *Q-form* of $\mathfrak{Str}_j$ in $\mathfrak{L}_N^\pi =_{Df}$ the expression formed from $\mathfrak{Str}_j$ by replacing every $\mathfrak{Z}_i$ occurring as a disjunctive component in $\mathfrak{Str}_j$ by its Q-form.

We found that the Q-form of a $\mathfrak{Z}$ corresponds to an *individual* distribution for all $\mathfrak{in}$ with respect to the Q-division. Therefore, the Q-form of any $\mathfrak{Str}_j$ corresponds to a *statistical* distribution (T6); they differ at most in the order of conjunctive and disjunctive components.

+T34-6. Any $\mathfrak{Str}_j$ in $\mathfrak{L}_N^\pi$ is L-equivalent to a statistical distribution for all $\mathfrak{in}$ in $\mathfrak{L}_N^\pi$ with respect to the Q-division. (From T1, D27-1, D26-6b, c.)

Any $\mathfrak{Str}_j$ in $\mathfrak{L}_N$ states those features of the domain of individuals of $\mathfrak{L}_N$ which are common to the isomorphic $\mathfrak{Z}$ belonging to $\mathfrak{Str}_j$. What isomorphic $\mathfrak{Z}$ in $\mathfrak{L}_N^\pi$ have in common is the ordered κ-tuple of Q-numbers (T3). Hence, *any* $\mathfrak{Str}_j$ *in* $\mathfrak{L}_N^\pi$ *states no more and no less than a certain set of* κ *Q-numbers.* Any $\mathfrak{Str}_j$ determines uniquely the Q-numbers, as seen from its Q-form. And, conversely, any arbitrary ordered κ-tuple of numbers whose sum is N determines, if taken as Q-numbers, uniquely a certain $\mathfrak{Str}_j$ in $\mathfrak{L}_N^\pi$; we find $\mathfrak{Str}_j$ by constructing the disjunction of all those $\mathfrak{Z}$ in $\mathfrak{L}_N^\pi$ (in the lexicographical order) which have the given numbers as Q-numbers. We have earlier talked loosely of the structure described by a $\mathfrak{Str}$. We may now give a more precise meaning to the term 'structure'. We might say, if we wish to, that, with respect to systems $\mathfrak{L}^\pi$, *the structure of* $\mathfrak{Z}_i$ *is the sequence* (ordered κ-tuple) *of the Q-numbers of* $\mathfrak{Z}_i$.

It is easily seen that the Q-numbers do indeed determine all structural features of the $\mathfrak{pr}$. The structure of a $\mathfrak{pr}$ of degree one or of the property designated by it is its cardinal number; all other structural properties (for instance, universality or emptiness) are determined by the cardinal number. The cardinal number n_i of any $\mathfrak{pr}_i$, for a given $\mathfrak{Z}_i$ or $\mathfrak{Str}_j$, is determined by the Q-numbers in the following way. $\mathfrak{pr}_i$ is L-equivalent to a disjunction of certain Q-predicates (T33-1a); since any two Q-predicates are L-exclusive (T31-2a), n_i is the sum of the Q-numbers of these Q-predicates. Likewise, the cardinal number of any molecular predicate expression and any molecular predicate is determined by the Q-numbers. (This follows analogously from T31-2f.)

We have defined the structure-descriptions ($\mathfrak{Str}$) only for finite systems. That a structure is determined by the κ Q-numbers holds also for $\mathfrak{L}^{\pi}_{\infty}$ (because of T4). However, in general, a structure in $\mathfrak{L}^{\pi}_{\infty}$ is not expressible by a sentence in this system $\mathfrak{L}^{\pi}_{\infty}$ itself. As mentioned earlier, we may regard classes of isomorphic $\mathfrak{Z}$ as representations of structures in $\mathfrak{L}^{\pi}_{\infty}$. However, they are classes of classes of sentences, and hence much more complex than sentences; we shall not use them within our theory. If a structure in $\mathfrak{L}^{\pi}_{\infty}$ fulfils a certain special condition, it is expressible by a sentence. This condition can easily be stated with the help of the Q-numbers.

We can find the condition in the following way. In $\mathfrak{L}_{\infty}$, as in any finite system, we can easily construct a sentence j_n which says that a given property, expressed by any matrix of the system in question, has a certain finite cardinal number. This may be done either in the customary way with the help of existential quantifiers and '=' (see Hilbert and Bernays [Grundlagen], I, 174) or, in $\mathfrak{L}_N$, also in the form of a disjunction as in the statistical distributions and the $\mathfrak{Str}$. However, there is no sentence in $\mathfrak{L}_{\infty}$ which says that the cardinal number of a given factual property is infinite or that it is finite; this can only be expressed by means of attribute variables, which do not occur in our systems $\mathfrak{L}$ (see the similar remark concerning the domain of individuals in the paragraph in small print at the end of § 20). [There are sentences in our systems from which it follows that the cardinal number of a certain property is finite or that it is infinite, which, however, say more than this. For instance, there is a sentence j which says that at most five individuals have the property M. It obviously follows from j that M is finite. And, in $\mathfrak{L}_{\infty}$, it follows from j that $\sim M$ is infinite, because it can be seen from the semantical rules of $\mathfrak{L}_{\infty}$ that the number of individuals is infinite, although this cannot be expressed by a sentence *in* $\mathfrak{L}_{\infty}$.] As we have seen, any structure in $\mathfrak{L}^{\pi}_{\infty}$ is determined by the Q-numbers. At least one Q-number is infinite; it is $\boldsymbol{a}_0$ (D40-8a), the smallest infinite cardinal number, because the number of individuals in $\mathfrak{L}_{\infty}$ is $\boldsymbol{a}_0$. Now let us consider a structure of which all Q-numbers except one are finite. Then there is a sentence i, which attributes to the $\kappa - 1$ finite Q-properties those finite cardinal numbers which they have in that structure. Since in $\mathfrak{L}^{\pi}_{\infty}$ at least one Q-number is $\boldsymbol{a}_0$, it follows from i that the one remaining Q-property has the cardinal number $\boldsymbol{a}_0$ (though this alone is not expressible in $\mathfrak{L}^{\pi}_{\infty}$). Thus, i states, explicitly or implicitly, all Q-numbers and hence describes the structure in question. We can easily see that this is only possible if all Q-numbers except one are finite. For, consider a structure of which two Q-numbers are infinite and the others finite. We can again construct a sentence j which attributes to these $\kappa - 2$ finite Q-properties their finite Q-numbers. It follows from j in $\mathfrak{L}^{\pi}_{\infty}$ that at least one of the other two Q-properties is infinite; but it does not follow that both are infinite. The structure in question cannot be described by a sentence in $\mathfrak{L}^{\pi}_{\infty}$. However, we can of course describe this and any other structure in our metalanguage (by means of the word 'infinite' or the sign '$\boldsymbol{a}_0$') and make statements about it.

§ 35. Some Numbers Connected with the Systems $\mathfrak{L}^\pi$

The numbers of the $\mathfrak{Z}$ and of the $\mathfrak{Str}$ in any system $\mathfrak{L}_N^\pi$ are stated (T1) in terms of N, π, and κ (§ 31). A table (T2) gives the values of these and other numbers for some small systems $\mathfrak{L}_N^\pi$. For any $\mathfrak{Z}_i$ in $\mathfrak{L}_N^\pi$, the number of those $\mathfrak{Z}$ which are isomorphic to $\mathfrak{Z}_i$ is given as a function of the Q-numbers of $\mathfrak{Z}_i$ (T4); this number will be used in inductive logic.

We have earlier (in § 29) introduced some numbers connected with the systems $\mathfrak{L}$: β (the number of the atomic sentences), ζ (the $\mathfrak{Z}$), ρ (the $\mathfrak{R}$), τ (in $\mathfrak{L}_N$, the $\mathfrak{Str}$; in $\mathfrak{L}_\infty$, the classes of isomorphic $\mathfrak{Z}$). We found that $\zeta = 2^\beta$ and $\rho = 2^\zeta$ (T29-1). These numbers apply, of course, also to the systems $\mathfrak{L}^\pi$, since these are merely special cases of systems $\mathfrak{L}$. For the systems $\mathfrak{L}^\pi$, we have further introduced the numbers π (the $\mathfrak{pr}$) and κ (the Q-predicates), where $\kappa = 2^\pi$ (T31-1).

We shall now state some theorems concerning these numbers with respect to the systems $\mathfrak{L}^\pi$. Important for our system of inductive logic is only T1d, stating the number of the $\mathfrak{Str}$.

T35-1. The following holds for any system $\mathfrak{L}_N^\pi$.

a. $\beta = \pi N$.

b. $\zeta = \kappa^N$.

Proof. $\zeta = 2^\beta$ (T29-1a), $= 2^{\pi N}$ (a), $= (2^\pi)^N = \kappa^N$ (T31-1). We can also obtain the theorem directly with the help of T40-31c, because the Q-forms of the $\mathfrak{Z}$ are the individual distributions of the N individuals among the κ Q-properties.

c. $\rho = 2^\zeta = 2^{\kappa^N}$. (From T29-1b, (b).)

+d. $\tau = \binom{N+\kappa-1}{\kappa-1}$, i.e., $\frac{(N+\kappa-1)!}{N!(\kappa-1)!}$.

(For these mathematical notations see D40-1 and 2.)

Proof. From T40-33b, since the $\mathfrak{Str}$, as their Q-forms show, correspond to the statistical distributions for the N in with respect to the Q-division.

The subsequent *table* T2 gives the values of β, τ, ζ, and ρ for some small systems $\mathfrak{L}_N^\pi$ with $\pi = 1$ to 3 and $N = 1$ to 10 (based on T1; or on T1a and d, T29-1a and b). The exact values are not important for our purposes. The table is intended merely to give a general impression of the order of magnitude of the values and, in particular, to show that ζ and, even more, ρ increase at an enormous rate with increasing π and N. ρ is also the number of propositions expressible by sentences in $\mathfrak{L}_N^\pi$ (see remark following T29-2). This number is finite, but, as the table shows, it takes immense values even for these very poor language systems; we see, for instance, that to write down the number ρ for $\mathfrak{L}_{10}^3$ in the ordinary decimal notation would take more than three hundred million digits.

T35-2. *The numbers of atomic sentences* (β), *of* $\mathfrak{Str}$ (τ), *of* $\mathfrak{Z}$ (ζ), *and of* $\mathfrak{R}$ (ρ) *for some small systems* $\mathfrak{L}^{\pi}_{N}$.

a. $\mathfrak{L}^{1}_{N}$: $\pi = 1$, $\kappa = 2$.

N	β	τ	ζ	ρ
1	1	2	2	4
2	2	3	4	16
3	3	4	8	256
4	4	5	16	65 536
5	5	6	32	4 294 967 296
6	6	7	64	1.85×10^{19}
7	7	8	128	3.42×10^{38}
8	8	9	256	1.17×10^{77}
9	9	10	512	1.37×10^{154}
10	10	11	1 024	1.88×10^{308}

b. $\mathfrak{L}^{2}_{N}$: $\pi = 2$, $\kappa = 4$.

N	β	τ	ζ	ρ
1	2	4	4	16
2	4	10	16	65 536
3	6	20	64	1.85×10^{19}
4	8	35	256	1.17×10^{77}
5	10	56	1 024	1.88×10^{308}
6	12	84	4 096	$1.25\times10^{1\,233}$
7	14	120	16 384	$2.43\times10^{4\,932}$
8	16	165	65 536	$3.52\times10^{19\,729}$
9	18	220	262 144	$1.53\times10^{78\,918}$
10	20	286	1 048 576	$5.52\times10^{315\,672}$

c. $\mathfrak{L}^{3}_{N}$: $\pi = 3$, $\kappa = 8$.

N	β	τ	ζ	ρ
1	3	8	8	256
2	6	36	64	1.85×10^{19}
3	9	120	512	1.37×10^{154}
4	12	330	4 096	$1.25\times10^{1\,233}$
5	15	792	32 768	$5.92\times10^{9\,864}$
6	18	1 716	262 144	$1.53\times10^{78\,918}$
7	21	3 432	2 097 152	$3.05\times10^{631\,345}$
8	24	6 435	16 777 216	$6.5\times10^{5\,050\,763}$
9	27	11 440	134 217 728	c. $10^{1.04\times10^{7}}$
10	30	19 448	1 073 741 824	c. $10^{3.23\times10^{8}}$

T35-3. Let m Q-predicates in $\mathfrak{L}^{\pi}_{N}$ be given ($0 \leqq m < \kappa$). Let τ_m be the number of those $\mathfrak{Str}$ in which these m Q-predicates (but not necessarily only these) are empty. Then

$$\tau_m = \binom{N + \kappa - m - 1}{\kappa - m - 1}, \text{ i.e., } \frac{(N + \kappa - m - 1)!}{N!(\kappa - m - 1)!}$$

Proof. From T40-33a, in analogy to T1d, since the $\mathfrak{Str}$ described correspond to the statistically different kinds of distributions of the N individuals among the remaining $\kappa - m$ Q-properties.

T4 will be of importance for inductive logic. It states the number ζ_i of those $\mathfrak{Z}$ in $\mathfrak{L}_N^\pi$ which are isomorphic to a given $\mathfrak{Z}_i$, as a function of the Q-numbers. The subsequent analogue for $\mathfrak{L}_\infty^\pi$ (T7) is less important.

+**T35-4.** Let the Q-numbers for $\mathfrak{Z}_i$ in $\mathfrak{L}_N^\pi$ be $N_1, N_2, \ldots, N_\kappa$. Let $\mathfrak{Str}_j$ be the one $\mathfrak{Str}$ corresponding to $\mathfrak{Z}_i$ (D27-1a). (Hence, $\mathfrak{Str}_j$ is characterized by the given Q-numbers.) Let ζ_i be the number of those $\mathfrak{Z}$ which belong to $\mathfrak{Str}_j$; in other words, those which are isomorphic to $\mathfrak{Z}_i$. Then

$$\zeta_i = \frac{N!}{N_1!\,N_2!\ldots N_\kappa!}$$

(From T34-1, T34-3, T40-32b.)

T6 and T7 are the analogues for $\mathfrak{L}_\infty^\pi$ to T1d and T4, respectively. They will not be used in inductive logic (see remark preceding T29-4).

T35-6. In $\mathfrak{L}_\infty^\pi$, $\tau = \alpha_0$.

Proof. Every $\mathfrak{Str}$ corresponds to an assignment of one of the values α_0, 0, 1, 2, . . . to each of the κ Q-properties in such a way that the value α_0 is assigned at least once. Therefore, τ, the number of the $\mathfrak{Str}$, is a finite multiple of the number of possibilities for assigning one of the values α_0, 0, 1, 2, . . . to each of $\kappa - 1$ Q-properties. The number of the values is α_0; hence the number of the possibilities described is $\alpha_0^{\kappa-1}$ (T40-31b), $= \alpha_0$ (T40-26e). Therefore, $\tau = \alpha_0$ (T40-26b).

T35-7. Let the Q-numbers for $\mathfrak{Z}_i$ in $\mathfrak{L}_\infty^\pi$ be $u_1, u_2, \ldots, u_\kappa$. (Each of these numbers is finite or α_0; at least one is α_0.) Let ζ_i be the number of those $\mathfrak{Z}$ which are isomorphic to $\mathfrak{Z}_i$.

a. If one Q-number is α_0 and all others are 0, then $\zeta_i = 1$.

b. If exactly one Q-number is α_0 and at least one other Q-number is positive, then $\zeta_i = \alpha_0$.

c. If more than one Q-number is α_0, then $\zeta_i = \alpha_1$.

Proof for (a), (b), (c). The $\mathfrak{Z}$ which are isomorphic to $\mathfrak{Z}_i$ represent those individual distributions of the α_0 individuals among the κ Q-properties in which the Q-properties have the given cardinal numbers $u_1, \ldots, u_\kappa$. Let n_1 of these κ Q-numbers be 0, n_2 of them finite and positive, and n_3 of them α_0 ($n_1 + n_2 + n_3 = \kappa$; $1 \leqq n_3 \leqq \kappa$; hence, $0 \leqq n_1 + n_2 \leqq \kappa - 1$). Suppose u_m is finite and positive; then the number of possibilities for selecting u_m from the α_0 individuals for Q_m is α_0 (T40-32f). After these u_m individuals have been removed, there remain still $\alpha_0 - u_m = \alpha_0$ individuals (T40-26a). Therefore, the number of possibilities for each of the n_2 finite and positive Q-numbers is the same as for u_m, hence α_0. Thus, the number of possibilities for these n_2

Q-properties together is $\alpha_0^{n_2}$. This is also the number of possibilities for the $n_2 + n_1$ finite Q-properties together, because for the n_1 empty Q-properties there is obviously only one possibility.

1. For (a) and (b). Here, $n_3 = 1$. For any distribution of individuals among the $\kappa - 1$ finite Q-properties, there is just one possibility for the infinite Q-property; it must contain all remaining individuals. Thus, the number of distributions is here the same as that for the $n_2 + n_1$ finite Q-properties, which we found to be $\alpha_0^{n_2}$. For (a), $n_2 = 0$; hence, $\zeta_i = \alpha_0^0 = 1$ (T40-26d). For (b), $n_2 > 0$; hence $\zeta_i = \alpha_0^{n_2} = \alpha_0$ (T40-26e).

2. For (c). Here $n_3 > 1$. We take the n_3 infinite Q-properties in any order. For the first of them, say, Q_p, the number of possibilities is the number of individual distributions of α_0 individuals among the two properties Q_p and $\sim Q_p$ in such a way that each of them has α_0 individuals, hence 2^{α_0} (T40-32g), $= \alpha_1$ (D40-8b). The same holds for each of the other infinite Q-properties except the last. Hence, the number of possibilities for $n_3 - 1$ of the n_3 infinite Q-properties is $\alpha_1^{n_3 - 1} = \alpha_1$ (T40-26e). The number of possibilities for the finite Q-properties is, as we found earlier, either 1 or α_0. If the distribution among all Q-properties except the last infinite Q-property is given, then there is only one possibility for the last infinite Q-property; it must contain all remaining individuals. Therefore, the number ζ_i in this case (c) is either $1\alpha_1$ or $\alpha_0\alpha_1$, hence α_1 (T40-26c).

§ 37. Simple Laws

A sentence consisting of a universal quantifier and a matrix as its scope which does not contain a quantifier is called a simple law (D1); if, moreover, neither '=' nor any in occurs in it, the sentence is called an unrestricted simple law (D2a). Let l be an unrestricted simple law in $\mathfrak{L}^\pi$. Then l asserts that a certain molecular property, say, M_1, is empty. If M_1 is a Q-property, l is called an unrestricted Q-law (D4b). Let the width (§ 32) of M_1 be $w > 0$; then M_1 is L-equivalent to a disjunction of w Q-properties. Therefore, l says in this case that these w Q-properties are empty, and hence can be transformed into a conjunction of w unrestricted Q-laws (T2b). l is then said to have the *strength* w (D6a).

We use the term 'law' here in the sense of 'natural law' or 'physical law', hence for universal sentences and chiefly for factual ones. (The so-called laws of logic are here rather called principles or theorems of logic.) In discussions of inductive logic, laws have always had a prominent place, and some authors have even gone so far as to define induction as a kind of non-deductive inference leading to laws. We conceive inductive logic in a much wider sense so that the hypothesis obtained or judged in induction may have any form whatever. We regard the case of a universal hypothesis as merely a special kind of induction, called universal induction. However, it is indeed a case of great importance. In preparation for the later treatment of laws in inductive logic, we shall here explain some of their properties in deductive logic (§§ 37 and 38).

Let l be a universal sentence $(i_k)(\mathfrak{M}_i)$. We shall chiefly deal with the simplest case where the scope $\mathfrak{M}_i$ is nongeneral, that is, does not contain a quantifier. In this case, we shall call l a *simple law* (D1).

Let l be a simple law. We shall define two special kinds; they are mutually exclusive but do not exhaust all possibilities. 1. If the scope $\mathfrak{M}_i$ contains neither '=' nor any $\mathfrak{in}$, then l speaks in a purely general way about the individuals of the system in question without referring to any particular individual. In this case, we shall call l an *unrestricted simple law* (D2a). [The exclusion of '=' in addition to that of the $\mathfrak{in}$ is inessential; for, if no $\mathfrak{in}$ occurs, $\mathfrak{i}_k$ is the only individual sign occurring; hence, '=' can occur only in the context $\mathfrak{i}_k = \mathfrak{i}_k$, which is L-interchangeable with 't' (T24-2a, T23-4c).] 2. Sometimes we wish to attribute a certain property M, not to all individuals without restriction, but to all individuals with the exclusion of some specified individuals, leaving it open whether or not these specified individuals have the property M. We can do this by a formulation like the following: '$(x)(x \neq a \,.\, x \neq b \supset Mx)$', where a and b are the individuals excluded; hence by '$(x)(x = a \vee x = b \vee Mx)$'. Simple laws of this kind will be called *restricted simple laws* (D2b).

D37-1. l is a ***simple law*** in a system $\mathfrak{L} =_{Df}$ l is a sentence of the form $(\mathfrak{i}_k)(\mathfrak{M}_i)$, where $\mathfrak{M}_i$ is nongeneral.

D37-2. Let l be a simple law $(\mathfrak{i}_k)(\mathfrak{M}_i)$ in $\mathfrak{L}$.

a. l is an *unrestricted simple law* $=_{Df}$ $\mathfrak{M}_i$ contains neither '=' nor any $\mathfrak{in}$.

b. l is a *restricted simple law* $=_{Df}$ $\mathfrak{M}_i$ is $\mathfrak{M}_j \vee \mathfrak{M}_k$, where $\mathfrak{M}_j$ is a disjunction of n components of the form $\mathfrak{i}_k = \mathfrak{in}$ with n distinct $\mathfrak{in}$ ($n \geqq 1$; in $\mathfrak{L}_N$, $n < N$) and $\mathfrak{M}_k$ contains neither '=' nor any $\mathfrak{in}$.

The discussion in this and the next section concerns simple laws in the systems $\mathfrak{L}^\pi$. We shall see that here the use of the Q-predicates will make the analysis of the deductive properties of laws very simple and effective; the same method will later be of great help in inductive logic.

Let l be an unrestricted simple law in $\mathfrak{L}^\pi$, say, $(\mathfrak{i}_k)(\mathfrak{M}_i)$, where $\mathfrak{i}_k$ is 'x'. Let 'M_1' be defined as a molecular predicate in such a way that 'M_1x' is L-equivalent to $\sim\mathfrak{M}_i$, and hence '$\sim M_1x$' is L-equivalent to $\mathfrak{M}_i$. Then l can be transformed into '$(x)(\sim M_1x)$' or '$\sim(\exists x)(M_1x)$'. This shows that every unrestricted simple law says that a certain molecular property, here M_1, is empty.

Example. Suppose that 'Swan' and 'White' are defined in some way or other as molecular predicates in $\mathfrak{L}^\pi$. Then 'all swans are white' can be formulated as an unrestricted simple law in $\mathfrak{L}^\pi$: '(x) (Swan $x \supset$ White x)', that is, '(x) ($\sim$Swan $x \vee$ White x)'. Now we define 'M_1' in the way described, transforming the negation of the scope in an obvious way: 'M_1x' for 'Swan $x \,.\, \sim$White x'. Thus, 'M_1' designates the property Non-White-Swan. Hence, the law says that this property is empty, in other words, that there are no non-white swans.

Let the logical width (D32-1a) of 'M_1' be w. Then 'M_1' is L-empty if and only if $w = 0$ (T32-2a). Otherwise, $w \geqq 1$, and 'M_1' is L-equivalent to a disjunction of w Q-predicates, say, 'Q_{n_1}', . . . , 'Q_{nw}'. Then, l is L-equivalent to '$(x)[\sim(Q_{n_1} \vee \ldots \vee Q_{nw})x]$', hence to '$(x)[\sim(Q_{n_1}x \vee \ldots \vee Q_{nw}x)]$', hence to '$(x)[\sim Q_{n_1}x \,.\, \ldots \,.\, \sim Q_{nw}x]$' (T21-5f(2)), hence to '$(x)(\sim Q_{n_1}x) \,.\, \ldots \,.\, (x)(\sim Q_{nw}x)$' (T22-9k). Thus we have here a conjunction of w components, each of which is a law whose scope is the negation of a Q-matrix. We shall call a law that has this form, or is L-equivalent to a sentence of this form, an unrestricted *Q-law* (D4b). It is a law in which the property declared empty is a Q-property. Thus we have obtained the result that, if l is not L-false and hence 'M_1' has a width $w \geqq 1$, then there is a unique set of w Q-predicates such that l can be transformed into a conjunction of w unrestricted Q-laws with these Q-predicates. Obviously, the greater the number w, the more is asserted by the law l. Therefore, we shall call w the (logical) *strength* of l (D6a). The relative width of 'M_1' is w/κ (D32-1b). This we shall call the *relative* (logical) *strength* of the law l (D6b). Each of the w Q-predicates occurring in the above transformation of l is declared empty by one of the Q-laws occurring as conjunctive components. Therefore we shall say that these w Q-predicates, and the Q-properties designated by them, are *excluded by the law* l (D5). Thus we lay down the following definitions.

+**D37-4.** For $\mathfrak{L}^\pi$.

a. l is a ***Q-law*** $=_{\text{Df}}$ l is a simple law, and the subdisjunction of the scope which contains those disjunctive components which are free of '$=$' is L-equivalent to the negation of a Q-matrix.

b. l is an *unrestricted Q-law* $=_{\text{Df}}$ l is an unrestricted simple law and a Q-law.

c. l is a *restricted Q-law* $=_{\text{Df}}$ l is a restricted simple law and a Q-law.

D37-5. Let l be a simple law in $\mathfrak{L}^\pi$. The Q-predicate $\mathfrak{A}_i$ (and the Q-property designated by it) is *excluded by* l $=_{\text{Df}}$ l L-implies a Q-law containing $\mathfrak{A}_i$.

D37-6. Let l be a simple law in $\mathfrak{L}^\pi$.

+**a.** The (logical) *strength* of l $=_{\text{Df}}$ the number of Q-predicates excluded by l.

b. The *relative* (logical) *strength* of l $=_{\text{Df}}$ w/κ, where w is the strength of l.

The following theorems hold on the basis of the definitions of this section and the theorems on logical width (§ 32), according to our previous explanations.

T37-1. Let l be a simple law in $\mathfrak{L}^\pi$ with the strength w and hence the relative strength $q = w/\kappa$.

a. l is L-true if and only if $w = 0$ and hence $q = 0$.
b. l is L-false if and only if $w = \kappa$ and hence $q = 1$.
c. l is factual if and only if $0 < w < \kappa$ and hence $0 < q < 1$. (From (a), (b).)

T37-2. Let l be a simple law in $\mathfrak{L}^\pi$ with the strength w.
a. l is a Q-law if and only if $w = 1$.
+b. If $w > 1$, then l is L-equivalent to a conjunction of w Q-laws with w distinct Q-predicates.

T37-3. Let 'M_1' be a molecular predicate with the width w.
a. '$(x)(\sim M_1 x)$' is an unrestricted simple law with the strength w.
b. '$(x)(\ldots \vee \sim M_1 x)$', where a disjunction of n =-matrices with 'x' and n distinct in ($n \geqq 1$) stands at the place of '. . .', is a restricted simple law with the strength w. (From D32-1a, D4, D5, D6.)

T37-4. Let l and l' be simple laws in $\mathfrak{L}^\pi$ with the strengths w and w', respectively.
a. If $\vdash l \equiv l'$ (but not only in this case), $w = w'$. (From T1, T2.)
b. If $\vdash l \supset l'$ (but not only in this case), $w \geqq w'$. (From T1, T2.)
c. If l and l' are unrestricted and $\vdash l \supset l'$ but not $\vdash l \equiv l'$, then $w > w'$. (From T1, T2.)
d. If l and l' are unrestricted and l is a Q-law and $\vdash l \supset l'$, then l' is either L-equivalent to l or L-true. (From T2a, (c), T1a.)

T4d says that, if l is an unrestricted Q-law, then there is no factual unrestricted simple law weaker than l.

§ 38. Simple Laws of Conditional Form

A law l of the form '$(x)(Mx \supset M'x)$' gives rise to a division of all individuals into four kinds (here represented by a diagram). The first of these kinds is designated by '$M \centerdot \sim M'$', abbreviated by 'M_1'; this is the property declared empty by l. We distinguish between those logical properties of l which are invariant with respect to L-equivalent transformations and those which are not.

Most laws in science have conditional form, for example: 'for every x (thing or space-time point or the like), if x fulfils such and such conditions, then such and such is the case with x'. Laws of this kind may be formulated as universal conditional sentences.

Let l be an unrestricted simple law of this form in $\mathfrak{L}^\pi$, say, $(\mathfrak{i}_k)(\mathfrak{M}_i \supset \mathfrak{M}_j)$. We can abbreviate $\mathfrak{M}_i$ by a full matrix of a molecular predicate, say, of 'M'; likewise $\mathfrak{M}_j$, with 'M''. Thus, l becomes '$(x)(Mx \supset M'x)$'. (For instance, if 'M' means Swan and 'M'' White, we have the example of § 37.) Obviously, l can be transformed into the following L-equivalent forms: '$(x)(\sim Mx \vee M'x)$', '$(x)[\sim(M \,.\, \sim M')x]$', and, if we define '$M_1$' as abbreviation for '$M \,.\, \sim M'$', into '$(x)(\sim M_1 x)$'. Thus we see, as in our discussion in the preceding section, that l says that the property M_1, that is, the property of being M but not M' (Non-White Swan) is empty. And here again, if the width of 'M_1' is $w > 0$, then 'M_1' is L-equivalent to a disjunction of w Q-predicates; and these w Q-predicates and no others are excluded by l; hence l has the strength w.

In a law of the form described, the two predicates 'M' and 'M'' are usually factual and, moreover, logically independent of each other (this means that it is not the case that either of them or its negation L-implies the other one or its negation). In this case, the two predicates give rise to a division of all individuals into four kinds. Let us designate these kinds by four molecular predicates, defined in the following way ('M_1' is the same as above):

'M_1' for '$M \,.\, \sim M'$',
'M_2' for '$M \,.\, M'$',
'M_3' for '$\sim M \,.\, M'$',
'M_4' for '$\sim M \,.\, \sim M'$'.

Under the assumptions made concerning 'M' and 'M'', we see that the four predicates 'M_p' ($p = 1$ to 4) are L-disjunct, that any two of them are L-exclusive, that each of them is factual, and hence that they form a division (in analogy to T31-2b, a, c, d).

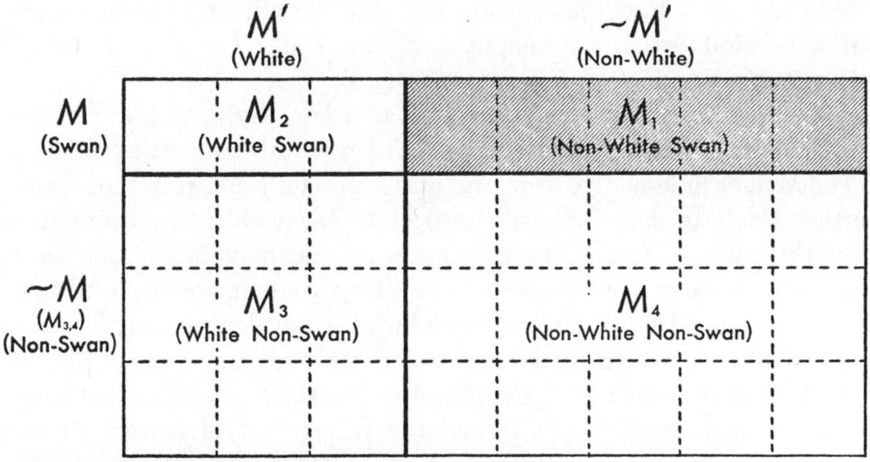

This division is represented by the accompanying *diagram;* references to the previous example are added. The whole rectangle represents the domain of individuals of the system $\mathfrak{L}^\pi$ in question. It is divided into four parts by the four properties M_1, M_2, M_3, and M_4. The thirty-two small squares separated by dotted lines represent the Q-properties (we have arbitrarily chosen $\kappa = 32$, and have divided this number into four parts in an arbitrary way). Let the widths of 'M_1', 'M_2', 'M_3', 'M_4' be w_1, w_2, w_3, w_4, respectively (in the diagram: 5, 3, 9, 15); hence, $w_1 + w_2 + w_3 + w_4 = \kappa$. The shaded area represents the property M_1 which is declared empty by the law l; hence the w_1 (five) small squares in this area correspond to the w_1 (five) Q-properties excluded by l. l can be transformed into a conjunction of w_1 Q-laws; each of them declares one of the w_1 small shaded squares to be empty. We have called w_1 the strength of l; this seems natural, for, the greater the number of Q-laws whose joint assertion is l, the more is said by l.

For many problems concerning the law l, the distinction between M_3 and M_4 is of little or no interest. (For instance, when we intend to test the law by the observation of individuals, then it is irrelevant whether a non-swan found is white or non-white.) Therefore, in our later discussion in inductive logic of laws of a form like l, we shall sometimes use a simplified division of only three kinds designated by 'M_1', 'M_2', and '$M_{3,4}$', where the latter predicate is defined by '$M_3 \vee M_4$', hence by '$\sim M$'; its width is $w_{3,4} = w_3 + w_4$.

At the beginning of this section we have mentioned several L-equivalent forms of the law l in terms of the predicates 'M' and 'M''. Of L-equivalent forms which use instead some of the four predicates of the division, '$(x)(\sim M_1 x)$' has already been mentioned; other simple forms of this kind are, for example, '$(x)(M_2 x \vee M_3 x \vee M_4 x)$', '$(x)(M_1 x \vee M_2 x \supset M_2 x)$', and '$(x)(M_1 x \vee M_3 x \supset M_3 x)$'.

When we carry out a logical analysis of a law, say, l, and, as a result, ascribe to it certain logical (that is, L-semantical) properties either in deductive or in inductive logic, we must distinguish between those properties which are invariant with respect to L-equivalent transformation and those which are not. The invariant properties may, in a certain sense, be called properties of the content of l (if by 'content' we mean, without giving an exact definition, something which L-equivalent sentences have in common; for a possibility of explication see § 73) or properties of the proposition expressed by l. On the other hand, the noninvariant properties of l are properties of the formulation rather than the content. Among the invariant properties of l are the L-concepts (for example, the properties of being factual, or L-true, or L-false, or L-implying such and such other sentences, or being an L-implicate of such and such other sentences, and the like); further, in inductive logic, the properties connected with the degree of confirmation of l or of a certain instance of l. Now let us examine the properties of l discussed earlier in this section. It is an invariant property of l that just the property M_1, which is the same as the property of being M but not M', is declared to be empty; likewise, that certain Q-predicates are excluded, that their number is w_1 (in the diagram: five), and hence that l has the strength w_1 (five). On the other hand, it belongs to the noninvariant properties of l dependent upon the formulation that the property referred to in the antecedent of the scope is M and that referred to in the consequent is M'; that these properties have certain widths (in the diagram: eight and twelve); that their conjunction is the property M_2 with the width w_2 (in the diagram: three), and the like. However, M and M' determine also an invariant property of l, viz., that the conjunction of the first and the negation of the second is the property M_1. To sum it up, all invariances of l are based on this one point, the emptiness of M_1.

In our later discussions of inductive logic, we shall find it important to distinguish two kinds of problems with respect to the situation just explained: (i) problems referring to a given law l; (ii) problems referring to a pair of properties M, M'. If the pair of properties is given, the corresponding law '$(x)(Mx \supset M'x)$' is uniquely determined. On the other hand, if the content of the law is given, the pair of properties is not uniquely determined; there are many different pairs of properties yielding the same content of the law. Thus, for example, the properties non-M', non-M lead to the formulation '$(x)(\sim M'x \supset \sim Mx)$', which is L-equivalent to the one above (by transposition, T21-5h(1)).

Let us calculate the *number p of different pairs of properties* which yield laws L-equivalent to a given factual unrestricted simple law j in $\mathfrak{L}^\pi$ with the strength w. (The result will not be used later but is merely intended to give a more precise picture of the situation.) We are referring to pairs of properties, not to pairs of matrices; the number of the latter pairs, in other words, of universal conditional sentences L-equivalent to j, is obviously infinite. Suppose the sentences $(i_k)(\mathfrak{M}_i \supset \mathfrak{M}_j)$ and $(i_k)(\mathfrak{M}'_i \supset \mathfrak{M}'_j)$ are both L-equivalent to j. If here $\mathfrak{M}_i$ is L-equivalent to $\mathfrak{M}'_i$ (D25-1g), then we say that the two matrices express the same property; if, in addition, $\mathfrak{M}_j$ is L-equivalent to $\mathfrak{M}'_j$, we say that the two sentences, though different, correspond to the same pair of properties, and hence we count them only as one for the number of pairs of properties.

j is supposed to be factual. Therefore, $0 < w < \kappa$ (T37-1c). Let $\mathfrak{K}_1$ be the class of those w Q-predicates which are excluded by j, and let 'M_1' be defined by the disjunction of these Q-predicates. Then 'M_1' has the width w and is factual. Now any pair of properties M, M' yields a law L-equivalent to j if and only if '$M \,.\sim M'$' is L-equivalent to 'M_1'. What we are searching for is the number of pairs of this kind. We find it as follows. We divide the class of all those Q-predicates which are not excluded by j—their number is $\kappa - w \geqq 1$—in an arbitrary way into three mutually exclusive subclasses $\mathfrak{K}_2$, $\mathfrak{K}_3$, and $\mathfrak{K}_4$, each of which may be empty. We define 'M' by the disjunction of the Q-predicates of $\mathfrak{K}_1 \cup \mathfrak{K}_2$, and '$M''$' by the disjunction of those of $\mathfrak{K}_2 \cup \mathfrak{K}_3$ (if this class is empty, we define 'M''' by any L-empty predicate expression, e.g., '$P \,.\, {\sim}P$'). Then '$M \,.\, {\sim}M''$' is L-equivalent to 'M_1', and hence the pair of the properties M, M' is one of those we are looking for. And, inversely, if any pair of properties M, M' is such that '$M \,.\, {\sim}M''$' is L-equivalent to 'M_1', then this pair can be obtained in the way described from one of the tripartitions of the $\kappa - w$ Q-predicates. It is easily seen that two pairs of properties are different if and only if they are based on two different tripartitions (regarded as ordered triples of subclasses). Therefore, the number p of pairs of properties searched for is the same as the number of the tripartitions, i.e., the individual distributions of $\kappa - w$ elements among three classes; hence $p = 3^{\kappa - w}$ (T40-31a). This number includes two extreme cases, viz., the pair in which M is L-universal (in this case M' is the negation of M_1) and the pair in which M' is L-empty (in this case M is the same as M_1). [If we wish to count only those pairs in which both properties are factual (represented by universal conditional sentences in which both the antecedent and the consequent matrices are factual), the number is $3^{\kappa - w} - 2$.] Thus we see that p is the greater, the smaller the strength w of the law j.

Examples. In the example of the above diagram we had $\kappa = 32$, $w_1 = 5$. Hence $p = 3^{27} \cong 7.6193 \times 10^{12}$. Suppose that in the given law j both components of the conditional are basic matrices; for instance, let j be '$(x)(P_1x \supset P_2x)$'. Then M_1 is a conjunction of two basic properties (in the example, 'M_1' is L-equivalent to '$P_1 \,.\, {\sim}P_2$'), and hence $w = 2^{\pi - 2}$ (T32-4a(2)) $= \kappa/4$. Hence, $\kappa - w = 3\kappa/4$, and $p = 3^{3\kappa/4}$. (For instance, in $\mathfrak{L}^4$ we have $\kappa = 16$; hence, $w = 4$ and $p = 3^{12} = 531{,}441$.) Here a few examples of pairs of properties for the sentence j mentioned above, represented by pairs of molecular predicate expressions: 'P_1', 'P_2'; '${\sim}P_2$', '${\sim}P_1$'; '$P_1 \vee P_2$', 'P_2'; '$P_1 \vee P_2$', '$P_2 \vee {\sim}P_1$'; 'P_1', '$P_2 \vee {\sim}P_1$'; 'P_1', '$P_2 \vee ({\sim}P_1 \,.\, {\sim}P_3)$'; '$P_3 \vee (P_1 \,.\, {\sim}P_2)$', '$P_2 \vee {\sim}P_1$'.

§ 40. Some Mathematical Definitions and Theorems

Some mathematical definitions and theorems are listed for later reference. The notations defined are: (*A*) '$n!$' (D1), '$\binom{m}{n}$' (D2), '$\left[\begin{smallmatrix} m \\ n \end{smallmatrix}\right]$' (D3, analogous to the preceding), '$\phi(u)$' (the normal function, D4a), '$\Phi(u)$' (the probability integral, D4b); (*B*) '$\lim f(n)$' (D6a); (*C*) 'α_0', 'α_1', etc., for infinite cardinal numbers (D8). *D.* Some theorems of combinatorics (T29–T33) state the number of permutations, of possible distributions, and the like.

In this section we list some mathematical definitions and theorems for the convenience of the reader. They are frequently used throughout this book, both in deductive logic, in the earlier sections of this chapter, and later in inductive logic. Almost all notations here defined are customary; the exceptions are D3 and D8. Almost all the theorems are well known. Therefore, we omit proofs in most cases.

'k', 'm', 'n', and 'p' are used as variables for natural numbers (0, 1, 2, etc.); 'q' and 'r' (and sometimes 'u') as variables for real numbers.

A. *Some Mathematical Functions*

+**D40-1.** Recursive definition of the ***factorial*** $n!$.

a. $0! =_{Df} 1$.

b. $(n + 1)! =_{Df} n!(n + 1)$.

c. If n is a negative integer, $n! = \infty$. (Seldom used.)

T40-1. If $n \geqq 1$, $n! = \prod_{p=1}^{n}(p)$ (i.e., $1 \times 2 \times 3 \times \ldots \times n$).

T40-2. *Table for the Factorial*

n	$n!$	log ($n!$)	n	$n!$	log ($n!$)
1	1	0	11	3.9917×10^{7}	7.60116
2	2	0.30103	12	4.7900×10^{8}	8.68034
3	6	0.77815	13	6.2270×10^{9}	9.79428
4	24	1.38021	14	8.7178×10^{10}	10.94041
5	120	2.07918	15	1.3077×10^{12}	12.11650
6	720	2.85733	16	2.0923×10^{13}	13.32062
7	5 040	3.70243	17	3.5569×10^{14}	14.55107
8	40 320	4.60552	18	6.4024×10^{15}	15.80634
9	362 880	5.55976	19	1.2165×10^{17}	17.08509
10	3 628 800	6.55976	20	2.4329×10^{18}	18.38612

(Here and in the following, 'log' is used for common logarithms, i.e., on the base 10.)

This table and the tables for other functions in this section are not intended for serious statistical work in science. For this purpose more extensive tables for these functions—and, moreover, for other functions not mentioned here—are given in textbooks on statistical methods and on the applications of the calculus of probabilities. Our tables are merely intended for the convenience of those readers who wish to calculate numerical examples in inductive logic. It is of course advisable in any mathematical discipline to study concrete examples in order to come to a better understanding of the abstract theorems. In inductive logic there is an important additional reason. We shall discuss various definitions for concepts of degree of confirmation or requirements for such definitions. We shall see that it is often hardly possible to judge the plausibility of definitions or requirements, that is, their adequacy for an explication of probability$_1$, by merely inspecting the definitions themselves. The judgment is rather to be based on an investigation of the consequences to which the definitions or requirements lead. Thus, the plausibility of a definition is judged by the plausibility of the theorems derived from it; and this in turn can often be judged in the easiest way by studying concrete numerical examples. We shall often give such examples; and some readers will wish to construct and analyze examples of their own.

The following two theorems give *approximations* for the factorial; they are convenient and frequently used. These approximations and those given in later theorems hold in the sense that the relative numerical error is the smaller the more the restricting condition is fulfilled (in T4, the larger n is; in T5a and b, the larger m is in relation to n^2, i.e., the larger m/n^2 is), in such a way that the limit of the relative error is 0. That one approximation is rougher than another means that the error is larger; in other words, the qualifying condition must be fulfilled to a higher degree in order to reduce the relative error to the same amount. ('$\cong$' is used as a sign of approximative equality.)

T40-4. ***Stirling's Theorem.*** For sufficiently large n, the following approximations hold.

a. $n! \cong \sqrt{2\pi n}\, n^n\, e^{-n}\, (1 + 1/12n)$.
('π' has here its usual mathematical meaning, which has, of course, nothing to do with our 'π' in § 31. $\pi \cong 3.14159$; $\sqrt{2\pi} \cong 2.5066$; $e \cong 2.71828$.)

b. (Rougher approximation.)
$n! \cong \sqrt{2\pi n}\, n^n\, e^{-n}$.
Even this approximation is already rather good for small n.

c. $\log (n!) \cong \log \sqrt{2\pi} + (n + 1/2) \log n - n \log e$. (From (b).)
($\log \sqrt{2\pi} \cong 0.39909$; $\log e \cong 0.43429$.)

T40-5. The following approximations hold if m is sufficiently large in relation to n^2.

a. $(m + n)! \cong m!\, m^n(1 + \frac{n(n+1)}{2m})$. (From T4.)

b. (Rougher approximation.)
$(m + n)! \cong m!\, m^n$. (From (a).)

+D40-2. The ***binomial coefficient*** $\binom{m}{n}$.
Let $n \geqq 0$.

a. For $m \geqq n$, $\binom{m}{n} =_{Df} \frac{m!}{n!(m-n)!}$.

b. (Seldom used.) For $m < n$, $\binom{m}{n} = 0$.

(This function is called binomial coefficient, because the coefficients in the binomial theorem T10a have this form. Other customary notations for it: '${}^mC_n$', 'C_n^m', '${}_mC_n$'.)

T40-7. ***Table for the Binomial Coefficient*** $\binom{m}{n}$

m	$\binom{m}{0}$	$\binom{m}{1}$	$\binom{m}{2}$	$\binom{m}{3}$	$\binom{m}{4}$	$\binom{m}{5}$	$\binom{m}{6}$	$\binom{m}{7}$	$\binom{m}{8}$	$\binom{m}{9}$	$\binom{m}{10}$
0	1										
1	1	1									
2	1	2	1								
3	1	3	3	1							
4	1	4	6	4	1						
5	1	5	10	10	5	1					
6	1	6	15	20	15	6	1				
7	1	7	21	35	35	21	7	1			
8	1	8	28	56	70	56	28	8	1		
9	1	9	36	84	126	126	84	36	9	1	
10	1	10	45	120	210	252	210	120	45	10	1
11	1	11	55	165	330	462	462	330	165	55	11
12	1	12	66	220	495	792	924	792	495	220	66
13	1	13	78	286	715	1 287	1 716	1 716	1 287	715	286
14	1	14	91	364	1 001	2 002	3 003	3 432	3 003	2 002	1 001
15	1	15	105	455	1 365	3 003	5 005	6 435	6 435	5 005	3 003
16	1	16	120	560	1 820	4 368	8 008	11 440	12 870	11 440	8 008
17	1	17	136	680	2 380	6 188	12 376	19 448	24 310	24 310	19 448
18	1	18	153	816	3 060	8 568	18 564	31 824	43 758	48 620	43 758
19	1	19	171	969	3 876	11 628	27 132	50 388	75 582	92 378	92 378
20	1	20	190	1 140	4 845	15 504	38 760	77 520	125 970	167 960	184 756

The value of $\binom{m}{n}$ for $10 < m \leqq 20$, $n > 10$, is found in the table with the help of T8d. For example, $\binom{18}{15} = \binom{18}{3} = 816$.

T40-8.

a. $\binom{m}{0} = 1$.

b. $\binom{m}{m} = 1$.

c. $\binom{m}{1} = m$.

d. $\binom{m}{n} = \binom{m}{m-n}$.

e. $n\binom{m}{n} = m\binom{m-1}{n-1}$.

f. $\binom{m-1}{n} + \binom{m-1}{n-1} = \binom{m}{n}$.

T40-9.

a. $\sum_{n=0}^{m} \binom{m}{n} = 2^m$.

b. $\sum_{n=0}^{k} \binom{n+m}{m} = \binom{k+m+1}{m+1}$.

c. $\sum_{n=0}^{m} \left[\binom{k}{n}\binom{k'}{m-n}\right] = \binom{k+k'}{m}$; (if $k < m$, it is sufficient to let the sum run from $n = 0$ to k, because of D2b).

d. $\sum_{n} \left[\binom{k}{n}\binom{k'}{n}\right] = \binom{k+k'}{k'}$; the sum runs from $n = 0$ to k or k'; it is sufficient to take the smaller of these two.

T40-10. Let r_1 and r_2 be any real numbers, and n a positive integer.

a. The ***Binomial Theorem*** (not to be confused with the Binomial Law, T95-1b, which is a theorem on probability based on the Binomial Theorem).

$$(r_1 + r_2)^n = \sum_{p=0}^{n}\left[\binom{n}{p} r_1^p r_2^{n-p}\right].$$

The function defined in D3 will be used very frequently in inductive logic. We choose for it a notation similar to that of the binomial coefficient, because we shall often state two analogous theorems, one (concerning an individual distribution) using this function while the other (concerning the corresponding statistical distribution) uses the binomial coefficient with the same arguments (see remark at the end of § 92). (Other notations: '${}_mP_n$', 'P_n^m'.)

+**D40-3.** For $n \geqq 0$, $m \geqq n$,

$$\begin{bmatrix} m \\ n \end{bmatrix} =_{\text{Df}} \frac{m!}{(m-n)!}.$$

T40-11. *Table for* $\begin{bmatrix} m \\ n \end{bmatrix}$

m	$\left[{m \atop 0}\right]$	$\left[{m \atop 1}\right]$	$\left[{m \atop 2}\right]$	$\left[{m \atop 3}\right]$	$\left[{m \atop 4}\right]$	$\left[{m \atop 5}\right]$	$\left[{m \atop 6}\right]$	$\left[{m \atop 7}\right]$	$\left[{m \atop 8}\right]$	$\left[{m \atop 9}\right]$	$\left[{m \atop 10}\right]$
0	1										
1	1	1									
2	1	2	2								
3	1	3	6	6							
4	1	4	12	24	24						
5	1	5	20	60	120	120					
6	1	6	30	120	360	720	720				
7	1	7	42	210	840	2 520	5 040	5 040			
8	1	8	56	336	1 680	6 720	20 160	40 320	40 320		
9	1	9	72	504	3 024	15 120	60 480	181 440	362 880	362 880	
10	1	10	90	720	5 040	30 240	151 200	604 800	1 814 400	3 628 800	3 628 800

T40-12. $\left[{m \atop n}\right] = m(m-1)(m-2)\ldots(m-n+1)$; this is a product of n descending factors, beginning with m.

T40-13.

a. $\left[{m \atop 0}\right] = 1$.

b. $\left[{m \atop 1}\right] = m$.

c. $\left[{m \atop m}\right] = m!$.

d. $\left[{m \atop m-1}\right] = m!$.

e. $\left[{m \atop n}\right] = \binom{m}{n} n!$.

T40-14. For $m \geqq n$, $\frac{m!}{n!} = \left[{m \atop m-n}\right]$.

T40-15. For $m_2 \geqq m_1$, $\dfrac{\left[{m_1 \atop n}\right]}{\left[{m_2 \atop n}\right]} = \dfrac{\left[{m_2 - n \atop m_2 - m_1}\right]}{\left[{m_2 \atop m_2 - m_1}\right]}$.

T15 shows a possible transformation for a quotient of two [ ]-expressions with the same lower argument. Quotients of this kind will often occur. The transformation is sometimes useful if $m_2 - m_1 < n$.

T17 and T18 give *approximations*, based on T5.

T40-17. If m is sufficiently large in relation to n^2, the following approximations hold.

a. (1) $\left[{m \atop n}\right] \cong (m-n)^n\left(1 + \frac{n(n+1)}{2m}\right)$.
   (2) (Rougher approximation) $\left[{m \atop n}\right] \cong (m-n)^n$.
   (3) (Still rougher) $\left[{m \atop n}\right] \cong m^n$.

b. (1) $\left[{m+n \atop n}\right] \cong m^n\left(1 + \frac{n(n+1)}{2m}\right)$.
   (2) (Rougher approximation) $\left[{m+n \atop n}\right] \cong m^n$.

T40-18. If m is sufficiently large in relation to n_1 and to n_2^2, the following approximations hold.

a. $\left[{m+n_1 \atop n_2}\right] \cong \left[{m \atop n_2}\right]$.

b. (Rougher approximation) $\left[{m+n_1 \atop n_2}\right] \cong m^{n_2}$.

D40-4.

a. The ***Normal Function:***

$$\phi(u) =_{\text{Df}} \frac{1}{\sqrt{2\pi}} \mathrm{e}^{-u^2/2}$$

('π' and 'e' have here their usual mathematical meanings; see remark on T40-4a.)

b. The ***Probability Integral:***

$$\Phi(u) =_{\text{Df}} \int_{-\infty}^{u} \phi(r)dr\ .$$

$\Phi(u)$ is the probability integral in the form of a cumulative distribution function. Sometimes the value of the above integral over ϕ but from $-u$ to u, designated by '$\alpha(u)$', or from 0 to u, which is $\alpha(u)/2$, is given in tables. In earlier books the following function is used more frequently, likewise under the term 'probability integral':

$$\Theta(u) =_{\text{Df}} \frac{2}{\sqrt{\pi}} \int_0^u e^{-r^2}dr\ .$$

The relation between the three functions is as follows: $\alpha(u) = \Theta(u/\sqrt{2}) = 2\Phi(u) - 1$; $\Phi(u) = \frac{1}{2}[1 + \alpha(u)]$. Unfortunately, the letters 'Θ', 'ϕ', and 'Φ' are used by various authors for different functions. We follow Cramér ([Statistics], p. 557) in the use of 'ϕ' and 'Φ'.

T40-19.

a. ϕ is an even function, i.e., $\phi(-u) = \phi(u)$.

b. $\phi(u)$ is always positive.

c. $\lim \phi(u)$ for $u \rightarrow \infty$ and $u \rightarrow -\infty$ is 0.
d. $\frac{d\phi(u)}{du} = -u\phi(u)$.
e. $\lim_{u \rightarrow -\infty} \Phi(u) = 0$.
f. $\lim_{u \rightarrow \infty} \Phi(u) = 1$.
g. $\Phi(0) = 1/2$.
h. $\Phi(-u) = 1 - \Phi(u)$.

T40-20. ***Table for the Normal Function $\phi(u)$ and the Probability Integral $\Phi(u)$***

u	$\phi(u)$	$\Phi(u)$	u	$\phi(u)$	$\Phi(u)$	u	$\phi(u)$	$\Phi(u)$
0.0	0.399	0.500	1.1	0.218	0.864	2.4	0.022 4	0.991 80
0.1	.397	.540	1.2	.194	.885	2.6	.013 6	.995 34
0.2	.391	.579	1.3	.171	.9032	2.8	.007 92	.997 44
0.3	.381	.618	1.4	.150	.9192	3.0	.004 43	.998 65
0.4	.368	.655	1.5	.130	.9332	3.2	.002 38	.999 31
0.5	.352	.691	1.6	.111	.9452	3.4	.001 23	.999 66
0.6	.333	.726	1.7	.0941	.9554	3.6	.000 61	.999 84
0.7	.312	.758	1.8	.0790	.9641	3.8	.000 29	.999 928
0.8	.290	.788	1.9	.0656	.9713	4.0	.000 13	.999 968
0.9	.266	.816	2.0	.0540	.9773	4.5	.000 016	.999 996 6
1.0	0.242	0.841	2.2	0.0355	0.9861	5.0	0.000 001 5	0.999 999 71

For negative values: $\phi(-u) = \phi(u)$; $\Phi(-u) = 1 - \Phi(u)$.

B. ***Limit***

+D40-5. Let an infinite sequence of elements of any kind be given, e.g., E_1, E_2, E_3, etc. (so that for every positive integer n there is exactly one nth member E_n in the sequence; but the same element may occur at different places, e.g., E_3 may be the same as E_5). A subsequence of the given sequence is a *final segment* of it $=_{Df}$ it consists of all members of the given sequence from some one member on, in the original order (e.g., E_5, E_6, E_7, etc.).

+D40-6. Let f be a function from natural numbers to real numbers, which is defined either for all natural numbers or at least for an infinite subsequence of them, say n_1, n_2, n_3, etc. (Hence, for any natural number n as argument, for which f is defined, its value $f(n)$ is a real number, and the values $f(0)$, $f(1)$, $f(2)$, etc., or $f(n_1)$, $f(n_2)$, $f(n_3)$, etc., form an infinite sequence of real numbers, which we call the *f-sequence*.)

a. The real number r is the ***limit*** of the function f for increasing n, or, the limit of the f-sequence (in symbols: '$r = \lim_{n \rightarrow \infty} f(n)$') $=_{Df}$ for every positive real number q (however small it may be chosen), there is a final segment of the f-sequence which lies entirely within the interval $r \pm q$.

b. The f-sequence (or the function f) is *convergent* (otherwise, *divergent*) $=_{\mathrm{Df}}$ there is a real number which is the limit of this sequence.

In the following theorems T1 and T2, 'lim (..)' is short for '$\lim_{n \to \infty}$ (..)'.

T40-21. Let f_1 and f_2 be convergent functions of the kind described in D6.

a. $\lim (f_1(n) + f_2(n)) = \lim f_1(n) + \lim f_2(n)$.

b. $\lim (f_1(n) - f_2(n)) = \lim f_1(n) - \lim f_2(n)$.

c. $\lim (f_1(n) \times f_2(n)) = \lim f_1(n) \times \lim f_2(n)$.

d. If all members of the f_1-sequence or of a final segment of it are equal to r, then $\lim f_1(n) = r$.

e. If every member of the f_1-sequence or of a final segment of it is equal to the corresponding member of the f_2-sequence or of a final segment of it, then $\lim f_1(n) = \lim f_2(n)$.

f. If for every m in a final segment of the sequence of natural numbers $f_1(m) \leqq f_2(m)$, then $\lim f_1(n) \leqq \lim f_2(n)$.

T40-22. Let r and m be constants, i.e., have the same value for all members of the sequence $n = 1, 2$, etc. Let r be an arbitrary positive real number, and m an arbitrary positive integer.

a. $\lim (r/n) = 0$.

b. $\lim (r/n^m) = 0$.

C. *Infinite Cardinal Numbers*

D40-8. Recursive definition for 'α_n'. (We shall use only 'α_0', 'α_1', and 'α_2'.)

a. $\alpha_0 =_{\mathrm{Df}}$ the cardinal number of the class of natural numbers. A class or property with the cardinal number α_0 is called *denumerable*.

b. $\alpha_{n+1} =_{\mathrm{Df}} 2^{\alpha_n}$.

[Assuming the general continuum hypothesis, from which it follows that 2^{α_n} is the cardinal number next higher than α_n, our alpha-numbers α_0, α_1, etc., are the smallest infinite cardinal numbers in order of magnitude, and hence are the same as Cantor's aleph-numbers. We prefer the letter alpha for typographical convenience.]

T40-25.

a. A class or property is denumerable, i.e., it has the cardinal number α_0, if and only if there is a one-one correlation between its elements and the natural numbers, in other words, if its elements can be ordered in an infinite sequence (in the sense of D5) without repetitions.

b. Each of the following classes has the cardinal number α_1: (1) the class of all classes of natural numbers; (2) the class of all real numbers; (3) the class of the real numbers in any interval (of positive length); (4) the class of all points on a straight line. (For this reason, α_1 is sometimes called the cardinal number of the continuum.)

c. Each of the following classes has the cardinal number α_2: (1) the class of all classes of real numbers; (2) the class of all functions of real numbers.

T40-26. Let μ be an infinite cardinal number, and n a positive finite cardinal number (a natural number > 0).

a. $\mu + n = \mu - n = \mu$.

b. $n\mu = \mu$.

c. $\alpha_0 \alpha_1 = \alpha_1$.

d. $\mu^0 = 1$.

e. $\mu^n = \mu$.

D. *Combinatorics*

T40-29. *Permutations.*

+a. The number of permutations of n elements (i.e., ways of ordering the elements in a linear order, in other words, finite sequences without repetitions) is $n!$.

Explanation. There are n possibilities of choosing an element as the first, then $n - 1$ possibilities of choosing one of the $n - 1$ remaining elements as the second, then $n - 2$ possibilities for the third, etc.; hence altogether $n(n - 1)(n - 2) \ldots = n!$.

b. For a given class of n elements, the number of one-one correlations having the given class both as domain and as converse domain is $n!$ (From (a).)

The following theorems T31, T32, and T33 refer to the possible ways for distributing ν (or n) elements among μ (or m) mutually exclusive properties. Let us call (here only) two such distributions of elements statistically equal, if the one distribution assigns to each of the properties the same number of elements as the other distribution; otherwise, statistically different. If the number of the elements in question is a finite number n, and if these elements are individuals in one of our systems $\mathfrak{L}$ and hence are designated by n in in $\mathfrak{L}$, and if the m properties are designated by the molecular predicates of a division in $\mathfrak{L}$ (D25-4), then any distribution of the n individuals can be described by a sentence in $\mathfrak{L}$ of the kind which we have called (D26-6a) an individually specified description of a distribution or, for short, an individual distribution for the *n* in. Statistically equal distributions of individuals are described by isomorphic individual distributions (meaning here sentences) for the in. And the common statistical features of statistically equal distributions of individuals are described by a sentence which we have called (D26-6c) a statistical description of a distribution or, for short, a statistical distribution for the in. Now the essential point in the earlier definitions mentioned (D26-6a and c) is that they have been framed in such a way that for every distribution of the individuals there is exactly one sentence called an individual distribution for the in. That is the reason why T31c states the same number as T31a, and T31i the same as T31d; and, further, T32b the same as T32a, and T32e the same as T32c. Similarly, every one of the statistically different kinds of statistically equal distributions of individuals is described by exactly one sentence called a statistical distribution for the in. Therefore, T33b states the same number as T33a.

T40-31. *Individual distributions.* Let ν and μ be any finite or infinite cardinal numbers, and *n* and *m* be finite.

+a. The number of possible distributions of ν elements among μ properties is μ^ν.

Explanation. There are μ possibilities of placing the first element, likewise μ for the second, etc.; hence altogether $\mu \times \mu \times \ldots = \mu^\nu$.

All the following items are simple corollaries of (a).

b. The number of functions which have one of μ values for each of ν arguments is μ^ν. (From (a).)

c. The number of individual distributions (sentences, in the sense of D26-6a) in $\mathfrak{L}$ for *n* given in with respect to a given division of *m* predicates is m^n. (From (a).)

d. The number of possible distributions of ν elements among two classes is 2^ν.

e. The number of functions which have one of two values for each of ν arguments is 2^ν. (From (b).)

f. The number of lines in a table with *n* arguments and two values (e.g., the truth-values in a truth-table (§ 21B), or the values + and − in the table of *Q*-predicates, A31-1) is 2^n. (From (e).)

g. The number of selections which contain exactly one element from each of ν mutually exclusive pairs of elements is 2^ν. (From (d).)

h. The number of subclasses of a given class *K* with ν elements (including the null class and *K* itself) is 2^ν. (From (d).)

i. The number of individual distributions (sentences) in $\mathfrak{L}$ for n given in with respect to the division of 'M' and '$\sim M$' is 2^n. (From (c).)

k. The number of possible distributions of n elements among m properties ($n \geqq m$) such that none of the properties is empty is as follows if $m \geqq 2$ (for $m = 1$, the number is 1):

(1) exactly $\sum_{k=0}^{m-1} [(-1)^k (m-k)^n \binom{m}{k}]$;

(2) approximation for the case that n is large in relation to m:

$m^n[1 - m(\frac{m-1}{m})^n]$.

l. The number of possible distributions of n elements among m properties such that p specified properties are empty and the others are not ($n \geqq m - p$) is as follows if $m - p \geqq 2$ (for $m - p = 1$, the number is 1):

(1) exactly $\sum_{k=0}^{m-p-1} [(-1)^k (m-p-k)^n \binom{m-p}{k}]$;

(2) approximation for the case that n is large in relation to m:

$(m-p)^n[1 - (m-p)(\frac{m-p-1}{m-p})^n]$. (From (k).)

m. (1), (2), (3). The number of possible distributions of n elements among m properties such that exactly p properties (no matter which ones) are empty ($n \geqq m - p$) is equal to the number specified under (l), form (1) or (2) or (3), respectively, multiplied by $\binom{m}{p}$. (From (l); cf. T32d.)

T40-32. *Individual distributions with given numbers.*

+a. The number of those (statistically equal) distributions of n individuals among m properties which assign n_1 individuals to the first property, n_2 to the second, . . . and n_m to the mth (where $n_1 + n_2 + \ldots + n_m = n$) is $\frac{n!}{n_1!n_2!\ldots n_m!}$.

Explanation. If the n individuals are ordered in a sequence, we may decide to assign the first n_1 individuals to the first property, the next n_2 to the second, etc., and the last n_m to the mth. In this way every ordering of the individuals determines uniquely a distribution with the required numbers n_1, n_2, etc. However, many different orderings determine the same distribution. If a certain order of the n individuals is given, we obtain another order determining the same distribution by rearranging the first n_1 individuals (the number of possible arrangements for them is $n_1!$, T29a); then the next n_2 individuals, etc.;

finally the last n_m individuals. Thus each distribution with the given numbers is determined by $n_1!n_2! \ldots n_m!$ distinct ways of ordering the n individuals. There are altogether $n!$ such ways (T29a). Therefore the number of distributions with the given numbers is $n!/(n_1!n_2! \ldots n_m!)$.

b. The number of (mutually isomorphic) individual distributions (sentences) in $\mathfrak{L}$ for n given in with respect to a given division of m predicates 'M_1', 'M_2', . . . , 'M_m', with the cardinal numbers $n_1, n_2, \ldots, n_m$, is $\frac{n!}{n_1!n_2! \ldots n_m!}$. (From (a).)

c. The number of (statistically equal) distributions of n individuals among two properties with the cardinal numbers n_1 and n_2 is $\frac{n!}{n_1!n_2!} = \binom{n}{n_1} = \binom{n}{n_2}$. (From (a).)

d. The number of subclasses with n_1 elements of a given class with n elements (often called *combinations* of n elements taken n_1 at a time) is $\binom{n}{n_1}$. (From (c).)

e. The number of (mutually isomorphic) individual distributions (sentences) in $\mathfrak{L}$ for n given in with respect to the division of 'M' and '$\sim M$' with the cardinal numbers n_1 and n_2 is $\binom{n}{n_1}$. (From (c).)

f. Let the class K have the infinite cardinal number ν, and let n be a positive finite number. The number of subclasses of K with n elements is ν.

g. Let ν be an infinite cardinal number. The number of (statistically equal) distributions of ν individuals among two classes such that each class contains ν individuals is 2^ν.

h. The number of ways of choosing n_1 elements from a given class of n elements and ordering them (sometimes called *permutations* of n elements taken n_1 at a time) is $\binom{n}{n_1}n_1! = \frac{n!}{(n-n_1)!} = \left[{n \atop n_1}\right]$. (From (d), T29a.)

i. Let m predicates 'M_1', . . . , 'M_m' form a division. Let K be a class of n individuals, of which n_1 have the property M_1, n_2 M_2, . . . , n_m M_m. Then the number of those subclasses of K which contain s individuals, and among them s_i ($i = 1, \ldots, m$) with the property M_i, is $\binom{n_1}{s_1}\binom{n_2}{s_2} \ldots \binom{n_m}{s_m}$. (From (d).)

T40-33. *Statistical distributions.*

a. The number of statistically different kinds of distributions of n individuals among m properties is $\binom{n+m-1}{m-1}$, i.e., $(n+m-1)!/n!(m-1)!$.

Explanation. The distributions in question may be represented by serial patterns consisting of n dots and $m-1$ strokes as follows: the number of individuals which have the first property is indicated by the number of dots preceding the first stroke; that of the second property by the dots between the first and second stroke, etc.; finally, that of the mth property by the dots following the last stroke. (For example, the pattern '. . . / / . /' indicates the numbers 3, 0, 1, 0 for the four properties.) Therefore the number sought is equal to the number of possible patterns with n dots and $m - 1$ strokes. These patterns may be produced by starting with a series of $n + m - 1$ dots and then replacing a subclass of $m - 1$ of them by strokes. The number of these subclasses is $\binom{n+m-1}{m-1}$ (T32d); therefore, this is also the number of possible patterns.

b. The number of statistical distributions (sentences, in the sense of D26-6c) in $\mathfrak{L}$ for n given in with respect to a given division with m predicates is $\binom{n+m-1}{m-1}$. (From (a).)

c. The number of statistically different distributions of n individuals among m properties such that none of the properties is empty is $\binom{n-1}{m-1}$.

Explanation. We first assign to each property one individual. Then the distributions described are made by distributing the remaining $n - m$ individuals among the m properties. There are $\binom{(n-m)+m-1}{m-1}$ ways of doing this (a).

d. The number of statistically different distributions of n individuals among m properties such that p specified properties are empty and the others are not is $\binom{n-1}{m-p-1}$. (From (c).)

e. The number of statistically different distributions of n individuals among m properties such that exactly p properties (no matter which ones) are empty is $\binom{m}{p}\binom{n-1}{m-p-1}$. (From (d), T32d.)

CHAPTER IV

THE PROBLEM OF INDUCTIVE LOGIC

This chapter contains some general, preliminary discussions concerning the nature of inductive logic and the problems of its possibility and use. These discussions are intended to remove some obstacles and prepare the way for the construction of a system of inductive logic, which we shall begin in the next chapter.

Inductive logic is here conceived as the theory of an explicatum for probability$_1$. The logical concept of probability$_1$ as explicandum is explained by interpreting it not only as evidential support but also as a fair betting quotient and as an estimate of relative frequency (§ 41). In this connection the problem of the presuppositions of the inductive method is discussed (§ 41F). The analogy between probability$_1$ and probability$_2$ (relative frequency) is discussed, and the change in the meaning of the word 'probability', which originally had only the sense of probability$_1$ and later acquired the second sense of probability$_2$, is explained (§ 42). Many philosophers have doubts whether inductive logic, and especially quantitative inductive logic, is possible, and some even assert its impossibility. Various reasons given for these beliefs are here discussed. They are often based on misconceptions of the nature and task of inductive logic. An attempt to clarify this nature is made by pointing out the close analogy between inductive and deductive logic and the lack of effective procedures for solving the chief problems in both these branches of logic (§ 43). A distinction is made between logical and methodological problems both for deduction and for induction; inductive logic has only the task of solving the logical problems. The principal kinds of inductive inference are explained (§ 44). Against those whose opposition to inductive logic is based on their general suspicions against abstractions, the usefulness and even indispensability of abstractions is emphasized, and it is shown that inductive logic, although based upon a simplified schema, is nevertheless applicable to problems in the actual world (§ 45). It must be admitted that the scientist's choice of a suitable hypothesis for the explanation of observed events is determined by factors of many different kinds. However, inductive logic has the task of representing the logical factors only, not those of a methodological or practical nature. The assertion that even the logical factors are in principle inaccessible to measurement can hardly be maintained (§ 46). On the other hand, even if we succeed in assigning numerical values to the logical factors, the task of determining how they should influence the degree of confirmation $\mathfrak{c}$ involves great difficulties. Therefore the doubts whether it is possible to solve the task, to give an adequate definition of $\mathfrak{c}$, seem understandable; however, the attempts so far made to prove the impossibility fall short of their aim (§ 47). Incidentally, the question is discussed how the concept of probability$_1$ is used in practical life and in science; it seems that it is used in a quantitative way within a much wider domain than the skeptics realize. This psychological fact concerning the use of the explicandum does not, of course, solve the logical problem of the possibility of a quantitative explicatum; nevertheless, it may encourage us to look for such an explicatum (§ 48). Assuming that quantitative inductive logic is possible, could it be usefully applied?

Its application has some essential limitations and involves certain difficulties which are similar to but still greater than those connected with deductive logic. On the other hand, inductive logic can be of great help within the theoretical domain of science, especially in cases where statistical descriptions and inferences are involved. Its development will also help to clarify the foundations of induction and thereby of the whole scientific method. Furthermore, inductive logic can and must be applied in order to serve, on the basis of our experiences, as a "guide of life" (§ 49). The problem of how a rule can be laid down for the determination of practical decisions with the help of inductive logic is discussed in detail. The inductive concept of an estimate plays an important part in a rule of this kind (§§ 50, 51).

In the last part of this chapter some more technical questions concerning $\mathfrak{c}$ are discussed. It is explained why we take as arguments of $\mathfrak{c}$ sentences rather than propositions or events, as is customary (§ 52). Some conventions are laid down which state certain fundamental, generally accepted properties of $\mathfrak{c}$ (§ 53). With the help of these conventions, it is shown how our problem of defining an adequate function $\mathfrak{c}$ for all language systems $\mathfrak{L}$ can be reduced to the problem of assigning suitable numbers to the state-descriptions ($\mathfrak{Z}$) in the finite systems $\mathfrak{L}_N$. Further, some additional requirements for $\mathfrak{c}$ are laid down (§ 54). The results of these informal considerations are meant merely as signposts to guide our steps when, in the next chapter, we shall begin the systematic construction of a quantitative inductive logic.

§ 41. The Logical Concept of Probability

Some further explanations are given concerning the meaning of probability$_1$ as an explicandum. *A*. In our original explanation, probability$_1$ was taken as a measure of evidential support. *B*. The value of probability$_1$ for a hypothesis *h* may be interpreted as a fair betting quotient for a bet on *h*. *C*. Let *h* be the prediction that the individual *b* has the property *M;* let *b* belong to the class *K;* let the relative frequency of *M* in *K* be *r*. If *r* is known, then *r* is the fair betting quotient for a bet on *h*. *D*. If *r* is not known, then the estimate *r'* of *r* is the fair betting quotient. Since the probability$_1$ of *h* was interpreted as the fair betting quotient, we may in the present case interpret the probability$_1$ of *h* as the estimate of the relative frequency of *M* in *K*. In a more general way the numerical value of probability$_1$ may be interpreted as the estimate of the relative frequency of truth among given equiprobable hypotheses. The logical relation between probability$_1$ and the general concept of the estimate of a magnitude (as explicanda) is explained; this relation will later be utilized for the definition of an explicatum for the concept of estimate (§ 100A). Since probability$_2$ means the relative frequency in the long run, the probability$_1$ of a singular prediction concerning *M* may be interpreted as the estimate of the probability$_2$ of *M*. This close relation between the two concepts of probability is the reason for a far-reaching analogy between certain theorems concerning these concepts. This relation also gives a psychological explanation for the fact that many authors since the classical period seem sometimes to shift inadvertently from probability$_1$ to probability$_2$. This is presumably the case when the authors infer a frequency from a probability or speak about unknown probabilities or the chance of a certain probability. *E*. Our conception is in agreement with Reichenbach's analysis of his two explicanda, the frequency concept of probability and the logical concept of probability or weight. But it is not in agreement with Reichenbach's explication of the latter concept, because he identifies this concept (like the former) with relative frequency instead of the estimate of relative frequency. *F*. What is needed as a presupposition for the validity of the inductive method and the justification of its application in determining practical decisions is not the principle of the uniformity of the world but only the statement that the uniformity is probable on the basis of the available evidence. This statement is an analytic statement in inductive logic and hence not in need of empirical confirmation. Thus the apparent vicious circle, which many philosophers believe to be involved in the validation of the inductive method, disappears.

We have previously (in chap. ii) distinguished two meanings of the word 'probability': the first ('probability$_1$') means weight of evidence or strength of confirmation, the second ('probability$_2$') means relative frequency. The chief topic of this book is the problem of an explication of probability$_1$. As explained earlier (§ 8), this problem may be approached on three different levels; we may try to define an explicatum for probability$_1$ in any one of the following three forms:

(i) a *classificatory* concept of confirmation ('the hypothesis *h* is confirmed by the evidence *e*');

(ii) a *comparative* concept of confirmation ('*h* is confirmed by *e* at least as highly as *h'* by *e'*');

(iii) a *quantitative* concept of confirmation, the concept of *degree of confirmation* ('*h* is confirmed by *e* to the degree *r*').

If a satisfactory explicatum of the kind (iii) could be found, it would obviously be the most desirable solution of our problem. A theory of the concept of degree of confirmation, founded upon an explicit definition of this concept, would constitute a *quantitative inductive logic*. If a satisfactory quantitative explicatum is not found or—as some authors believe—can never be found, then we should have the more modest task of defining a comparative explicatum. This would lead to a *comparative inductive logic*.

This chapter will contain preliminary discussions clearing the ground for the later construction of a quantitative inductive logic. The nature and meaning of probability$_1$ as an explicandum will be clarified. Some circumstances will be examined which seem to make the task of a quantitative explication of probability$_1$ difficult or, in the opinion of some philosophers, even insoluble. The possibility of applying inductive logic for the determination of practical decisions will be examined. And, finally, some steps will be outlined for the construction of inductive logic. In later chapters, systems of inductive logic both in a quantitative and in a comparative form will be developed.

For any quantitative explicatum for probability$_1$—not only for the one we shall define later—we use the term 'degree of confirmation' or often briefly 'confirmation', when the context makes sufficiently clear that the degree of confirmation is meant and not the act of confirming; as symbol, likewise in the metalanguage, we use 'c'. Thus, '$c(h,e) = r$' is merely a shorter formulation for 'the degree of confirmation (or: the confirmation) of h on the evidence e is r'; 'c' is often also used within a word sentence as abbreviation for '(degree of) confirmation'.

In the present section we shall explain in greater detail the nature and meaning of probability$_1$, the logical concept of probability. These explanations are not yet meant as an explication but merely as a clarification of the explicandum. Such a clarification is a necessary preparation for the later task of explication. In order to judge whether a proposed concept is adequate as an explicatum for a given explicandum, we must be sufficiently clear as to what we mean by the explicandum.

The concept of probability$_1$ will be explained in this section from three different points of view. The probability$_1$ of a hypothesis h with respect to given evidence e represents

(A) a measure of the evidential support given to h by e;
(B) a fair betting quotient;
(C) an estimate of relative frequency.

A. *Probability$_1$ as a Measure of Evidential Support*

The first aspect of probability$_1$ is the one explained earlier (§§ 8–10). To say that the probability$_1$ of h on e is high means that e gives strong support to the assumption of h, that h is highly confirmed by e, or, in terms of application to a knowledge situation: if an observer X knows e, say, on the basis of direct observations, and nothing else, then he has good reasons for expecting the unknown facts described by h.

Although this explanation may be said to outline the primary and simplest meaning of probability$_1$, it alone is hardly sufficient for the clarification of probability$_1$ as a quantitative concept. For a comparative use, especially in the simpler cases involving three instead of four arguments (§ 8, examples (b) and (c)), the explanation seems fairly clear. Scientists use and understand statements to the effect that one assumption h_1 is more highly confirmed by given observations e than another one h_2. But it is not immediately clear what it should mean to say that h_1 is twice as much confirmed by e than h_2; and still less clear what it might mean to say that the strength of support given to h by e is 3/4 or even that it is 5. (Why should this not be a possible value?)

One might perhaps say that under certain plausible assumptions the meanings of numerical values for the strength of support become clear.

Let us assume (i) that this strength is to be measured by nonnegative numbers $\leqq 1$, and (ii) that, if two hypotheses h_1 and h_2 are L-exclusive, then the support given by e to $h_1 \vee h_2$ is to be measured by the sum of the numbers which measure the support given by e to h_1 and to h_2 separately. If now we know the meaning of the comparative concepts of stronger support and of equal support, we may obtain an interpretation for numerical values of the strength of support as follows. Suppose h and $\sim h$ are equally supported by e. Since $h \vee \sim h$ is L-true, no sentence can be more certain on any evidence. Therefore the strength of support for $h \vee \sim h$ on e must have the highest possible value, which is 1, according to (i). According to (ii), this is the sum of the values for h and for $\sim h$ separately. Since these two values are equal, each is $1/2$. Similarly, if we have n hypotheses which are such that necessarily one and only one of them must hold (in technical terms, they are L-disjunct and L-exclusive in pairs, D20-1e and g) and which are equally supported by e, then the strength of support by e for each of them is $1/n$, and that for a disjunction j_m of m of them is m/n. To say of any other hypothesis h' that it is supported by e to the degree m/n means that h' and j_m are equally supported by e. In this way we obtain an interpretation for rational numbers of the interval (0, 1) as values of the strength of support in certain cases and thus of probability$_1$ as a quantitative concept.

I think the reasoning just outlined is correct once the assumptions (i) and (ii) are accepted. However, with respect to the concept of strength of evidential support, these two assumptions are entirely arbitrary. True, it is customary to make these assumptions in theories of probability$_1$, and we shall make them too in our system to be constructed later. But in order to show that these assumptions express essential features of probability$_1$, we have to go beyond an explanation of this concept as strength of evidential support. This will be seen by the following discussions of the second and the third aspects of probability$_1$.

B. *Probability$_1$ as a Fair Betting Quotient*

Since the classical period of the theory of probability, games of chance and bets have very frequently served as convenient examples of application and, moreover, have often been used for the purpose of explaining the very meaning of the concept of probability in the sense of probability$_1$. Among contemporary authors, Borel and Reichenbach especially have made extensive use of betting situations in the clarification of probability.

A ***bet,*** in the widest sense, may be regarded as a contract between two partners X_1 and X_2 to the effect that X_1 promises to confer a certain benefit upon X_2 if a certain prediction h is not fulfilled, and X_2 promises a benefit to X_1 in the case of h. We assume that the benefits promised in any bet by X_1 and X_2 are amounts of money, u_1 and u_2, called the *stakes*. u_1 and u_2 are nonnegative; in general, both are positive; but we admit also the two extreme cases that either u_1 or u_2 is 0, but not both; hence $u_1 + u_2$ is always positive. We look at the result from the point of view of X_1: in the favorable case, that is, if h is true, he wins the amount u_2; if h is false, he loses u_1 or, as we shall say for the sake of a more uniform terminology, he wins $-u_1$. We call the ratio $u_1 : u_2$ the *betting ratio* (usually called the odds) and $u_1/(u_1 + u_2)$ the ***betting quotient***. If the betting quotient q is given, the betting ratio is obviously $q : (1 - q)$; only this ratio, not the amounts u_1 and u_2 themselves, is determined by q. We assume that X_1 and X_2 pool their knowledge before they make a bet concerning h; let e express their common body of information. The statement

'The probability$_1$ of h with respect to the evidence e has the value q'

can now be interpreted as saying that a bet on h with a betting quotient q for the two bettors whose knowledge is e is *a fair bet*. A bet is fair or equitable if it does not favor either partner. Therefore the probability statement means that if a person is permitted to choose either the side of X_1 (i.e., betting on h with q) or the side of X_2 (i.e., betting on $\sim h$ with $1 - q$), one choice is as good as the other. It follows that if a person is offered a cheaper bet on h, i.e., with a betting quotient less than the probability$_1$ value q, it is advisable for him to accept it (with a certain qualification to be explained later); if he is offered a higher bet, it is advisable to reject it.

The interpretation of probability$_1$ as a fair betting quotient is in accord with its first interpretation as evidential support, because the stronger the support given to h by e is, the higher can a bet on h be. But this second interpretation is more specific than the first because it leads to numerical values. The question as to how a value of probability$_1$ as a fair betting quotient is to be determined has not yet been answered; we shall soon come back to it. Nevertheless, we shall see now that the second interpretation leads immediately to two simple results concerning the values.

The stakes u_1 and u_2 may be any nonnegative numbers. Since $q = u_1/(u_1 + u_2)$, $0 \leqq q \leqq 1$ (if $u_1 = 0$ and $u_2 > 0$, $q = 0$; if $u_1 > 0$ and $u_2 = 0$, $q = 1$). Thus the interpretation of probability$_1$ as a fair betting quotient leads to this result:

(1) The values of probability$_1$ belong to the interval (0, 1), both end points included.

This justifies the assumption (i) mentioned above under (A).

If X_1 bets against X_2 on h with $q = u_1/(u_1 + u_2)$, then this is for X_2 a bet on $\sim h$ with the betting quotient $u_2/(u_1 + u_2) = 1 - q$. A bet is fair if it favors neither partner; therefore a fair bet is fair for both partners. It follows that, if q is a fair betting quotient for h on e, then $1 - q$ is a fair betting quotient for $\sim h$ on e. Since the probability$_1$ of h on e is meant as a fair betting quotient for h on e, the following holds:

(2) If the probability$_1$ of h on e is q, the probability$_1$ of $\sim h$ on e is $1 - q$.

C. *Probability$_1$ and Relative Frequency*

We have said that probability$_1$ may be regarded as determining a fair betting quotient. But the latter concept is itself in need of further clarification. We shall now try to throw some light on it, at least for the most important kind of betting situation, namely, the case where the hypothesis h is a singular sentence saying that a particular individual, say, b, has a certain property, say, M.

In order to judge the fairness or bias of a bet between X_1 and X_2 concerning h, we regard it as an element of a whole set of n similar bets concerning the n individuals of a class K, one of which is b. e is supposed to be such that it does not say for any individual in K whether or not it has the property M or any other factual property. We consider the case where X_1 makes n simultaneous bets with X_2; for every individual x in K, X_1 bets u_1 against u_2, hence with the betting quotient $q = u_1/(u_1 + u_2)$, that x has the property M. Suppose that actually rn of the n individuals in K are M, whether the two bettors know it or not; hence the relative frequency of M in K is r. What will be the final result after all individuals of K have been observed and all debts paid? X_1 wins rn bets; thus he receives the amount of rnu_2. He loses $(1 - r)n$ bets; thus he has to pay $(1 - r)nu_1$. Therefore, his total balance is $rnu_2 - (1 - r)nu_1 = n(u_1 + u_2)(r - q)$. Since $u_1 + u_2$ is always positive, X_1 will come out with a gain if $q < r$; with a loss if $q > r$; and just even if $q = r$.

Let us assume that X_1 is a rational bettor who is not willing to pay a price merely for the fun of the excitement, as a player in a commercial lottery does. He makes a bet only if it is not unfavorable in view of his chance, and he determines his chance in each case with the help of rational inductive methods on the basis of the evidence e available to him. X_2 is likewise supposed to be a rational bettor. How will a bet between the two then be made?

We consider first the case that the common knowledge e contains the information that exactly rn of the n elements of K are M, although it is not known which elements are M. It is clear that in this case the two bettors will not make the set of n bets concerning K with any betting quotient q different from r. For if $q > r$, the bet is unfavorable for X_1. He will not make the set of those bets in this case because, as we have seen, that would with certainty lead to a loss in the final balance. If he makes only a part of the bets or perhaps only one, then the over-all loss is not certain, a gain is possible. Nevertheless, X_1, being a rational bettor, will not even conclude one bet with any q greater than the known r because it is unfavorable for him in this sense: it is one case out of a whole class of logically similar cases for which the mean result is a loss. Similarly, X_2 will not make a bet with $q < r$. Thus the only possibility for a bet is one on the basis of $q = r$. There is no point for X_1 and X_2 in making the totality of n bets with this quotient because the end result is foreseeable with certainty: neither will gain or lose anything. But they might conclude one bet or a proper part of all the bets with $q = r$. In this case the result is uncertain, as it ought to be in a genuine bet; and the betting quotient is fair, that is, not clearly favorable to either side.

Thus we have obtained the following result. If the relative frequency of M in a class to which b belongs is known to be r, then the fair betting quotient for the hypothesis that b is M, and hence the probability$_1$ of this hypothesis, is r.

D. *Probability$_1$ as an Estimate of Relative Frequency*

Now we shall consider the more frequent and more interesting case that the two bettors have no knowledge about the relative frequency r of M in K. X_1 knows that the final balance for the total class of bets depends upon this value r. If he knew this value, he would regard it as a fair betting quotient, as we have seen. Since he does not know the value, he will try, if possible, to make an estimate of it on the basis of his knowledge e of observations of other things and regard this estimate as a fair betting quotient. Since the probability$_1$ of h on e is intended to represent a fair betting quotient, it will not seem implausible to require that the probability$_1$ of h on e determine an *estimate of the relative frequency* of M in K. Thus we shall try to interpret the statement 'The probability$_1$ of the assumption that b is M with respect to the evidence e not mentioning b is q' as saying that the estimate with respect to e of the relative frequency of M in a class K of individuals not mentioned in e is q. However, before we can accept this interpretation, a closer examination will be necessary. In particular, we shall have to clarify the concept of an estimate, and then we must show that the interpretation of probability$_1$ just given is in accord with the interpretations given earlier.

To find an estimate u' of the unknown value u of a magnitude on the basis of given evidence e is an inductive procedure, not a deductive one, because there is no certainty that the estimate u' is equal or even near to the actual value u. The concept of estimate is indeed one of the most important concepts of inductive logic; it will be discussed in detail later (chap. ix). At the present moment it may be sufficient to indicate briefly the connection between the general concept of the estimate of a magnitude and probability$_1$. Suppose that it is known, either by the definition of the magnitude in question or by the information e, that there are n possible values of the magnitude, say, $u_1, u_2, \ldots, u_n$. Then we may take as the estimate of u with respect to e the weighted mean of these possible values with probability$_1$ as weight. This we call the probability$_1$-weighted mean or, briefly, the probability$_1$-mean. (The probability$_1$-mean is, in the terminology of the classical theory of probability, the expectation value of the magnitude.) Hence we define as follows:

(3) The ***estimate*** (more explicitly, the probability$_1$-mean estimate) of the unknown value of a magnitude with respect to given evidence $e =_{Df}$ the probability$_1$-mean, that is, the sum of the products formed by multiplying each of the possible values of the magnitude with the probability$_1$ of its occurrence with respect to e.

Throughout this chapter we shall understand the term 'estimate' always in the sense defined by (3). Note that (3) gives merely a clarification of the term 'estimate' as an explicandum, not yet an explication, because the term 'probability$_1$' is so far not explicated. (Later we shall explicate probability$_1$ by the degree of confirmation $\mathfrak{c}$ (chap. v) and hence the probability$_1$-mean by the $\mathfrak{c}$-mean as estimate-function (chap. ix).) As an example, suppose that the possible gain for X_1 in a game or business venture is known to be either g_1 or g_2. The actual gain g is unknown. We assume that X_1 is able to determine the value of probability$_1$ for any hypothesis with respect to any possible evidence and, in particular, with respect to the evidence actually available to him. If, with respect to the available knowledge e, the two possible outcomes have equal probability$_1$, the estimate g' of the gain is $g_1/2 + g_2/2 = (g_1 + g_2)/2$, hence the arithmetic mean. If, however, the probability$_1$ of g_1 is $3/4$ and hence that of g_2 $1/4$, then g' is $3g_1/4 + g_2/4$. g' represents for X_1 the money value of his share in the game or business. As a rational man he is not willing to buy this share for more than g' nor to sell it for less.

Let us now apply the concept of estimate as defined by (3) to the set of n bets described under (C). We found that if X_1 makes these bets with the betting quotient q $(= u_1/(u_1 + u_2))$ and the relative frequency of M in K is r, then his total gain g (positive or negative) will be $n(u_1 + u_2)(r - q)$. There are $n + 1$ possible values of the number m of individuals in K which are M (0, 1, 2, . . . , n) and hence $n + 1$ possible values of $r = m/n$ and of $g = n(u_1 + u_2)(r - q)$. Each of these $n + 1$ possible cases has a certain probability$_1$ with respect to e. Thus X_1 can determine, according to (3), the estimate m' of m, the estimate r' of r, and the estimate g' of g with respect to e. It can easily be shown on the basis of the definition (3) that, no matter what the particular probability$_1$ values are, the following equations hold:

(4) $r' = m'/n;$

(5) $g' = n(u_1 + u_2)(r' - q).$

[The reason is that r is a linear function of m, and g is a linear function of r; cf. T100-5 on the basis of D100-1.] Consequently, X_1 will reject any offered bet with a betting quotient $q > r'$ because the estimate g' of his gain would be negative; he may accept a bet with $q \leqq r'$. Thus the situation here is similar to that discussed earlier in which r was known, but it is not quite the same. In the former situation X_1 knew that the total set of bets with $q = r$ will leave him without gain or loss, and the set with $q < r$ will result in a final gain. In the present situation, however, the result of the total set of bets with $q = r'$ cannot be foreseen; the estimate r' of the relative frequency may be greater than its actual value r, and in this case the total result will be a loss. But there is also the possibility of a gain. Thus, in the present situation, not only the outcome of a single bet or a few bets is uncertain, but even that of the total set of bets. Since, however, uncertainty is of the essence of a bet, this fact alone will not deter X_1 from betting, provided the conditions of the bet are not unfavorable to him. They are unfavorable to him if $q > r'$, and unfavorable to X_2 if $q < r'$; they are neither favorable nor unfavorable to either side only if $q = r'$. *The bet is fair if and only if the estimate of the gain is zero for both partners;* and this is the case if and only if the betting quotient q for h is equal to r':

(6) For a bet on the singular prediction that an individual belonging to a class K of unknown individuals has the property M on the basis of the available knowledge e, *the fair betting quotient is the estimate of the relative frequency* of M in K on the basis of e.

Here, however, two difficulties seem to appear. Suppose that X_1 considers a bet with X_2 on the hypothesis that an unknown individual b is M on the basis of their common knowledge e. He asks what would be a fair betting quotient for h on e. Let us assume that X_1 knows how to determine values of probability$_1$ and hence also, according to (3), estimates of relative frequency. Our first answer is given by (6): take a class K of n unknown individuals containing b and determine the estimate of the relative frequency of M in K; this is a fair betting quotient. Here the first difficulty arises: which number n should X_1 choose, and which class of n individuals? What if the estimate has different values for different classes? Now it can be shown that the latter case is impossible, because the following holds:

(7) For any given evidence e and any given molecular property M, the estimate (probability$_1$-mean) of the relative frequency of M in a non-empty class K has always the same value no matter how many and which individuals belong to K, provided only that e does not say anything about these individuals.

We shall later prove an important theorem (T106-1d) to the effect that the independence stated in (7) holds generally for a comprehensive class of functions (called symmetrical c-functions) containing among others all those functions which can be considered as adequate explicata of probability$_1$. Thus X_1 will find one value as estimate of the relative frequency of M within any class K of unobserved individuals, no matter whether K is small or consists of the total unobserved part of the universe.

The second difficulty seems to arise from the fact that we have given two different rules for the determination of a fair betting quotient for h on e: this quotient was equated in (6) to the estimate of the relative frequency but, earlier, to the probability$_1$ of h on e. Now it can be shown that these two values always coincide:

(8) Let e be any (non-L-false) evidence, M any molecular property, b an individual and K any class of individuals not mentioned in e, and h the hypothesis to the effect that b is M, then the estimate (probability$_1$-mean) of the relative frequency of M in K is equal to the probability$_1$ of h on e.

This holds likewise generally for the class of functions mentioned above.

It is easily seen that (8) follows from (7). Let r' be the estimate of the relative frequency in K, and r'' that in $\{b\}$, the class consisting of b alone. Then, according to (7), $r' = r''$. The relative frequency in $\{b\}$ has only two possible values: 1 if h is true, 0 if $\sim h$ is true. Therefore, according to (3), $r'' = 1 \times$ probability$_1$ of h on $e + 0 \times$ probability$_1$ of $\sim h$ on $e =$ probability$_1$ of h on e. Hence $r' =$ probability$_1$ of h on e. This is (8).

The result (8) justifies the earlier interpretation mentioned tentatively:

the probability$_1$ of a singular hypothesis concerning M can be interpreted as the estimate of the relative frequency of M in an unknown class *K*. The result (8) is, in fact, a special case of the following:

(9) Let *e* be any (non-L-false) evidence and $\mathfrak{K}_i$ be any non-null class of sentences each of which has the same probability$_1$-value *q* with respect to *e*. Then the estimate of the relative frequency of true sentences in $\mathfrak{K}_i$ is equal to *q*.

The later theorems corresponding to (8) and (7) (T106-1c and d) will be derived from a much more general theorem (T104-2c) which corresponds to (9). While (8) concerns individuals and one given property *M*, in other words, hypotheses which are full sentences of the same predicate '*M*' differing only in the individual constants occurring, (9) refers to a class of sentences without restriction; these sentences may have any forms whatever, and there may be deductive relations between them (e.g., L-implication, L-exclusiveness, or even L-equivalence). The result (9) can be used to explain probability$_1$ as a quantitative concept in terms of the following two concepts: (1) probability$_1$ as a comparative concept and, in particular, the relation of one hypothesis h_1 being equally probable to another one h_2 with respect to the same evidence, and (2) the concept of estimation, in particular, the estimate of the frequency of truth with respect to a given evidence *e*. Suppose that *X* understands these two concepts as explicanda; that is to say, he knows roughly what he means by them, although he may not be able to explicate them, i.e., to give exact rules for their use. Then, with the help of (9), we can explain to him probability$_1$ as a quantitative explicandum in the following way: if you have a class of *s* hypotheses which have equal probability$_1$ on *e*, then take as numerical value for the probability$_1$ of each of them the estimate of the relative frequency of truth among them (in other words, the estimate of the number of true sentences in the given class, divided by *s*). Thus *the common probability$_1$ value of several hypotheses can be interpreted as the estimate of the relative frequency of truth among them.*

In the foregoing discussions we have interpreted the concept of probability$_1$ in terms of an estimate of relative frequency, either of a property *M* among given individuals or of truth among given sentences. These estimates are special cases of the general concept of estimate; and this concept again was explained in terms of probability$_1$. In a system of definitions a circular procedure of this kind would, of course, be inadmissible. But our present discussions aim only at a clarification of certain concepts as explicanda. In such a clarification it is not only admissible but expedient to go back and forth and in circles, illuminating the network of concepts by analyzing the logical relations holding between any two of them. In the later construction of a system containing explicata of those explicanda, a chain of definitions not involving any circle will be built up. First, the regular c-functions (confirmation-functions) will be defined (§ 55A); they comprehend possible explicata for probability$_1$. With their help, a general concept of an estimate-function ('c-mean estimate') will be introduced by a definition (D100-1) which corresponds to (3) above. The relations between the degree of confirmation and the estimate of relative frequency will then be stated by theorems (T104-2c and T106-1c) corresponding to (9) and (8).

If we take a sufficiently large unknown class K, then the relative frequency of M in K may be regarded as representing the relative frequency "in the long run". But this is the explicandum of probability$_2$, the statistical concept of probability. Thus we find an important connection between the two probability concepts: in certain cases *probability*$_1$ *may be regarded as an estimate of probability*$_2$.

The relation between probability$_2$ and probability$_1$ is hence seen to be a special instance of the logical relation which holds generally between an empirical, e.g., physical, quantitative concept and the corresponding inductive-logical concept of its estimate with respect to given evidence. This relation explains, on the one hand, the different nature of the two probability concepts, but, on the other hand, also the far-reaching analogy between them which we shall repeatedly observe in our further discussions.

The interpretation of probability$_1$ as an estimate of relative frequency for future observations may help us in clearing up a problem which has been much discussed since classical times. Consider the following three sentences:

(i) 'The available knowledge e contains the information that this die has symmetrical shape, and hence in geometrical respects its six sides are alike. e does not contain any information concerning other respects in which the sides may differ.'

(ii) 'The *probability* that any future throw of this die will yield an ace is 1/6.'

(iii) 'If a sufficiently long series of throws of this die is made, the *relative frequency* of aces will be 1/6.'

The problem is whether (iii) can be inferred from (ii). Earlier authors have sometimes made inferences of this kind from probability to relative frequency. They meant the term 'probability' in (ii) in the sense of probability$_1$ with respect to the evidence e characterized in (i); this interpretation is clear from their reference to symmetry. On the basis of this interpretation, however, no valid inference can lead from (ii) to (iii), because the statement (ii) is purely logical while (iii) is factual. Later authors have correctly criticized inferences of this kind. This was first done by Mises (1919), who later said concerning the invalid inference just described: "I still believe that unearthing the fallacy of the classical argument is the cornerstone of what is called the frequency theory of probability" [Comments 2].

On the other hand, let us modify the inference by taking either of the following two statements instead of (iii):

(iv) 'The *estimate of the relative frequency* of aces in any future series of throws of this die is 1/6.'

(v) 'The probability$_1$ of the prediction that the relative frequency of aces in a future series of throws of this die will be within the small interval $1/6 \pm \epsilon$ is high (and can even be brought as near to 1 as wanted) if the series is made sufficiently long.'

(iv) does indeed follow from (ii), as is seen from our previous discussion. According to classical conceptions, also (v) follows from (ii) in virtue of Bernoulli's theorem. (This theorem will be discussed later (§ 96); we shall see that it can be applied only under certain restricting conditions, which may make its use in the above example questionable; but we may leave this problem aside for our present discussion.) Now the inferences in question made by earlier authors are usually not formulated in very clear and unambiguous terms. The conclusion is seldom formulated in a way similar to (iii). Sometimes phrases are used like 'we may anticipate' or 'it is to be expected' or something similar. In these cases it might not be implausible to assume that what the author actually meant is not a factual assertion like (iii) but an inductive statement concerning either an estimate like (iv) or a high probability$_1$ like (v). If so, the author cannot be accused of committing the fallacy earlier explained. Those cases in which the fallacy of inferring (iii) is actually committed can now be explained psychologically: they arise from a confusion of an estimate of frequency with the frequency itself.

The difference between probability$_1$ and probability$_2$ may be further elucidated by analyzing the sense of the customary references to *unknown probabilities*. The value of a certain probability$_2$ may be unknown to us at a certain time in the sense that we do not possess sufficient factual information for its calculation. On the other hand, the value of a probability$_1$ for two given sentences cannot be unknown in the same sense. (It may, of course, be unknown in the sense that a certain logicomathematical procedure has not yet been accomplished, that is, in the same sense in which we say that the solution of a certain arithmetical problem is at present unknown to us.) As we have seen earlier (§ 12B), the classical authors on probability deal, on the whole, with probability$_1$. However, they sometimes refer to unknown probabilities or to the probability (or chance) of certain probability values, e.g., in formulations of Bayes' theorem. This would not be admissible for probability$_1$. Perhaps the authors here inadvertently go over to probability$_2$. Since a probability$_2$ value for a given case is a physical fact like a temperature, we may very well inquire into the probability$_1$, on a given evidence, of a certain probability$_2$. However, a question about the probability$_1$ of a probability$_1$ statement has no more point than a question about the probability$_1$ of the statement that $2 + 2 = 4$ or that $2 + 2 = 5$, because a probability$_1$ statement is, like an arithmetical statement, either L-true or L-false; therefore its probability$_1$, with respect to any evidence, is either 1 or 0.

E. *Some Comments on Other Conceptions*

On the basis of the preceding discussions it will now be possible to clarify the relation between our conception of probability$_1$ and Reichenbach's conception. Since Reichenbach is one of the leading representatives of the frequency conception, it might at first appear as if our views must be fundamentally opposed. However, a closer examination of Reichenbach's argumentation shows that the two points of view are actually quite close to each other. As long as Reichenbach discusses the two explicanda of probability before he proposes his explicatum, our views are in agreement on all basic points. He explains that there are two forms of probability or two kinds of application ([Experience] § 32). The one is the frequency concept, our probability$_2$. The other is called by him the "logical concept of probability" or "weight". When we see that he refers to it also as "predictional value" (*op. cit.*, p. 315) and says that it is determined not only by the event in question but "also by the state of our knowledge", it becomes clear that this explicandum is the same as, or something similar to, our probability$_1$. Now it is interesting to see that Reichenbach's analysis of this concept and its function in determining decisions, especially in the case of wagers, leads him to the procedure of estimation ("appraising"); thus he comes very close to our interpretation of probability$_1$. He distinguishes between the actual value and an estimate ("appraisal") of a magnitude, e.g., the funds needed for a new factory or the spatial distance estimated by an artillery officer (p. 319). This analysis is then applied to the case of a wager. "The man who bets on the outcome of a boxing match, or a horse race, or a scientific investigation . . . makes use of such instinctive appraisals of the weight; the height of his stakes indicates the weight appraised." From his preceding discussions it is clear that the magnitude to be estimated in these cases is the relative frequency of events of the kind in question within a reference class to which the event referred to in the bet belongs. Therefore, the statement quoted may be understood as saying that the bettor's estimate of this relative frequency determines the betting quotient at which he is willing to make the bet. Thus it seems that Reichenbach is aware of the distinction between the actual relative frequency in the future, which is unknown at present, and the estimate of it, and that he recognizes that it is the latter, not the former, which determines the bettor's decision concerning a betting quotient. Up to this point our views agree. But now Reichenbach takes a step which marks the parting of our ways. After identifying probability, in the sense of probability$_2$, with relative frequency, he declares that weight, that is, probability$_1$, must likewise be explicated by identifying it with relative frequency. It seems to me that it would be more in accord with Reichenbach's own analysis if his concept of weight were identified instead with the *estimate* of relative frequency. If Reichenbach's theory is modified in this one respect, our conceptions would agree in all fundamental points.

Reichenbach criticizes the logical concept of probability, that is, probability$_1$, in the forms in which it has been proposed and systematized by Laplace and Keynes. It must be admitted that some of his objections are correct. However, Reichenbach cannot reject the concept of probability$_1$ in our interpretation either because of its alleged apriorism or for any other reason, because this concept, at least in certain cases of application, coincides with a concept used by Reichenbach himself, namely, the concept of an estimate of relative frequency. His own detailed and illuminating discussions of the role of inductive thinking, both in science and in everyday life, make it clear how important a systematic theory of estimation and, in particular, of the estimation of relative frequency would be. In our conception this is one of the tasks of inductive logic. If Reichenbach were to add such an inductive theory of estimation to his theory of frequency, then, but not otherwise, his system would become complete. This follows from a consistent development of his own basic conception.

Some philosophers believe that the logical concept of probability$_1$ super sedes the concept of truth. They regard the latter concept as an illegitimate idealization; instead of saying that a given statement is true we should say more correctly that it is highly confirmed or highly probable. In a similar way Reichenbach ([Experience] §§ 22, 35) believes that the values of probability (the logical concept of probability$_1$) ought to take the place of the two truth-values, truth and falsity, of ordinary logic, or, in other words, that probability logic is a multivalued logic superseding the custumary two-valued logic. I think that these views are based on a lack of distinction between 'true', on the one hand, and 'known to be true', 'absolutely certain', 'completely verified', 'confirmed to the maximum degree', 'having the probability$_1$ 1', on the other. The concept expressed by the latter phrases in their strictest sense is indeed an absolutistic concept that should be replaced by the concept of probability$_1$ with its continuous scale of degrees. Both these concepts refer to given evidence; the concept of truth, however, does not and thus is seen to be of an entirely different nature, and, hence, values of probability$_1$ are fundamentally different from truth-values. Therefore, inductive logic, although it introduces the continuous scale of probability$_1$ values, remains two-valued, like deductive logic. While it is true that to the multiplicity of probability$_1$ values in inductive logic only a dichotomy corresponds in deductive logic, nevertheless this dichotomy is not between truth and falsity of a sentence but between L-implication and non-L-implication for two sentences. If, for example, the probability$_1$ of h on e is 2/3, then h is still either true or false and does not have an intermediate truth-value of 2/3. [For more detailed discussions on the relations and the distinctions between truth, verification, and probability$_1$ see [Concepts] § VI and [Remarks] § 3.]

F. *Presuppositions of Induction*

The concept of probability$_1$ and the concept of estimation based on probability$_1$ not only are of theoretical interest but are also essential for those deliberations which are intended to guide our practical decisions. We have discussed the relevance of probability$_1$ and of an estimate of relative frequency for judging whether a proposed bet is fair or not. Later we shall show in detail how values of probability$_1$ or of estimates of various magnitudes may be used in determining practical decisions (§§ 50, 51). Leaving the technical details of this procedure for the later discussion, we shall at present examine its validity and presuppositions. Let us assume that a man X generally decides his actions in accordance with the probabilities of relevant predictions with respect to the observational evidence available to him. Is this an arbitrary habit, or can we give a justification for this general way of procedure? Can X be sure that his activities if determined in this way will be successful?

Suppose that X would like to know whether the prediction

(1) 'It will rain tomorrow'

is true or false, because this is relevant for a practical decision he has to take now. Some reflection will show him that for questions of this kind certainty is not attainable but only probability. Thus he will be content to take the following statement (2) instead of (1) as a basis of his decision:

(2) 'With respect to the available evidence, the probability$_1$ that it will rain tomorrow is high'.

This is all he can know at the present moment. And it is sufficient as a basis of his decision. For example, he may decide to take his umbrella along; or, if the probability is numerically determined, say as 4/5, he may decide to make a bet with this value as the betting quotient. X is aware that he cannot be sure that the action thus determined will be successful. It may be that the event predicted with high probability will not occur. But is he perhaps right in expecting success in the average of a long series, though not in each single case? He asks himself whether there are good reasons for accepting the following prediction:

(3) 'If X continues to make decisions with the help of the inductive method, that is to say, taking account of the values of probability$_1$ or estimation with respect to the available evidence, then he will be successful in the long run. More specifically, if X makes a sufficiently long series of bets, where the betting quotient is never higher than the probability$_1$ for the prediction in question, then the total balance for X will not be a loss.'

If X could know this, then he would clearly be justified in following the inductive method. It is clear that the truth of (3) is not logically necessary but depends on the contingency of facts. Statements like (3) which assert success in the long run for the inductive method would be true if the world as a whole had a certain character of uniformity to the effect, roughly speaking, that a kind of events which have occurred in the past very frequently under certain conditions will under the same conditions occur very frequently in the future. Therefore many philosophers have asserted that the assumption of the uniformity of the world is a necessary presupposition for the validity of inductive inferences (probability inferences) and hence for the justification of applying the inductive method in the determination of practical decisions. Among the many different formulations of this *principle of uniformity*, which are similar to each other but not necessarily logically equivalent, two may be given here:

(4) 'The degree of uniformity of the world is high.'

(5) 'If the relative frequency of a property in a long initial segment of a series is high (say, r), then it will likewise be high (approximately equal to r) in a sufficiently long continuation of the series.'

We give to the principle of uniformity the form (4) rather than the customary one: 'The world is uniform', because it is preferable to use the concept of uniformity in a quantitative form instead of the usual classificatory form, as we shall see later. The questions as to whether the principle of uniformity is true and, if so, whether and how we can know it, has been much discussed by philosophers. There is no doubt that the principle is synthetic, that it makes a factual assertion about the world; it is conceivable that it is false, that is, that the world is chaotic or at least that it has a low degree of uniformity. Many philosophers maintain that the principle is fundamentally different from other factual hypotheses about the world, e.g., physical laws. The latter hypotheses can be empirically tested on the basis of observational evidence and thereby either confirmed or disconfirmed inductively. But any attempt to confirm inductively the principle of uniformity would contain a vicious circle, according to these philosophers, because the inductive method presupposes this principle. Some of these philosophers conclude that skepticism is the only tenable position: we have to reject the validity of inductive inference. Other philosophers maintain that we must abandon the principle of empiricism which says that a synthetic statement can be accepted only if it is empirically confirmed.

Are these conclusions actually inescapable? Let us examine what kind of assurance would justify X's implicit habit or explicit general decision to determine all his specific decisions with the help of the inductive method. We can easily see that he need not know with certainty that this procedure will be successful in the long run; it would be sufficient for him to have the assurance that success in the long run is *probable.* Just as in the case of the prediction of a single event it was clear that only probability but not certainty can be obtained and that probability gives a sufficient basis for the specific decision, thus analogously for the question of success in the long run it would suffice for X to obtain, instead of the earlier statement (3), an inductive statement either in terms of probability$_1$ like (6a) or in terms of an estimate like (6b):

(6a) 'If X makes a long series of bets such that the betting quotient is never higher than the probability$_1$ for the prediction in question, then it is highly *probable* that the total balance for X will not be a loss.'

(6b) 'If X makes a long series of bets as described, then the *estimate* of his total balance will not be negative.'

It seems that, indeed, many contemporary philosophers, perhaps the majority, in contradistinction to those of the last century, agree that probability of success in the long run would be sufficient for the validity of inductive inference. Accordingly, it is agreed that what is needed as a presupposition of the validity of the inductive method is not certainty of the uniformity of the world but only probability. Therefore we replace now the earlier statements (4) and (5) by corresponding inductive statements (7) and (8); we formulate each of them again in two alternative ways, in terms of a probability or an estimate:

(7a) 'On the basis of the available evidence it is very *probable* that the degree of uniformity of the world is high.'

(7b) 'On the basis of the available evidence, the *estimate* of the degree of uniformity of the world is high.'

(8a) 'On the basis of the evidence that the relative frequency of a property in a long initial segment of a series is high (say, r), it is very *probable* that it will likewise be high (approximately equal to r) in a long continuation of the series.'

(8b) 'On the basis of the evidence described, the *estimate* of the relative frequency in a continuation of the series is likewise high (has a certain value near to r).'

These are alternative formulations for the principle which is needed as a presupposition for the validity of the inductive method. This means that a demonstration or confirmation of this principle would constitute a justification for the inductive method. Some of those philosophers who agree that the principle need not assert uniformity with certainty but merely with probability believe nevertheless that the difficulty earlier described remains essentially the same. The statement of the probability of uniformity is regarded by them as a synthetic, factual statement (usually interpreted in terms of the frequency concept probability$_2$). But it cannot be confirmed empirically because such a procedure would use the method of induction which in turn presupposes the statement. Thus, they say, at this point empiricism must be sacrificed. This is, for instance, the conclusion to which Bertrand Russell comes in a detailed and thoroughgoing analysis of the presuppositions of science ([Knowledge], chaps. v and vi).

Our conception of the nature of inductive inference and inductive probability leads to a different result. It enables us to regard the inductive method as valid without abandoning empiricism. According to our conception, the theory of induction is inductive *logic*. Any inductive statement (that is, not the hypothesis involved, but the statement of the inductive relation between the hypothesis and the evidence) is purely logical. Any statement on probability$_1$ or estimation is, if true, analytic. This holds also for the statements of the probability of uniformity or the estimate of uniformity ((7a) and (7b), and likewise (8a) and (8b)). Since they are not synthetic, no empirical confirmation is required. Thus the earlier difficulty disappears. The opponents would perhaps say that the statement of the probability of uniformity must be taken as a factual statement because otherwise *X* would have no assurance of success in the long run. Our reply is: it is not possible to give *X* an assurance of success even in the long run, but only of the probability of success, as in statement (6a); and this statement is itself analytic. But can *X* take a practical decision if he has as a basis merely an analytic statement, one that does not say anything about the world? In fact, *X* has as a basis for his decision two statements: first a factual statement of his total observational evidence, and second an analytic statement of probability$_1$. The latter does not add anything to the factual content of the first, but it makes explicit an inductive-logical relation between the evidence and the hypothesis in question. In our earlier example this inductive statement has the form (2) for the hypothesis (1). Thus *X* learns from (2) that his evidence gives more support to the prediction of rain than to that of non-rain. Therefore it is reasonable for him to take suitable action; for example, to take his umbrella or to bet on rain rather than on non-rain. For a practical decision is reasonable if it is made according to the probabilities with respect to the available evidence, even if it turns out to be not successful. Going back to the general problem, it is reasonable for *X* to take the general decision of determining all his specific decisions with the help of the inductive method, because the uniformity of the world is probable and therefore his success in the long run is probable on the basis of his evidence, even though he may find at the end of his life that he actually was not successful and that his competitor who made his decisions in accordance not with probabilities but with arbitrary whims was actually successful.

Later (in Vol. II), after constructing a definition of degree of confirmation as an explicatum of probability$_1$ (compare § 110A) and, based upon this, a definition of an estimate-function (compare § 100A), we shall show that inductive statements on the uniformity of the world of a kind similar to (8a) or (8b) are indeed analytic, because deductively provable on the basis of the definitions mentioned. We shall also propose definitions as tentative explications for the degree of uniformity and its opposite, the degree of randomness. This will make it possible to formulate and prove also statements similar to (7a) or (7b). The whole problem of the justification and the presuppositions of the inductive method, and in particular of its application in the determination of practical decisions, will then be discussed in greater detail and in more exact, technical terms. What has been said here should be regarded merely as preliminary remarks in non-exact terms of the explicanda, intended to show in outline the direction in which we look for a solution of the problem.

§ 42. Probability$_1$ and Probability$_2$

A. The word 'probability' had originally only the sense of probability$_1$. It is no more than about a hundred years ago that some writers used it in the sense of probability$_2$. This shift in sense was made inadvertently. It seems that the ambiguity of elliptical formulations of probability statements and a lack of distinction between frequency and an estimate of frequency played some part in the historical origin of the new sense. *B*. Many probability statements made by scientists, actuaries, and practical statisticians are based on statistical results concerning observed frequencies and lead to expectations of certain frequencies in the future. An analysis of these statements shows that they can be interpreted not only as statements on probability$_2$ but also as statements on probability$_1$ with respect to statistical evidence (in the traditional terminology, probability statements "a posteriori").

A. *The Shift in Meaning of the Word 'Probability'*

We have seen that the word 'probability' used in contemporary science has sometimes the meaning of probability$_1$, that is, degree of confirmation, and sometimes that of probability$_2$, that is, relative frequency. Thus the questions arise: what was the original meaning of the word, and how did it acquire a second meaning?

The first question is easily answered. The etymology of the word 'probable' and corresponding words in other languages, e.g., German 'wahrscheinlich', French 'vraisemblable', Latin 'probabilis' and 'verisimilis', shows clearly that these words were used originally in everyday speech for something that is not certain but may be expected to happen or presumed to be the case. It is easily seen how this common use led to the similar but somewhat more specific use in early books on probability, where the term 'probability' was meant in the sense of 'evidential support for an assumption (or event)' or 'rational credibility of an assumption', and, more specifically, as 'numerical degree of this support or credibility'. In other words, the word 'probability' had the sense of what we have called probability$_1$. Its use in the sense of probability$_2$ is of relatively recent date; it goes back not more than about a hundred years. The development of this new meaning out of the older one can be made understandable from each of two different points of view, referring to two different situations in which the word in its older sense was used. We shall now analyze both of them in turn.

Let us begin with the assumption that, within a certain group of scientific writers about the middle of the last century, the word 'probability' was commonly used in the sense of probability$_1$. It was more or less clear that it was applicable to an unknown event or hypothesis with respect to a given body of evidence, although the customary formulations often omitted explicit reference to this evidence. Now let us consider the case in which the evidence gives statistical information concerning a certain population and, in particular, states the relative frequency of a certain property M within the population, and the hypothesis is the assumption that an individual, whose characteristics are unknown except that he belongs to the population, has the property M. (This will later be called a case of the direct inductive inference, § 44B.) As an example, suppose that an observer X has the following knowledge:

(1) 'The relative frequency of myopia among the inhabitants of Chicago is 1/5',

and considers the hypothesis:

(2) 'John Doe is myopic',

where 'John Doe' is defined as 'the inhabitant No. 117 of Chicago' so that the statement 'John Doe is an inhabitant of Chicago' is analytic. If now X wanted to make a statement concerning the probability, in the sense of probability$_1$, of the assumption (2), a complete formulation would have to be of the following form:

(3) 'The probability of (2) with respect to (1) is 1/5'.

The numerical value of the probability is in this case equal to the known relative frequency. This equality was generally assumed on the basis of the classical conception of probability, and our theory will lead to the same result (T94-1e). However, complete formulations like (3) were seldom used before Keynes, as mentioned earlier (§ 10A). X, as a man of the last century, was apt to use instead the following elliptical formulation:

(4) 'The probability that John Doe is myopic is 1/5'.

X was, of course, aware that this probability statement had something to do with the frequency statement (1). But he did not clearly recognize that the frequency statement ought to be an essential part of the probability statement; he regarded it merely as the ground, the given knowledge, from which he had derived the latter. Therefore, if he felt instinctively the need of referring to the frequency in connection with the probability, he might do it in a form like this:

(5) 'Since the relative frequency of myopia among inhabitants of Chicago is 1/5, the probability that John Doe is myopic is 1/5'.

He might also assert a generalized statement in conditional form:

(6) 'If the relative frequency of a property *M* in a population *K* is *q*, then the probability of an element of *K* being *M* is *q*',

and the following as a substitution instance of it:

(7) 'If the relative frequency of myopia among inhabitants of Chicago is 1/5, the probability that John Doe is myopic is 1/5.'

As explained earlier (§ 10A), conditional formulations of this kind, although not quite correct and sometimes misleading, were quite customary; in particular, (6) has the customary form of a general theorem in the traditional theory of probability. Therefore *X* would regard (6) as analytic, and likewise (7), since it is an instance of (6). Furthermore, since in the case of a relative frequency different from 1/5 the probability would likewise be different from 1/5, *X* might regard the converse of (7) likewise as true and analytic. This would naturally lead him to the belief that the two components in (7), that is, (1) and (4), were logically equivalent. Thus it becomes understandable that *X*, when he wished to communicate the statistical fact (1) concerning the relative frequency of *M*, would use the formulation:

(8) 'The probability of an inhabitant of Chicago being *M* is 1/5',

which seemed to him to follow from (1) and indeed to have the same meaning. In this way, the word 'probability' became for him synonymous with 'relative frequency (in the whole population)' and hence acquired the sense of probability$_2$.

In the second situation to be considered now the evidence *e* describes an observed sample taken from a population *K* and the hypothesis *h* says that an unobserved element of *K* has the property *M*. (A case of this kind will be called a singular predictive inference, § 44B.) Suppose *X* finds the following result:

(9) 'The probability$_1$ of *h* with respect to *e* is 1/3.'

As we have seen previously (§ 41D (8)), this statement is logically equivalent to the following:

(10) 'The estimate of the relative frequency of *M* in any unobserved class, and hence also in the whole unobserved part of *K*, on the evidence *e* is 1/3.'

Although earlier authors did not state explicitly the equivalence of (9) to (10) and presumably were not aware of it with full clarity, it seems that they, nevertheless, felt this connection more or less instinctively. This is shown by the fact that they often made a transition from a statement on probability to one on an expected relative frequency in a form like this: 'The probability of an individual's being *M* is 1/3; therefore we may expect to find among future cases one-third who will exhibit the property *M*.' The phrase 'we may expect to find' is rather ambiguous. As explained earlier (§ 41D), the author is right if the phrase is meant to refer to an estimate but wrong if it expresses a prediction. Now it seems that sometimes a writer was not quite clear in his own mind whether he meant to state an estimate or a prediction of the future relative frequency. In a case of this kind it may happen that a statement containing the word 'probability' is first meant in the traditional sense, that is, probability$_1$, then correctly interpreted as stating an estimate of relative frequency, and, finally, due to a lack of distinction between an estimate and a predicted value, acquires a new interpretation as a factual statement on the future relative frequency; in other words, 'probability' is inadvertently shifted from the old sense of probability$_1$ to the new sense of probability$_2$.

Thus the transition from the old conception of probability to the newer one is sometimes concealed by ambiguous formulations, as a picture on a screen blurs over into a new one so that it is impossible to mark a clear-cut point at which the change occurs. It seems to me that this is exemplified in certain formulations by Leslie Ellis, which Keynes regards as the first appearance of the frequency conception of probability ([Probab.], pp. 92 f.). In a paper read in 1842 (hence before the appearance of Cournot's work to be mentioned soon) and published in 1844 (not, as Keynes says, 1843), Ellis says: "If the probability of a given event be correctly determined, the event will on a long run of trials tend to recur with frequency proportional to their [*sic*] probability. This is generally proved mathematically. It seems to me to be true *a priori*. . . . I have been unable to sever the judgment that one event is more likely to happen than another from the belief that in the long run it will occur more frequently" ([Foundations], pp. 1 f.). The phrase "the belief that" shows the typical ambiguity earlier discussed. It can be interpreted as an unclear reference to an estimate, but also as a formulation, unnecessarily psychologistic, of a plain prediction of relative frequency. The phrase "will tend to recur with frequency . . ." in the first sentence quoted is likewise ambiguous. Presumably it is not meant in the sense of "will recur . . .", since that would obviously be false. More likely is it to be interpreted in the sense that the specified frequency has a high probability, hence as a loose formulation of Bernoulli's theorem; this interpretation seems confirmed by the subsequent sentence: "This is generally proved mathematically". The phrase "true *a priori*" in the third sentence means probably "immediately following from a definition". The whole quotation and later passages of a similar nature (*op. cit.*, p. 3) give the impression that Ellis felt that there is some relation between probability and relative frequency without being able to make it clear to himself whether a probability value q means an estimate q of relative frequency, or a high probability of a relative frequency q, or simply a relative frequency q. His reflections are perhaps to be regarded as the historically first step in the transition of the meaning of the word 'probability' from probability$_1$ to probability$_2$, and we see that this first step was made in—and was perhaps psychologically due to—a foggy state of mind characterized by a lack of distinction between various closely related but nonidentical concepts.

The next step was made by A. Cournot ([Exposition] [1843]). He likewise combines the classical definition of probability, hence probability$_1$, with an interpretation in terms of relative frequency ([Exposition], p. iii, quoted by Keynes [Probab.], p. 92 n.) without being aware of their incompatibility. [It seems to me that George Boole ([Laws] [1854]) cannot be regarded as a representative of the frequency conception as is sometimes done. It is true that on a few occasions he makes indications toward a frequency interpretation. But they are not meant as a general definition of probability. The basic concept used throughout most of his systematic developments is unmistakably probability$_1$.]

John Venn ([Logic] [1866]), more than twenty years after Cournot, was the first to advocate the frequency concept of probability$_2$ unambiguously and systematically as explicandum and also the first to propose as explicatum for it the concept of the limit of relative frequency in an infinite series. Although his conception influenced the views of some other writers, among them Charles Sanders Peirce (1878), it was only half a century later that comprehensive systematic theories were constructed which took probability$_2$ as their basis. This was done, on the one hand, by Hans Reichenbach and Richard von Mises and, on the other hand, by R. A. Fisher and subsequently by the majority of contemporary mathematical statisticians. [Reichenbach used the frequency concept first in [Begriff] (1915), the limit concept in [Kausalität] (1930); the systematic construction of the theory was given in [Axiomatik] (1932) and further developed in [Wahrsch.] (1935). Mises defined probability as the limit of relative frequency first in [Grundlagen] (1919); the systematic development of his whole theory was given in [Wahrsch.] (1931). Fisher constructed the foundations of his theory in [Foundations] (1922) and developed it in numerous further publications.]

It is surprising to see that hardly any one of these representatives of the frequency conception, beginning with Venn, seems to be aware of the fundamental change that has taken place in the meaning of the word 'probability'. It is true that they criticize Bayes, Laplace, and other classical and later authors. But they seem to believe that their new conception involves merely a modification and sometimes a rejection of certain assertions, theorems or rules, concerning probability made by the earlier writers, due to the choice of an improved explicatum. They do not seem to recognize that the explicandum itself has been changed and that, consequently, their theories deal with a subject matter entirely different from that of the earlier writers. This may be due, at least partly, to the fact explained above that the first steps in the transition from probability$_1$ to probability$_2$ were involved in ambiguities and confusions. It should be noticed that the criticism just made is by no means directed against the frequency theories themselves. These theories are of great importance for statistical work and therefore for the whole of science. Our remarks are only intended to point out the historical fact that the basic concept and the problems of the classical theory of probability differ in a more fundamental sense from these theories than is usually recognized.

B. *On the Interpretation of Given Probability Statements*

The previous discussion on probability$_1$ and, in particular, its explanation as an estimate of frequency (§ 41D), and, further, the remarks just made concerning the historical development leading from probability$_1$ to probability$_2$, also make it clear that the concept of probability$_1$ is closely connected with the concept of frequency. Therefore, it is often not easy to discover whether a given statement on probability is to be interpreted in terms of probability$_1$ or probability$_2$. In the following we shall analyze certain probability statements which involve frequency and therefore may appear at first as statements on probability$_2$, but we shall find that they may be interpreted as dealing with probability$_1$.

Many writers since the classical period have said of certain probability statements that they are 'based on frequencies' or 'derived from frequencies'. Nevertheless, these statements often, and practically always if made before the time of Venn, speak of probability$_1$, not of probability$_2$. In our terminology they are probability$_1$ statements referring to an evidence involving frequencies. We have explained earlier (§ 10A) that in cases of this kind the frequency statement is not a premise of the probability statement but part of its subject matter, and hence the customary phrase 'derived from frequencies' is misleading. It would be more correct to say that in these cases the probability is determined with the help of a given frequency and its value is either equal or close to that of the frequency. The frequency stated in the evidence may either refer to the whole population or to an observed sample. (As mentioned above, we speak in the first case of a direct probability or a direct inductive inference, in the second case of a predictive one.) In the traditional terminology the probability in the second case was often called a 'probability a posteriori', in distinction to a 'probability a priori'. The latter term was used in cases where the evidence did not state a frequency but was very weak or even tautological (a 'statement of ignorance') and the value of the probability was determined chiefly by the use of the principle of indifference. Consider, for example, a statement to the effect that the probability of throwing an ace with a given die is 1/6. If the evidence, which was usually not referred to explicitly in the probability statement but merely indicated by the description of the situation, said only that the die had the shape of a regular cube, the statement would be said to give a probability a priori. If, on the other hand, the evidence described the results of six thousand throws made with the die and stated that one thousand of them were aces, the probability was called a posteriori. Thus, even in the latter case, the concept of probability involved is probability$_1$, not probability$_2$, although its value is determined on the basis of a frequency. It is important to notice this fact, because some writers have regarded the use of probability a posteriori as an indication of the frequency conception. That this use is actually still a case of probability$_1$ is clearly seen from the general description of the two methods by Bernoulli, who introduced the terms 'a priori' and 'a posteriori' for them ([Ars], Part IV, chap. iv). Nevertheless, the fact that in the course of the last century the use of the principle of indifference was more and more regarded with suspicion and, consequently, the use of probability a posteriori was more emphasized, was presumably one of the psychological factors which helped in preparing the way for the frequency conception.

We have earlier (§ 9) taken the statement 'The probability of throwing an ace with this die is 1/6' as a typical example of probability$_2$. The preceding discussion shows, however, that the same statement may also be interpreted as referring to probability$_1$. In order to discover which interpretation the person X who makes the statement has actually in mind, we have to take into consideration the context of the statement and the use X makes of it. Let us analyze the situation somewhat more in detail; we shall find that certain circumstances which frequentists might be inclined to regard as indicative of probability$_2$ do not in fact preclude an interpretation in terms of probability$_1$. Let us consider a modified example of an irregular or loaded die with a probability different from 1/6. The frequentists have pointed out, correctly, that in this case the classical definition of probability in terms of possible and favorable cases is not applicable, at least not without rather artificial constructions; from this they have inferred the conclusion, which we shall question, that in this case only the concept of probability$_2$ is applicable. Suppose X asserts the following statement:

(13) 'The probability of throwing an ace with this die is 0.15.'

We want to determine in which sense this statement is meant by X. Here, as often, it is not advisable to ask direct questions like 'What do you mean?' or 'Which meaning does the word 'probability' have for you?' We ask instead: 'What is the basis of your assertion? What observations led you to the value stated?' The frequentists emphasize the fact that a probability statement in their sense is not obtained by a merely logicoarithmethical procedure like counting possible and favorable cases but by statistical observations. Therefore, in order to fit our example to this conception, let us assume that X answers as follows:

(14) 'I have made 1,000 throws with this die, of which 150 yielded an ace; no other results of throws with this die are known to me.'

The frequentists will be inclined to take this answer as indicating an interpretation of the original statement (13) in the sense of probability$_2$. It is true that this interpretation is possible, but it is not the only one possible. We may try to clarify the situation by asking X to state more explicitly the connection between (14) and (13) as he sees it. Suppose he replies as follows:

(15) 'Since there were 150 aces among the observed 1,000 throws, the probability of an ace is 0.15.'

He may even add: 'This will be obvious for anyone who uses the word 'probability' in the same sense as I do.' But this sense is still not unambiguously determined by (15). It is true, this statement may suggest the sense of probability$_2$. However, it is also possible that it is meant by *X* in the traditional sense of a probability a posteriori, that is, in the following sense:

(16) 'The probability$_1$ of the assumption that a future throw with this die will yield an ace with respect to the evidence (14) is 0.15.'

[The use of a formulation like (15) in the sense of (16) is customary but not quite correct; see the above discussion of (5); the present situation is analogous to the earlier one but slightly different because it involves a predictive probability, not a direct one.]

Since probability$_2$ means relative frequency in the long run, let us formulate a statement concerning the future frequency:

(17) 'The relative frequency of aces among future throws of this die in the long run will be 0.15',

and then let us ask *X* for his judgment about this prediction from the point of view of his original statement (13) and the observational report (14); perhaps his answer will reveal whether his probability statement (13) was meant in the sense of probability$_2$. We may assume that his answer will be somewhat like this:

(18) 'It is not possible, of course, to make predictions with certainty; but, in view of the observational report (14), it seems sensible to expect a frequency of about the value 0.15 predicted in (17).'

A frequentist might now argue that by this answer *X* has accepted the statement (17) and, since this is a statement of probability$_2$, *X* has hereby shown that also his original statement (13) was meant in the sense of probability$_2$. Against this argument it must be pointed out that *X* did not in (18) accept (17) as an outright prediction but rather as a reasonable expectation. It seems more adequate to interpret this as an inductive statement. [In Reichenbach's terminology, (18) would be said to express an anticipation of a relative frequency as a "posit" ([Experience], p. 352). It seems to me that here again Reichenbach introduces, apparently without being aware of it, concepts which belong to inductive logic in our sense and hence can be based only on probability$_1$, not on probability$_2$.] In particular, (18) may be interpreted in either one of the following two senses (19) or (20):

(19) 'There is a *high probability*$_1$ with respect to the evidence (14) for the prediction that the relative frequency of aces in a long series of future throws with this die will lie within an interval around 0.15.'

(20) 'The *estimate* of the relative frequency of aces in a series of future throws with this die with respect to the evidence (14) is 0.15.'

Both (19) and (20) are statements of inductive logic. The latter is, according to our earlier explanations (§ 41D (8)), logically equivalent to (16); therefore, it would suggest an interpretation of the original statement (13) in the sense of probability$_1$.

The result of our analysis of the simple probability statement (13) holds, of course, likewise for any other probability statement based on statistical evidence and leading to expectations concerning certain future relative frequencies. Thus it holds, for example, for the statements of a physicist concerning the probability that the velocity of a molecule in a given body of gas belongs to a certain value region, or concerning the probability that the number of α-particles emitted by a given radioactive body during the next hour lies in a certain interval, or the statement of an actuary concerning the probability of death within the next year for a fifty-year-old steel worker in Chicago. Any statement of this kind can be explicated in two different ways; either (i) in the sense that the relative frequency in the long run, in other words, probability$_2$, is q, or (ii) in the sense that the probability$_1$ of a single instance of the kind in question with respect to given statistical evidence, e.g., an observed relative frequency, is q. Both reformulations contain the same numerical value q. Most of those scientists who have not made a special study of the problems of probability, and hence have not become partisans either of the Keynes-Jeffreys school of probability$_1$ or of the frequency school of probability$_2$, will perhaps refuse to tie themselves down to one of the two interpretations; they will perhaps regard the distinction as of merely academic interest. In a certain sense they are right. There is not much difference between the practical consequences drawn from (i) or (ii), since, as we have seen earlier, (ii) means the same as the statement that the estimate of relative frequency is q. Therefore, the scientist will proceed in either case in certain respects as if he knew that the relative frequency will be q. There is, however, the following difference. In the case (i) the statement in question is complete and has factual content, while in the case (ii) it is elliptical and analytic, expressing a logical relation between two factual statements. Consequently, there will be a difference concerning the future procedure in the following respect, if further observations exhibit a value of the relative frequency deviating considerably from q. The statement in sense (i) is rejected as probably false; the statement in sense (ii), however, remains valid but becomes irrelevant for practical purposes and is replaced by a new, likewise analytic, statement referring to the increased evidence.

§ 43. Inductive and Deductive Logic

A. Can a system of inductive logic as a theory of the degree of confirmation contain *exact rules?* This is sometimes denied for the reason that the procedure of induction is not rational but intuitive. Now it must be admitted that there is no effective procedure for finding a suitable hypothesis h for the explanation of a given observational report e, nor, if a hypothesis h is proposed, for determining $\mathfrak{c}(h,e)$. However, this is no reason against the possibility of an inductive logic because in deductive logic there is likewise no effective procedure for the solution of the corresponding problems. On the other hand, there are effective procedures for testing whether an alleged proof for a logical theorem is correct, e.g., in deductive logic for a theorem of the form 'e L-implies h', and in inductive logic for a theorem of the form '$\mathfrak{c}(h,e) = r$'.

B. Inductive logic is constructed from deductive logic by the adjunction of a definition of $\mathfrak{c}$. Hence inductive logic presupposes deductive logic. The analogy between these two fields of logic is illustrated by examples both for purely logical statements and for those involving the application to knowledge situations. However, truth and knowledge of the evidence e, although relevant for these applications, are irrelevant for the validity of the statements in inductive logic, as for those in deductive logic.

A. *On the Possibility of Exact Rules of Induction*

The question whether an inductive logic with exact rules is at all possible is still controversial. But in one point the present opinions of most philosophers and scientists seem to agree, namely, that the inductive procedure is not, so to speak, a mechanical procedure prescribed by fixed rules. If, for instance, a report of observational results is given, and we want to find a hypothesis which is well confirmed and furnishes a good explanation for the events observed, then there is no set of fixed rules which would lead us automatically to the best hypothesis or even a good one. It is a matter of ingenuity and luck for the scientist to hit upon a suitable hypothesis; and, if he finds one, he can never be certain whether there might not be another hypothesis which would fit the observed facts still better even before any new observations are made. This point, the impossibility of an automatic inductive procedure, has been especially emphasized, among others, by Karl Popper ([Logik] §§ 1–3 and elsewhere), who also quotes a statement by Einstein: "There is no logical way leading to these . . . laws, but only the intuition based upon a sympathetic understanding of experience" (". . . die auf Einfühlung in die Erfahrung sich stützende Intuition") (*Mein Weltbild* [1934], p. 168); compare also Einstein, *On the Method of Theoretical Physics* (Oxford, 1933), pages 11–12. The same point has sometimes been formulated by saying that it is not possible to construct an inductive machine. The latter is presumably meant as a mechanical contrivance which, when fed an observational report, would furnish a suitable hypothesis, just as a computing machine when supplied with two factors furnishes their product. I am completely in agreement that an inductive machine of *this* kind is not possible. However, I think we must be careful not to draw too far-reaching negative consequences from this fact. I do not believe that this fact excludes the possibility of a system of inductive logic with exact rules or the possibility of an inductive machine with a different, more limited, aim. It seems to me that, in this respect, the situation in inductive logic is similar to that in deductive logic. This will become clear by a comparison of the tasks of these two parts of logic.

When considering the kinds of problems dealt with in any branch of logic, deductive or inductive, one distinction is of fundamental importance. For some problems there is an effective procedure of solution, but for others there can be no such procedure. A procedure is called *effective* if it is based on rules which determine uniquely each step of the procedure and if in every case of application the procedure leads to the solution in a finite number of steps. A *procedure of decision* ('Entscheidungsverfahren') for a class of sentences is an effective procedure either, in semantics, for determining for any sentence of that class whether it is true or not (the procedure is usually applied to L-determinate sentences and hence the question is whether the sentence is L-true or L-false), or, in syntax, for determining for any sentence of that class whether it is provable in a given calculus (cf. Hilbert and Bernays [Grundlagen], Vol. II, § 3). A concept is called *effective* or *definite* if there is a procedure of decision for any given case of its application (Carnap [Syntax] § 15; [Formalization] § 29). An effective arithmetical function is also called *computable* (A. M. Turing, *Proc. London Math. Soc.*, Vol. 42 [1937]).

Now let us compare the chief kinds of problems to be solved in deductive logic and in inductive logic. Our aim is to discover whether inductive procedures are less regulated by exact rules than deductive procedures, as some philosophers believe.

In order to simplify the comparison, let us regard deductive logic, including mathematics, as the theory of L-implication, the explicatum for logical entailment (§ 20), and inductive logic as the theory of degree of confirmation, the quantitative explicatum of $probability_1$. At this stage in our discussions we do not yet know whether it is possible to find an adequate quantitative explicatum for $probability_1$. Therefore the following explanations are meant at present merely in a hypothetical sense: *if* there is an adequate explicatum $\mathfrak{c}$ and hence a quantitative inductive logic as its theory, what is its nature in comparison with deductive logic?

In each of the two branches of logic we may distinguish three kinds of fundamental problems concerning the application of the fundamental concepts, viz., L-implication or $\mathfrak{c}$, respectively.

1. First Problem: To Find a Conclusion

a. Deductive logic. Given: a sentence *e* as a premise (it may be a conjunction of a set of premises); wanted: a conclusion *h* L-implied by *e* and suitable for a certain purpose. For instance, a set of axioms for geometry is given; theorems concerning certain configurations are wanted. The essential point is the fact that there is no effective procedure for the solution of problems of this kind. The work of a logician or a mathematician consists to a great extent in attempts to solve problems of this kind. Some laymen imagine a mathematician to be chiefly occupied with computation, though of a sort more complicated than computation in elementary arithmetic. In fact, however, there is a difference in principle, not only in degree of complexity, between the two kinds of activities. To find the product of 15 and 17 is a simple task; to compute the square root of 7 to five decimals is more complicated; to compute the value of a number defined by a definite integral, e.g., e or π, to five decimals is still more complicated. All these tasks of computation, however, are fundamentally of the same nature, irrespective of the degree of complexity; for all of them there is an effective procedure; and this is characteristic of computation. The mathematician, on the other hand, cannot find fruitful and interesting new theorems, say, in geometry, in algebra, in the infinitesimal calculus, by computation or by any other effective procedure. He has to find them by an activity in which rational and intuitive factors are combined. This activity is not guided by fixed rules; it requires a creative ability, which is not required in computation.

b. Inductive logic. Given: a sentence *e* as evidence; wanted: a hypothesis *h* which is highly confirmed by the evidence *e* and suitable for a certain purpose. For instance, a report concerning observations of certain phenomena on the surface of the sun is given; a hypothesis concerning the physical state of the sun is wanted which, in combination with accepted physical laws, furnishes a satisfactory explanation for the observed facts. Or, a historical report about some acts of Napoleon is given; a hypothesis concerning his character, his knowledge at the time in question, and his conscious and unconscious motives is wanted which would make his acts understandable. There is no effective procedure for solving these problems; that is the point emphasized by Einstein and Popper, as mentioned above. However, we see now that this feature is by no means characteristic of inductive thinking; it holds in just the same way for the corresponding deductive problems.

II. Second Problem: To Examine a Result

a. Deductive logic. Given: two sentences *e* and *h;* wanted: an answer to the question whether *e* L-implies *h*. For instance, on the basis of an axiom set *e* of geometry, a mathematician finds, as a conjecture, an interesting sentence *h* concerning the angles of a triangle; this constitutes a tentative solution of a problem of the first kind; now he wants to find out whether *h* is actually deducible from *e*. Here, again, there is, in general, no effective procedure; in other words, L-implication is, in general, not an effective concept. Problems of this kind are again an essential part of any work in logic and mathematics. They are closely connected with problems of the first kind; for when a mathematician has found a theorem, he wants to give an exact proof for it so as to compel the assent of others. Finding a theorem is largely a matter of extrarational factors, not guided by rules. Constructing a proof is often called a rational procedure because here fixed rules have to be taken into consideration. However, the decisive point must not be overlooked: the rules of deduction are not rules of prescription, but rules of permission and of prohibition. That is to say, the rules do not tell the logician *X* which step to take at a given point in the course of a deduction; in other words, they do not constitute an effective procedure. The rules tell *X* merely which steps are permitted and thereby they say implicitly that all other steps are prohibited; they leave it to *X* to choose one of the steps permitted. Thus, here again, it depends upon *X*'s ingenuity and luck whether he solves the problem, that is, whether he finds a series of steps permitted by the rules, such that they lead from *e* to *h*.

More specifically, the situation is this. Only in the most elementary part of logic, in propositional logic (see above, § 21) is there a general method of decision, viz., the customary method of truth-tables (see § 21B). As soon as we enter the next higher field of logic, the so-called lower functional logic as represented, for instance, by our language system $\mathfrak{L}$ (§§ 15 ff.), there cannot be a method of decision for all sentences. [This has been shown by Alonzo Church; see *Amer. Journal of Math.*, 58 (1936), 345, and *Journal of Symbolic Logic*, 1 (1936), 40.] This holds a fortiori in the higher parts of logic, including arithmetic and the higher branches of mathematics. This does not exclude the possibility of methods of decision restricted to special kinds of sentences; and indeed several such methods for certain kinds within lower functional logic have been developed and are used as helpful instruments.

b. Inductive logic. Here, the problems of the second kind occur in two different forms, because here we are concerned not only with two sentences but, in addition, with a third item, a number. (i) Given: two sentences *e* and *h;* wanted: the value of $\mathfrak{c}(h,e)$, i.e., the degree of confirmation of *h* on the evidence *e.* (ii) Given: two sentences *e* and *h* and a number *r;* wanted: an answer to the question whether $\mathfrak{c}(h,e) = r$. For instance, a physicist has found, as a conjecture, a hypothesis *h* which he believes to be a good explanation for the results *e* of certain experiments; this is his solution, intuitively found, of a problem of the first kind; now he wants to find out whether *h* is indeed highly confirmed by *e* and, more precisely, (i) what is the value of $\mathfrak{c}(h,e)$; or, if he has made the guess that this value is *r*, he wants to find out (ii) whether indeed $\mathfrak{c}(h,e) = r$. There is, in general, no effective procedure for these problems; in other words, $\mathfrak{c}$ is, in general, not a computable function. This does not exclude the existence of methods of computation for $\mathfrak{c}$ in restricted classes. We shall later, in our system of quantitative inductive logic, give such methods for the following cases: (1) for all cases where *h* and *e* are molecular sentences in any system $\mathfrak{L}$, (2) for all cases where *h* and *e* are sentences of any form, molecular or general, in any finite system $\mathfrak{L}_N$, (3) for certain cases in a system $\mathfrak{L}_\infty^\pi$ (i.e., an infinite system containing only primitive predicates of degree one, § 31). More methods of this kind could be found for other restricted classes of cases. However, no general method of computation for $\mathfrak{c}$ is possible with respect to an infinite system $\mathfrak{L}_\infty$ which contains also relations; because such a method would immediately yield a method of decision for all sentences of this system, which is known to be impossible, as stated under (a). Thus, if *e* and *h* do not belong to one of the classes for which a method of computation exists and is known, the inductive logician *X* who wants to determine the value of $\mathfrak{c}(h,e)$ cannot simply follow a way prescribed by fixed rules, but just has to try to hit upon a way to a solution by his skill and good luck. This, however, is not a peculiar feature of inductive logic but holds in just the same way for deductive logic, as we have seen.

Thus it is true that an inductive machine is impossible for finding a suitable hypothesis (first problem) and also for examining whether a given hypothesis is suitable (second problem). But, then, a deductive machine is likewise impossible if it is intended to solve the corresponding deductive problems of finding a suitable L-implied theorem or of examining whether a proposed theorem is indeed L-implied. However, for a restricted domain as described above, an inductive machine for the determination of $\mathfrak{c}(h,e)$ is possible, for example, for all cases in which *e* and *h* do not contain variables with an infinite range of values; just as a deductive machine is possible which decides whether or not *e* L-implies *h*.

III. Third Problem: To Examine a Given Proof

a. Deductive logic. Given: *e*, *h*, and an alleged proof that *e* L-implies *h;* wanted: an answer to the question whether the alleged proof is actually a proof, that is, whether it is in accordance with the rules of deductive logic. For instance, a mathematician believes to have not only a solution of the first problem, for instance, a geometrical theorem *h*, but also a solution of the second problem, a proof that the axiom set *e* L-implies the theorem *h;* he wants to make sure that his belief is right, that is, that the proof is correct. For the solution of this problem there is an effective procedure, provided the proof is given completely. We have to distinguish here two different methods which are in customary use for proving that *e* L-implies *h*. (i) The first method consists in the construction of a sequence of sentences in the object language, leading from *e* to *h* in accordance with rules of deduction. (ii) The second method consists in a proof in the metalanguage, leading to the semantical statement '*e* L-implies *h*'. Strictly speaking, an effective method for testing proofs can only be applied if a set of deductive rules has been laid down and if the proof to be tested is formulated in such a detailed form that every step in it consists in a single application of one of the rules. This condition is not often fulfilled in method (i) and almost never in method (ii). The method for testing proofs, as they are usually formulated, is not effective in the strictest sense. However, we may say that it is *practically effective* in the following sense. Suppose a mathematician shows, by either method (i) or method (ii), that the theorem *h* is deducible from the geometrical axioms *e;* and suppose he uses in his proof, as is customary in geometry, the ordinary word language without explicit rules of deduction. Then we know what we have to do in order to examine the correctness of the proof. We examine for every single step in the proof whether it is an instance of a simple deductive procedure which we know to be valid. The mathematician has made the steps in such a way that he expects us to be able to carry out this examination for every step and to come to an affirmative result. If he has not overestimated our ability to recognize instances of L-implication, we shall affirm step for step and thereby recognize the whole proof as correct. Otherwise we have to ask him to split up the step which we are unable to judge into more and simpler steps, for which we are able to decide the question of correctness. Thus, in this examination of the proof, we are not entirely left to guessing, to a trial-and-error method as in problems of the first and second kind; instead, we know practically how to proceed and we expect that, under normal conditions, we shall reach a result in a finite number of operations, viz., the examinations of the steps of the given proof. In this sense we may say that we have a practically effective method. The result may also be formulated in this way: while L-implication is not an effective concept, the concept of proof for L-implication is effective, at least practically.

The situation may be described more in detail as follows. A method of the kind (i) is usually applied in syntax with respect to a calculus *K;* here the rules constitute a definition of 'direct C-implicate (directly derivable) in *K*' (see, e.g., [Semantics] §§ 26–28). Now it is possible, although not customary, to apply an exactly analogous method in semantics, with respect to a semantical system *S*. Essentially the same rules are here formulated as definition of 'direct L-implicate in *S*'. [Instead of constructing a chain leading from the premise *e* to *h* (called a derivation in the technical sense) one may also construct a chain without a premise leading to $e \supset h$ (called a derivation with the null class of premises or a proof in the technical sense; see [Semantics] § 26, formulation B); the difference is merely a technical one, the result is the same (for languages without free variables in sentences), see T20-1b.] Even if this method is used in a symbolic language for which explicit rules of deduction have been laid down, the proofs are rarely given in a complete form. They usually proceed by larger steps, such that each step consists of several applications of the rules and hence would be divided into several steps in a complete formulation. This abbreviated formulation is, of course, convenient and even necessary in order to avoid enormous length of the proofs. In many cases, the object language used in method (i) is the ordinary word language (supplemented by some technical terms and symbols) without explicit rules of deduction; and in almost all cases this holds for the metalanguage used in method (ii). This is customary for the formulations of deductions in mathematics and in science. Likewise in this book, we use method (ii); the proofs are formulated in the word language as our metalanguage (as an example, see the proof of T19-3). Thus, in all these cases, the method of examining the proofs has only the weaker and somewhat vague practical effectiveness described above.

b. Inductive logic. Given: *e*, *h*, and *r*, and an alleged proof that $\mathfrak{c}(h,e) = r$; wanted: an answer to the question whether the alleged proof is correct. For instance, a physicist believes he has found a solution of a problem of the first kind, say, a suitable hypothesis *h* on the basis of an observational report *e*, and, moreover, a solution of the problem of the second kind for this case, viz., what appears to him like a proof that $\mathfrak{c}(h,e) = r$; he wants to determine whether this is a correct proof. For the solution of this problem, as for the analogous problem in deductive logic, there is a procedure which is at least practically effective. However, there is this difference: of the two methods (i) and (ii) earlier described, there is an analogue here only to the second, that is, a proof in the metalanguage for the semantical sentence '$\mathfrak{c}(h,e) = r$'. No analogue to the first method is known; and it seems doubtful whether a simple and convenient method of this kind could be found. [One might perhaps think of a procedure consisting in the construction of a sequence of sentences, with a real number expression attached to each sentence expressing the $\mathfrak{c}$ of that sentence on the fixed evidence *e*. The sentence *e* itself with '1' attached to it would be the beginning of the sequence, and *h* with an expression for the number *r* attached to it would be the end. The sentences would belong to the object language, as in a proof in method (i), but the numerical expressions would still be in the metalanguage.] Thus the situation is here the same as described earlier for method (ii) in deductive logic. A proof is given, formulated in the word language, which serves as a semantical metalanguage; and we test the correctness of the proof by examining for each step whether it is valid on the basis of the tacitly presupposed standards. Thus the procedure is practically effective in just the same sense as explained earlier (although it is not effective in the strictest sense unless deductive rules are laid down for the metalanguage).

B. ***The Relation between Deductive and Inductive Logic***

Deductive logic may be regarded as the theory of the L-concepts, especially L-implication. These concepts can be based on the semantical concept of range, as we have seen (§ 20). Thus deductive logic, in this sense, is seen to be a part of semantics, that part which we sometimes call L-semantics. Inductive logic, in its quantitative form, may be regarded as the theory of $\mathfrak{c}$. As we shall see later, $\mathfrak{c}$ is also based on the concept of range. The theorems of inductive logic deal not only with $\mathfrak{c}$ but also with L-implication and the other L-concepts. Thus, inductive logic is likewise a part of semantics; it presupposes deductive logic; it may be regarded as constructed out of deductive logic by the introduction of the definition for $\mathfrak{c}$. In a sense, we may say that the definition of L-implication represents the rules of deduction; in the same sense, the definition of $\mathfrak{c}$ represents the rules of induction. Except for this difference with respect to the definitions used, the procedures for constructing proofs for theorems are the same in inductive logic as in deductive logic. We have earlier spoken of proofs for theorems of the form '*e* L-implies *h*' in deductive logic (see IIIa, method (ii)), and later of proofs for theorems of the form '$\mathfrak{c}(h,e) = r$' in inductive logic (see IIIb). If we look not at the definitions used but at the forms of inference used in these two kinds of proof, we find that they are the same in both cases. Not only in proofs of theorems of deductive logic but also in those of inductive logic we apply the implicit *deductive* procedures which are customarily applied in the word language. Thus any procedure of proof in any field, also in inductive logic, is ultimately a deductive procedure. This does not mean, of course, that induction is a kind of deduction. We must clearly distinguish between theorems of inductive logic, e.g., '$\mathfrak{c}(h,e) = 3/4$', and sentences like *e* and *h* about which the theorems speak. The former belong to the metalanguage; the latter belong to the object language and hence are not a part of inductive logic but its subject matter. The previous remark concerns only the former; it means that these theorems, although belonging to inductive logic, are reached by deduction. On the other hand, the relation between *e* and *h*, as stated by the theorem mentioned, is inductive, not deductive. No deductive procedure leads from *e* to *h;* but, if we may say so, an inductive procedure, characterized by the number 3/4, connects *e* with *h*.

The far-reaching analogy which holds between inductive and deductive logic in spite of the important differences between these two fields were repeatedly emphasized in the preceding discussions. The principal common characteristic of the statements in both fields is their independence of the contingency of facts. This characteristic justifies the application of the common term 'logic' to both fields. The following representation of examples in two parallel columns will perhaps help in further clarifying the analogy.

Deductive Logic	**Inductive Logic**
The subsequent statements in deductive logic refer to these example sentences:	The subsequent statements in inductive logic refer to these example sentences:
Premise e: 'All men are mortal, and Socrates is a man.'	*Evidence* (or premise) *e:* 'The number of inhabitants of Chicago is three million; two million of these have black hair; *b* is an inhabitant of Chicago.'
Conclusion h: 'Socrates is mortal.'	*Hypothesis* (or conclusion) *h:* '*b* has black hair.'
The following is an example of an elementary statement in deductive logic:	The following is an example of an elementary statement in inductive logic:
D1. '*e* L-implies *h* (in *E*).' (*E* is here either the English language or a semantical language system based on English.)	**I1.** '$\mathfrak{c}(h,e) = 2/3$ (in *E*).'

DEDUCTIVE LOGIC—*Continued*

D_2. The statement D_1 can be established by a logical analysis of the meanings of the sentences *e* and *h*, provided the definition of 'L-implication' is given.

D_3. D_1 is a complete statement. We need not add to it any reference to specific deductive rules (e.g., the mood Barbara). However, the definition of 'L-implication' is, of course, presupposed for establishing D_1.

The following is a consequence of D_2.

D_4. The question whether the premise *e* is known (well established, highly confirmed, accepted), is irrelevant for D_1. This question becomes relevant only in the *application* of D_1 (see D_6 and D_7).

D_5 follows from D_1:

D_5. 'If *e* is true, then *h* is true.'

D_6 and D_7 are consequences of D_1 concerning *applications* to possible knowledge situations. D_6 represents the theoretical application (that is, the result refers again to the knowledge situation); D_7 represents the practical application (that is, the result refers to a decision).

D_6. 'If *e* is *known* (accepted, well established) by the person *X* at the time *t*, then *h* is likewise.' [Here, 'to know' is understood in a wide sense, including not only items of *X*'s explicit knowledge, that is, those which he is able to declare explicitly, but also those which are implicitly contained in *X*'s explicit knowledge.]

D_7. 'If *e* is known by *X* at *t*, then a decision of *X* at *t* based on the assumption *h* is rationally justified.'

INDUCTIVE LOGIC—*Continued*

I_2. The statement I_1 can be established by a logical analysis of the meanings of the sentences *e* and *h*, provided the definition of 'degree of confirmation' is given.

I_3. I_1 is a complete statement. We need not add to it any reference to specific inductive rules (e.g., for I_1, a rule of the direct inductive inference). However, the definition of 'degree of confirmation' is, of course, presupposed for establishing I_1.

The following is a consequence of I_2.

I_4. The question whether the premise (evidence) *e* is known (well established, highly confirmed, accepted), is irrelevant for I_1. This question becomes relevant only in the *application* of I_1 (see I_6 and I_7).

There is here no analogue to D_5. From I_1 and '*e* is true' nothing can be inferred (see § 10A).

I_6 and I_7 are consequences of I_1 concerning *applications* to possible knowledge situations. I_6 represents the theoretical application, I_7, the practical application.

I_6. 'If *e* and nothing else is *known* by *X* at *t*, then *h* is confirmed by *X* at *t* to the degree 2/3.' [Here, the term 'confirmed' does not mean the logical (semantical) concept of degree of confirmation occurring in D_1 but a corresponding pragmatical concept; the latter is, however, not identical with the concept of degree of (actual) belief but means rather the degree of belief justified by the observational knowledge of *X* at *t*.] The phrase 'and nothing else' in I_6 is essential; see § 45B concerning the requirement of total evidence.

I_7. 'If *e* and nothing else is known by *X* at *t*, then a decision of *X* at *t* based on the assumption of the degree of certainty 2/3 for *h* is rationally justified (e.g., the decision to accept a bet on *h* with a betting quotient not higher than 2/3).'

It should be noticed that in inductive logic, just as in deductive logic, the reference to the knowledge of X does not occur in the purely logical statements (e.g., I_1) but only in the statements of application (I_6 and I_7). It is true that statements of inductive logic, like those of deductive logic, are usually applied both in everyday life and in science to a premise or evidence that is known, i.e., well established by observations. Nevertheless, it is irrelevant for the *validity* as distinguished from the practical value or applicability, of a statement of inductive logic, just as for one of deductive logic, whether the evidence is true or not and, if it is true, whether its truth is known or not.

We shall later (§ 55B) clarify the relation between deductive and inductive logic in still another way with the help of the concept of range. We shall see that a statement of deductive logic like 'e L-implies h' means that the entire range of e is included in that of h, while a statement of inductive logic like '$\mathfrak{c}(h,e) = 3/4$' means that three-fourths of the range of e is included in that of h. This shows again the similarity and at the same time the difference between the two fields.

§ 44. Logical and Methodological Problems

A. With respect to deductive procedures, we distinguish between the problems of deductive logic proper, including mathematics, and those of the methodology of deduction. The latter concern the choice of suitable deductive procedures for given purposes. Analogously we distinguish between inductive logic and methodology of induction. The latter gives no exact rules but only advice how best to apply inductive procedures for given purposes. Bacon's and Mill's theories on induction belong chiefly, not to inductive logic, but to the methodology of induction. On the other hand, the beginnings of an inductive logic are found in the classical theory of probability.

B. An inductive inference does not, like a deductive inference, lead to the acquisition of a new sentence but rather to the determination of a degree of confirmation. Inductive inferences usually concern a population (of persons or things) and samples; in many cases they deal with frequencies (statistical inferences). The principal kinds of inductive inference are briefly characterized: (1) direct inference, (2) predictive inference, (3) inference by analogy, (4) inverse inference, (5) universal inference.

A. *Methodological Problems*

In order to clarify the aim of our construction of inductive logic, it seems useful to emphasize a certain distinction between two kinds of problems. The problems of the one kind constitute the field which we call inductive logic; the problems of the other kind may be called, for lack of a better term, methodological problems and, more specifically, problems of the methodology of induction. Before explaining this distinction, let us look at deductive logic, where an analogous distinction can be made which is easier to understand. Here we have first the field of deductive logic proper, including pure mathematics. To this field belong, for instance, the theorems stated in §§ 20–40 above. Then there is a second field, closely connected but not identical with deductive logic. In this second field, methods are described for practically carrying out the procedures of deductive logic and mathematics, and suggestions are made for the use of these methods in various situations and for various purposes. Here we learn, for instance, how best to look for a proof of a conjectured theorem or for a simplification of a given proof; some hints are given as to the conditions under which an indirect proof may be useful; devices are explained for proving the independence of a certain sentence from a given set of postulates, or the consistency of the set, or its completeness; other devices are given for finding convenient approximating functions for the purpose of numerical calculations (for example, T40-4 above; this theorem itself and other similar ones in § 40A belong to mathematics and hence to deductive logic; but the more or less vague general rules which tell us how to find an approximating function of this kind when we need it belong to the second field). This second field may be called methodology of deductive logic and mathematics.

Analogously, inductive logic (in its quantitative form) contains statements which attribute a certain value of $\mathfrak{c}$ to a certain case, that is, a pair of sentences e,h, or speak about relations between values of $\mathfrak{c}$ in different cases. On the other hand, the methodology of induction gives advice how best to apply the methods of inductive logic for certain purposes. We may, for instance, wish to test a given hypothesis h; methodology tells us which kinds of experiments will be useful for this purpose by yielding observational data e_2 which, if added to our previous knowledge e_1, will be inductively highly relevant for our hypothesis h, that is, such that $\mathfrak{c}(h,e_1 \cdot e_2)$ is either considerably higher or considerably lower than $\mathfrak{c}(h,e_1)$. Sometimes, not one hypothesis but a set of competitive hypotheses is given, and we wish to come to an inductive decision among them by finding observational material which gives to one of the hypotheses a considerably higher $\mathfrak{c}$ than to the others. In another case, we may have found observational results which are not explainable by the hypotheses accepted so far and perhaps even incompatible with one of them; here, we wish to find a new hypothesis which not only is compatible with the observations but explains them as well as possible. As explained in the preceding section (problem I), there is no effective procedure leading to this aim, no more than there is in mathematics for finding a theorem suitable for a given purpose. Nevertheless, it is possible in both cases to give some useful hints in which direction and by which means to look for a result of the kind wanted; these hints are given by methodology. Inductive and deductive logic cannot give them; they are indifferent to our needs and purposes both in practical life and in theoretical work. By emphasizing the distinction between logic and methodology, we do not intend to advocate a separation of the two kinds of problems within scientific inquiry. They are usually treated in close connection, and that is very useful. There is hardly any book in mathematics—except perhaps a table of logarithms—that does not add to the mathematical theorems some indications as to how they may usefully be applied either in mathematics itself or in empirical science. Similarly, to our later theorems in inductive logic, we shall often add some remarks about their use. Some of these remarks concern the use within inductive logic, for instance, the utilization of a given theorem in proofs of later theorems; other remarks concern the use outside of inductive logic, for instance, the possibility of a practical application either of inductive logic in general or of a given theorem to knowledge situations. Remarks of both kinds belong, not to inductive logic itself, but to the methodology of induction. [Examples of methodological discussions concerning the application of inductive logic in general are our discussions of the requirements of logical independence and completeness (above, § 18B), of the requirement of total evidence (below, § 45B), and the detailed discussions of the application of inductive logic for determining practical decisions (below, §§ 49–51); examples of methodological remarks concerning the application of particular theorems to possible knowledge situations are found at many places in the subsequent chapters, e.g., in §§ 60, 61, and generally whenever in the comments on given theorems terms like 'observation', 'known', 'unknown', 'expectation', 'prediction', 'decision', 'betting', and similar ones occur.] However, the principal purpose of this book is the discussion and, if possible, solution of problems of inductive logic itself; in other words, the proof of theorems on the degree of confirmation. The discussions of problems of the methodology of induction, on the other hand, are only incidental, although for practical reasons they may be useful and sometimes even indispensable. A theoretical book on geometry need not discuss in detail, if at all, the application of geometrical theorems for the calculation of the area of a garden or the distance of the moon, because the reader can be expected to be familiar with the connection between theoretical geometry and its application to spatial relations of physical bodies. In the case of inductive logic, on the other hand, there is at the present time not yet sufficient clarity and agreement even among the writers in the field concerning the nature of the theory and the connection between theory and practical application. Therefore today a book on inductive logic is compelled to devote a considerable part of its space to a discussion of methodological problems.

One of the purposes in emphasizing the distinction between inductive logic proper and the methodology of induction is to make it clear that certain books, investigations, and discussions concerning induction do not belong to inductive logic although they are often attributed to it. This holds in particular for the works of Francis Bacon and John Stuart Mill; their discussions on induction, including Mill's methods of agreement, difference, etc., belong chiefly to the methodology of induction and give hardly a beginning of inductive logic. On the other hand, the beginnings of a systematic inductive logic can be found in another class of works, some of them written a long time before Mill, although in many of these works the word 'induction' does not even occur. I am referring to all those works which deal with the theory of probability$_1$; as previously explained (§ 12), most of the classical works on the theory of probability belong to this class, as do most of those modern books on probability which are not based on the frequency conception of probability. In most of these theories, probability has numerical values; hence, they are systems of quantitative inductive logic. Keynes's theory is an example of a comparative inductive logic supplemented by a very restricted part of quantitative inductive logic, since, according to his conception, probability has numerical values only in some cases of a special kind, while in general only a comparison is possible leading to the result that one hypothesis is more probable than another. Jeffreys starts with axioms on the primitive notion 'given p, q is more probable than r', hence with a comparative inductive logic; on its basis, a quantitative inductive logic is constructed by laying down conventions for the assignment of numerical values.

B. *Inductive Inferences*

What we call inductive logic is often called the theory of nondemonstrative or nondeductive inference. Since we use the term 'inductive' in the wide sense of 'nondeductive', we might call it the theory of inductive inference. We shall indeed often speak of inductive inferences because the term is customary and convenient. However, it should be noticed that the term 'inference' must here, in inductive logic, not be understood in the same sense as in deductive logic. Deductive and inductive logic are analogous in one respect: both investigate logical relations between sentences;

the first studies the relation of L-implication, the second that of degree of confirmation which may be regarded as a numerical measure for a partial L-implication, as we shall see (§ 55B). The term 'inference' in its customary use implies a transition from given sentences to new sentences or an acquisition of a new sentence on the basis of sentences already possessed. However, only deductive inference is inference in this sense. If an observer *X* has written down a list of sentences stating facts which he knows, then he may add to the list any other sentence which he finds to be L-implied by sentences of his list. If, on the other hand, he finds that his knowledge confirms another sentence to a certain degree, he must not simply add this other sentence. The result of his inductive examination cannot be formulated by the sentence alone; the value found for the degree of confirmation is an essential part of the result. If we want to give a schematized (and hence somewhat oversimplified) picture of *X*'s procedure, we may imagine that he writes two lists of sentences; for the sake of simplicity we assume that the sentences of both lists are molecular. The first list contains the sentences which he knows; additions to this list are made in two ways: (*a*) basic sentences formulating the results of new observations which he makes and (*b*) sentences L-implied by those on the list. Only the additions of the kind (*a*) change the logical content of the list. Let us assume that the atomic sentences of *X*'s language are logically independent of each other (according to the requirement of independence, § 18B). Then *X* need never cross out a sentence once written on the first list. The second list contains inductive results. These are formulated by sentences, each of them marked with a numerical value, its degree of confirmation with respect to the first list. These values, however, hold only for a certain time; as soon as a new observation sentence is added to the first list, the numerical values on the second list have to be revised. These values could be provided by an inductive machine, into which the observation sentences of the first list, kind (*a*), are fed. (In order to make the procedure effective and accessible to a machine, it must be restricted to a finite system.)

This picture makes it clear that an inductive inference does not, like a deductive inference, result in the acquisition of a sentence but in the determination of its degree of confirmation. It is in this sense, and only in this sense, that we shall use the term 'inductive inference' further on.

The most important kinds of inductive inference or, in other words, of general theorems concerning $\mathfrak{c}$ deal with cases where either or both of the sentences *e* and *h* give information about frequencies, for instance, in the form of an individual or statistical distribution (§ 26B) for some individuals with respect to a division. In these cases we might speak of *statistical inductive inferences*.

Following the usage of statisticians, we call the class of all those individuals to which a given statistical investigation refers the *population*. Any proper subclass of the population, defined by an enumeration of its elements, not by a common property, is called a *sample* from the population. The population need not necessarily consist of human beings; it may consist of things or events of any kind, persons, animals, births, deaths, molecules, electrons, specimens of grain, products of a factory, etc. The population is usually not the whole universe of individuals but only a part of it. For example, the universe may be the totality of physical things; one investigation may take as population the present inhabitants of Chicago, another may take the inhabitants of Boston in 1900, etc.; the fact that these and other populations are parts of the same universe of individuals makes it possible first to formulate these investigations in the same language system and also, if desired, to consider later a more comprehensive population containing the original ones as parts and studying their relations.

We shall now briefly characterize some of the most important kinds of inductive inference; they are neither exhaustive nor mutually exclusive.

1. The *direct inference*, that is, the inference from the population to a sample. (It might also be called internal inference or downward inference.) e may state the frequency of a property M in the population, and h the same in a sample of the population.

2. The *predictive inference*, that is, the inference from one sample to another sample not overlapping with the first. (It might also be called external inference.) This is the most important and fundamental inductive inference. From the general theorems concerning this kind we shall later (in Vol. II) derive the theorems concerning the subsequent kinds. The special case where the second sample consists of only one individual is called the *singular predictive inference*. We have indicated earlier (§ 41D) and we shall show in detail later (T108-1) that the results of the singular predictive inference stand in a close relation to the estimation of relative frequency.

3. The *inference by analogy*, the inference from one individual to another on the basis of their known similarity.

4. The *inverse inference*, the inference from a sample to the population. (It might also be called upward inference.) This inference is of greater importance in practical statistical work than the direct inference because we usually have statistical information only for some samples actually ob-

served and counted and not for the whole population. Methods for the inverse inference (often called 'inverse probability') have been much discussed both in the classical period and in modern statistics. One of the chief stimulations for the developments of modern statistical methods came from the controversies concerning the validity of the classical methods for the inverse inference.

5. The *universal inference*, the inference from a sample to a hypothesis of universal form. This inference has often been regarded as the most important kind of inductive inference. The term 'induction' was in the past often restricted to universal induction. Our later discussion will show that actually the predictive inference is more important not only from the point of view of practical decisions but also from that of theoretical science.

§ 45. Abstraction in Inductive Logic

A. The application of logic, which is not a task of logic itself but of methodology, has to do with states of observing, believing, knowing, and the like. On the other hand, logic itself, both deductive and inductive, deals not with these states but instead with sentences subject to exact rules. Thus logic gains exactness by abstracting from the vague features of actual situations. *B*. In the application of inductive logic still another difficulty is involved, which does not concern inductive logic itself. This difficulty consists in the fact that, if an observer wants to apply inductive logic to an expectation concerning a hypothesis h, he has to take as evidence e a complete report of all his observational knowledge. Many authors on probability$_1$ have not given sufficient attention to this *requirement of total evidence*. They often leave aside a great part of the available information as though it were irrelevant. However, cases of strict irrelevance are much more rare than is usually assumed. *C*. The simple structure of our language systems, the earlier requirement of completeness (§ 18B), and now the requirement of total evidence compel us to construct all examples of the application of inductive logic in a fictitious simplified form. This fact, however, does not prevent the approximative application of inductive logic to actual knowledge situations in our actual world, just as certain idealized concepts of physics can be practically applied. *D*. Abstractions may be very fruitful and even necessary for the progress of science, as the example of geometry shows. Some students reject all abstractions; others use them excessively and neglect certain features of reality. These extremes are harmful. We should rather combine both tendencies, that emphasizing the concrete as well as that emphasizing the abstract. As to inductive logic, we should overlook neither the fact that its ultimate purpose lies in its application in practical life nor the fact that it cannot be efficient without using abstract methods.

A. *Abstraction in Deductive and Inductive Logic*

Our theory of inductive logic will be applied not to the whole language of science with its great complexities, its large variety of forms of expression, and its variables of higher levels (e.g., for real numbers), but only to the simple language systems $\mathfrak{L}$ explained in the preceding chapter. This involves a certain simplification and schematization of inductive procedures in comparison with those actually used in the practice of science. Other kinds of schematization here involved are still more important; they will be discussed in this section. The first of them is inherent in any logical method; it could not be avoided even if we took the whole language of science as our object language, and it is a necessary factor even in deductive logic. It consists in the fact that the pure systems of both deductive and inductive logic refer simply to sentences (or to the propositions expressed by them) rather than to states of knowing, believing, assuming, etc., while any *application* of logic to an actual situation has to do with these states. This application is outside of pure logic itself; it belongs to the subject matter of the methodology of logic, as we have seen in the preceding section.

Let us first take an example from deductive logic. One of the simplest theorems of deductive logic says that i L-implies $i \vee j$. One kind of application of this theorem consists in the following rule, which is not a logical but a methodological rule: if X has good reasons for believing i, then the same reasons entitle him to believe $i \vee j$. This, however, is a crude formulation using 'believing' as a classificatory concept. A more adequate formulation would use it as a quantitative or at least as a comparative concept: if X at the time t has reasons for a belief in i to the degree r, then he has at the same time reasons for a belief in $i \vee j$ at least to the degree r. For instance, I look at a tree and, on the basis of what I see, I am convinced that a certain leaf is green; then I have the right to be convinced at least as strongly that this leaf is green or smooth. In this way, some rather vague and perhaps even problematic concepts enter the situation. Am I actually convinced? How am I to measure the strength of my conviction or at least to compare two convictions as to their strength? Is the color I want to express described accurately by 'green', or should I perhaps rather say 'greenish-blue'? We have here all the vaguenesses and other difficulties which arise on the way from an observation to the utterance of a corresponding observation sentence and our report about the belief in it. Within logic, however, all these difficulties do not appear. Not that they have been overcome; we just leave them outside, we 'abstract' from them. The advantage of this procedure is that in logic we deal only with clear-cut entities without vagueness. We have predicates and they are assumed to designate properties, and further we have other signs and their designata. The actual vagueness of the boundary line between green and blue is disregarded and likewise the vagueness of the other properties and all other designata. Furthermore, logic contains other semantical rules determining the meaning of the sentences on the basis of these designata (e.g., in the form of rules of ranges, as explained in § 18D). With the help of these rules, we determine whether or not the relation of L-implication holds between given sentences, and thus we reach one of the chief aims of deductive logic. (For instance, we show that i L-implies $i \vee j$ by showing that the range of i is contained in that of $i \vee j$.) All these procedures within deductive logic deal with neat, clear-cut entities according to exact rules and thus are not blurred by any vagueness. However, we must necessarily pay a price for this advantage; by the abstraction which we carry out in order to construct our system of logic, we disregard certain features; they remain outside the scope of logic. However, we must be careful in the characterization of this situation. Some philosophers say that, in consequence of the abstraction leading to logic or, in a similar way, to quantitative physics, certain features of reality (for instance, the 'genuine qualities' or 'qualia') remain forever outside our grasp. I do not agree with this view; although it sounds similar to what I said earlier, there is a fundamental difference. This may become clearer by the following analogy. Suppose a circular area is given, and we want to cover some of it with quadrangles which we draw within the circle and which do not overlap. This can be done in many different ways; but, whichever way we do it and however far we go with the (finite) procedure, we shall never succeed in covering the whole circular area. However, it is not true that—in analogy to the philosophical view mentioned—there is any point in the area which cannot be covered. On the contrary, for every point and even for every finite number of points there is a finite set of quadrangles covering all of them. The situation with abstraction is analogous. In any construction of a system of logic or, in other words, of a language system with exact rules, something is sacrificed, is not grasped, because of the abstraction or schematization involved. However, it is not true that there is anything that cannot be grasped by a language system and hence escapes logic. For any single fact in the world, a language system can be constructed which is capable of representing that fact while others are not covered. For instance, if we find ourselves unable to describe a certain subtle difference between two shades of color with simple predicates like 'green' and 'blue', we may make our net finer and finer by introducing more and more predicates like 'bluish-green', 'greenish-blue', etc., or by introducing quantitative scales (as in the color systems of W. Ostwald or A. C. Hardy); in this way, our language becomes more and more precise with respect to colors. Perhaps this process of introducing more and more precise terms can never come to an end, so that some vagueness always remains. On the other hand, there is no difference in color shade, however slight, that remains forever inexpressible.

B. *The Requirement of Total Evidence*

Suppose that inductive logic supplies a simple result of the form '$\mathfrak{c}(h,e) = r$', where h and e are two given sentences and r is a given real number. How is this result to be applied to a given knowledge situation? This question is answered by the following rule, which is not a rule of inductive logic but of the methodology of induction:

(1) If e expresses the total knowledge of X at the time t, that is to say, his total knowledge of the results of his observations, then X is justified at this time to believe h to the degree r, and hence to bet on h with a betting quotient not higher than r.

One of the decisive points in this rule is the fact that it lays down the following stipulation:

(2) *Requirement of total evidence:* in the application of inductive logic to a given knowledge situation, the total evidence available must be taken as basis for determining the degree of confirmation.

There is no analogue to this requirement in deductive logic. If deductive logic says that e L-implies h and if X knows e, then he is entitled to assert h irrespective of any further knowledge he may possess. On the other hand, if inductive logic says that $\mathfrak{c}(h,e) = r$, then the mere fact that X knows e does not entitle him to believe h to the degree r; obviously it is required either that X know nothing beyond e or that the totality of his additional knowledge i be ***irrelevant*** for h with respect to e, i.e., that it can be shown in inductive logic that $\mathfrak{c}(h,e \centerdot i) = \mathfrak{c}(h,e)$. It cannot even be said that X may believe h at least to the degree r; by the addition of i, the $\mathfrak{c}$ for h may as well decrease as increase. The theoretical validity of the requirement of total evidence cannot be doubted. If a judge in determining the probability of the defendant's guilt were to disregard some relevant facts brought to his knowledge; if a businessman tried to estimate the gain to be expected from a certain deal but left out of consideration some risks he knows to be involved; or if a scientist pleading for a certain hypothesis omitted in his publication some experimental results unfavorable to the hypothesis, then everybody would regard such a procedure as wrong.

The requirement has been recognized since the classical period of the theory of probability. Keynes ([Probab.], p. 313) refers to "Bernoulli's maxim, that in reckoning a probability, we must take into account all the information which we have". Although in the second axiom referred to by Keynes, Bernoulli speaks in somewhat weaker terms ("everything that can come to our knowledge" [Ars], p. 214), the formulation of the third axiom ("Not only those arguments must be considered which are favorable to an affair but also all those which can be advanced against it, so that after pondering both it becomes clear which ones outweigh the others", p. 215) and the examples given in connection with both axioms leave no doubt that the requirement of total evidence is meant. The requirement is expressed more clearly by C. S. Peirce: "I cannot make a valid probable inference without taking into account whatever knowledge I have . . . that bears on the question" ([Theory], p. 461). However, many writers since the classical period, although presumably acknowledging the requirement in theory, did not give sufficient attention to it in questions of practical application. Laplace himself, for instance, raised the following question: According to the reports of history, the sun has never failed to rise every twenty-four hours for five thousand years or 1,826,213 days; what is the probability of its rising again tomorrow morning? Using his rule of succession, Laplace gave the answer: $1 - 1/1{,}826{,}215$. Since we cannot assume that he was unaware of the fact that history reports besides sunrises also a number of other events, we must conclude that he either regarded all other known events as irrelevant for his problem or failed to consider the question of relevance. Many examples of a similar nature were constructed. Later writers criticized these examples. Aside from criticisms of the methods used for the solutions, for example, the rule of succession, the objection was raised that series of events of this kind are not a proper subject matter for the theory of probability because we have a causal explanation for them and therefore cannot regard them as matters of chance. I should prefer to give this objection a different form. I agree with Laplace against his critics in the view that the theory of probability or inductive logic applies to *all* kinds of events, including those which seem to follow so-called causal laws, that is, general formulas of physics, for instance, in the example of the sun, the laws of mechanics applied to the earth and the sun. On the other hand, I agree with the critical judgment of the later writers that Laplace's application of the theory in cases of this kind is not correct because our knowledge of mechanics is disregarded. I would say that the requirement of total evidence is here violated because there are many other known facts which are relevant for the probability of the sun's rising tomorrow. Among them are all those facts which function as confirming instances for the laws of mechanics. They are relevant because the prediction of the sunrise for tomorrow is a prediction of an instance of these laws.

Modern authors on probability are in general more careful in the construction of their examples; but I think that even they are often not cautious enough in their tacit or explicit assumptions as to irrelevance. The cases of strict irrelevance are considerably more rare than is usually believed. Later, in the construction of our system of inductive logic, examples will be found where we might be inclined at the first look to assume irrelevance, while a closer investigation shows that it does not hold.

C. *The Applicability of Inductive Logic*

We have seen earlier (§ 18B) that the requirement of completeness compels us to imagine for the purpose of the application of inductive logic a simplified world, a universe which is not more complex in structure or more abundant in variety than the simple language system which we are able to manipulate in inductive logic. Now the requirement of total evidence compels us in the construction of examples of application to imagine in the simplified universe an observer X with a simplified biography. While every adult person in our actual world has observed an enormous number of events with an immense variety transcending all possibilities of complete description, let alone calculatory inductive analysis, we have to imagine an observer X whose entire wealth of experience is so limited that it can easily be formulated and taken as a basis for inductive procedures. Thus, examples of the application of inductive logic must necessarily show certain fictitious features and deviate more from situations which can actually occur than is the case in deductive logic. This fact, however, does not make inductive logic a fictitious theory without relevance for science or practical life. A man who wants to calculate the areas of islands and countries begins with studying geometrical theorems illustrated by examples of simple forms like triangles, rectangles, circles, etc., although none of the countries in which he is interested has any of these forms. He knows that by beginning with simple forms he will learn a method which can be applied also to more and more complex forms approximating more and more the areas in which he is interested. Analogously, the method of inductive logic, although first applied only to fictitious simple situations, can, if sufficiently developed, be applied to more and more complex cases which approximate more and more the situations in which we find ourselves in real life. Physics likewise uses certain simplified, idealized conceptions which would hold strictly only in a fictitious universe, for example, those of frictionless movement, an absolutely rigid lever, a perfect pendulum, a mass point, an ideal gas, etc. These concepts are found to be useful, however, because the simple laws stated for these ideal cases hold approximately whenever the ideal conditions are approximately fulfilled. Similarly, there are actual situations which may be regarded as approximately representing the ideal conditions dealt with in our inductive logic referring to the simple systems $\mathfrak{L}$.

Suppose, for instance, that spherical balls of equal size are drawn from an urn; the surface of these balls is in general white, but some are marked with a red point, others not; some (without regard to whether they have a red point or not) have a blue point, others not; and some have a yellow point, others not. A simple inspection does not reveal other differences between the balls. Then we may apply our system $\mathfrak{L}$ to the balls and their observed marks; we take as individuals the balls, or rather the events of the appearance of the single balls, abstracting from the fact that the actual balls have distinguishable parts and that the very markings by which we distinguish them are parts of the balls. And we take the three kinds of markings as primitive properties as though they were the only qualitative properties of the balls, abstracting from the fact that a careful inspection of the actual balls would reveal many more properties in which they differ. Suppose we have drawn one hundred balls and found that forty of them had the property M of bearing a red point and a blue point. Suppose that this is all the knowledge we have concerning the balls and that we are interested in the probability of the hypothesis h that the next ball (if and when it appears) will have the property M. Then we shall take as our evidence e the observation results concerning the hundred balls just described. This is again an idealization of the actual situation because in fact we have, of course, an enormous amount of knowledge concerning other things. We leave this other knowledge i aside because we regard it as plausible that it is not very relevant for h with respect to e, that is to say, that the value of $\mathfrak{c}(h,e)$, which we can calculate, does not differ much from the value of $\mathfrak{c}(h,e \cdot i)$, which ought to be taken according to the requirement of total evidence but which would make the calculation too complicated. (Of course, we may be mistaken in the assumption of the near-irrelevance of i; that is to say, a closer investigation might show that, in order to come to a sufficient approximation, certain other parts of the available knowledge must be included in the evidence; just as a physicist who assumes that the influence of the friction in a certain case is so small that he may neglect it may find by a closer analysis that its influence is considerable and therefore must be taken into account.) If the temporal order of the hundred ball drawings is known and seems to be relevant (for instance, if the sequence of the colors in their temporal order of appearance shows a high degree of regularity), then we shall include in our evidence the description of this order according to one of the methods earlier explained (§ 15B). If the temporal order of the hundred drawings is not known (for instance, if we counted only the number of each kind without paying attention to the order) or if it is known but assumed to be not very relevant, then we shall take as evidence the conjunction of three hundred sentences, each of which says of one of the hundred balls whether or not it has one of the three primitive properties. It will even be sufficient to take as evidence a conjunction of one hundred sentences, each of which says of one of the hundred balls whether or not it is *M*. For certain rules of induction or definitions of degree of confirmation, it can be shown that the additional knowledge contained in the three hundred sentences is strictly irrelevant in this case.

Let us suppose that we have decided to take the latter conjunction of one hundred sentences concerning *M* and non-*M* as our evidence *e*. Then a system of inductive logic, although formulated for a simplified universe, may be applied to the actual knowledge situation just described. The application consists in calculating the value of the degree of confirmation c for the hypothesis *h* and the evidence *e* specified and taking this value as the probability sought.

It is important to recognize clearly the nature of the difficulties which have just been explained. They do not occur in inductive logic itself but only in the application of inductive logic to actual situations of knowledge; hence they belong to the methodology of induction. Like deductive logic, inductive logic has to do only with clear-cut entities without any vagueness; it deals with sentences of a constructed language system; it ascribes to a pair of sentences *h*,*e* a real number *r* as the degree of confirmation according to exact rules. Here, as in deductive logic, the exactness, the freedom from vagueness, is obtained by abstraction and therefore at a sacrifice.

D. *Dangers and Usefulness of Abstraction*

Some scientists and philosophers feel a strong disinclination against all abstractions or schematizations. They demand that any methodological or even logical analysis of science should never lose sight of the actual behavior of scientists both in the laboratory and at the desk. They warn against neglecting any of the factors which a good scientist takes into consideration in inventing and testing his hypotheses; they emphasize that the complex judgment on the acceptability of a hypothesis cannot be based on just one number, the degree of confirmation. I think that this view contains a correct and important idea. Whenever we make an abstraction, we certainly ought to be fully aware of what we are doing and not to forget that we leave aside certain features of the real processes and that these features from which we abstract at the moment must not be entirely overlooked but must be given their rightful place at some point in the full investigation of science. On the other hand, if some authors exaggerate this valid requirement into a wholesale rejection of all abstractions and schematizations, an attitude which sometimes develops into a veritable abstractophobia, then they deprive science of some of its most fruitful methods.

The history of science is full of examples for the usefulness and immense fertility of abstractions. One of the most outstanding examples is geometry. It was created by an act of abstraction: attention was directed toward the spatial properties and relations of bodies, while all other properties, color, substance, weight, etc., were disregarded. Then another bold step was taken, leading away from the world of concrete things with their directly observable properties to a schema consisting of constructs: geometry was transformed into a theory of certain spatial configurations whose properties are completely and exactly determined. This geometry no longer deals with wooden or iron balls but with spheres, perfect spheres of which the balls are only more or less rough approximations. It deals with infinite straight lines, of which at best some finite segments are approximately represented by certain threads and edges of bodies. Both these steps of abstraction were taken in ancient times; we will not discuss here some later steps which went even much farther in the same direction by transforming geometry into a theory of certain sets of real numbers (Descartes), into a formal axiom system (Hilbert), and finally into a special branch of the logic of relations (Russell). The important point for our discussion appears already in the effect of the first two steps of abstraction. Today it is clear that the magnificent development of geometry through its history of more than two thousand years would have been impossible without those abstractions and that the development of physics would have been impossible without that of geometry. Thus the end result is that, not only from the point of view of the mathematician but also from that of the physicist, the abstractions in geometry are immensely useful and even practically indispensable. Although the aim remains the investigation not of the abstract configurations but of the observable spatial properties of concrete things, nevertheless it turns out that abstract geometry supplies the most efficient method for this investigation, much more efficient than any method dealing directly with observable spatial properties. Numerous other methods of abstraction or schematization have proved fruitful in physics. This shows that, if we want to obtain knowledge of the things and events of our environment as a help for our decisions in practical life, then the roundabout way which leads first away from these things to an abstract schema may in the long run be better than the direct way which stays close to the things and their observable properties.

The situation in logic is analogous. Both in deductive and in inductive logic we deal with abstract schemata, with sentences which belong to constructed language systems and are manipulated according to exact rules. This is admittedly a step away from the actual situations of observing, believing, etc., in which we find ourselves in practical life. The choice of this procedure is not based on the assumption that the actual situations are unimportant and that the exact schemata are all that matters. On the contrary, the final aim of the whole enterprise of logic as of any other cognitive endeavor is to supply methods for guiding our decisions in practical situations. (This does, of course, not mean that this final aim is also the motive in every activity in logic or science.) But here, as in physics, the roundabout way through an abstract schema is the best way also for the practical aim. Some philosophers who shy away from all abstractions have suggested that in the logical analysis of science we should not make abstractions but deal with the actual procedures, observations, statements, etc., made by scientists; we should give up the concept of truth as defined in pure semantics with respect to a constructed language system and use instead the pragmatical concept 'accepted (or verified or highly confirmed) by *X* at the time *t*'; likewise, instead of the semantical concept of L-truth (see § 20), we should use a related pragmatical concept defined in about this way: '*i* is a sentence of such a kind that, for any sentence *j*, the utterance of the conjunction *i* . *j* by *X* to *Y* has the same effect on *Y* as the utterance of *j* alone'. A theory of pragmatical concepts would certainly be of interest, and a further development of such a theory from the present modest beginnings is highly desirable. However, I think the repudiation of pure radical semantics and L-semantics, and thereby both of pure deductive and of inductive logic, in favor of a merely pragmatical analysis of the language of science would lead to a method of very poor efficiency, analogous to a geometry restricted to observable spatial properties. Inductive logic deals with schemata; but it is developed not for the sake of these schemata, but finally for the purpose of giving help to the man who wants to know how certain he can be that his crop will not be destroyed by a drought, to the insurance company which wants to calculate a premium rate for life insurance that is not too high but still profitable, to the engineer who wants to find the degree of certainty that the bridge he constructs will be able to carry a certain load, to the physicist who wants to find out which of a set of competing theories is best supported by the experimental results known to him. The decisive point is that just for these practical applications the method which uses abstract schemata is the most efficient one.

One of the factors contributing to the origin of the controversy about abstractions is a psychological one; it is the difference between two constitutional types. Persons of the one type (extroverts) are attentive to and have a liking for nature with all its complexities and its inexhaustible richness of qualities; consequently, they dislike to see any of these qualities overlooked or neglected in a description or a scientific theory. Persons of the other type (introverts) like the neatness and exactness of formal structures more than the richness of qualities; consequently, they are inclined to replace in their thinking the full picture of reality by a simplified schema. In the field of science and of theoretical investigation in general, both types do valuable work; their functions complement each other, and both are indispensable. Students of the first type are the best observers; they call our attention to subtle and easily overlooked features of reality. They alone, however, would not be able to reach generalizations of a high level, because abstractions are needed for this purpose. Therefore, a science developed by them alone would be rich in details but weak in power of explanation and prediction. (This is a warning to those who are afraid of abstractions, especially in inductive logic.) Students of the second type are the best originators and users of abstract methods which, when sufficiently developed, may be applied as powerful instruments for the purpose of description, explanation, and prediction. Their chief weakness is the ever present temptation to overschematize and oversimplify and hence to overlook important factors in the actual situation; the result may be a theory which is wonderful to look at in its exactness, symmetry, and formal elegance, and yet woefully inadequate for the task of application for which it is intended. (This is a warning directed at the author of this book by his critical super-ego.)

It seems to me that the contrast between the two types, as long as its expression is a controversy between thesis and antithesis, the danger of abstractions versus their usefulness, is futile. It may become fruitful if expressed as a difference in emphasis rather than in assertion; either type emphasizes one side of the whole method of research and works as a safeguard against its neglect. History and personal experiences show us that either type is tempted to underestimate the value of the work of the other type. However, it is clear that science can progress only by the cooperation of both types, by the combination of both directions in the working method.

The foregoing distinction of two types is a customary but obviously oversimplified description of the situation. Instead of speaking of two types, one directed toward the concrete, the other toward the abstract, it would be more correct to apply a continuous scale of comparison: a person X tends less toward the concrete and more toward the abstract than another person Y. (In other words, a comparative concept is here more adequate than the two classificatory concepts; see § 4.)

§ 46. Is a Quantitative Inductive Logic Impossible?

Some students regard a quantitative degree of confirmation and hence a quantitative inductive logic as impossible because there are very many different factors determining the choice of the "best" hypothesis, and some of them cannot be numerically evaluated. However, the task of inductive logic is not to represent all these factors, but only the logical ones; the methodological (practical, technological) and other nonlogical factors lie outside its scope. Some authors, among them Kries, believe (1) that even the logical factors, for example, the extension, precision, and variety of the confirming material, are in principle inaccessible to numerical evaluation; and (2) that it is impossible to define a quantitative degree of confirmation dependent upon these factors. The first of these assertions is easily refuted.

The different attitude of the two psychological types discussed above manifested itself clearly each time in the development of modern science when attempts were made to introduce quantitative concepts, measurement, and mathematical methods into a new field, for instance, psychology, social sciences, and biology. Those who made these attempts were convinced from the beginning that the application of mathematical methods was possible though perhaps difficult. Even if they had to admit that the initial steps taken were far from perfect, they were not discouraged; they did not believe that these defects were necessary, due to an inherent nonquantitative character of the field in question. They expected that the method could and would be improved and that, when further developed, it would yield many new results unobtainable by the traditional methods alone. The opponents, on the other hand, believed either that it was impossible in principle to apply quantitative concepts to the special field ("How should it be possible to measure an intensive magnitude like a degree of intelligence, the intensity of an emotion, the similarity of two color sensations?") or that the quantitative method would only furnish trivial results and could not contribute to the real understanding of the phenomena, or even that the application of this method would do harm by giving a one-sided and distorted picture. The developments in quite a number of fields have shown in the meantime that the proponents of quantitative methods were right in their basic idea; on the other hand, they would themselves admit today that certain features of the methods applied at the beginning were not adequate, that the method is in need of continuous correction and improvement, and also that it is advisable to keep always in mind which features of the events under investigation are adequately represented by the quantitative concepts used and which are not.

The attempt to construct a quantitative inductive logic is not quite analogous to the cases just discussed, since here we have to do with a field of logic, and there with fields of empirical science. Nevertheless, the psychological situation is similar. It is therefore not surprising that also in this case objections are raised against the use of the quantitative method. And it seems that here the opposition is even stronger than in other cases. Many philosophers and scientists who object neither to the abstractions generally involved in logic nor to the introduction of the quantitative method into other fields are skeptical about its application in inductive logic or even declare this application to be impossible. For example, Kries believes that numerical values of probability$_1$ are applicable only in situations similar to those in games of chance, while in other cases at best a comparative statement is possible; he says, for instance, that an expectation based upon an inference by analogy "is always only more or less probable. The logical relation which holds here has nothing that can be represented numerically" ([Prinzipien], p. 26). Likewise, Keynes thinks that probability$_1$ is measurable only in cases of a very special kind. More recently, Ernest Nagel has expressed serious doubts concerning the possibility of a quantitative concept of degree of confirmation ([Principles], pp. 68–71). He points out the various factors which a scientist takes into consideration in judging and then either accepting or rejecting a proposed theory on the basis of given observational evidence. He explains the difficulties involved in any attempt to take into account these factors; some of these difficulties will be discussed in the next section. Because of the multiplicity of the factors involved, Nagel doubts whether it is possible to arrange theories in a linear order of increasing confirmation on a given evidence; if this is impossible, a quantitative degree of confirmation is obviously impossible.

Quantitative inductive logic, when fully developed—as it has not been so far and will not be in this book—so as to be applicable to the whole language of physics, is intended to enable us to determine, for instance, which of two hypotheses in physics is more supported by the given set of observational results and hence, so to speak, inductively preferable. Those who are skeptical with respect to quantitative inductive logic point to the fact—and here they are certainly correct—that in the practice of science factors of very different kinds influence the choice of a hypothesis. Some seem to think that to determine this choice by a simple calculatory schema would be just as preposterous as to propose rules of calculation which are to determine for every man which of the available women is the best for him to marry.

In judging objections of the kind described, it is important to be clearly aware of what is and what is not the nature and task of inductive logic and especially of its distinction from the methodology of induction (§ 44A). Inductive logic alone does not and cannot determine the best hypothesis on a given evidence, if the best hypothesis means that which good scientists would prefer. This preference is determined by factors of many different kinds, among them logical, methodological, and purely subjective factors. In the case of deductive logic it is clear that its task is not the representation of the actual procedures of thinking and forming beliefs by good scientists, still less of the ways in which they make their practical decisions. It is directed only toward one particular logical side of these procedures. Take, for example, a physicist who is pondering about logical consequences of certain premises, say, a set of well-established physical laws. In which direction his thinking goes, and which particular consequence he finds step for step as he goes along, is determined by a great number of factors of very different kinds, for instance, certain new observations for which he would like to discover whether or not, and if so, how, they can be explained with the help of those laws, the satisfaction he expects to feel if he succeeded in refuting another physicist's assumption, the fact that he is more familiar with certain mathematical techniques than with other ones, the strength and peculiar character of his imagination. All these factors are outside the realm of deductive logic. The rules of deductive logic do not in general guide his reflections; they can help him only at one point, in proving that a certain sentence considered by him is actually a logical consequence of the premises, that is, entailed, logically implied, implicitly given with the premises. He will reach this result only if deductive logic is sufficiently developed and if he is skilful and lucky enough to find a way leading from the premises to the conclusion in accordance with the rules. The situation with inductive logic is analogous. If a physicist deliberates whether or not to accept one hypothesis rather than another one on the basis of given observational results, then inductive logic can be of use to him only in one respect. It tells him whether one hypothesis is more supported than the other one; and, if the inductive logic applied is not only comparative but quantitative, it tells him to what degree the hypothesis considered is supported by the observations; this is, so to speak, the degree of partial entailment or partial logical implication. And he can obtain this help only if inductive logic is sufficiently developed and if he is able to find a way of applying it to his special case. All the other factors influencing his thinking and his decision are outside the scope of inductive logic. Thus the task and function of inductive logic is analogous and complementary to that of deductive logic.

Even if we distinguish clearly the logical factors from the methodological and other nonlogical factors, the question of the possibility of a quantitative inductive logic is still far from being settled. There remain still two problems: (1) Can the logical factors be measured, that is, given numerical values? (2) Is it possible to find a mathematical function of these numerical values which would represent the degree of confirmation, that is, an adequate quantitative explicatum of probability$_1$? These problems are still controversial. We shall discuss the first problem in this section, the second in the next section.

Some students regard as doubtful or impossible the numerical evaluation even of some of those factors which we characterize as logical. Let us examine, as examples, the factors mentioned in this connection by Kries. After discussing the inference by analogy (see the quotation above), he speaks about the universal inductive inference which leads from experience to laws, that is, sentences of a universal content. "Especially if a sentence of this kind", he says ([Prinzipien], pp. 29 f.), "possesses a great variety of consequences and is applicable in many cases and hence can be founded on experiential results of many different kinds, then it cannot be denied that a numerical measure of this foundation or empirical confirmation does not exist. To look for a numerical value of the certainty, for example, of the law of inertia or the principle of the conservation of energy would be an entirely illusory attempt; and the same holds for other, less well-established theorems of the same or other fields. For any sentence of this kind, extension and precision of its empirical confirmation, richness and fertility of its applications, and no less the objections against it which have to be eliminated by new assumptions, all these are factors which defy in principle any numerical determination." By saying "in principle", Kries indicates that he intends to disregard the difficulties caused by the fact that the methods of inductive logic may not yet be sufficiently developed at the present moment and further by the fact that the immense complexity of the situation with respect to his examples may practically prevent us from carrying out the numerical evaluation. Of the factors he mentions, the following are of a logical nature, and a quantitative inductive logic is therefore required to take them into account for the calculation of the degree of confirmation: (i) the extension of the confirming observational material, (ii) the variety of the confirming material, (iii) the precision of the confirming material, (iv) the extension (and likewise the other factors just mentioned) of the disconfirming material ("the objections", in the original: "die etwa entgegenstehenden Bedenken"). In the passage quoted, Kries makes two different statements concerning these factors, constituting negative answers to the two questions earlier mentioned. He says (1) that "all these are factors which defy in principle any numerical determination" and (2) that therefore "a numerical measure of this . . . empirical confirmation does not exist". Now the great difficulty involved in (2) must be admitted; it will be discussed in greater detail in the next section. The assertion (1), however, seems rather surprising, because the contrary appears nearly obvious and fairly generally assumed by scientists.

Let us subject this assertion to a closer examination. It says that it is impossible in principle to give numerical values to the factors mentioned—quite aside from the other question whether we can use these values for determining the degree of confirmation. There is first the problem of counting the number of confirming and of disconfirming cases for a given universal hypothesis *h* in a given observational report *e*. It is true, there are some serious difficulties involved in this problem, though often overlooked. It is usually assumed that, for all practical purposes, it is sufficiently clear what is meant by a confirming case and by a disconfirming case for *h*, and hence what is meant by the number of cases of those kinds occurring in *e*. The difficulties involved in these concepts were first pointed out by Carl G. Hempel in his investigations of the concept of confirmation, which we shall later discuss in detail (§§ 87 f.). Let us briefly indicate the chief difficulty. Let *h* be a simple law: '$(x)(Mx \supset M'x)$', where 'M' and 'M'' are molecular predicates; *h* may say, for instance, that all swans are white. Let *i* be '$Mb \, . \, M'b$' ('*b* is a white swan'). Then it seems natural to call *b* a confirming case for the law *h*. Let *j* be '$Mc \, . \, {\sim}M'c$' ('*c* is a non-white swan'). Then it seems natural to call *c* a disconfirming case for *h*. Now, let *i′* be '$\sim Md \, . \sim M'd$' ('*d* is a non-white non-swan'). At first, we might be tempted to regard *d* as an irrelevant case for *h*, that is, as neither confirming nor disconfirming. However, let *h′* be the law '$(x)(\sim M'x \supset \sim Mx)$' ('all non-white things are non-swans'); then *i′* has the same relation to *h′* as *i* to *h*, and hence *d* is a confirming case for *h′*. Now *h* and *h′* are L-equivalent; they express the same law and differ merely in their formulations. Therefore any observation must either confirm both or neither of them. On the other hand, if somebody who intends to test the law that all swans are white finds a non-swan, say, a stone, and observes that it is not white but brown, then he would probably hesitate to regard this observation as a confirming case for the law. We propose to call this puzzling situation *Hempel's paradox* because Hempel first pointed it out and offered a solution for it; this will be discussed later (in Vol. II). Hempel offers a definition for the concept of confirming case which is supposed to overcome this and other difficulties involved. Even if there are some doubts whether the particular definition chosen by Hempel may not be too narrow (see below, § 88), it seems plausible to assume that an adequate definition can be found. At any rate, nobody has so far given any reasons why it should be impossible in principle to find an adequate definition. On the contrary, scientists speak frequently about the number of confirming cases. A physicist would say, for instance, that he made six experiments in order to test a certain law and that he found it confirmed in all six cases. A physician would report that he tried out a new drug in twenty cases of a certain disease and found it successful in twelve cases, not successful in five, while in three cases the result was not clear either way; he hereby refers to confirming, disconfirming, and irrelevant cases for the hypothesis that the drug has a favorable effect in all cases of the disease in question. In other situations, the application of the concept of a confirming case would be less clear. This, however, shows merely that the concept is rather vague in certain respects; but all explicanda are more or less vague, and this fact certainly does not prove the impossibility of an explicatum.

Thus let us assume, as most scientists seem to do implicitly, that the concept of a confirming case can be defined; the concept of a disconfirming case is then easily definable. Then we can determine the number of confirming cases contained in the observational report *e*. If these cases are of different kinds, we can determine the number of confirming cases of each kind. Then it is not difficult to define a measure for the degree of variety in the distribution of the cases, on the basis of the number of kinds and the numbers of cases of each of the kinds. If the differences between the kinds are not only qualitative (for instance, male and female persons; or human beings, dogs, and guinea pigs) but quantitative (for instance, persons of different age, weight, blood pressure, etc.), then the degree of variety will also depend upon the dispersion of the cases with respect to each of the relevant magnitudes (measured, for instance, by the standard deviation). In this way we obtain numbers characterizing what Kries calls the extension and the variety of empirical confirmation. In the same way, the extension and the variety of the disconfirming material can be numerically determined.

That Kries should regard the precision with which the observations fulfil the law as a factor inaccessible to numerical evaluation is still more surprising. This factor comes into consideration only if the law contains quantitative concepts, for instance, physical magnitudes, and the report *e* refers to results of measurement of these magnitudes. Methods for measuring the precision in the sense here in question were developed a long time ago in the branch of mathematical statistics called the theory of errors and are constantly applied in many branches of science; for instance, a value inversely proportional to the standard deviation is often taken as a measure of precision. [In our theory of inductive logic the problem of the precision with which the observations fulfil a law does not arise because quantitative magnitudes do not occur in our object languages $\mathfrak{L}$. It may be remarked that, once this factor is measured, it is certainly possible in a more comprehensive system of inductive logic to take it into consideration for the determination of the $\mathfrak{c}$ of the hypothesis; Jeffreys has discussed ways of doing this ([Probab.], chap. iii).]

It is not quite clear what Kries means when he says that a law is "applicable in many cases" and refers to the "richness and fertility of its applications". Perhaps he means by "applications" of the law observable consequences; then the phrases just quoted do not refer to a new factor but are simply a repetition with other words of what he has said before. Or else he means by "applications" of the law its practically useful technological applications. In this case the factor referred to is not logical but methodological or technological. Hence, for the concept of degree of confirmation, it is neither required nor possible to take account of this factor.

Our discussion has shown that the first of the two arguments by which Kries and other authors try to prove the impossibility of a quantitative degree of confirmation is rather weak and can easily be refuted. The assertion is that certain logical factors, of which it is said correctly that the degree of confirmation depends upon them, are in principle inaccessible to numerical evaluation. We have seen that, on the contrary, it is rather plausible that they can be evaluated numerically. The second argument is more serious; it will be discussed in the next section.

§ 47. Some Difficulties Involved in the Problem of Degree of Confirmation

There remains the problem whether the degree of confirmation can be adequately defined if the factors earlier mentioned on which it depends can be evaluated numerically. Our discussion tries to show that there is no sufficient reason for the assertion that it is impossible. However, there are serious difficulties involved. We discuss the following points: (*A*) the degree of confirmation for a singular prediction on the evidence of an observed frequency; further, the degree of confirmation for a law with respect to different bodies of evidence; (*B*) an evidence which contains only confirming cases; (*C*) a more complex evidence containing cases which might be regarded as partially confirming; (*D*) an evidence which contains confirming and disconfirming cases. *E*. The degree of confirmation for a law should also depend upon the variety of confirming cases. *F*. In all these situations, the difficulty consists not in the fact that there is no adequate function but rather that it is not easy to see how best to make a choice among the infinite number of functions—a choice which would not seem entirely arbitrary. Whether and how the difficulties can be overcome will be seen later.

After the elimination of the first of the two arguments by which Kries and other authors try to prove the impossibility of a quantitative degree of confirmation, the second argument may be formulated like this: Even if it is true that numerical values can be attributed to each of the factors earlier mentioned, on which the degree of confirmation depends, it is still impossible to find a definition of a quantitative concept of degree of confirmation which adequately represents this dependence, because the parts played by the various factors differ from one another and vary with the situations and therefore cannot be summed up in one number.

Although this argument does not constitute a cogent proof of the impossibility asserted, the circumstances to which it refers deserve careful consideration, because they involve serious difficulties which any attempt toward a quantitative inductive logic has to meet. In this section some of these difficulties will be explained without making an attempt to solve them. The discussion is chiefly intended to make us realize how hard the task is that lies before us.

A. *Singular Prediction*

One of the most important and, in a certain sense, also most elementary problems of inductive logic concerns the singular predictive inference (§ 44B). If we have observed the frequency of a certain property, what is the probability$_1$ that a new object of the kind in question has this property? Let the evidence *e* available to *X* be a report about an observed sample of *s* (say, a hundred) individuals; *e* says that among them s_1 (say, eighty) have the property *M*.

Let the hypothesis *h* be the singular prediction that a certain individual *c* not belonging to the sample is *M*. The question is, what is the probability$_1$ of *h* with respect to *e*; in other words, when we look for a suitable definition of degree of confirmation $\mathfrak{c}$ as an explicatum of probability$_1$, what value do we want it to attribute to $\mathfrak{c}(h,e)$? We might perhaps first think that this value should be the same as the relative frequency observed, hence $\mathfrak{c}(h,e) = s_1/s$. This answer seems quite natural at the first glance, and it has indeed sometimes been proposed and even made the basis of various inductive methods, which we shall later examine in detail (in Vol. II). This solution, which we call the *Straight Rule*, might perhaps be accepted as a simple first approximation, but there are reasons which make it doubtful whether a definition of $\mathfrak{c}$ which leads exactly to this result is adequate as an explication of probability$_1$. This is shown by certain consequences to which such a definition would lead, especially in the case $s_1 = s$. In this case, in which all observed things are *M*, $\mathfrak{c}$ would become 1. Is this an adequate value? Perhaps someone might think that the value $\mathfrak{c} = 1$ could be accepted if the number *s* of individuals in the sample is large. Suppose we accept it for $s = 1{,}000$; should we then also accept it for $s = 20$, or 3, or even 1? And, if not, where should we draw the line? However, it is doubtful whether the value $\mathfrak{c} = 1$ is acceptable for any *s* because it would mean that it would be reasonable for *X* to bet with any betting quotient, however large, on the prediction that *c* is *M*. It seems clear that this would not be reasonable; I should like to find somebody who is willing in such a case to bet with me one million dollars against one. To put it in another way, $\mathfrak{c} = 1$ means that, if *X* knows *e*, *h* is practically certain for him (and, as we shall see later, *h* is even logically certain, that is, L-implied by *e*, if the number of individuals involved is finite, as in the case under discussion); and this does, of course, not hold in the case described.

Considerations of this kind, of which we can give here only brief indications, show that, if the observed relative frequency $r = s_1/s$ is 1, we must take $\mathfrak{c} < r$. This makes it plausible to take $\mathfrak{c} < r$ also if *r* is a proper fraction sufficiently near to 1. Then, however, the difficulty arises how to choose the difference between $\mathfrak{c}$ and *r*. If $r = 1$, should we take $\mathfrak{c} = 0.99$ or 0.99999 or what? If $r = 0.8$, as in the example above, which value smaller than 0.8 should be taken for $\mathfrak{c}$? Every possible choice seems unsatisfactory because completely arbitrary. Laplace, in his so-called rule of succession, takes $\mathfrak{c} = (s_1 + 1)/(s + 2)$. This value is $1/2$ if $r = 1/2$, and otherwise always between r and $1/2$; hence it fulfils the above requirement that it is smaller than r if r is equal to or near 1. Furthermore, this function is very simple and may appear to some as less arbitrary. Unfortunately, however, the general application of Laplace's rule leads to contradictions, as we shall see later.

Thus the situation is as follows. If e and h are of the kind described, $\mathfrak{c}(h,e)$ should in some way or other depend upon the numbers s and s_1 (the question whether it should, in addition, depend on other numbers may be left aside at the moment). Now, it is easy to state functions of s and s_1 which would seem fairly adequate for determining $\mathfrak{c}$. Hence the argument as originally meant by Kries and others does not hold; it is not at all impossible to find an adequate function for the case in question. There is actually a difficulty here; however, it is of a nature opposite to that asserted. There is not a lack of suitable functions but an overabundance, indeed an infinity of them. [For instance, for a given property M, we might take $\mathfrak{c} = (s_1 + m)/(s + 2m)$ with a positive constant m arbitrarily chosen; $m = 0$ is inadequate, as explained above (straight rule); $m = 1$ gives Laplace's function; contradictions are avoided if for other properties other suitable functions are chosen.] The difficulty is that we do not know how to make a choice among these functions without an arbitrary and hence implausible stipulation. In the other points to be discussed in this section we shall find situations involving difficulties of essentially the same kind.

B. *Confirming Cases for a Law*

In the preceding section we have seen that the task of defining the concepts of confirming case and of disconfirming case involves some difficulties but that, nevertheless, a solution seems possible. Let us now assume that we have satisfactory definitions for these concepts so that we can count the number of confirming and of disconfirming cases contained in an observational report e with respect to a hypothesis h, for instance, a law.

Let us first consider situations where e contains no cases disconfirming h but n confirming cases. Here it seems natural to determine $\mathfrak{c}(h,e)$ as a function of n (leaving aside, at present, other determining factors). It seems plausible that this function should be never decreasing. But which of the infinitely many functions of this kind should we choose? It is not difficult to lay down some more requirements for the function which seem plausible, for instance, that its relative increase by one additional confirming case should be less for higher *n*. But even after this condition and similar ones have been stated, there is still an infinite number of functions left from which to choose. Many authors have regarded the task as unsolvable; they believe that in the situation described, which is often called 'induction by simple enumeration', it is impossible to express in a quantitative way the evidential support given by the *n* confirming cases. I see no reason why this should be impossible. It must, however, be admitted that this point again shows that it is difficult to define $\mathfrak{c}$ without making quite arbitrary decisions.

C. *More Complex Evidence*

Let us assume again that we have an adequate definition for the concept of confirming case. Then it may happen that the evidence *e* available to *X* does not quite suffice to make the individual *b* a confirming case. For example, let *h* be the law '$(x)(Mx \supset M'x)$' ('all swans are white'), and let *e* contain '$Mb \cdot (M'b \vee Pb)$' ('*b* is a swan and is either white or small') and nothing else about *b*. Here, *X* does not know whether the swan *b* is white or not; but, still, the information that *b* is either white or small is more than nothing. Should it not count for something in weighing the evidence for the law *h*? But how much? Perhaps as half a confirming case? Or should it be left aside as an irrelevant case? Suppose, furthermore, that another part of the evidence *e* says that, of 100 observed small things, 90 were white. Then the assumption that *b* is white becomes much more probable. Therefore it seems no longer justified to disregard *b* entirely in determining $\mathfrak{c}(h,e)$. Although it cannot be counted as a whole confirming case, it must be counted in some way. Perhaps as 9/10 of a confirming case? Or perhaps as somewhat more than 9/10, according to the reasoning under (A)? At any rate, counting of whole cases does not seem sufficient. Thus the problem becomes rather complicated, although the evidence considered has still a fairly simple form. The difficulties would increase immensely if we were to consider more complex molecular sentences or even general sentences as the evidence or as conjunctive components of it. How can we hope to find a definition of degree of confirmation that gives plausible values in all these cases?

D. *Disconfirming Cases*

Now let us consider the situation where the evidence *e* describes a sample of *s* individuals among which s_1 violate the law (non-white swans), while the remaining s_2 do not. As hypothesis *h* we take here not the unrestricted law but a corresponding restricted law (D37-2b) which says that all swans not mentioned in *e* are white. Let s_2 be a fixed number, say, 100; we consider different values of s_1. It seems plausible that $\mathfrak{c}(h,e)$ is considerably less for $s_1 = 1$ than for $s_1 = 0$; but how much less? It seems further plausible that, with increasing s_1, $\mathfrak{c}$ decreases monotonically; but in which way? Suppose that r_0 and r_1 are the values of $\mathfrak{c}$ for $s_1 = 0$ and $s_1 = 1$, respectively, that is, just before and just after finding the first disconfirming case; then $r_1 < r_0$, as above. Suppose that all further observations in an increasing number s_2' contain no disconfirming cases. How many additional cases are required for outbalancing the one disconfirming case? That is to say, for which number s_2' does $\mathfrak{c}$ come back to its original value r_0? Suppose somebody defines $\mathfrak{c}$ in such a way that 5 additional cases balance the one disconfirming case, while somebody else offers a definition according to which 5,000 additional cases are required, and a third definition is such that no finite number of additional cases brings $\mathfrak{c}$ back to its original value. Which of these definitions—and of an infinite number of others—ought to be chosen? Would any decision on this point not seem arbitrary?

E. *The Variety of Instances*

One of the principles of the methodology of induction says that in testing a law we should vary as much as possible those conditions which are not specified in the law. This principle is generally recognized, and scientists followed it long before it was formulated explicitly. The theoretical justification for this methodological principle must lie in a theorem of either comparative or quantitative inductive logic to the effect that by following the principle, that is, by distributing the test cases among a wider variety of different kinds, a higher degree of confirmation is obtained. Therefore, a definition for $\mathfrak{c}$ would not be adequate unless it yielded a theorem of this kind; hence $\mathfrak{c}$ should, in certain situations, depend also upon the extent to which the principle of variety is heeded, that is to say, upon the number of different kinds from which the test cases are taken and the number of cases for each of these kinds. The problem is whether it is possible to find a definition of $\mathfrak{c}$ such that this requirement is fulfilled and, moreover, fulfilled without arbitrary stipulations *ad hoc*. Nagel has clearly shown, by a detailed discussion of numerical examples, how great the difficulty is in fulfilling the requirement mentioned ([Principles], pp. 68–71). Although I do not agree with his view that this difficulty makes it impossible to find an adequate definition for $\mathfrak{c}$, I admit that the difficulty is a very serious one. In a later chapter (in Vol. II) Nagel's views on this point will be discussed in detail, and then it will be examined with reference to his numerical examples how our system of inductive logic fulfils the requirement (cf. below, § 110I).

F. *The Task before Us*

The points (A) to (E) just explained are only a few of the difficulties which must be overcome if we are to construct an adequate quantitative inductive logic. It cannot be denied that these difficulties exist and that they are by no means negligible. However, they are not of the nature of a barrier thwarting our path; on the contrary, we see many open paths before us; the difficulty consists rather in the fact that we do not know at present which path will be the best for attaining our aim. The task is to find a function which is to fulfil certain requirements; it must depend, under certain conditions, on certain factors in certain ways which are only vaguely characterized. In order to show that a solution of this task is impossible, it would be necessary to prove that the various requirements are logically incompatible. It seems to me that the arguments of those who assert the impossibility are very far from proving this point or even making it plausible.

How shall we approach this task? One might perhaps consider the following procedure: we take up, one after the other, the points mentioned in this section and other ones in which there is a choice of several possibilities; at each point we take a choice which seems suitable for that specific problem; maybe we are sometimes compelled to change an earlier decision in order to make possible a suitable decision in a later point; in this way we might hope to work out, so to speak, a compromise solution which considers the various requirements. To be more specific, we might perhaps think of first deciding on ways for attributing numerical values to the factors discussed in the preceding section and to others and then to define $\mathfrak{c}$ as a function of these factors, fulfilling the requirements mentioned in this section.

We shall, however, not try to solve the task in this way. A procedure of this kind, consisting of a series of decisions only loosely connected and all of them more or less arbitrary, would lead to a patchwork solution that in the end would not appear satisfactory to anybody; very likely, a solution of this kind would lead to consequences, not immediately recognized, which are unplausible or even quite inacceptable. We shall approach the task from an entirely different angle. At the end of this chapter we shall discuss a way of laying the general foundations of a quantitative inductive logic (§§ 52–54). Then these foundations will actually be constructed in the next chapter. However, they will determine only those features of inductive logic which are in no way controversial, that is, those in which practically all workers in the field agree. Later (in Vol. II) our own system of inductive logic will be constructed, based on a definition of degree of confirmation. This definition will be reached on the basis of the common foundation, not by a large number of single decisions involving choices of particular numerical values, but by only two, so to speak, over-all decisions, decisions of a very general nature, not involving references to any of the factors earlier mentioned or to any numerical values (see Appendix, § 110A). Afterward we shall develop the consequences of this definition and then examine how the particular problems explained in this section and many other problems are solved. Then we shall have to judge whether these solutions seem adequate.

How is the adequacy of a function $\mathfrak{c}$, proposed as a quantitative explicatum of probability$_1$, to be judged? The simplest approach is the following. We imagine a knowledge situation and describe it in a sentence *e*, and further a hypothesis which we formulate by a sentence *h*. We choose *e* and *h* such that (1) they are simple enough so that they can be formulated in our systems $\mathfrak{L}$ and the given definition of $\mathfrak{c}$ can be applied to them, and (2) such that we have an intuitive impression of the value of probability$_1$ of *h* on *e* to which customary ways of inductive thinking would lead. In constructing these examples of application, we must be careful to make sure that the interpretation chosen fulfils the requirements of independence and completeness (§ 18B) and that *e* fulfils the requirement of total evidence (§ 45B). Then we examine whether the value of $\mathfrak{c}(h,e)$ calculated on the basis of the given definition is sufficiently in agreement with the intuitive value. Since the intuitive determination of a value is in general rather vague, an approximate agreement will be regarded as sufficient. If the calculated value differs considerably from the intuitive one, we shall regard the definition as inadequate in the case in question. It will seldom occur that a proposed definition will generally yield inadequate values. More frequently we shall find that it furnishes inadequate values only in certain special instances. In this case the definition need not be entirely abandoned; it may be that a suitable modification for it can be found. I believe that this is the case with several of those inductive methods which have been proposed by other authors and which will be examined, together with our own definition, with respect to adequacy (in Vol. II).

The discussion in this section does not claim to prove that a quantitative inductive logic is possible; it indicates merely that the arguments of opponents which are meant to prove its impossibility are insufficient. Thus the discussion is intended to remove an obstacle which might discourage us from even making an attempt toward the construction of a quantitative inductive logic. On the other hand, any overoptimism may be dampened by the explanation of the great difficulties involved in the task. Whether the attempt can and will be successful remains to be seen.

§ 48. Is Probability$_1$ Used as a Quantitative Concept?

A. Here the question is considered, not what the nature of probability$_1$ actually is or what an explicatum for it would be, but rather how people use the concept of probability$_1$. It appears plausible that many and perhaps most people in practical life and in science, who do not know any theory of probability, use the concept of probability$_1$ in the following way. They use probability$_1$ not only as a classificatory concept but also as a *comparative* concept ('more probable'). Furthermore, they use probability$_1$ in the following cases even as a *quantitative* concept: (*B*) with respect to predictions of results of games of chance, (*C*) with respect to a hypothesis concerning an individual in a field where a relevant relative frequency is known. *D*. In other cases we can determine which numerical value they implicitly attribute to a probability$_1$, even if they do not state it explicitly, by observing their reactions to betting proposals. *E*. If two people attribute considerably different probability$_1$ values to the same hypothesis on the same evidence, then they are inclined to offer theoretical arguments; this shows that they regard probability$_1$ as an *objective concept*. All these are merely psychological facts; they do not prove that there is an objective quantitative explicatum for probability$_1$. However, they may encourage us to make an attempt to find such an explicatum.

A. *Probability$_1$ Is Used as a Comparative Concept*

Our problem is to define an adequate quantitative concept of confirmation or, failing this, at least an adequate comparative concept. At the present stage of our discussions in this chapter, we do not yet know whether this is possible. The consideration of the difficulties explained in the preceding section may make us rather skeptical. Now we shall look at certain facts which may revive some hope. These facts do not concern the problem of probability$_1$ itself but only what people seem to believe about this concept or rather how they are inclined to use this concept. This, of course, provides no logical argument; but it may nevertheless be a practical factor influencing our expectations with respect to the solubility of the logical problem of an explication of probability$_1$.

Before we raise the more important question concerning the quantitative concept, let us examine whether in everyday life and in science, before an explication for probability$_1$ and a systematic theory is constructed, the concept of probability$_1$ is used as a comparative concept (for instance, in the form '*h* is confirmed by *e* more than *h'* by *e''*) or only as a classificatory concept ('*e* gives confirming evidence for *h*'). (These concepts have been explained in § 8.) It seems that most authors on probability$_1$ agree that the comparative concept is frequently used in cases of the following kind. These cases are characterized by having only one body of evidence, that is, *e* is the same as *e'*, while *h* and *h'* may be different from each other. For example, statements similar to the following ones are often made, where it is understood that the common evidence *e* for both hypotheses is the total knowledge of the speaker at the time of speaking: (1) 'It is more likely to rain tomorrow than not'; (2) 'Peter will probably come by train rather than by bus'. Comparisons of this kind are obviously necessary for all our practical decisions. Sometimes, a comparison is made for the same hypothesis with respect to two pieces of evidence, for example, (3) 'Now, in view of today's weather, the chances for good weather next Sunday are better than before'; (4) 'By the results of Koch's experiments the assumption that tuberculosis is caused by bacilli gained much in weight'. I believe that the customary use of probability$_1$ as a comparative concept covers a much wider field than the two special kinds of cases described, including many cases where *e* and *e'* are different and even independent of one another (while in the examples mentioned one body of evidence L-implies the other) and simultaneously *h* and *h'* are different and even independent. However, this point is controversial. My view on it will become clear from what I shall say about the quantitative concept.

B. *Probability$_1$ and Games of Chance*

Is the concept of probability$_1$ customarily used also in a quantitative way and, if so, under which conditions? A few authors seem to believe that the concept is never used quantitatively by reasonable and careful people. However, I think that the majority of authors believe that at least in a special kind of case, namely, for predictions of results of games of chance, numerical values are attributed customarily—and, they would add, rightly so—to probability$_1$. [Kries ascribes numerical values to probability only in cases analogous to those of games of chance; Keynes does it only in a very restricted kind of cases to which presumably those of games of chance belong; Nagel, as mentioned above (§§ 46 and 47E), doubts in general the possibility of assigning numerical values to the degree of confirmation, in contradistinction to probability$_2$; however, he discusses chiefly universal theories and does not mention in this connection games of chance.] For example, let us consider a case of the singular predictive inference. Let *e* contain the information that a certain die is symmetrically built, that 6,000 throws have been made with it under the ordinary conditions, and that 1,000 of them have yielded an ace; let *h* be the prediction that the next throw with this die will result in an ace; then there will be almost general agreement that the probability$_1$ of *h* on *e* is (exactly or approximately) 1/6. It is true, there are a few theoreticians who would refuse to make any statement in terms of 'probability' with respect to *h* because, according to their conception, a probability statement with respect to a single event is meaningless; in our terminology, they recognize only the concept of probability$_2$ and believe there is no such concept as probability$_1$ or at least no quantitative concept. However, the man in the street and the practical scientist in the laboratory have no such scruples. If we give them the information *e* and ask them what is the probability or chance of *h*, the overwhelming majority will not hesitate to give an answer, and the overwhelming majority of the answers will show good agreement with one another. And even among those who hesitate to use here a term like 'probability' or 'chance', many will answer affirmatively if we ask them whether between two people who have the information *e* a bet on *h* of one against five is to be regarded as equitable. This answer shows that they attribute the same probability$_1$ value as we do and that they merely reject our terminology.

C. *Probability$_1$ and Direct Inference*

The situation is not very different in cases of the direct inference, even if they do not concern a game of chance. Here the evidence *e* contains suitable statistical information concerning a class to which the individual referred to in *h* belongs. Suppose that *h* is 'W_2c', that the only information which *e* gives concerning *c* is 'W_1c', and that *e*, furthermore, says that the total number of individuals with the property W_1 is 1,000 and that 800 of them have the property W_2. For instance, *e* says that the person *c* is one of the 1,000 inhabitants of the village Norville among whom there are 800 of Norwegian ancestry; *h* says that *c* is one of the latter. Certainly many people will be prepared to assign here a numerical value to the probability$_1$ of *h* on *e*, and practically all of them will take the value 0.8 and hence will regard as equitable a bet of four against one on *h* between two bettors who have no other information than *e*. This is justified by our previous discussion in § 41C.

D. *Probability$_1$ and Betting Behavior*

Now let us consider predictions which do not concern games of chance and where no clearly relevant statistical information is available. Suppose

X makes the following statement: 'My friend Peter will probably come by train, not by bus', which we interpret as an elliptical statement on probability$_1$. Perhaps we think first that his expectation is chiefly influenced by some knowledge about relative frequencies; so we ask him: 'Do you think so because you know that usually many more passengers on this trip take train than bus?' 'Oh, no, I am not thinking of the other people; it's just that I know my friend.' 'Is it then that you have observed that he takes a train much more frequently than a bus?' 'No, he is a thrifty man and often prefers a bus. However, he will probably decide that for this long distance a bus trip would be too tiring.' Our question is whether people like X, whom we suppose to know neither the mathematical calculus of probability nor any philosophical theories on probability, are usually willing to assign a numerical value to the probability, in the sense of probability$_1$, in cases like the example just given. Another example of this kind: 'Thirty years from now most international conferences will probably use an international auxiliary language'. The chief difficulty with these examples is not the fact that they refer to a single event; that is likewise the case with the examples under (B) and (C). The important difference is the fact that here we cannot simply take a known relative frequency as the value of the probability$_1$ in question. Also in these cases, to be sure, there are relative frequencies—either exactly known or vaguely estimated —which belong to the relevant facts known to X and influence his probability judgment; but he will presumably not take simply one of these frequencies as the probability value.

Some authors seem to think that ordinary people like X do not attribute any numerical value at all to the probability in cases of this kind. It may indeed very well be that, if we asked people who make probability statements of this kind whether the probability asserted has a numerical value and whether they could express it in terms of a percentage, many and perhaps even most of them would answer in the negative; perhaps they would even be rather surprised that we expected of them such an "obviously impossible" thing as measuring the probabilities in these cases. However, this does not prove the point. From the fact that X tells us that his probability concept, as used in cases of the kind here discussed, is a nonquantitative concept, we cannot infer that his concept is actually nonquantitative. We have earlier (at the beginning of § 11) called attention to the discrepancy frequently found between what people, even scientists, say about the meaning and nature of their statements and terms and the way in which they actually use these statements and terms. Although our direct question to X does not succeed in eliciting a numerical evaluation of the probability, maybe his response to a certain situation which induces him to take a practical decision might show us nevertheless that the probability which he ascribes to a certain prediction has a numerical value. Since probability$_1$ means a fair betting quotient (§ 41B), we might offer *X* bets on the prediction in question with various betting quotients and see which of them he accepts. If *X* refuses to bet because he does not like to risk a loss, we may change the situation slightly by offering a reward instead of a bet. We can use here a device proposed by Émile Borel ([Valeur], p. 85) and other authors; it consists in inducing *X* to reveal to us by an act of choice how he compares the probability in question to the probability in a simple situation of a game of chance; we assume that he evaluates this latter probability in accordance with the general consent. This may, for instance, be done in the following way with respect to the first example above. We promise to pay *X* $10 under certain conditions; we allow him to choose one of the following conditions (*a*) or (*b*): (*a*) we shall wait until Peter comes; if he comes by train, we shall give *X* $10, otherwise not; (*b*) *X* shall cast his die, which he and we know to be normal; if the result is not an ace, we shall give him $10. If he chooses (*a*), he thereby implicitly reveals that he regards the probability of Peter's coming by train as not less than 5/6; if he chooses (*b*), he regards the probability as not more than 5/6. By a series of experiments of this kind, either in the form of bets or of rewards, with different values as standards of comparison, we find narrower and narrower intervals which include the value, unknown to us, of the probability$_1$ which *X* attributes to the prediction; in other words, we measure this unknown value with greater and greater precision. This procedure is not only analogous to the ordinary procedure of measuring the value of an empirical magnitude, say, the length or weight of a body, but is itself an instance of such a measurement. The magnitude measured here is not the semantical, logical concept of probability$_1$ or its explicatum, the degree of confirmation (for which we cannot speak of 'unknown values', see § 41D), but the corresponding pragmatical, psychological concept 'the probability or degree of belief of the prediction *h* at the time *t* for *X*'.

It seems plausible to assume that many people would react to experiments of this kind in a consistent way, as long as we do not take too narrow intervals. If this assumption is right, it means that many people do attribute numerical values to the probability$_1$ of their predictions, no matter whether or not they are able to state these values directly and explicitly on a direct question. In this point I am in agreement with Reichenbach. whose concept of weight corresponds to our concept of probability$_1$ (see above, § 41E); he says: "There are a great many germs of a metrical [= quantitative] determination of weights contained in the habits of business and daily life. The habit of betting on almost every thing unknown but interesting to us shows that the man of practical life knows more about weights than many philosophers will admit" ([Experience], pp. 318 f.).

E. *Probability$_1$ Is Used as an Objective Concept*

Assuming that our preceding considerations and expectations as to many people's reactions are correct, they merely show certain subjective habits. The problem whether there is an objective concept of quantitative probability$_1$ or degree of confirmation is thereby not answered. This problem will not be discussed in this section; but we shall now briefly consider the question, again of a pragmatical, psychological nature, as to what is the ordinary people's attitude to this problem. Here again we shall not ask them directly: 'What is your answer to this problem?' We shall rather try to observe whether the people's habits of behavior reveal an implicit belief in an underlying *objective* concept of probability$_1$.

First let us look at the other side. How do people behave when they regard a certain concept as purely or chiefly subjective? Suppose X appreciates Grieg's music much more than that of Chopin, while his friend Y shows the opposite preference. We see X playing his Grieg records to Y, trying to call his attention to certain features of them, praising them in words of emotional appeal, etc. We observe Y doing something similar with Chopin records to X. Suppose that afterward we find each of them expressing his preference unchanged. Still neither of them tries to prove by theoretical arguments that the other is wrong; rather they agree: 'We seem to have different tastes', and there the matter remains. In other cases of fundamentally the same nature, more objective, factual factors are involved. Suppose X says: 'I should buy this house if I could get it for $6,000', while Y replies: 'I should not take it for $2,000'. There may first be certain facts concerning the house, advantageous or disadvantageous, which one of the two friends has discovered and communicates to the other. If, however, after they have shared all relevant factual information, they still find that their appreciations, expressed by the price either of them would be willing to pay, differ considerably, then they agree again on their disagreement, and that settles the matter. Either of them may be surprised by the other's different appreciation, but neither of them says that the other is wrong. We infer from the behavior of X and Y in both these cases that they regard a judgment of appreciation or preference in music or in things of everyday life (except for factual components like usefulness for a certain purpose, etc.) as subjective.

Now take a case of the other kind. Suppose *X* and *Y* look at the moon and discuss its distance. They do not know astronomy, and they do not think of any other method of measuring distances than by rods or chains; and they agree that here this method is impracticable because of technical difficulties. Thus they content themselves with making the best estimate they can of the distance, just from the impression they have by looking at the moon. *X* estimates the distance as one hundred miles, *Y* as one million miles. It looks at first as if the situation were similar to that in the former cases of appreciation of music or of a house. After each has tried to influence the other's opinion by calling his attention to certain features which he may have overlooked, they find their estimates are still unchanged. They agree: 'We just have quite different estimates', and they give up the hope of coming to an agreement. However, in spite of the similarity with the earlier cases up to this point, there is a fundamental difference between their attitudes here and there. Both admit that they have no very good reasons for their estimates; but each of them says: '*If* I am right, then you are wrong'. And although they have no hope of actually deciding the question, each of them still says: 'Too bad that we cannot measure the distance by rods and do not know another method. *If only* we found a way of measuring, then the question would be decided. If the result turned out different from my estimate, I should, of course, give up the estimate. Thus we should come to an agreement.' In this way we see that *X* and *Y* regard distance as an objective concept. This is not altered by the fact that their estimates differ very much, that they feel rather uncertain as to the accuracy of their estimates, and that they do not know any feasible procedure for deciding the question.

Now we come back to the quantitative statements of probability$_1$ made by *X*, who is an ordinary man not prejudiced by any knowledge of theories on probability. Does *X* regard these statements as subjective or as objective, as merely an expression of his personal attitude like an appreciation of music, or rather as an assertion about something that is independent of personal taste, such that if *X* and *Y* attribute, on the basis of their common knowledge *e*, different values to the probability$_1$ of *h* (considerably different values, since they are in most cases merely meant as rough estimates) then at least one of them must be wrong? I think that many and perhaps most people have the latter attitude. We must, of course, be careful not to confuse the relativity of probability$_1$ with respect to a body of evidence with subjectivity. As to the relativity, there is now general agreement among authors on probability$_1$ (see above, § 10A); hence we may suppose that *X* will agree with us when we explain to him that the ordinary probability$_1$ statements are often elliptical and that a complete statement has the form: 'The probability$_1$ of the hypothesis *h* with respect to the evidence *e* is *r*'. Thus, if *X* says: 'The probability that it will rain tomorrow is 1/2', and *Y* says: 'The probability that it will rain tomorrow is 3/4', then it is possible that both are right. This obvious fact should not be referred to as subjectivity of probability, as earlier authors have often done, but rather as relativity, here concealed by the omission of references to the evidence. If the two elliptical statements are made complete by the insertion of references to the evidence meant, viz., the knowledge of *X* and the knowledge of *Y*, respectively, then the appearance of a contradiction disappears. The question of subjectivity or objectivity must be raised with respect to these complete statements. Suppose *X* and *Y* make two probability$_1$ statements not only for the same hypothesis *h* but also with respect to the same evidence *e*. This may happen either if both have the same relevant knowledge, for instance, by pooling their information, or if they do not take as evidence their own knowledge but something else, say, a fictitious state of knowledge. Thus, for instance, *X* may say to *Y*: 'If we did not know of the person *c*, as we actually do know, that he is not of Norwegian ancestry, but knew only that he is an inhabitant of Norville, and if, in addition, we had our present knowledge that among the 1,000 inhabitants of Norville there are 800 of Norwegian descent, which value *r* should we attribute to the probability of the assumption that *c* is of Norwegian descent? In other words, which betting quotient *r* would be equitable between us?' Suppose that *X* himself answers this question with '$r = 4/5$' and *Y* with '$r = 1/2$'. The decisive point now is the reaction of *X* to this divergence. If he says: 'Well, we seem to differ here, just as we do in our tastes in music; and that's all there is to it', then this shows that he regards probability$_1$ as a subjective concept. If, on the other hand, he offers theoretical arguments with the professed intention of refuting the value stated by *Y*, then this shows that he regards probability$_1$ as objective. And the same holds even if *X* reacts only in the following much weaker way: 'Well, I feel I am right but I am not quite sure. And I am not clever enough to find arguments which might convince you. Hence our disagreement remains unsolved, just as our disagreement concerning the distance of the moon. One thing is sure though, here as there; *if* I am right, then you are wrong.' I think that most people, including practically working scientists, would react in this latter way, and hence regard probability$_1$ as objective.

Even if this assumption is right, it is no more than a certain historical, psychological fact: many people show certain behavior habits which reveal an implicit, underlying belief in the objectivity of probability_1. From this fact it does, of course, by no means follow that probability_1 is actually an objective concept or that it is possible to find an objective concept which is an adequate explicatum for probability_1. On the other hand, the fact that many reasonable persons think and act successfully on the basis of an implicit belief in an objective concept of probability_1, although they are not able to give a definition of it, may give us some hope of finding an objective quantitative explicatum in spite of the difficulties explained in the preceding section.

§ 49. The Question of the Usefulness of Inductive Logic

A. Theoretical usefulness. If a quantitative inductive logic can be constructed either for simple language systems, as will be done in this book, or for the whole language of science, what help would it give to work in empirical science? The use of inductive logic in science is similar to that of deductive logic. In many cases, the situation is too complicated for an application of inductive logic. In other cases, however, application is practically possible. This holds especially for the cases of inductive inference in which the evidence or the hypothesis or both are of a statistical nature. Inductive logic, if sufficiently developed, will serve as a logical foundation for the methods of mathematical statistics. We see today the first steps in this direction, which, if continued, will lead to greater clarity and exactness of the basic concepts of statistics. The development of inductive logic will furthermore help in clarifying the problems of the nature and validity of inductive reasoning.

B. Practical usefulness. The value of an empirical magnitude, for example, the length of a rod, will often be an important factor in determining the decisions of a person X, provided X knows this value. If he does not know it, he has instead to take an estimate as the basis of his decision. It is often said that probability is a guide of life. For which of the two probability concepts does this hold? The statements concerning probability_2, the relative frequency in the long run, are empirical like those about length. Such a statement can serve as a basis for a practical decision only if it is known. However, it can never be known directly if probability_2, according to the customary conceptions, refers to an infinite population and is explicated as a limit. Therefore X must base his decision on an estimate of probability_2, hence a value of probability_1. It becomes clear that neither empirical science alone nor inductive logic alone can serve as a guide of life, but only both in co-operation.

Although we do not yet know whether our aim, a system of inductive logic, can be reached, it is worth while to consider the question whether and how such a system would be useful *if* it could be constructed. Some philosophers and scientists are skeptical in this respect. If their doubts were right, it would be a waste of time to try to construct a system of inductive logic. But there are good reasons against their doubts. These will now be discussed. Let us assume hypothetically, for the sake of this discussion, that it is possible to construct a system of quantitative inductive logic, based on a concept of degree of confirmation as a quantitative explicatum for probability$_1$, first for simple languages like our systems $\mathfrak{L}$, and then extended to languages containing quantitative concepts, for example, a systematized language of physics with real numbers as space-time coordinates and with signs for mathematical and physical functions. We shall now discuss the question of the usefulness of this system in two respects: (A) What assistance will this system give in the field of *theoretical* work, especially in empirical science? (B) How could the system be used in making *practical* decisions?

A. *Theoretical Usefulness of Inductive Logic in Science*

The possibility of applying inductive logic in science and also the limitations to this application, some of them essential but others merely technical, can best be clarified by the analogy with deductive logic. Scientists carry out their deductive inferences in most cases, especially where mathematical transformations are not yet involved, in an intuitive, instinctive way, that is, without the use of explicitly formulated rules of logic; and they are in general quite successful in doing so. Therefore we cannot expect that the development and systematization of deductive logic should have the effect of immediately increasing the correctness or efficiency of the inferential procedures of the scientist. Many cases with which he has to deal in his work are so simple that the use of explicit logical rules is unnecessary. In other cases, the premises with which he works are so complex that he is either not able or not willing to take the trouble of formulating them explicitly and exhaustively; this may sometimes not prevent him from recognizing—with more or less clarity and more or less certainty—that a given conclusion follows from the premises; but it prevents the application of explicit rules. On the other hand, there are certain cases where deductive logic has proved to be very useful for the scientist, especially since its very extensive development in these last hundred years; and we may expect the number of these cases to increase with the further development. For instance, the axiomatic method in its more exact modern form has been possible only on the basis of modern logic; and this method becomes more and more important in mathematics and its applications, and also in physics and other fields of science. Furthermore, I think we may assume that certain errors in deductive procedure which have earlier been made in science would have been avoided if the methods of modern logic had been available at that time. Prominent examples are the alleged deductions of Euclid's parallel axiom from the other axioms; if one of the most fertile fields of modern logic, the logic of relations, had been known at that time, it would have prevented those errors because it makes it possible to represent the derivation of a conclusion from the axioms in an exact, formal way, avoiding the earlier pitfalls of a nonformal method, especially the inadvertent use of an additional, nonformulated premise on the basis of intuition.

The situation with inductive logic is similar. There is first its essential limitation to logical factors, to the exclusion of methodological factors (§ 44A). This limitation does by no means make inductive logic useless, for, if it gives to a scientist a numerical value of the degree of confirmation which embodies all logical factors, it thereby does not prevent him from taking into consideration for his decision also as many nonlogical factors as he wants to; on the contrary, it facilitates this task. However, there are many situations in science which by their complexity make the application of inductive logic practically impossible. For instance, we cannot expect to apply inductive logic to Einstein's general theory of relativity, to find a numerical value for the degree of confirmation of this theory (or, rather, of an instance of it, § 110G) on the basis of the whole observational material known to physicists at the time when the theory was first stated, or for the increase in the degree in consequence of the observations of the solar eclipse of 1919. The same holds for the other steps in the revolutionary transformation of modern physics, especially those in connection with quantum theory. In all these cases the relevant observational material is immensely extensive; it is not at all restricted to those crucial experiments which we usually associate with the origin of the new theories. Furthermore, the structure of the new physical theory in each of these cases is so comprehensive and complicated that no physicist at any stage in the development has given a complete and exact formulation of it (according to the rigorous standards of modern logic), let alone a complete and exact formulation of the observational evidence. Therefore an application of inductive logic in these cases is out of the question.

On the other hand, there are also cases in which there are good reasons for the expectation that the application of inductive logic will become useful for the scientist, or in which the useful application is already possible today. This holds especially for those fields of science where statistical methods are used for the description of distributions of certain properties. As we shall see later, the inductive inferences (§ 44B) are of special importance in the form of statistical inferences, that is, in cases where the hypothesis or the evidence or both give statistical information, for instance, by stating relative frequencies. Suppose a scientist knows the statistical distribution of certain properties within a given population (of persons or bacteria or atoms or whatever else) and, on this basis, wants to find out the probability$_1$ of a certain assumption as to their distribution in an as yet unobserved sample (direct inference); or, conversely, the distribution in a sample is known and a hypothesis is made concerning the distribution either in the whole population (inverse inference) or in another sample (predictive inference); for these and similar cases of statistical inferences, inductive logic can be of immediate help.

Many of the methods of mathematical statistics are essentially inductive methods, especially those which have been developed during the last decades and have found very fruitful application in agriculture, medicine, industrial production, insurance, and many other fields, among them methods of estimation, curve-fitting, significance tests, etc. These methods, as applied today by most statisticians, are usually not based on a system of inductive logic, but developed independently. Similarly, deductive mathematics (arithmetic, analysis, theory of functions, infinitesimal calculus, etc.) was first developed independently of logic for more than two thousand years. Finally, Frege, Russell, and Whitehead succeeded in basing the concepts and principles of mathematics on those of deductive logic and thereby making mathematics a part of logic itself. Although this achievement changed hardly anything in the content of mathematics, it was very important because it established mathematics for the first time on a solid foundation and contributed greatly to the clarity and exactness of the basic concepts of mathematics. It is obvious that this achievement was possible only through the utilization of symbolic logic. In my view, the situation with inductive statistics is quite analogous. If it is possible to construct quantitative inductive logic to the extent indicated at the beginning of this section, again, of course, with the help of symbolic logic, then it will be possible to base statistics upon it and thereby make it a part of inductive logic. (Obviously, this holds only for the inductive part of statistics, the theory of statistical inference, as distinguished from the deductive part, usually called descriptive statistics, which belongs to (deductive) mathematics and hence is part of deductive logic.) It may be expected that mathematical statistics will thereby gain for the first time a solid foundation, a systematic unity of its various methods, and a clarity and exactness of its basic concepts. In spite of the great wealth in methods and results achieved in modern mathematical statistics, and especially its great fruitfulness in practical application, it is clearly in need of the theoretical virtues just mentioned, more urgently than deductive mathematics was before Frege.

The system of inductive logic which will be developed in this book has by far not yet the extension indicated above. But even in this limited domain it will be possible to introduce a general concept of estimation and to find with its help some simple but new and important results concerning the predictive and inverse estimates of relative frequency (chap. ix). And in the same limited domain the founding of statistical methods on the basis of inductive logic will in certain cases even lead to corrections in some general theorems and, consequently, in numerical results. It will be shown (in Vol. II) that certain numerical values obtained by some methods widely used today in mathematical statistics are not quite adequate and that the values supplied by the methods of our inductive logic are more adequate. This holds, for example, for predictive and inverse estimates of relative frequency based on small samples. From a practical point of view, these corrections are of minor importance because the numerical difference is small for samples of those sizes with which statisticians usually work. But from a theoretical and fundamental point of view, the fact of this correction is interesting because it means a change, though only a slight one, in content. [One would have an analogue in the reduction of deductive mathematics to deductive logic if, for example, Frege in the course of his logical work had found that certain results obtained by earlier uncritical uses of divergent series had to be corrected, a discovery which actually was made already by A. L. Cauchy (1823).]

Jeffreys was the first, and is so far the only one, to attempt a solution of the difficult problem of founding mathematical statistics on a system of inductive logic comprehensive enough to be applied to the quantitative language of physics. He came to this problem not from logic but from empirical science. His work in fields of science where statistical methods are frequently applied, above all in his special field of geophysics, showed him the necessity of a theory of probability$_1$ sufficiently developed to serve as a logical foundation for the use of statistical methods (see his [Probab.], Preface). Throughout his work he emphasizes the requirement that a system of inductive logic must be applicable in the actual work of scientists, and he himself gives numerous examples for the application of his methods to special problems in geophysics and other branches of physics. It seems to me that Jeffreys' examples provide ample illustration for the usefulness and even indispensability of inductive logic for the practical work in empirical science. Irrespective of whether or not we agree with all details of his method, there can be no doubt that he has done valuable pioneer work in bridging the gap between inductive logic and the domain of statistical methods dealing with quantitative physical magnitudes. [We may leave aside here the objections which we shall raise in a later chapter against certain features which Jeffreys' theory has in common with the classical theory of probability; we shall show in the construction of our theory how the difficulties here involved can be overcome; the present discussion concerns not the correctness of a particular theory but the usefulness of inductive logic in general, provided a good theory can be found.]

It seems to me that there is still another direction in which the development both of deductive and of inductive logic becomes important for scientific thinking in general. The development of deductive logic not only has made possible the application in numerous concrete cases but has, in addition, thrown light on certain fundamental problems of a more general nature. Seen from a historical and psychological angle, it has been a side effect of the development of modern deductive logic—though, from a philosophical point of view, it may be regarded as an achievement of outstanding importance—that today we have a better understanding of the foundations of deductive inference, of the reasons for its validity, and of the nature of the sentences which state purely logical connections. Thereby also remarkable progress has been made in the clarification of the nature of mathematics and especially of the relation between mathematics and empirical science. I believe that, in a similar way, the development of inductive logic will, over and above the applications in concrete cases, yield results of a more general, we might say, a philosophical character: a clarification of the foundations of induction (in the wide sense in which we use this term), of the presuppositions of induction, which are hardly ever made explicit, and the meaning and conditions of its validity. This includes the old, much-debated but still controversial question concerning the justification of induction or of special kinds of inductive inference, for example, those mentioned earlier. It belongs to the aims of this book not only to construct a system of inductive logic but also to contribute to the clarification of these more general problems. In both respects, this book cannot do more than take a few steps. I am convinced that the future development will soon not only improve the technical methods of inductive logic and widely extend their scope, but simultaneously also increase our insight, today still clouded in many points, into the nature and validity of inductive reasoning.

B. *Practical Usefulness of Inductive Logic: Probability as a Guide of Life*

Since the earliest beginnings of the development of the calculus of probability the mathematicians and philosophers who worked on it emphasized its applicability to practical problems. At first the field of application was chiefly that of games of chance; the calculus claimed to provide methods by which a gambler could calculate the chances in a game and thereby determine under what conditions it would be advisable to accept an offered game or a bet, and to judge whether the rules of the game were fair, that is, not favoring any of the players. Soon it was recognized that the decisions made in more serious affairs, individual decisions in private life or political decisions in the life of a community, are not different in principle from those made in a game; the situations here are more complicated and cannot be analyzed as easily into their determining factors, and the number of relevant factors is often much greater. But this difference in complexity seems to be merely a difference in degree. Therefore, it was hoped that, as soon as science would furnish a more thoroughgoing analysis of the laws of nature and society, the calculus of probability would become one of the most efficient instruments of the human mind, helping one to find in any given situation the most reasonable decision, that is, the decision giving the best hope of success. The authors during the period of the Enlightenment were most optimistic in this respect. Contemporary authors agree in principle but are usually more moderate in their expectations concerning the benefits to be obtained by the application of probability. On the other hand, they are able, within certain limited fields, to speak not only of hopes but of accomplished results. They can point out the many fruitful applications of probability considerations and statistical methods based upon probability in such various fields as insurance, public health, genetics, theoretical physics, astronomy, the design of agricultural experiments, quality control in industrial mass production, the analysis of economic trends and of personality factors, and many more. These applications lead not only to theoretical results but also to practical decisions concerning insurance rates, public health measures, the choice of special breeds of wheat, changes in methods of mass production and inspection, etc.

The basic fact that makes inductive logic useful and even necessary for obtaining rational decisions is the impossibility of knowing the future with certainty. Any man *X* has to base his decisions on expectations concerning events which are independent of his actions and also concerning events which might happen in consequence of certain acts which he might decide to carry out. For expectations of both kinds, *X* has no certainties but only probabilities. And if his decision is to be rational, it must be determined by these probabilities. "To us probability is the very guide of life", as Bishop Joseph Butler said (in the Preface of *The analogy of religion* [1736], quoted from Keynes [Probab.], p. 309).

Since we have found two concepts of probability fundamentally different in nature, the question arises as to what part each of them plays in determining practical decisions. Those who want to restrict the theory of probability to probability$_2$, the frequency concept, believe that only this concept can be of help in practical life. Their principal argument for this belief is the fact that only a statement on probability$_2$ says something about the facts of nature, while a statement on probability$_1$, being purely logical, has no factual content. This characterization of the two concepts is certainly correct, but it remains to examine the question whether the conclusion follows that the logical concept of probability$_1$ is not applicable for practical purposes.

According to our previous discussion (§ 41D), the distinction between a probability$_2$ statement for a property M and a probability$_1$ statement for a singular hypothesis concerning M may be regarded as a special case of the general distinction between the following two kinds of statements: (1) a statement about the actual value of a physical magnitude in a given case, a value which is either unknown to the observer or at least not known exactly, and (2) a statement about the *estimate* of this value with respect to given evidence. Let us consider an example of a familiar kind for this distinction; this may help us in clarifying the situation with respect to the two probability concepts. Let us suppose that the evidence e available to the observer X contains the information that the length of a given rod has been measured three times, with the results, say, 80.0, 80.1, 80.5. Let us assume that the measurements were made under the same conditions. Then there is no reason for regarding any one of the three results as more reliable than any other. Therefore X will take as the estimate of the length of the rod the arithmetic mean of the three values, that is, 80.2. He cannot assert with certainty that the actual length is 80.2 (not even if this figure is understood as an abbreviated expression for the interval 80.15–80.25). The value 80.2 is merely an estimate; that means, it is a guess; not an arbitrary guess but a reasonable guess. It is indeed the best guess the observer can make in the present situation, as long as no results of further measurements are available to him. Now let us compare the following two sentences which occur in this example; the first belongs, not to our language systems $\mathfrak{L}$, but to the more comprehensive, quantitative language of physics:

(1) 'The actual length of the rod is 80.2.'

(2) 'The estimate of the length of the rod with respect to the given evidence e is 80.2.'

The sentence (1) is an empirical sentence; it has factual content. (We need not discuss in detail the problem of its exact interpretation in terms of observations; it may be interpreted, for example, as saying that the arithmetic mean of the results of the first n measurements would, with increasing n, converge toward 80.2.) The second sentence, on the other hand, is analytic. It is based upon a definition of the concept of estimate. (This definition may be similar to, but more complicated than, the one indicated in § 41D (3) because of the occurrence of a magnitude with a continuous scale of values.) Let us assume that this definition is constructed in such a manner that it implies that, for simple cases like the one under discussion, the estimate is the mean of the observed values. The sentence (2) cannot be either confirmed or disconfirmed by any future observations. Even if the results of future measurements tend toward a value considerably different from 80.2, it still remains true that 80.2 is the estimate *with respect to the evidence e* containing the three values stated earlier.

Let us suppose that X has to make a practical decision concerning the use of the given rod, a decision which depends upon the length of the rod. Then he may act in certain respects as though he knew that the length was 80.2. Now let us analyze the theoretical basis of this behavior. This is not meant as a psychological question concerning the actual process by which X arrives at his decision, but rather as a rational reconstruction of this process. How does X utilize the sentences (1) and (2)? We might perhaps be tempted to say that he must make use of (1) rather than (2), because only the sentence (1) can tell him what the actual length is. X would certainly make use of (1) if this sentence were known to him. However, in the situation assumed in our example, X does not know the actual length but only the results of the three measurements. Sentence (1) is at the present moment for X neither certain nor even probable, that is to say, it does not follow from the observational results expressed by e and is not even highly confirmed by e. [Under certain plausible assumptions concerning a concept of degree of confirmation $\mathfrak{c}$ as an explicatum for probability$_1$ it can be shown that, for the hypothesis that the actual length is exactly 80.2, $\mathfrak{c}$ on e is 0; and for the hypothesis that the actual length is between 80.15 and 80.25, $\mathfrak{c}$ on e is considerably less than 1/2.] With respect to sentence (1), X can do nothing else but wait and see in which direction future observations will point; they may highly confirm it and hence suggest its acceptance or highly disconfirm it and hence suggest its rejection. Therefore X cannot find a theoretical basis for his decision in sentence (1). But he finds it in sentence (2), because this sentence is analytic and hence both true and known to him; and, added to his evidence *e* containing the results of the three measurements, it states the estimated value 80.2 which determines his decision.

Generally speaking, situations of this kind may be characterized as follows. Practical decisions of a man are often dependent upon values of certain magnitudes for the things in his environment. If he does not know the exact value, he has to base his decision on an estimate. This estimate is given in a statement of the form: 'The estimate for the magnitude in question with respect to such and such observational results is so and so.' This statement is purely analytic. Nevertheless it may serve as a basis for the decision. It cannot, of course, do so by itself, since it has no factual content; but it may do so in combination with the observational results to which it refers.

Now let us return to the problem of the concept of probability$_1$. The situation here is to some extent analogous to that in the example just discussed. Suppose that *X* has taken a sample of eighty persons from the population of Chicago and has found that sixty of these persons possess a property *M*. This constitutes his present evidence *e*. Let *h* be a singular hypothesis, namely, the prediction that the person *b* taken at random from the nonobserved part of the population will be found to have the property *M*. For the present discussion the exact value of the probability$_1$ of *h* on *e* does not matter. It seems plausible that this value does not differ much, if at all, from the relative frequency of *M* in the observed sample, which is 3/4. To make the example more concrete, let us arbitrarily assume that the probability$_1$ of *h* on *e* is 0.73. [The reason for choosing here a value not equal to but slightly different from the observed relative frequency is merely the intention of stressing the fact that the estimate to be discussed is equal to the value of the probability$_1$, here 0.73, and not necessarily equal to the observed relative frequency, here 3/4.] Now let us compare the following sentences concerning the present example; we shall see that they are analogous to the earlier sentences concerning the actual length of a rod and the estimate of its length.

(3) 'The actual relative frequency of *M* in the population of Chicago is 0.73.'

(4) 'The probability$_1$ of the singular hypothesis *h* with respect to the evidence *e* concerning the observed sample is 0.73.'

According to our earlier discussion (§ 41D(8)), the estimate (in the sense of the probability$_1$-mean) of the relative frequency of *M* in the whole population of Chicago with respect to the evidence *e* is equal to the probability$_1$ of *h* on *e*, hence likewise 0.73. Therefore (4) is logically equivalent to the following:

(5) 'The estimate of the relative frequency of *M* in the whole population with respect to the evidence *e* is 0.73.'

Suppose that *X* has to make a practical decision, perhaps of an administrative or legislative nature, a decision depending upon his knowledge concerning the relative frequency of *M* in the population of Chicago. It is clear what he will do; he will act in certain respects as though he knew that the relative frequency was 0.73. But it is perhaps not immediately clear what the theoretical basis for his action is—in other words, which rational procedure would lead to his action. Should he take (3) or (5) as a basis for his decision? The proponents of the frequency conception of probability will perhaps say that only (3) can serve as a basis because this is a statement about the relative frequency in the whole and hence a probability statement in their sense. They are right to this extent: if *X* knew (3), he would take it as a basis. However, (3) is not known to *X* as long as his knowledge is restricted to the evidence *e* concerning the eighty observed individuals; (3) is not even highly confirmed on the basis of the evidence *e*. It is rather the other statement that may serve as a basis for the decision. This statement is known to *X* because it is, in either of the two equivalent formulations (4) and (5), analytic; (4) follows from the presupposed definition of probability$_1$, and (5) from the definition of the estimate of a function. The statement (5) is quite analogous to the earlier statement (2) concerning the estimate of the length of a rod. Here, again, the statement about the estimate cannot be either confirmed or disconfirmed by any future observations. Even if a complete census of the population of Chicago showed that the actual relative frequency were quite different from 0.73, this would by no means refute the statement that the estimate *with respect to the evidence e* is 0.73. Here, as in the earlier case, the decision can be based on the given observational evidence *e* and the analytic statement which gives the estimate with respect to this evidence *e*. It is the value of this estimate or, in other words, the value of probability$_1$ that justifies the decision.

We obtain the same result if we consider the following situation. Suppose that *X* wants to make a bet on the prediction that an arbitrarily chosen individual has the property *M*. This prediction is the hypothesis *h*, to which the statement (4) ascribes the probability$_1$ 0.73 with respect to the available evidence *e*. Thus on the basis of this statement (4) *X* will decide to accept no bet on *h* with a betting quotient higher than 0.73. The same decision could also, of course, be based on the statement (5) concerning the estimate of the relative frequency.

These considerations show the following. In a sense it is correct to say that empirical statements concerning the values of physical magnitudes are important for determining our practical decisions. This holds, in particular, for the relative frequency in the long run of a property *M*, in other words, the probability$_2$ of *M*, because the final balance of the totality of future bets on singular predictions concerning *M* is determined by the probability$_2$ of *M* (§ 41C). Thus empirical statements and, in particular, statements on probability$_2$, may indeed serve as a guide of life. However, they can do so only if they are known. But the exact value of an empirical magnitude is in general not known; and if the value of a magnitude is defined as the limit of an infinite sequence of observed values, as is the case, for example, with length as interpreted above and with probability$_2$ as explicated by Mises and Reichenbach, then the exact value cannot possibly ever be known. This fact does not make concepts of this kind either meaningless or unsuitable for practically useful application. But it has the consequence that inductive logic is needed for utilizing these concepts. The hypothesis that the actual value of a certain magnitude lies within a given small interval may be highly probable, although it is not certain; that is to say, it may not follow from the available observational knowledge *e* but its probability$_1$ with respect to *e* may be high. And even if this is not the case for any small interval, as in the examples discussed above, we may still calculate the estimate of the value of the magnitude with respect to *e*. In these cases the magnitudes remain practically important; but they can be utilized only by way either of a high probability$_1$ or of an estimate, defined with the help of probability$_1$; without the use of these concepts of inductive logic those magnitudes would become useless. Thus we see that neither empirical science (which includes probability$_2$) nor inductive logic (which is based upon probability$_1$) can serve alone as a guide of life but only both in co-operation. Science makes observations and constructs theories. Inductive logic is necessary in order to obtain judgments concerning the credibility of theories or singular predictions on the basis of given observational results. And these judgments concerning expected events serve as a basis for our practical decisions. In analogy to a well-known dictum of Kant, we might say that inductive logic without observations is empty; observations without inductive logic are blind.

§ 50. The Problem of a Rule for Determining Decisions

A. Our problem is to find a rule which tells a man *X*, with the help of inductive logic, which decisions it would be reasonable for him to make in view of his past experiences. Such a rule does not belong to inductive logic itself but involves the methodology of induction and of psychology. In this section four tentative forms of the rule are discussed, each more adequate than the preceding ones. The final rule will be explained in the next section. *B*. Rule R_1: 'Act on the expectation that events with a high probability$_1$ will happen'. *C*. Rule R_2: 'Among several possibilities, act on the expectation of the one with the highest probability$_1$.' *D*. Rule R_3: 'If your decision depends upon a magnitude whose value *u* is unknown, determine its estimate *u'* on the available evidence and then act in certain respects as though you knew with certainty that *u* were equal or near to *u'*.' *E*. Rule R_4: 'Choose that action for which the estimate of the resulting gain has its maximum.' From this is derived a specialized rule R_4^*: 'If an offer is favorable (i.e., the estimated gain in case of accepting is greater than in case of rejecting), accept it; if it is unfavorable, reject it.' Even this apparently obvious rule leads in certain exceptional cases to unreasonable decisions and hence is in need of further modification.

A. *The Problem*

The discussions in the preceding section have thrown some light on the question as to how considerations of probability$_1$ influence expectations of future events and thereby practical decisions. We shall now investigate this question in greater detail. We presuppose that the observer *X* is in possession of a system of inductive logic as a theory of probability$_1$. This theory applies to the sentences of *X*'s language (which may be more comprehensive than our systems $\mathfrak{L}$), in which *X* can formulate the results of his observations and his predictions of future events. *X* formulates the results of all observations which he has made up to the present time in one comprehensive report *e*. We assume that he is able to calculate the value of probability$_1$ on the evidence *e* for any hypothesis *h* in which he is interested. We disregard here the question of how *X* calculates these values; we are at present interested only in the question of how he utilizes them. In other words, we wish to formulate a rule which tells *X* how he is to make his decisions with the help of the values of probability$_1$, if he wants his decisions to be rational. For *X* to act rationally means to learn from experience and hence to take as evidence what he has observed. It means further that he should avoid considering only a biased selection from his experiences and disregarding any available information that might be relevant; therefore, we assume that he takes as basis the total evidence *e* available.

The problem now to be investigated concerning the determination of decisions with the help of probability$_1$ goes beyond the boundaries of inductive logic itself. Inductive logic has only the task of finding statements concerning probability$_1$; these statements may give the values of probability$_1$ for particular cases or state general properties or relations of such values. Inductive logic itself is not concerned with the practical applications of its theorems, any more than pure arithmetic is concerned with the application of arithmetical theorems for the purposes of planning a family budget, or pure geometry is concerned with the application of geometrical theorems for the purposes of navigation. In the later construction of a system of inductive logic we shall not deal with the problems of application. But in the present preliminary discussions it seems advisable to do so. While nobody doubts the theoretical validity and the practical applicability of arithmetic and geometry, the same does not hold for inductive logic; not only its usefulness but even its theoretical possibility is still controversial. Therefore, a clarification at least of the general features of an application of inductive logic for practical purposes may be helpful in contributing to a clarification of its nature and purpose. The distinction between the system of pure inductive logic and the procedures and rules of its application for practical decisions is emphasized chiefly for the following reason. The analysis of the application involves, as we shall soon see, in addition to considerations of the general methodology of induction (§ 44A) also certain assumptions and concepts of a psychological nature (for instance, concerning the measurement of preference and valuation). Now it is important to see clearly that the problems and difficulties here involved belong to the methodology of a special branch of empirical science, the psychology of valuations as a part of the theory of human behavior, and that therefore they should not be regarded as difficulties of inductive logic.

The following discussion will lead, step for step, from customary crude formulations of a rule for the determination of practical decisions with the help of inductive logic to more adequate formulations. Four versions of the rule will be discussed in this section, the fifth and final one in the next section.

B. *The Rule of High Probability*

Many writers on the calculus of probability and its application have declared that it is reasonable to expect that those events will happen which are highly probable. This suggests the following rule directed toward X and referring to the total evidence e available to X.

Rule R_1. Assume that those events will occur which have a high value of probability$_1$ on evidence e, and act as though you knew that these events were certain.

This is a crude rule-of-thumb which is often useful. As we shall see, however, it would in many cases lead to a wrong decision, that is, one which would not be regarded as reasonable by sensible people. Furthermore, it has the disadvantage of being applicable only if one of the possible cases has a high $probability_1$.

C. *The Rule of Maximum Probability*

In order to avoid the disadvantage just mentioned of rule R_1, some writers have said that the most probable among the possible events should be expected, even if its probability is not high. This suggests the following rule.

Rule R_2. With respect to an exhaustive set of mutually exclusive events (that is, in semantical terms, a set of hypotheses which are L-disjunct and L-exclusive in pairs with respect to *e*) expect that event which has the highest $probability_1$, and act as though you knew that this event is certain.

This rule works satisfactorily in a case of the following kind.

Example of the bookshop. X has a bookshop and wants to order copies of a certain book that is in steady use in order to have them on hand for the beginning of the academic year. He has experience with the past sale of this book over a number of years. On the basis of this and perhaps other relevant information, he finds that the assumption of a sale of 80 copies has a probability which, although small, is higher than that of any other case; the probability for the number 79 is somewhat less, for 78 still less, and so it goes down for smaller numbers, first slowly, then steeply; similarly, the probability decreases for higher numbers, first slowly, then more steeply, in such a way that the curve showing the probability as a function of the number of copies has a bell-shaped form, which has its maximum for 80 and declines symmetrically from this maximum toward both sides. If *X* follows the rule R_2, he assumes that there will be a demand of 80 copies, and therefore he provides for this number. This decision would not be unreasonable (although, as we shall see later, a slightly different decision might be still better). This example shows also that the rule R_2 is better than R_1; the latter rule is not applicable to the cases of the various numbers of copies, because none of them has a high probability.

In other cases, however, rule R_2 does not work so well. This is seen by the following example which at first might appear as quite analogous to the one just given.

Example of the restaurant. X runs a dining place and decides how much of every dish is to be prepared today. He knows from previous experience concerning one particular dish that the number of people who order it on one day varies between 0 and 5; and, in particular, the probability that the number of people who will order it today will be 0, 1, 2, . . . , 6, is 0.20, 0.19, 0.18, 0.17, 0.16, 0.10, 0, respectively. The dish must be prepared in advance. Thus the problem for *X* is: for how many people should he have it prepared? Rule R_1 is again inapplicable, since none of the cases has a high probability. What would be the effect of rule R_2? The most probable assumption is that nobody will order this dish. If *X* follows rule R_2, he will act on this assumption and not prepare this dish. But this decision does not seem to be the best in view of the fact that the assumption that nobody will order the dish has only the probability 1/5; thus, it is probable to the degree 4/5 that at least one person will order it.

In each of the following two examples only two possible cases need be considered, one of which has a very high probability. Thus in these examples, both rules R_1 and R_2 are applicable. Both these rules advise *X* to act on the assumption of the event which has the high probability; but this advice is wrong in both examples.

Example of the lottery. The lottery consists of one hundred tickets; it is known (that is, it follows from *e*) that exactly one ticket will win; the prize is $100; the information concerning the lottery mechanism is such that all hundred tickets have an equal chance of winning. *X* has one ticket. Thus the probability of his winning is 0.01, that of his not winning is 0.99. If now *X* were to take either rule R_1 or R_2 literally, he would act as if he knew for certain that his ticket will not win. This would lead, for example, to the unreasonable decision of selling his ticket to somebody who offers 10 cents for it.

Example of the fire insurance. *X* owns a house whose value is $10,000. His knowledge *e* contains statistical information concerning a large number of houses which were under similar conditions and of which a certain fraction burned down during a certain period. *X* finds that with respect to this information the probability of the assumption *h* that his house will burn down during the next year is 0.001; thus the probability of $\sim h$ is 0.999. Should *X* take out fire insurance if the premium for one year were $5.00? This would be a very cheap insurance, and it would certainly be advisable to take it. However, if *X* were again to follow either rule R_1 or R_2 literally, he would act as though he knew with certainty that his house was not going to burn down within the next year and therefore he would decide against insurance.

Thus we have found that rule R_2, though better than R_1, nevertheless leads to wrong decisions in certain situations. Therefore, we have to look for a better rule.

D. *The Rule of the Use of Estimates*

Let us examine, in the example of the lottery, why rule R_2 went wrong and how it should be changed. It is clear that $1.00 would be a fair price for a ticket, because, if all tickets are sold at this price, the man who arranges the lottery comes out even, and so do the buyers of tickets taken together. Therefore X should not buy a ticket for more than $1.00 nor sell it for less (with a certain qualification to be explained later). This shows that the amount which should determine X's decision is neither the most probable gain (as rules R_1 and R_2 would have it) because this is zero, nor the one possible positive gain, which is $100, but rather the *estimate* of his gain with respect to the available evidence e. (Here again we use the term 'estimate' in the sense of 'probability$_1$-mean estimate' as defined by (3) in § 41D.) This estimate is $1.00, as is easily seen from the definition mentioned. Therefore X, as a rational agent, will regard $1.00 as the money value of his ticket. We assume that X is able to calculate not only the values of probability$_1$ on evidence e but also, on their basis, the values of estimates on e.

These considerations suggest the following rule:

Rule R_3. Suppose that your decision depends upon a certain magnitude u unknown to you, in the sense that, *if* you knew u, then this would determine your decision (that is, there is a function F such that a certain feature of your decision would take the value $F(u)$). Then calculate the estimate u' of u with respect to the available evidence e and act in certain respects as though you knew with certainty that the value of u were either equal to u' (that is, let the feature in question take the value $F(u')$) or near to u'.

It is easily seen that this rule is much better than the two previous ones; but we shall find that it still has some weak points. In the example of the bookshop the estimate of the number of books demanded is equal to the number with the highest probability, that is, 80, because of the symmetry of the probability curve (this follows from the definition of the probability$_1$-mean estimate). Therefore, rule R_3 leads, just as R_2, to the decision of keeping 80 copies in stock. This decision seems fairly reasonable.

In the example of the restaurant the estimate of the number of persons ordering the dish is found to be 2.2. Therefore, according to rule R_3, X expects that two persons will order and hence prepares for two orders. Now it becomes clear why the previous rule R_2 worked well in the case of the bookshop but not in that of the restaurant, although the situations seem similar. The reason is that in the case of the bookshop, but not in that of the restaurant, the estimated value is equal to the most probable value. This holds in many cases but by far not in all. Only in those cases where it holds is the frequently used formulation R_2 adequate.

In the example of the lottery, the estimate of *X*'s gain is \$1.00. Therefore, according to rule R_3, *X* is not willing to pay for a ticket more than this amount or to sell it for less. In the example of the fire insurance, the estimate of *X*'s loss from fire within the next year is \$10.00. Thus rule R_3 leads *X* to the decision of taking out insurance if the premium is not more than this amount.

In all four cases the decisions determined by rule R_3 seem quite reasonable. In one case (bookshop) the decision is the same as that determined by rule R_2; in the other three cases the decisions by R_3 are much more reasonable than those by R_2.

However, the same rule R_3, if applied without qualification to other aspects of the four examples, would lead to quite unreasonable decisions. This is the reason for the qualifying phrase 'in certain respects' in the formulation of the rule. The weakness of the rule is the vagueness of this phrase; the rule does not specify in which respects *X* may act as if he knew that the estimate were the actual value and in which respects he may not. That there are certain respects in which the described way of acting would not be reasonable is easily seen as follows. If, in the example of the bookshop, *X* were to act in every respect as though he knew with certainty that exactly 80 copies will be demanded, then he would be willing to bet a thousand against one on the prediction that the number of copies demanded will be exactly 80—obviously an unreasonable decision. For this reason the rule was formulated in such a manner as to admit the weaker expectation that the actual value is, if not equal, then near to the estimate. But if *X* acted in every respect as though he knew that the number of copies demanded will be between, say, 60 and 100, then he would be willing to bet one thousand against one on this prediction, which would again be unreasonable. We might perhaps consider modifying the rule somehow to the effect of advising *X* not to regard as certain even the weaker prediction that the actual value is near the estimate and hence to bet upon this prediction only at moderate odds. But a modified rule of this kind, although working all right in the case just discussed, would in other cases still lead to wrong decisions. In the example of the lottery it would make *X* willing to bet at moderate odds on the prediction that his gain will be near to \$1.00, say, between 50 cents and \$2.00, although *X* knows from the available information *e* that such an outcome is impossible.

Many cases are similar to this example in so far as the estimate is not even near to any of the possible values.

The difficulty which we have discussed consists in the fact that rule R_3 does not specify in which respects it should be applied and in which not. But there is another, more serious, difficulty which would remain even if we found a way of overcoming the first. Let us assume that we had succeeded in making the required specification in an adequate way, although it is not easy to see how this could be done in a general way. In particular, let us assume that the modified rule were such that *X* could apply it in our examples only in the following respects: in the example of the lottery, only for the determination of the price at which he is willing to buy or sell a ticket; in the example of the fire insurance, only for the determination of the premium he is willing to pay; in the example of the bookshop, only for the determination of the number of copies to be provided; in the example of the restaurant, only for the determination of the number of servings to be prepared. Even then the decisions determined by the rule in these and similar cases are not always the best that could be taken in the situation in question. If a bookseller estimates the number of copies that will be demanded at 80, he will actually order not this number, but a somewhat larger number. For if he has fewer books than will be demanded, he misses a profitable business, while if he has more books, he incurs merely the minor disadvantage of having to store the unsold copies for a later occasion or to return them to the publisher.

Let us try to describe the essential features of this situation in general terms. *X*'s decision depends upon an unknown value u. Suppose he chooses, no matter by what means, rational or irrational, a value u'' and acts so as to be prepared for this value. If then the actual value of u happens to be u'', *X* is properly prepared and hence in a favorable situation. If, however, the actual value u turns out to be either higher or lower than u'', the case is unfavorable for *X*. If it is a financial matter, for instance, a business affair or a game or a bet, *X* suffers a loss in this case. Now the decisive point is that in certain situations the losses to be expected are not symmetrically distributed but are higher on one side. If *X* has to expect a higher loss in case he is underprepared (i.e., $u'' < u$) than in case he is overprepared (i.e., $u'' > u$), then he should guard more against underpreparedness than against overpreparedness. This means that he should choose as the value u'' for which he prepares not the estimate u' of u, but a somewhat higher value in order to make the unfavorable result of underpreparedness less probable. In his choice of the value u'' he must take into consideration not only the possible values of u but also, and essentially, his gains (including losses as negative gains) in all the possible cases and their probabilities. The choice of a particular decision is ultimately to be determined by the estimates of his gains for the various possible decisions rather than by estimates of the other magnitudes involved.

E. *The Rule of Maximizing the Estimated Gain*

The preceding considerations suggest a new rule involving only estimates of one magnitude, the gain of X, and saying roughly that X should choose that course of action for which the estimate of his gain has the highest possible value. We consider at the present moment only gains or losses of money or of such other things as can be bought for money, for example, a book, a meal, a concert, the advice of a lawyer, a trip to the mountains. The problem of the so-called imponderables, that is, advantages that cannot be bought and disadvantages that cannot be bought off, will be discussed in the next section, because the solution of this problem is closely connected with the concept of utility involved in the next rule.

There is a set of actions which are possible for X at the present moment out of which he has to choose one. Let these possible actions be described by the sentences $j_1, j_2, \ldots, j_i, \ldots$. Let the possible events which might result from any of these actions, together with other factors in the situation not influenced by X, be described by the sentences $h_1, h_2, \ldots, h_k, \ldots$. If X carries out a particular action j_i, then some of these events may become impossible; others, which remain possible, may change their probabilities. [For the sake of simplicity we assume in the present informal discussion that both the number of possible actions and the number of possible resulting events are finite. The analysis for infinite sets of possibilities would merely be somewhat more complicated mathematically, but the basic features would remain the same. Note that the j-sentences are L-exclusive in pairs and L-disjunct with respect to e; and the same holds for the h-sentences.] We assume that X is able to assess in terms of money units the value of his wealth in any possible situation. Let us call this value his *fortune* in the situation in question. Let f_0 be the fortune of X at the present moment, and f_{ik} the fortune he would have in case he carried out the action j_i and the event h_k occurred. By his *gain* g_{ik} in this case we mean the increase of his fortune in consequence of his action j_i and the event h_k; hence $g_{ik} = f_{ik} - f_0$. A loss is here taken as a negative gain. Suppose X considers one of the possible actions, say, j_i, at the present moment, before he actually chooses and carries out any of the actions. He does not know what will be the actual gain g_i in case of his action j_i, because this gain depends also upon the unknown *h*-events. Nevertheless, *X* can make an estimation of this gain. He is able to calculate the probability which any of the possible events, say, h_k, would have if he were to carry out the considered action j_i, that is, the probability$_1$ of h_k on the evidence $e \cdot j_i$; let the value which he finds for this probability be q_{ik}. With the help of the probabilities $q_{i1}, q_{i2}, \ldots, q_{ik}, \ldots$ for the events $h_1, h_2, \ldots, h_k, \ldots$, he can now calculate the estimate g_i' of the gain g_i in case of the action j_i. According to our definition of an estimate (in the sense of the probability$_1$-mean, § 41D(3)), $g_i' = \sum_k [g_{ik} \times q_{ik}]$. In this way *X* can calculate for each of the possible actions the estimate of his gain resulting from this action. Then the reasonable thing for him to do is to decide upon that action for which this estimate has its maximum. Thus the general rule must say in effect: '*Maximize your estimated gain!*' It may be formulated as follows:

Rule R_4. Among the possible actions choose that one for which the estimate of your gain, determined with the help of the probabilities of the possible outcomes, is not lower than for any other possible action. If several actions lead to the maximum value of the estimate, you may choose any one of them, it does not matter which one.

This rule is essentially better than R_3. It eliminates both difficulties which we discussed in connection with R_3. The first difficulty resulted from the fact that rule R_3 advised *X* to act in certain respects as if he knew that the actual value was equal to the estimate. To act as if one knew what in fact one does not know is a risky procedure. Rule R_4 does not contain any such as-if clause; the procedure prescribed does not involve any pretension to knowledge not actually available. The second difficulty consisted in the fact that in certain cases the reasonable action conforms, not to the estimate itself of a certain magnitude, but to a value differing slightly from the estimate in one direction, provided the expected losses are less in this direction. In cases of this kind, rule R_4, in distinction to R_3, leads to the action for which the least loss is to be expected. (For instance, a closer examination would easily show that in the example of the bookshop rule R_4 would lead *X* to the decision of ordering a certain number of books somewhat greater than eighty, if certain plausible assumptions concerning the losses in the various cases are made.)

In certain simple cases rule R_4 leads to the same decision as R_3; for instance, if the decision concerns the acceptance of a bet or the buying or selling of a lottery ticket. In many other cases rule R_3 leads to a decision which is, if not the best, at least near to the best decision. Therefore, rule

R_3 need not be entirely discarded; it may be regarded as a cruder form whose use is often convenient because of its greater simplicity. Thus, although the more refined rule R_4 applies the procedure of estimation to values of only one magnitude, the gain resulting for a person, nevertheless the estimates of many other magnitudes are still useful under certain conditions. This holds especially for the estimates of absolute and relative frequency.

The situation in which X finds himself is often of such a kind that he has to choose between two alternatives only. For instance, he may either do a certain thing or refrain from doing it. For example, somebody offers X a bet or a business deal under specified conditions which X is not allowed to change; he has merely the choice of either accepting or declining the offer. Let the two actions be described by j_1 and j_2. Let the fortune of X which would actually result in the case of the action j_1 be f_1. f_1 is unknown. Let the estimate of f_1 with respect to $e \centerdot j_1$ be f'_1. Then the gain g_1 in this case is $f_1 - f_0$, and its estimate g'_1 is $f'_1 - f_0$. Let f_2, f'_2, g_2, and g'_2 be the analogous values for the action j_2. If $f'_1 > f'_2$ (and hence $g'_1 > g'_2$), we call the first action *favorable* for X and the second *unfavorable*. If $f'_1 = f'_2$ (and hence $g'_1 = g'_2$), we call both actions *neutral* for X; the deal or game or bet offered will likewise be called neutral in this case. In other words, an action is favorable or unfavorable or neutral if the difference between the estimates of fortune (or of gain) is positive, negative, or zero, respectively. (Sometimes the situation is such that in the case of one of the two decisions, the fortune of X is expected to remain unchanged; in other words, the estimate of the gain is zero. In this case the other decision is favorable, unfavorable, or neutral if the estimate of gain for this decision is positive, negative, or zero, respectively.)

If rule R_4 is applied to the case of an offer made to X in the form of an alternative, it leads to the following specialized rule:

Rule R_4^*: If the offer is favorable for you, accept it; if it is unfavorable, reject it; if it is neutral, you may accept or reject it.

This special rule seems in accord with common sense. It may even appear as too obvious and trivial to deserve explicit statement. This appearance, however, is deceptive. Rule R_4 and likewise the specialized form R_4^* lead indeed to reasonable decisions in the great majority of cases. But there are certain cases where the resulting decisions are not the best ones. We shall now consider such exceptional cases; their examination will lead to a further refinement of the rule.

Example of the bet on a coin. The present fortune of X is 10,000 (with the dollar as value unit). Somebody offers X a bet on the outcome of a throw of a coin. The coin is known to both bettors to be symmetrical; hence the probability of either result is 1/2. (i) Suppose the bet is offered at even odds; then it is neutral for X, and hence rule R_4^* permits him to accept. (ii) Suppose that X's stake is smaller than the other; then the bet is favorable for X and hence the rule commands acceptance. The rule determines these decisions irrespective of the absolute amount of X's stake in the bet. Suppose, however, that X's stake is 8,000 and his partner's stake either (i) 8,000 or (ii) 8,001; then all sensible people would regard X's acceptance of the bet as very unreasonable. Some would tell him that under no condition should a reasonable man risk a considerable part of his fortune on the flip of a coin. Others might perhaps be less severe; they would permit such a risk if the offer were extremely favorable, say, at odds of eight thousand to a million.

How should we then modify rule R_4^*? Should we make it more restrictive in such a manner that it requires for acceptance not only that the deal be favorable but that it be favorable to a sufficient degree dependent upon the ratio between X's stake and his fortune? But a modification of this kind would not do. We shall see that there are other cases which suggest, not a restriction, but a liberalizing of the rule; cases in which it is reasonable to accept an offer although it is unfavorable.

A simple case of this kind is provided by the example of the fire insurance. Suppose that X's present possessions consist of a house valued at 10,000 and 100 in cash; hence his present fortune is $f_0 = 10{,}100$. He has to choose between two actions: j_1 consists in taking out fire insurance for one year for his house at the full value of 10,000, for which he pays a premium in the amount of r; j_2 consists in not taking insurance. There are two possible events relevant for the outcome; h_1: the house will burn down during the year of insurance, and h_2, which is $\sim h_1$: the house will not burn down. According to our previous assumption for this example, X's knowledge e contains information of previous experiences concerning similar houses of such a kind that the probability of h_1 with respect to e is 0.001. Let us assume that insuring or not-insuring does not influence the chance of a conflagration; this means that the probability of h_1 is likewise 0.001 with respect to $e \cdot j_1$ and to $e \cdot j_2$. Then on each of the evidences e, $e \cdot j_1$, and $e \cdot j_2$, the probability of h_2 is 0.999. We assume for the sake of simplicity that X has no gains or losses during the year except those connected with the insurance and a possible conflagration. Let us first assume that X takes out the insurance. Hence he pays the premium r. If now the house burns down (h_1), he has a loss of 10,000 but is reimbursed for it; thus his gain is $g_{11} = -r$. If the house does not burn down, his gain g_{12} is likewise $-r$. Thus, in the case of insurance (j_1), his gain g_1 is certainly $-r$, irrespective of the probability of a conflagration; hence the estimate g'_1 is here, in a trivial way, $=g_1 = -r$. Now suppose that X does not insure (j_2). If then the house burns down (h_1), his gain is $g_{21} = -10{,}000$; the probability for this is $p_{21} = 0.001$. If the house does not burn down (h_2), his gain is $g_{22} = 0$; hence the probability for this case is irrelevant. Thus the estimate of gain in the case of noninsurance (j_2) is $g'_2 = (-10{,}000) \times 0.001 = -10$. Therefore insurance is favorable, unfavorable, or neutral for X, if the premium r is <10, >10, or $=10$, respectively. Suppose that the insurance company has the same information as X concerning the statistics of past conflagrations. Then it will certainly demand a premium $r > 10$, because the premiums received will not only have to balance the payments for damage by fire but must cover also the administrative expenses and maybe yield a profit. Let us therefore assume that the premium is 12. Then the insurance is unfavorable for X, and hence rule R_4^* would prohibit it. On the other hand, to take out insurance under the circumstances described would be regarded by everybody as reasonable, and not to do it would be regarded by most as unreasonable.

We have found that rule R_4^*, demanding the acceptance of favorable offers and the rejection of unfavorable ones, works satisfactorily in most cases but not in certain exceptional cases. There are cases in which it would be reasonable to reject a favorable offer and other cases in which it would be reasonable to accept an unfavorable offer. Thus a further refinement of rule R_4^* and thereby of rule R_4, from which R_4^* was derived, seems necessary.

Such a refined version of the rule will be developed in the next section.

§ 51. The Rule of Maximizing the Estimated Utility

A. The decisive factor for *X*'s choice of an action is not the physical gain, i.e., the monetary value of the goods acquired, but rather the moral gain or utility, i.e., the measure of the satisfaction derived by *X* from the goods. Therefore, the last of the rules for determining decisions discussed in the preceding section (R_4) must be replaced by the following rule R_5: 'Choose that action for which the estimate of the resulting utility has its maximum'. The use of this rule presupposes that utility can be measured and that there is a quantitative law stating the utility as a function of the gain.

B. Daniel Bernoulli has stated two laws which are relevant here, a general law in comparative terms and a more specific law in quantitative terms. The first says that the utility of a fixed physical gain added to an initial fortune is the smaller the larger the initial fortune (1); the second says that it is inversely proportional to the initial fortune (2). These are psychological hypotheses.

C. If we assume these laws, or at least the first, we obtain the following results. Even a fair bet or game of chance is morally unfavorable for both partners, that is to say, the estimate of the utility is negative. Further, it is morally favorable to take out fire insurance even at a premium somewhat higher than the fair premium (i.e., the estimate of loss by fire). Thus the new rule R_5 leads to reasonable decisions even in those exceptional cases where rule R_4 did not.

A. *The Rule of Maximizing the Estimated Utility*

In the preceding section we have examined the rule R_4, which prescribes that action for which the estimate of gain is a maximum, and the special rule R_4^*, which says that a favorable offer must be accepted and an unfavorable rejected. These rules lead to reasonable decisions in most cases but not in all. We found, in particular, two examples of exceptional cases. (1) The offer of a *bet* on heads at 8,000 against 8,001 is favorable; however, if X's fortune is 10,000, it would not be reasonable for him to accept it. (2) The offer of *fire insurance* at a premium of 12 is unfavorable under the conditions described; however, it would be reasonable for X to insure.

These two cases are alike in the following respect. There is a possibility of a loss for X which is not small in relation to his fortune; therefore, as a cautious man, he ought to choose the decision which avoids the large loss, although this decision is slightly unfavorable for him. This might suggest a restriction of rule R_4^* to the effect that X should choose a favorable action only if none of the losses which are possible on the basis of this decision is large in relation to his fortune. And it has indeed often been said that in the case of a bet the probability may be regarded as representing a betting quotient for a fair bet, neither favorable nor unfavorable for either side, only if the stake of each partner is small in relation to his fortune. Restricting the rule in this way seems well in accord with common conceptions of reasonable decisions. However, this procedure would merely limit the field of application of the old rule. The new rule would not tell us what to do in the excluded cases, those involving the possibility of large losses. Our problem is to state a *general* rule applicable in any case no matter whether the risks involved are small or large. It would not do to stipulate that large risks must be avoided at any price. There are certainly situations in which each of the possible decisions involves a large risk. And even in a situation where one of two possible decisions involves a large risk while the other does not, it may be advisable not to take the latter decision if the price is too high. In the example of the fire insurance it seems reasonable for X to insure even if the premium is more than 10 and hence the insurance is unfavorable, provided it is not too unfavorable. If the only opportunity of fire insurance for X involves a premium of 300, it seems questionable whether it would not be wiser for X to leave the house uninsured. What is needed is a general rule that says in a case like this exactly where the boundary line of the too unfavorable decision is.

A way to a solution might be found if we could answer the question why it is that those possible cases which involve a large loss for X ought to be given special consideration; in other words, why X, in choosing his decision, ought to assign to such a case not only a weight proportional to the amount of the loss involved—as is done by rule R_4—but a still higher weight. The answer is: the weight of a large loss should be more than proportional because X would suffer from a large loss disproportionately. If X has a fortune of 10,000, then he would suffer from a loss of 8,000 not only eight times as much as from a loss of 1,000, but much more because it would mean his near ruin. If X were to lose by ten successive accidents 1,000 each time, then every loss would hurt him more than the preceding ones, and the last would be the worst. Inversely, if X, with an initial fortune of zero, were to make ten or any other number of successive gains of 1,000 each, the satisfaction derived from the first gain would be the greatest, and those derived from the subsequent gains would be smaller and smaller.

Following the terminology of economists, we shall call the capacity of a certain amount of money or goods for satisfying the needs of a certain person the ***utility*** of that amount for this person. [Other terms used for this concept are 'moral gain' (Laplace) and 'subjective value'.] It seems that the following law holds generally within a wide field.

(1) ***Law of diminishing marginal utility.*** If a certain gain (a certain amount of goods or money) is added to an initial fortune f_0, then the utility of this gain is the smaller, the higher f_0.

This is, of course, not a law of inductive logic but an empirical law concerning the reactions of human beings, hence a law of psychology; but it is of importance for the application of inductive logic in determining practical decisions. This law was first pronounced by Daniel Bernoulli. It is well known in economics.

The aim of X in all his actions is the satisfaction of his needs and the avoidance of suffering, which we may regard as negative satisfaction. Gains in money or goods are appreciated as means of obtaining satisfaction; thus what counts is their utility. Therefore X's decisions must be guided by the principle of maximizing the utility of his gains rather than the gains themselves. Since, however, he cannot foresee future events, gains, and utilities with certainty but only with probability, he must apply the maximizing principle to the estimate of utility rather than to the unknown utility itself. This, however, presupposes that certain problems are solved which involve serious difficulties: first, utility must be measurable, and, further, a law must be known determining the utility of gains.

The first problem is to find *a method for measuring the* (positive or negative) *utility* of a gain (or a loss as a negative gain) for a certain person at a certain time; the (positive or negative) gain may consist in the acquisition (or loss) of money, goods, or other advantages. In other words, a quantitative explicatum must be found for the inexact concept of utility as an explicandum, which is perhaps not quantitative but merely comparative. The basic problem consists in measuring the utility of money. If this is possible, then it might be possible to measure the utility of other goods and advantages (or disadvantages) by establishing utility equivalences between them and amounts of money. This seems possible at least for those goods which can be exchanged, bought, and sold. But it might not be impossible even for the so-called imponderables, for example, a disease or the recovery from it, the positive or negative prestige gained by composing a good or a bad symphony, the gaining or losing of the love of a woman. It may be possible, at least theoretically, to determine the utility of events of this kind for X by determining his preferential reactions. Even if neither X nor the medical authorities accessible to him know how to cure a certain disease (which he has, or if he had it), nevertheless he can imagine a fairy confronting him with the alternative of either curing the disease or giving him a certain amount of money. Although the situation is imaginary, X can ask himself what he would prefer, and his answer measures his actual valuation. There are amounts of money which he will value less than the cure, and perhaps others which he will value more; and there will be intermediate amounts with respect to which he has no clear preference either way and which thus will represent a money equivalent for the utility of the advantage or disadvantage in question. It must be admitted that there are some serious problems involved in this assumption of the possibility of measuring the utility of all advantages and disadvantages for a given person at a given time on the basis of one common, one-dimensional scale. But something like this assumption is usually taken as a basis of an analysis of what is called 'rational behavior' in many parts of social science, especially in economics and ethics; and it is indeed hard to see how such an analysis could be made without this assumption. For our present purpose, we need not enter into a critical examination of the assumption. That belongs to the task of the methodology of the fields mentioned. We presuppose here the general methodological assumptions underlying an analysis of rational behavior. Our present task is merely to clarify the functions which the inductive concepts of probability$_1$ and estimate have in determining rational behavior.

The problem of the *measurability of utility* is much discussed in mathematical economics. See, e.g., Ragnar Frisch, *New methods of measuring marginal utility* (Tübingen, 1932); Oscar Lange, "The determinateness of the utility function", *Review of Economic Studies*, 1 (1933–34), 218–25; Harold T. Davis, *The theory of econometrics* (Bloomington, Ind., 1941), chap. iii; Paul A. Samuelson, *Foundations of economic analysis* (Cambridge, Mass., 1947), pp. 90 ff. and 173 ff. John von Neumann and Oskar Morgenstern ([Games], pp. 15–31, 617–32) discuss the problem of a quantitative concept of utility and construct an axiom system for it. Against those economists who propose to use the concept of utility merely in a comparative form (e.g., in the method of indifference curves introduced by Pareto), they advance the following argument. Let us assume that the system of preferences of the person X is complete not only with respect to alternative events which, when chosen, occur with certainty but also with respect to uncertain events with given numerical probabilities; this means that X is able to say, for example, which of the following two alternative events he prefers or whether they are equally desirable to him: (1) he receives $1.00 in cash, or (2) he receives a lottery ticket which represents a chance of obtaining $100 with the probability 0.01. The authors show that this complete system of the preferences of X determines a quantitative concept of utility for X in all its essential features, leaving open only the choice of a zero point and a unit of the utility scale. The resulting numerical utility is "that thing for which the calculus of mathematical expectations is legitimate" (p. 28).

Many investigations by economists concerning decisions made by a person X (including the discussion of utility by Neumann and Morgenstern just mentioned) are restricted to cases in which X knows the values of probability for certain events, especially for anticipated consequences of possible actions. The term 'probability' is understood in these investigations in the sense of probability$_2$, i.e., relative frequency. According to our conception, however, the determination of a practical decision can be based on the values of probability$_1$; knowledge of the values of probability$_2$ is not necessary. Now it is true that, if a value of probability$_2$ is known to X, that is, contained in the evidence available to X, then the corresponding value of probability$_1$ with respect to this evidence is equal to the value of probability$_2$, that is, the known relative frequency. (This follows from our considerations in § 41C. It will be shown in more exact terms later; see the remarks on T94-1e.) Therefore the numerical values obtained for probability or mathematical expectation in those investigations can be accepted from the point of view of our theory, because these values may be reinterpreted as values of the corresponding inductive concepts. But the approach described has a serious disadvantage: its domain of application has very narrow limits. Although the relevant values of probability_2 are known in certain cases, e.g., in many of those concerning games of chance, they are unknown in the great majority of cases concerning ordinary economic decisions, e.g., buying, selling, investing, and the like. Thus the method described excludes most of the problems relevant for economics. Now the decisive point is that the limitation mentioned is entirely unnecessary, if inductive logic is accepted. If the investigations in question were to use the concept of probability_1 instead of probability_2, the limitations would disappear, because the values of probability_1 cannot be unknown in the same sense as those of probability_2 (see § 41D, the last paragraph). If *X* knows the frequency of a relevant property *M* only for a sample which he has observed, then the probability_2, i.e., the relative frequency of *M* in the whole population, is unknown to him. But he can calculate the probability_1 of a hypothesis which ascribes *M* to an unobserved individual. This value of probability_1 is simultaneously the estimate of the unknown value of probability_2 in question (§ 41D). This value is sufficient as a basis for *X*'s decision.

When a method for measuring utility is found, a law must be established which states a functional relation between a gain, either in money or in goods having a money equivalent, and the utility of this gain (in other terms: between a physical gain and the corresponding moral gain, an objective value and the corresponding subjective value). The law of diminishing marginal utility is a law of this kind. But, although of great importance, it is not sufficient because it states a relation merely in comparative terms. What is needed is a quantitative law which enables *X* to determine beforehand the utility of an expected gain in money or goods. This is necessary for him in order to calculate the estimate of the resulting utility for each of his possible actions. And this again is required in order to enable him to choose the most promising course of action. The problem of a quantitative law will soon be discussed further. At the moment let us assume that it were solved. Then the maximizing principle could be stated in the form of the following rule:

Rule $\mathbf{R}_5$. Among the possible actions choose that one for which the estimate of the resulting utility is a maximum.

This rule is analogous to the previous rule R_4 (§ 50E). The difference is merely that R_5 refers to the utility instead of the money amount of the gain. Within those limits where the utility is proportional to the gain, the old rule arrives at the same results as the new one. This holds for those situations in which the absolute amount of any possible gain of X is small in relation to his initial fortune.

If the fortune changes from f_0 to f_1 and hence the gain is $g = f_1 - f_0$, we designate the corresponding utility by '$\mathbf{g}$'. We shall also speak of the total utilities $\mathbf{f}_0$ and $\mathbf{f}_1$ corresponding to the fortunes f_0 and f_1, respectively. However, these terms will occur in our calculations merely as auxiliary terms; the result will always be expressed, not as a value of the total utility itself, but as a difference between two values of total utility, that is, as a utility gain. Thus '$\mathbf{f}_0$' and '$\mathbf{f}_1$' are not interpreted separately, but only a term like '$\mathbf{f}_1 - \mathbf{f}_0$'; the latter is to be understood as the utility, positive or negative, which would result for X if his fortune were to change from f_0 to f_1.

B. *Daniel Bernoulli's Law of Utility*

That the distinction between the amount of money gained and its utility value is of great importance in practical applications of probability was recognized very early in the development of the theory of probability. Daniel Bernoulli, a nephew of the great Jacob Bernoulli, was the first to investigate this distinction clearly and systematically in his work [Specimen] published in 1738. He even proposed a particular quantitative law connecting the two magnitudes; see (2) below. This law enabled him to solve a number of problems, among them the so-called Petersburg Paradox. His theory was later reproduced and further developed by Laplace in a chapter of his chief work called "De l'espérance morale" ([Théorie], pp. 432–45). In Laplace's terminology the distinction is made between the 'physical fortune' measured in monetary units and the 'moral fortune', and hence between the 'physical gain' and the 'moral gain', that is, the satisfaction or utility. The estimate of the physical gain was usually called 'mathematical expectation'; Laplace contrasts to it the 'moral expectation' or 'moral hope' ('espérance morale'), i.e., the probability-mean estimate of the moral gain.

(2) ***Daniel Bernoulli's law of marginal utility.*** Suppose that X's fortune changes from f_0 to $f_0 + \Delta f$, where the gain Δf (positive or negative) is small in comparison with f_0. Then the marginal utility $\Delta\mathbf{f}$ (positive or negative) of this change for X is

(*a*) proportional to the gain Δf,

(*b*) inversely proportional to the initial fortune f_0.

Hence: $\Delta\mathbf{f} = k\frac{\Delta f}{f_0}$, where k is a constant which is characteristic of the person X at the time in question.

The stipulation (a) seems rather obvious. If X's fortune is large, say, 10,000, then he will derive from a positive gain of 2 twice as much satisfaction as from one of 1; and he will suffer from a loss of 2 twice as much as from one of 1. The decisive point in the law is (b). This is in accord with the law of diminishing utility (1) but is more specific. (1) says merely that, for the same gain Δf, the marginal utility $\Delta \mathfrak{f}$ decreases with increasing f_0; (2) states quantitatively how it decreases. It says that the utility for X of a positive gain of 1 is twice as high if his fortune is 5,000 than if it is 10,000.

The following theorem (3) refers to any change in fortune, whether small in relation to the initial fortune or not. It is mathematically deduced from (2) by dividing a large change (say, from 10,000 to 11,000) into many small changes (say, a thousand additions of 1 each), to which (2) can be applied; it is assumed that the utility of the large change is equal to the sum of the utilities of the small changes. (Exactly speaking, (3) is deduced by integration from the differential form of Bernoulli's law; see below.)

(3) *Corollary to Daniel Bernoulli's law.* Two changes (positive or negative, small or large) in fortune, say, from f_0 to f_1 and from f_2 to f_3, have equal utilities (positive or negative) if and only if the ratios of increase are equal:

$$\mathfrak{f}_1 - \mathfrak{f}_0 = \mathfrak{f}_3 - \mathfrak{f}_2 \text{ if and only if } f_1/f_0 = f_3/f_2 \, .$$

Thus, in order to cause equal increases in utility (the total utility growing in an arithmetic progression), the fortune must increase by equal ratios, hence in a geometric progression (e.g., 100, 200, 400, 800, etc.).

There is a striking analogy between Daniel Bernoulli's law and the Weber-Fechner psychophysical law, which says that the intensity of a sensation, e.g., the pressure sensation in the skin, grows by equal amounts if the physical intensity of the stimulus, e.g., the physical force of a body pressing the skin, grows by equal ratios. The fortune corresponds to the stimulus, the (total) utility to the sensation.

Bernoulli's law and some consequences of it, which are explained in the text in a less technical form, will here be stated briefly in their exact technical form. For the sake of simplicity, we have formulated (2) in terms of a small increase Δf. The actual form of Bernoulli's law states the same relation for the limiting case, that is, it has the differential form

(4) $$d\mathfrak{f} = k\, df/f \, .$$

Suppose that the fortune changes from f_0 to f_1, and hence the gain is $g = f_1 - f_0$. Then the utility corresponding to this change is $\mathfrak{g} = \mathfrak{f}_1 - \mathfrak{f}_0 = k\int_{f_0}^{f_1} df/f$.

Hence:

(5) $$g = k\,(\log f_1 - \log f_0) = k \log f_1/f_0\,.$$

The corollary (3) follows immediately from this.

Let X have the fortune f_0. Let $g_1, g_2, \ldots$, be the possible gains resulting from a certain action, and $q_1, q_2, \ldots$, their probabilities. Then the utility in the case of g_1 is, according to (5), $\mathbf{g}_1 = k[\log(f_0 + g_1) - \log f_0]$. $\mathbf{g}_2$, etc., are analogous. Therefore, the estimate of the utility is (§ 41D(3))

(6) $$\begin{aligned} \mathbf{g}' &= k[q_1 \log(f_0 + g_1) + q_2 \log(f_0 + g_2) \ldots - (q_1 + q_2 \ldots) \log f_0] \\ &= k[\log[(f_0 + g_1)^{q_1}(f_0 + g_2)^{q_2} \ldots] - \log f_0]\,. \end{aligned}$$

We shall now determine that gain which, if it occurred on the basis of f_0, would cause the utility $\mathbf{g}'$ (which does not actually occur but has just been determined as an estimate); let us call it '$*\mathbf{g}'$'. According to (5), $\mathbf{g}' = k[\log(f_0 + *\mathbf{g}') - \log f_0]$. This, together with (6), yields:

(7) $$*\mathbf{g}' = (f_0 + g_1)^{q_1}(f_0 + g_2)^{q_2} \ldots - f_0\,.$$

This is Daniel Bernoulli's main theorem, from which he draws important consequences for various problems. We shall illustrate in the text some of his theorems with the help of our examples; for the sake of easier understanding, we shall not make use of (5) or (7) but derive the results by elementary means, using only the corollary (3).

For a given f_0, $*\mathbf{g}'$ increases with increasing $\mathbf{g}'$. Therefore our rule R_5, referring to the maximum value of $\mathbf{g}'$, could as well refer to that of $*\mathbf{g}'$.

The content of Daniel Bernoulli's treatise is summarized by Todhunter ([History], pp. 213–22). His conception and its consequences are discussed in many books on probability; see, e.g., Czuber [Wahrsch.], I, 235–45, Keynes [Probab.], pp. 317 f. (the formula at the top of p. 318, corresponding to our (7), is misprinted), Fry [Probab.], pp. 195 f. Bernoulli's law, chiefly in its comparative form (1), the law of diminishing marginal utility, has become the foundation of the modern theory of value in economics, which was founded by Stanley Jevons (1871), Carl Menger (father) (1871), and Léon Walras (1874), and is based on the concept of marginal utility.

On the other hand, the quantitative form of Bernoulli's law is usually regarded by modern authors as an oversimplification. It is pointed out that different kinds of commodities may require different forms of a quantitative law and that the simultaneous consideration of several commodities ought to take into account their relationships (Vilfredo Pareto: 'complementary goods' and 'competitive goods'). Furthermore, doubts have been expressed concerning the adequacy of the particular form of the law chosen by Bernoulli, and other forms have been proposed. Compare: Ludwig Frick [Einleitung], H. E. Timerding [Bernoulli], Ch. Jordan [Bernoulli], Harold T. Davis, *The theory of econometrics* (Bloomington, Ind., 1941). Gerhard Tintner introduces the concept of a risk preference functional: with its help he explains economic behavior, e.g., in betting or business, as dependent upon the *entire* probability function rather than merely upon its mean or other parameters ([Choice], [Contribution]; further: "The theory of production under non-static conditions", *Journal of Political Economy*, 50 [1942], 645 ff.). Karl Menger (son) [Wertlehre] has made a careful analysis of the whole problem. (This analysis leads to a clarification of the so-called Petersburg Paradox, which seems more satisfactory than the various earlier attempts of a solution.) After a critical examination of the laws proposed by Daniel Bernoulli and others he shows that the law, in order to represent the actual behavior of most people, would have to possess the following features among others, in addition to satisfying the principle of diminishing marginal utility. The utility of a gain approaches zero as the initial fortune grows. There is a certain saturation value which the curve of the total utility does not exceed but approaches asymptotically. Further, X does not simply try to maximize the probability$_1$-mean, in other words, the effect of an expected gain on the decision of X is not measured by the product of its utility and its probability; instead, very small probabilities are "underestimated", that is to say, their effect is smaller than the product mentioned and becomes even 0 for sufficiently small, though still positive, probabilities. Probabilities near to 1 are likewise "underestimated", while certain intermediate probabilities are "overestimated". Then there is a certain fraction q_X, usually < 1, such that X, possessing the fortune f_0, is not willing to risk more than the amount $q_X f_0$ even for the best of chances; q_X depends upon the person X and to some extent also on the situation. Menger does not propose any particular law either for the utility or for the determination of X's decision. He believes that the form of such a law changes from person to person and would therefore have to contain many parameters characteristic of person or situation. Although the law would have a quantitative form, it could not be used for the actual determination of quantitative values with respect to a given person X without first measuring the values for X of all the parameters involved. Menger regards as the essential features of such a law not so much its quantitative form and the values of the parameters involved, but rather certain comparative characteristics, some of which are stated by him in a general, comparative form.

In the case of an alternative, we called one of the two possible actions favorable, unfavorable, or neutral, respectively, if g'_1 (the estimate of the gain in the case of this action) is greater, less, or equal, respectively, to g'_2. On the basis of the distinction between the gain g and its utility (or subjective value) $\boldsymbol{g}$, we should use now the more explicit terms 'objectively favorable', etc., and contrast them with 'subjectively favorable', etc. If the estimate of the utility is higher for one action than for the other, the first may be called subjectively favorable, the second subjectively unfavorable; if the estimates are equal, the actions and the offer are called subjectively neutral.

C. *Consequences of Bernoulli's Law*

We shall now explain two important conclusions which Daniel Bernoulli has derived from his law. They will be illustrated by application to those of our previous examples in which the earlier rule R_4 (§ 50E) led to unreasonable decisions. Then the application of the new rule R_5 to these cases will be discussed. We shall find that this rule leads to reasonable decisions also in these cases; thus it overcomes the difficulties previously explained (§ 50E).

For the more general, comparative, form of the results, we shall use only the comparative law of diminishing utility (1). For the more specific quantitative results, we shall assume Bernoulli's law; it will, however, be sufficient to use its corollary (3). We do not mean to adopt the law. To decide whether and to what extent the law holds is the task of psychology, not of inductive logic; therefore, we abstain from a judgment on this question.

If we wanted to calculate actual numerical values of the utility of gains, we should have to specify the numerical value of the parameter k occurring in Bernoulli's law. If, furthermore, we wanted to calculate numerical values of total utilities themselves and not only of their differences, we should have to specify the numerical value of another parameter (the constant of integration appearing when (4) is integrated). However, this can be avoided by a device which was used by Bernoulli and Laplace: instead of characterizing a utility $\boldsymbol{g}$ (with respect to an initial fortune f_0) by its numerical value on the psychological scale of utility, which actually has not been established, it is characterized by the equivalent money gain, which we designate by '$*\boldsymbol{g}$'. This is meant as that gain in money which (on the basis of f_0) would have the utility $\boldsymbol{g}$. Analogously, $f_0 + *\boldsymbol{g}$ is designated by '$*\boldsymbol{f}$'. If we start from a gain g and then consider its utility $\boldsymbol{g}$, there is, of course, no point in using the concept and symbol just introduced, because $*\boldsymbol{g}$ is simply g. However, if the utility $\boldsymbol{g}$ has not been determined as that of a given money gain but in some other way, for instance, as an estimate, then the use of '$*\boldsymbol{g}$' will be convenient, as we shall see.

The first important result is that even a game or bet which is fair, that is, objectively neutral for either partner, is subjectively unfavorable for both. Let us take our example of a bet at even odds on a throw of a symmetrical coin. Let X's initial fortune be f_0 and the stake u. Then the resulting fortune is either $f_1 = f_0 + u$ or $f_2 = f_0 - u$. The estimate f' of the resulting fortune is the arithmetic mean of the two possible and equiprobable results, that is, f_0. Hence the estimate of the gain is $g' = 0$. However, with respect to the utility the situation is quite different. Let $\boldsymbol{f}_0$, $\boldsymbol{f}_1$, and $\boldsymbol{f}_2$ be the total utilities corresponding to f_0, f_1, and f_2, respectively. Since the two results $\boldsymbol{f}_1$ and $\boldsymbol{f}_2$ are equiprobable, the estimate $\boldsymbol{f}'$ of the resulting total utility is their arithmetic mean; hence (i) $\boldsymbol{f}_1 - \boldsymbol{f}' = \boldsymbol{f}' - \boldsymbol{f}_2$. According to the law of diminishing marginal utility (1), the utility corresponding to a change in fortune from f_0 to $f_1 = f_0 + u$ is less than that which would correspond to a change from $f_2 = f_0 - u$ to f_0, because $f_0 > f_2$. In other words, (ii) $\boldsymbol{f}_1 - \boldsymbol{f}_0 < \boldsymbol{f}_0 - \boldsymbol{f}_2$. Hence with (i): (iii) $\boldsymbol{f}' < \boldsymbol{f}_0$. The estimate $\boldsymbol{g}'$ of the utility $\boldsymbol{g}$ is $\boldsymbol{f}' - \boldsymbol{f}_0$; according to (iii), this is negative. Therefore, accepting the bet is subjectively unfavorable, although objectively neutral.

Now let us examine the same situation quantitatively, with the help of the corollary (3) to Bernoulli's law. Let $*f'$ be the fortune corresponding to f'; that is to say, if a change in fortune from f_0 to $*f'$ were to occur, it would cause a change in total utility from $\boldsymbol{f}_0$ to $\boldsymbol{f}'$ and hence the additional utility would be $\boldsymbol{f}' - \boldsymbol{f}_0$. Applying (3) to the equality of differences in total utility (i), we obtain an equality of ratios of the corresponding fortunes: (iv) $f_1 : *f' = *f' : f_2$; in other words, $*f'$ is the geometric mean between f_1 and f_2. Since the geometric mean of two positive numbers is always less than their arithmetic mean, we have: (v) $*f' < f_0$. This is a merely comparative result, essentially the same as the earlier result (iii). But (iv) is a quantitative result allowing numerical calculations. In our previous example, the initial fortune was $f_0 = 10{,}000$, the stake $u = 8{,}000$; hence $f_1 = 18{,}000$ and $f_2 = 2{,}000$. $*f'$ is the geometric mean of the latter two values, hence 6,000. Therefore the monetary equivalent $*\boldsymbol{g}'$ of the estimate $\boldsymbol{g}'$ of the utility has the negative value of $-4{,}000$. This means that if X accepts the bet with the stake of 8,000, the estimate of his resulting total utility corresponds to a fortune of only 6,000; in other words, acceptance of the bet is equivalent in utility to throwing 4,000 out of the window; hence it is rather disadvantageous. Rule R_5 prescribes maximization of the estimate of the utility. Therefore it prohibits the acceptance of the bet, in agreement with common sense. Thus rule R_5 overcomes the first of the difficulties we found in connection with rules R_4 and R_4^*.

In the case just considered, the negative utility, measured by the equivalent monetary loss of 4,000, is enormous. This is due to the large stake. The accompanying table shows also the results for smaller values

Stake u	$*f'$	Money Equivalent of the Estimate of the Resulting Utility $*g'$
8,000	6,000	−4,000
1,000	9,949.88	− 50.12
100	9,999.50	− 0.50
10	9,999.995	− 0.005
1	9,999.99995	− 0.00005

of the stake u, the initial fortune being always $f_0 = 10{,}000$. The calculation is as follows: $*f'$ is the geometric mean between $10{,}000 + u$ and $10{,}000 - u$; $*g' = *f' - 10{,}000$. We see from the last column of the table that the absolute amount of the monetary equivalent of the estimate of the utility decreases rapidly with decreasing stake.

So far the decisions resulting from rule R_5 seem to be in accord with common sense. But now the question arises whether this rule is not too rigorous by declaring *all* fair bets as disadvantageous even if the stake of X is small in relation to his fortune. We feel that a reasonable friend, although he would warn X against a bet of a thousand dollars, would not try to dissuade him from a bet of one dollar, and perhaps not even from one of ten dollars. The estimate of the utility is found to be equivalent to a loss of one two-hundredth of a cent in the first case and one-half of a cent in the second. One might say that these amounts, though practically negligible, are anyway negative amounts and hence indicate that even bets for these moderate stakes are, strictly speaking, disadvantageous; one might think that if the rule prohibits these bets, it seems questionable whether it is in accord with sound common sense. However, the rule does not unconditionally prohibit these bets. It says merely that the bet is disadvantageous *if* the positive utility from winning and the negative utility from losing are all the utility factors involved. If there are other factors in the situation, they must be introduced into the calculation, and then the result may be different. It may be, for example, that X derives some pleasure from the excitement of the bet or from pleasing his friend who wishes to bet. Even if this pleasure is small, it may easily be sufficient to outweigh the displeasure equivalent to the loss of a fraction of one cent. If so, the rule leads to the decision of accepting the bet of ten dollars. If the stake is one hundred dollars, the estimate of the utility is equivalent to the loss of fifty cents. If the additional pleasures are not worth to X half a dollar, the rule will result in X's decision to decline the bet.

It is important to recognize clearly that rule R_5 does not tell X in any way how to valuate things; whether he should prefer the excitement of gambling or the peace of mind caused by abstaining from gambling; whether to help Y in his business affairs, or to defeat him by honest but ruthless operations, or to cheat him. The rule is not a moral rule but a rule of applied logic. (Therefore Laplace's terms 'moral fortune', 'moral gain', and 'moral expectation' are somewhat misleading.) This means that the rule does not lay down value standards by which to judge, to approve or to disapprove our desires. It presupposes that X has a fixed set of interests or needs; the rule has merely the task of helping X in finding out which actions are consistent with his needs and which are not. It does so, not a priori, but on the basis of the empirical knowledge which X has collected by his previous experiences.

Now let us examine the second difficulty which we found in connection with the previous rule R_4. This rule prohibits taking out fire insurance if it is unfavorable, that is, if the premium, as is usually the case, is higher than the fair premium, i.e., the estimate of loss by fire. Common sense, on the other hand, advises one to insure provided the premium is not exorbitant. In our example, X has the opportunity to insure his house, valued at 10,000, for one year against fire at a premium of $r > 10$. The probability that the house will burn down during the year is 1/1,000. The problem is whether from the point of view of utility it is advisable for him to buy the insurance. The answer depends not only upon the amount r of the premium but also upon the present fortune f_0 of X. If f_0 is not much larger than 10,000, in other words, if X does not own much besides the house, then the destruction of the house, if not insured, would reduce X's fortune to a small fraction of its present value. This reduction would cause a very great negative satisfaction, not only a thousand times as great as the expense of 10 but much more. Therefore, in this case, X would do well to pay the premium r, even though it is more than 10, provided it is not too high.

In order to obtain quantitative values, let us assume again Bernoulli's law. Suppose that X has, in addition to the house, only 100 in cash; hence $f_0 = 10{,}100$. If he buys the insurance, his loss is r. If he does not, there are two possible cases: the house may burn down or not. In the first case the resulting fortune is $f_1 = 100$; in the second case, $f_2 = 10{,}100$. The probability of the first case is $q_1 = 0.001$; that of the second, $q_2 = 0.999$. Let the total utilities corresponding to the fortunes f_0, f_1, and f_2 be $\mathbf{f}_0, \mathbf{f}_1$, and $\mathbf{f}_2$, respectively. Then the estimate $\mathbf{f}'$ of the resulting total utility is, according to the definition of estimate (§ 41D(3)), $q_1 f_1 + q_2 f_2$, that is, $0.001\, \mathbf{f}_1 + 0.999\, \mathbf{f}_2 = \mathbf{f}_1 + 0.999\, (\mathbf{f}_2 - \mathbf{f}_1)$. In other words, if we divide the distance between $\mathbf{f}_1$ and $\mathbf{f}_2$ on the $\mathbf{f}$-scale in one thousand equal parts, $\mathbf{f}'$ is the last dividing point preceding $\mathbf{f}_2$. Now, according to the corollary (3), to equal differences on the $\mathbf{f}$-scale correspond equal ratios on the f-scale. Therefore, in order to find the value $^*f'$ on the f-scale corresponding to $\mathbf{f}'$, we have to divide the segment of the f-scale between f_1 and f_2 in one thousand parts, not parts of equal length but parts for which the quotient of one value divided by the preceding one is always the same, say, q. Thus the successive points on the f-scale have the values $f_1, f_1q, f_1q^2, f_1q^3, \ldots, f_1q^{999}$, $f_1q^{1{,}000} = f_2$. Hence q is to be calculated as the thousandth root of f_2/f_1. For $f_2 = 10{,}100$ and $f_1 = 100$, we find $q = 1.004626$. Then $^*f'$ is found as the last value preceding f_2, hence f_1q^{999} or $f_2/q = 10{,}053.50$. This amount is less by 46.50 than the initial fortune $f_0 = 10{,}100$. This result means that, if X does not insure the house, the estimate of his resulting total utility corresponds to a fortune of 10,053.50; hence the estimate of the resulting increase in utility is negative. It is measured by the corresponding gain $*g' = *f' - f_0$, which we found to be -46.50. Therefore, if the premium r is less than 46.50, rule R_5 advises X to buy the insurance, because in this case the estimate of the utility (corresponding to a gain of $-r$) is higher than in the case of noninsurance (where it corresponds to -46.50).

In this example the premium which is subjectively neutral (46.50) is rather large in comparison with the premium which is fair, i.e., objectively neutral (10). This is due to the fact that in this example the value of the house constitutes a large part of the initial fortune (10,100), indeed nearly all of it. The accompanying table shows the results for other values of the

Initial Fortune f_0	f_0/h	q	Subjectively Neutral Premium $-*g'$
10,100	1.01	1.004 626	46.50
15,000	1.5	1.001 100	16.50
20,000	2	1.000 693	13.86
40,000	4	1.000 288	11.52
100,000	10	1.000 105 4	10.54

initial fortune f_0, but always for the same value of the house ($h = 10{,}000$). The calculation is as follows:

$$q = [f_0/(f_0 - 10{,}000)]^{0.001} ;$$
$$*f' = f_0/q ; \quad -*g' = f_0 - *f' = f_0(1 - 1/q) .$$

The table shows that, the higher the initial fortune f_0, the lower the subjectively neutral premium. If f_0 is ten times the value of the house, the subjectively neutral premium is only 10.54, hence not much higher than the fair, that is, objectively neutral premium (10). Since the premium demanded by an insurance company will usually be higher than 10.54, this result means that, in the last case, insurance at available rates is not only objectively but even subjectively unfavorable. This result is in accord with what is regarded as sound thinking in business. Even people of cautious character often prefer to leave a certain item, a house, a car, or the like, uninsured in view of prevailing insurance rates if the value of this item is only a small part of their whole fortune.

Thus we see that the present rule R_5, making the estimate of the utility rather than that of the money gain decisive in the choice of actions, overcomes the difficulties involved in the previous rule R_4. It may be assumed that the present rule or a similar one using likewise inductive concepts like probability$_1$, estimate, etc., would be adequate as a "guide of life," that is, as an explicatum for the vague concept of a reasonable decision as explicandum *if* the following two requirements were fulfilled. (i) A quantitative law must be found which states either the value of the total utility as a function of the fortune or (like (2)) the value of the increase in utility as a function of the gain and the initial fortune. This law will contain certain parameters whose values depend upon person and time. As mentioned earlier, it seems today plausible to assume that this law cannot have the simple form stated by Daniel Bernoulli but must have a more general and more complicated form. This is a problem to be solved by psychological investigation. (ii) The rule uses the concept of estimate. Therefore an adequate explicatum of this concept is required. If an adequate quantitative explicatum for probability$_1$ can be found, a concept of estimate can be defined as the probability$_1$-mean (§ 41D(3)). An alternative procedure would consist in constructing an independent definition of estimate (i.e., one not based on probability$_1$) or various methods of estimation for various magnitudes. Some contemporary statisticians investigate methods of estimation which are independent in this sense, because they do not believe in the possibility of an adequate quantitative explicatum for probability$_1$ (see § 98). In any case the development of methods of estimation, whether based on probability$_1$ or independent, is a task of quantitative inductive logic.

§ 52. On the Arguments of Degree of Confirmation

We may choose between two logical types for the arguments of degree of confirmation. In method (1) the arguments are entities expressed by sentences, e.g., propositions, events, or the like. In method (2) the arguments are sentences, and hence names of sentences are written as argument expressions. In method (1) the sentences about degree of confirmation belong to the object language, in (2) to the semantical metalanguage. (1) is more customary; we shall however use (2), because here the language can be extensional (truth-functional) and we do not need a modal logic as basis. At any rate, the difference is only a technical one; all our theorems of inductive logic can easily be translated into form (1). Incidentally, the analogous problem for probability$_2$ (relative frequency) is discussed; here, the customary formulation (1) in the object language seems preferable. The degree of confirmation is relative not only with respect to the evidence, but, like all semantical concepts, also with respect to the language system.

In the rest of this chapter (§§ 52–54), some preliminary considerations will be made which will help us to find a way for solving our task, the construction of a quantitative inductive logic for our systems $\mathfrak{L}$. This construction will then be begun in the following chapter.

We aim at finding, as a basis for inductive logic, a definition for the degree of confirmation $\mathfrak{c}$ as a quantitative explicatum for probability$_1$. It is essential that $\mathfrak{c}$ is a function of two arguments, because, as explained earlier (§ 10A), probability$_1$ is a relative concept which is dependent not only upon the hypothesis in question but also upon the evidence.

Whether propositions or sentences expressing the propositions are taken as arguments of the degree of confirmation is merely a technical question, not a question of the conception of the nature of probability$_1$. We shall now discuss both alternatives; thereby the reason why we prefer the second will become clear.

1. Both in the classical theory and in more recent theories of probability$_1$, nearly all authors have taken as arguments (or, in the older period when the relativity of probability$_1$ was not yet clearly recognized, as the one argument) not sentences but something expressed or described by sentences, variously designated as events, possible cases, occurrences, or, by more modern authors, for example, Keynes and Jeffreys, as propositions. For our present problem we need not discuss here the controversial question whether or not events, facts, etc., belong to the same type as propositions; we need not even pay attention to the particular terms used by the authors for the arguments. The essential point is that the authors of this group write sentences (or variables of the type of sentences) as argument expressions. In words, this is done in the customary formulation:

(a) 'the probability that . . . (on the evidence that - - -) is 1/6'.

Using a language of symbolic logic, Keynes writes, for example, '$P(a/h) = 1/6$' or briefly '$a/h = 1/6$', and similarly Jeffreys '$\mathrm{P}(q|p) = 1/6$'; 'a', 'h', 'p', 'q' are variables for which sentences may be substituted. This way of formulation has an important consequence; probability$_1$ becomes here a function of the kind known as intensional (non-extensional, non-truth-functional). Therefore the theory of probability$_1$ in this form must be based not on the form of logical system ordinarily used in symbolic logic but on an intensional, modal system. Not even the authors mentioned above, although they use symbolic logic, seem to be aware of this fact. That probability$_1$ is here not a truth-function is obvious. [For instance, from the schema (a) we can first form a true sentence (a_1) by writing a suitable sentence in the place of the three dashes and another sentence which happens to be true in the place of the three dots; and then we can form another sentence (a_2) which is false by putting for the dashes the same as before but for the dots another true sentence.] How modal logic comes in may be seen from the following example. In our theory, which belongs to the second kind, there is the following theorem (T59-1b):

(b) 'For any sentences e and h, if e is not L-false and the sentence $e \supset h$ is L-true (in other words, e L-implies h), then $\mathfrak{c}(h,e) = 1$.'

In order to transfer this theorem to the present form of theory, we need first, instead of '$\mathfrak{c}$', a corresponding symbol, say, 'c' (or Keynes's and Jeffreys' 'P'), which takes sentences as argument expressions, and further a modal sign, say, 'N' for logical necessity, which corresponds to 'L-true' (or '$\vdash$') but takes a sentence as argument expression. Then the theorem corresponding to (b) can be formulated in the following way either in words (c) or in symbols (c′):

(c) 'For any p and q, if p is not impossible and if it is necessary that $p \supset q$ (in other words, if p strictly implies q), then $c(q,p) = 1$.'

(c′) '$(p)(q)[\sim N \sim p \,.\, N(p \supset q) \supset c(q,p) = 1]$'.

If one wants to be more explicit, he may write in (c) after 'any' a suitable noun, say, 'propositions' or 'cases' or 'events' or whichever term of this kind he prefers; this is, however, not necessary; it is sufficient to stipulate the type of the variables 'p' and 'q', for instance, by the customary rule that sentences may be substituted for them. In contradistinction to (b), which belongs to the metalanguage, (c) and (c′) belong to the object language. This becomes still clearer when we take a substitution instance of (c′), e.g., with 'Pa' for 'p' and '$Pa \vee Pb$' for 'q':

(d) '$\sim N \sim (Pa) \,.\, N(Pa \supset Pa \vee Pb) \supset c(Pa \vee Pb, Pa) = 1$'.

If a suitable system of modal logic is used, then the two conjunctive components of the antecedent can be proved, and hence we obtain:

(e) '$c(Pa \vee Pb, Pa) = 1$'.

2. The second method of formulation takes sentences as arguments. Therefore here, not sentences, but names of sentences (or, in general theorems, variables for names of sentences, like our 'h', 'i', etc.), are written as argument expressions. Thus here, the sentences about probability$_1$ or degree of confirmation belong to the metalanguage and, in particular, to its semantical part, not to the same language as the sentences to which they refer. This method has only recently been used by a few authors, for instance, Mazurkiewicz and Hosiasson; and we shall use it too. Instead of (c) or (c′), we have here the form (b). Here, again, we may form a substitution instance corresponding to (d). Taking '$\mathfrak{S}_1$' as a name (not an abbreviation!) for 'Pa' and '$\mathfrak{S}_2$' for 'Pb', we have:

(f) 'If $\mathfrak{S}_1$ is not L-false and $\mathfrak{S}_1 \supset \mathfrak{S}_1 \vee \mathfrak{S}_2$ is L-true, then $\mathfrak{c}(\mathfrak{S}_1 \vee \mathfrak{S}_2, \mathfrak{S}_1) = 1$'.

Since the two conditions are fulfilled, we may omit the conditional clause; thus we obtain, corresponding to (e):

(g) '$\mathfrak{c}(\mathfrak{S}_1 \vee \mathfrak{S}_2, \mathfrak{S}_1) = 1$'.

This second method has the advantage that here the language to which the sentences about probability$_1$ or $\mathfrak{c}$ belong may be extensional. Thus here a simpler structure can be taken for the underlying deductive logic than in the first method. The fact that here we cannot stay within the object language but have to use a metalanguage does not seem too high a price for the advantage mentioned.

The choice between the two methods (1) and (2) here discussed for the formulation of inductive logic is analogous to the much-discussed choice between two well-known methods for the formulation of deductive logic. The latter can take the form either (1) of a modal logic in an intensional object language, like Lewis' system of strict implication, or (2) of a theory of L-concepts within semantics, as here in the earlier chapter on deductive logic (§§ 20–24). (Concerning modal logic and its relation to semantics cf. [Modalities] § 1 and [Meaning] § 39.) The concepts of L-truth, L-falsity, and L-implication in method (2) correspond to the modal concepts of necessity, impossibility, and strict implication, respectively, in (1). There is so far no agreement as to which of these two methods for deductive logic is preferable. Those who prefer here the semantical method (2) will presumably also prefer our semantical method (2) for inductive logic. However, as said before, the difference is only a technical one; all theorems of our inductive logic stated in later chapters can easily be translated into formulations according to method (1), as shown by the examples (b) and (c) (or (c′)) above.

Some remarks may be made incidentally on the analogous problem for probability$_2$, that is, relative frequency. As explained earlier (§ 10B), we have here likewise two arguments. Method (1) takes properties as arguments; method (2) predicates designating those properties. In method (1), a probability$_2$ sentence is formulated in the object language; but here, in distinction to probability$_1$, the language need not be intensional. Since coextensive properties have obviously the same cardinal number, and probability$_2$ is definable as a function of cardinal numbers (in the simplest form, as a relative frequency, hence a quotient of two cardinal numbers), the value of probability$_2$ does not change if one argument property is replaced by another one of the same extension. Therefore here, in distinction to probability$_1$, there is no advantage in taking method (2) and thereby going to the metalanguage. The formulation of probability$_2$ sentences in the object language has the great advantage that these sentences, which are not, like the probability$_1$ sentences, purely logical but have a factual content, can be dealt with on a par with other factual sentences of science. Thus we can, for example, in physics, combine laws of a deterministic form with probability$_2$ laws without any difficulties. Therefore it is understandable that, as far as I am aware, all authors on probability$_2$ have used method (1).

In most applications of probability$_1$, the first argument, which we call the hypothesis, is an assumption about facts not known or insufficiently known; it may be a prediction of a single event or a physical law or an existential assumption or a complex theory consisting of general and nongeneral sentences. In order not to restrict the applicability unduly, we shall admit as first argument for $\mathfrak{c}$ any sentence of our systems $\mathfrak{L}$ of whatever form; a theory consisting of various statements will then be formulated as a conjunction. The second argument of probability$_1$, which we call the evidence, is often a report on observations, which may be formulated as a conjunction of basic sentences (D16-6b). However, we shall not restrict the second argument of $\mathfrak{c}$ to this form but again admit sentences of all forms, including general ones, with the sole exception of L-false sentences (the term 'L-false' is explained and defined in § 20). To make this exception is customary and convenient. [We shall see later that $\mathfrak{c}(h,e)$ may be represented as a quotient of two numbers (§ 54B). If e is L-false, both these numbers are 0. In arithmetic the function of quotient is not defined for the case that both arguments are zero; this restriction is found convenient because otherwise (that is, if we were to make an *ad hoc* stipulation for the value of '0/0') some general arithmetical theorems would not hold in their customary simple form. For the same reasons it is convenient to exclude the case of an L-false second argument (evidence) from the domain of definition of the function $\mathfrak{c}$.]

We have earlier (§ 10A) emphasized the relativity of probability$_1$ or degree of confirmation $\mathfrak{c}$ with respect to the evidence. But it is relative in still another way, viz., with respect to the language system. $\mathfrak{c}$ is, as we shall see, closely related to the semantical L-concepts and may even be regarded as a quantitative semantical L-concept. Therefore, like all semantical concepts, $\mathfrak{c}$ is dependent upon a language system; any $\mathfrak{c}$-sentence must, in complete formulation, contain a reference to a language system, for instance: '$\mathfrak{c}(h,e) = r$ in the system $\mathfrak{L}$'. For '$\mathfrak{c}$ in the system $\mathfrak{L}_N$' we shall sometimes write '${}_N\mathfrak{c}$' and for '$\mathfrak{c}$ in the system $\mathfrak{L}_\infty$' '${}_\infty\mathfrak{c}$'. More frequently, we shall omit for the sake of brevity the reference to the language system if either it is not essential for the point under discussion or the context makes sufficiently clear which system or systems are meant; this formulation is in line with the customary elliptic formulations of other semantical concepts (e.g., 'true' instead of 'true in $\mathfrak{L}$'). The relativity with respect to language has generally been overlooked, even by those modern authors who use symbolic logic. Leaving aside language systems of a more complex structure and with other kinds of variables and considering only our language systems $\mathfrak{L}$, there are especially two features of a system which may influence $\mathfrak{c}$. (i) The number of $\mathfrak{in}$ in the language system, and hence the number of individuals in the domain of individuals of the system, is obviously of influence upon $\mathfrak{c}$ if general sentences are involved; for, as we have seen earlier (§ 15A), the meaning and hence the L-semantical properties of a general sentence change with the number of $\mathfrak{in}$. (ii) The influence of the $\mathfrak{pr}$ in $\mathfrak{L}$ upon $\mathfrak{c}$ in $\mathfrak{L}$ is not so obvious; we shall see later that in certain cases the value of $\mathfrak{c}(h,e)$ in $\mathfrak{L}$ depends upon what other $\mathfrak{pr}$ besides those occurring in h and e belong to $\mathfrak{L}$. [One reason for this dependence is the fact that sometimes $\mathfrak{c}(h,e)$ in $\mathfrak{L}^\pi$ (§ 31) is influenced by the logical width (D32-1a) of a molecular predicate expression occurring in h or e and that this width is dependent upon the total number π of $\mathfrak{pr}$ including those not occurring in h or e.]

§ 53. Some Conventions on Degree of Confirmation

Some conventions concerning $\mathfrak{c}$ are laid down. They are not part of our system of inductive logic but serve merely for heuristic purposes; they will be used only in the preliminary considerations in the next section. The conventions, among them the customary principles of multiplication and addition, are plausible and fulfilled by all adequate quantitative explicata of probability$_1$.

Since the task of defining a quantitative concept of confirmation seems rather complicated in view of the difficulties some of which have been discussed in this chapter, we shall make an attempt in the next section of reducing this task to simpler tasks. In order to do so, we shall have to make use of some simple, fundamental properties of degree of confirmation. In this section we shall lay down some of these properties by way of conventions. The first convention C1 states only properties which it seems clear any adequate quantitative explicatum must have. And it seems that indeed practically all authors who use probability$_1$ as a quantitative concept, even if only within a restricted field, have accepted these properties. Some authors have laid down these conditions, or similar ones from which these follow, as axioms. We shall not do so; our system of inductive logic will not be based on axioms but only on explicit definitions. The conventions here made will be used only for heuristic purposes, for the preliminary considerations in this and the next section; they will not be used later on. C1 is not a definition of adequacy; the conditions (a) to (d) are necessary, but they together do not form a sufficient condition for adequacy. That is to say, a concept fulfilling these conditions may still be inadequate; but no concept which violates one of these conditions can be regarded as adequate.

C53-1. ***Convention on adequacy.*** A quantitative function $\mathfrak{c}$ defined for some pairs of sentences of a system $\mathfrak{L}$ is not adequate as a quantitative explicatum for probability$_1$ unless it fulfils the following conditions (a) to (d) with respect to any sentences in $\mathfrak{L}$ for which it is defined.

- **a.** *L-equivalent evidences.* If e and e' are L-equivalent, then $\mathfrak{c}(h,e) = \mathfrak{c}(h,e')$.
- **b.** *L-equivalent hypotheses.* If h and h' are L-equivalent, then $\mathfrak{c}(h,e) = \mathfrak{c}(h',e)$.
- **c.** *General Multiplication Principle.* $\mathfrak{c}(h\,.\,j,e) = \mathfrak{c}(h,e) \times \mathfrak{c}(j,e\,.\,h)$.
- **d.** *Special Addition Principle.* If $e\,.\,h\,.\,j$ is L-false, then $\mathfrak{c}(h \vee j,e) = \mathfrak{c}(h,e) + \mathfrak{c}(j,e)$.

It seems plausible to require the four conditions C1a to d for any explicatum $\mathfrak{c}$ for probability$_1$. (a) says that the value of $\mathfrak{c}$ does not change if one evidence is replaced by another L-equivalent one; (b) says the same for hypotheses. These requirements seem natural, since L-equivalent sentences have the same content, give the same information about the facts, and differ at most in their formulations. It seems obvious that the value of probability$_1$ depends not upon the formulation but merely upon the content. Those theories of probability$_1$ which take as arguments, not sentences as our theory does, but propositions (§ 52, method (1)), do not need principles corresponding to (a) and (b), since L-equivalent sentences express the same proposition. (c) and (d) are generally accepted in practically all modern theories of probability$_1$ (and, incidentally, their analogues occur in all theories of probability$_2$). Earlier authors have usually given simpler forms instead of (c) and (d), but later it was recognized that those simpler forms hold only under certain restricting conditions. (c) and (d) are in accordance with what reasonable people think in terms of probability$_1$ and, in particular, what they are willing to bet on certain assumptions.

Examples. (1) for (c). Suppose X has the knowledge e concerning the present political situation in the United States and is willing to bet with the betting quotient r_1 (§ 41B) on the hypothesis h that a certain candidate Y will be nominated by one of the parties as presidential candidate for the next election;

suppose further that he makes up his mind that, if he knew *h* in addition to *e*, then he would be willing to bet with the quotient r_2 on the second hypothesis *j*, that *Y* will be elected president; then *X* will be willing, on the basis of his actual present knowledge *e*, to bet with the quotient $r_1 r_2$ on the combined hypothesis $h \,.\, j$ that *Y* will be first nominated and then elected. (2) for (d). Suppose again that *X*, on the basis of his knowledge *e*, is willing to bet with the quotient r_1 on the hypothesis *h* of *Y*'s nomination as candidate of one of the parties, and further with the quotient r_3 on the hypothesis *h'* of the nomination of another candidate *Y'* by the same party; suppose, moreover, that it follows from *e* that only one person can be nominated by the same party, so that $h \,.\, h'$ is incompatible with *e* and hence $e \,.\, h \,.\, h'$ is L-false; then *X* will be willing, on the basis of *e*, to bet with the quotient $r_1 + r_3$ on the disjunction $h \vee h'$, that is, the hypothesis that either *Y* or *Y'* will be nominated.

The convention C1 does not imply that there actually is an adequate quantitative explicatum but merely that, *if* there is any such explicatum, then it will fulfil the four conditions (a) to (d).

Which interval of numbers is chosen for the values of $\mathfrak{c}$ is a matter of an inessential convention as long as $\mathfrak{c}$ is interpreted only as evidential support. But in view of the fact that we interpret $\mathfrak{c}$ more specifically as value of a fair betting quotient (§ 41B), and, in certain cases, as an estimate of relative frequency (§ 41D), we take the real numbers of the interval 0 to 1, both end points included. This is in accordance with the customary use since the beginning of the classical theory. Since the tautological sentence '*t*' (§ 15A) is necessarily true in all possible cases, its probability$_1$ has the maximum value on any (not L-false) evidence, hence the value 1. Therefore we lay down the following convention C2.

C53-2. ***Convention concerning the maximum value.*** For any not L-false *e*, $\mathfrak{c}(t,e) = 1$.

The following theorem states some simple consequences of the conventions C1 and C2. They are not part of our system of inductive logic but will be used only in the preliminary considerations in the next section.

T53-1. Let $\mathfrak{c}$ be a quantitative function which (i) fulfils the conditions C1a to d, (ii) is defined for every pair of sentences in $\mathfrak{L}$ the second of which is not L-false, and (iii) fulfils C2. Then the following holds, provided *e* is not L-false.

a. $\mathfrak{c}(e \,.\, h,t) = \mathfrak{c}(e,t) \times \mathfrak{c}(h,e)$.

Proof. From C1c by substitutions. In the last factor, we replace the evidence $t \,.\, e$ by *e* (C1a), which is L-equivalent (T21-5s(1)).

b. If $\mathfrak{c}(e,t) \neq 0$, $\mathfrak{c}(h,e) = \frac{\mathfrak{c}(e \,.\, h,t)}{\mathfrak{c}(e,t)}$. (From (a).)

c. Addition principle for multiple disjunction. Let $e \,.\, h \,.\, h'$ be L-false for any pair h,h' of different sentences taken from the sentences $h_1, h_2, \ldots, h_n$. Then $\mathfrak{c}(h_1 \vee h_2 \vee \ldots \vee h_n, e) = \sum_{m=1}^{n} \mathfrak{c}(h_m, e)$. (From C1d, by mathematical induction.)

d. $\mathfrak{c}(h,e) + \mathfrak{c}(\sim h,e) = 1$.

Proof. $\mathfrak{c}(h,e) + \mathfrak{c}(\sim h,e) = \mathfrak{c}(h \vee \sim h,e)$ (C1d), $= \mathfrak{c}(t,e)$ (C1b), $= 1$ (C2).

e. $\mathfrak{c}(\sim t,e) = 0$.

Proof. $\mathfrak{c}(\sim t,e) = 1 - \mathfrak{c}(t,e)$ (d), $= 1 - 1$ (C2), $= 0$.

f. If h is L-false, $\mathfrak{c}(h,e) = 0$. (From (e), C1b.)

Let $\mathfrak{Z}_i$ be an arbitrary $\mathfrak{Z}$ (state-description, D18-1a) in a finite system $\mathfrak{L}_N$. $\mathfrak{Z}_i$ is a certain conjunction of basic sentences which is factual (T20-5b), not L-false; it represents one of a finite number of possible cases. Before an observer makes any observations concerning the individuals of $\mathfrak{L}_N$, he cannot know whether the possible case represented by $\mathfrak{Z}_i$ is the actual one or not. To attribute to $\mathfrak{Z}_i$ the probability$_1$ 0 on the basis of the tautological evidence t, that is, without any knowledge of facts, would be an a priori decision not to reckon with the occurrence of this possible case. This seems entirely unjustified. Therefore we lay down the convention C3 to the effect that in this case $\mathfrak{c}$ should be positive. This convention applies only to finite systems $\mathfrak{L}_N$; the situation in $\mathfrak{L}_\infty$ is different because the number of $\mathfrak{Z}$ is infinite.

C53-3. For any $\mathfrak{Z}_i$ in $\mathfrak{L}_N$, $\mathfrak{c}(\mathfrak{Z}_i,t) > 0$.

This convention C3, in distinction to the earlier ones, does not seem to be generally recognized. We shall later (in Vol. II) examine a number of inductive methods which have been proposed in the form of a theory either of probability$_1$ or of estimation. We shall find that some of these methods are in conflict with C3, but only implicitly, in the following sense. They do not assign any value to probability$_1$ on a tautological evidence, nor do they speak of state-descriptions. However, the values which they assign to probability$_1$ or to estimates with respect to a factual evidence correspond, in a certain sense, to the assignment of the probability$_1$ 0 on the tautological evidence to some state-descriptions. It will be shown that some of the values which these methods actually yield with respect to factual evidence are not adequate. It seems that all adequate explicata of probability$_1$ are in accord with the convention C3.

§ 54. Reduction of the Problem of Degree of Confirmation

Some considerations are made which will help us in finding a way toward our aim, a definition of $\mathfrak{c}$ as an explicatum of probability$_1$. (A) to (C) show how this problem can be reduced to simpler problems; (D) and (E) concern further requirements for an adequate $\mathfrak{c}$. *A*. $\mathfrak{c}(h,e)$ in *the infinite system* may be defined as limit of the sequence of values $\mathfrak{c}(h,e)$ in $\mathfrak{L}_N$ with increasing N, provided this sequence is convergent (1). *B*. $\mathfrak{c}_0(j)$ is defined as the confirmation on the tautological evidence, $\mathfrak{c}(j,t)$, called the *null confirmation* (2). Then it follows from the conventions in § 53 that in $\mathfrak{L}_N$ $\mathfrak{c}(h,e) = \mathfrak{c}_0(e \,.\, h)/\mathfrak{c}_0(e)$ (3). *C.* $\mathfrak{c}_0(j)$ in $\mathfrak{L}_N$ is the sum of the $\mathfrak{c}_0$-values for those *state-descriptions* ($\mathfrak{Z}$) in $\mathfrak{L}_N$ in which j holds (4). Thus our problem is reduced to the problem of finding, for every system $\mathfrak{L}_N$, a suitable function $\mathfrak{c}_0$ for the $\mathfrak{Z}$ in $\mathfrak{L}_N$. *D.* A function $\mathfrak{c}_0$ for the $\mathfrak{Z}$ in $\mathfrak{L}_N$ must be such that (*a*) it is positive for every $\mathfrak{Z}$, and (*b*) the sum of the $\mathfrak{c}_0$-values for all $\mathfrak{Z}$ in $\mathfrak{L}_N$ is 1. *E.* A further requirement (6) is laid down in order to make sure that $\mathfrak{c}_0$-functions chosen for different systems $\mathfrak{L}_N$ fit together. The results here found will guide us in the construction of the system of inductive logic in the following chapters.

In this section we shall carry out some preliminary considerations; in particular, we shall try to reduce the problem of finding a definition for degree of confirmation for the language systems $\mathfrak{L}$ step by step to simpler problems without, however, restricting the general scope of our task. These considerations are informal, without any claim to exactness; they are merely intended to find a way, or a first part of a way, which may lead to our aim. In the next chapter we shall begin the systematic construction of inductive logic, guided by what we find here.

A. *Degree of Confirmation in the Infinite System*

Our aim is to find a function $\mathfrak{c}$ for the system $\mathfrak{L}_\infty$ and for every one of the systems $\mathfrak{L}_N$ such that (i) $\mathfrak{c}$ has a numerical value in any of the systems $\mathfrak{L}_N$ for every pair h,e of sentences where e is not L-false and in $\mathfrak{L}_\infty$ for as many of these pairs as seems feasible; (ii) $\mathfrak{c}$ is adequate as a quantitative explicatum for probability$_1$; (iii) hence $\mathfrak{c}$ fulfils the conditions of adequacy C53-1a to d; (iv) $\mathfrak{c}$ fulfils furthermore the conventions C53-2 and 3. For the considerations in this section we shall not consider the requirement (ii) but only the weaker requirement (iii), which follows from the former. In later chapters, when we go beyond the partial solution to be here discussed, we shall of course have to take into consideration the stronger requirement (ii). From (iii) and (iv) it follows that $\mathfrak{c}$ must have the properties stated in T53-1.

If tentative steps are made toward a solution of the problem indicated, it soon becomes clear that one of the chief difficulties involved consists in the infinity of $\mathfrak{L}_\infty$. The task seems less difficult for the finite systems $\mathfrak{L}_N$. Now the latter systems become, with growing N, practically more and more similar to $\mathfrak{L}_\infty$ so that, for instance, a system with a billion billion individuals is practically not much different from $\mathfrak{L}_\infty$, although theoretically there is, of course, always a fundamental difference between the infinite system and any finite system however large. For any pair of sentences h,e in $\mathfrak{L}_\infty$ there is an n (viz., the largest subscript of an $\mathfrak{in}$ occurring in *h* or *e*, or 1 if no in occurs) such that *h* and *e* occur likewise in every $\mathfrak{L}_N$ with $N \geqq n$. If now we had a definition of $\mathfrak{c}$ for all systems $\mathfrak{L}_N$ and it did turn out that the sequence of the values ${}_N\mathfrak{c}(h,e)$ converges with increasing N toward a limit r (D40-6), then it would not appear unplausible to take r as the value of ${}_\infty\mathfrak{c}(h,e)$. The condition of convergence will later be examined for the function $\mathfrak{c}^*$ which we shall define (in Vol. II); it will be seen that it is fulfilled for nongeneral sentences throughout and for general sentences at least in a comprehensive class of cases. Thus the following definition is suggested:

(1) $${}_\infty\mathfrak{c}(h,e) =_{\text{Df}} \lim_{N \to \infty} {}_N\mathfrak{c}(h,e) .$$

Hereby our problem is reduced to the problem of a definition of $\mathfrak{c}$ for all systems $\mathfrak{L}_N$.

B. ***The Null Confirmation***

For the next step in the reduction we make use of T53-1b. This theorem shows that $\mathfrak{c}(h,e)$ is the quotient of the $\mathfrak{c}$-values of certain sentences with respect to the tautological evidence '*t*'. Since '*t*' does not give any factual information—we say sometimes that it has the null content (T73-1b)—$\mathfrak{c}(j,t)$ is the extreme case of $\mathfrak{c}$ before any factual knowledge is available; we call it the *null confirmation* of *j*. Since this concept is often used in inductive logic, we introduce a simple notation for it:

(2) $$\mathfrak{c}_0(j) =_{\text{Df}} \mathfrak{c}(j,t) .$$

Now we use T53-1b, but restricted to the systems $\mathfrak{L}_N$. There is first the condition that $\mathfrak{c}_0(e) \neq 0$. We shall see later that for all $\mathfrak{c}$-functions which come into consideration as explicata for probability$_1$, ${}_N\mathfrak{c}_0(e) = 0$ only if *e* is L-false. (This holds only for $\mathfrak{L}_N$, not for $\mathfrak{L}_\infty$; that is the reason why we make the present step of reduction after the first.) Thus we obtain from T53-1b:

(3) In any system $\mathfrak{L}_N$, if *e* is not L-false,
$$\mathfrak{c}(h,e) = \frac{\mathfrak{c}_0(e.h)}{\mathfrak{c}_0(e)} .$$

Hereby, the task of finding a suitable function $\mathfrak{c}$ for the pairs of sentences in $\mathfrak{L}_N$ is reduced to the task of finding a suitable function $\mathfrak{c}_0$ for the sentences in $\mathfrak{L}_N$.

C. ***Reduction to State-Descriptions***

For the next step, we make use of the theorem (T21-8c) that any non-L-false sentence *j* in $\mathfrak{L}_N$ is L-equivalent to a disjunction *j'* whose *n* components ($n \geqq 1$) are those n $\mathfrak{Z}$ (state-descriptions, D18-1a) in which j holds, in other words, the $\mathfrak{Z}$ belonging to $\mathfrak{R}_j$ (the range of j, D18-6a). Therefore, $\mathfrak{c}_0(j) = \mathfrak{c}_0(j')$ (C53-1b, with the evidence 't'). If h and h' are any two different $\mathfrak{Z}$ in $\mathfrak{L}_N$, then $h \,.\, h'$ is L-false (T21-8a) and hence also $t \,.\, h \,.\, h'$. Therefore, according to the addition principle (T53-1c) the following (4a) holds for $\mathfrak{c}_0(j')$, and hence likewise for $\mathfrak{c}_0(j)$.

(4) **a.** If j is not L-false, $\mathfrak{c}_0(j)$ is the sum of the $\mathfrak{c}_0$-values for all $\mathfrak{Z}$ in $\mathfrak{R}_j$.

b. If j is L-false, $\mathfrak{c}_0(j) = 0$ (T53-1f).

Thus the task of finding a suitable function $\mathfrak{c}_0$ for all sentences in $\mathfrak{L}_N$ is reduced to the task of finding a suitable function $\mathfrak{c}_0$ for all $\mathfrak{Z}$ in $\mathfrak{L}_N$, hence for a very restricted, special kind of sentences in $\mathfrak{L}_N$. This ends the reduction of our problem.

D. *Null Confirmation for the State-Descriptions*

We shall now consider requirements which a function $\mathfrak{c}_0$ for the $\mathfrak{Z}$ in $\mathfrak{L}_N$ should fulfil. If a function $\mathfrak{c}_0$ for the $\mathfrak{Z}$ is chosen, then it determines uniquely a function $\mathfrak{c}_0$ for the sentences according to (4), and a function $\mathfrak{c}$ for the pairs of sentences according to (3).

First let us see which restricting conditions are imposed upon the choice of a function $\mathfrak{c}_0$ for the $\mathfrak{Z}$ in $\mathfrak{L}_N$ by the requirement that $\mathfrak{c}$ fulfil also the conventions C53-2 and 3.

Since 't' holds in every $\mathfrak{Z}$ (D18-4c), $\mathfrak{c}_0(t)$ is the sum of the $\mathfrak{c}_0$-values for all $\mathfrak{Z}$ in $\mathfrak{L}_N$. On the other hand, $\mathfrak{c}_0(t) = 1$ (C53-2). This leads to the second one of the following requirements; the first is given by C53-3.

(5) *Requirements for $\mathfrak{c}_0$-functions for the $\mathfrak{Z}$ in $\mathfrak{L}_N$.*

a. For any $\mathfrak{Z}_i$ in $\mathfrak{L}_N$, $\mathfrak{c}_0(\mathfrak{Z}_i) > 0$.

b. The sum of the $\mathfrak{c}_0$-values for all $\mathfrak{Z}$ in $\mathfrak{L}_N$ is 1.

Suppose we start with some $\mathfrak{c}_0$-function for the $\mathfrak{Z}$ which fulfils these two requirements; it determines a $\mathfrak{c}_0$-function for the sentences according to (4); and this, in turn, determines a $\mathfrak{c}$-function according to (3). Then the latter will be called a ***regular*** ***$\mathfrak{c}$-function***.

E. *The Requirement of Fitting Together*

There is still another point to be considered in choosing a suitable $\mathfrak{c}_0$-function for the finite language systems. For a given system $\mathfrak{L}_N$, there are many $\mathfrak{c}$-functions adequate as explicata for probability$_1$, and indeed an infinite number of them. This is analogous to the situation with the temperature concept (§ 5); there is an infinite number of quantitative explicata for the comparative explicandum Warmer, that is to say, an infinite number of possible scale forms for temperature, several of which have actually been used in physics (among them several scales based on various thermometrical substances, as mercury, alcohol, hydrogen, etc., and the thermodynamic scale). This does not mean that all these concepts, either in the case of temperature or in the case of $\mathfrak{c}$, are equally good as explicata; one concept may have certain advantages and another concept may have advantages in other respects, and some concepts may be clearly inferior to certain others. It means merely that every one of these concepts is not entirely inadequate as explicatum, although there is, of course, no sharp boundary line. Now suppose that we choose a sequence of $\mathfrak{c}_0$-functions, one for each system $\mathfrak{L}_N$, say, ${}_1\mathfrak{c}_0$ for $\mathfrak{L}_1$, ${}_2\mathfrak{c}_0$ for $\mathfrak{L}_2$, etc. Then it may very well happen that each one of these $\mathfrak{c}_0$-functions is adequate for its system, that is to say, it leads to a $\mathfrak{c}$-function adequate as an explicatum for probability$_1$, and that nevertheless the different $\mathfrak{c}_0$-functions of the sequence do not fit together. In other words, the choices of one $\mathfrak{c}_0$-function for each of the systems $\mathfrak{L}_N$ should not be made independently of one another. As we have seen earlier (§ 15A), any nongeneral sentence has the same meaning in all systems $\mathfrak{L}_N$ in which it occurs. Therefore it is to be required that, for any nongeneral sentences h and e, $\mathfrak{c}(h,e)$ have the same value in all systems $\mathfrak{L}_N$ in which both sentences occur; and hence it is to be required that, for any nongeneral sentence j, $\mathfrak{c}_0(j)$ have the same value in all systems $\mathfrak{L}_N$ in which j occurs. However, we choose a function $\mathfrak{c}_0$ for the $\mathfrak{Z}$, not for the sentences in general; the corresponding function $\mathfrak{c}_0$ for the sentences is determined by the function $\mathfrak{c}_0$ for the $\mathfrak{Z}$. Therefore we have now to examine what the requirement just stated means for the latter function.

Let i be any $\mathfrak{Z}$ in $\mathfrak{L}_N$. Then i is a nongeneral sentence in $\mathfrak{L}_N$ and hence also in $\mathfrak{L}_{N+1}$; but it is not a $\mathfrak{Z}$ in $\mathfrak{L}_{N+1}$. $\mathfrak{R}_i$ in $\mathfrak{L}_N$ is $\{i\}$ (T19-6). $\mathfrak{R}_i$ in $\mathfrak{L}_{N+1}$ is the class of those $\mathfrak{Z}$ in $\mathfrak{L}_{N+1}$ of which i is a subconjunction (T19-5b). Therefore (see (4a) above), ${}_{N+1}\mathfrak{c}_0(i)$ is the sum of the $\mathfrak{c}_0$-values for all those $\mathfrak{Z}$ in $\mathfrak{L}_{N+1}$ of which i is a subconjunction. This suggests the following requirement.

(6) *Requirement of fitting together:* for every N and for every $\mathfrak{Z}_i$ in $\mathfrak{L}_N$, ${}_N\mathfrak{c}_0(\mathfrak{Z}_i)$ must be equal to the sum of the ${}_{N+1}\mathfrak{c}_0$-values for all those $\mathfrak{Z}$ in $\mathfrak{L}_{N+1}$ of which $\mathfrak{Z}_i$ is a subconjunction.

If we fulfil this requirement in our choices of $\mathfrak{c}_0$-functions, one for each system $\mathfrak{L}_N$, then these choices are dependent upon one another in the following way. Suppose we have chosen a $\mathfrak{c}_0$-function for $\mathfrak{L}_{N+1}$; then a certain

$\mathfrak{c}_0$-function for $\mathfrak{L}_N$ is thereby uniquely determined, and the choice of a $\mathfrak{c}_0$-function for $\mathfrak{L}_{N+2}$ is, although not determined uniquely, restricted within rather narrow limits. In the next chapter we shall deal with those sequences of functions ${}_1\mathfrak{c}_0$, ${}_2\mathfrak{c}_0$, . . . , ${}_N\mathfrak{c}_0$, . . . for the systems $\mathfrak{L}_1$, $\mathfrak{L}_2$, . . . , $\mathfrak{L}_N$, . . . , which fulfil the requirement (6), and with the sequences of functions ${}_1\mathfrak{c}$, ${}_2\mathfrak{c}$, . . . , ${}_N\mathfrak{c}$, . . . based upon the $\mathfrak{c}_0$-functions in the manner earlier explained; the latter sequences will be called *fitting sequences* of $\mathfrak{c}$-functions. When we shall speak in inductive logic about $\mathfrak{c}$ with respect to different systems $\mathfrak{L}_N$, we shall usually presuppose that the $\mathfrak{c}$-functions for the different systems $\mathfrak{L}_N$ fit together in the sense of forming a sequence of the kind just described.

In the next chapter we shall not yet choose a particular function $\mathfrak{c}$. Instead we shall study the common properties of all regular $\mathfrak{c}$-functions. This will be a general inductive logic. Only much later (in Vol. II) shall we choose a particular one among the regular $\mathfrak{c}$-functions, designated by '$\mathfrak{c}^*$' (see Appendix, § 110). Then we shall base our special theory of inductive logic on this function $\mathfrak{c}^*$.

CHAPTER V

THE FOUNDATION OF QUANTITATIVE INDUCTIVE LOGIC: THE REGULAR c-FUNCTIONS

According to the plan previously outlined (in § 54), we lay down the following definitions. We start with a measure function for the $\mathfrak{Z}$ (state-descriptions) in a finite system $\mathfrak{L}_N$; this is any distribution of positive real numbers, whose sum is 1, among the $\mathfrak{Z}$ (D55-1). Then we define $\mathfrak{m}(j)$ for a sentence j as the sum of the $\mathfrak{m}(\mathfrak{Z})$ for those $\mathfrak{Z}$ in which j holds (D55-2), and $\mathfrak{c}(h,e)$ as $\mathfrak{m}(e \,.\, h)/\mathfrak{m}(e)$ (D55-3 and 4). All $\mathfrak{m}$-functions and $\mathfrak{c}$-functions constructed in this way are called ***regular***. Thus $\mathfrak{c}$ (i.e., any regular $\mathfrak{c}$-function), which is the fundamental concept of inductive logic, measures the extent to which one range is partially included in another; on the other hand, L-implication, which is the fundamental concept of deductive logic, corresponds to total inclusion of one range in another (see diagrams in § 55B). The values of $\mathfrak{m}$- and of $\mathfrak{c}$-functions for the infinite system $\mathfrak{L}_\infty$ are defined as limits of the values for finite systems (§ 56). The task of this chapter is to construct, on the basis of the definitions mentioned, the theory of the regular $\mathfrak{c}$-functions as the fundamental part of quantitative inductive logic. The null confirmation $\mathfrak{c}_0(h)$ is defined as the $\mathfrak{c}$ of h on the tautological evidence 't', hence as the confirmation of h before any factual knowledge is available (D57-1). It turns out that $\mathfrak{c}_0$ coincides with $\mathfrak{m}$ (T57-3). For any L-true sentence j, $\mathfrak{m}(j)$ (and hence $\mathfrak{c}_0(j)$) $= 1$; but it happens sometimes (however, only among general sentences in $\mathfrak{L}_\infty$) that also **a** factual sentence i has the $\mathfrak{m}$-value 1; in this case, i is said to be almost L-true (D58-1a). Among the *theorems concerning regular $\mathfrak{c}$-functions* (§§ 59, 60, 61), we find the fundamental theorems of the classical theory, e.g., the general and the special addition theorem (T59-1k and l), and the general multiplication theorem (T59-1n); furthermore, among the theorems dealing with the confirmation of a hypothesis on the basis of relevant observations (§§ 60 and 61), we find the general division theorem (T60-1c) and the much-debated *Bayes's theorem* (T60-6).

An examination of some ***modern axiom systems*** for probability$_1$ shows that they are all rather weak (§ 62); they are contained in what we call the theory of regular $\mathfrak{c}$-functions. In our view, this theory is only a small part of inductive logic. We shall construct the remaining parts in later chapters.

§ 55. Regular $\mathfrak{m}$- and $\mathfrak{c}$-Functions for Finite Systems

A. Following the plan outlined in § 54, we lay down the following definitions. A function $\mathfrak{m}$ (corresponding to $\mathfrak{c}_0$ in § 54B) is called a regular $\mathfrak{m}$-function under the following conditions; first, $\mathfrak{m}$ is applied to the $\mathfrak{Z}$ in $\mathfrak{L}_N$ and assigns to them positive real numbers whose sum is 1 (D1); then $\mathfrak{m}$ is extended to all sentences in $\mathfrak{L}_N$ by taking as $\mathfrak{m}(j)$ the sum of the $\mathfrak{m}$-values for all $\mathfrak{Z}$ in $\mathfrak{R}_j$ (D2). If $\mathfrak{m}$ is regular and $\mathfrak{c}(h,e)$ is defined as $\mathfrak{m}(e \,.\, h)/\mathfrak{m}(e)$, $\mathfrak{c}$ is called a ***regular $\mathfrak{c}$-function***

(D3, D4). The regular c-functions are just those which fulfil the conventions in § 53; they seem to include all functions which might be regarded as adequate explicata for probability$_1$.

B. By these definitions, the difference between deductive and inductive logic becomes clear. Deductive logic deals with L-implication, hence with the case of total inclusion of one range in another. Inductive logic deals with c, which is the ratio of partial inclusion of one range in another, measured by m; hence, c is, so to speak, partial L-implication (see the diagrams).

C. Incidentally, probability$_2$, i.e., relative frequency, is likewise the ratio of partial inclusion of one class in another. This explains the analogy between the theories of probability$_1$ and probability$_2$. However, there remains this fundamental difference: for probability$_2$, the partial inclusion is a factual matter, and hence the value of probability$_2$ is established empirically; on the other hand, probability$_1$ concerns partial inclusion of ranges, which is of a purely logical nature.

A. *Regular m- and c-Functions*

In this chapter we begin the construction of quantitative inductive logic. However, here we shall not yet select one function c but rather deal with a very comprehensive class of functions, which we call the regular c-functions. All functions which I would regard as adequate quantitative explicata for probability$_1$ belong to this class.

The fundamental conception which leads us to the definition of the regular c-functions is very simple. Briefly speaking, they are those functions which fulfill the conventions laid down in § 53. Therefore, our construction here will follow the plan outlined in § 54.

We call a numerical function m for the $\mathfrak{Z}$ in $\mathfrak{L}_N$ a ***regular measure function*** or regular m-function (D1) if it fulfils the two requirements for c_0 stated in § 54D: the values are positive, and their sum is 1. [At this step, we do not use the symbol 'c_0', but a neutral symbol 'm'. Later, 'c_0' will be defined as confirmation on the basis '*t*' (D57-1); and then it can easily be shown that c_0 and m coincide (T57-3).] Then, according to § 54C, we extend a function m for the $\mathfrak{Z}$ in $\mathfrak{L}_N$ so as to apply to all sentences in $\mathfrak{L}_N$, by defining m(*j*) as the sum of the m-values for all $\mathfrak{Z}$ in $\mathfrak{R}_j$ (D2). [If m is a function for the $\mathfrak{Z}$, then, strictly speaking, we should have to use another symbol, say, 'm′', for the corresponding function for the sentences. However, the definition would easily show (with T19-6) that, for any sentence *j* which is a $\mathfrak{Z}$, m′(*j*) = m(*j*); in other words, m′ is merely an extension of the function m. Therefore it is convenient to use the same symbol for both functions.] Then, in accordance with § 54B, on any function m we may base a function c by defining c(*h*,*e*) as m(*e* . *h*)/m(*e*) (D3). If c is based in this way on a regular m-function, we call it a ***regular c-function*** (D4).

+D55-1. $\mathfrak{m}$ is a ***regular measure function*** (or, briefly, a regular $\mathfrak{m}$-function, or a regular $\mathfrak{m}$) for the $\mathfrak{Z}$ in $\mathfrak{L}_N =_{Df}$ $\mathfrak{m}$ fulfils the following two conditions.

a. For every $\mathfrak{Z}_i$ in $\mathfrak{L}_N$, $\mathfrak{m}(\mathfrak{Z}_i)$ is a positive real number.

b. The sum of the values of $\mathfrak{m}$ for all $\mathfrak{Z}$ in $\mathfrak{L}_N$ is 1.

T55-1. Let $\mathfrak{m}$ be a regular $\mathfrak{m}$-function for the $\mathfrak{Z}$ in $\mathfrak{L}_N$. Then, for every $\mathfrak{Z}_i$ in $\mathfrak{L}_N$, $0 < \mathfrak{m}(\mathfrak{Z}_i) < 1$. (From D1.)

+D55-2. Let $\mathfrak{m}$ be a regular $\mathfrak{m}$-function for the $\mathfrak{Z}$ in $\mathfrak{L}_N$. We extend $\mathfrak{m}$ to a *regular* $\mathfrak{m}$-*function for the sentences* in $\mathfrak{L}_N$ in the following way.

a. For any L-false sentence j in $\mathfrak{L}_N$, $\mathfrak{m}(j) =_{Df} 0$.

b. For any non-L-false sentence j in $\mathfrak{L}_N$, $\mathfrak{m}(j) =_{Df}$ the sum of the values of $\mathfrak{m}$ for the $\mathfrak{Z}$ in $\mathfrak{R}_j$.

D3 introduces merely an auxiliary term for D4.

D55-3. Let $\mathfrak{m}$ be a numerical function for the sentences in $\mathfrak{L}_N$, and $\mathfrak{c}$ be a numerical function for pairs of sentences in $\mathfrak{L}_N$. $\mathfrak{c}$ is *based upon* $\mathfrak{m} =_{Df}$ for any sentences e and h in $\mathfrak{L}_N$, where $\mathfrak{m}(e) \neq 0$, $\mathfrak{c}(h,e) = \frac{\mathfrak{m}(e \cdot h)}{\mathfrak{m}(e)}$; for any e, where $\mathfrak{m}(e) = 0$, $\mathfrak{c}(h,e)$ has no value.

+D55-4. $\mathfrak{c}$ is a ***regular confirmation function*** (or, briefly, a regular $\mathfrak{c}$-function, or a regular $\mathfrak{c}$) for $\mathfrak{L}_N =_{Df}$ $\mathfrak{c}$ is based (D3) upon a regular $\mathfrak{m}$-function for the sentences in $\mathfrak{L}_N$.

Instead of '$\mathfrak{m}$ for $\mathfrak{L}_N$' and '$\mathfrak{c}$ for $\mathfrak{L}_N$', we shall sometimes write '${}_N\mathfrak{m}$' and '${}_N\mathfrak{c}$', respectively.

T2 is an immediate consequence of the given definitions; it serves as lemma for later theorems.

T55-2. Let $\mathfrak{c}$ be a regular $\mathfrak{c}$-function for $\mathfrak{L}_N$. Then there is a regular $\mathfrak{m}$ for the sentences of $\mathfrak{L}_N$ (namely, that upon which $\mathfrak{c}$ is based) such that the following holds.

a. For any pair of sentences h,e in $\mathfrak{L}_N$, where $\mathfrak{m}(e) \neq 0$, $\mathfrak{c}(h,e) = \frac{\mathfrak{m}(e \cdot h)}{\mathfrak{m}(e)}$. (From D4, D3.)

b. $\mathfrak{c}$ has a value for a pair of sentences h,e in $\mathfrak{L}_N$ if and only if $\mathfrak{m}(e) \neq 0$, hence if and only if e is not L-false in $\mathfrak{L}_N$. (From D4, D3, D2.)

Remarks on the exclusion of an L-false evidence. Let $\mathfrak{c}$ be regular and based upon $\mathfrak{m}$. According to our definitions, if e is L-false and hence $\mathfrak{m}(e) = 0$, $\mathfrak{c}(h,e)$ has no value (T2b). This is not the only possible procedure. As an alternative, let us consider a definition D3′ which is like D3 except for stating that, if $\mathfrak{m}(e) = 0$, $\mathfrak{c}(h,e) = 1$; D4 remains unchanged. Here, $\mathfrak{c}$ has a value for every pair of sentences in $\mathfrak{L}_N$. If we want at all to assign a value to $\mathfrak{c}$ in the case mentioned, the value 1 seems the most natural. For our original definitions have the effect that, except for L-false e, if $\vdash e \supset h$ (i.e., e L-implies h), $\mathfrak{c}(h,e) = 1$ (see below, T59-1b);

now, if e is L-false, then, for every h, $\vdash e \supset h$ (T20-2h); hence D3′ yields the result that, without exception, if $\vdash e \supset h$, $\mathfrak{c}(h,e) = 1$. In a similar way, most of the theorems to be stated later are valid on the basis of the alternative definition D3′ in a more general way, with omission of the restricting condition 'if the evidence is not L-false'. On the other hand, there are some theorems which must retain this restricting condition even on the basis of D3′. For instance, this holds obviously for the theorem (T59-1f) that, if h is L-false, $\mathfrak{c}(h,e) = 0$; for, if e is also L-false, D3′ would yield here $\mathfrak{c} = 1$. The same holds for the special addition theorem (T59-1l); for, if e is L-false, on the basis of D3′ $\mathfrak{c}(h,e) = 1$ and likewise $\mathfrak{c}(\sim h,e) = 1$; however, $\mathfrak{c}(h \vee \sim h,e)$ cannot be the sum of these two values, i.e., 2, because no $\mathfrak{c}$-value exceeds 1. These and similar consequences of D3′ cannot be regarded as disadvantages in comparison with D3, because they mean merely that on the basis of D3′ some theorems must contain a certain restricting condition, which on the basis of D3 many more theorems must contain.

The disadvantages of D3′ appear when we come to $\mathfrak{L}_\infty$. Here, $\mathfrak{m}$ and $\mathfrak{c}$ will be defined (in § 56) as limits of their values for the finite systems $\mathfrak{L}_N$, in accordance with § 54A. In $\mathfrak{L}_N$ the chief difference between D3 and D3′ consists in the fact that in certain cases D3′ gives a value to $\mathfrak{c}$ where D3 does not. In $\mathfrak{L}_\infty$ we find the opposite; in some special cases, D3′ gives no value where D3 does. This happens when the additional values of $\mathfrak{c}$ in the finite systems on the basis of D3′ destroy the existence of a limit. [For exemplification, let us refer to those functions $\mathfrak{m}$ and $\mathfrak{c}$ which we shall later select as basis for inductive logic (they will then be designated by '$\mathfrak{m}^*$' and '$\mathfrak{c}^*$', § 110A). Let e be a purely general sentence containing the primitive predicates 'P' and 'R' of degree one and two, respectively, and saying that the relation R constitutes a one-one correspondence between those individuals which have the property P and those which have not. Obviously, if e is true, P and non-P must have the same cardinal number, which is impossible if N is an odd number. Therefore, in every $\mathfrak{L}_N$ with an odd N, e is L-false and hence $\mathfrak{m}(e) = 0$; but in every $\mathfrak{L}_N$ with an even N, e is factual and hence $\mathfrak{m}(e) > 0$. We shall find later that these positive $\mathfrak{m}$-values converge toward the limit 0 with increasing N. Let h be any factual, molecular sentence such that $\mathfrak{c}(h,e) = \mathfrak{c}(h,t)$ (hence e is initially irrelevant for h, D65-2d) $= \mathfrak{m}(h)$ (T57-3) $= r$, where r is constant, i.e., independent of N and $0 < r < 1$. On the basis of D3, $\mathfrak{c}(h,e)$ has no value in the odd systems, but in all even systems its value is always r. Thus, for the even systems we have an infinite sequence with the constant value r; hence its limit is r; therefore, in $\mathfrak{L}_\infty$, $\mathfrak{c}(h,e) = r$. On the other hand, the situation is quite different with D3′. Here, in every odd system, $\mathfrak{c}(h,e) = 1$, while in every even system, as before, $\mathfrak{c}(h,e) = r < 1$. Thus, here, $\mathfrak{c}(h,e)$ oscillates between two constant values and hence has no limit; therefore, $\mathfrak{c}(h,e)$ has no value in $\mathfrak{L}_\infty$.]

The convention that no value is assigned to the function $\mathfrak{c}$ in the case of an L-false evidence seems generally accepted, if the point is at all discussed. We find it, for instance, in Keynes's theory of probability ([Probab.], p. 116) and in Hosiasson's theory of degree of confirmation ([Confirmation], p. 133). Some authors even of more exactly formulated modern systems fail to make a convention either way; this, however, leads to contradictions (see § 62).

B. *Deductive and Inductive Logic*

D3 may help us to see clearly both the similarity and the difference between deductive and inductive logic. The fundamental concept of deductive logic is L-implication. Hence an elementary sentence of deductive logic has the form '*e* L-implies *h*'. This sentence holds if and only if $\mathfrak{R}_e$ (the range of *e*) is entirely contained in $\mathfrak{R}_h$. On the other hand, the fundamental concept of inductive logic is degree of confirmation. Hence an elementary sentence of inductive logic has the form '$\mathfrak{c}(h,e) = r$'. This sentence says, according to D3, that $\frac{\mathfrak{m}(e \cdot h)}{\mathfrak{m}(e)} = r$. We may regard $\mathfrak{m}(e)$ as the measure assigned to $\mathfrak{R}_e$. Then $\mathfrak{m}(e \cdot h)$ is the measure assigned to $\mathfrak{R}(e \cdot h)$; this class is $\mathfrak{R}(e) \frown \mathfrak{R}(h)$, in other words, that part of $\mathfrak{R}(e)$ which is contained in $\mathfrak{R}_h$. Thus, for example, '$\mathfrak{c}(h,e) = 3/4$' says that not the whole of $\mathfrak{R}_e$ is contained in $\mathfrak{R}_h$ but only a part of it which, measured by $\mathfrak{m}$, is three-fourths of $\mathfrak{R}_e$. This is shown in the accompanying diagram, where the areas represent the ranges of the sentences.

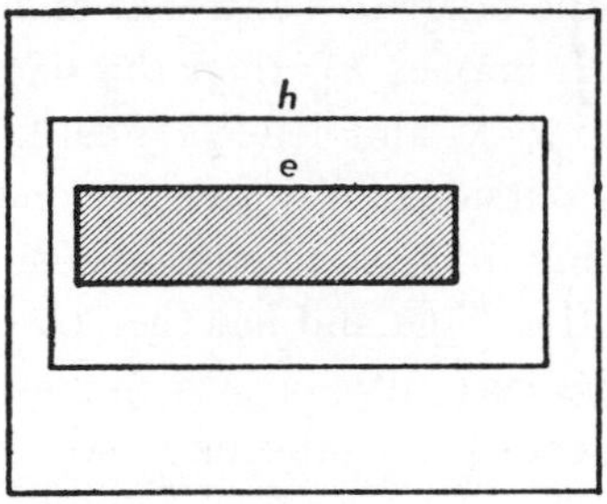

Deductive Logic

'*e* L-implies *h*' means that the range of *e* is entirely contained in that of *h*.

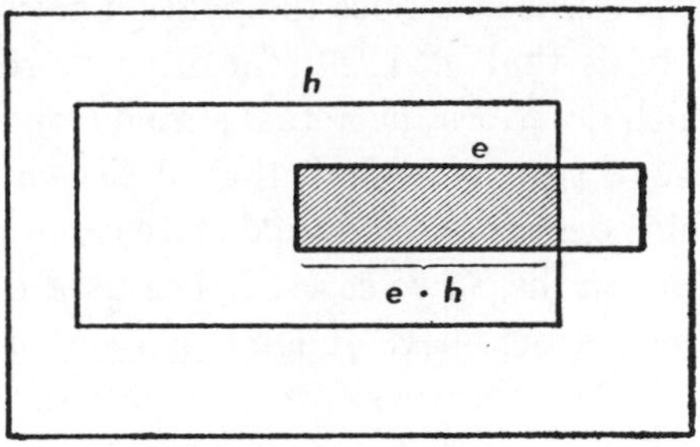

Inductive Logic

'$\mathfrak{c}(h,e) = 3/4$' means that three-fourths of the range of *e* is contained in that of *h*.

Thus both deductive and inductive logic concern relations between the ranges of sentences. The range of a sentence is independent of any facts, dependent merely upon the meaning of the sentence as determined by the semantical rules of the language system in question. If these rules are given, then both the relations studied in deductive logic and those studied in inductive logic can be established; no knowledge of facts (that is, extra-linguistic, contingent facts) is required. This characterizes both theories as branches of logic. Deductive logic deals with the relation of total inclusion between ranges. Inductive logic deals with the relation of partial inclusion between ranges, so to speak, partial L-implication. Therefore, inductive logic (here always meant as quantitative inductive logic) requires the introduction of a new concept, a numerical, additive measure function for the ranges. This may be illustrated by an analogy with geometry. A sentence like 'The whole of Illinois is contained in the United States' expresses a purely topological relation and hence does not require a measure function. On the other hand, a sentence of the form 'Three-fourths of Illinois lies north of 39° lat.' presupposes a measure function for geographical areas.

We can now see more clearly what the definition of c by D3 amounts to if we remember what the range of a sentence is. $\mathfrak{R}_e$ was defined as the class of those $\mathfrak{Z}$ (state-descriptions) in which the sentence *e* holds (D18-6a). The $\mathfrak{Z}$ describe the possible states of the domain of individuals (§ 18A). Suppose the whole knowledge which an observer *X* has gained by observations of the individuals is expressed by the sentence *e*. Then all he knows is that the actual state of the domain of individuals is one of those described by the $\mathfrak{Z}$ in $\mathfrak{R}_e$; but he does not know which one of these it is. Suppose now that *X* is interested in a certain hypothesis *h;* he wants to obtain a judgment about *h* on the basis of his knowledge. For this purpose, he examines the relation between the range of *e* and that of *h*. If he finds that $\mathfrak{R}_e \subset \mathfrak{R}_h$ (in other words, *e* L-implies *h*), then the one $\mathfrak{Z}$ which describes the actual state belongs also to $\mathfrak{R}_h$ and hence *h* must likewise be true. If he finds that $\mathfrak{R}_e$ lies entirely outside of $\mathfrak{R}_h$, then the one $\mathfrak{Z}$ which describes the actual state cannot belong to $\mathfrak{R}_h$ and hence *h* must be false. In these two cases, *X* has used deductive logic and has thereby obtained a definitive judgment about *h*. [The certainty of *X*'s judgment about *h*, either positive or negative, is of course not absolute but only relative to *e;* that is to say, he knows either *h* or $\sim h$ with at least the same degree of certainty as he knows *e*.] If, however, he finds that only a part of the range of *e* is contained in that of *h*, then he must use inductive logic. In this case, as long as he does not make new observations beyond those expressed in *e*, he cannot find certainty concerning *h;* he can only determine a probability, a degree of confirmation of *h* on the evidence *e*. He knows that the actual state is described by one of the $\mathfrak{Z}$ in $\mathfrak{R}_e$ (and is hence represented by one of the points in the area *e* in the right-hand diagram above). If now the actual state were described by one of those $\mathfrak{Z}$ which belong to the part of $\mathfrak{R}_e$ contained in $\mathfrak{R}_h$ (and hence were represented by a point in the shaded area of the diagram), then *h* would be true; otherwise, *h* would be false. Therefore, the larger the part of $\mathfrak{R}_e$ overlapping with $\mathfrak{R}_h$ is in relation to the whole of $\mathfrak{R}_e$, in other words, the more of those possibilities which are still left open by *e* are such that *h* would hold in them, the more reason has *X*, who knows *e*, for expecting *h* to be true. Thus the definition of c by the quotient in D3 becomes plausible. [One might perhaps think at first that the introduction of a special measure function m for the ranges was not necessary, that we could simply take the quotient of the number of $\mathfrak{Z}$ in $\mathfrak{R}(e \,.\, h)$ by the number of $\mathfrak{Z}$ in $\mathfrak{R}_e$. There is such a quotient because here, where we speak of the finite systems $\mathfrak{L}_N$, the number of $\mathfrak{Z}$ is finite. However, this definition would not yield an adequate explicatum for probability$_1$. This definition would amount to taking that regular $\mathfrak{m}$-function which has the same value for all $\mathfrak{Z}$. We shall later discuss this $\mathfrak{m}$-function $\mathfrak{m}\dagger$ and the $\mathfrak{c}$-function $\mathfrak{c}\dagger$ based upon it; then we shall find that the latter is inadequate (see § 110A). Therefore, in order to obtain an adequate explicatum, we must not simply count the $\mathfrak{Z}$ but, so to speak, weight them; in other words, we must find a distribution of $\mathfrak{m}$-values among the $\mathfrak{Z}$ which does not assign equal values but is nevertheless not arbitrary. This constitutes one of the main problems we shall have to solve.]

On the basis of an idea of Wittgenstein ([Tractatus] *5.15), Friedrich Waismann ([Wahrsch.], pp. 236 f.) gives a definition of probability as a quotient of measures of ranges, like our D3. (For the requirements which Waismann lays down concerning the measure function see below, § 62.) Our explanation above of L-implication as inclusion of ranges and $\mathfrak{c}$ as partial inclusion of ranges is in its essential features suggested by Waismann's discussion. Thus the foundations of our inductive logic are in complete agreement with his conception. However, our further construction of inductive logic seems to differ in the following point from Waismann's plan, which is only indicated but not carried out. He says that the choice of the measure function is to be made in such a manner that "we obtain accordance with statistical experience" (*op. cit.*, p. 242). In our theory, on the other hand, the choice of an $\mathfrak{m}$-function is regarded as a purely logical question; we shall later define a certain $\mathfrak{m}$-function $\mathfrak{m}^*$ as basis for inductive logic. According to our conception, the empirical knowledge of facts enters inductive logic only at one point, viz., as formulated in the evidence *e;* but it cannot determine the definition of $\mathfrak{c}$. (Compare, however, the following discussion.)

Some philosophers seem to have feelings against choosing a measure function $\mathfrak{m}$ once for all, independently of our experiences, so to speak, a priori. They believe that it would be more in accord with the scientific method or with the principle of empiricism if the measure function were to change with the accumulating experiences (compare the above reference to Waismann). I think our method is in perfect accord with empiricism and, in particular, with the requirement that inductive procedure should be based on our empirical knowledge *e*. This requirement is fulfilled because in our theory the value of $\mathfrak{c}$ is dependent upon *e*. If someone wishes $\mathfrak{c}$ to be based upon a measure function for the ranges which changes with the changing experiences, his wish can be fulfilled within our theory in the following way. Suppose that a regular $\mathfrak{m}$-function $\mathfrak{m}$ is chosen; however, it is now regarded not as the basic measure function but merely as a calculatory convenience. As the basic measure function we take now a new function $\mathfrak{m}_e$ which is defined with the help of $\mathfrak{m}$ as follows, first for the $\mathfrak{Z}$ in $\mathfrak{L}_N$ with respect to any non-L-false *e*:

(1) a. If e does not hold in $\mathfrak{Z}_i$, $\mathfrak{m}_e(\mathfrak{Z}_i) = 0$.

b. If e holds in $\mathfrak{Z}_i$, $\mathfrak{m}_e(\mathfrak{Z}_i) = \frac{\mathfrak{m}(\mathfrak{Z}_i)}{\mathfrak{m}(e)}$.

Thus $\mathfrak{m}_e$ is dependent upon e and hence fulfils the requirement that its value change with the changing experiences. Then $\mathfrak{m}_e(j)$ for any other sentence j in $\mathfrak{L}_N$ is defined (in analogy to D2) as the sum of the values of $\mathfrak{m}_e$ for the $\mathfrak{Z}$ in $\mathfrak{R}_j$ or as 0 if j is L-false. Then the function $\mathfrak{c}'$ is simply defined as follows:

(2) For any pair of sentences e,h in $\mathfrak{L}_N$, where e is not L-false, $\mathfrak{c}'(h,e) =_{Df} \mathfrak{m}_e(h)$.

It is easily seen that this function $\mathfrak{c}'$ coincides with the function $\mathfrak{c}$ based upon $\mathfrak{m}$ according to our method (D3); hence the method just outlined is essentially the same as our method and differs from it only in the form of representation.

Proof. $\mathfrak{c}'(h,e) = \mathfrak{m}_e(h) = \Sigma[\mathfrak{m}(\mathfrak{Z}_i)]/\mathfrak{m}(e)$, where the sum extends over those $\mathfrak{Z}$ in $\mathfrak{R}_h$ in which e holds, hence the $\mathfrak{Z}$ in $\mathfrak{R}(e\,.\,h)$. Therefore the sum is $\mathfrak{m}(e\,.\,h)$. Hence the quotient is $\mathfrak{m}(e\,.\,h)/\mathfrak{m}(e) = \mathfrak{c}(h,e)$.

C. *Probability$_1$ and Probability$_2$*

We have earlier (§ 41D) analyzed the relation between probability$_1$ and probability$_2$ by showing that, under certain conditions, probability$_1$ may be regarded as an estimate of probability$_2$. This relation explains the striking analogy between theorems of the two fields. We are now in a position to throw some light on this analogy from a different angle, looking at the logical forms of the two concepts rather than at their meanings. Both concepts may be represented as quotients of measures of certain classes. This was shown for probability$_1$ by the above diagrams. We can now use the same diagrams for representing probability$_2$, if we give them a new interpretation. For the sake of simplicity, let us here consider a finite domain of individuals. The largest rectangle in each of the two diagrams is now taken as representing, not the class of the $\mathfrak{Z}$ in $\mathfrak{L}_N$, but the class of all N individuals dealt with in $\mathfrak{L}_N$. Let 'M_1' and 'M_2' designate two factual properties, say, Swan and White, respectively. Let the rectangle marked by 'e' in each diagram now represent the extension of M_1 (the class of swans), and that marked by 'h' the extension of M_2 (the class of white things). Then the left-hand diagram shows the situation where all swans are white, and the right-hand diagram shows the situation where three-fourths of the swans are white. Now, the probability$_2$ of M_2 with respect to M_1 (the probability$_2$ of a swan being white) is the relative frequency $\mathrm{nc}(M_1\,.\,M_2)/\mathrm{nc}(M_1)$, where 'nc(. . .)' stands for 'the cardinal number of . . .'; in the diagram this probability$_2$ is 3/4. We see a perfect analogy between this definition for probability$_2$ and that given in D3 for $\mathfrak{c}$ or probability$_1$. Consequently, the theory of probability$_2$ contains theorems analogous to those for probability$_1$ ($\mathfrak{c}$) which we shall base on D3 (among them also theorems of multiplication, addition, and division analogous to those we shall state in the following sections). However, there are the following important differences between the two concepts of probability. 1. In the case of probability$_1$, there is an infinite number of regular $\mathfrak{c}$-functions based on an infinite number of regular $\mathfrak{m}$-functions; in order to obtain numerical $\mathfrak{c}$-values, we have to choose one of these functions. On the other hand, in the case of probability$_2$, we take simply the cardinal numbers in order to find the relative frequency (or its limit, if the domain of individuals is infinite). [It is only in cases of a special kind that also for probability$_2$ a measure function must be chosen. This becomes necessary if not only properties like M_1 and M_2 are involved but physical magnitudes with a continuous realm of values; this occurs only in languages essentially richer than our systems $\mathfrak{L}$. The traditional term for this case is 'geometrical probability', because in the earliest examples of this kind the magnitudes involved were spatial extensions.] 2. If a factual property M_1 is given, then the questions as to which things have this property and what is their number are factual questions; the answers are to be found empirically, by observations of the things involved. Therefore, the statement of a probability$_2$ value for two given properties is a factual statement. On the other hand, the question as to which $\mathfrak{Z}$ belong to the range of a given sentence e is a logical, not an empirical, question; because, in order to answer it, it is sufficient to understand the meaning of e, technically speaking, to know the semantical rules for e; we need not know the facts referred to by e. And further, if a function $\mathfrak{m}$ is defined, then, on the basis of its definition, we can determine the value of $\mathfrak{m}(e)$, again without knowledge of facts. Thus, according to D3, we find the value of $\mathfrak{c}(h,e)$ in a purely logical way. Hence statements of probability$_1$, in contradistinction to statements of probability$_2$, are not factual but purely logical. This difference has been indicated earlier (in § 10); now we have a clearer understanding of the situation, since we know now how the ranges are determined by the semantical rules and the values of probability$_1$ are determined with the help of the measures ascribed to the ranges. The comparison of probability$_1$ and probability$_2$ may be summed up as follows. Both concepts may be regarded as expressing a numerical ratio for the partial inclusion of one class in another. For probability$_2$ the two classes are, in general, determined by factual properties; therefore the value is found empirically. For probability$_1$ the two classes are ranges of sentences and hence determined logically; therefore, the value is found in a purely logical way.

§ 56. Regular Functions for the Infinite System

In accordance with an earlier consideration (in § 54A), we define now $\mathfrak{m}(j)$ for $\mathfrak{L}_\infty$ as the limit of its values in the finite systems (D1), and analogously $\mathfrak{c}(h,e)$ for $\mathfrak{L}_\infty$ as the limit of its values in the finite systems (D2).

We have so far applied the concepts of regular $\mathfrak{m}$- and $\mathfrak{c}$-functions only to the finite systems $\mathfrak{L}_N$. Now we shall apply them to the infinite system $\mathfrak{L}_\infty$. In accordance with our previous considerations (in § 54A), we define the values of those functions in $\mathfrak{L}_\infty$ as limits of the values in finite systems (D1 and D2). In what follows, 'lim(. .)' is always meant, unless otherwise indicated, as short for '$\lim\limits_{N\to\infty}$(. .)'. (For the definition of this concept, see D40-6a.)

+D56-1. Let $_1\mathfrak{m}$, $_2\mathfrak{m}$, etc., be a sequence of regular $\mathfrak{m}$-functions for the sentences in $\mathfrak{L}_1$, $\mathfrak{L}_2$, etc. $\mathfrak{m}$ is the *regular* $\mathfrak{m}$*-function for the sentences in* $\mathfrak{L}_\infty$ corresponding to this sequence $=_{\text{Df}}$ for every sentence j in $\mathfrak{L}_\infty$ for which the limit exists, $\mathfrak{m}(j) = \lim {}_N\mathfrak{m}(j)$; if the limit does not exist, $\mathfrak{m}$ has no value for j.

+D56-2. Let $_1\mathfrak{c}$, $_2\mathfrak{c}$, etc., be a sequence of regular $\mathfrak{c}$-functions for $\mathfrak{L}_1$, $\mathfrak{L}_2$, etc. $\mathfrak{c}$ is the *regular* $\mathfrak{c}$*-function for* $\mathfrak{L}_\infty$ corresponding to this sequence $=_{\text{Df}}$ for any pair of sentences h,e in $\mathfrak{L}_\infty$ for which the limit exists, $\mathfrak{c}(h,e) = \lim {}_N\mathfrak{c}(h,e)$; if the limit does not exist, $\mathfrak{c}$ has no value for h,e.

Instead of '$\mathfrak{m}$ for $\mathfrak{L}_\infty$' and '$\mathfrak{c}$ for $\mathfrak{L}_\infty$' we shall sometimes write '$_\infty\mathfrak{m}$' and '$_\infty\mathfrak{c}$', respectively.

Now let us see what is stated by D1 and D2. Suppose a sentence j in $\mathfrak{L}_\infty$ is given. Then j occurs also in finite systems; suppose it occurs in $\mathfrak{L}_m$, then it occurs likewise in every $\mathfrak{L}_n$ where $n > m$. To j as a sentence in $\mathfrak{L}_m$, a certain real number r_m is assigned as its $_m\mathfrak{m}$-value; likewise, to j as a sentence in $\mathfrak{L}_{m+1}$, a real number r_{m+1} (not necessarily different from r_m) as its $_{m+1}\mathfrak{m}$-value, etc. Now, D1 says this: if the sequence of the numbers r_m, r_{m+1}, r_{m+2}, etc., possesses a limit r, then this number r is taken as $_\infty\mathfrak{m}(j)$, i.e., as the value of the function $_\infty\mathfrak{m}$ ascribed to j as a sentence in $\mathfrak{L}_\infty$. The situation with D2 is analogous. Suppose the sentences h and e in $\mathfrak{L}_\infty$ are given. Then h and e occur also in a finite system, say, $\mathfrak{L}_m$; and hence also in $\mathfrak{L}_{m+1}$, $\mathfrak{L}_{m+2}$, etc. Then $_m\mathfrak{c}(h,e)$ has a value in all those systems of this sequence in which e is not L-false (T55-2b). Now D2 says this: if the sequence of these $\mathfrak{c}$-values possesses a limit q, then q is taken as ${}_\infty\mathfrak{c}(h,e)$, i.e., as the value of the function ${}_\infty\mathfrak{c}$ for h and e as sentences in $\mathfrak{L}_\infty$.

We shall briefly indicate the reason for our decision to base ${}_\infty\mathfrak{m}$ on the sequence of the functions ${}_N\mathfrak{m}$ (i.e., ${}_1\mathfrak{m}$, ${}_2\mathfrak{m}$, etc.) and analogously ${}_\infty\mathfrak{c}$ on the sequence of the functions ${}_N\mathfrak{c}$. Without closer examination, one might perhaps think that ${}_\infty\mathfrak{m}$ could be directly introduced as a function for the $\mathfrak{Z}$ in $\mathfrak{L}_\infty$ in analogy to D55-1 and then extended to the sentences in $\mathfrak{L}_\infty$ in analogy to D55-2, i.e., by defining ${}_\infty\mathfrak{m}(j)$ as the sum of ${}_\infty\mathfrak{m}(\mathfrak{Z}_i)$ for all $\mathfrak{Z}$ in $\mathfrak{R}_j$. However, this procedure is not possible for the following reasons. First, the number of $\mathfrak{Z}$ in $\mathfrak{L}_\infty$ is not only infinite but nondenumerable; it is $\boldsymbol{a}_1$ (T29-4c), hence equal to the cardinal number of the continuum (T40-25b). Second, for many sentences j in $\mathfrak{L}_\infty$, the number of $\mathfrak{Z}$ in $\mathfrak{R}_j$ is infinite; in many cases, for instance if j is any non-L-false molecular sentence, the number is again $\boldsymbol{a}_1$. It would be possible to introduce the $\mathfrak{m}$-functions as additive measure functions (in the sense of point-set theory) for those classes of $\mathfrak{Z}$ in $\mathfrak{L}_\infty$ which are ranges of sentences in $\mathfrak{L}_\infty$ (see the remark following D58-1). In accordance with the intended meaning of universal sentences, these functions should fulfil the following condition. Let i be a universal sentence (e.g., '$(x)(Mx)$'); let j_n be the instance of its scope with 'a_n' ('Ma_n'); let k_n be the conjunction $j_1 \centerdot j_2 \centerdot \ldots \centerdot j_n$; then $\mathfrak{m}(i) = \lim \mathfrak{m}(k_n)$ (for $n \rightarrow \infty$). This, however, is not essentially different from our present procedure using the systems $\mathfrak{L}_N$, as can be seen in the following way. In our procedure we define ${}_\infty\mathfrak{m}(i)$ as $\lim {}_N\mathfrak{m}(i)$ (D1). Now, i is L-equivalent in $\mathfrak{L}_N$ to k_N. Therefore, ${}_N\mathfrak{m}(i) = {}_N\mathfrak{m}(k_N)$. Hence, ${}_\infty\mathfrak{m}(i) = \lim {}_N\mathfrak{m}(k_N)$. Furthermore, the procedure indicated would involve certain additional complications, because if we were to define (directly in $\mathfrak{L}_\infty$) $\mathfrak{c}(h,e)$ simply as $\mathfrak{m}(e \centerdot h)/\mathfrak{m}(e)$, which seems the most natural way, then this procedure would have the serious disadvantage explained below for W′ (see: Discussion of an alternative procedure).

Let ${}_N\mathfrak{m}$, ${}_\infty\mathfrak{m}$, ${}_N\mathfrak{c}$, and ${}_\infty\mathfrak{c}$ be regular. Although ${}_N\mathfrak{m}$ has a value for every sentence in $\mathfrak{L}_N$ (D55-2), we see from D1 that ${}_\infty\mathfrak{m}$ does not necessarily have a value for every sentence in $\mathfrak{L}_\infty$. ${}_N\mathfrak{c}$ has a value for sentences h and e in $\mathfrak{L}_N$ only under a certain condition (T55-2b). A still stronger condition must be fulfilled for ${}_\infty\mathfrak{c}$ to have a value. The following theorems state the domains of the functions ${}_\infty\mathfrak{m}$ and ${}_\infty\mathfrak{c}$, i.e., the conditions which the arguments must fulfil in order to assure values for the functions.

T56-1. Let ${}_N\mathfrak{m}$ (N = 1, 2, etc.) be a sequence of regular $\mathfrak{m}$-functions for sentences and ${}_\infty\mathfrak{m}$ the regular $\mathfrak{m}$-function for sentences in $\mathfrak{L}_\infty$ corresponding to the sequence. Then, for a sentence j in $\mathfrak{L}_\infty$, ${}_\infty\mathfrak{m}$ has a value if and only if the sequence of the numbers ${}_N\mathfrak{m}(j)$ is convergent (D40-6b).

T56-2. Let ${}_N\mathfrak{c}$ (N = 1, 2, etc.) be a sequence of regular $\mathfrak{c}$-functions based on the functions ${}_N\mathfrak{m}$, and ${}_\infty\mathfrak{c}$ the regular $\mathfrak{c}$-function for $\mathfrak{L}_\infty$ corresponding to the sequence. Then, for a pair of sentences h,e in $\mathfrak{L}_\infty$, ${}_\infty\mathfrak{c}$ has a value if and only if the following two conditions are fulfilled.

a. Those N for which ${}_N\mathfrak{m}(e) \neq 0$ (and hence e is not L-false in $\mathfrak{L}_N$) form an infinite sequence.

b. For these N, the sequence of the numbers ${}_N\mathfrak{c}(h,e)$ is convergent. (From T55-2b, D2.)

Discussion of an alternative procedure. On the basis of a function ${}_N\mathfrak{m}$ for the sentences in $\mathfrak{L}_N$, ${}_N\mathfrak{c}$ is defined (D55-3 and 4). On the same basis, ${}_\infty\mathfrak{m}$ is defined (D1). Then there are two possible ways for defining ${}_\infty\mathfrak{c}$. The way W, which we have chosen, is expressed by D2; here, ${}_\infty\mathfrak{c}$ is defined as the limit of ${}_N\mathfrak{c}$, in analogy to D1. The alternative way W′ would consist in defining ${}_\infty\mathfrak{c}$ not on the basis of ${}_N\mathfrak{c}$ but on the basis of ${}_\infty\mathfrak{m}$; in analogy to D55-3 and 4, ${}_\infty\mathfrak{c}(h,e)$ would be defined as ${}_\infty\mathfrak{m}(e \centerdot h)/{}_\infty\mathfrak{m}(e)$. In all cases where W′ assigns a value to ${}_\infty\mathfrak{c}$, our way W yields the same value (see below, T4a). On the other hand, W′ does not assign a value in certain cases where W does. For W′ to assign a value to ${}_\infty\mathfrak{c}(h,e)$, it is required that ${}_\infty\mathfrak{m}(e) \neq 0$, in analogy to T55-2b. The requirement in the case of W, which has been stated in T2, is weaker. For there may be sentences e of the following kind (for our function $\mathfrak{m}^*$, any sentence of the form '$(x)(Mx)$' would be an example, see the remark following (5) in § 110A). e is factual both in the systems $\mathfrak{L}_N$ and in $\mathfrak{L}_\infty$; nevertheless, ${}_\infty\mathfrak{m}(e) = 0$ because the sequence ${}_N\mathfrak{m}(e)$, although consisting of positive numbers, converges toward the limit 0 (as, e.g., in T40-22). (In this case we shall later call e almost L-false, D58-1b.) If e is of this kind, the procedure W′ assigns no value to ${}_\infty\mathfrak{c}(h,e)$. On the other hand, for every N, ${}_N\mathfrak{c}(h,e)$ has a value; and if the sequence of these values has a limit, say, r, then, on the basis of W, i.e., D2, ${}_\infty\mathfrak{c}(h,e)$ has the value r. For instance, for every N, ${}_N\mathfrak{c}(t,e) = 1$ (T59-1d), and hence ${}_\infty\mathfrak{c}(t,e) = 1$. This feature of W′ is a serious disadvantage.

T56-4. Let ${}_N\mathfrak{m}$ ($N = 1, 2$, etc.) be any sequence of regular $\mathfrak{m}$-functions for the $\mathfrak{Z}$. Let the following functions be defined on this basis: the sequence of functions ${}_N\mathfrak{m}$ for sentences (D55-2), the function ${}_\infty\mathfrak{m}$ (D1), the sequence of functions ${}_N\mathfrak{c}$ (D55-3 and 4), and the function ${}_\infty\mathfrak{c}$ (D2).

a. For any sentences h and e in $\mathfrak{L}_\infty$, if ${}_\infty\mathfrak{m}$ has values for $e \centerdot h$ and for e and the latter value is not 0, then

$$ {}_\infty\mathfrak{c}(h,e) = \frac{{}_\infty\mathfrak{m}(e \centerdot h)}{{}_\infty\mathfrak{m}(e)} . $$

Proof. Let the conditions be fulfilled. Then there is an m (T1) such that, for every $N > m$, ${}_N\mathfrak{m}(e) > 0$ and ${}_N\mathfrak{c}(h,e) = {}_N\mathfrak{m}(e \centerdot h)/{}_N\mathfrak{m}(e)$ (D55-4 and 3), hence ${}_N\mathfrak{c}(h,e) \times {}_N\mathfrak{m}(e) = {}_N\mathfrak{m}(e \centerdot h)$. Therefore $\lim({}_N\mathfrak{c}(h,e)) \times \lim({}_N\mathfrak{m}(e)) = \lim({}_N\mathfrak{m}(e \centerdot h))$ (T40-21c), and hence ${}_\infty\mathfrak{c}(h,e) \times {}_\infty\mathfrak{m}(e) = {}_\infty\mathfrak{m}(e \centerdot h)$ (D2, D1). Since the second factor is assumed to be positive, the theorem follows.

b. If e is L-false in $\mathfrak{L}_\infty$, then ${}_\infty\mathfrak{c}(h,e)$ has no value.

Proof. If the condition is fulfilled, there is an m such that, for every $N > m$, e is L-false in $\mathfrak{L}_N$ (T20-11b) and hence ${}_N\mathfrak{c}(h,e)$ has no value (T55-2b). Hence the theorem (T2a).

In connection with T4a, it is to be noted that, as mentioned earlier, ${}_\infty\mathfrak{c}(h,e)$ has sometimes a value even in cases where ${}_\infty\mathfrak{m}(e) = 0$; here, also,

$_\infty\mathfrak{m}(e \,.\, h) = 0$, and hence the $_\infty\mathfrak{c}$-value cannot be represented as a quotient of the two $_\infty\mathfrak{m}$-values. (See the discussion preceding T4.)

For the sake of simplicity, the definitions and theorems concerning $\mathfrak{m}$- and $\mathfrak{c}$-functions are formulated in this book only for sentences as arguments. They can, however, easily be extended so as to apply also to *classes of sentences.* The definitions of 'range' (D18-6b) and of the L-concepts (D20-1) are applicable to classes of sentences. In a finite system $\mathfrak{L}_N$, the $\mathfrak{m}$- and $\mathfrak{c}$-functions can be applied in a simple way to classes of sentences. For every such class there is a sentence representing it in the sense of being L-equivalent to it (T21-8e); hence we can define the values of those functions for any given classes by their values for the representing sentences. In the infinite system $\mathfrak{L}_\infty$, this simple procedure cannot be used; but the same aim can be achieved by other means.

A procedure for $\mathfrak{L}_\infty$ may briefly be indicated. If a class of sentences $\mathfrak{K}_i$ in $\mathfrak{L}_\infty$ is given, we define the corresponding class $_N\mathfrak{K}_i$ in $\mathfrak{L}_N$ as the class of those sentences of $\mathfrak{K}_i$ which occur in $\mathfrak{L}_N$. Then we define $_\infty\mathfrak{m}(\mathfrak{K}_i)$ as the limit of $_N\mathfrak{m}(_N\mathfrak{K}_i)$, and analogously for $_\infty\mathfrak{c}$. Let $\mathfrak{K}_i$ be the class of all full sentences of '*M*' in $\mathfrak{L}_\infty$. Then the corresponding class $_N\mathfrak{K}_i$ contains the full sentences of '*M*' with 'a_1' through 'a_N'. In this case, there is a sentence in $\mathfrak{L}_\infty$ L-equivalent to $\mathfrak{K}_i$, viz., '$(x)(Mx)$'; let this be i. This same sentence i in $\mathfrak{L}_N$ is L-equivalent to the corresponding class $_N\mathfrak{K}_i$ in $\mathfrak{L}_N$. Thus in a case of this kind the new definition for $\mathfrak{m}(\mathfrak{K}_i)$ is in accord with the old definition in this sense: $\mathfrak{m}$ has for $\mathfrak{K}_i$ the same value as for the sentence i representing $\mathfrak{K}_i$. Therefore it seems plausible to accept the same definition also for any class for which there is no L-equivalent sentence.

§ 57. Null Confirmation; Fitting Sequences

A. Some fundamental theorems concerning regular $\mathfrak{m}$-functions are stated (T1).

B. The confirmation of a hypothesis j on the tautological evidence 't', in other words, the confirmation of j before any factual knowledge is available, is called the *null confirmation* (or initial confirmation) of j, in symbols: '$\mathfrak{c}_0(j)$' (D1). It turns out that $\mathfrak{c}_0$ coincides with $\mathfrak{m}$ (T3).

C. Suppose we have a sequence of regular $\mathfrak{m}$-functions $_1\mathfrak{m}$, $_2\mathfrak{m}$, etc., one for each finite system. If these functions fit together in a certain sense, the sequence is called a fitting $\mathfrak{m}$-sequence (D3, D4). And the sequence of regular $\mathfrak{c}$-functions based upon those $\mathfrak{m}$-functions is called a fitting $\mathfrak{c}$-sequence (D5). That the functions of a fitting sequence actually fit together is shown by the following results: for a nongeneral sentence, all $\mathfrak{m}$-functions of the sequence have the same value (T5); and for a pair of nongeneral sentences, all $\mathfrak{c}$-functions of the sequence have the same value (T6).

A. *Theorems on Regular $\mathfrak{m}$-Functions*

The theorems in T1 concern regular $\mathfrak{m}$-functions for finite or infinite systems. These theorems serve chiefly for two purposes: (i) as lemmas for later theorems concerning regular c-functions, and (ii) as theorems concerning the null confirmation $\mathfrak{c}_0$, since this function coincides with $\mathfrak{m}$ (T3).

T57-1. Let ${}_N\mathfrak{m}$ (N = 1, 2, etc.) be a sequence of regular $\mathfrak{m}$-functions, and ${}_\infty\mathfrak{m}$ the corresponding regular $\mathfrak{m}$-function for $\mathfrak{L}_\infty$. Then the following assertions (a) to (x) hold both (1) if $\mathfrak{m}$ is any ${}_N\mathfrak{m}$ (with respect to any sentences in $\mathfrak{L}_N$), and (2) if $\mathfrak{m}$ is ${}_\infty\mathfrak{m}$ (with respect to any sentences in $\mathfrak{L}_\infty$ for which ${}_\infty\mathfrak{m}$ has a value, compare T56-1). The proofs or references indicating proofs concern ${}_N\mathfrak{m}$ under (1), and ${}_\infty\mathfrak{m}$ under (2). (Concerning the use of '$\vdash$', see the remark preceding T20-1.)

+a. If $\vdash i \equiv j$, then $\mathfrak{m}(i) = \mathfrak{m}(j)$. (1. From D20-1d, D55-2. 2. From T20-11, T40-21e.)

+b. If i is L-false, $\mathfrak{m}(i) = 0$. (1. From D55-2a. 2. From T20-11b, T40-21e.) (For a restricted converse of this theorem, applying to all sentences in $\mathfrak{L}_N$ and to the nongeneral sentences in $\mathfrak{L}_\infty$, see T58-1a.)

c. $\mathfrak{m}(\sim t) = 0$. (From (b).)

+d. If i is L-true, $\mathfrak{m}(i) = 1$. (1. From D20-1a, D55-2b, D55-1b. 2. From T20-11a, T40-21e.) (For a restricted converse see T58-1c.)

e. $\mathfrak{m}(t) = 1$. (From (d).)

f. If $0 < \mathfrak{m}(i) < 1$, then i is factual. (From (b), (d).) (For a restricted converse see T58-1e.)

+g. $0 \leqq \mathfrak{m}(i) \leqq 1$. (1. From D55-2 and 1. 2. From D56-1.)

+h. If $\vdash i \supset j$, then $\mathfrak{m}(i) \leqq \mathfrak{m}(j)$. (1. From D20-1c, D55-2, D55-1a. 2. From T20-11, T40-21f.)

i. $\mathfrak{m}(i \cdot j) \leqq \mathfrak{m}(i)$. (From (h).)

j. $\mathfrak{m}(i) \leqq \mathfrak{m}(i \vee j)$. (From (h).)

+k. $\mathfrak{m}(i \vee j) = \mathfrak{m}(i) + \mathfrak{m}(j) - \mathfrak{m}(i \cdot j)$.

Proof. 1. $\mathfrak{R}(i \vee j)$ is $\mathfrak{R}_i \cup \mathfrak{R}_j$ (T18-1f). Therefore, ${}_N\mathfrak{m}(i \vee j) = \Sigma {}_N\mathfrak{m}(\mathfrak{Z})$ for the $\mathfrak{Z}$ in $\mathfrak{R}_i \cup \mathfrak{R}_j$ = $\Sigma {}_N\mathfrak{m}(\mathfrak{Z})$ for the $\mathfrak{Z}$ in $\mathfrak{R}_i$ plus $\Sigma {}_N\mathfrak{m}(\mathfrak{Z})$ for the $\mathfrak{Z}$ in $\mathfrak{R}_j$ minus $\Sigma {}_N\mathfrak{m}(\mathfrak{Z})$ for the $\mathfrak{Z}$ in $\mathfrak{R}_i \cap \mathfrak{R}_j$ (the latter sum must be subtracted because these $\mathfrak{Z}$ belong both to $\mathfrak{R}_i$ and to $\mathfrak{R}_j$ and hence their ${}_N\mathfrak{m}$-values are counted twice in the first two terms). Hence theorem (with T18-1g). 2. From T40-21a and b.

l. $\mathfrak{m}(i \cdot j) = \mathfrak{m}(i) + \mathfrak{m}(j) - \mathfrak{m}(i \vee j)$. (From (k).)

+m. If $\mathfrak{m}(i \cdot j) = 0$, hence in particular (from (b)) if i and j are L-exclusive (in other words, $i \cdot j$ is L-false, $\vdash i \supset \sim j$), then $\mathfrak{m}(i \vee j) = \mathfrak{m}(i) + \mathfrak{m}(j)$. (From (k), (b).)

n. See v.

+p. $\mathfrak{m}(\sim i) = 1 - \mathfrak{m}(i)$. (1. From T18-1e, D55-2, D55-1. 2. From (1), T40-21b.)

q. If $\mathfrak{m}(i \cdot j) = 1$, then $\mathfrak{m}(i) = \mathfrak{m}(j) = 1$. (From (i), (g).)

r. $\mathfrak{m}(i) = \mathfrak{m}(i \cdot j) + \mathfrak{m}(i \cdot \sim j)$. (From T21-5j(2), (a), (m).)

s. If $\mathfrak{m}(i) = 0$, $\mathfrak{m}(i \cdot j) = 0$. (From (i).)

t. If $\mathfrak{m}(i \vee j) = 1$, hence in particular (from (d)) if i and j are L-disjunct (i.e., $\vdash i \vee j$), then $\mathfrak{m}(i \cdot j) = \mathfrak{m}(i) + \mathfrak{m}(j) - 1$. (From (l).)

u. If $\mathfrak{m}(i \cdot \sim j) = 0$, hence (from (p)) $\mathfrak{m}(\sim i \vee j) = 1$, then
(1) $\mathfrak{m}(i) = \mathfrak{m}(i \cdot j)$ (from (r));
(2) $\mathfrak{m}(i) \leq \mathfrak{m}(j)$. (From (1), (i).)

v. Let j be $j_1 \vee j_2 \vee \ldots \vee j_n$ ($n \geqq 2$). For any two different components j_m and j_p, let $\mathfrak{m}(j_m \cdot j_p) = 0$. (This is the case in particular if $j_1, \ldots, j_n$ are L-exclusive in pairs (D20-1g).) Then

$$\mathfrak{m}(j) = \sum_{p=1}^{n} \mathfrak{m}(j_p).$$

Proof. 1. The assertion holds for $n = 2$ (m). 2. For $n > 2$, let us assume that the assertion holds for $n - 1$; we shall show that then it holds likewise for n. Let j' be $j_1 \vee j_2 \vee \ldots \vee j_{n-1}$. $j' \cdot j_n$ is L-equivalent to $(j_1 \cdot j_n) \vee (j_2 \cdot j_n) \vee \ldots \vee (j_{n-1} \cdot j_n)$ (T21-5m(2)). For every component of the latter disjunction $\mathfrak{m} = 0$, hence also for the conjunction of any two of these components (s). The disjunction has $n - 1$ components. Therefore, according to our assumption, $\mathfrak{m}(j' \cdot j_n)$ is the sum of the $\mathfrak{m}$ of the components, hence 0. Therefore, since j is $j' \vee j_n$, $\mathfrak{m}(j) = \mathfrak{m}(j') + \mathfrak{m}(j_n)$ (m). Again according to our assumption, $\mathfrak{m}(j') = \sum_{p=1}^{n-1} \mathfrak{m}(j_p)$. Hence $\mathfrak{m}(j) = \sum_{p=1}^{n} \mathfrak{m}(j_p)$. The assertion for every $n \geqq 2$ follows from (1) and (2) by mathematical induction.

w. If $\mathfrak{m}(i) = \mathfrak{m}(j) = 0$, then $\mathfrak{m}(i \vee j) = 0$.

Proof. $\mathfrak{m}(i \cdot j) = 0$ (i). Hence the assertion with (k).

x. If $\mathfrak{m}(i) = \mathfrak{m}(j) = 1$, then $\mathfrak{m}(i \cdot j) = 1$.

Proof. $\mathfrak{m}(i \vee j) = 1$ (j). Hence the assertion with (l).

B. *Null Confirmation*

In accordance with an earlier preliminary explanation (in § 54B), we shall now introduce the symbol '$\mathfrak{c}_0$' for the ***null confirmation*** or initial confirmation, i.e., the confirmation on the tautological basis 't' (D1). Then it can easily be shown that $\mathfrak{c}_0$ coincides with $\mathfrak{m}$ (T3); hence T1 applies also to $\mathfrak{c}_0$.

+D57-1. Let $\mathfrak{c}$ be a regular $\mathfrak{c}$-function for a finite or infinite system $\mathfrak{L}$. For every sentence j in $\mathfrak{L}$,

$$\mathfrak{c}_0(j) =_{\text{Df}} \mathfrak{c}(j,t)\ .$$

+T57-3. Let $\mathfrak{m}$ be a regular $\mathfrak{m}$-function for the sentences of a finite or infinite system $\mathfrak{L}$. Let $\mathfrak{c}$ be the corresponding regular $\mathfrak{c}$-function for $\mathfrak{L}$, and

$\mathfrak{c}_0$ the corresponding null confirmation (D1). Then, for every sentence j in $\mathfrak{L}$ (in $\mathfrak{L}_\infty$, provided $\mathfrak{m}$ has a value for j)

$$\mathfrak{c}_0(j) = \mathfrak{m}(j) .$$

Proof. $\mathfrak{c}_0(j) = \mathfrak{c}(j,t)$ (D1), $= \mathfrak{m}(t \,.\, j)/\mathfrak{m}(t)$ (T55-2a for $\mathfrak{L}_N$, T56-4a for $\mathfrak{L}_\infty$), $= \mathfrak{m}(j)$ (T21-5s(1), T1a, T1e).

The concept of null confirmation is very important for inductive logic. $\mathfrak{c}_0(h)$ is the degree of confirmation of the hypothesis h on the evidence 't' and hence on any L-true evidence, in other words, the degree of confirmation of h before any factual information is available. This concept may look suspicious at the first glance; one might perhaps think that, as long as we have no factual knowledge, we have no right to say anything about h. An objection of this kind, however, is based on a misconception of the nature of $\mathfrak{c}$ and of its explicandum, probability$_1$. As earlier explained (§ 10A), a statement of probability$_1$ is, if true, L-true, not factual; hence the same holds for a sentence of the form '$\mathfrak{c}(h,e) = r$'. This sentence is a semantical and, more specifically, an L-semantical sentence which states a logical relation between the sentences h and e of the object language but does not say anything about facts. In this respect it has the same nature as an L-semantical sentence of the form 'e L-implies h'. Consequently, a sentence of the form '$\mathfrak{c}_0(h) = q$' states a certain logical property of the sentence h without saying anything about facts. More specifically, it states a numerical value of a purely logical function for the argument h; this value is dependent only upon what is usually called the meaning of h or, in more technical terms, the range of h as determined by the semantical rules of the language system $\mathfrak{L}$ to which h belongs; it is not dependent in any way upon the contingency of facts, e.g., upon the question whether h is true or false. We shall later come back to the question of the legitimacy of the concept of null confirmation (§ 107, *A* and *B*).

Earlier authors in the theory of probability$_1$ have sometimes used the term 'probability a priori' for the concept under discussion. Later authors have preferred to avoid this term because of its ambiguity and to use instead other terms, e.g., 'initial probability' ('Anfangswahrscheinlichkeit'). The term 'probability a priori' and its counterpart 'probability a posteriori' have been used in at least three different meanings. 1. 'Probability a priori' for confirmation by L-true evidence, 'probability a posteriori' for confirmation by a factual evidence. 2. In theories of probability based on the principle of indifference, the term 'probability a priori' is often used in cases where the probability is calculated chiefly with the help of that principle, even if factual knowledge is used, provided this knowledge is not of a statistical nature. On the other hand, a probability is called 'a posteriori' if it is calculated chiefly on the basis of statistical information (reports of experiments, social statistics, and the like). In particular, with respect to results of games of chance, 'probability a priori' is used if the evidence gives information only about the general conditions of the game (e.g., symmetry of a die or roulette, physical similarity of cards, and the like), while 'probability a posteriori' refers to evidence including statistical results of earlier games. 3. Let *h* be a law or another hypothesis, and *i* a prediction concerning the result of a new experiment which we plan to make in order to test *h;* let *e* express the knowledge we have before we observe the result of the new experiment; *e* may include the results of any number of previous observations relevant to *h*. Then 'probability a priori' is sometimes used for $\mathfrak{c}(h,e)$, and 'probability a posteriori' for $\mathfrak{c}(h,e\,.\,i)$. (We shall later use the terms 'prior confirmation' and 'posterior confirmation' instead; see § 60.) It seems to me that, if the two terms are to be used at all, (1) is the only appropriate use, because the only one in accordance with the customary, Kantian meanings of the terms 'a priori' and 'a posteriori'. The usages (2) and (3) should be avoided; the use of 'probability a priori' in these cases, when the evidence is factual and empirical, is quite misleading.

It must be admitted that some earlier authors have violated the principle of empiricism by certain statements concerning probability a priori. Other authors were right in criticizing these statements (cf. §§ 41D and 42B). The decisive point for our present discussion is the fact that the violation is to be blamed not on the concept $\mathfrak{c}_0$ itself but on its misuse. This misuse was chiefly due to a lack of distinction between probability$_1$ and probability$_2$. There is no analogue to $\mathfrak{c}_0$ for probability$_2$, since relative frequency has no value within the null class.

C. *Fitting Sequences*

The remainder of this section deals with a technical problem which has, however, no fundamental significance. We have found earlier that $\mathfrak{m}$-functions (or $\mathfrak{c}_0$-functions) for different finite systems must fulfil a certain requirement in order to fit together (§ 54E(6)). We now call a sequence of regular $\mathfrak{m}$-functions for $\mathfrak{Z}$ for all finite systems a ***fitting*** $\mathfrak{m}$***-sequence*** if they fulfil this requirement (D3). The concept of a fitting $\mathfrak{m}$-sequence for sentences is then defined on this basis (D4), in analogy to our earlier extension of $\mathfrak{m}$-functions for $\mathfrak{Z}$ to $\mathfrak{m}$-functions for sentences (D55-2). Finally, the concept of a ***fitting*** $\mathfrak{c}$***-sequence*** is defined on this basis in an obvious way (D5), in analogy to D55-4. (In what follows, the $\mathfrak{Z}$ in $\mathfrak{L}_N$ are designated by '${}_N\mathfrak{Z}$', and the ranges in $\mathfrak{L}_N$ by '${}_N\mathfrak{R}$'.)

D57-3. A sequence of functions ${}_1\mathfrak{m}$, ${}_2\mathfrak{m}$, ${}_3\mathfrak{m}$, etc., is a regular fitting sequence of $\mathfrak{m}$-functions for $\mathfrak{Z}$ or, briefly, a ***fitting*** $\mathfrak{m}$-***sequence*** for $\mathfrak{Z}$ $=_{\text{Df}}$ the following two conditions are fulfilled.

a. For every N (= 1, 2, etc.), ${}_N\mathfrak{m}$ is a regular $\mathfrak{m}$-function for the $\mathfrak{Z}$ in $\mathfrak{L}_N$.

b. For every N and every ${}_N\mathfrak{Z}_j$ (i.e., $\mathfrak{Z}_j$ in $\mathfrak{L}_N$), ${}_N\mathfrak{m}({}_N\mathfrak{Z}_j)$ is equal to the sum of the ${}_{N+1}\mathfrak{m}$-values for all those ${}_{N+1}\mathfrak{Z}$ of which ${}_N\mathfrak{Z}_j$ is a subconjunction.

D57-4. A sequence of functions ${}_1\mathfrak{m}$, ${}_2\mathfrak{m}$, ${}_3\mathfrak{m}$, etc., is a regular fitting sequence of $\mathfrak{m}$-functions for sentences or, briefly, a *fitting* $\mathfrak{m}$-*sequence for sentences* $=_{\text{Df}}$ there is a fitting $\mathfrak{m}$-sequence for $\mathfrak{Z}$, ${}_1\mathfrak{m}'$, ${}_2\mathfrak{m}'$, etc., and, for every N, ${}_N\mathfrak{m}$ is a regular $\mathfrak{m}$-function for the sentences in $\mathfrak{L}_N$ such that, for every non-L-false sentence j in $\mathfrak{L}_N$, ${}_N\mathfrak{m}(j)$ is the sum of the ${}_N\mathfrak{m}'$-values for the $\mathfrak{Z}$ in $\mathfrak{R}_j$.

D57-5. A sequence of functions ${}_1\mathfrak{c}$, ${}_2\mathfrak{c}$, ${}_3\mathfrak{c}$, etc., is a regular fitting sequence of confirmation functions or, briefly, a ***fitting*** $\mathfrak{c}$-***sequence*** $=_{\text{Df}}$ there is a fitting $\mathfrak{m}$-sequence for sentences ${}_1\mathfrak{m}$, ${}_2\mathfrak{m}$, etc., such that, for every N, ${}_N\mathfrak{c}$ is the regular $\mathfrak{c}$-function based upon ${}_N\mathfrak{m}$ (D55-3).

The following theorem T5 says that, with respect to a fitting $\mathfrak{m}$-sequence, any nongeneral sentence j has the same $\mathfrak{m}$ in all systems $\mathfrak{L}$. This is as it should be, since a nongeneral sentence has the same meaning in all systems (§ 15A). Thus, T5 shows that D3 and D4 are adequate, i.e., that these definitions define indeed the "fitting together" of $\mathfrak{m}$-functions for different systems in the sense intended. It is then easily seen that D5 is likewise adequate, i.e., that it effects the "fitting together" of $\mathfrak{c}$-functions; this is stated in T6.

T57-5. Let ${}_1\mathfrak{m}$, ${}_2\mathfrak{m}$, etc., be a fitting $\mathfrak{m}$-sequence for sentences, and ${}_\infty\mathfrak{m}$ the corresponding regular $\mathfrak{m}$-function for $\mathfrak{L}_\infty$. Let j be a *nongeneral* sentence in $\mathfrak{L}_N$, and hence also in $\mathfrak{L}_{N+1}$, in $\mathfrak{L}_{N+m}$ for any m, and in $\mathfrak{L}_\infty$.

a. ${}_N\mathfrak{m}(j) = {}_{N+1}\mathfrak{m}(j)$.

Proof. 1. Let j be L-false in $\mathfrak{L}_N$. Then it is likewise L-false in $\mathfrak{L}_{N+1}$ (T20-8b). Therefore, in both systems, $\mathfrak{m} = 0$ (D55-2a). 2. Let j be not L-false in $\mathfrak{L}_N$. Then it is not L-false in $\mathfrak{L}_{N+1}$ (T20-8b). Therefore, neither ${}_N\mathfrak{R}_j$ (i.e., the range of j in $\mathfrak{L}_N$) nor ${}_{N+1}\mathfrak{R}_j$ is null. ${}_{N+1}\mathfrak{R}_j$ is the class of those ${}_{N+1}\mathfrak{Z}$ of which the sentences in ${}_N\mathfrak{R}_j$ are subconjunctions (T19-8); and for every ${}_{N+1}\mathfrak{Z}$ in ${}_{N+1}\mathfrak{R}_j$, there is just one ${}_N\mathfrak{Z}$ in ${}_N\mathfrak{R}_j$ which is a subconjunction of it. Let ${}_N\mathfrak{Z}_i$ be any $\mathfrak{Z}$ in ${}_N\mathfrak{R}_j$. Then $\Sigma\,{}_{N+1}\mathfrak{m}(\mathfrak{Z})$ for those ${}_{N+1}\mathfrak{Z}$ which contain ${}_N\mathfrak{Z}_i$ as a subconjunction equals ${}_N\mathfrak{m}({}_N\mathfrak{Z}_i)$ (D3b). Therefore, $\Sigma\,{}_N\mathfrak{m}(\mathfrak{Z})$ for the ${}_N\mathfrak{Z}$ in ${}_N\mathfrak{R}_j$ equals $\Sigma\,{}_{N+1}\mathfrak{m}(\mathfrak{Z})$ for the ${}_{N+1}\mathfrak{Z}$ in ${}_{N+1}\mathfrak{R}_j$. ${}_N\mathfrak{m}(j)$ is the first of these two sums (D55-2b), ${}_{N+1}\mathfrak{m}(j)$ is the second. Hence these two $\mathfrak{m}$-values are equal.

b. ${}_N\mathfrak{m}(j) = {}_{N+m}\mathfrak{m}(j)$ for any m. (From (a), by mathematical induction.)

c. ${}_\infty\mathfrak{m}(j) = {}_N\mathfrak{m}(j)$. (From (b), T40-21d.)

T57-6. Let ${}_1\mathfrak{c}$, ${}_2\mathfrak{c}$, etc., be a fitting $\mathfrak{c}$-sequence, and ${}_\infty\mathfrak{c}$ the corresponding regular $\mathfrak{c}$-function for $\mathfrak{L}_\infty$. Let e and h be *nongeneral* sentences in $\mathfrak{L}_N$ (and hence in $\mathfrak{L}_{N+1}$, in $\mathfrak{L}_{N+m}$ for any m, and in $\mathfrak{L}_\infty$), and e be not L-false in $\mathfrak{L}_N$.

a. e is not L-false in $\mathfrak{L}_{N+1}$; and ${}_N\mathfrak{c}(h,e) = {}_{N+1}\mathfrak{c}(h,e)$. (From T20-8b; T55-2a, T5a.)

b. For any m, e is not L-false in $\mathfrak{L}_{N+m}$; and ${}_N\mathfrak{c}(h,e) = {}_{N+m}\mathfrak{c}(h,e)$. (From T5b.)

c. e is not L-false in $\mathfrak{L}_\infty$; and ${}_\infty\mathfrak{c}(h,e) = {}_N\mathfrak{c}(h,e)$. (From T20-10b; (b), T40-21d.)

§ 58. Almost L-true Sentences

If i is not L-true but, as for L-true sentences, $\mathfrak{m}(i) = 1$, then we call i an almost L-true sentence (D1a). i is called almost L-false if i is not L-false but $\mathfrak{m}(i) = 0$ (D1b, T3a). Sentences of this kind can occur only among general sentences in $\mathfrak{L}_\infty$ (T3d, e). The terms 'almost L-implies' and 'almost L-equivalent' are defined analogously (D1c, d).

General sentences (i.e., sentences containing variables) in $\mathfrak{L}_N$ can always be transformed into L-equivalent nongeneral sentences (T22-3). In $\mathfrak{L}_\infty$, however, this does in general not hold. Therefore, certain theorems in inductive logic are stated for all sentences in finite systems but only for nongeneral sentences in $\mathfrak{L}_\infty$. The following theorem T1 concerning $\mathfrak{m}$-functions belongs to this kind, and later T59-5 concerning $\mathfrak{c}$-functions.

T58-1. The subsequent assertions (a) to (l) hold under each of the following two assumptions: (i) Let $\mathfrak{m}$ be a regular $\mathfrak{m}$-function for the sentences in $\mathfrak{L}_N$ and $\mathfrak{m}'$ (in (h) to (k)) any other such function; let i and j be any sentences in $\mathfrak{L}_N$. (ii) Let $\mathfrak{m}$ be a regular $\mathfrak{m}$-function for the sentences in $\mathfrak{L}_\infty$ (D56-1) corresponding to any fitting $\mathfrak{m}$-sequence for sentences (D57-4), and $\mathfrak{m}'$ (in (h) to (k)) any other such function corresponding to any other such sequence; let i and j be any *nongeneral* sentences in $\mathfrak{L}_\infty$. (The proofs and references given below are for the assertions in case (i); the assertions in case (ii) follow with the help of T20-10 and T57-5c.)

a. If i is not L-false, $\mathfrak{m}(i) > 0$. (From D20-1b, D55-2b, D55-1a.)

+b. $\mathfrak{m}(i) = 0$ if and only if i is L-false. (From D55-2a; (a).)

c. If i is not L-true, $\mathfrak{m}(i) < 1$. (From D20-1a, D55-2, D55-1.)

+d. $\mathfrak{m}(i) = 1$ if and only if i is L-true. (From T57-1d; (c).)

e. If i is factual, $0 < \mathfrak{m}(i) < 1$. (From (a), (c).)

+f. $0 < \mathfrak{m}(i) < 1$ if and only if i is factual. (From T57-1f; (e).)

g. If $\vdash i \supset j$ but not $\vdash j \supset i$, then $\mathfrak{m}(i) < \mathfrak{m}(j)$.

Proof. Let the conditions be fulfilled. Then $\mathfrak{R}_i \subset \mathfrak{R}_j$ but not the converse (D20-1c). Thus, all $\mathfrak{Z}$ of $\mathfrak{R}_i$ belong to $\mathfrak{R}_j$, but there is a $\mathfrak{Z}_k$ in $\mathfrak{R}_j$ which does not belong to $\mathfrak{R}_i$. $\mathfrak{m}(\mathfrak{Z}_k) > 0$ (D55-1a); hence the theorem (with D55-2).

h. If $\mathfrak{m}(i) = 0$, $\mathfrak{m}'(i) = 0$. (From (b).)

i. If $\mathfrak{m}(i) > 0$, $\mathfrak{m}'(i) > 0$. (From (h).)

j. If $\mathfrak{m}(i) = 1$, $\mathfrak{m}'(i) = 1$. (From (d).)

k. If $\mathfrak{m}(i) < 1$, $\mathfrak{m}'(i) < 1$. (From (j).)

l. Let i be a factual sentence in $\mathfrak{L}$; hence $0 < \mathfrak{m}(i) < 1$ (e). Let r be an arbitrary real number such that $0 < r < 1$. Then there is a regular $\mathfrak{m}$-function $\mathfrak{m}''$ for the sentences in $\mathfrak{L}$ such that $\mathfrak{m}''(i) = r$.

Proof (for $\mathfrak{L}_N$). $\mathfrak{R}_i$ is neither empty nor does it contain all $\mathfrak{Z}$ (in $\mathfrak{L}_N$). We construct $\mathfrak{m}''$ as a function for the $\mathfrak{Z}$ (D55-1) by distributing r in an arbitrary way, e.g., in equal amounts, among the $\mathfrak{Z}$ in $\mathfrak{R}_i$, and $1 - r$ in an arbitrary way, e.g., in equal amounts, among the remaining $\mathfrak{Z}$. Then we extend $\mathfrak{m}''$ to a function for the sentences (D55-2). Then $\mathfrak{m}''(i) = r$.

Some of the theorems in T1 are restricted converses of theorems which hold without restriction for all sentences in $\mathfrak{L}_\infty$. In this way, T1a, c, e correspond to T57-1b, d, f, respectively. We shall now explain why the restriction to nongeneral sentences in $\mathfrak{L}_\infty$ is necessary. This will give occasion for the introduction of new terms, the 'almost-L'-terms.

As mentioned earlier (in § 56, Discussion of an alternative procedure), for a given sequence ${}_N\mathfrak{m}$ of regular $\mathfrak{m}$-functions and the corresponding function ${}_\infty\mathfrak{m}$ the following may happen. (For our function $\mathfrak{m}^*$, '$(x)(Mx)$' was mentioned as an example.) There is a sentence e of the following kind. e is factual both in $\mathfrak{L}_\infty$ and in the systems $\mathfrak{L}_N$; hence, ${}_N\mathfrak{m}(e) > 0$ for every N; and, in particular, these positive values are such that they converge with increasing N toward 0; hence ${}_\infty\mathfrak{m}(e) = 0$ (D56-1). e has the latter property in common with L-false sentences (T57-1b), although e is not L-false but factual. We shall call sentences of this kind ***almost L-false*** (D1b). Because of the existence of almost L-false sentences, T1a and hence T1b cannot be asserted without restriction. Since we have proved T1a for all sentences in finite systems and for all nongeneral sentences in $\mathfrak{L}_\infty$, almost L-false sentences can only occur among the general sentences in $\mathfrak{L}_\infty$ (T3e). If e has the properties mentioned, then $\sim e$ is not L-true; nevertheless, $\sim e$ has the ${}_\infty\mathfrak{m}$-value 1 (T57-1p) like L-true sentences (T57-1d). We shall call sentences of this kind ***almost L-true*** (D1a). Because of their existence, T1c and hence T1d cannot be asserted without restriction. The concepts of almost L-true and almost L-false sentences will prove useful in our system of inductive logic; that is the reason why we introduce special terms for them. Other 'almost-L'-terms will be defined analogously (D1c and d), but they are less important.

D58-1. Let $\mathfrak{m}$ be a regular $\mathfrak{m}$-function for the sentences in $\mathfrak{L}_\infty$, and i and j be sentences in $\mathfrak{L}_\infty$.

+**a.** i is ***almost L-true*** (in $\mathfrak{L}_\infty$, with respect to $\mathfrak{m}$) $=_{\text{Df}}$ i is not L-true (in $\mathfrak{L}_\infty$) but $\mathfrak{m}(i) = 1$.

+**b.** i is ***almost L-false*** (in $\mathfrak{L}_\infty$, with respect to $\mathfrak{m}$) $=_{\text{Df}}$ $\sim i$ is almost L-true.

c. i ***almost L-implies*** j (in $\mathfrak{L}_\infty$, with respect to $\mathfrak{m}$) $=_{\text{Df}}$ $i \supset j$ is almost L-true.

d. i is ***almost L-equivalent*** to j (in $\mathfrak{L}_\infty$, with respect to $\mathfrak{m}$) $=_{\text{Df}}$ $i \equiv j$ is almost L-true.

A remark on the *choice of the term 'almost L-true'*. Let $\mathfrak{m}$ be a regular $\mathfrak{m}$-function for the sentences in $\mathfrak{L}_\infty$. For every sentence i in $\mathfrak{L}_\infty$ for which $\mathfrak{m}(i)$ has a value (T56-1), let us assign this value to the class $\mathfrak{R}_i$ as its measure. Thereby, in the domain whose elements are the $\mathfrak{Z}$ in $\mathfrak{L}_\infty$, we have defined an *additive measure function* for some classes of elements. A measure function f is called additive if the following holds: for any two mutually exclusive classes $\mathfrak{K}_i$ and $\mathfrak{K}_j$ for which f has values, $f(\mathfrak{K}_i \cup \mathfrak{K}_j) = f(\mathfrak{K}_i) + f(\mathfrak{K}_j)$. This condition is fulfilled for the function described. [Proof. Let i and j be any sentences in $\mathfrak{L}_\infty$ for which $\mathfrak{m}$ has values, and let $\mathfrak{R}_i$ and $\mathfrak{R}_j$ be exclusive classes, i.e., $\mathfrak{R}_i \cap \mathfrak{R}_j$, and hence $\mathfrak{R}(i \,.\, j)$, is empty. Then $i \,.\, j$ is L-false in $\mathfrak{L}_\infty$. Therefore $f(\mathfrak{R}_i \cup \mathfrak{R}_j) = \mathfrak{m}(i \vee j) = \mathfrak{m}(i) + \mathfrak{m}(j)$ (T57-1m), $= f(\mathfrak{R}_i) + f(\mathfrak{R}_j)$.] Now, in the terminology of mathematics (theory of measure functions, based on set theory), with respect to the elements of a domain within which an additive measure function for certain classes is defined, one says that *almost all* elements have a certain property if all elements have this property with the exception of some whose class has the measure zero. According to this usage, if a sentence i in $\mathfrak{L}_\infty$ is not L-true but such that $\mathfrak{m}(i) = 1$, we should say that i holds in almost all $\mathfrak{Z}$. [This is seen as follows. The $\mathfrak{Z}$ in which i does not hold are those belonging to $\mathfrak{R}(\sim i)$ (T18-1e). The measure of $\mathfrak{R}(\sim i)$ is $\mathfrak{m}(\sim i) = 1 - \mathfrak{m}(i)$ (T57-1p), $= 0$.] Since now a sentence which holds in all $\mathfrak{Z}$ is called L-true (D20-1a), it seems not unnatural to call i, which holds in almost all $\mathfrak{Z}$, *almost L-true*. Analogously, $\sim i$ fails to hold in all $\mathfrak{Z}$ except those of $\mathfrak{R}(\sim i)$, which is a class of measure zero; hence, $\sim i$ fails to hold in almost all $\mathfrak{Z}$. Thus it seems natural to call $\sim i$ almost L-false. [The phrase 'almost all' is sometimes used in mathematical terminology in a somewhat different sense, meaning 'all elements (of an infinite domain) except a finite number of them'. It may be noted that in this sense the phrase does not apply to our case. The class of those $\mathfrak{Z}$ in which an almost L-true sentence i does not hold, namely, $\mathfrak{R}(\sim i)$, is in general infinite; the essential point is that its measure is nevertheless zero.]

T58-3. Let $\mathfrak{m}$ be a regular $\mathfrak{m}$-function for the sentences in $\mathfrak{L}_\infty$, and i and j be sentences in $\mathfrak{L}_\infty$. Then the following holds (with respect to $\mathfrak{m}$, in $\mathfrak{L}_\infty$).

+**a.** i is almost L-false if and only if i is not L-false but $\mathfrak{m}(i) = 0$. (From D1b, T57-1p.)

b. i almost L-implies j if and only if i does not L-imply j but $\mathfrak{m}(i \supset j) = 1$ (hence, $\mathfrak{m}(i \,.\, \sim j) = 0$). (From D1c.)

c. i is almost L-equivalent to j if and only if i is not L-equivalent to j but $\mathfrak{m}(i \supset j) = \mathfrak{m}(j \supset i) = 1$. (From D1d, T57-1q.)

+d. If i is almost L-true, then i is general (i.e., contains a variable). (From T1c(ii).)

+e. If i is almost L-false, then i is general. (From D1b, (d).)

f. If i is almost L-true and $\vdash i \supset j$, then $\mathfrak{m}(j) = 1$, and hence j is either L-true or almost L-true. (From T57-1h.)

g. If j is almost L-false and $\vdash i \supset j$, then $\mathfrak{m}(i) = 0$, and hence i is either L-false or almost L-false. (From T57-1h.)

h. If i is almost L-true, then i is factual in $\mathfrak{L}_\infty$.

Proof. 1. i is not L-true (D1a). 2. i is not L-false, because otherwise $\mathfrak{m}(i) = 0$ (T57-1b).

i. If i is almost L-false, then i is factual in $\mathfrak{L}_\infty$. (From D1b, (h), T20-6.)

Let us go back to the question why the restriction of T1(ii) to nongeneral sentences in $\mathfrak{L}_\infty$ is necessary. Let i be almost L-true and hence $\sim i$ almost L-false. T1a to d have been explained earlier. T1e and f hold neither for i nor for $\sim i$. The following is a counterexample for T1g as applied to general sentences. '$\sim t$' L-implies $\sim i$, like every sentence (T20-2h); but the converse does not hold because $\sim i$ is not L-false; nevertheless, for both '$\sim t$' and $\sim i$, $\mathfrak{m} = 0$. This yields also examples for D1c and d. From what has just been said, it follows that $\sim i \supset \sim t$ is not L-true; but it is almost L-true, because $\mathfrak{m}(\sim i \supset \sim t) = \mathfrak{m}(i \vee \sim t) = \mathfrak{m}(i) = 1$. Therefore, $\sim i$ almost L-implies '$\sim t$'; and 't' almost L-implies i. Furthermore, since $\vdash \sim t \supset \sim i$, $\mathfrak{m}(\sim t \supset \sim i) = 1$. Therefore, $\sim i$ and '$\sim t$' are almost L-equivalent (T3c); likewise, i and 't'.

The following theorems T4a, b and T5a, b are chiefly of interest if $\mathfrak{L}$ is $\mathfrak{L}_\infty$ and j is almost L-false, because otherwise j is L-false (T1b) and then the assertions are obvious. Analogously, T5c, d are chiefly of interest if $\mathfrak{L}$ is $\mathfrak{L}_\infty$ and j is almost L-true.

T58-4. Let $\mathfrak{m}$ be a regular $\mathfrak{m}$-function for the sentences of a system $\mathfrak{L}$ (finite or infinite), and let $\mathfrak{m}(j) = 0$.

a. $\mathfrak{m}(j \,.\, i) = 0$. (From T57-1i.)

b. $\mathfrak{m}(j \vee i) = \mathfrak{m}(i)$. (From T57-1k, (a).)

T58-5. Let $\mathfrak{m}$ be a regular $\mathfrak{m}$-function for the sentences of $\mathfrak{L}$; let i, i', j, and j' be sentences in $\mathfrak{L}$ such that i' is formed from i by replacing one or several (not necessarily all) occurrences of j in i with j'.

a. If $\mathfrak{m}(j) = 0$ and j' is '$\sim t$', then $\mathfrak{m}(i) = \mathfrak{m}(i')$.

Proof. $\mathfrak{m}(i) = \mathfrak{m}(j \vee i)$ (T4b), $= \mathfrak{m}(j \vee i')$ (T23-6b, T57-1a), $= \mathfrak{m}(i')$ (T4b).

b. If $\mathfrak{m}(j) = \mathfrak{m}(j') = 0$, then $\mathfrak{m}(i) = \mathfrak{m}(i')$. (From (a).)

c. If $\mathfrak{m}(j) = 1$ and j' is 't', then $\mathfrak{m}(i) = \mathfrak{m}(i')$.

Proof. $\mathfrak{m}(i)$ remains unchanged if i is transformed as follows. First we replace the occurrences in question of j by $\sim\sim j$ (T23-1b, T57-1a); then, at these places, we replace $\sim j$, whose $\mathfrak{m}$-value is 0 (T57-1p), by '$\sim t$' (a). Thus, the original j is replaced by '$\sim\sim t$'; for this, we put 't' (T23-1b, T57-1a).

d. If $\mathfrak{m}(j) = \mathfrak{m}(j') = 1$, then $\mathfrak{m}(i) = \mathfrak{m}(i')$. (From (c).)

T5b and d are inductive theorems of replacement, analogous to the deductive theorem T23-1b. They say that $\mathfrak{m}(i)$ remains unchanged if any subsentence in i is replaced by any other sentence such that either both have the $\mathfrak{m}$-value 0 or both have the $\mathfrak{m}$-value 1. While $\mathfrak{m}(i)$ may have any value whatever, for the sentences exchanged it is not sufficient that they have equal $\mathfrak{m}$, but it is required that their $\mathfrak{m}$ has one of the two extreme values. [The necessity of this restriction is shown by the following counterexample. Let j be a factual sentence such that $\mathfrak{m}(j) = \mathfrak{m}(\sim j)$, and hence both values are $1/2$. (For the function $\mathfrak{m}^*$ to be introduced later, this holds, e.g., for every atomic sentence.) Then, $\mathfrak{m}(j \vee \sim j) = 1$ (T57-1d); on the other hand, $\mathfrak{m}(j \vee j) = \mathfrak{m}(j)$ (T57-1a), $= 1/2$.]

§ 59. Theorems on Regular c-Functions

Some theorems concerning regular c-functions are stated, among them fundamental theorems of the classical theory, e.g., the general and the special addition theorems (T1k and l) and the general multiplication theorem (T1n). One important result is as follows. In general, if, for a given pair of sentences h,e, we choose arbitrarily a real number r between 0 and 1, then we can find a regular $\mathfrak{c}$ such that $\mathfrak{c}(h,e) = r$ (T5f). This shows that the class of regular c-functions contains not only concepts which may be regarded as adequate explicata for probability$_1$ but also concepts which are entirely inadequate. Therefore, all those theories of probability$_1$ which contain only theorems valid for all regular c-functions are very weak.

In this and the two subsequent sections, theorems are stated which hold for all regular c-functions. Among them are the most fundamental theorems of inductive logic. Many of these theorems are well known, either to be found in modern theories on probability$_1$ (e.g., the systems of Keynes, Jeffreys, Hosiasson, and others; see § 62), or already in the classical theory. The present section contains theorems of a very general nature. The next two sections will deal with the complex of problems traditionally associated with the name of Bayes.

All theorems of §§ 59, 60, and 61, with the sole exception of T59-5, hold for all finite and infinite systems (that is to say, they hold both if c is any regular c-function $_N\mathfrak{c}$ for $\mathfrak{L}_N$, and also if c is any regular c-function $_\infty\mathfrak{c}$ for $\mathfrak{L}_\infty$ corresponding to any sequence of regular c-functions for the finite systems), provided the following conditions (A), (B), and (C) are fulfilled.

A. For $\mathfrak{L}_N$. The sentences occurring belong to $\mathfrak{L}_N$; and no sentence occurring as evidence (i.e., as second argument of c) is L-false in $\mathfrak{L}_N$.

B. For $\mathfrak{L}_\infty$. The sentences occurring belong to $\mathfrak{L}_\infty$; and the arguments of c are such that every c-expression occurring has a value (in other words, the arguments fulfil the conditions stated in T56-2).

C. The value of every c-expression occurring as a denominator is positive.

Some of the proofs or references indicating proofs are divided into (I) and (II); in these cases, (I) concerns $_N\mathfrak{c}$, (II) $_\infty\mathfrak{c}$.

T59-1.

a. $0 \leqq \mathfrak{c}(h,e) \leqq 1$. (I. From T55-2a, T57-1g and i. II. From D56-2.)

+b. If $\vdash e \supset h$, $\mathfrak{c}(h,e) = 1$. (I. From T55-2a, T20-2l, T57-1a. II. From T20-11, T40-21d.) (The converse of (b) holds only in a restricted way, see T5b.)

c. If h is L-true, $\mathfrak{c}(h,e) = 1$. (From (b).)

d. $\mathfrak{c}(t,e) = 1$. (From (c).)

+e. If $\vdash e \supset \sim h$ (in other words, $e \centerdot h$ is L-false, e and h are L-exclusive), then $\mathfrak{c}(h,e) = 0$. (I. From T55-2a, D55-2a. II. From T20-11, T40-21d.)

f. If h is L-false, $\mathfrak{c}(h,e) = 0$. (From (e).)

g. $\mathfrak{c}(\sim t,e) = 0$. (From (f).)

+h. *L-equivalent evidences.* If $\vdash e_1 \equiv e_2$ (e_1 and e_2 are L-equivalent), $\mathfrak{c}(h,e_1) = \mathfrak{c}(h,e_2)$. (I. From T57-1a. II. From T40-21e.)

+i. *L-equivalent hypotheses.* If $\vdash h_1 \equiv h_2$ (h_1 and h_2 are L-equivalent), $\mathfrak{c}(h_1,e) = \mathfrak{c}(h_2,e)$. (I. From T57-1a. II. From T40-21e.)

+k. *General addition theorem.* $\mathfrak{c}(h \vee i,e) = \mathfrak{c}(h,e) + \mathfrak{c}(i,e) - \mathfrak{c}(h \centerdot i,e)$. (I. From T55-2a, T57-1k. II. From T40-21a and b.)

+l. *Special addition theorem.* Let $\mathfrak{c}(h \centerdot i,e) = 0$. (This condition is fulfilled in particular if $e \centerdot h \centerdot i$ is L-false (e), hence also if $h \centerdot i$ is L-false.) Then $\mathfrak{c}(h \vee i,e) = \mathfrak{c}(h,e) + \mathfrak{c}(i,e)$. (From (k).)

+m. *Special addition theorem for multiple disjunction.* If the sentences h_1, $h_2, \ldots, h_n$ ($n \geqq 2$) are L-exclusive in pairs with respect to e (hence always if these sentences are L-exclusive in pairs), then $\mathfrak{c}(h_1 \vee h_2 \vee \ldots \vee h_n,e) = \sum_{p=1}^{n} \mathfrak{c}(h_p,e)$. (From (l), by mathematical induction.)

+**n.** *General multiplication theorem.*

(1) $\mathfrak{c}(h \cdot i,e) = \mathfrak{c}(h,e) \times \mathfrak{c}(i,e \cdot h)$.

(2) $\phantom{\mathfrak{c}(h \cdot i,e)} = \mathfrak{c}(i,e) \times \mathfrak{c}(h,e \cdot i)$.

Proof. I. Since $e \cdot h$ is not L-false (A), $\mathfrak{m}(e \cdot h) > 0$ (T58-1a). Therefore, $\frac{\mathfrak{m}(e \cdot h \cdot i)}{\mathfrak{m}(e)} = \frac{\mathfrak{m}(e \cdot h)}{\mathfrak{m}(e)} \times \frac{\mathfrak{m}(e \cdot h \cdot i)}{\mathfrak{m}(e \cdot h)}$. Hence (1) (with T55-2a). (2) from (1) with (i). II. From T40-21c.

+**p.** $\mathfrak{c}(\sim h,e) = 1 - \mathfrak{c}(h,e)$.

Proof. $\mathfrak{c}(h,e) + \mathfrak{c}(\sim h,e) = \mathfrak{c}(h \vee \sim h,e)$ (l), $= 1$ (c). Hence the theorem.

q. $\mathfrak{c}(i \cdot j,e) = \mathfrak{c}(i,e) + \mathfrak{c}(j,e) - \mathfrak{c}(i \vee j,e)$. (From (k).)

r. If $\vdash e \supset i \vee j$ (hence, in particular, if i and j are L-disjunct), $\mathfrak{c}(i \cdot j,e) = \mathfrak{c}(i,e) + \mathfrak{c}(j,e) - 1$. (From (q), (b).)

s. $\mathfrak{c}(i \vee j,e) = \mathfrak{c}(i,e) + \mathfrak{c}(j \cdot \sim i,e)$. (From (i), T21-5p(3), (l).)

t. Let the sentences $h_1, h_2, \ldots, h_n$ ($n \geqq 2$) be L-exclusive in pairs with respect to e (this is the case, in particular, if they are L-exclusive in pairs) and L-disjunct with respect to e (this is the case, in particular, if they are L-disjunct), then $\sum_{p=1}^{n} \mathfrak{c}(h_p,e) = 1$. (From (m), (b).)

u. $\mathfrak{c}(h,e) = \mathfrak{c}(h \vee \sim e,e)$. (From (k), (e).)

v. Let h be the conjunction $h_1 \cdot h_2 \cdot \ldots \cdot h_n$ ($n \geqq 2$). Let $\mathfrak{c}(h_1,e) = \mathfrak{c}(h_2,e \cdot h_1) = \mathfrak{c}(h_3,e \cdot h_1 \cdot h_2) = \ldots = \mathfrak{c}(h_n,e \cdot h_1 \cdot h_2 \cdot \ldots \cdot h_{n-1})$. Then $\mathfrak{c}(h,e) = [\mathfrak{c}(h_1,e)]^n$.

Proof. By repeated application of (n) (1), $\mathfrak{c}(h,e) = \mathfrak{c}(h_1,e) \times \mathfrak{c}(h_2,e \cdot h_1) \times \mathfrak{c}(h_3,e \cdot h_1 \cdot h_2) \times \ldots \times \mathfrak{c}(h_n,e \cdot h_1 \cdot h_2 \cdot \ldots \cdot h_{n-1})$.

w. Let $h \cdot i$ be L-false. Then $\mathfrak{c}(h,h \vee i) + \mathfrak{c}(i,h \vee i) = 1$. (From (l), (b).)

T59-2.

a. $\mathfrak{c}(i,e) = \mathfrak{c}(h \cdot i,e) + \mathfrak{c}(\sim h \cdot i,e)$.

Proof. i is L-equivalent to $(h \cdot i) \vee (\sim h \cdot i)$ (T21-5j(2)). Hence the theorem with T1i and l.

b. $\mathfrak{c}(i,e) = \mathfrak{c}(h,e) \times \mathfrak{c}(i,e \cdot h) + \mathfrak{c}(\sim h,e) \times \mathfrak{c}(i,e \cdot \sim h)$. (From (a), T1n.)

d. If $\vdash h_1 \supset h_2$ or $\vdash e \cdot h_1 \supset h_2$, then $\mathfrak{c}(h_1,e) \leqq \mathfrak{c}(h_2,e)$.

Proof. I. $\vdash e \cdot h_1 \supset e \cdot h_2$. Hence, for every regular $\mathfrak{m}$, $\mathfrak{m}(e \cdot h_1) \leqq \mathfrak{m}(e \cdot h_2)$ (T57-1h). Hence the theorem (with T55-2a). II. From T20-11, T40-21f.

e. $\mathfrak{c}(h \cdot i,e) \leqq \mathfrak{c}(h,e)$. (From (d).)

f. $\mathfrak{c}(h,e) \leqq \mathfrak{c}(h \vee i,e)$. (From (d).)

g. $\mathfrak{c}(h \vee i,e) \leqq \mathfrak{c}(h,e) + \mathfrak{c}(i,e)$. (From T1k.)

h. If $\vdash e \cdot h \supset j$, then $\mathfrak{c}(h \cdot j,e) = \mathfrak{c}(h,e)$.

Proof. I. $\vdash e \,.\, h \,.\, j \equiv e \,.\, h$ (T20-2l). Therefore, $\mathfrak{m}(e \,.\, h \,.\, j) = \mathfrak{m}(e \,.\, h)$ (T57-1a). Hence the theorem (with T55-2a). II. From T20-11, T40-21e.

i. $\mathfrak{c}(h \,.\, e,e) = \mathfrak{c}(h,e)$. (From (h).)

j. If $\vdash e \,.\, h_1 \supset h_2$ and $\vdash e \,.\, h_2 \supset h_1$ (in other words, if $\vdash e \supset (h_1 \equiv h_2)$, h_1 is L-equivalent to h_2 with respect to e), then $\mathfrak{c}(h_1,e) = \mathfrak{c}(h_2,e)$.

Proof. I. $\mathfrak{m}(e \,.\, h_1) = \mathfrak{m}(e \,.\, h_2)$ (T57-1a). Hence the theorem (with T55-2a). II. From T20-11, T40-21e.

k. Let $\mathfrak{m}$ be the regular $\mathfrak{m}$-function corresponding to $\mathfrak{c}$ (for $\mathfrak{L}_N$ or $\mathfrak{L}_\infty$; for $\mathfrak{L}_\infty$, let $\mathfrak{m}$ have a value for h). If $\vdash h \supset e$ and $\mathfrak{m}(e) > 0$, then $\mathfrak{c}(h,e) = \frac{\mathfrak{m}(h)}{\mathfrak{m}(e)}$.

Proof. Since $\vdash h \supset e$, $\vdash e \,.\, h \equiv h$ (T20-2l). Therefore, $\mathfrak{m}(e \,.\, h) = \mathfrak{m}(h)$ (T57-1a). Hence (I) from T55-2a; (II) from T56-4a.

l. Let $\mathfrak{m}$ be the regular $\mathfrak{m}$-function corresponding to $\mathfrak{c}$ (for $\mathfrak{L}_N$ or $\mathfrak{L}_\infty$); for $\mathfrak{L}_\infty$, let $\mathfrak{m}$ have a value for $e \,.\, h$ and a positive value for e. Then $\mathfrak{c}(h,e) = \frac{\mathfrak{m}(e \,.\, h)}{\mathfrak{m}(e \,.\, h) + \mathfrak{m}(e \,.\, \sim h)}$. (From T57-1r, (I) T55-2a; (II) T56-4a.)

m. $\mathfrak{c}(h,e_1 \vee e_2) = \mathfrak{c}(h \,.\, e_1,e_1 \vee e_2) + \mathfrak{c}(h \,.\, e_2,e_1 \vee e_2) - \mathfrak{c}(h \,.\, e_1 \,.\, e_2,e_1 \vee e_2)$. (From (i), T1i, T1k.)

n. If $e_1 \,.\, e_2$ is not L-false, $\mathfrak{c}(h,e_1 \vee e_2) = \mathfrak{c}(h,e_1) \times \mathfrak{c}(e_1,e_1 \vee e_2) + \mathfrak{c}(h,e_2) \times \mathfrak{c}(e_2,e_1 \vee e_2) - \mathfrak{c}(h,e_1 \,.\, e_2) \times \mathfrak{c}(e_1 \,.\, e_2,e_1 \vee e_2)$. (From (m), T1n(2), T21-5p(2).)

o. If $h \,.\, e_1 \,.\, e_2$ is L-false, then $\mathfrak{c}(h,e_1 \vee e_2) = \mathfrak{c}(h,e_1) \times \mathfrak{c}(e_1,e_1 \vee e_2) + \mathfrak{c}(h,e_2) \times \mathfrak{c}(e_2,e_1 \vee e_2)$. (From (m), T1f.)

p. If $e_1 \,.\, e_2$ is L-false, than $\mathfrak{c}(h,e_1 \vee e_2) = \mathfrak{c}(h,e_1) \times \mathfrak{c}(e_1,e_1 \vee e_2) + \mathfrak{c}(h,e_2) \times (1 - \mathfrak{c}(e_1,e_1 \vee e_2))$. (From (o), T1w.)

q. Let $e_1 \,.\, e_2$ be L-false. Let r be the maximum and r' the minimum of the values $\mathfrak{c}(h,e_1)$ and $\mathfrak{c}(h,e_2)$. (In the case of $\mathfrak{L}_\infty$, it is assumed that the values $\mathfrak{c}(e_1,e_1 \vee e_2)$ and $\mathfrak{c}(e_2,e_1 \vee e_2)$ exist.) Then $r' \leqq \mathfrak{c}(h,e_1 \vee e_2) \leqq r$.

Proof. 1. Let $\mathfrak{c}(h,e_1) = \mathfrak{c}(h,e_2)$. Then $\mathfrak{c}(h,e_1 \vee e_2) = \mathfrak{c}(h,e_2)$ (p), $= r = r'$. 2. Let $\mathfrak{c}(h,e_1) > \mathfrak{c}(h,e_2)$; hence the first is r, the second r'. Let $\mathfrak{c}(e_1, e_1 \vee e_2) = q$. Then $\mathfrak{c}(h, e_1 \vee e_2) = rq + r'(1 - q)$ (p), $= r' + q(r - r') \geqq r'$. Similarly we obtain: $\mathfrak{c}(h,e_1 \vee e_2) \leqq r$ (from (p), with e_1 and e_2 interchanged). 3. Let $\mathfrak{c}(h,e_1) < \mathfrak{c}(h,e_2)$. The proof is analogous to (2).

The following theorem deals with multiple disjunctions; it makes use of the special addition theorem for multiple disjunction (T1m).

T59-3. Let j be $j_1 \vee j_2 \vee \ldots \vee j_n$ ($n \geqq 2$).

a. Let $\vdash e \,.\, h \supset j$. (This condition is always fulfilled if $\vdash j$, in other words, if $j_1, j_2, \ldots, j_n$ are L-disjunct.) Let the sentences $e \,.\, h \,.\, j_1, \ldots, e \,.\, h \,.\, j_n$ be L-exclusive in pairs. (This condition is always fulfilled if $j_1, j_2, \ldots, j_n$ are L-exclusive in pairs.) Then

$$(1)\quad \mathfrak{c}(h,e) = \sum_{p=1}^{n} \mathfrak{c}(h \cdot j_p,e)\ ;$$

$$(2)\quad = \sum_{p=1}^{n} [\mathfrak{c}(j_p,e) \times \mathfrak{c}(h,e \cdot j_p)]\ .$$

Proof. (1). $e \cdot h$ is L-equivalent to $e \cdot h \cdot j$ (T20-2l). $\mathfrak{c}(h,e) = \mathfrak{c}(e \cdot h,e)$ (T2i), $= \mathfrak{c}(e \cdot h \cdot j,e)$ (T1i), $= \mathfrak{c}(h \cdot j,e)$ (T2i), $= \mathfrak{c}(h \cdot (j_1 \vee \ldots \vee j_n), e) = \mathfrak{c}((h \cdot j_1) \vee \ldots \vee (h \cdot j_n), e)$ (by distribution). Hence (1) by T1m. (2) from (1) by T1n(2).

b. Let h have the same $\mathfrak{c}$ on each of the sentences $e \cdot j_1, \ldots, e \cdot j_n$ as evidence. Let these sentences $e \cdot j_1, \ldots, e \cdot j_n$ be L-exclusive in pairs. Let $\mathfrak{c}(j,e) > 0$. Then $\mathfrak{c}(h,e \cdot j) = \mathfrak{c}(h,e \cdot j_m)$ for any m (from 1 to n).

Proof. $h \cdot j$ is L-equivalent (by distribution) to $(h \cdot j_1) \vee (h \cdot j_2) \vee \ldots \vee (h \cdot j_n)$. Therefore (T1m), $\mathfrak{c}(h \cdot j,e) = \sum_{p=1}^{n} \mathfrak{c}(h \cdot j_p,e) = \sum_{p=1}^{n} [\mathfrak{c}(j_p,e) \times \mathfrak{c}(h,e \cdot j_p)]$ (T1n (2)). For any m (from 1 to n), the second factor in each term of the last-mentioned sum equals $\mathfrak{c}(h,e \cdot j_m)$. Therefore, $\mathfrak{c}(h \cdot j,e) = \mathfrak{c}(h,e \cdot j_m) \times \sum_{p=1}^{n} \mathfrak{c}(j_p,e)$. The latter sum equals $\mathfrak{c}(j,e)$ (T1m). Thus, $\mathfrak{c}(h \cdot j,e) = \mathfrak{c}(h,e \cdot j_m) \times \mathfrak{c}(j,e)$. On the other hand (T1n (2)), $\mathfrak{c}(h \cdot j,e) = \mathfrak{c}(j,e) \times \mathfrak{c}(h,e \cdot j)$. By forming an equation of the two right-hand sides and dropping the factor $\mathfrak{c}(j,e)$, since it is assumed to be positive, we obtain the theorem.

c. (Corollary to (b).) Let h have the same $\mathfrak{c}$ on each of the sentences $j_1, \ldots, j_n$ as evidence. Let the sentences $j_1, \ldots, j_n$ be L-exclusive in pairs. Let $\mathfrak{c}_0(j) > 0$. Then $\mathfrak{c}(h,j) = \mathfrak{c}(h,j_m)$ for any m (from 1 to n). (From (b), with 't' as e. It follows also from (d).)

d. Let the sentences $j_1, \ldots, j_n$ be L-exclusive in pairs. Let r be the maximum and r' the minimum of the values $\mathfrak{c}(h,j_i)$ ($i = 1, \ldots, n$). (In the case of $\mathfrak{L}_\infty$, it is assumed that the values $\mathfrak{c}(j_i,j)$ exist.) Then $r' \leq \mathfrak{c}(h,j) \leq r$. (From T2q, by mathematical induction with respect to n.)

It is clear that a *chain of inferences* is valid in deductive logic in this sense: if we can deduce each, except the first, in a series of sentences from the preceding one, then the last one is deducible from the first. This holds because of the transitivity of the relation of L-implication: if i L-implies j and j L-implies k, then i L-implies k (T20-2b); the theorem concerning a series of any length follows from this by mathematical induction. Let us now examine the problem whether an analogous procedure is valid in inductive logic. To a superficial inspection it might appear as if inferences of the following kind were not only frequently used in everyday life but also valid: suppose that on the basis of given evidence e, the hypothesis h_1 is highly probable and that h_1 gives high probability to h_2; then h_2 is highly probable on e. But in this form the chain of inference is not generally valid. Although the relation of a high degree of confirmation is in certain respects similar to L-implication, it is not transitive. There are cases in which $\mathfrak{c}(h_1,e)$ and $\mathfrak{c}(h_2,h_1)$ are both very high and, nevertheless, $\mathfrak{c}(h_2,e)$ is very low or even zero. This holds if the ranges of the sentences involved, measured by any given $\mathfrak{m}$, fulfil the following conditions: $\mathfrak{R}(e \cdot h_1)$ is a large part of $\mathfrak{R}(e)$ but only a small part of $\mathfrak{R}(h_1)$; that makes it possible for $\mathfrak{R}(h_2)$ to cover a large part of $\mathfrak{R}(h_1)$ without overlapping with $\mathfrak{R}(e)$. [Example. Let $\mathfrak{m}(e \cdot h_1 \cdot h_2) = 0$; $\mathfrak{m}(e \cdot h_1 \cdot \sim h_2) = 0.000{,}049{,}95$; $\mathfrak{m}(e \cdot \sim h_1 \cdot h_2) = 0$; $\mathfrak{m}(e \cdot \sim h_1 \cdot \sim h_2) = 0.000{,}000{,}05$; $\mathfrak{m}(\sim e \cdot h_1 \cdot h_2) = 0.0999$; $\mathfrak{m}(\sim e \cdot h_1 \cdot \sim h_2) = 0.000{,}050{,}05$. The six sentences mentioned are L-exclusive in pairs (D20-1g); hence their ranges are mutually exclusive. Since $e \cdot \sim h_1$ is L-equivalent to $e \cdot \sim h_1 \cdot h_2 \vee e \cdot \sim h_1 \cdot \sim h_2$ (T21-5m(1), T21-5s(1)), $\mathfrak{m}(e \cdot \sim h_1)$ is the sum of the $\mathfrak{m}$-values of the disjunctive components (T57-1m), hence $0.000{,}000{,}05$. In a similar way it is found that $\mathfrak{m}(e \cdot h_1) = 0.000{,}049{,}95$; $\mathfrak{m}(e) = 0.000{,}05$; hence $\mathfrak{c}(\sim h_1,e) = 0.001$ (D55-3), and $\mathfrak{c}(h_1,e) = 0.999$ (T1p). Further, $\mathfrak{m}(h_1 \cdot h_2) = 0.0999$; $\mathfrak{m}(h_1 \cdot \sim h_2) = 0.0001$; $\mathfrak{m}(h_1) = 0.1$; hence $\mathfrak{c}(h_2,h_1) = 0.999$. On the other hand, $\mathfrak{m}(e \cdot h_2) = 0$; hence $\mathfrak{c}(h_2,e) = 0$.] Are then the chains of inductive reasoning customarily made in everyday life, in law courts, and in science invalid? I think that many of them can be defended as valid. They are valid if they do not have the simple form mentioned above but rather the following cumulative form: The evidence e available to X gives strong confirmation to h_1; therefore X believes h_1 *together with e;* h_2 is highly probable with respect to $e \cdot h_1$ (but not necessarily with respect to h_1 alone); therefore X regards h_2 as highly confirmed also by his actual evidence e. This is a valid procedure. The chain may even be longer: X believes now in $e \cdot h_1 \cdot h_2$; if this gives a high probability to h_3, then he adds h_3 to his belief, etc. Generally speaking, if the values $\mathfrak{c}(h_1,e)$, $\mathfrak{c}(h_2,e \cdot h_1)$, $\mathfrak{c}(h_3,e \cdot h_1 \cdot h_2)$, etc., are all very high, then the $\mathfrak{c}$ of the last hypothesis h_n on e is also high or at least fairly high, provided the chain is not too long. This follows from the subsequent theorem T4b, which says that $\mathfrak{c}(h_n,e)$ is at least as high as the product of the afore-mentioned values.

+T59-4. ***A cumulative confirmation chain***

a. For any $n \geqq 2$, $\mathfrak{c}(h_1 \cdot h_2 \cdot \ldots \cdot h_n,e) = \mathfrak{c}(h_1,e) \times \mathfrak{c}(h_2,e \cdot h_1) \times \mathfrak{c}(h_3,e \cdot h_1 \cdot h_2) \times \ldots \times \mathfrak{c}(h_n,e \cdot h_1 \cdot h_2 \cdot \ldots \cdot h_{n-1})$.

Proof. 1. The assertion holds for $n = 2$ (T1n(1)). 2. Let k_n be the conjunction of the n h-sentences, and k_{n-1} that of the first $n-1$ of them; hence k_n is $k_{n-1} \cdot h_n$. Let Π_n be the n-term product in the theorem, and Π_{n-1} the product of its first $n - 1$ terms; hence $\Pi_n = \Pi_{n-1} \times c(h_n, e \cdot k_{n-1})$. Let us assume that the assertion holds for $n - 1$, that is to say, $c(k_{n-1}, e) = \Pi_{n-1}$; we shall show that it holds then likewise for n. From T1n(1): $c(k_n, e) = c(k_{n-1}, e) \times c(h_n, e \cdot k_{n-1}) = \Pi_{n-1} \times c(h_n, e \cdot k_{n-1})$ (according to our assumption) $= \Pi_n$. 3. The assertion for every $n \geqq 2$ follows from (1) and (2) by mathematical induction.

b. For any $n \geqq 2$, $c(h_n, e) \geqq c(h_1, e) \times c(h_2, e \cdot h_1) \times c(h_3, e \cdot h_1 \cdot h_2) \times \ldots \times c(h_n, e \cdot h_1 \cdot h_2 \cdot \ldots \cdot h_{n-1})$. (From (a), T2e.)

The following theorem T5 is, like T58-1, on which it is based, restricted so as not to apply to general sentences in $\mathfrak{L}_\infty$.

T59-5. The subsequent assertions (a) to (f) hold under each of the following two assumptions:

(i) Let c be a regular c-function for $\mathfrak{L}_N$, and let e and h be any sentences in $\mathfrak{L}_N$ such that e is not L-false in $\mathfrak{L}_N$.

(ii) Let c be a regular c-function for $\mathfrak{L}_\infty$ (D56-2) corresponding to any fitting c-sequence (D57-5), and let e and h be any *nongeneral* sentences in $\mathfrak{L}_\infty$ such that e is not L-false in $\mathfrak{L}_\infty$. (Hence, e is not L-false in $\mathfrak{L}_N$ (T20-10b), and $c(h,e)$ has a value in $\mathfrak{L}_\infty$ which is the same as that in $\mathfrak{L}_N$ (T57-6c).)

The proofs refer to (i); then (ii) follows with T57-6c.

a. If not $\vdash e \supset h$, then $c(h,e) < 1$.

Proof. If not $\vdash e \supset h$, then not $\vdash e \supset e \cdot h$. However, $\vdash e \cdot h \supset e$; therefore $m(e \cdot h) < m(e)$ (T58-1g). Hence theorem (with T55-2a).

b. If $c(h,e) = 1$, then $\vdash e \supset h$. (From (a).)

c. If $c(h,e) = 0$, then $\vdash e \supset \sim h$, in other words, $e \cdot h$ is L-false, e and h are L-exclusive. (From T1p, (b).)

d. If $e \cdot h$ is not L-false (in other words, not $\vdash e \supset \sim h$), $c(h,e) > 0$. (From (c), T1a.)

e_1. If $c(h,e) = 0$, then $c(e,h) = 0$. (From (c), T1e.)

e_2. If $c(h,e) > 0$, then $c(e,h) > 0$. (From (e_1).)

e_3. If $c(h,e) = 1$, then $c(\sim e, \sim h) = 1$ and $c(e, \sim h) = 0$. (From (b), T1b, T1p.)

+f. Let h be not L-dependent upon e (i.e., neither $\vdash e \supset h$ nor $\vdash e \supset \sim h$); let r be an arbitrary real number such that $0 < r < 1$. Then there is a regular c (and, moreover, in general, an infinite number of them) such that $c(h,e) = r$.

Proof. Let j_1 be $\sim e$, j_2 be $e \cdot h$, j_3 be $e \cdot \sim h$. These three sentences are L-disjunct (i.e., $\vdash j_1 \vee j_2 \vee j_3$, D20-1e) and L-exclusive in pairs (D20-1g); hence every $\mathfrak{Z}$ belongs to exactly one of the three ranges. Under the conditions stated, j_2 and j_3 are not L-false. Let m be any regular m-function. Then $m(j_1) + m(j_2) + m(j_3) = 1$ (T57-1n and d). e is L-equivalent to $j_2 \vee j_3$, hence $m(e) = m(j_2) +$

$\mathfrak{m}(j_3)$ (T57-1a and $\mathfrak{m}$). Therefore (T55-2a) $\mathfrak{c}(h,e) = \mathfrak{m}(j_2)/\mathfrak{m}(e) = \mathfrak{m}(j_2)/\mathfrak{m}(j_2) + \mathfrak{m}(j_3)$. Now we distinguish two cases, I and II. I. Let j_1 be L-false. Then $\vdash e$, hence $\mathfrak{m}(e) = 1$. In this case, we choose any regular $\mathfrak{m}$ such that $\mathfrak{m}(j_2) = r$. (This is possible according to T58-1l.) Then $\mathfrak{c}(h,e) = r$. II. Let j_1 be not L-false. Then we choose any q such that $0 < q < 1$ and any regular $\mathfrak{m}$ such that $\mathfrak{m}(j_1) = q$, $\mathfrak{m}(j_2) = (1 - q)r$, and $\mathfrak{m}(j_3) = (1 - q)(1 - r)$. (An $\mathfrak{m}$ of this kind can easily be constructed; the sum of the three values just stated is 1; all we have to do is to divide each of the three values in an arbitrary way, e.g., in equal amounts, among the $\mathfrak{Z}$ of the range of the sentence in question.) Then $\mathfrak{c}(h,e) = (1 - q)r/((1 - q)r + (1 - q)(1 - r)) = r$.

T5b (part (ii), for $\mathfrak{L}_\infty$) is a restricted converse of T1b, likewise T5c of T1e. The reason for the restrictions is here, as in T58-1, the existence of almost L-true and almost L-false sentences. Let ${}_\infty\mathfrak{m}$ correspond to ${}_\infty\mathfrak{c}$ (i.e., be defined on the basis of the same $\mathfrak{m}$-sequence), and let i be almost L-true (with respect to ${}_\infty\mathfrak{m}$). Then i is general (T58-3d), and $\sim i$ is almost L-false. As we found earlier (in connection with T58-1), 't' almost L-implies i but not $\vdash t \supset i$. Nevertheless, ${}_\infty\mathfrak{c}(i,t) = 1$ (T56-4a), because ${}_\infty\mathfrak{m}(t) = 1$ and ${}_\infty\mathfrak{m}(t \,.\, i) = {}_\infty\mathfrak{m}(i) = 1$. Hence, T5a and b do not hold without restriction. Furthermore, since ${}_\infty\mathfrak{m}(\sim i) = 0$, ${}_\infty\mathfrak{c}(\sim i,t) = 0$, but not $\vdash t \supset \sim\sim i$. Thus, T5c and d must be restricted. In general (provided the $\mathfrak{m}$- and $\mathfrak{c}$-values involved exist), the following holds. If $\mathfrak{c}(h,e) = 1$, then e either L-implies or almost L-implies h; if $\mathfrak{c}(h,e) = 0$, then e either L-implies or almost L-implies $\sim h$.

The following example shows the necessity of the restriction not in terms of our technical concepts (regular $\mathfrak{m}$- and $\mathfrak{c}$-functions) but instead in terms of usual conceptions concerning the explicandum, viz., probability$_1$. Let e say that all individuals except two of a given infinite domain have the property M; and let h say that a certain individual b of which nothing is known except that it belongs to the given domain has the property M. [In our system $\mathfrak{L}_\infty$, e is '$(\exists x)(\exists y)\,[x \neq y \,.\, \sim Mx \,.\, \sim My \,.\, (z)(z \neq x \,.\, z \neq y \supset Mz)]$', and h is 'Mb'.] Then I think that most scientists who use a quantitative concept of probability$_1$ in cases of this kind would ascribe to h on the evidence e the probability$_1$ 1 and, consequently, to $\sim h$ the probability$_1$ 0. However, h is obviously not a logical consequence of e, since the individual b may be one of the two exceptions; and hence $\sim h$ is not logically incompatible with e. This shows that, with respect to an infinite domain of individuals, probability$_1$ 1 is not the same as certainty or necessity (in the sense of relative necessity with respect to evidence e, in other words, logical entailment by e), as has sometimes been assumed by earlier authors. Likewise, probability$_1$ 0 is not the same as impossibility (in the sense of relative impossibility, i.e., logical incompatibility). In both cases the inductive relation is wider than the deductive one. Most modern authors recognize this difference.

T5f corresponds to T58-1l. It shows that the class of regular c-functions does by no means comprehend only those functions which may be regarded as fairly adequate explicata for probability$_1$. On the contrary, this class comprehends also functions which, in any given case, deviate from a value which may appear as plausible to any extent in either direction. As an example, let *e* be a conjunction of one thousand different atomic sentences with the same predicate '*P*', and *h* be another atomic sentence with '*P*'. Thus, *e* reports that a thousand things have been observed and that all of them had the property *P;* and *h* predicts that a new thing will likewise be *P*. Now it is one of the characteristic features of inductive thinking that, on the evidence of a high relative frequency of a certain kind among a sufficient number of observed things, the probability$_1$ that the next thing will belong to the same kind is high. (This has earlier been discussed; see § 47A.) Thus a value of c(*h*,*e*) equal or close to 1 would appear as plausible to most scientists, while a considerably lower value, e.g., 1/2, would hardly seem acceptable to anyone. Now, at the present moment, we do not assert that c must be close to 1 in this case. We merely call attention to the fact that there are regular c-functions which have in this case any value however small (but still positive), e.g., one-millionth.

We shall see later (in § 62) that those modern theories of probability$_1$ which, in distinction to the classical theory, do not contain something similar to the principle of indifference state only such axioms and hence such theorems as hold for all regular c-functions. T5f shows that these systems do not effect a narrow selection of c-functions but admit, in addition to adequate concepts, also concepts which are entirely inadequate as explicata for probability$_1$. In a certain sense, we might even say that these systems hardly make any selection at all, inasmuch as they admit as basic m-function any distribution of arbitrary positive values with the total amount 1 among the $\mathfrak{Z}$. This is no objection against these theories; they are certainly correct as far as they go, because they state only those properties of c which any adequate explicatum of probability$_1$ must certainly have. Our result shows merely that these theories are very weak. And thus it shows too how far from our aim we still are in the present stage of our construction of a quantitative inductive logic; in other words, how much remains to be done in order to restrict the very comprehensive class of regular c-functions and finally to select one c-function as explicatum. Anticipating later discussions, it may be remarked that we shall reach the aim not by many small steps but by two big steps. The first step will consist in selecting a special kind of regular $\mathfrak{c}$-functions to be called the symmetrical $\mathfrak{c}$-functions (chap. viii). The second step will lead, by way of one additional requirement, to the function $\mathfrak{c}^*$ which will be proposed as explicatum (§ 110A).

The following theorems T6 deal with $\mathfrak{c}$-values 0 and 1. They are listed here for reference purposes only. They are chiefly of interest with respect to $\mathfrak{L}_\infty$, especially for general sentences. For any sentences in finite systems and for nongeneral sentences in $\mathfrak{L}_\infty$, the $\mathfrak{c}$-values 0 and 1 coincide with certain L-concepts, as we have seen (T5a, b, c, d); hence in this case the following theorems follow directly from simple theorems in deductive logic, e.g., T6a from the theorem 'If $e \cdot h$ is L-false, $e \cdot h \cdot i$ is L-false'. In $\mathfrak{L}_\infty$, however, $\mathfrak{c}(h,e)$ may be 0 while $e \cdot h$ is not L-false but only almost L-false; thus in this case the theorems are of interest. [Most of the theorems in T6 have been stated by Keynes ([Probab.], pp. 140–46); his proofs, however, are of little value because they hold only for finite systems, since he identifies probabilities 0 and 1 with the corresponding deductive concepts (see below, § 62).]

T59-6.

a. If $\mathfrak{c}(h,e) = 0$, $\mathfrak{c}(h \cdot i,e) = 0$. (From T2e.)

b. If $\mathfrak{c}(h,e) = 0$ and $\mathfrak{c}(i,e) > 0$, then $\mathfrak{c}(h,e \cdot i) = 0$.

Proof. $\mathfrak{c}(h \cdot i,e) = 0$ (from (a)), $= \mathfrak{c}(i,e) \times \mathfrak{c}(h,e \cdot i)$ (from T1n (2)). Since the first factor is not 0, the second must be 0.

c. If $\mathfrak{c}(h,e) = 1$ and $\mathfrak{c}(i,e) > 0$, then $\mathfrak{c}(h,e \cdot i) = 1$.

Proof. $\mathfrak{c}(\sim h,e) = 0$ (T1p). Hence $\mathfrak{c}(\sim h,e \cdot i) = 0$ (from (b)). Hence the assertion (T1p).

d. If $\mathfrak{c}(h,e) = 1$, then $\mathfrak{c}(h \cdot i,e) = \mathfrak{c}(i,e \cdot h) = \mathfrak{c}(i,e)$.

Proof. (1) Let $\mathfrak{c}(i,e) > 0$. $\mathfrak{c}(h \cdot i,e) = \mathfrak{c}(i,e) \times \mathfrak{c}(h,e \cdot i) = \mathfrak{c}(h,e) \times \mathfrak{c}(i,e \cdot h)$ (T1n). Since $\mathfrak{c}(h,e) = 1$, $\mathfrak{c}(h,e \cdot i) = 1$ (c); hence the assertion. (2) Let $\mathfrak{c}(i,e) = 0$. Then assertion from (a) and (b).

e. If $\mathfrak{c}(h \cdot i,e) = 1$, then $\mathfrak{c}(h,e) = 1$ and $\mathfrak{c}(i,e) = 1$. (From T2e.)

f. If $\mathfrak{c}(h_1 \supset h_2,e) = 1$, $\mathfrak{c}(h_1,e) \leqq \mathfrak{c}(h_2,e)$.

Proof. $1 = \mathfrak{c}(h_1 \supset h_2,e) = \mathfrak{c}(\sim h_1 \vee h_2,e) \leqq \mathfrak{c}(\sim h_1,e) + \mathfrak{c}(h_2,e)$ (from T2g), $= 1 - \mathfrak{c}(h_1,e) + \mathfrak{c}(h_2,e)$ (T1p). Hence $0 \leqq -\mathfrak{c}(h_1,e) + \mathfrak{c}(h_2,e)$. Hence the assertion.

g. If $\mathfrak{c}(h_1 \equiv h_2,e) = 1$, $\mathfrak{c}(h_1,e) = \mathfrak{c}(h_2,e)$.

Proof. $h_1 \equiv h_2$ is L-equivalent to $(h_1 \supset h_2) \cdot (h_2 \supset h_1)$. Therefore $\mathfrak{c}(h_1 \supset h_2,e) = 1$ and $\mathfrak{c}(h_2 \supset h_1,e) = 1$ (e). Hence assertion by (f).

h. If $c(h,e) = 1$, then (1) $c(i \vee h,e) = 1$. (From T2f.)
(2) $c(i \supset h,e) = 1$. (From (1).)

i. If $c(i \equiv j,e) = 1$, $c(i,e) > 0$, and $c(j,e) > 0$, then $c(h,e \cdot i) = c(h,e \cdot j)$.

Proof. T1n(2) yields these two equations: (1) $c(h \cdot i,e) = c(i,e) \times c(h,e \cdot i)$, (2) $c(h \cdot j,e) = c(j,e) \times c(h,e \cdot j)$. $c(h \supset (i \equiv j),e) = 1$ (from (h2)). Hence $c(h \cdot i \equiv h \cdot j,e) = 1$ (T21-5o). Hence the left-hand sides in (1) and (2) are equal (g). Therefore the right-hand sides are equal. Since the first factors are equal (g) and positive, the second factors are equal.

j. If $c(i \equiv j, e) = 1$, $c(i, e) > 0$, $c(j, e) > 0$, and $c(k, e) > 0$, then $c(i, e \cdot k) = c(j, e \cdot k)$.

Proof. T1n yields these two equations: (1) $c(k,e) \times c(i,e \cdot k) = c(i,e) \times c(k,e \cdot i)$, (2) $c(k,e) \times c(j,e \cdot k) = c(j,e) \times c(k,e \cdot j)$. On the right-hand sides the first factors are equal (g), and likewise the second factors (i). Therefore the right-hand sides are equal, and hence the left-hand sides. Hence the assertion, since $c(k,e)$ is positive.

k. If $c(h,e) = 0$ and $c(i,e) > 0$, then $c(h \cdot e,i) = 0$.

Proof. $c(h,e \cdot i) = 0$ (b). From T1n(2): $c(h \cdot e,i) = c(e,i) \times c(h,e \cdot i) = 0$.

l. If $c(h \cdot i,e) = 0$ and $c(i,e) > 0$, then $c(h,e \cdot i) = 0$. (From T1n(2).)

m. If $c(h,e) = 1$ and $c(i,e) > 0$, then $c(e \supset h,i) = 1$.

Proof. $c(\sim h,e) = 0$ (T1p). Hence $c(\sim h \cdot e,i) = 0$ (k). Hence $c(\sim(\sim h \cdot e),i) = 1$ (T1p). Hence the assertion (T21-5g(1)).

n. If $c(i \supset h,e) = 1$ and $c(i,e) > 0$, then $c(h,e \cdot i) = 1$.

Proof. $c(i \cdot \sim h,e) = 0$ (T21-5g(2), T1p). Therefore $c(\sim h,e \cdot i) = 0$ (l). Hence the assertion by T1p.

o. If $c(i \supset (h_1 \equiv h_2),e) = 1$ and $c(i,e) > 0$, then $c(h_1,e \cdot i) = c(h_2,e \cdot i)$. (From (n), (g).)

p. Let $c(h,i) = 1$ and $c(h,j) = 0$. Then
(1) either $c(i,j)$ or $c(j,i)$ is 0;
(2) if $c(e,i) > 0$ and $c(e,j) > 0$, $c(i \cdot j,e) = 0$.

Proof. (1). From T1n: $c(i,j) \times c(h,j \cdot i) = c(h,j) \times c(i,j \cdot h)$. Since $c(h,j) = 0$, the left-hand product is 0 and hence at least one of its factors is 0. Again from T1n: $c(j,i) \times c(\sim h,i \cdot j) = c(\sim h,i) \times c(j,\sim h \cdot i)$. $c(\sim h,i) = 0$ (T1p). Therefore the left-hand product is 0 and hence at least one of its factors is 0. Thus (1) holds, because otherwise $c(h,i \cdot j) = 0$ and simultaneously $c(\sim h,i \cdot j) = 0$, hence $c(h,i \cdot j) = 1$ (T1p), which is impossible. (2). From (1) by (k).

q. If $c(h,e) = 0$, $c(e,i) = 1$, and $c(i,e) > 0$, then $c(h,i) = 0$.

Proof. $c(h \cdot e,i) = 0$ (k). Therefore $c(h,i) \times c(e,i \cdot h) = 0$ (T1n(1)). Hence $c(h,i) = 0$, because otherwise $c(e,i \cdot h)$ would be 1 (c), which leads again to $c(h,i) = 0$.

r. If $\mathfrak{c}(h,e) = 0$, $\mathfrak{c}(h,\sim e) = 0$, $\mathfrak{c}(i,e) > 0$, and $\mathfrak{c}(i,\sim e) > 0$, then $\mathfrak{c}(h,i) = 0$.

Proof. $\mathfrak{c}(h \cdot e,i) = 0$ (k), and $\mathfrak{c}(h \cdot \sim e,i) = 0$ (k). $\mathfrak{c}(h,i)$ is the sum of these two $\mathfrak{c}$-values (T2a) and hence is 0.

s. If $\mathfrak{c}(h \vee i,e) = 0$, then $\mathfrak{c}(h,e) = 0$. (From T2f.)

t. If $\mathfrak{c}(h,e) = 0$ and $\mathfrak{c}(i,e) = 0$, then $\mathfrak{c}(h \vee i,e) = 0$. (From (a), T1k.)

u. If $\mathfrak{c}(h,e) = 0$, then $\mathfrak{c}(h \supset i,e) = 1$. (From (h(1)), with $\sim h$ for h, and T1p.)

v. If $\mathfrak{c}(h,e_1 \vee e_2) = 0$ and $\mathfrak{c}(e_1,e_1 \vee e_2) > 0$, then $\mathfrak{c}(h,e_1) = 0$.

Proof. $\mathfrak{c}(h \cdot (e_1 \vee e_2),e_1) = 0$ (k). Hence $\mathfrak{c}(h \cdot e_1,e_1) = 0$ (s). Hence the assertion by T2i.

w. If $\mathfrak{c}(h,e_1 \vee e_2) = 1$ and $\mathfrak{c}(e_1,e_1 \vee e_2) > 0$, then $\mathfrak{c}(h,e_1) = 1$. (From (v) with $\sim h$ for h, and T1p.)

x. If $\mathfrak{c}(h,e_1) = 0$ and $c(h,e_2) = 0$, then $\mathfrak{c}(h,e_1 \vee e_2) = 0$.

Proof. $\mathfrak{c}(h \cdot e_1,e_1 \vee e_2) = 0$ (k), since $\mathfrak{c}(e_1 \vee e_2,e_1) = 1$ (T1b), > 0. Analogously, $\mathfrak{c}(h \cdot e_2,e_1 \vee e_2) = 0$. Therefore $\mathfrak{c}(h \cdot (e_1 \vee e_2),e_1 \vee e_2) = 0$ (from (t), T21-5m(1)). Hence assertion by T2i.

y. If $\mathfrak{c}(h,e_1) = 1$ and $\mathfrak{c}(h,e_2) = 1$, then $\mathfrak{c}(h,e_1 \vee e_2) = 1$. (From (x) with $\sim h$ for h, and T1p.)

§ 60. Confirmation of Hypotheses by Observations: Bayes's Theorem

This section deals with the following situation. e formulates our present knowledge, say, a report on results of earlier observations. h is a hypothesis. i is a prediction of a future observation, which, if we hypothetically assume h, has a certain probability$_1$ (i.e., $\mathfrak{c}(i,e \cdot h)$), which we call the likelihood of i. $\mathfrak{c}(h,e)$ is called the prior confirmation of h, $\mathfrak{c}(h,e \cdot i)$ its posterior confirmation. The question is raised: how much is the confirmation of h increased when the observation predicted by i actually occurs? The answer is given by the *general division theorem* (T1c and d): the ratio of increase of the confirmation of h (i.e., the posterior confirmation divided by the prior confirmation) is equal to the likelihood of i divided by $\mathfrak{c}(i,e)$. *Bayes's theorem* (T6) applies this result to the case of n competing hypotheses of which it is known that one and only one of them holds. Bayes's theorem has often been criticized, and it must be admitted that some formulations of it and many applications of it (using the principle of indifference) are objectionable. However, there can hardly be any doubts as to its validity (if formulated correctly), since it is founded on assumptions which seem accepted by all quantitative theories of probability$_1$. The question whether and how the theorem can be applied for the actual computation of a posterior confirmation will be dealt with in a later chapter.

The theorems of this section are formulated in a general way, with respect to any sentences. However, they are especially important for practical application in situations of the following kind. Let e be a formulation of the evidence available to the observer X at the present moment, say, a report about the observations made by X. h is a hypothesis concerning things not known to X; in other words, neither h nor $\sim h$ follows from e. Moreover, h is not simply a prediction of some future directly observable events. Thus X does not expect to acquire complete knowledge about h in the future; all he hopes for is to find some evidence which might give indirect and partial confirmation for h. And, in particular, there is a sentence i formulating a future observable event which is connected with h in such a manner that either it follows from $e \cdot h$ or at least seems probable to a certain degree if h is assumed together with e. We call $\mathfrak{c}(h,e)$, i.e., the confirmation of h before the new observation formulated by i is made, the ***prior confirmation*** of h; and its confirmation after the observation i, i.e., $\mathfrak{c}(h,e \cdot i)$, the ***posterior confirmation*** of h. [Note that 'prior confirmation' does not mean a priori confirmation or null confirmation, i.e., $\mathfrak{c}(h,t)$; in general, e is factual and may contain information relevant for h, e.g., the results of earlier observations similar to i; 'prior' means merely 'prior to the new observation in question'.] We are chiefly interested in determining the posterior confirmation of h and its relation to the prior confirmation, in particular, whether the confirmation of h is increased when the observation i is made. If it is increased, we shall say later that i is *positively relevant* to h on the evidence e (D65-1a); the problems of positive and negative relevance and irrelevance will be studied in detail in the next chapter. As mentioned above, we suppose that i has a certain connection with h such that if X assumes h hypothetically together with e, then he is in a position to predict i with a certain probability or even with certainty. We call this probability, i.e., $\mathfrak{c}(i,e \cdot h)$, the ***likelihood*** of the observation i (with respect to the hypothesis h and the evidence e). $\mathfrak{c}(i,e)$, the probability of i on e alone, without regard to the hypothesis h, will be called the ***expectedness*** of the observation i. In this section the problem is discussed in a general way for any value of the likelihood. The next section will deal with the special case that the likelihood is 1, that is, where the observation i can be predicted with certainty (or almost certainty) with the help of h.

The terms 'prior confirmation' and 'posterior confirmation' are adaptations of Jeffreys' terms 'prior probability' and 'posterior probability'. The term 'likelihood' is likewise taken from Jeffreys, who uses it in the sense explained above; it was earlier introduced by R. A. Fisher in a related but somewhat different sense (in [Foundations]). The term 'expectedness' was suggested to me by Herbert Bohnert.

Examples. 1. Let the evidence e of the observer X include the statement that the weather today is of the kind M. i is a forecast of the weather situation M' for tomorrow. h is a meteorological law saying that a weather situation M is in 70 per cent of the cases followed by one of the kind M' on the next day. Suppose that, for a given c-function, the likelihood of i is 0.7. (This value would result, e.g., for all symmetrical c-functions, as we shall find later; see T94-1e.) The problem is: How will the confirmation of h increase if X observes tomorrow that the expected weather M' actually occurs? If h is not a merely statistical law but a deterministic law saying that M is always followed by M', then we have the special case of the likelihood 1. 2. h is the assumption, so far not sufficiently tested by X, that a person Y has a certain disease D. e contains reports about earlier occurrences of this disease and its correlation with certain symptoms and, in addition, a report about a few, inconclusive symptoms observed by X in Y's case. X intends to make a blood test; i formulates the positive result of this test, i.e., the one which would be expected as probable if Y were known to have the disease D. The probability of this expected result is what we call the likelihood of i.

The theorems of this section hold both for finite and for infinite systems under the conditions (A), (B), and (C) stated at the beginning of § 59. In these theorems, c-expressions occur frequently as denominators or as factors in a denominator; it is to be noted that, according to (C), the theorems in question presuppose that those c-expressions have positive values.

Our question as to the posterior confirmation and its relation to the prior confirmation is answered by the *general division theorem* T1c, which was already known in the classical theory of probability; it leads to Bayes's Theorem to be stated later (T6). We see from this theorem T1c that the posterior confirmation of the hypothesis h is (i) proportional to the prior confirmation of h, (ii) proportional to the likelihood of the observation i, (iii) inversely proportional to the expectedness of the observation i; this means that, the more surprising the new observation i is, in other words, the less X could expect it on the basis of his prior evidence e, the more does its occurrence increase the confirmation of the hypothesis h. In the example (2) above, this means that, if the result i of the blood test is known to X to occur very seldom in the population in general and hence its occurrence in the case of Y has a low expectedness, then its actual occurrence in this case strengthens the c of h considerably.

From T1c, T1d follows immediately. It concerns the quotient of the posterior and the prior confirmation; in other words, the ratio of increase of the confirmation of h because of the addition of the new observation i to X's knowledge. This will later be called the *relevance quotient* of i for

h on e (§ 66). T1d says that this relevance quotient is equal to that of h for i on e, i.e., the ratio in which the confirmation of i would be increased by the addition of h to the knowledge e.

T60-1.

a. $\mathfrak{c}(i,e \,.\, h) = \frac{\mathfrak{c}(h \,.\, i,e)}{\mathfrak{c}(h,e)}$. (From T59-1n (1).)

b. $\mathfrak{c}(h,e) \times \mathfrak{c}(i,e \,.\, h) = \mathfrak{c}(i,e) \times \mathfrak{c}(h,e \,.\, i)$. (From T59-1n.)

+**c.** *General Division Theorem*
$\mathfrak{c}(h,e \,.\, i) = \frac{\mathfrak{c}(h,e) \times \mathfrak{c}(i,e \,.\, h)}{\mathfrak{c}(i,e)}$. (From (b).)

+**d.** $\frac{\mathfrak{c}(h,e \,.\, i)}{\mathfrak{c}(h,e)} = \frac{\mathfrak{c}(i,e \,.\, h)}{\mathfrak{c}(i,e)}$. (From (c).)

e. $\mathfrak{c}(i,e \,.\, h) = \frac{\mathfrak{c}(h \,.\, i,e)}{\mathfrak{c}(h \,.\, i,e) + \mathfrak{c}(h \,.\, \sim i,e)}$. (From (a), T59-2a.)

The following theorem T2 deals with the *comparison of two hypotheses* h_1 and h_2, both of which make the expected observation i probable. Since the expectedness $\mathfrak{c}(i,e)$ is the same, independently of the hypotheses, the general division theorem (T1c) leads here to the result (T2b) that, in order to find a comparison of the posterior confirmations of the two hypotheses, we need only compare the first two of the three factors mentioned earlier, viz., (i) the prior confirmation of the hypotheses, and (ii) the likelihood of i for each of the hypotheses. Consequently, if the hypotheses had approximately the same prior confirmation, but the observation i is considerably more probable on the assumption of h_1 than on that of h_2, then the posterior confirmation of h_1 will be considerably higher than that of h_2. [In the example (2) above, suppose that, before the blood test, two diseases D_1 and D_2 come into consideration with about equal prior confirmation; and that the likelihood of the result i, if it is assumed that the patient has D_1, is five times as strong as if D_2 is assumed; then, after i is observed, the confirmation of D_1 is about five times as high as that of D_2.]

T60-2.

a. (Lemma.) $\mathfrak{c}(h_1,e) \times \mathfrak{c}(i,e \,.\, h_1) \times \mathfrak{c}(h_2,e \,.\, i) = \mathfrak{c}(h_1,e \,.\, i) \times \mathfrak{c}(h_2,e) \times \mathfrak{c}(i,e \,.\, h_2)$. (From T1b.)

b. $\frac{\mathfrak{c}(h_1,e \,.\, i)}{\mathfrak{c}(h_2,e \,.\, i)} = \frac{\mathfrak{c}(h_1,e) \times \mathfrak{c}(i,e \,.\, h_1)}{\mathfrak{c}(h_2,e) \times \mathfrak{c}(i,e \,.\, h_2)}$. (From (a).)

In the following theorem T3, the effects of *two observations* i_1 and i_2 on the confirmation of the same hypothesis h are compared. Since $\mathfrak{c}(h,e)$ is the same in both cases, only the influence of the last two of the three factors earlier mentioned is different: (ii) the likelihood of i_1 or i_2, respectively, and (iii) the expectedness of i_1 or i_2, respectively. (T3a is essentially the same as T2a, only with different letters.) [In the example of the medical diagnosis, this theorem is applicable if X has to choose between two different tests T_1 and T_2; in the first test the result i_1 would confirm the assumption that the patient has the disease *D;* in the second test, the result i_2 would confirm the same assumption. Before *X* makes the tests, he wants to know which of the two results would lead to a higher posterior confirmation of his assumption; perhaps he prefers that test whose positive result would give him more certainty. T3b gives the answer. This theorem would lead *X* to the following decisions. (1) If the two test results have about equal expectedness (i.e., probability before the tests), then *X* chooses the test whose positive result has higher likelihood, i.e., is known to occur more frequently in cases of the disease *D*. (2) If the two test results have about equal likelihood, then *X* chooses the test whose positive result has a lower expectedness, i.e., is known to him to occur less frequently in the population in general. Incidentally, in our discussion of these examples, we have assumed that, the higher the observed relative frequency of a property, the higher is the confirmation of a future instance of this property. This is a customary feature of inductive thinking (cf. § 48B). In our inductive logic this result will appear much later, in the theory of the predictive inference (§ 110C).]

T60-3.

a. (Lemma.) $\mathfrak{c}(i_1,e) \times \mathfrak{c}(h,e \,.\, i_1) \times \mathfrak{c}(i_2,e \,.\, h) = \mathfrak{c}(i_1,e \,.\, h) \times \mathfrak{c}(i_2,e) \times \mathfrak{c}(h,e \,.\, i_2)$. (From T2a.)

b. $\frac{\mathfrak{c}(h,e \,.\, i_1)}{\mathfrak{c}(h,e \,.\, i_2)} = \frac{\mathfrak{c}(i_1,e \,.\, h)}{\mathfrak{c}(i_2,e \,.\, h)} \times \frac{\mathfrak{c}(i_2,e)}{\mathfrak{c}(i_1,e)}$. (From (a).)

The following theorems T5 and T6 apply the general division theorem (T1c) to the case of *several competing hypotheses*. T5 deals with the case of two competitive hypotheses, for instance, two contradictory hypotheses *h* and $\sim h$; T6 concerns the general case of *n* hypotheses of which it is known (either logically, or by the evidence *e*, or at least after the observation *i*, i.e., by $e \,.\, i$) that one and only one of them holds; but it is not known which one holds. T6, together with other related theorems, sometimes also T5, bears traditionally the name of *Bayes's Theorem*. The theorem which Thomas Bayes [Essay] actually stated and proved may be interpreted as a special case of T6b concerning the inverse inductive inference; this will be discussed later (in Vol. II).

T60-5. Let $\mathfrak{c}(i,e) \neq 0$. Let $\mathfrak{c}(h_1,e \,.\, i) + \mathfrak{c}(h_2,e \,.\, i) = 1$. (This condition is fulfilled if h_2 is $\sim h_1$.)

a. $\mathfrak{c}(h_1,e \,.\, i) = \frac{\mathfrak{c}(h_1,e) \times \mathfrak{c}(i,e \,.\, h_1)}{\mathfrak{c}(h_1,e) \times \mathfrak{c}(i,e \,.\, h_1) + \mathfrak{c}(h_2,e) \times \mathfrak{c}(i,e \,.\, h_2)}$.

Proof. We replace in T2a '$\mathfrak{c}(h_2,e \,.\, i)$' by '$1 - \mathfrak{c}(h_1,e \,.\, i)$' and multiply out.

b. Let $\mathfrak{c}(h_1,e) = \mathfrak{c}(h_2,e)$.
Then $\mathfrak{c}(h_1,e \,.\, i) = \frac{\mathfrak{c}(i,e \,.\, h_1)}{\mathfrak{c}(i,e \,.\, h_1) + \mathfrak{c}(i,e \,.\, h_2)}$. (From (a).)

+**T60-6.** ***Bayes's Theorem.*** Let $\mathfrak{c}(i,e) > 0$. Let $h_1, h_2, \ldots, h_n$ ($n \geqq 2$) be such that (1) $\vdash e \,.\, i \supset h_1 \vee h_2 \vee \ldots \vee h_n$, and (2) the sentences $e \,.\, i \,.\, h_1$, $e \,.\, i \,.\, h_2, \ldots, e \,.\, i \,.\, h_n$ are L-exclusive in pairs (D20-1g). Let h be any one of the n h-sentences.

a. (1) $\mathfrak{c}(h,e \,.\, i) = \dfrac{\mathfrak{c}(i \,.\, h,e)}{\sum\limits_{p=1}^{n} \mathfrak{c}(i \,.\, h_p,e)}$. (From T1c, T59-3a(1).)

(2) $\phantom{\mathfrak{c}(h,e \,.\, i)} = \dfrac{\mathfrak{c}(h,e) \times \mathfrak{c}(i,e \,.\, h)}{\sum\limits_{p=1}^{n} [\mathfrak{c}(h_p,e) \times \mathfrak{c}(i,e \,.\, h_p)]}$. (From (1), T59-1n(2).)

b. Let $\mathfrak{c}(h_p,e)$ have the same value for every p (from 1 to n). Then $\mathfrak{c}(h,e \,.\, i) = \dfrac{\mathfrak{c}(i,e \,.\, h)}{\sum\limits_{p=1}^{n} \mathfrak{c}(i,e \,.\, h_p)}$. (From (a)(2).)

T6 refers to n hypotheses $h_1, \ldots, h_n$. The evidence $e \,.\, i$ shows (1) that at least one of them holds (they may, e.g., be L-disjunct), and (2) that at most one of them holds (they may, e.g., be L-exclusive in pairs, D20-1g). For h_p ($p = 1$ to n), let $\mathfrak{c}(h_p,e) \times \mathfrak{c}(i,e \,.\, h_p)$, i.e., the product of the prior confirmation of h_p and the likelihood of i, have the value r_p. Then we know from the general division theorem (T1c) that the posterior confirmation of h_p is proportional to r_p; now, Bayes's theorem T6a says that the posterior confirmation is $r_p/\Sigma r_p$.

T6b concerns the special case where the prior confirmations for all n hypotheses are equal. Thus here, of the three factors influencing the posterior confirmation of a hypothesis, only the likelihood is different for the various hypotheses; and T6b says that the posterior confirmation of h_p is simply the likelihood of i with respect to h_p divided by the sum of the likelihoods of i with respect to all n hypotheses.

Objections have frequently been raised against Bayes's theorem and many applications of it. It must be admitted, I think, that the customary formulations in the classical period, beginning with Bayes's own formulation, contain an obscure point (e.g., phrases like 'the chance that the probability of the event lies in a certain interval'). It seems to me that this obscurity is chiefly due to a confusion of probability$_1$ with probability$_2$. Further, the theorem has sometimes (not by Bayes himself) been applied to cases where it led to strange or even absurd results. This was mostly due to an uncritical use of the principle of indifference. These mistakes give no reasons for objections against a formulation like our T6a. This theorem is provable on the basis of our definition of regular c-functions, and hence likewise on the basis of those weak assumptions which practically all theories of probability$_1$ seem to have in common.

Therefore for anybody who accepts at all any of these theories, there can be no doubt concerning the validity of Bayes's theorem in the form T6a. The question as to its usefulness is not so easy to answer. First, this theorem—like all theorems in this chapter except those which state a c-value 0 or 1—does not enable us actually to compute the c for any given pair of sentences but says merely how some c-values are connected with other c-values. In order to apply any of the theorems, we must already know some c-values. How do we find the first ones? In the classical theory this was done with the help of the principle of indifference. However, since this principle leads to contradictions, we have to give it up. Those modern axiom systems for probability$_1$ which dispense with this principle give no means to compute any c-value (except 0 or 1). Our later construction of inductive logic will have the task to furnish other, consistent rules by which to compute c-values. At the present stage of our discussion, the situation with respect to Bayes's theorem is not worse than for the other theorems; it is just as valid as the other ones, and the other ones are just as inapplicable as this one.

It has often been said that Bayes's theorem is essentially different from the other theorems (those given by us in § 59), that it is of little use or even of no use because its application by an observer X requires that he knows, for each one of the n hypotheses, not only the likelihood of i but also the prior confirmation of h; to find the latter is regarded as more difficult or even as impossible in many or in all cases. If we take the theorem in the general form given above, there is no essential difference between the two c-values. However, with respect to the problem of the inverse inductive inference, for which the theorem has mostly been used since Bayes, there is a certain core of truth in the view mentioned. Let e say that a certain population (e.g., the inhabitants of a certain town or the balls in a certain urn) consists of 1,000 individuals; let i say that in a certain sample of 10 individuals of this population 8 have the property M (black-haired persons, black balls); let h_p (p = 8 to 998) say that the whole population contains p individuals with the property M. The task of finding $c(i,e \cdot h)$ would be a case of the direct inductive inference; the determination of $c(h,e \cdot i)$ would be an inverse inductive inference (§ 44B).

Bayes's theorem is usually applied for the second purpose. We see from T6a that the solution of this second task requires (1) the knowledge of $c(i,e \cdot h)$ and hence the solution of the first task, and (2) the knowledge of $c(h,e)$, that is, the prior confirmation for all possible frequencies in the population before we observe the sample. Both tasks require new rules in addition to those available in this chapter and in the consistent theories of probability$_1$ known today. We shall see later that the solution of the first problem requires only a rather weak and very plausible additional rule, which has been used implicitly by many authors, to the effect that c is symmetrical (chap. viii). For the second problem, on the other hand, a much stronger additional rule is needed. The latter rule is so strong that it makes our system of quantitative inductive logic complete; it leads to the definition of c* (§ 110A).

§ 61. Confirmation of a Hypothesis by a Predictable Observation

This section deals with a special case of the situation discussed in the preceding section, the case where *the likelihood* $c(i,e \cdot h)$ *is* 1, in other words, $e \cdot h$ L-implies (or almost L-implies) i. We express this condition also by saying that the observation i is *predictable* under the hypothetical assumption of h, or that h is a suitable hypothesis for the explanation of i. The most important of the theorems holding for this case is the *special division theorem* (T3b and c) which says that the ratio of increase of the c of h in consequence of the observation i is the reciprocal of the expectedness of i (i.e., $1/c(i,e)$). Thus, for different hypotheses explaining i, the ratio of the increase of c is the same (T6f).

This section deals with an important special case of the situation discussed in the preceding section, viz., the case that $c(i,e \cdot h)$, the likelihood of the observation i, is 1.

In order to clarify the meaning of this condition, let us use two customary phrases of the word language (not in our technical terminology, but only in the informal discussion in this section and in similar discussions later). A certain relation between a hypothesis h and an observation i (on the basis of given evidence e) may be expressed by saying: 'i is *predictable* under the hypothetical assumption of h (together with e)' or 'h is a hypothesis capable of *explaining* i (on the evidence e)'. The first phrase seems more natural at a time before the observation i is made, the second seems more natural afterward; however, the logical relation between the three sentences which the phrases describe is of course independent of the time point from which we look at the situation; therefore we may take the two phrases as synonymous. Strictly speaking, however, each of the phrases may be understood either in a strong sense or in a slightly weaker sense. They may either be taken as describing the deductive relation that $e \cdot h$ L-implies i, or as describing the inductive relation that $c(i,e \cdot h) = 1$. For $\mathfrak{L}_N$, the two relations coincide (T59-1b, T59-5b). For $\mathfrak{L}_\infty$, however, the latter relation is slightly weaker, because it holds not only if $e \cdot h$ L-implies i but also if $e \cdot h$ almost L-implies i. Thus we have to distinguish between predictability (or explanation) in the strong deductive sense and in the weaker inductive sense. The latter sense is meant in the condition assumed in this section. If i is predictable in the stronger deductive sense, the theorems of this section hold likewise.

For the examples (1) and (2), this special case has already been explained in § 60. If the meteorological law h in example (1) is deterministic, the likelihood of i becomes 1. In example (2), the likelihood of i is 1, if the assumption h of the disease D makes the result i of the blood test certain or almost certain.

Many theorems in this section (but in a weaker version, with the stronger deductive condition that $\vdash e \cdot h \supset i$) have been stated by Janina Hosiasson (see below, § 62).

T61-1. Let $\mathfrak{c}(i, e \cdot h) = 1$. Then the following holds.

a. $\mathfrak{c}(h \cdot i, e) = \mathfrak{c}(h, e)$. (From T59-1n.)

b. $\mathfrak{c}(i, e) = \mathfrak{c}(h, e) + \mathfrak{c}(i \cdot \sim h, e)$. (From T59-2a.)

c. $\mathfrak{c}(i, e) = \mathfrak{c}(h, e) + \mathfrak{c}(\sim h, e) \times \mathfrak{c}(i, e \cdot \sim h)$. (From (b), T59-1n.)

d. Let the sentences $h, h_1, h_2, \ldots, h_n$ fulfil the following two conditions: (1) $\vdash e \cdot i \supset h \vee h_1 \vee h_2 \vee \ldots \vee h_n$ (this condition is always fulfilled if the h-sentences are L-disjunct); (2) the sentences $e \cdot i \cdot h$, $e \cdot i \cdot h_1$, $e \cdot i \cdot h_2, \ldots, e \cdot i \cdot h_n$ are L-exclusive in pairs (this condition is always fulfilled if the h-sentences are L-exclusive in pairs). Then

$$\mathfrak{c}(i, e) = \mathfrak{c}(h, e) + \sum_{p=1}^{n} [\mathfrak{c}(h_p, e) \times \mathfrak{c}(i, e \cdot h_p)].$$

Proof. From (1): $\vdash e \cdot i \cdot \sim h \supset h_1 \vee h_2 \vee \ldots \vee h_n$ (T21-5h(7)). From (2): for every p (from 1 to n), $e \cdot i \cdot h_p \cdot h$ is L-false, hence $\vdash h_p \cdot e \cdot i \supset \sim h$, hence $\vdash h_p \supset (e \cdot i \supset \sim h)$ (T21-5k(1)); therefore, $\vdash h_1 \vee \ldots \vee h_n \supset (e \cdot i \supset \sim h)$ (T21-5n(4)), hence $\vdash e \cdot i \cdot (h_1 \vee \ldots \vee h_n) \supset \sim h$ (T21-5k(1)). Therefore, $e \cdot i \cdot \sim h$ is L-equivalent to $e \cdot i \cdot (h_1 \vee \ldots \vee h_n)$ and hence, by distribution, to $e \cdot [(i \cdot h_1) \vee \ldots \vee (i \cdot h_n)]$. Therefore $\mathfrak{c}(i \cdot \sim h, e) = \mathfrak{c}((i \cdot h_1) \vee \ldots \vee (i \cdot h_n), e)$ (T59-2j), $= \sum_{p=1}^{n} \mathfrak{c}(i \cdot h_p, e)$ (T59-1m), $= \sum_{p=1}^{n} [\mathfrak{c}(h_p, e) \times \mathfrak{c}(i, e \cdot h_p)]$ (T59-1n (2).) Hence theorem with (b).

e. $e \cdot h$ either L-implies or almost L-implies i.

Proof. If in T59-6m 'i' is taken for 'h', '$e \cdot h$' for 'e', and 't' for 'i', the conditions in the theorem are fulfilled. Hence $\mathfrak{c}(e \cdot h \supset i, t) = 1$, $= \mathfrak{m}(e \cdot h \supset i)$ (T57-3). Therefore $e \cdot h \supset i$ is either L-true or almost L-true (D58-1a). Hence the assertion (D58-1c).

T61-2. Let $\mathfrak{c}(h_2, e \cdot h_1) = \mathfrak{c}(h_1, e \cdot h_2) = 1$.

a. $e \cdot h_1$ and $e \cdot h_2$ are either L-equivalent or almost L-equivalent.

Proof. $\mathfrak{m}$ has the value 1 for the following sentences: $e \cdot h_1 \supset h_2$ (see proof of T1e), $e \cdot h_1 \supset e \cdot h_2$, $e \cdot h_2 \supset e \cdot h_1$ (analogously). Hence the assertion (T58-3c).

b. $\mathfrak{c}(h_1, e) = \mathfrak{c}(h_2, e)$. (From T1a, T59-1i.)

In the following theorem T3, especially the items (b) and (c) are important. Since we assume now that the likelihood of the observation *i* is 1, only the first and third of the three factors influencing the posterior confirmation of *h* remain. Thus, the general division theorem (T60-1c) leads here to the special division theorem T3b, and further to T3c. The latter says that the ratio of the increase of the c of *h* by the observation *i* is simply the reciprocal of the expectedness of this observation. This means the following. Before *X* makes the observation *i*, he can compute its expectedness, i.e., its c with respect to the available evidence, without regard to any hypothesis. As an example, let us assume that the expectedness of *i* is 1/10. Suppose now that *X* actually makes the observation *i* so that his evidence increases from *e* to *e* . *i*. Then T3c says this: if *h* is any hypothesis which would explain the observation *i*—in the sense that *e* . *h* L-implies or almost L-implies *i*—then the c of *h* grows by the observation *i* to ten times its prior value. There are of course many different hypotheses each of which is capable of explaining *i* in the sense indicated; some of them are strong, others weak; for some the prior c is very low, for others not quite so low (it cannot be higher than 0.1); irrespective of these differences, the c of each of these hypotheses grows, when *X* makes the new observation *i*, to ten times its prior value (cf. T6f below).

T61-3. Let $\mathfrak{c}(i,e \cdot h) = 1$. Then the following holds.

a. $\mathfrak{c}(h,e) = \mathfrak{c}(i,e) \times \mathfrak{c}(h,e \cdot i)$. (From T60-1b.)

+b. *Special Division Theorem.*
$\mathfrak{c}(h,e \cdot i) = \frac{\mathfrak{c}(h,e)}{\mathfrak{c}(i,e)}$. (From (a).)

+c. $\frac{\mathfrak{c}(h,e \cdot i)}{\mathfrak{c}(h,e)} = \frac{1}{\mathfrak{c}(i,e)}$. (From (b).)

d. (Lemma for T7.) $\mathfrak{c}(h,e \cdot i) - \mathfrak{c}(h,e) = \mathfrak{c}(h,e)\left(\frac{1}{\mathfrak{c}(i,e)} - 1\right)$. (From (b).)

e. $\mathfrak{c}(h,e \cdot i) \geqq \mathfrak{c}(h,e)$. (From (a), T59-1a.)

f. If $\mathfrak{c}(i,e) = 1$, then $\mathfrak{c}(h,e \cdot i) = \mathfrak{c}(h,e)$. (From (a).)

g. If $\mathfrak{c}(h,e \cdot i) = \mathfrak{c}(h,e) > 0$, then $\mathfrak{c}(i,e) = 1$. (From (a).) (This is a restricted converse of (f).)

h. If $\mathfrak{c}(h,e \cdot i) > \mathfrak{c}(h,e)$, then $\mathfrak{c}(i,e) < 1$. (From (a).)

i. Let $\mathfrak{c}(h,e \cdot i) > 0$. If $\mathfrak{c}(i,e) < 1$, then $\mathfrak{c}(h,e \cdot i) > \mathfrak{c}(h,e)$. (From (a).) (This is a restricted converse of (h).)

k. If $\mathfrak{c}(h,e) = 1$, then likewise $\mathfrak{c}(h,e \cdot i) = 1$. (From (e), T59-1a.)

l. (For $\mathfrak{L}_\infty$, let $\mathfrak{c}(i,e) > 0$.) If $\mathfrak{c}(h,e) = 0$, then likewise $\mathfrak{c}(h,e \cdot i) = 0$. (From (a).) [For $\mathfrak{L}_N$, the restricting condition need not be stated, because, according to assumption (A), *e* . *i* is not L-false, and hence the condition is fulfilled (T59-3d).]

T3e says that the confirmation of *h* cannot decrease by the observation *i* but either remains the same or increases. T3f to i deal with the latter two cases separately. They say roughly this: the confirmation of h remains the same if and only if the expectedness of the observation i is 1, i.e., if this observation was certain or almost certain beforehand; the confirmation of h increases if and only if the expectedness of i is <1, i.e., if i was not certain beforehand but represents a new fact. T3k and l say that, if the prior confirmation of h has one of the extreme values 1 or 0, then it remains unchanged by i.

The following theorem deals with the *comparison of two observations* i_1 and i_2, which are predictable by the same hypothesis h.

T61-5. Let $c(i_1,e\,.\,h) = c(i_2,e\,.\,h) = 1$. (For $\mathfrak{L}_N$, this means that $e\,.\,h$ L-implies both i_1 and i_2.)

a. (Lemma.) $c(i_1,e) \times c(h,e\,.\,i_1) = c(i_2,e) \times c(h,e\,.\,i_2)$. (From T60-3a.)

b. $\frac{c(h,e\,.\,i_1)}{c(h,e\,.\,i_2)} = \frac{c(i_2,e)}{c(i_1,e)}$. (From (a).)

c. Let $c(i_1,e) > 0$. If $c(h,e\,.\,i_1) < c(h,e\,.\,i_2)$, then $c(i_1,e) > c(i_2,e)$.

Proof. If the two conditions are fulfilled, the two denominators in (b) are positive. Hence theorem from (b).

d. Let $c(h,e\,.\,i_2) > 0$. If $c(i_1,e) > c(i_2,e)$, then $c(h,e\,.\,i_1) < c(h,e\,.\,i_2)$. (From (b), like (c).)

e. If $c(h,e\,.\,i_1) = c(h,e\,.\,i_2) > 0$, then $c(i_1,e) = c(i_2,e)$. (From (a).)

f. If $c(i_1,e) = c(i_2,e) > 0$, then $c(h,e\,.\,i_1) = c(h,e\,.\,i_2)$. (From (a).)

The following theorems T6 and T7 concern *two hypotheses* h_1 and h_2, each of which explains the observation i in the sense of giving to it, together with the evidence e, the confirmation 1.

T61-6. Let $c(i,e\,.\,h_1) = c(i,e\,.\,h_2) = 1$. (For $\mathfrak{L}_N$, this means that both $e\,.\,h_1$ and $e\,.\,h_2$ L-imply i.)

a. (Lemma.) $c(h_1,e) \times c(h_2,e\,.\,i) = c(h_1,e\,.\,i) \times c(h_2,e)$. (From T60-2a.)

b. $\frac{c(h_1,e\,.\,i)}{c(h_2,e\,.\,i)} = \frac{c(h_1,e)}{c(h_2,e)}$. (From (a).)

c. Let $c(h_2,e) > 0$. (Hence, likewise $c(h_2,e\,.\,i) > 0$, T3e.) $c(h_1,e\,.\,i) < c(h_2,e\,.\,i)$ if and only if $c(h_1,e) < c(h_2,e)$. (From (b), like T5c.)

d. If $c(h_1,e\,.\,i) = c(h_2,e\,.\,i) > 0$, then $c(h_1,e) = c(h_2,e)$. (From (a).)

e. If $c(h_1,e) = c(h_2,e) > 0$, then $c(h_1,e\,.\,i) = c(h_2,e\,.\,i)$. (From (a).)

f. $\frac{c(h_1,e\,.\,i)}{c(h_1,e)} = \frac{c(h_2,e\,.\,i)}{c(h_2,e)}$. (From (a).)

T7 differs from T6 by the additional assumption that the expectedness of i is neither 0 nor 1. For $\mathfrak{L}_N$, this means that i is not L-dependent upon e, i.e., that e L-implies neither i nor $\sim i$. In the situation earlier discussed, it was assumed that i describes a possible new observation; in this case, the condition mentioned is obviously fulfilled.

T61-7. Let $\mathfrak{c}(i,e \cdot h_1) = \mathfrak{c}(i,e \cdot h_2) = 1$, and $0 < \mathfrak{c}(i,e) < 1$. We write '$D_1$' as short for '$\mathfrak{c}(h_1,e \cdot i) - \mathfrak{c}(h_1,e)$' and '$D_2$' for '$\mathfrak{c}(h_2,e \cdot i) - \mathfrak{c}(h_2,e)$'.

a. $\mathfrak{c}(h_1,e)$, $\mathfrak{c}(h_1,e \cdot i)$, and D_1 are either all three positive or all three 0. Likewise with $\mathfrak{c}(h_2,e)$, $\mathfrak{c}(h_2,e \cdot i)$, and D_2.

b. If $\mathfrak{c}(h_2,e) \geqq \mathfrak{c}(h_1,e)$, then $D_2 \geqq D_1$.

c. If $\mathfrak{c}(h_2,e) > \mathfrak{c}(h_1,e)$, then $D_2 > D_1$.

d. If $\mathfrak{c}(h_2,e) = \mathfrak{c}(h_1,e)$, then $D_2 = D_1$.

Proof for (a), (b), (c), (d). Since $\mathfrak{c}(i,e) > 0$, T3d can be applied. Accordingly, $D_1 = \mathfrak{c}(h_1,e)\left(\frac{1}{\mathfrak{c}(i,e)} - 1\right)$; D_2 is analogous. Since $\mathfrak{c}(i,e) < 1$, $\frac{1}{\mathfrak{c}(i,e)} - 1$ is positive; it has the same value for h_1 and for h_2. Hence (a) (with T3a), (b), (c), (d).

Let us now clarify the content of the theorems T6 and T7. h_1 and h_2 are two hypotheses each of which, together with the prior evidence e, explains the new observation i. Let us assume that the prior and posterior confirmations of both hypotheses are positive. Then the ratio of the posterior confirmations of the two hypotheses is the same as that of their prior confirmations (T6b); hence the $\mathfrak{c}$ of h_2 is higher than that of h_1 after the observation if and only if the same holds before (T6c); and the two $\mathfrak{c}$ are equal afterward if and only if they are equal before (T6d,e). The *ratio of the increase* of $\mathfrak{c}$, which will later be called the relevance quotient (§ 66), is the same for both hypotheses (T6f). In T7, we make the additional assumption that i is a possible new fact ($0 < \mathfrak{c}(i,e) < 1$). T7 speaks about the *absolute increase* of $\mathfrak{c}$ (D_1 and D_2, respectively). T7a says that, in this situation, there are only two possible cases for a hypothesis; either its prior confirmation is 0, then its posterior confirmation is likewise 0, and hence the absolute increase is 0; or the prior confirmation is positive, then the posterior confirmation is likewise positive and greater than the prior confirmation. T7c says this: if the prior confirmation is higher for h_2 than for h_1, then the absolute increase is likewise higher for h_2. T7d says that if the prior confirmations for the two hypotheses are equal, then the absolute increases of $\mathfrak{c}$ are equal too.

§ 62. On Some Axiom Systems by Other Authors

Some modern axiom systems for probability$_1$ (by Keynes, Waismann, Mazurkiewicz, Hosiasson, Jeffreys, Koopman, and Wright) are examined. It is found that their axioms, and hence also their theorems, hold for all regular $\mathfrak{c}$-functions. (Other theories, which contain the principle of indifference, are inconsistent; if this principle is omitted, then the remainder holds likewise for all $\mathfrak{c}$-functions.) A theory which holds for all regular $\mathfrak{c}$-functions and thus, in other words, admits all possible measure functions, is very weak; it comprises only a small part of inductive logic. Our task will be to construct the rest of inductive logic by narrowing the class of $\mathfrak{c}$-functions and finally selecting one of them. This will be done in later chapters.

In this section we examine some theories of probability$_1$, especially modern axiom systems, from the point of view of our inductive logic. Our chief aim is to find out whether these theories contain parts which go beyond the theory of regular c-functions as represented in the earlier sections of this chapter.

The great merit of John Maynard ***Keynes***'s work [Probab.] (1921), to which we have repeatedly referred, lies in his careful critical analysis of earlier conceptions and theories; the most important point is his criticism and rejection of the principle of indifference in its classical form. Furthermore, his positive analyses and discussions contain valuable constructive contributions to the development of inductive logic. He has also made the first attempt to construct an axiom system for probability$_1$ ([Probab.], chap. xii); however, this formal part of his work is less satisfactory. Although symbolic logic is used, some points are not quite clear. As I understand the axioms and those of the so-called definitions which must be regarded as axioms, they hold, as far as they apply to numerical values, for all regular c-functions with respect to a finite domain of individuals.

Keynes's inductive logic is chiefly of a comparative form; only in cases of a special kind are numerical values attributed to probabilities. Since we want to examine here only the quantitative part of his theory, we take his axioms and definitions as referring to numbers. Then some of the axioms and definitions become purely arithmetical (e.g., the commutative principle of multiplication, and the like) and may therefore be left aside for the purpose of our comparison; these are Definitions XI, XII, and Axioms (iv), (v), and (vi). We may likewise leave aside the genuine, explicit definitions, i.e., those introducing a term in such a manner that it can be eliminated; this holds for Definitions I, VI, VII, VIII, XIII, XIV. (However, we have of course to make use of these definitions when their terms occur in axioms.) The remaining so-called Definitions are no definitions at all in the sense indicated; they must rather be regarded as axioms; this holds for Definitions II, III, IV, V, IX, and X.

We shall now compare the latter Definitions and the remaining Axioms with theorems which have been stated in this chapter, chiefly in § 59. We add the mark '(F)' to those of our theorems which hold without restriction only for a finite domain of individuals. The result is as follows. Keynes's Definition II corresponds to our theorems T59-1b and T59-5b (F); likewise, III to T59-1e and T59-5c (F); IV to T59-5a (F); V to T59-5d (F); IX to T59-2a; X to T59-1n. Further, Keynes's Axiom (i) corresponds to our T55-2b (we state this for $\mathfrak{L}_N$ only, but it could, in another system, be made valid for $\mathfrak{L}_\infty$ too); Axiom (ii) follows from T59-1h; Axiom (iii) consists of five parts, the first four of which are special cases of T59-1c. The fifth part of Axiom (iii) is somewhat obscure because the term 'equivalent' occurs here in an absolute way, although it has been introduced by Definition VIII only as a term relative to a premise (evidence). Perhaps the term 'equivalent' is here meant in the sense of our 'L-equivalent'; if so, the fifth part corresponds to our T59-5b (F) (in view of T20-2l).

We see that a number of Keynes's principles hold only for a finite domain of individuals. This is the case especially for his identification of certainty with probability 1 and of impossibility with probability 0 (Definitions II and III, see also *op. cit.*, p. 128); compare the discussion above, following T59-5. It is not clear whether he had the intention to restrict his theory to finite domains or whether he believed that his principles held also in an infinite domain; the latter seems more likely because, when he speaks about the assumption that the number of independent qualities is not infinite (p. 256), he remarks that this assumption does not limit the number of entities or objects. In consequence of this restriction, whether intentional or not, many theorems and their proofs are considerably simpler than would otherwise be the case.

Thus the result of the comparison is this: Keynes's definitions and axioms, and therefore likewise his theorems, hold for all regular c-functions with respect to a finite domain of individuals.

As earlier mentioned (see § 55B), Friedrich ***Waismann*** ([Wahrsch.] 1931) defines probability with the help of measures assigned to sentences (or propositions, "Aussagen"). For the measure of sentences, Waismann lays down three requirements (*op. cit.*, p. 236); they correspond to our T57-1g (first part: the measure is a nonnegative real number), D55-2b (or T57-1b), T57-1m. He then defines the probability of one sentence with respect to another as in our D55-3; here, the requirement should be added that the measure of the evidence is not 0, because otherwise the quotient has no value. Waismann says that, on the basis described, Keynes's axioms can be proved and hence all theorems of "the Calculus of Probability" (*op. cit.*, p. 239). However, this obviously does not hold for all theorems of the classical theory of probability and, in particular, not for those which are proved with the help of the principle of indifference, but only for those which hold for all regular c-functions. It seems that Waismann regards only this part of what we call inductive logic as belonging to logic; the determination of the measure function is, in his view, not the task of logic but is to be made on the basis of statistical experience (*op. cit.*, p. 242).

Stefan ***Mazurkiewicz*** ([Axiomatik] 1932) constructs an axiom system for probability. Janina ***Hosiasson*** ([Confirmation] 1940, [Induction] 1941) adopts Mazurkiewicz' four axioms but formulates them in terms of degree of confirmation. She leaves open the question whether degree of confirmation is the same as probability ([Induction], p. 354). However, it seems clear that both authors have in mind the same concept of probability$_1$. The four axioms I, II, III, and IV of these two authors correspond to our theorems T59-1b, l, n, and h, respectively. Therefore all theorems derivable from their axioms hold likewise in our theory of regular c-functions. In the two articles mentioned, Hosiasson derives a number of theorems and uses them for interesting discussions concerning the degree of confirmation. They include those corresponding to our theorems T59-3a, T61-1c and d, T61-3f, i, k, and l, T61-5d, T61-7c. Most of them concern the confirmation of a hypothesis by the observation of an event which is predictable with the help of the hypothesis (the condition of predictability is taken in the narrower, deductive sense).

Harold ***Jeffreys'*** work ([Probab.], 1939) is especially valuable in his extensive application of the theory of probability$_1$ or inductive logic to mathematical problems in statistics. But it contains also more general discussions which (if we leave aside some negative remarks concerning the frequency conception of probability, see above, § 9) contribute positively to the clarification of the nature of inductive logic and its role within the method of science. It is to be desired that these discussions find as much attention among logicians and authors on scientific method as they deserve. The axiom system for probability which Jeffreys constructs (*op. cit.*, chap. i) begins with a comparative concept of probability$_1$: "given *p*, *q* is more probable than *r*", where *p*, *q*, and *r* are propositions. Later, real numbers are assigned to the probabilities by certain rules, which are called "conventions" in order to emphasize their nature as inessential, logically arbitrary stipulations in distinction to the axioms proper. In this way, a quantitative inductive logic is constructed on the basis of the original comparative one. The advantage of this procedure lies in the fact that it shows clearly which of the theorems are based merely on the original, purely comparative assumptions; this is analogous to constructing an axiom system of geometry by first laying down a system of topology and then strengthening it by additional axioms to a system of metrical geometry. Now let us compare Jeffreys' system with the theory of regular c-functions. His system contains certain parts which are due to the particular procedure just described and which would become superfluous if the system were constructed from the beginning as a system of quantitative probability$_1$; these items are Axioms 1, 2, 4, and 5, and Convention 1 (Axiom 4 becomes superfluous because of Convention 2). There are no analogues to these items in the theory of regular c-functions. The other items in Jeffreys' system correspond to certain theorems in our theory in this way: his Convention 2 corresponds to our T59-1l; his Axiom 3 yields, together with Convention 2, our T59-1e, and, together with Convention 3, our T59-1b; Axiom 6 corresponds to T59-2h. A number of the theorems which we have stated in the earlier sections of this chapter have been proved by Jeffreys on the basis of his axioms and conventions; among them especially T59-2a, e, g, T59-3b, T61-2.

There are two points in Jeffreys' axiom system where, it seems to me, corrections are necessary; the first is inessential, the second essential.

1. Jeffreys' axioms and conventions do not contain any restricting condition for the statements of evidence (although Keynes had already excluded impossible (logically self-contradictory) propositions (corresponding to L-false sentences) as evidence). Consequently, a contradiction is derivable from Axiom 3 and Conventions 2 and 3 as follows. $p \cdot \sim p$ entails both p and $\sim p$. [This holds certainly if 'entailment' is used either in the sense of Lewis' 'strict implication' or in the sense of our 'L-implication'. And it seems that it holds likewise in Jeffreys' sense, because I understand the footnote on page 17 (*op. cit.*) as indicating that Jeffreys intends to use the term in such a way that a conjunction entails each of its components.] Therefore, Convention 3 ("If p entails q, then $P(q|p) = 1$", p. 21) and Theorem 2 ("If p entails $\sim q$, then $P(q|p) = 0$", p. 20), which is based on Axiom 3 and Convention 2, lead to the results that the probability of p on basis $p \cdot \sim p$ is both 1 and 0. This defect is of course inessential; it can easily be removed without diminishing the intended power of the system; all that is needed is the exclusion of self-contradictory propositions as evidence. Perhaps the author tacitly intended this restriction to be imposed.

2. The second point is more important. Convention 1 says: "We assign the larger number on given data to the more probable proposition (and therefore equal numbers to equally probable propositions)" (*op. cit.*, p. 19). Let us examine the second part, the one included in parentheses. It says obviously no more than this: "*If* p and q are equally probable on evidence r (in the sense of the comparative, not yet numerical concept of equality of probability), then equal numbers are to be assigned to p and q as their probability values on evidence r". In particular, it does not say anything at all as to the conditions for p, q, and r under which we are to regard p and q as equally probable on evidence r (in the comparative sense); nor are these conditions stated anywhere else in the system. Therefore the rule mentioned can never be applied to any particular instances in the system. However, later in the book (p. 34), the author interprets Convention 1 surprisingly in such a way that the principle of indifference (Laplace's principle of insufficient reason) is "an immediate application" of it; and, moreover, this principle is taken in a rather strong sense: "If there is no reason to believe one hypothesis rather than another, the probabilities are equal". And the principle in this strong sense, allegedly derived from Convention 1, is then used in proofs of theorems (e.g., p. 104 for (2); p. 111, in 3.23 for (1); p. 193 for (1)). We shall see later (in Vol. II) that the principle of indifference in the general form leads to contradictions. Thus Convention 1, not in the sense expressed in

its clear and simple wording, but in the sense in which it is interpreted and used by the author, makes the system inconsistent. This contradiction is essential to the system; if we remove its source, the principle of indifference, we deprive the system of some important results. If we take the system without the principle of indifference, then all its axioms and theorems hold for all regular c-functions, as our earlier comparison shows.

B. O. ***Koopman*** has constructed an axiom system for a comparative concept of probability$_1$ ([Axioms], 1940). It seems that his primitive concept "*h* on the presumption that *e* is true is equally or less probable than *h'* on the presumption that *e'* is true", if interpreted in quantitative terms, corresponds to '$c(h,e) \leqq c(h',e')$'. Interpreted in this way, his axioms hold for all regular c-functions. This will be shown later by a comparison with our system of comparative inductive logic (§ 83B).

Georg Henrik von ***Wright*** lays down six axioms for probability ([Induction], 1941, pp. 106 f.). The axioms A_1, A_2, A_3, A_5, and A_6 correspond to our theorems T59-1a, b, e, n, and k, respectively. A_4 says: "For a given *h* and a given *a* the expression $P(a|h)$ has one and only one value". Here, however, the restricting condition should be inserted that *h* is not L-false; otherwise A_2 and A_3 lead to a contradiction in the same way as explained above in connection with Jeffreys' Axiom 3. In a later work ([Wahrsch.], 1945), Wright constructs an axiom system which, according to his intention, should be interpretable in terms of both probability$_2$ ("relative frequency") and probability$_1$ ("inductive probability", "reliability of predictions"). His Axiom I states the uniqueness of the probability value (as A_4 in the former system). Axioms II, III, IV, V correspond to the following of our theorems, respectively: part of T59-1a ($c \geqq 0$), T59-1b, p, n. Axioms VI and VII correspond to special cases of T59-1i and h, respectively.

We have examined only modern axiom systems of probability$_1$. The question may be raised as to the relation between these systems and the ***classical theory*** of probability. Is the classical theory not essentially stronger than the modern systems? It is hardly possible to describe the structure and strength of the classical theory in precise terms, because its formulations fall far short of the standards of exactness of modern logic. Furthermore, the formulations by different authors vary to some extent. However, it seems that an examination of the principles and the procedure of the classical theory would yield, on the whole, the following result.

At the first look, the classical theory seems to be much stronger than the modern axiom systems; in other words, stronger than a mere theory of regular c-functions. And we find indeed many stronger theorems stated by classical authors. However, a closer examination shows that the proofs for these stronger theorems make use, explicitly or implicitly, of the principle of indifference. The classical theory claims to give a definition for probability, based on the concept of equipossible cases. The only rule given for the application of the latter concept is the principle of indifference; since we know today that this principle leads to a contradiction, there is in fact no definition for the concept of equipossibility. In order to base the classical theory on a consistent foundation, we may proceed in the following way. We regard it, not as an interpreted theory as it was intended, but as an uninterpreted axiom system with 'equipossible cases' as undefined, primitive term without interpretation. Then we take the classical definition of 'probability' based on 'equipossible.' Thus this definition is here an uninterpreted axiomatic definition. If we do so (and, in addition, make some other necessary modifications, e.g., by inserting references to evidence, which are often omitted in classical formulations), then we obtain a consistent axiom system. This axiom system, however, is as weak as the modern systems described above; it holds likewise for all regular c-functions.

Our discussion in this section leaves aside those axiom systems for probability which are intended to be interpreted in terms of the *frequency concept* of probability$_2$. These systems are different from those for probability$_1$ not only in the interpretations intended but also in their logical form aside from all interpretations. The chief difference lies in the logical type of the arguments. The arguments of probability$_2$ are properties (classes); those of probability$_1$ are propositions or sentences. The primitive term in an axiom system for probability$_2$, say, 'probability' or '*P*', can, of course, be interpreted in many different ways, not only by the concept of probability$_2$. However, this term cannot be interpreted directly by probability$_1$ because of the type distinction mentioned. This holds as long as we take either sentences or propositions as arguments of probability$_1$; if we took as arguments the ranges of the sentences, hence classes of a certain kind, then this modified concept of probability$_1$ could be taken as interpretation for '*P*'. All axiom systems for probability$_2$, if thus interpreted in terms of probability$_1$, are as weak as the systems for probability$_1$ discussed above; their axioms and theorems hold for all regular c-functions. Axiom systems for probability$_2$ have been given, among others, by the following authors: S. Bernstein (1917, in Russian, see Kolmogoroff [Wahrsch.]), Reichenbach ([Axiomatik], [Wahrsch.] §§ 12–14), Kolmogoroff [Wahrsch.], Dörge [Axiomatisierung], Evans and Kleene [Probab.], Cramér ([Statistics], pp. 145 ff.). The system by Copeland [Postulates] presumably belongs here too, but the formulation is not quite clear in this respect; that the system is intended for probability$_2$ seems likely because the author maintains the frequency conception of probability (see [Fundamental]). Mises' theory of probability is not an uninterpreted axiom system but an interpreted theory based on an explicit definition of probability$_2$; what he calls axioms are actually parts of this definition.

Let us sum up the result of our discussion. We have examined the axiom systems for probability$_1$ constructed by Keynes, Waismann, Mazurkiewicz, Hosiasson, Jeffreys, Koopman, and Wright. We have found that the axioms of these systems correspond to or are immediate consequences of theorems on regular c-functions stated in this chapter. Therefore, these axioms, and hence likewise all theorems provable in these axiom systems, hold for all regular c-functions. Other theories (e.g., the classical theory and Jeffreys' system not as formulated but as used by its author) contain the principle of indifference; if we omit this principle, because it leads to contradictions, then the remainder holds likewise for all regular c-functions.

What follows from this result? If the axioms of a system hold for all regular c-functions, then that system represents only a very small part of the theory of probability$_1$. This part, it is true, is of great importance because it contains the fundamental relations between c-values. But its weakness becomes apparent from the following facts. Let *e* and *h* be factual sentences in $\mathfrak{L}_N$ such that *e* L-implies neither *h* nor $\sim h$. Then a theory of the kind mentioned does not determine the value of $c(h,e)$. Moreover, it does not even impose any restricting conditions upon this value; the assignment of any arbitrarily chosen real number between 0 and 1 is compatible with the theory. We have seen this earlier, in connection with T59-5f. A theory of this kind states merely relations between c-values; thus, if some c-values are given, others can be computed with the help of the theorems. There is an analogous restriction in the theory of probability$_2$; however, here the restriction is necessary. The statement of a particular value of probability$_2$ for two given properties is, in general, a factual statement (§ 10B). Therefore, a logicomathematical theory of probability$_2$ cannot yield statements of this kind but must restrict itself to stating relations between probability$_2$ values. On the other hand, in the case of a theory of probability$_1$, there is no reason for this restriction. A sentence of the form '$c(h,e) = r$' is not factual but L-determinate. Therefore, a logicomathematical theory of probability$_1$, in other words, a system of inductive logic, can state sentences of this form. The fact that the axiom systems for probability$_1$ restrict themselves to statements which hold for all regular c-functions makes these systems unnecessarily weak.

Thus it becomes clear what our task is to be if we want to construct a system of inductive logic that can furnish the answer to inductive problems and enables us, among other things, to compute the value of c for given sentences. The theory of regular c-functions dealt with in this chapter is no more than the first step. We have to lay down further requirements in addition to regularity, and thereby finally come to the selection of one particular c-function. The additional requirements are to achieve what the classical theory intended to achieve by the principle of indifference; they must, however, avoid the absurd results which have been derived with the help of this principle and the contradictions which can be derived. Moreover—and this involves a more serious problem—the c-function to which the requirements lead must be an adequate explicatum for probability$_1$.

CHAPTER VI

RELEVANCE AND IRRELEVANCE

The theory of relevance and irrelevance deals chiefly with the following situation, which has been briefly discussed earlier (§ 60). On the basis of prior evidence e, a hypothesis h is considered, and the change in the confirmation of h due to an additional evidence i is examined. If the $\mathfrak{c}$ of h is increased by the addition of i to e, i is said to be positively relevant or *positive* to h on the evidence e; if $\mathfrak{c}$ is decreased, i is said to be *negative* (to h on e). In these cases i is called *relevant* (to h on e), otherwise *irrelevant* (§ 65).

These relevance concepts can be represented in various ways by numerical functions of triples of sentences i, h, e. One of these functions is the relevance quotient $\mathfrak{c}(h,e \,.\, i)/\mathfrak{c}(h,e)$. It is clear that i is positive, negative, or irrelevant to h on e, if the relevance quotient is >1, <1, or 1, respectively. Theorems on this quotient, developed by W. E. Johnson and Keynes are briefly reported here (§ 66); but this concept is not used further on.

A new numerical function, the *relevance measure* $\mathfrak{r}$, is introduced (§ 67) and then applied as the fundamental concept of the theory of relevance developed in this chapter. $\mathfrak{r}(i,h,e)$ is defined on the basis of $\mathfrak{m}$-values. It is shown that i is positive, negative, or irrelevant to h on e, if $\mathfrak{r}(i,h,e)$ is positive, negative, or 0, respectively. If i is replaced by $\sim i$ or h by $\sim h$, $\mathfrak{r}$ changes to the opposite value. Some of the chief problems here discussed and solved concern the relations between the relevance of two new observations i and j (to h on e) and the relevance of their connections, especially $i \,.\, j$ and $i \vee j$ (§§ 68, 69); further, the relations between the relevance of i to two hypotheses h and k (on e) and the relevance of i to their connections, especially to $h \,.\, k$ and $h \vee k$ (§§ 70, 71). It is found that $\mathfrak{r}$ is additive in two respects (§ 68): (1) the $\mathfrak{r}$ of a disjunction with L-exclusive components (to h on e) is the sum of the $\mathfrak{r}$-values for the components; (2) the $\mathfrak{r}$ of a conjunction with L-disjunct components is the sum of the $\mathfrak{r}$-values for the components. (1) can be applied, in particular, to the ultimate disjunctive components of i; these are the state-descriptions $\mathfrak{Z}$ in the range $\mathfrak{R}(i)$. Thus, the $\mathfrak{r}$ of i (to h on e) is the sum of the $\mathfrak{r}$-values for these $\mathfrak{Z}$ (§ 72). If i is positive to h on e and none of these $\mathfrak{Z}$ is negative, i is said to be extremely positive to h on e (§ 74). The second additivity (2) can be applied especially to the ultimate conjunctive components of i; these are the negations of the $\mathfrak{Z}$ in $\mathfrak{R}(\sim i)$; we call them the content-elements of i. Thus the $\mathfrak{r}$ of i (to h on e) is the sum of the $\mathfrak{r}$-values for the content-elements of i (§ 73). If i is positive to h on e and none of the content-elements of i is negative, i is said to be completely positive to h on e (§ 75).

§ 65. The Concepts of Relevance and Irrelevance

Suppose the new evidence i is added to the prior evidence e for a hypothesis h. If the posterior confirmation $\mathfrak{c}(h,e \,.\, i)$ is higher than the prior confirmation $\mathfrak{c}(h,e)$, i is said to be *positive* to h on the evidence e (D1a). If it is lower, i is said to be negative (D1b). In both cases, i is called *relevant* (D1c). If the c-values are equal or if $e \cdot i$ is L-false (in which case $\mathfrak{c}(h,e \cdot i)$ has no value), i is called *irrelevant*. The most interesting among the theorems answer the questions how relevance and irrelevance are influenced by exchanging i and h and by negating either or both of them. Among the answers are the theorems of symmetry: if i is positive to h on e, then h is positive to i on e (T6a); similarly for negative relevance (T6b) and irrelevance (T6d). If i is positive to h on e, then $\sim i$ is negative to h on e (T6e) and i is negative to $\sim h$ on e (T6h(1), (6)). If i is irrelevant to h on e, then likewise $\sim i$ to h on e (T6g) and i to $\sim h$ on e (T6k). The special multiplication theorem (T6l) says that, if i is irrelevant to h on e, then the c-value for $h \cdot i$ (on e) is the product of those for h and for i. Initial relevance is defined as relevance on the tautological evidence (D2).

The situation which we shall study in this section, and indeed throughout this chapter, is essentially the same as that discussed in § 60: an observer X is interested in a hypothesis h; he possesses some prior evidence e and obtains now additional evidence i or considers the possibility of obtaining it. The chief question to be investigated is, how the $\mathfrak{c}$ of h is influenced by the addition of i to e. If the posterior confirmation $\mathfrak{c}(h,e \cdot i)$ is higher than the prior confirmation $\mathfrak{c}(h,e)$, we shall say that the additional evidence i is ***positively relevant*** or, simply, ***positive*** to the hypothesis h on the evidence e (D1a). If it is lower, we shall say that i is ***negatively relevant*** or ***negative*** to h on e (D1b). If the $\mathfrak{c}$ of h remains unchanged, and also in another case, where $\mathfrak{c}$ cannot be applied, we shall say that i is ***irrelevant*** to h on e (D1d). Here, as in § 60, the definitions and theorems are formulated in a general way for any sentences i, h, and e; but they are especially of interest when applied to situations of the kind described.

These simple, nonnumerical relevance concepts will be discussed in this section. The subsequent sections of this chapter will investigate the same situation with the help of relevance functions which ascribe a numerical value to a triple of sentences i, h, e. This will be done in the next section by using the relevance quotient, which has been introduced and studied by W. E. Johnson and Keynes, and in the remainder of this chapter with the help of a new function, which we shall call the relevance measure $\mathfrak{r}$.

The investigation of the problems of relevance and irrelevance in this chapter form a part of the general theory of regular c-functions, which was begun in the preceding chapter. Only later shall we restrict the consideration to a special subclass of the regular c-functions (chap. viii), and still later to one particular c-function (§ 110). Thus the results to be found in the present chapter hold generally, no matter which particular c-function anybody may prefer as an explicatum for the concept of degree of confirmation.

+**D65-1.** Let $\mathfrak{L}$ be any finite or infinite system, $\mathfrak{c}$ be a regular $\mathfrak{c}$-function in $\mathfrak{L}$, and *h*, *e*, and *i* be sentences in $\mathfrak{L}$.

a. *i* is ***positively relevant*** or, briefly, ***positive*** to *h* on evidence *e* (with respect to $\mathfrak{c}$ in $\mathfrak{L}$) $=_{Df}$ $\mathfrak{c}(h,e \cdot i) > \mathfrak{c}(h,e)$.

b. *i* is ***negatively relevant*** or, briefly, ***negative*** to *h* on evidence *e* (with respect to $\mathfrak{c}$ in $\mathfrak{L}$) $=_{Df}$ $\mathfrak{c}(h,e \cdot i) < \mathfrak{c}(h,e)$.

c. *i* is ***relevant*** to *h* on evidence *e* (with respect to $\mathfrak{c}$ in $\mathfrak{L}$) $=_{Df}$ *i* is either positively relevant or negatively relevant to *h* on evidence *e*.

d. *i* is ***irrelevant*** to *h* on evidence *e* (with respect to $\mathfrak{c}$ in $\mathfrak{L}$) $=_{Df}$ either (1) $\mathfrak{c}(h,e \cdot i) = \mathfrak{c}(h,e)$, or (2) $e \cdot i$ is L-false.

These concepts (with the term 'favourably relevant' instead of 'positively relevant') and some of the subsequent theorems (T6a, d, g) are due to Keynes ([Probab.], pp. 55, 146 f.). For the definition of irrelevance, he uses only the condition (d) (1). He suggests also another, stronger definition for irrelevance, which we shall discuss later (at the end of § 75). We add the condition (2) in (d), because it turns out that hereby the theorems on irrelevance become simpler. If $e \cdot i$ is L-false, $\mathfrak{c}(h,e \cdot i)$ has no value; if $e \cdot i$ is not L-false, then in $\mathfrak{L}_N$ both $\mathfrak{c}(h,e \cdot i)$ and $\mathfrak{c}(h,e)$ have values. Thus the addition of (2) has the effect that in $\mathfrak{L}_N$ any sentence *i* is either relevant or irrelevant to *h* on *e* (T4g).

Let us briefly indicate some other consequences of the addition of the condition (2), anticipating later explanations and discussions. The criterion for irrelevance in terms of $\mathfrak{m}$-values becomes simpler; it holds in $\mathfrak{L}_N$ without exceptions (T4f). Further, due to (2), the theorem of the symmetry of irrelevance holds in $\mathfrak{L}_N$ without exceptions (T6d). Take the following example in $\mathfrak{L}_N$: let $e \cdot h$ be L-false; then $\mathfrak{c}(h,e \cdot i) = \mathfrak{c}(h,e) = 0$; thus *i* is irrelevant to *h* on *e*, and (by D1d(2)) *h* is irrelevant to *i* on *e*. On the other hand, since $\mathfrak{c}(i,e \cdot h)$ has no value, *i* is not irrelevant in the narrower sense (d)(1) to *h* on *e;* if (2) were omitted, *i* would be said to be neither relevant nor irrelevant to *h* on *e*.

Another simplification effected by (2) is the strict parallelism in $\mathfrak{L}_N$ between the relevance concepts defined by D1 and the relevance measure $\mathfrak{r}$ (D67-1, T67-10). If (2) were omitted, we should have to say: '$\mathfrak{r}(i,h,e) = 0$ if and only if *i* is irrelevant to *h* on *e* or $e \cdot i$ is L-false.' We shall find that the numerical concept $\mathfrak{r}$ is more fruitful, leads to more simple and interesting theorems, than the simple relevance concepts. Therefore it seems preferable to adjust the latter concepts to $\mathfrak{r}$ rather than vice versa.

It is to be noticed that for general sentences in $\mathfrak{L}_\infty$ and, in particular, for almost L-false sentences, a gap between relevance and irrelevance and hence a discrepancy between the relevance concepts and $\mathfrak{r}$ remains. Let $e \cdot i$ be almost L-false (D58-1b); then $e \cdot i$ is not L-false but $\mathfrak{m}(e \cdot i) = 0$ (T58-3a) and hence $\mathfrak{m}(e \cdot i \cdot h) = 0$. We shall see that in this case $\mathfrak{r} = 0$ but that nevertheless the following may happen: $\mathfrak{c}(h,e \cdot i)$ has a value and is greater than $\mathfrak{c}(h,e)$ (see the example following T67-9), hence *i* positive to *h* on *e*. This shows also that the condition (2) cannot be replaced by the condition that $\mathfrak{m}(e \cdot i) = 0$.

An *alternative explication for the relevance concepts* will here be indicated briefly. Consider the case in $\mathfrak{L}_\infty$ that $\vdash e \cdot i \supset h$, hence $\mathfrak{c}(h,e \cdot i) = 1$; further, not $\vdash e \supset h$, but, for a given $\mathfrak{c}$, nevertheless $\mathfrak{c}(h,e) = 1$. In other words, e almost L-implies h, $e \cdot \sim h$ is almost L-false (D58-1). Thus $\mathfrak{c}$ is not increased by the addition of i to e. Therefore, according to D1, i is called irrelevant to h on e. On the other hand, the addition of i changes our knowledge concerning h; before this addition, h was only almost certain (i.e., almost L-implied by the evidence e available); after the addition, h is certain (i.e., L-implied by the available evidence $e \cdot i$). [*Example.* Let h be '$(\exists x)Px$' and i be 'Pb' in $\mathfrak{L}_\infty$. As prior evidence e we take the tautology 't'. With respect to many adequate $\mathfrak{c}$-functions, among them our function $\mathfrak{c}^*$ to be introduced later, h is almost L-true; hence $\mathfrak{c}(h,t) = \mathfrak{c}(h,t \cdot i) = 1$. On the evidence '$t$', h is not certain, although almost certain; that is to say, X cannot know whether h holds or not. However, as soon as X makes the observation that b is P, h follows. Thus his knowledge concerning h has clearly changed in a favorable way, although this change is not represented by an increase in the value of $\mathfrak{c}$.] It might not seem implausible to call i in this case positively relevant instead of irrelevant. This suggests the following alternative to D1a:

(D′) i is *positive* to h on $e =_{\text{Df}}$ either (1) $\mathfrak{c}(h,e \cdot i) > \mathfrak{c}(h,e)$ or (2) $\vdash e \cdot i \supset h$ and not $\vdash e \supset h$ and $\mathfrak{c}(h,e) = \mathfrak{c}(h,e \cdot i) = 1$.

Analogously, the definition of negative relevance would be modified so as to include the case in which $\mathfrak{c}(h,e \cdot i) = \mathfrak{c}(h,e) = 0$, $\vdash e \cdot i \supset \sim h$ but not $\vdash e \supset \sim h$ (hence $e \cdot h$ is almost L-false). And the definition of irrelevance would be made narrower by excluding the two cases. This alternative definition coincides with D1 as far as any sentences in $\mathfrak{L}_N$ and nongeneral sentences in $\mathfrak{L}_\infty$ are concerned; it differs from D1 only in some special cases of general sentences in $\mathfrak{L}_\infty$ (where either $e \cdot \sim h$ or $e \cdot h$ is almost L-false). Most of the theorems in this chapter exclude this special case and thus would remain unchanged if D1 were replaced by the alternative definitions. In a few theorems, slight changes would have to be made. For instance, T67-8 and T67-10 would remain unchanged. T67-9 contains the condition that $e \cdot i$ is not almost L-false; here we would have to insert in (a) the additional condition that $e \cdot \sim h$ is not almost L-false, in (b) that $e \cdot h$ is not almost L-false, and in (c) and (d) both. Similar additions would be made in T65-4 and some other theorems.

In the following theorems it is always presupposed that $\mathfrak{m}$ is any regular $\mathfrak{m}$-function in the system $\mathfrak{L}$ in question, that $\mathfrak{c}$ is the regular $\mathfrak{c}$-function corresponding to $\mathfrak{m}$, and that the relevance concepts are meant with respect to this $\mathfrak{c}$.

We shall use throughout this chapter the following abbreviations 'k_1', etc., for certain conjunctions, and '$\mathfrak{m}_1$', etc., for their $\mathfrak{m}$-values:

n	k_n	$\mathfrak{m}_n = \mathfrak{m}(k_n)$
1	k_1: $e \cdot i \cdot h$	$\mathfrak{m}_1$
2	k_2: $e \cdot i \cdot \sim h$	$\mathfrak{m}_2$
3	k_3: $e \cdot \sim i \cdot h$	$\mathfrak{m}_3$
4	k_4: $e \cdot \sim i \cdot \sim h$	$\mathfrak{m}_4$

The $\mathfrak{m}$-values for other sentences which we need can then easily be represented as sums of these $\mathfrak{m}$-values:

T65-1. Lemma.

a. $\mathfrak{m}(e \cdot i) = \mathfrak{m}_1 + \mathfrak{m}_2$.

b. $\mathfrak{m}(e \cdot \sim i) = \mathfrak{m}_3 + \mathfrak{m}_4$.

c. $\mathfrak{m}(e \cdot h) = \mathfrak{m}_1 + \mathfrak{m}_3$.

d. $\mathfrak{m}(e \cdot \sim h) = \mathfrak{m}_2 + \mathfrak{m}_4$.

e. $\mathfrak{m}(e) = \mathfrak{m}_1 + \mathfrak{m}_2 + \mathfrak{m}_3 + \mathfrak{m}_4$.

(From T57-1r.)

T65-2. Let e' be L-equivalent to e; let i' be L-equivalent (or L-equivalent with respect to e) to i, and likewise h' to h. If i is positive (or negative, or relevant, or irrelevant, respectively) to h on e, then so is i' to h' on e'. (From T59-1h and i, T59-2j.)

T65-3. If i is relevant to h on e, then $e \cdot i$ and e are not L-false. (From D1c, b, a, T55-2b, T56-4b.)

In the following theorem T4, the items (c), (d), (e), and (f) give sufficient and necessary conditions for the four concepts defined in D1. Concerning condition (B) in T4 and T6: to say of a sentence which has an $\mathfrak{m}$-value that it is not almost L-false means that either it is L-false or its $\mathfrak{m}$-value is > 0 (T58-3a).

+**T65-4.** Let e, h, and i be either (i) any sentences in $\mathfrak{L}_N$, or (ii) any nongeneral sentences in $\mathfrak{L}_\infty$, or (iii) any sentences in $\mathfrak{L}_\infty$ fulfilling the following two conditions: (A) $\mathfrak{m}$ has values for k_1, k_2, k_3, and k_4 (and hence for e, $e \cdot h$, $e \cdot i$, and $e \cdot i \cdot h$, T1) and (B) neither e nor $e \cdot i$ is almost L-false. Then the following holds.

a. Lemma. Either e is L-false or

$$\mathfrak{c}(h,e) = \mathfrak{m}(e \cdot h)/\mathfrak{m}(e).$$

Proof. If e is not L-false, $\mathfrak{m}(e) > 0$ (for $\mathfrak{L}_N$, from T58-1a; for $\mathfrak{L}_\infty$, from (B), T58-3a). Hence the assertion (for $\mathfrak{L}_N$, from D55-3; for $\mathfrak{L}_\infty$, from T56-4a).

b. Lemma. Either $e \cdot i$ is L-false or

$$\mathfrak{c}(h,e \cdot i) = \mathfrak{m}(e \cdot i \cdot h)/\mathfrak{m}(e \cdot i).$$ (Analogous to (a).)

c. i is *positive* to h on e

(1) if and only if $\mathfrak{m}(e \cdot i \cdot h) \times \mathfrak{m}(e) > \mathfrak{m}(e \cdot h) \times \mathfrak{m}(e \cdot i)$;

(2) if and only if $\mathfrak{m}_1 \times \mathfrak{m}_4 > \mathfrak{m}_2 \times \mathfrak{m}_3$.

Proof. 1. I. Let $e \cdot i$ be L-false. Then $\mathfrak{c}(h,e \cdot i)$ has no value and hence i is not positive. $\mathfrak{m}(e \cdot i) = 0$, and hence $\mathfrak{m}(e \cdot i \cdot h) = 0$ (T57-1s); thus the condition in (1) is not fulfilled. II. Let $e \cdot i$ not be L-false. Then e is not L-false, and $\mathfrak{m}(e \cdot i)$ and $\mathfrak{m}(e)$ are >0. Hence the assertion (1) by (a) and (b). 2. From (1), T1.

d. i is *negative* to h on e

(1) if and only if $\mathfrak{m}(e \cdot i \cdot h) \times \mathfrak{m}(e) < \mathfrak{m}(e \cdot h) \times \mathfrak{m}(e \cdot i)$;

(2) if and only if $\mathfrak{m}_1 \times \mathfrak{m}_4 < \mathfrak{m}_2 \times \mathfrak{m}_3$.
(Analogous to (c).)

e. *i* is *relevant* to *h* on *e*
(1) if and only if $\mathfrak{m}(e \,.\, i \,.\, h) \times \mathfrak{m}(e) \neq \mathfrak{m}(e \,.\, h) \times \mathfrak{m}(e \,.\, i)$;
(2) if and only if $\mathfrak{m}_1 \times \mathfrak{m}_4 \neq \mathfrak{m}_2 \times \mathfrak{m}_3$.
(From (c), (d).)

f. *i* is *irrelevant* to *h* on *e*
(1) if and only if $\mathfrak{m}(e \,.\, i \,.\, h) \times \mathfrak{m}(e) = \mathfrak{m}(e \,.\, h) \times \mathfrak{m}(e \,.\, i)$;
(2) if and only if $\mathfrak{m}_1 \times \mathfrak{m}_4 = \mathfrak{m}_2 \times \mathfrak{m}_3$.

Proof. 1. I. Let $e \,.\, i$ be L-false. Then *i* is irrelevant (D1d(2)). $\mathfrak{m}(e \,.\, i) = 0$, and hence $\mathfrak{m}(e \,.\, i \,.\, h) = 0$ (T57-1s). Therefore the condition in (1) is fulfilled. II. Let $e \,.\, i$ not be L-false. Then *e* is not L-false, and $\mathfrak{m}(e \,.\, i)$ and $\mathfrak{m}(e)$ are >0. Hence the assertion (1) by D1d(1), (a), (b). 2. From (1), T1.

g. *i* is either relevant or irrelevant to *h* on *e*. (From (e), (f).)

T65-5. Let *e*, *h*, and *i* be either (i) any sentences in $\mathfrak{L}_N$, or (ii) any non-general sentences in $\mathfrak{L}_\infty$.

a. Let $\mathfrak{m}'$ and $\mathfrak{m}''$ be regular $\mathfrak{m}$-functions, $\mathfrak{c}'$ be based upon $\mathfrak{m}'$ and $\mathfrak{c}''$ upon $\mathfrak{m}''$ such that *i* is *positive* to *h* on *e* with respect to $\mathfrak{c}'$ but *negative* with respect to $\mathfrak{c}''$. Then, for every regular $\mathfrak{m}$-function $\mathfrak{m}$, $\mathfrak{m}_1$, $\mathfrak{m}_2$, $\mathfrak{m}_3$, and $\mathfrak{m}_4$ are >0, and all four *k*-sentences are non-L-false.

Proof. $\mathfrak{m}_1' \times \mathfrak{m}_4' > \mathfrak{m}_2' \times \mathfrak{m}_3'$ (T4c(2)). Hence $\mathfrak{m}_1'$ and $\mathfrak{m}_4'$ are >0. Therefore k_1 and k_4 are non-L-false (T57-1b). Hence, for every regular $\mathfrak{m}$, $\mathfrak{m}_1$ and $\mathfrak{m}_4$ are >0 (T58-1a). $\mathfrak{m}_1'' \times \mathfrak{m}_4'' < \mathfrak{m}_2'' \times \mathfrak{m}_3''$ (T4d(2)). Hence $\mathfrak{m}_2''$ and $\mathfrak{m}_3''$ are >0. Therefore k_2 and k_3 are non-L-false. Hence, for every regular $\mathfrak{m}$, $\mathfrak{m}_2$ and $\mathfrak{m}_3$ are >0.

b. Let the conditions in (a) be fulfilled. Then there is a regular $\mathfrak{c}$-function $\mathfrak{c}$ such that *i* is *irrelevant* to *h* on *e* with respect to $\mathfrak{c}$.

Proof. The four *k*-sentences are L-exclusive in pairs and non-L-false (a). Their disjunction is L-equivalent to *e*. Therefore we can construct a regular $\mathfrak{m}$-function $\mathfrak{m}$ such that $\mathfrak{m}_1 = \mathfrak{m}_2 = \mathfrak{m}_3 = \mathfrak{m}_4 = \mathfrak{m}(e)/4$. Let $\mathfrak{c}$ be based upon $\mathfrak{m}$. Then *i* is irrelevant to *h* on *e* with respect to $\mathfrak{c}$ (T4f).

c. Let *i* be relevant to *h* on *e* with respect to *every* regular $\mathfrak{c}$-function. Then *i* is either positive with respect to every regular $\mathfrak{c}$-function or negative with respect to every regular $\mathfrak{c}$-function. (From (b).)

The following theorem shows how relevance and irrelevance are influenced by exchanging *i* and *h* and by negating either or both of them.

+T65-6. Let *e*, *h*, and *i* be either (i) any sentences in $\mathfrak{L}_N$, or (ii) any nongeneral sentences in $\mathfrak{L}_\infty$, or (iii) any sentences in $\mathfrak{L}_\infty$ fulfilling the following two conditions: (A) $\mathfrak{m}$ has values for k_1, k_2, k_3, and k_4 (and hence for *e*, $e \,.\, i$, $e \,.\, {\sim}i$, $e \,.\, h$, $e \,.\, {\sim}h$, T1); (B) none of the sentences *e*, $e \,.\, i$,

$e \cdot \sim i$, $e \cdot h$, and $e \cdot \sim h$ is almost L-false (hence each of them either is L-false or its m-value is >0). Then the following holds.

a. *Symmetry of positive relevance.* If i is positive to h on e, then h is positive to i on e.

Proof. The condition T4c(1) remains the same if i and h are exchanged, since $\mathfrak{m}(e \cdot h \cdot i) = \mathfrak{m}(e \cdot i \cdot h)$.

Keynes remarks here: "This constitutes a formal demonstration of the generally accepted principle that, if a hypothesis helps to explain a phenomenon, the fact of the phenomenon supports the reality of the hypothesis" ([Probab.], p. 147).

b. *Symmetry of negative relevance.* If i is negative to h on e, then h is negative to i on e. (From T4d(1).)

c. *Symmetry of relevance.* If i is relevant to h on e, then h is relevant to i on e. (From (a), (b).)

d. *Symmetry of irrelevance.* If i is irrelevant to h on e, then h is irrelevant to i on e. (From T4f(1).)

e. If i is positive to h on e, then $\sim i$ is negative to h on e.

Proof. $\mathfrak{m}(e \cdot i \cdot h) \times \mathfrak{m}(e \cdot \sim i \cdot \sim h) > \mathfrak{m}(e \cdot i \cdot \sim h) \times \mathfrak{m}(e \cdot \sim i \cdot h)$ (T4c (2)). Hence $\mathfrak{m}(e \cdot \sim i \cdot h) \times \mathfrak{m}(e \cdot i \cdot \sim h) < \mathfrak{m}(e \cdot \sim i \cdot \sim h) \times \mathfrak{m}(e \cdot i \cdot h)$. Hence the assertion (T4d(2) with '$\sim i$' for 'i').

f. If i is negative to h on e, then $\sim i$ is positive to h on e. (From T4d(2) and T4c(2), in analogy to (e).)

g. If i is irrelevant to h on e, then so is $\sim i$. (From T4f(2), in analogy to (e).)

h. The following eight conditions are logically equivalent to one another, that is to say, if any one of them holds, all others hold too.

(1) i is positive to h on e.
(2) h is positive to i on e.
(3) $\sim i$ is negative to h on e.
(4) $\sim h$ is negative to i on e.
(5) h is negative to $\sim i$ on e.
(6) i is negative to $\sim h$ on e.
(7) $\sim h$ is positive to $\sim i$ on e.
(8) $\sim i$ is positive to $\sim h$ on e.

Proof. (1) is logically equivalent to (2) (from (a)); likewise (1) to (3) (from (e), (f), and T2); (2) to (4) (from (e) and (f)); (3) to (5) (from (b)); (4) to (6) (from (b)); (5) to (7) (from (e) and (f)); (6) to (8) (from (e) and (f)).

i. The following eight conditions are logically equivalent to one another.

(1) $\sim i$ is positive to h on e.
(2) h is positive to $\sim i$ on e.
(3) i is negative to h on e.
(4) $\sim h$ is negative to $\sim i$ on e.
(5) h is negative to i on e.
(6) $\sim i$ is negative to $\sim h$ on e.
(7) $\sim h$ is positive to i on e.
(8) i is positive to $\sim h$ on e.

Proof. We change in (h) 'i' into '$\sim i$'. Thereby '$\sim i$' is changed into '$\sim\sim i$', which may then be changed into 'i' (T2).

j. If any sentence in one of the two classes $\{i, \sim i\}$ and $\{h, \sim h\}$ is relevant on e to some sentence in the other class, then each sentence in either class is relevant on e to each sentence in the other class. (From (h) and (i).)

k. If any sentence in one of the two classes $\{i, \sim i\}$ and $\{h, \sim h\}$ is irrelevant on e to some sentence in the other class, then each sentence in either class is irrelevant on e to each sentence in the other class. (From (d) and (g).)

l. *Special multiplication theorem.* If i is irrelevant to h on e (and hence h irrelevant to i on e, (d)) and e is not L-false, then $\mathfrak{c}(h \centerdot i,e) = \mathfrak{c}(i,e) \times \mathfrak{c}(h,e)$.

Proof. $\mathfrak{m}(e) > 0$; hence the three c-values exist (as in T4a). If $e \centerdot i$ is L-false, $e \centerdot i \centerdot h$ is L-false; hence the first two c-values are 0 and the equation is fulfilled. If $e \centerdot i$ is not L-false, $\mathfrak{c}(h,e \centerdot i) = \mathfrak{c}(h,e)$ (D1d); hence the assertion by T59-1n(2).

From T6h and i we see the following. Suppose a true statement is given saying that one sentence is positive (or negative) to another sentence on e. Then this statement remains true if we exchange the first and the second sentence; and likewise if we carry out any two of the following three changes:
(1) in the first sentence we add or drop the sign of negation;
(2) in the second sentence we add or drop the sign of negation;
(3) we change 'positive' to 'negative' (or vice versa).

The condition (B) in T6 requires for $\mathfrak{L}_\infty$ that certain sentences be not almost L-false. In order to show the necessity of this restriction, let us consider the following counterexample in $\mathfrak{L}_\infty$ with an almost L-false sentence $e \centerdot h$. Let h be the law '$(x)Mx$', where 'M' is a factual molecular predicate. Let e be '$Ma_1 \centerdot Ma_2 \centerdot \ldots \centerdot Ma_s$'; hence e describes a sample of s cases fulfilling the law h. $\vdash h \supset e$; hence $e \centerdot h$ is L-equivalent to h. Let j be 'Mc', where 'c' is an in not occurring in e. Then $\vdash h \supset j$, hence $\mathfrak{c}(j,e \centerdot h) = 1$ and $\mathfrak{c}(\sim j,e \centerdot h) = 0$. $\mathfrak{c}(j,e) < 1$ (T59-5a); hence $\mathfrak{c}(\sim j,e) > 0$ (T59-1p). Therefore h is positive to j on e, and negative to $\sim j$ on e. On the other hand, the following holds for the function $\mathfrak{c}^*$ to be introduced later (§ 110F (12)) and likewise for many other regular $\mathfrak{c}$-functions. $\mathfrak{c}^*(h,e)$ and $\mathfrak{c}^*(h,e \,.\, j)$ are 0. Since $\vdash \sim j \supset \sim h$, $\mathfrak{c}(h,e \,.\, \sim j) = 0$. Therefore j and $\sim j$ are irrelevant to h on e. Thus here positive relevance, negative relevance, relevance, and irrelevance are not symmetric. The example would violate T6a, b, c, and d, if these theorems were formulated without restrictions. However, in this example $\mathfrak{m}^*(e \,.\, h) = \mathfrak{m}^*(h) = 0$. Therefore h, since it is factual, is almost L-false (T58-3a); and the same holds for $e \,.\, h$.

The following two theorems deal with two special cases of irrelevance.

T65-7. Let $e \,.\, h$ be L-false in $\mathfrak{L}$; in other words, $\vdash e \supset \sim h$. (This holds in $\mathfrak{L}_N$, if, but not only if, $\mathfrak{c}(h,e) = 0$.) Then the following holds.

a. Lemma. If e is not L-false, $\mathfrak{c}(h,e) = 0$. (From T59-1e.)

b. Lemma. For any i such that $e \,.\, i$ is not L-false, $\mathfrak{c}(h,e \,.\, i) = 0$. (From T59-1e.)

c. Every sentence is irrelevant to h on e. (From D1d, (a), (b).)

T7 says for $\mathfrak{L}_N$ that if we once have the confirmation 0 for h, then this remains so no matter what additional evidence we may find. In this form the statement is restricted to $\mathfrak{L}_N$; it does not hold generally in $\mathfrak{L}_\infty$. It may happen in $\mathfrak{L}_\infty$ that $\mathfrak{c}(h,e) = 0$ and still $e \,.\, h$ is not L-false but only almost L-false. It may then be that, to take a trivial example, $\mathfrak{c}(h,e \,.\, h)$ has a value (which is, of course, impossible if $e \,.\, h$ is L-false); if so, this value is 1 (T59-1b), and hence h itself is positive to h on e. There are also nontrivial cases of a relevant sentence i, that is to say, cases in which i is not so strong that $\vdash e \,.\, i \supset h$.

In order to construct a nontrivial example of this kind in $\mathfrak{L}_\infty$, we use again the sentences h, e, and j of the example to T6 and our function $\mathfrak{c}^*$. Let i be '$(x)[x \neq c \supset Mx]$'; it says that M holds for all individuals distinct from c. We see easily that $\vdash i \supset e$; further $\vdash h \equiv i \,.\, j$, and hence $\vdash h \supset i$, but not $\vdash e \,.\, i \supset j$ and hence not $\vdash e \,.\, i \supset h$. ${}_N\mathfrak{c}^*(h,e)$ is >0 but converges with increasing N toward 0; therefore in $\mathfrak{L}_\infty$ $\mathfrak{c}^*(h,e) = 0$. On the other hand, $\mathfrak{c}^*(h,e \,.\, i) = \mathfrak{c}^*(h,i)$ (T59-1h, because $\vdash i \supset e$), $= \mathfrak{c}^*(i \,.\, j,i)$ (because $\vdash h \equiv i \,.\, j$), $= \mathfrak{c}^*(j,i)$ (T59-2i). Since not $\vdash i \supset j$, ${}_N\mathfrak{c}^*(j,i) < 1$; but it converges toward 1, and therefore in $\mathfrak{L}_\infty$ $\mathfrak{c}^*(h,e \,.\, i) = \mathfrak{c}^*(j,i) = 1$. Thus i is positive to h on e, although $\mathfrak{c}^*(h,e) = 0$.

The following theorem T8 is analogous to T7.

T65-8. Let $e \,.\, \sim h$ be L-false in $\mathfrak{L}$; in other words, $\vdash e \supset h$. (This holds in $\mathfrak{L}_N$ if $\mathfrak{c}(h,e) = 1$.) Then the following holds.

a. Lemma. If e is not L-false, $\mathfrak{c}(h,e) = 1$. (From T59-1b.)

b. Lemma. For any i such that $e \,.\, i$ is not L-false, $\mathfrak{c}(h,e \,.\, i) = 1$. (From T59-1b.)

c. Every sentence is irrelevant to h on e. (From D1d, (a), (b).)

T8 says for $\mathfrak{L}_N$ that, once h is confirmed to the maximum degree 1, then this will not be changed by any additional evidence. This does not hold generally for $\mathfrak{L}_\infty$.

To give a counterexample in $\mathfrak{L}_\infty$, we take again the function $\mathfrak{c}^*$ and the sentences h, j, and i of the former example. Then $\mathfrak{c}^*(h,i) = 1$. Nevertheless, $\sim j$ is negative to h on i because $\vdash h \supset j$, hence $\vdash \sim j \supset \sim h$, hence $\mathfrak{c}^*(h,i \,.\, \sim j) = 0$.

T65-9. Let $e \,.\, \sim i$ be L-false in $\mathfrak{L}$; in other words, $\vdash e \supset i$. Let h be any sentence. For $\mathfrak{L}_\infty$, let either e be L-false or $\mathfrak{c}(h,e)$ have a value. Then i is irrelevant to h on e.

Proof. $e \,.\, i$ is L-equivalent to e (T21-5i(1)). If $e \,.\, i$ is L-false, i is irrelevant (D1d(2)). If $e \,.\, i$ is not L-false, then e is not L-false, and $\mathfrak{c}(h,e \,.\, i) = \mathfrak{c}(h,e)$; hence again i is irrelevant (D1d(1)).

Relevance of a state-description $\mathfrak{Z}_i$ in $\mathfrak{L}_N$:

T65-11. Let e be a sentence in $\mathfrak{L}_N$ which holds in $\mathfrak{Z}_i$. (Hence e is not L-false.) Let h be any sentence not L-implied by e and likewise holding in $\mathfrak{Z}_i$.

a. $\mathfrak{Z}_i$ is positive to h on e.

Proof. Since not $\vdash e \supset h$, $\mathfrak{c}(h,e) < 1$ (T59-5a). $\vdash \mathfrak{Z}_i \supset h$ and $\vdash \mathfrak{Z}_i \supset e$ (T20-2t); hence $e \,.\, \mathfrak{Z}_i$ is L-equivalent to $\mathfrak{Z}_i$ (T21-5i(1)). Therefore $\mathfrak{c}(h,e \,.\, \mathfrak{Z}_i) = \mathfrak{c}(h,\mathfrak{Z}_i)$, $= 1$ (T59-1b). Hence the assertion.

b. $\sim \mathfrak{Z}_i$ is negative to h on e. (From (a), T6e.)

Later, after the introduction of the relevance measure $\mathfrak{r}$, we shall make a more detailed investigation of the relevance of state-descriptions and their negations (§§ 72, 73).

We shall now introduce concepts of relevance and irrelevance which are analogous to those defined above but apply to the special case where the evidence e is tautological. This means that we judge the relevance of i to h before any factual knowledge is available. If i is relevant to h on the tautological evidence 't', we shall say that i is ***initially relevant*** to h. For the probability$_1$ on the evidence 't', classical authors used the term 'probability a priori' and later authors 'initial probability'. We have used the terms 'null confirmation' and 'initial confirmation' (and the symbol '$\mathfrak{c}_0$', D57-1). For the present concept, the term 'relevance a priori' might be taken, but the term 'initial relevance' is probably less in danger of being misinterpreted. The concepts here defined will seldom be used in the following.

D65-2. Let $\mathfrak{c}$ be a regular $\mathfrak{c}$-function in $\mathfrak{L}$, and let h and i be sentences in $\mathfrak{L}$.

a. i is *initially positive* to h (with respect to $\mathfrak{c}$ in $\mathfrak{L}$) $=_{\mathrm{Df}}$ i is positive to h on evidence 't'.

b. i is *initially negative* to h (with respect to $\mathfrak{c}$ in $\mathfrak{L}$) $=_{\mathrm{Df}}$ i is negative to h on evidence 't'.

c. i is *initially relevant* to h (with respect to $\mathfrak{c}$ in $\mathfrak{L}$) $=_{\mathrm{Df}}$ i is relevant to h on evidence 't'.

d. i is *initially irrelevant* to h (with respect to $\mathfrak{c}$ in $\mathfrak{L}$) $=_{\mathrm{Df}}$ i is irrelevant to h on evidence 't'.

The following theorem T13 is analogous to T4. The items (a) to (d) give convenient other forms of sufficient and necessary conditions for the four concepts introduced by D2.

T65-13. Let h and i be either (i) any sentences in $\mathfrak{L}_N$, or (ii) any non-general sentences in $\mathfrak{L}_\infty$, or (iii) any sentences in $\mathfrak{L}_\infty$ fulfilling the following two conditions: (A) $\mathfrak{m}$ has values for $i \,.\, h$, $i \,.\, \sim h$, $\sim i \,.\, h$, and $\sim i \,.\, \sim h$ (and hence also for i and h), and (B) i is not almost L-false (hence either i is L-false or $\mathfrak{m}(i) > 0$). Then the following holds.

a. i is *initially positive* to h
  (1) if and only if $\mathfrak{c}(h,i) > \mathfrak{c}_0(h)$; (from D2a, D1a, D57-1);
  (2) if and only if $\mathfrak{m}(i \,.\, h) > \mathfrak{m}(i) \times \mathfrak{m}(h)$. (From T4c(1).)

b. i is *initially negative* to h
  (1) if and only if $\mathfrak{c}(h,i) < \mathfrak{c}_0(h)$;
  (2) if and only if $\mathfrak{m}(i \,.\, h) < \mathfrak{m}(i) \times \mathfrak{m}(h)$. (Analogous to (a).)

c. i is *initially relevant* to h
  (1) if and only if $\mathfrak{c}(h,i) \neq \mathfrak{c}_0(h)$;
  (2) if and only if $\mathfrak{m}(i \,.\, h) \neq \mathfrak{m}(i) \times \mathfrak{m}(h)$. (From (a), (b).)

d. i is *initially irrelevant* to h
  (1) if and only if $\mathfrak{c}(h,i) = \mathfrak{c}_0(h)$ or i is L-false;
  (2) if and only if $\mathfrak{m}(i \,.\, h) = \mathfrak{m}(i) \times \mathfrak{m}(h)$. (Analogous to (a).)

e. i is initially either relevant or irrelevant to h. (From T4g.)

T65-14. Let h be L-false or L-true in $\mathfrak{L}$. Then every sentence is initially irrelevant to h. (From T7c, T8c.)

T14 is analogous to T7 and T8. Analogues to the other previous theorems on relevance and irrelevance hold obviously here too; they are simply special cases with 't' taking the place of e.

§ 66. The Relevance Quotient

The simple relevance quotient, symbolized by '$\{i_1,i_2\}_e$', is defined as $\mathfrak{c}(i_1,e \,.\, i_2)/\mathfrak{c}(i_1,e)$, hence as the quotient of the posterior and prior confirmations of i_1 (D1a). A related function for more arguments is defined analogously

(D1b). Among the theorems are the following. It is clear that i is positive, negative, or irrelevant to h on e if $\{h,i\}_e$ is >1, <1, or $=1$, respectively (T2). The $\mathfrak{c}$ of a conjunction is the product of the $\mathfrak{c}$-values for the conjunctive components and the corresponding relevance quotient (T3). The relevance quotient is commutative (T4). The definition and the theorems of this section are due to W. E. Johnson and Keynes. They will not be used further on in this book.

In this and the subsequent sections we shall deal with numerical functions of three sentences. They belong to the kind of functions which might be called relevance functions, since for each of them the value for a triple of sentences i, h, e is characteristic for i being positive or negative or irrelevant to h on e. In the present section we shall briefly explain a function which W. E. Johnson and Keynes have discussed, but which will not be used further on in this book. In the next section we shall introduce a new relevance function.

The relevance concepts defined in the preceding section have to do with the change in the confirmation of h when a new evidence i is added to the prior evidence e, that is, with the change from $\mathfrak{c}(h,e)$ to $\mathfrak{c}(h,e \cdot i)$. i was called positive if the latter value was greater than the former. Now let us look for means which will make it possible not only to say that i is positively relevant but, so to speak, to measure the positive relevance of i. There are obviously two simple ways for doing so; we may either take the quotient $\mathfrak{c}(h,e \cdot i)/\mathfrak{c}(h,e)$ or the difference $\mathfrak{c}(h,e \cdot i) - \mathfrak{c}(h,e)$. i is positively relevant if the quotient is >1, and also if the difference is >0. Thus both functions are relevance functions. The first of them, which we call the ***relevance quotient***, will be dealt with in this section, following Keynes. Another function which is closely related to the difference will be introduced in the next section and used throughout the remainder of this chapter.

Keynes ([Probab.], pp. 150–55) gives a definition of the relevance quotient, which he calls the coefficient of influence, and a series of theorems on this concept, based upon unpublished notes by W. E. Johnson. The following exposition follows Keynes in the main lines; we use, however, a slightly modified symbol and transfer the whole into our terminology and symbolism.

D66-1. Let $\mathfrak{c}$ be a regular $\mathfrak{c}$-function in the finite or infinite system $\mathfrak{L}$. Let e, i_1, i_2, etc., be sentences in $\mathfrak{L}$ whose conjunction is not L-false, and h any sentence in $\mathfrak{L}$. We define recursively (with respect to $\mathfrak{c}$ in $\mathfrak{L}$):

a. *Simple relevance quotient.* $\{i_1,i_2\}_e =_{Df} \frac{\mathfrak{c}(i_1,e \cdot i_2)}{\mathfrak{c}(i_1,e)}$.

b. *Multiple relevance quotient* ($n \geqq 2$). $\{i_1,i_2, \ldots ,i_{n+1}\}_e =_{Df} \{i_1,i_2, \ldots , i_{n-1},i_n \cdot i_{n+1}\}_e \times \{i_n,i_{n+1}\}_e$.

Keynes writes instead of (b) '$\{i_1{}^e i_2{}^e i_3{}^e \ldots {}^e i_{n+1}\}$'. Since all superscripts in any expression of this form are alike, it seems simpler to indicate the evidence only once.

Thus we have, for instance, for three arguments:

$$\{h,i,j\}_e = \{h,i \cdot j\}_e \times \{i,j\}_e = \frac{\mathfrak{c}(h,e \cdot i \cdot j)}{\mathfrak{c}(h,e)} \times \frac{\mathfrak{c}(i,e \cdot j)}{\mathfrak{c}(i,e)} .$$

In the following theorems we omit for brevity the reference 'with respect to $\mathfrak{c}$ in $\mathfrak{L}$'. However, the relativity with respect to $\mathfrak{c}$ must be kept in mind. We cannot determine the numerical value of a relevance quotient unless we choose a specific $\mathfrak{c}$-function.

T66-1. Let e' be L-equivalent to e, and for every p = 1 to n ($n \geqq 2$), let i'_p be L-equivalent to i_p with respect to e. Then $\{i'_1,i'_2, \ldots ,i'_n\}_{e'} = \{i_1,i_2, \ldots ,i_n\}_e$. (From D1, T59-1h, T59-2j.)

+T66-2.

a. i is *positive* to h on evidence e if and only if $\{h,i\}_e > 1$. (From D1a, D65-1a.)

b. i is *negative* to h on e if and only if $\{h,i\}_e < 1$. (From D1a, D65-1b.)

c. i is *relevant* to h on e if and only if $\{h,i\}_e \neq 1$. (From D65-1c, (a), (b).)

d. i is *irrelevant* to h on e if and only if either (1) $\{h,i\}_e = 1$, or
(2) $\mathfrak{c}(h,e \cdot i) = \mathfrak{c}(h,e) = 0$, or
(3) $e \cdot i$ is L-false.
(From D65-1d, D1a.) (In case (2) the relevance quotient has no value; in case (3), $\mathfrak{c}(h,e \cdot i)$, and hence the relevance quotient too, has no value.)

For the following theorems it is presupposed that e, h, i, i_1, i_2, etc., are sentences in $\mathfrak{L}$ such that the { }-expressions and $\mathfrak{c}$-expressions occurring have values.

T3 shows how the relevance quotient makes it possible to express the confirmation of a conjunction in terms of the confirmations of the components separately.

+T66-3.

a. $\mathfrak{c}(h \cdot i,e) = \{h,i\}_e \times \mathfrak{c}(h,e) \times \mathfrak{c}(i,e)$. (From T59-1n(2), D1a.)

b. $\mathfrak{c}(h \cdot i \cdot j,e) = \{h,i,j\}_e \times \mathfrak{c}(h,e) \times \mathfrak{c}(i,e) \times \mathfrak{c}(j,e)$.

Proof. $\mathfrak{c}(h \cdot i \cdot j,e) = \{h,i \cdot j\}_e \times \mathfrak{c}(h,e) \times \mathfrak{c}(i \cdot j,e)$ (from (a)). $\mathfrak{c}(i \cdot j,e) = \{i,j\}_e \times \mathfrak{c}(i,e) \times \mathfrak{c}(j,e)$ (from (a)). Hence assertion by D1b.

c. $\mathfrak{c}(i_1 \cdot i_2 \cdot \ldots \cdot i_n,e) = \{i_1,i_2, \ldots ,i_n\}_e \times \prod_{p=1}^{n} \mathfrak{c}(i_p,e)$.

Proof analogous to (b), by mathematical induction.

T4 states the *commutativity* of the relevance quotient. T4a is simply the general division theorem (T60-1d) rewritten in the present notation.

+T66-4.

a. $\{h,i\}_e = \{i,h\}_e$. (From T60-1d.)

b. $\{i_1,i_2,\ldots,i_n\}_e = \{i_{p_1},i_{p_2},\ldots,i_{p_n}\}_e$, where the right-hand expression contains the same terms as the left-hand expression but in an arbitrary different order.

Proof. From T3c, because of the commutativity of multiple conjunction and multiplication.

Note that T4a holds only if *both* { }-expressions have values. In $\mathfrak{L}_N$, either both have values (this is the case if and only if $e \,.\, i$ and $e \,.\, h$ are not L-false) or both have not. In $\mathfrak{L}_\infty$, however, this does not hold. [It may occur in $\mathfrak{L}_\infty$ that $\mathfrak{c}(h,e) = 0$ and hence the first { }-expression has no value; but nevertheless $e \,.\, h$ is not L-false, $\mathfrak{c}(i,e \,.\, h)$ has a value, and $\mathfrak{c}(i,e) > 0$, and hence the second { }-expression has a value.]

T66-5. $\{\ldots,i \,.\, j,\ldots\}_e \times \{i,j\}_e = \{\ldots,i,j,\ldots\}_e$, where the last { }-expression is like the first except for containing in the place of the term '$i \,.\, j$' the two terms 'i' and 'j' separately. (From D1c, T4b.)

T7 is W. E. Johnson's "Cumulative Formula".

T66-7. Let i be the conjunction $i_1 \,.\, i_2 \,.\, \ldots \,.\, i_n \,.\, i_{n+1}$ $(n \geqq 1)$.

$$\frac{[\mathfrak{c}(h,e)]^n \times \mathfrak{c}(h,e \,.\, i)}{[\mathfrak{c}(h',e)]^n \times \mathfrak{c}(h',e \,.\, i)} = \frac{\{i_1,i_2,\ldots,i_{n+1}\}_{e\,.\,h} \times \prod_{p=1}^{n+1} \mathfrak{c}(h,e \,.\, i_p)}{\{i_1,i_2,\ldots,i_{n+1}\}_{e\,.\,h'} \times \prod_{p=1}^{n+1} \mathfrak{c}(h',e \,.\, i_p)}\,.$$

Proof. With respect to a variation of h, the following proportionalities hold. $\mathfrak{c}(h,e \,.\, i)$ prop. $\mathfrak{c}(h,e) \times \mathfrak{c}(i,e \,.\, h)$ (T60-2b). Hence

$$[\mathfrak{c}(h,e)]^n \times \mathfrak{c}(h,e \,.\, i) \text{ prop. } [\mathfrak{c}(h,e)]^{n+1} \times \mathfrak{c}(i,e \,.\, h)\,. \qquad (1)$$

From T3c:

$$[\mathfrak{c}(h,e)]^{n+1} \times \mathfrak{c}(i,e \,.\, h) = [\mathfrak{c}(h,e)]^{n+1} \times \{i_1,i_2,\ldots,i_{n+1}\}_{e\,.\,h} \times \prod_{p=1}^{n+1} \mathfrak{c}(i_p,e \,.\, h)\,. \quad (2)$$

If we apply T60-2b to each of $i_1,i_2,\ldots,i_{n+1}$ instead of i and then equate the product of the left sides to the product of the right sides and finally exchange the two sides, we obtain:

$$[\mathfrak{c}(h,e)]^{n+1} \times \prod_{p=1}^{n+1} \mathfrak{c}(i_p,e \,.\, h) \text{ prop. } \prod_{p=1}^{n+1} \mathfrak{c}(h,e \,.\, i_p)\,. \qquad (3)$$

The assertion follows from (1), (2), and (3).

As Keynes remarks (p. 152, in different terminology), the accumulative formula is to be applied in the following situation. X has accumulated the items of evidence $i_1, i_2, \ldots, i_{n+1}$ in addition to his prior evidence e; he desires to know the ratio of the $\mathfrak{c}$-values of h and h' and maybe other hypotheses under consideration, while he knows already the confirmation of these hypotheses on the evidence of each of the items i_1, i_2, etc., separately, together with e. Besides the confirmations just mentioned, viz., $\mathfrak{c}(h,e \cdot i_p)$ and $\mathfrak{c}(h',e \cdot i_p)$ for every p, the knowledge of two other sets of values is required: (1) the prior confirmation of the hypotheses (i.e., $\mathfrak{c}(h,e)$ and $\mathfrak{c}(h',e)$), and (2) the relevance quotients $\{i_1,i_2, \ldots, i_{n+1}\}$ both on $e \cdot h$ and on $e \cdot h'$. Keynes remarks that the latter two values for $e \cdot h$ and $e \cdot h'$ are not related in any way, even when h' is L-equivalent to $\sim h$.

I omit some further theorems stated by Keynes. The concept explained will hardly be used in the remainder of this book. It has been represented in this section in order to call attention to an interesting concept which deserves further investigation. It seems useful for problems of accumulative evidence, especially within a theory which (like Keynes's, in distinction to the theory which will later be based on the function $\mathfrak{c}^*$) deals only with $\mathfrak{c}$-functions in general without choosing a specific one. In the following sections we shall study problems of relevance with the help of another relevance function to be introduced, which turns out to be useful for our purposes. We shall see that this new function is additive in certain respects; that makes it helpful for finding the relevance of connections like $i \cdot j$ and $i \vee j$, etc., on the basis of the relevances of i and j.

§ 67. The Relevance Measure

The numerical function $\mathfrak{r}(i,h,e)$ is defined as follows: $\mathfrak{r}(i,h,e) =_{\mathrm{Df}} \mathfrak{m}(e \cdot i \cdot h) \times \mathfrak{m}(e) - \mathfrak{m}(e \cdot h) \times \mathfrak{m}(e \cdot i)$ (D1). We call it the relevance measure of i (to h on e), because (in $\mathfrak{L}_N$ always and in $\mathfrak{L}_\infty$ under a certain condition) $\mathfrak{r}(i,h,e)$ is >0, <0, or 0, if and only if i is (to h on e) positive, negative, or irrelevant, respectively (T8, T9, T10). $\mathfrak{r}$ is commutative, that is, $\mathfrak{r}(i,h,e) = \mathfrak{r}(h,i,e)$ (T3). If i or h is replaced by its negation, $\mathfrak{r}$ changes to the opposite value (T5). These properties of $\mathfrak{r}$ correspond to those of the relevance concepts. $\mathfrak{r}$ turns out to be a suitable means for characterizing relevance situations and will therefore be used continually in the following sections. The chief advantages of $\mathfrak{r}$, its additivity in two respects, will be explained later (§§ 72, 73).

We have earlier seen that the regular $\mathfrak{m}$-functions may be regarded as measure functions for the ranges, because the $\mathfrak{m}$-value for the class-sum (union) of two mutually exclusive ranges is the sum of the $\mathfrak{m}$-values for the two ranges. In terms of sentences, this means that, if i and j are L-exclusive, $\mathfrak{m}(i \vee j) = \mathfrak{m}(i) + \mathfrak{m}(j)$ (T57-1m). Analogously, the $\mathfrak{c}$-functions may be regarded as measure-functions for the ranges because they fulfil an analogous condition as stated in the special addition theorem (T59-1l). In this section we shall introduce a relevance function $\mathfrak{r}$ which possesses the same additivity with respect to exclusive ranges. This is the reason why we call this relevance function, in distinction to that discussed in the preceding section, the ***relevance measure***. [r is, however, different from ordinary measure functions like length, area, volume, etc., by admitting also negative values.] It will turn out further, that this function r, in contradistinction to m- and c-functions, is simultaneously a measure function for the contents of sentences (§ 73).

It is the purpose of relevance functions in general to represent the change in the confirmation of *h* on *e* by the addition of a new evidence *i*. The relevance quotient did this by way of the quotient of the posterior confirmation $c(h,e \cdot i)$ and the prior confirmation $c(h,e)$. Another relevance function is the difference $c(h,e \cdot i) - c(h,e)$; let us call it D_1 for the moment. D_1 is the amount of the increase of the c of *h* by the addition of *i* to *e*. It can easily be shown that D_1 has the additivity mentioned above for r. Therefore it could be taken as a relevance measure. The disadvantage of D_1 is that it is not commutative with respect to *h* and *i*. If we exchange *h* and *i*, we obtain the different function $c(i,e \cdot h) - c(i,e)$; let us call it D_2. D_2 measures the increase of the c of *i* by the addition of *h* to *e*. It is likewise additive. Each of the two functions D_1 and D_2 has the property that its value is >0 if *i* is positive to *h* on *e* and hence also *h* is positive to *i* on *e*. Positive relevance on a given *e* is a symmetrical relation between *i* and *h* (T65-6a). Therefore, instead of using two different functions D_1 and D_2, it will be more convenient to represent the mutual relevance of *i* and *h* on *e* by one function which is commutative with respect to *i* and *h*, that is, which has the same value for *i,h,e* as for *h,i,e*. That is the chief reason for introducing the function r instead of the two functions D_1 and D_2. r is closely related to both of them; it is proportional to D_1 in one respect (T4b) and proportional to D_2 in another (T4e). r also characterizes mutual positive relevance of *i* and *h* by positive values and negative relevance by negative values (T8, T9, T10). It is true that the functions D_1 and D_2 have the advantage that it is easier to understand the meaning of their values as characteristics of the knowledge situations to which they are applied. It turns out, however, that the function r, although less intuitive, is a more convenient theoretical tool for the analysis of problems of relevance. We shall make extensive use of this function throughout the remainder of this chapter.

We shall find in the next section that r is additive in two respects. First, the r-value for a disjunction with L-exclusive components is the sum of the values for the components (T68-1). This is especially useful in view of the fact that every sentence can be transformed into the disjunction of the $\mathfrak{Z}$ in its range; and these $\mathfrak{Z}$ are L-exclusive (§ 72). Second, the $\mathfrak{r}$-value for a conjunction with L-disjunct components is the sum of the values for the components (T68-2); this will later be used for an analysis of the relevance of a sentence based on the relevances of its content-elements, i.e., its ultimate conjunctive components (§ 73).

+D67-1. Let $\mathfrak{L}$ be any finite or infinite system, $\mathfrak{m}$ be a regular $\mathfrak{m}$-function in $\mathfrak{L}$, and i, h, and e be any sentences in $\mathfrak{L}$. The ***relevance measure*** (with respect to $\mathfrak{m}$ in $\mathfrak{L}$) $\mathfrak{r}(i,h,e) =_{\mathrm{Df}} \mathfrak{m}(e \,.\, i \,.\, h) \times \mathfrak{m}(e) - \mathfrak{m}(e \,.\, h) \times \mathfrak{m}(e \,.\, i)$.

This function is suggested in an obvious way by one form of our previous criteria for relevance and irrelevance (T65-4c(1), d(1), e(1), and f(1)). The other form (T65-4c(2), d(2), e(2), and f(2)) corresponds to the subsequent theorem T1.

+T67-1. $\mathfrak{r}(i,h,e) = \mathfrak{m}(e \,.\, i \,.\, h) \times \mathfrak{m}(e \,.\, \sim i \,.\, \sim h) - \mathfrak{m}(e \,.\, i \,.\, \sim h) \times \mathfrak{m}(e \,.\, \sim i \,.\, h)$; hence (in the notation of § 65) $= \mathfrak{m}_1 \times \mathfrak{m}_4 - \mathfrak{m}_2 \times \mathfrak{m}_3$. (From D1, T65-1.)

T67-2. The *domain of definition* of $\mathfrak{r}$.

a. In $\mathfrak{L}_N$, $\mathfrak{r}$ has a value for every triple of sentences i,h,e.

b. In $\mathfrak{L}_\infty$, $\mathfrak{r}$ (with respect to a given $\mathfrak{m}$) has a value for i,h,e

(1) if and only if $\mathfrak{m}$ has values for the four sentences e, $e \,.\, h$, $e \,.\, i$, and $e \,.\, i \,.\, h$ (from D1);

(2) if and only if $\mathfrak{m}$ has values for the four sentences $e \,.\, i \,.\, h$, $e \,.\, i \,.\, \sim h$, $e \,.\, \sim i \,.\, h$, and $e \,.\, \sim i \,.\, \sim h$. (These are the sentences k_1, k_2, k_3, and k_4 in the notation of § 65.) (From T1.)

Thus for the existence of $\mathfrak{r}$-values there are no restrictions in a finite system and only weak restricting conditions in the infinite system; the latter conditions require only that certain $\mathfrak{m}$-values exist, not that they are positive. For some $\mathfrak{m}$-functions, this condition is fulfilled for all sentences. [For example, we shall find later that our function $\mathfrak{m}^*$ has a value for every sentence in $\mathfrak{L}_\infty^\pi$ (§ 110A).] For the subsequent theorems here and throughout this chapter, the following is tacitly presupposed if not otherwise indicated. $\mathfrak{L}$ is any finite or infinite system; $\mathfrak{m}$ is any regular $\mathfrak{m}$-function for $\mathfrak{L}$; $\mathfrak{c}$ is the regular $\mathfrak{c}$-function for $\mathfrak{L}$ corresponding to $\mathfrak{m}$; $\mathfrak{r}$ is the relevance measure with respect to $\mathfrak{m}$ in $\mathfrak{L}$; the concepts of positive and negative relevance and irrelevance are meant with respect to $\mathfrak{c}$ in $\mathfrak{L}$. It is further presupposed that the sentences occurring as arguments of one of the functions $\mathfrak{m}$, $\mathfrak{c}$, or $\mathfrak{r}$ are such that this function has a value for them.

+T67-3. *Commutativity.* $\mathfrak{r}(h,i,e) = \mathfrak{r}(i,h,e)$. (From D1, T57-1a.)

The following theorem connects $\mathfrak{r}$ with the two differences of $\mathfrak{c}$-values discussed above and with the relevance quotient discussed in the preceding section.

T67-4.

a. $\mathfrak{r}(i,h,e) = [\mathfrak{c}(h,e \cdot i) - \mathfrak{c}(h,e)] \times \mathfrak{m}(e) \times \mathfrak{m}(e \cdot i)$.

Proof. 1. Let $\mathfrak{m}(e \cdot i) = 0$. Then $\mathfrak{m}(e \cdot i \cdot h) = 0$ (T57-1s). Hence both sides of the equation are 0. 2. Let $\mathfrak{m}(e \cdot i) > 0$. Then $\mathfrak{m}(e) > 0$ (T57-1s). Then $\mathfrak{c}(h,e \cdot i) = \mathfrak{m}(e \cdot i \cdot h)/\mathfrak{m}(e \cdot i)$, and $\mathfrak{c}(h,e) = \mathfrak{m}(e \cdot h)/\mathfrak{m}(e)$ (for $\mathfrak{L}_\infty$, T56-4a). Hence the assertion.

b. With respect to a variation of h, $\mathfrak{r}(i,h,e)$ is proportional to $\mathfrak{c}(h,e \cdot i) - \mathfrak{c}(h,e)$. (From (a).)

c. If $\mathfrak{m}(e \cdot i) > 0$ (and hence $\mathfrak{m}(e) > 0$, T57-1s), then $\mathfrak{c}(h,e \cdot i) - \mathfrak{c}(h,e) = \mathfrak{r}(i,h,e)/\mathfrak{m}(e) \times \mathfrak{m}(e \cdot i)$. (From (a).)

d. $\mathfrak{r}(i,h,e) = [\mathfrak{c}(i,e \cdot h) - \mathfrak{c}(i,e)] \times \mathfrak{m}(e) \times \mathfrak{m}(e \cdot h)$.

Proof, by exchanging in (a) 'i' and 'h', and then applying T3.

e. With respect to a variation of i, $\mathfrak{r}(i,h,e)$ is proportional to $\mathfrak{c}(i,e \cdot h) - \mathfrak{c}(i,e)$. (From (d).)

f. If $\mathfrak{m}(e \cdot h) > 0$ (and hence $\mathfrak{m}(e) > 0$), then $\mathfrak{c}(i,e \cdot h) - \mathfrak{c}(i,e) = \mathfrak{r}(i,h,e)/\mathfrak{m}(e) \times \mathfrak{m}(e \cdot h)$. (From (d).)

h. $\mathfrak{r}(i,h,e) = [\{h,i\}_e - 1] \times \mathfrak{m}(e \cdot h) \times \mathfrak{m}(e \cdot i)$.

Proof. 1. Let at least one of the two values $\mathfrak{m}(e \cdot h)$ and $\mathfrak{m}(e \cdot i)$ be 0. Then both sides of the equation are 0 (as in the proof of (a)(1)). 2. Let both $\mathfrak{m}(e \cdot h) > 0$ and $\mathfrak{m}(e \cdot i) > 0$. Then $\mathfrak{m}(e) > 0$ (T57-1s). If we transform the expression in square brackets according to D66-1a, and then the $\mathfrak{c}$-expressions occurring as in the proof of (a)(2), we obtain the assertion.

i. If both $\mathfrak{m}(e \cdot h) > 0$ and $\mathfrak{m}(e \cdot i) > 0$, then

$$\{h,i\}_e = 1 + \frac{\mathfrak{r}(i,h,e)}{\mathfrak{m}(e \cdot h) \times \mathfrak{m}(e \cdot i)}. \text{ (From (h).)}$$

If $\mathfrak{r}(i,h,e)$ is known, then (c) shows how to determine the increase in the $\mathfrak{c}$ of h caused by the addition of i to e, and (f) shows how to determine the increase in the $\mathfrak{c}$ of i caused by the addition of h to e. The amounts of these two increases are in general different. The value of $\mathfrak{r}$, however, is the same for both cases (T3).

T5 determines the relevance measure for the cases that i or h or both are negated.

+T67-5.

a. $\mathfrak{r}(\sim i,h,e) = -\mathfrak{r}(i,h,e)$.

Proof. $\mathfrak{r}(\sim i,h,e) = \mathfrak{m}(e \cdot \sim i \cdot h) \times \mathfrak{m}(e \cdot i \cdot \sim h) - \mathfrak{m}(e \cdot \sim i \cdot \sim h) \times \mathfrak{m}(e \cdot i \cdot h)$ (T1), $= \mathfrak{m}(e \cdot i \cdot \sim h) \times \mathfrak{m}(e \cdot \sim i \cdot h) - \mathfrak{m}(e \cdot i \cdot h) \times \mathfrak{m}(e \cdot \sim i \cdot \sim h) = -\mathfrak{r}(i,h,e)$ (T1)

b. $\mathfrak{r}(i, \sim h, e) = -\mathfrak{r}(i,h,e)$. (From T3, (a).)
c. $\mathfrak{r}(\sim i, \sim h, e) = \mathfrak{r}(i,h,e)$. (From (a), (b).)

T5 says that $\mathfrak{r}$ changes its sign if either i is replaced by its negation (a) or h is replaced by its negation (b). Hence $\mathfrak{r}$ remains unchanged if both replacements are made simultaneously (c). Since, as we shall soon see, a positive value of $\mathfrak{r}$ is characteristic of positive relevance and a negative value of negative relevance, these results are in accord with earlier theorems on positive and negative relevance (T65-6h). However, the present theorems are stronger inasmuch as they not only assert the change from positive to negative relevance but specify the numerical value of the relevance measure. The fact that this value does not change its absolute amount but simply its sign, both for the change of i and for that of h, makes the function $\mathfrak{r}$ appear as an especially simple means for characterizing relevance situations.

The following theorem T6 says that in certain extreme cases $\mathfrak{r}$ becomes 0. This holds in particular if e is L-false (b) or e L-implies either h (c) or $\sim h$ (a) or i (e) or $\sim i$ (d). [In $\mathfrak{L}_\infty$, the theorem applies also to nontrivial cases, where one of the sentences e, $e \,.\, h$, $e \,.\, \sim h$, $e \,.\, i$, and $e \,.\, \sim i$ is almost L-false.]

T67-6.

a. Let $\mathfrak{m}(e \,.\, h) = 0$. (This is in particular the case if $\vdash e \supset \sim h$, in other words, $e \,.\, h$ is L-false, e and h are L-exclusive.) Then, for every i, $\mathfrak{r}(i,h,e) = 0$.

Proof. $\mathfrak{m}(e \,.\, h \,.\, i) = 0$ (T57-1s). Hence the assertion by D1.

b. Let $\mathfrak{m}(e) = 0$. (This is the case if e is L-false.) Then for every i and h, $\mathfrak{r}(i,h,e) = 0$. (From T57-1s, (a).)

c. Let $\mathfrak{m}(e \,.\, \sim h) = 0$. (This is the case if $\vdash e \supset h$.) Then, for every i, $\mathfrak{r}(i,h,e) = 0$.

Proof, from (a) with '$\sim h$' for 'h', and T5b.

d. Let $\mathfrak{m}(e \,.\, i) = 0$. (This is the case if $\vdash e \supset \sim i$, in other words, $e \,.\, i$ is L-false, e and i are L-exclusive; and in particular if i is L-false.) Then, for every h, $\mathfrak{r}(i,h,e) = 0$. (Analogous to (a).)

e. Let $\mathfrak{m}(e \,.\, \sim i) = 0$. (This is the case if $\vdash e \supset i$; and in particular if i is L-true.) Then, for every h, $\mathfrak{r}(i,h,e) = 0$. (From (d), T5a.)

The following theorems T8 to T10 show that $\mathfrak{r}$ fulfils its purpose of serving as a relevance function; under certain conditions, positive relevance is characterized by a positive value of $\mathfrak{r}$, negative relevance by a negative value, and irrelevance by the value 0. There are certain exceptions in $\mathfrak{L}_\infty$, which will soon be explained.

+T67-8.

a. If $\mathfrak{r}(i,h,e) > 0$, then i is positive to h on e.

Proof. $\mathfrak{m}$ has values for e, $e \cdot h$, $e \cdot i$, and $e \cdot i \cdot h$ (T2b(1)). $\mathfrak{m}(e)$ and $\mathfrak{m}(e \cdot i)$ are >0 (T6b, d). Hence $\mathfrak{c}(h,e \cdot i)$ and $\mathfrak{c}(h,e)$ exist (T56-4a), and their difference is >0 (T4c). Hence the assertion by D65-1a.

b. If $\mathfrak{r}(i,h,e) < 0$, then i is negative to h on e. (Analogous to (a).)

c. If $\mathfrak{r}(i,h,e) \neq 0$, then i is relevant to h on e. (From (a), (b).)

d. If i is irrelevant to h on e, then $\mathfrak{r}(i,h,e) = 0$. (From (c).)

The statements in T9 are restricted converses to those in T8.

+T67-9. Let $e \cdot i$ not be almost L-false; in other words, either $e \cdot i$ is L-false or $\mathfrak{m}(e \cdot i) > 0$. Then the following holds.

a. If i is positive to h on e, then $\mathfrak{r}(i,h,e) > 0$.

Proof. $e \cdot i$ is not L-false (T65-3); hence $\mathfrak{m}(e \cdot i) > 0$; hence $\mathfrak{m}(e) > 0$ (T57-1s). $\mathfrak{c}(h,e \cdot i) - \mathfrak{c}(h,e) > 0$ (D65-1a). Hence the assertion by T4a.

b. If i is negative to h on e, then $\mathfrak{r}(i,h,e) < 0$. (Analogous to (a).)

c. If i is relevant to h on e, then $\mathfrak{r}(i,h,e) \neq 0$. (From (a), (b).)

d. If $\mathfrak{r}(i,h,e) = 0$, then i is irrelevant to h on e.

Proof. Let $e \cdot i$ not be L-false (otherwise the assertion follows from D65-1d(2)). Then $\mathfrak{m}(e \cdot i) > 0$, and hence $\mathfrak{m}(e) > 0$. Therefore $\mathfrak{c}(h,e \cdot i) = \mathfrak{m}(e \cdot i \cdot h)/\mathfrak{m}(e \cdot i)$, and $\mathfrak{c}(h,e) = \mathfrak{m}(e \cdot h)/\mathfrak{m}(e)$ (T56-4a). [This, the existence of the two $\mathfrak{c}$-values, is the decisive point in this proof; because of this point, we cannot derive (d) directly from (c).] The difference of the two $\mathfrak{c}$-values is 0 (T4c). Hence the assertion by D65-1d(1).

The *restricting condition* in T9 requiring that $e \cdot i$ not be almost L-false applies, of course, only to $\mathfrak{L}_\infty$. It must be required for $\mathfrak{L}_\infty$ because here the following can happen: $\mathfrak{c}(h,e \cdot i)$ and $\mathfrak{c}(h,e)$ have values, hence $e \cdot i$ is not L-false; the first of the two values is greater, hence i is positive to h on e; however, $\mathfrak{m}(e \cdot i) = 0$ ($e \cdot i$ is almost L-false) and hence $\mathfrak{m}(e \cdot i \cdot h) = 0$; therefore $\mathfrak{r}(i,h,e) = 0$. As an example, take the sentences e, h, and i mentioned in the discussions following T65-6 and T65-7. Then the following holds in $\mathfrak{L}_\infty$ for certain $\mathfrak{m}$ and $\mathfrak{c}$ (among them our functions $\mathfrak{m}^*$ and $\mathfrak{c}^*$): i and h and hence $e \cdot i$ and $e \cdot h$ are almost L-false; $\mathfrak{c}(h,e) = 0$, $\mathfrak{c}(h,e \cdot i) = 1$, hence i is positive to h on e; on the other hand, $\mathfrak{m}(i) = 0$, hence $\mathfrak{m}(e \cdot i) = \mathfrak{m}(e \cdot i \cdot h) = 0$, hence $\mathfrak{r}(i,h,e) = 0$.

T10 says that the parallelism between the relevance concepts and $\mathfrak{r}$ holds in $\mathfrak{L}_N$ without any restriction. The same holds for $\mathfrak{L}_\infty$, if e and i are nongeneral, since in this case $e \cdot i$ cannot be almost L-false (T58-3e).

+T67-10. For $\mathfrak{L}_N$.

a. The following four conditions are logically equivalent, that is to say, if any of them holds, all others hold too:

(1) $\mathfrak{r}(i,h,e) > 0$;
(2) i is positive to h on e;
(3) $\mathfrak{r}(h,i,e) > 0$;
(4) h is positive to i on e.
(From T8a, T9a; T3.)

b. The following four conditions are logically equivalent:
(1) $\mathfrak{r}(i,h,e) < 0$;
(2) i is negative to h on e;
(3) $\mathfrak{r}(h,i,e) < 0$;
(4) h is negative to i on e.
(From T8b, T9b; T3.)

c. The following four conditions are logically equivalent:
(1) $\mathfrak{r}(i,h,e) \neq 0$;
(2) i is relevant to h on e;
(3) $\mathfrak{r}(h,i,e) \neq 0$;
(4) h is relevant to i on e.
(From T8c, T9c; T3.)

d. The following four conditions are logically equivalent:
(1) $\mathfrak{r}(i,h,e) = 0$;
(2) i is irrelevant to h on e;
(3) $\mathfrak{r}(h,i,e) = 0$;
(4) h is irrelevant to i on e.
(From T8d, T9d; T3.)

T10 will be used frequently in the following sections, often without explicit reference.

§ 68. Relevance Measures for Two Observations and Their Connections

The problems discussed in this section and the next one concern the relations between the relevance measures $\mathfrak{r}$ of i and of j (to h on e), on the one hand, and those of certain connections of i and j, especially $i \vee j$ and $i \cdot j$, on the other. Two theorems of additivity are found: (1) if i and j are L-exclusive with respect to e, then the $\mathfrak{r}$-value for $i \vee j$ (to h on e) is the sum of the values for i and for j (T1b); (2) if i and j are L-disjunct with respect to e, then the $\mathfrak{r}$-value for $i \cdot j$ (to h on e) is the sum of the values for i and for j (T2b). The first result is analogous to the special addition theorems for $\mathfrak{m}$ and for $\mathfrak{c}$; the second result marks an essential difference between $\mathfrak{r}$ and those two functions. The twofold additivity of $\mathfrak{r}$ is important for our further analysis of relevance.

If the $\mathfrak{r}$-values (to h on e) for $i \cdot j$, $i \cdot \sim j$, $\sim i \cdot j$, and $\sim i \cdot \sim j$ are given, the $\mathfrak{r}$-values for i, j, and $i \vee j$ can be obtained as sums of one, two, or three of those four $\mathfrak{r}$-values. This is done first generally (T3) and then for all possible cases of deductive relations between i and j on the evidence e (T4).

In this section we shall develop theorems which tell us whether and how the relevance measures of two sentences i and j (to h on e) determine the relevance measures of their connections, especially of $i \,.\, j$ and $i \vee j$. These theorems will enable us to deal with problems like this: suppose we know that i is positive to h on e (or negative, or irrelevant) and further that j is positive to h on e (or negative, or irrelevant), what can we infer concerning the relevance of $i \,.\, j$, or of $i \vee j$? Problems of this kind occur frequently in science and in everyday life. For example, some scientists are jointly interested in a certain hypothesis h, which may be a general theory or a singular prediction; they pool their prior evidence e; then they start separately to look for further observational material relevant to h. Suppose now one of these scientists reports to the group that he has made observations (i) which are positive to h (on e); then another one reports that he has found evidence (j) which is positive (or negative or irrelevant) to h. Thereupon the group wishes to know what is the relevance to h of the two reports i and j taken together, that is, of the conjunction $i \,.\, j$. In other situations, the problem concerns the relevance of the disjunction $i \vee j$. Suppose, for example, X is interested in a hypothesis concerning the influence of certain rarely occurring conditions on pneumonia. Since he knows so far of only a small number of relevant cases, he is interested in every new report on a case where those particular conditions occurred, even if the report is not as specific as he might wish. Now he receives a new report: the particular conditions did occur, and many other details are reported; however, it has not been examined whether it was a case of virus pneumonia or of bacillus pneumonia. After careful deliberation, X comes to the conclusion that, if the report had stated the first, it would have positive relevance to his hypothesis; if the second, it would be positive too (or negative, or irrelevant). And now he wishes to answer the question, what is the relevance of the actual report from which he learns merely that either the one or the other was the case?

There are analogous problems concerning two hypotheses. If we know the relevance of i to h on e, and also that of i to k on e, what is the relevance of i to $h \,.\, k$ or to $h \vee k$? These problems will be discussed in a later section (§ 70).

Even in a complete system of inductive logic, that is to say, a theory based upon a specific c-function, it is useful to have general theorems saying under what conditions the c increases or decreases, because these theorems might often save us the trouble of computing the prior and posterior confirmations and thus determining the increase or decrease. The importance of general theorems of this kind is still greater in the theory dealt with in this and the preceding chapters, the general theory of regular c-functions. As long as we do not go beyond this theory and choose a specific c-function as our concept of degree of confirmation, we cannot determine any c-values (except the extreme values 0 and 1), and thus there is no other way of determining positive or negative relevance than with the help of general theorems. It is true that we shall later take the further step to a complete inductive logic. However, we cannot expect to find general agreement with our specific choice of a function, while there is a practically general agreement with respect to those assumptions which underlie the theory of regular c-functions (see § 62). Therefore it is important to establish as many results as possible on this basis common to all theories. Thus, for example, it would be of great interest to discover whether the following statement holds generally: if *i* is positive to *h* on *e* and *j* is irrelevant, then $i \vee j$ is positive; or, if this does not hold generally, whether at least the weaker statement holds that under those conditions $i \vee j$ is not negative to *h* on *e*.

One might perhaps think that questions of this kind could be answered without elaborate technical analyses; that, for example, statements of the following kind could be established simply by common sense: (i) if *i* is positive to *h* on *e* and *j* is negative, then for $i \,.\, j$ three cases are possible depending upon the particular nature of the sentences involved: $i \,.\, j$ may be positive (if *i* has, so to speak, a stronger influence than *j*), or negative (in the inverse case), or it may be irrelevant (if *i* and *j* cancel out each other); (ii) if both *i* and *j* are positive to *h* on *e*, then $i \,.\, j$ is positive too. To this it should be remarked first that it is always at least of theoretical interest to reconstruct plausible and even indubitable relationships within a systematic theory, for example, to prove in the propositional calculus that from $i \,.\, j$ we can derive $j \,.\, i$. Furthermore, the superficial appearance of plausibility in inductive logic is very often entirely misleading. Thus, for example, of the two statements mentioned (i) is right, but (ii) is wrong; the conjunction of two sentences which are positive to *h* on *e* may indeed be positive too, but it may also be irrelevant and even negative. In other words, it is possible that each of two reports *i* and *j*, if added to our prior evidence, increases the probability of a certain future event, and nevertheless the simultaneous addition of both reports makes the event less probable. This is the first of four possible cases listed below which may appear rather surprising at first glance. The possibilities are meant in this way: for any c-function that comes at all into consideration as an explicatum, we can easily find sentences *e*, *h*, *i*, and *j* which exhibit these relationships.

The following cases are possible:

1. Both i and j are positive to h on e, but $i \cdot j$ is nevertheless negative to h on e.
2. Both i and j are positive to h on e, but $i \vee j$ is negative.
3. i is positive both to h and to k on e, but it is negative to $h \cdot k$.
4. i is positive both to h and to k on e, but it is negative to $h \vee k$.

These possibilities will not only be proved technically but also made plausible, intuitively understandable, with the help of simple examples. The cases (3) and (4) will be dealt with in the later discussion concerning connections of two hypotheses (§ 71).

In the following discussions we shall often make use of the relative L-terms 'with respect to (the given evidence) e' (see D20-2).

In the following two theorems, the parts T1b and T2b are of especial importance. They state the additivity of $\mathfrak{r}$ for disjunctions and conjunctions under certain conditions and are fundamental for a great part of our further discussions in this chapter.

T68-1. *Additivity for disjunctions.*

a. $\mathfrak{r}(i \vee j,h,e) = \mathfrak{r}(i,h,e) + \mathfrak{r}(j,h,e) - \mathfrak{r}(i \cdot j,h,e)$.

Proof. $\mathfrak{r}(i \vee j,h,e) = \mathfrak{m}(e \cdot h \cdot (i \vee j)) \times \mathfrak{m}(e) - \mathfrak{m}(e \cdot h) \times \mathfrak{m}(e \cdot (i \vee j))$ (D67-1),
$= \mathfrak{m}[(e \cdot h \cdot i) \vee (e \cdot h \cdot j)] \times \mathfrak{m}(e) - \mathfrak{m}(e \cdot h) \times \mathfrak{m}[(e \cdot i) \vee (e \cdot j)]$ (T21-5m(1)),
$= [\mathfrak{m}(e \cdot h \cdot i) + \mathfrak{m}(e \cdot h \cdot j) - \mathfrak{m}(e \cdot h \cdot i \cdot j)] \times \mathfrak{m}(e) - \mathfrak{m}(e \cdot h) \times [\mathfrak{m}(e \cdot i) + \mathfrak{m}(e \cdot j) - \mathfrak{m}(e \cdot i \cdot j)]$ (T57-1k),
$= [\mathfrak{m}(e \cdot h \cdot i) \times \mathfrak{m}(e) - \mathfrak{m}(e \cdot h) \times \mathfrak{m}(e \cdot i)] + [\mathfrak{m}(e \cdot h \cdot j) \times \mathfrak{m}(e) - \mathfrak{m}(e \cdot h) \times \mathfrak{m}(e \cdot j)] - [\mathfrak{m}(e \cdot h \cdot i \cdot j) \times \mathfrak{m}(e) - \mathfrak{m}(e \cdot h) \times \mathfrak{m}(e \cdot i \cdot j)]$.
Hence the assertion by D67-1.

+b. Let $\mathfrak{m}(e \cdot i \cdot j) = 0$. (This is the case in particular if $e \cdot i \cdot j$ is L-false, in other words, i and j are *L-exclusive* with respect to e.) Then $\mathfrak{r}(i \vee j,h,e) = \mathfrak{r}(i,h,e) + \mathfrak{r}(j,h,e)$.

Proof. $\mathfrak{r}(i \cdot j,h,e) = 0$ (T67-6d). Hence the assertion by (a).

c. Let i be a disjunction with n ($\geqq 2$) components: $i_1 \vee i_2 \vee \ldots \vee i_n$. For any two distinct components i_m and i_p, let $\mathfrak{m}(e \cdot i_m \cdot i_p) = 0$. (This is the case if $i_1, \ldots, i_n$ are L-exclusive in pairs with respect to e.) Then $\mathfrak{r}(i,h,e) = \sum_{p=1}^{n} \mathfrak{r}(i_p,h,e)$.

Proof. Let i' be $i_1 \vee i_2 \vee \ldots \vee i_{n-1}$. Then $e \cdot i' \cdot i_n$ is L-equivalent to $(e \cdot i_1 \cdot i_n) \vee (e \cdot i_2 \cdot i_n) \vee \ldots \vee (e \cdot i_{n-1} \cdot i_n)$ (T21-5m(2)). For any component in the latter disjunction and hence (T57-1s) also for any conjunction of two or more of them, $\mathfrak{m} = 0$. Hence $\mathfrak{m}(e \cdot i' \cdot i_n) = 0$ (T57-1v). Therefore, since i is

$i' \vee i_n$, $\mathfrak{r}(i,h,e) = \mathfrak{r}(i',h,e) + \mathfrak{r}(i_n,h,e)$ (b). If the assertion of the theorem holds for $n - 1$, then $\mathfrak{r}(i',h,e) = \sum_{p=1}^{n-1} \mathfrak{r}(i_p,h,e)$; hence, with the result just found, the assertion for n follows. The assertion holds for $n = 2$ (b). Therefore, by mathematical induction, it holds for every $n \geqq 2$.

One of the characteristics of those numerical functions of classes which are called measure functions is the following property: for any such function, its value for the class-sum of two classes is always the sum of its values for the two classes minus its value for the class-product; it is clear that the latter value must be subtracted, because by summing the measures of the two classes their common part has been counted twice. This is the reason for the general addition theorem concerning $\mathfrak{m}$ (T57-1k); this theorem was the basis for the general addition theorem concerning $\mathfrak{c}$ (T59-1k) and is here the basis for the general addition theorem concerning $\mathfrak{r}$ (T1a). We shall see later that the necessity of the subtraction of the last term in T1a brings about the possibility of the case (2) mentioned earlier: even if both i and j are positive to h on e, $i \vee j$ may be negative. We see from T1a that this would happen if the $\mathfrak{r}$-values for i, j, and $i \,.\, j$ are positive and the last one greater than the sum of the first and second. The question whether and under what conditions this can occur will be examined later.

In the case of mutually exclusive classes, the measure functions have simple additivity: the value for the class-sum is the sum of the values of the two classes; this is the chief characteristic of measure functions. Therefore we had, under the condition of L-exclusivity of the sentences, which corresponds to the exclusivity of the ranges, the special addition theorem for $\mathfrak{m}$ (T57-1m). Based on it are the special addition theorem for $\mathfrak{c}$ (T59-1l) and now that for $\mathfrak{r}$ (T1b). In addition to these theorems for simple disjunction, we have the special addition theorems for multiple disjunction concerning $\mathfrak{m}$ (T57-1v), $\mathfrak{c}$ (T59-1m), and $\mathfrak{r}$ (T1c).

T68-2. *Additivity for conjunctions.*

a. $\mathfrak{r}(i \,.\, j,h,e) = \mathfrak{r}(i,h,e) + \mathfrak{r}(j,h,e) - \mathfrak{r}(i \vee j,h,e)$. (From T1a.)

+b. Let $\mathfrak{m}(e \,.\, \sim i \,.\, \sim j) = 0$. (This is the case in particular if $\vdash e \supset i \vee j$, in other words, if i and j are *L-disjunct* with respect to e.) Then $\mathfrak{r}(i \,.\, j,h,e) = \mathfrak{r}(i,h,e) + \mathfrak{r}(j,h,e)$.

Proof. $\mathfrak{m}(e \,.\, \sim(i \vee j)) = 0$. Therefore $\mathfrak{r}(i \vee j,h,e) = 0$ (T67-6e). Hence the assertion by (a).

c. Let i be a conjunction with n ($\geqq 2$) components: $i_1 \,.\, i_2 \,.\, \ldots \,.\, i_n$. For any two distinct components i_m and i_p, let $\mathfrak{m}(e \,.\, \sim i_m \,.\, \sim i_p) = 0$.

(This is the case if i_m and i_p are L-disjunct with respect to e, i.e., $\vdash e \supset i_m \vee i_p$.) Then $\mathfrak{r}(i,h,e) = \sum_{p=1}^{n} \mathfrak{r}(i_p,h,e)$.

Proof, from T1c by substituting '$\sim i$' for 'i' and '$\sim i_p$' (for every p = 1 to n) for 'i_p', and T67-5a.

T2a is still analogous to theorems on $\mathfrak{m}$ (T57-1l) and $\mathfrak{c}$ (T59-1q). However, the analogy does not go farther. For $\mathfrak{r}$ we have here a special addition theorem for conjunction (T2b), while the corresponding theorem for $\mathfrak{m}$ (T57-1t) has not this simple form; the reason for this difference is that if i and j are L-disjunct, $i \vee j$ is L-true, and hence $\mathfrak{r}(i \vee j,h,e) = 0$ while $\mathfrak{m}(i \vee j)$ is not 0 but 1. The corresponding theorem for $\mathfrak{c}$ (T59-1r) is analogous to that for $\mathfrak{m}$, hence likewise not as simple as that for $\mathfrak{r}$. Thus the result is that, under suitable conditions, $\mathfrak{r}$ is additive with respect to disjunctions, like $\mathfrak{m}$ and $\mathfrak{c}$, but further also additive with respect to conjunctions, in distinction to $\mathfrak{m}$ and $\mathfrak{c}$.

Suppose two sentences i and j are given. Let us consider the four sentences $i \,.\, j$, $i \,.\, \sim j$, $\sim i \,.\, j$, and $\sim i \,.\, \sim j$. They correspond to the four lines of the truth-table for i and j (see the explanation preceding T21-7). Let l be any non-L-false sentence constructed out of i and j with the help of any connectives. Then l can be transformed into a disjunction of n of the four sentences ($1 \leqq n \leqq 4$) (T21-7d); for example, $i \vee j$ is L-equivalent to the disjunction of the first three of them. Since the four sentences are L-exclusive in pairs (T21-7a), $\mathfrak{r}(l,h,e)$ can be represented as a sum of some of the $\mathfrak{r}$-values for the four sentences. Thus these four $\mathfrak{r}$-values are a convenient basis for studying the relations between the $\mathfrak{r}$-values of i, j, and their connections. This method will be applied in T3.

We shall use in this section and the next one the following abbreviations for the four $\mathfrak{r}$-values:

$\mathfrak{r}_1 = \mathfrak{r}(i \,.\, j,h,e)$,

$\mathfrak{r}_2 = \mathfrak{r}(i \,.\, \sim j,h,e)$,

$\mathfrak{r}_3 = \mathfrak{r}(\sim i \,.\, j,h,e)$,

$\mathfrak{r}_4 = \mathfrak{r}(\sim i \,.\, \sim j,h,e)$.

T68-3. Let e, h, i, j be sentences in $\mathfrak{L}$.

a. $\mathfrak{r}_1 + \mathfrak{r}_2 + \mathfrak{r}_3 + \mathfrak{r}_4 = 0$.

Proof. Let k be $(i \,.\, j) \vee (i \,.\, \sim j) \vee (\sim i \,.\, j) \vee (\sim i \,.\, \sim j)$. The components of this disjunction are L-exclusive in pairs (T21-7a), hence also L-exclusive in pairs with respect to e. Therefore (T1c) $\mathfrak{r}(k,h,e)$ is the sum of the four $\mathfrak{r}$-values as stated above. On the other hand, k is L-true (T21-7b), hence $\vdash e \supset k$. Therefore $\mathfrak{r}(k,h,e) = 0$ (T67-6e).

b. $\mathfrak{r}(i,h,e) = \mathfrak{r}_1 + \mathfrak{r}_2$.

Proof. i is L-equivalent to $(i \cdot j) \vee (i \cdot \sim j)$ (T21-5j(2)). Hence the assertion by T1b.

c. $\mathfrak{r}(j,h,e) = \mathfrak{r}_1 + \mathfrak{r}_3$. (Analogous to (b).)
d. (1) $\mathfrak{r}(i \vee j,h,e) = \mathfrak{r}_1 + \mathfrak{r}_2 + \mathfrak{r}_3$;
(2) $= -\mathfrak{r}_4$.

Proof. 1. $i \vee j$ is L-equivalent to $(i \cdot j) \vee (i \cdot \sim j) \vee (\sim i \cdot j)$ (T21-7d). Hence the assertion by T1c. 2. From (1) and (a).

If any deductive relations (L-concepts) hold between i and j, then one or two or three of the four sentences $i \cdot j$, $i \cdot \sim j$, $\sim i \cdot j$, and $\sim i \cdot \sim j$ are L-false (for example, if $\vdash i \supset \sim j$, $i \cdot j$ is L-false; if $\vdash i \equiv j$, then $i \cdot \sim j$ and $\sim i \cdot j$ are L-false); then for these L-false sentences $\mathfrak{r} = 0$ (T67-6d). This provides a simple method for studying how deductive relations between i and j, and also e, affect the r-values of i, j, and their connections. This method will be applied in T4. There we shall use not the strong deductive condition that a certain sentence is L-false but rather the condition that its m-value is 0; the latter condition is weaker in $\mathfrak{L}_\infty$.

T68-4.

a. Let $\mathfrak{m}(e \cdot i \cdot j) = 0$. (This is the case in particular if $e \cdot i \cdot j$ is L-false, in other words, $\vdash e \cdot i \supset \sim j$, i and j are L-exclusive with respect to e.) Then the following holds.
(1) $\mathfrak{r}_1 = 0$. (From T67-6d.)
(2) $\mathfrak{r}_2 + \mathfrak{r}_3 + \mathfrak{r}_4 = 0$. (From T3a, (1).)
(3) $\mathfrak{r}(i,h,e) = \mathfrak{r}_2$. (From T3b, (1).)
(4) $\mathfrak{r}(j,h,e) = \mathfrak{r}_3$. (From T3c, (1).)
(5) $\mathfrak{r}(i \vee j,h,e) = \mathfrak{r}_2 + \mathfrak{r}_3 = -\mathfrak{r}_4$. (From T3d, (1).)

b. Let $\mathfrak{m}(e \cdot i \cdot \sim j) = 0$. (This is the case if $e \cdot i \cdot \sim j$ is L-false, hence $\vdash e \cdot i \supset j$.)
(1) $\mathfrak{r}_2 = 0$. (From T67-6d.)
(2) $\mathfrak{r}_1 + \mathfrak{r}_3 + \mathfrak{r}_4 = 0$. (From T3a, (1)).
(3) $\mathfrak{r}(i,h,e) = \mathfrak{r}_1$. (From T3b, (1).)
(4) $\mathfrak{r}(j,h,e) = \mathfrak{r}(i \vee j,h,e) = \mathfrak{r}_1 + \mathfrak{r}_3 = -\mathfrak{r}_4$. (From T3c, T3d, (1).)

c. Let $\mathfrak{m}(e \cdot \sim i \cdot j) = 0$. (This is the case if $e \cdot \sim i \cdot j$ is L-false, hence $\vdash e \cdot j \supset i$.)
(1) $\mathfrak{r}_3 = 0$. (From T67-6d.)
(2) $\mathfrak{r}_1 + \mathfrak{r}_2 + \mathfrak{r}_4 = 0$. (From T3a, (1).)
(3) $\mathfrak{r}(j,h,e) = \mathfrak{r}_1$. (From T3c, (1).)
(4) $\mathfrak{r}(i,h,e) = \mathfrak{r}(i \vee j,h,e) = \mathfrak{r}_1 + \mathfrak{r}_2 = -\mathfrak{r}_4$. (From T3b, T3d, (1).)

d. Let $\mathfrak{m}(e \cdot \sim i \cdot \sim j) = 0$. (This is the case if $e \cdot \sim i \cdot \sim j$ is L-false, in other words, $\vdash e \supset i \vee j$, i and j are L-disjunct with respect to e.)

(1) $\mathfrak{r}_4 = 0$. (From T67-6d.)
(2) $\mathfrak{r}_1 + \mathfrak{r}_2 + \mathfrak{r}_3 = 0$. (From T3a, (1).)
(3) $\mathfrak{r}(i,h,e) = \mathfrak{r}_1 + \mathfrak{r}_2 = -\mathfrak{r}_3$. (From T3b, (2).)
(4) $\mathfrak{r}(j,h,e) = \mathfrak{r}_1 + \mathfrak{r}_3 = -\mathfrak{r}_2$. (From T3c, (2).)
(5) $\mathfrak{r}(i \vee j,h,e) = 0$. (From T3d(1), (2).)

e. Let $\mathfrak{m}(e \cdot i \cdot j) = \mathfrak{m}(e \cdot i \cdot {\sim}j) = 0$; in other words, $\mathfrak{m}(e \cdot i) = 0$. (This is the case if $e \cdot i$ is L-false, hence $\vdash e \supset {\sim}i$.)
(1) $\mathfrak{r}_1 = \mathfrak{r}_2 = 0$. (From (a)(1), (b)(1.))
(2) $\mathfrak{r}_3 + \mathfrak{r}_4 = 0$. (From T3a, (1).)
(3) $\mathfrak{r}(i,h,e) = 0$. (From (a)(3), (1).)
(4) $\mathfrak{r}(j,h,e) = \mathfrak{r}(i \vee j,h,e) = \mathfrak{r}_3 = -\mathfrak{r}_4$. (From (b)(4), (1).)

f. Let $\mathfrak{m}(e \cdot i \cdot j) = \mathfrak{m}(e \cdot {\sim}i \cdot j) = 0$; in other words, $\mathfrak{m}(e \cdot j) = 0$. (This is the case if $e \cdot j$ is L-false, hence $\vdash e \supset {\sim}j$.)
(1) $\mathfrak{r}_1 = \mathfrak{r}_3 = 0$. (From (a)(1), (c)(1).)
(2) $\mathfrak{r}_2 + \mathfrak{r}_4 = 0$. (From T3a, (1).)
(3) $\mathfrak{r}(j,h,e) = 0$. (From (c)(3), (1).)
(4) $\mathfrak{r}(i,h,e) = \mathfrak{r}(i \vee j,h,e) = \mathfrak{r}_2 = -\mathfrak{r}_4$. (From (c)(4), (1).)

g. Let $\mathfrak{m}(e \cdot i \cdot j) = \mathfrak{m}(e \cdot {\sim}i \cdot {\sim}j) = 0$; in other words, $\mathfrak{m}(e \cdot (i \equiv j)) = 0$. (This is the case if $e \cdot (i \equiv j)$ is L-false, hence $\vdash e \supset (i \equiv {\sim}j)$.)
(1) $\mathfrak{r}_1 = \mathfrak{r}_4 = 0$. (From (a)(1), (d)(1).)
(2) $\mathfrak{r}_2 + \mathfrak{r}_3 = 0$. (From T3a, (1).)
(3) $\mathfrak{r}(i,h,e) = \mathfrak{r}_2 = -\mathfrak{r}_3$. (From (d)(3), (1).)
(4) $\mathfrak{r}(j,h,e) = \mathfrak{r}_3 = -\mathfrak{r}_2 = -\mathfrak{r}(i,h,e)$. (From (d)(4), (1).)
(5) $\mathfrak{r}(i \vee j,h,e) = 0$. (From (d)(5).)

h. Let $\mathfrak{m}(e \cdot i \cdot {\sim}j) = \mathfrak{m}(e \cdot {\sim}i \cdot j) = 0$; in other words, $\mathfrak{m}(e \cdot {\sim}(i \equiv j)) = 0$. (This is the case if $e \cdot {\sim}(i \equiv j)$ is L-false, hence $\vdash e \supset (i \equiv j)$, i and j are L-equivalent with respect to e.)
(1) $\mathfrak{r}_2 = \mathfrak{r}_3 = 0$. (From (b)(1), (c)(1).)
(2) $\mathfrak{r}_1 + \mathfrak{r}_4 = 0$. (From T3a, (1).)
(3) $\mathfrak{r}(i,h,e) = \mathfrak{r}(j,h,e) = \mathfrak{r}(i \vee j,h,e) = \mathfrak{r}_1 = -\mathfrak{r}_4$. (From (b)(3), (b)(4), (1).)

i. Let $\mathfrak{m}(e \cdot i \cdot {\sim}j) = \mathfrak{m}(e \cdot {\sim}i \cdot {\sim}j) = 0$; in other words, $\mathfrak{m}(e \cdot {\sim}j) = 0$. (This is the case if $e \cdot {\sim}j$ is L-false, hence $\vdash e \supset j$.)
(1) $\mathfrak{r}_2 = \mathfrak{r}_4 = 0$. (From (b)(1), (d)(1).)
(2) $\mathfrak{r}_1 + \mathfrak{r}_3 = 0$. (From T3a, (1).)
(3) $\mathfrak{r}(i,h,e) = \mathfrak{r}_1 = -\mathfrak{r}_3$. (From (b)(3), (2).)
(4) $\mathfrak{r}(j,h,e) = \mathfrak{r}(i \vee j,h,e) = 0$. (From (b)(4), (2).)

j. Let $\mathfrak{m}(e \cdot {\sim}i \cdot j) = \mathfrak{m}(e \cdot {\sim}i \cdot {\sim}j) = 0$; in other words, $\mathfrak{m}(e \cdot {\sim}i) = 0$. (This is the case if $e \cdot {\sim}i$ is L-false, hence $\vdash e \supset i$.)
(1) $\mathfrak{r}_3 = \mathfrak{r}_4 = 0$. (From (c)(1), (d)(1).)

(2) $\mathfrak{r}_1 + \mathfrak{r}_2 = 0$. (From T3a, (1).)

(3) $\mathfrak{r}(i,h,e) = \mathfrak{r}(i \vee j,h,e) = 0$. (From (c)(4), (2).)

(4) $\mathfrak{r}(j,h,e) = \mathfrak{r}_1 = -\mathfrak{r}_2$. (From (c)(3), (2).)

k. Let any three of the four sentences $i \,.\, j$, $i \,.\, \sim j$, $\sim i \,.\, j$, and $\sim i \,.\, \sim j$ be selected. Let $\mathfrak{m} = 0$ for the three conjunctions of e with each of the selected sentences. (This is the case if these three conjunctions are L-false, and hence e L-implies the one sentence among the four which has not been selected.)

(1) $\mathfrak{r}_1 = \mathfrak{r}_2 = \mathfrak{r}_3 = \mathfrak{r}_4 = 0$.

Proof. For each of the three selected sentences, $\mathfrak{r} = 0$ (T67-6d). Therefore the same holds for the one remaining sentence (T3a).

(2) For i, j, $i \vee j$, and $i \,.\, j$ (to h on e), $\mathfrak{r} = 0$. (From T3b, c, d, and (1).)

l. Let $\mathfrak{m}(e \,.\, i \,.\, j) = \mathfrak{m}(e \,.\, i \,.\, \sim j) = \mathfrak{m}(e \,.\, \sim i \,.\, j) = \mathfrak{m}(e \,.\, \sim i \,.\, \sim j) = 0$; in other words, $\mathfrak{m}(e) = 0$. (This is the case if e is L-false.)

(1) $\mathfrak{r}_1 = \mathfrak{r}_2 = \mathfrak{r}_3 = \mathfrak{r}_4 = 0$.

(2) For i, j, $i \vee j$, and $i \,.\, j$ (to h on e), $\mathfrak{r} = 0$. (From (k); or directly from T67-6b.)

T4 has dealt with all those cases where one, two, three, or all four of the sentences $e \,.\, i \,.\, j$, $e \,.\, i \,.\, \sim j$, $e \,.\, \sim i \,.\, j$, and $e \,.\, \sim i \,.\, \sim j$ have the $\mathfrak{m}$-value 0, which includes the cases where these sentences are L-false. Thereby all possibilities of deductive relations (L-concepts) between i and j on the basis e are dealt with, in other words, all nonquantitative relations (like inclusion, exclusion, emptiness, etc.) between those parts of $\mathfrak{R}_i$ and $\mathfrak{R}_j$ which are within $\mathfrak{R}_e$. The purpose of T3 and T4 is this. If the relevance measures of the four L-exclusive sentences $i \,.\, j$, $i \,.\, \sim j$, $\sim i \,.\, j$, and $\sim i \,.\, \sim j$ are given, then the theorems determine the relevance measures for i, j, and $i \vee j$, and enable us to find easily those for any other connections of i and j. T3 does this in general, and T4 for all cases of deductive relations.

§ 69. The Possible Relevance Situations for Two Observations and Their Connections

Suppose that the relevance situation for four sentences e, h, i, and j is described in the following way: for each of the sentences $i \,.\, j$, $i \,.\, \sim j$, $\sim i \,.\, j$, $\sim i \,.\, \sim j$, i, j, and $i \vee j$, not the numerical value of $\mathfrak{r}$ (to h on e) is given, but merely the sign of $\mathfrak{r}$, that is to say, it is stated whether $\mathfrak{r} > 0$, < 0, or $= 0$. (These indications for the seven sentences are, of course, not independent of each other.) A table (T1a) is given which contains a complete list of all seventy-five possible relevance situations thus described in terms of signs of $\mathfrak{r}$. With the help of this table, general theorems about possible relevance situations are derived, first in terms of signs of r (T2), and then in terms of the relevance concepts (T3). Four kinds of relevance situations, whose possibility seems surprising at first glance, are studied more in detail; among them are the following: (1a) *i* and *j* are both positive (to *h* on *e*) but $i \,.\, j$ is negative; (2a) *i* and *j* are both positive but $i \vee j$ is negative. These situations are illustrated and made plausible by examples with numerical values. Finally, the following is shown by a general theorem (T5) and by examples: if it is known that *j* is L-implied either by *i* alone or by $e \,.\, i$, then from the relevance of *i* (to *h* on *e*) nothing can be inferred concerning the relevance of *j*, or vice versa.

The problems which we have discussed in the preceding section and shall further discuss here concern the following situation. The prior evidence *e* is given; the hypothesis *h* is considered; *i* and *j* are pieces of additional evidence, for example, reports of new observations. The questions to be answered concern the relevance to *h* on *e* of *i* and *j* and their connections. We had two theorems (T68-3 and T68-4) which state the relations between the relevance measures of the four sentences $i \,.\, j$, $i \,.\, \sim j$, $\sim i \,.\, j$, and $\sim i \,.\, \sim j$, on the one hand, and those of *i*, *j*, and $i \vee j$, on the other. We shall now turn to nonnumerical questions of relevance; that is to say, we ask for each sentence *l* among those mentioned, not what is its relevance measure to *h* on *e*, but merely whether *l* is positive, negative, or irrelevant to *h* on *e*. Or, more exactly, we ask not about the numerical value of r for *l* (to *h* on *e*) but merely for what we shall call the *sign of* r, that is, whether r for *l* is >0, <0, or 0. These three cases correspond in general to positive relevance, negative relevance, and irrelevance. [However, as we have seen earlier, this correspondence holds without restrictions only in $\mathfrak{L}_N$ and for nongeneral sentences in $\mathfrak{L}_\infty$. If $e \,.\, l$ is an almost L-false sentence in $\mathfrak{L}_\infty$ (and hence contains a variable, T58-3e), then $\mathfrak{m}(e \,.\, l) = 0$ and hence $\mathfrak{m}(e \,.\, l \,.\, h) = 0$ and hence $\mathrm{r}(l,h,e) = 0$ (D67-1); nevertheless, *l* is in this case not necessarily irrelevant to *h* on *e* but may be positive or negative.]

We shall now consider the possible relevance situations to *h* on *e* for the sentences mentioned above (viz., $i \,.\, j$, $i \,.\, \sim j$, $\sim i \,.\, j$, $\sim i \,.\, \sim j$; *i*, *j*, and $i \vee j$), characterized in a nonnumerical way by the signs of r for these sentences. With the help of the theorems in the preceding section it will now be possible to state *a complete list of all possible relevance situations* in this sense for the sentences mentioned; their number is 75. This list will be given in *the subsequent table* T1a. The table contains, aside from the enumeration at the left-hand side, seven columns for the seven sentences mentioned above. (At present, we pay attention only to those headings of the columns which are given on the line **a**; the line **b** refers to another interpretation T1b of the same table, to be discussed later (§ 71).) The table is constructed in such a manner that every case listed is possible and that no possible case is omitted. It will later provide the basis for general theorems on possible relevance situations in terms of relevance concepts (T3).

The procedure for constructing the table T1a is as follows. We begin by filling the columns (1) to (4) only. '+', '−', and 'o' mean that $\mathfrak{r} > 0$, $\mathfrak{r} < 0$, and $\mathfrak{r} = 0$, respectively, for the sentence indicated at the head of the column, always to *h* on *e*. We list all those distributions of '+', '−', and 'o' among the four sentences which are possible; these distributions are those which satisfy the following rule:

R1. If '+' occurs in one of the columns (1) to (4), then '−' must occur in another of these columns; if '−' occurs in one, '+' must occur in another.

This follows from T68-3a. $\mathfrak{r}_1$, $\mathfrak{r}_2$, $\mathfrak{r}_3$, and $\mathfrak{r}_4$ in this theorem are the $\mathfrak{r}$-values for the four sentences to which the columns refer. T68-3a says that the sum of these four values is 0; therefore, if one value is >0, another is <0, and vice versa. Therefore, there are fourteen distributions without 'o' (Nos. 1 to 14); because there are all together sixteen distributions of two values among four items (T40-31e), and two of them are here excluded by R1, viz., '++++' and '− − − −'. Now we come to the cases where $\mathfrak{r} = 0$ for just one of the four sentences. If $\mathfrak{r} = 0$ for (1) only, we have six cases for (2), (3), and (4) (Nos. 15–20), because there are eight distributions of '+' and '−' (T40-31e) and again two of them are excluded by R1, viz., '+++' and '− − −'. There are likewise six cases each if $\mathfrak{r} = 0$ for (2) only, or for (3) only, or for (4) only (Nos. 21 to 38). Then we have the cases where $\mathfrak{r} = 0$ for two sentences (Nos. 39–50); here, according to R1, one of the two remaining sentences must have '+' and the other '−'. That exactly three sentences have 'o' is excluded by R1. Hence there remains only the last case (No. 51), where all four sentences have 'o'.

Now we turn to column (5) for *i*. Here we have to determine the sign of $\mathfrak{r}$ for *i* on the basis of the earlier columns. T68-3b says that the $\mathfrak{r}$-value for *i* is the sum of the $\mathfrak{r}$-values for the sentences (1) and (2). Thus we have the following rules for filling in column (5) (R5 will presently be explained):

R2. If in columns (1) and (2) we find '++' or '+o' or 'o+', we write in column (5) '+'.

R3. If we find '− −' or '−o' or 'o−', we write '−'.

R4. If we find 'oo', we write 'o'.

R5. Suppose we find in columns (1) and (2) one '+' and one '−'.
- *a.* If there is still another '+' (in column (3) or (4)) but no other '−', we write in column (5) '−'.
- *b.* If there is still another '−' but no other '+', we write '+'.
- *c.* If we find 'o' in both (3) and (4), we write 'o' in (5).
- *d.* If we find in (3) and (4) one '+' and one '−', then there are for (5) all three possibilities, '+', '−', and 'o'. This occurs in Nos. 5, 6, 9, and 10.

R2, R3, and R4 are obvious, in view of T68-3b. R5a applies if there is one '−' but two or three '+' (and hence one or no 'o'). Consider the case where

$\mathfrak{r}_1$ is negative, say, $-r_1$, $\mathfrak{r}_2$ and $\mathfrak{r}_3$ are positive, say, r_2 and r_3, and $\mathfrak{r}_4$ is either positive, say, r_4, or 0. Then (T68-3a) $r_1 = r_2 + r_3$ or $r_2 + r_3 + r_4$, hence $r_1 > r_2$; therefore $\mathfrak{r}$ for i, which is $\mathfrak{r}_1 + \mathfrak{r}_2$ (T68-3b) $= -r_1 + r_2$, is negative. R5b is analogous to R5a. In the case of R5c, $\mathfrak{r}_1 + \mathfrak{r}_2 = 0$ (T68-3a). In the case of R5d, we see easily that $\mathfrak{r}$ for i may be >0 or <0 or $= 0$. As an example, take case No. 5. If the $\mathfrak{r}$-values for the sentences (1) to (4) are, say, $2r$, $-r$, r, and $-2r$, respectively, where r is any positive real number, then $\mathfrak{r}$ for i, which is the sum of the first two values, is r, hence > 0; if the four values are r, $-2r$, $2r$, $-r$, then $\mathfrak{r}$ for i is $-r$, hence <0; if those values are r, $-r$, $2r$, $-2r$, then $\mathfrak{r}$ for i is 0.

Now we come to column (6) for j. According to T68-3c, the $\mathfrak{r}$-value for j is the sum of the values for the sentences (1) and (3). Thus the procedure is here analogous to that for column (5). Here likewise, we have sometimes all three possibilities: $\mathfrak{r}$ for j may be >0, <0, or 0; this occurs in cases Nos. 3, 6, 9, and 12. In two of these cases, Nos. 6 and 9, we had already three possibilities for i in (5). In these cases the three possibilities for j in (6) are independent of the three possibilities for i in (5); that is to say, all nine combinations are possible. This is shown for the nine combinations A to I in No. 6 by the following nine examples; they are to be understood in the same manner as the above examples for the application of R5d to No. 5; examples for No. 9 can easily be constructed analogously.

	(1) +	(2) −	(3) −	(4) +	(5) =(1)+(2)	(6) =(1)+(3)
6 *A*	$3r$	$-2r$	$-2r$	r	r	r
B	$2r$	$-r$	$-3r$	$2r$	r	$-r$
C	$2r$	$-r$	$-2r$	r	r	0
D	$2r$	$-3r$	$-r$	$2r$	$-r$	r
E	r	$-2r$	$-2r$	$3r$	$-r$	$-r$
F	r	$-2r$	$-r$	$2r$	$-r$	0
G	$2r$	$-2r$	$-r$	r	0	r
H	r	$-r$	$-2r$	$2r$	0	$-r$
I	r	$-r$	$-r$	r	0	0

Finally we fill in column (7) for $i \vee j$ according to the following rule:

R6. If in column (4) we find '+', '−', or '0', then we write in column (7) '−', '+', or '0', respectively.

This follows from the fact that $\mathfrak{r}$ for $i \vee j$ is $-\mathfrak{r}_4$ (T68-3d(2)). R6 determines every item in column (7) uniquely.

T69-1. ***The possible relevance situations.***

a. Signs of $\mathfrak{r}$ for i, j, and their connections, to h on e.

b. Signs of $\mathfrak{r}$ for i to h, k, and their connections, on e.

'+', '−', and '0' indicate that $\mathfrak{r} > 0$, $\mathfrak{r} < 0$, and $\mathfrak{r} = 0$, respectively.

	(1)	(2)	(3)	(4)	(5)	(6)	(7)
T1a.	$i \cdot j$	$i \cdot \sim j$	$\sim i \cdot j$	$\sim i \cdot \sim j$	i	j	$i \vee j$
T1b.	$h \cdot k$	$h \cdot \sim k$	$\sim h \cdot k$	$\sim h \cdot \sim k$	h	k	$h \vee k$
No. 1	+	+	+	−	+	+	+
2	+	+	−	+	+	−	−
3 A						+	
3 B	+	+	−	−	+	−	+
3 C						o	
4	+	−	+	+	−	+	−
5 A					+		
5 B	+	−	+	−	−	+	+
5 C					o		
6 A					+	+	
6 B					+	−	
6 C					+	o	
6 D					−	+	
6 E	+	−	−	+	−	−	−
6 F					−	o	
6 G					o	+	
6 H					o	−	
6 I					o	o	
7	+	−	−	−	+	+	+
8	−	+	+	+	−	−	−
9 A					+	+	
9 B					+	−	
9 C					+	o	
9 D					−	+	
9 E	−	+	+	−	−	−	+
9 F					−	o	
9 G					o	+	
9 H					o	−	
9 I					o	o	
10 A					+		
10 B	−	+	−	+	−	−	−
10 C					o		
11	−	+	−	−	+	−	+
12 A						+	
12 B	−	−	+	+	−	−	−
12 C						o	
13	−	−	+	−	−	+	+
14	−	−	−	+	−	−	−
15	o	+	+	−	+	+	+
16	o	+	−	+	+	−	−
17	o	+	−	−	+	−	+
18	o	−	+	+	−	+	−
19	o	−	+	−	−	+	+
20	o	−	−	+	−	−	−
21	+	o	+	−	+	+	+
22	+	o	−	+	+	−	−
23	+	o	−	−	+	+	+
24	−	o	+	+	−	−	−
25	−	o	+	−	−	+	+
26	−	o	−	+	−	−	−
27	+	+	o	−	+	+	+
28	+	−	o	+	−	+	−
29	+	−	o	−	+	+	+
30	−	+	o	+	−	−	−
31	−	+	o	−	+	−	+
32	−	−	o	+	−	−	−

	(1)	(2)	(3)	(4)	(5)	(6)	(7)
T1a.	$i \centerdot j$	$i \centerdot \sim j$	$\sim i \centerdot j$	$\sim i \centerdot \sim j$	i	j	$i \vee j$
T1b.	$h \centerdot k$	$h \centerdot \sim k$	$\sim h \centerdot k$	$\sim h \centerdot \sim k$	h	k	$h \vee k$
33	+	+	−	0	+	−	0
34	+	−	+	0	−	+	0
35	+	−	−	0	+	+	0
36	−	+	+	0	−	−	0
37	−	+	−	0	+	−	0
38	−	−	+	0	−	+	0
39	0	0	+	−	0	+	+
40	0	0	−	+	0	−	−
41	0	+	0	−	+	0	+
42	0	−	0	+	−	0	−
43	0	+	−	0	+	−	0
44	0	−	+	0	−	+	0
45	+	0	0	−	+	+	+
46	−	0	0	+	−	−	−
47	+	0	−	0	+	0	0
48	−	0	+	0	−	0	0
49	+	−	0	0	0	+	0
50	−	+	0	0	0	−	0
51	0	0	0	0	0	0	0

We can read from the table T1a which combinations of signs of r are possible for i, j, $i \centerdot j$, and $i \vee j$. Thus we find the results stated in the following theorem T2; it serves chiefly as a lemma for T3, which deals with the possible combinations of relevance properties for those sentences.

T69-2. Let four sentences e, h, i, and j in $\mathfrak{L}$ be given. (a), (b), (c), and (d) deal with four cases concerning the signs of r for i and for j; they are always meant to h on e. It is easily seen that for any four sentences exactly one of these cases (a) to (d) applies.

a. Let r either be >0 for both i and j, or >0 for one of them and 0 for the other. Then the following holds.

(1) For at least one of the sentences $i \centerdot j$ and $i \vee j$ $\mathfrak{r} > 0$.

(2) If for $i \centerdot j$ $\mathfrak{r} > 0$, then for $i \vee j$ r may be >0, <0, or 0.

(3) If for $i \vee j$ $\mathfrak{r} > 0$, then for $i \centerdot j$ r may be >0, <0, or 0.

(4) Let $\mathfrak{m}(e \centerdot i \centerdot j) = 0$. (This is the case in particular if $e \centerdot i \centerdot j$ is L-false, in other words, i and j are L-exclusive with respect to e.) Then for $i \centerdot j$ $\mathfrak{r} = 0$, and for $i \vee j$ $\mathfrak{r} > 0$. (From T67-6d; T68-1b.)

(5) Let $\mathfrak{m}(e \centerdot \sim i \centerdot \sim j) = 0$. (This is the case if $e \centerdot \sim i \centerdot \sim j$ is L-false, hence $\vdash e \supset i \vee j$.) Then for $i \vee j$ $\mathfrak{r} = 0$, and for $i \centerdot j$ $\mathfrak{r} > 0$. (From T67-6e; T68-2b.)

b. Let r either be <0 for both i and j, or <0 for one of them and 0 for the other. Then the following holds.

(1) For at least one of the sentences $i \cdot j$ and $i \vee j$ $\mathfrak{r} < 0$.
(2) If for $i \cdot j$ $\mathfrak{r} < 0$, then for $i \vee j$ $\mathfrak{r}$ may be >0, <0, or 0.
(3) If for $i \vee j$ $\mathfrak{r} < 0$, then for $i \cdot j$ $\mathfrak{r}$ may be >0, <0, or 0.
(4) Let $\mathfrak{m}(e \cdot i \cdot j) = 0$. Then for $i \cdot j$ $\mathfrak{r} = 0$, and for $i \vee j$ $\mathfrak{r} < 0$. (From T67-6d; T68-1b.)
(5) Let $\mathfrak{m}(e \cdot \sim i \cdot \sim j) = 0$. Then for $i \vee j$ $\mathfrak{r} = 0$, and for $i \cdot j$ $\mathfrak{r} < 0$. (From T67-6e; T68-2b.)

c. Let $\mathfrak{r}$ be >0 for one of the sentences i and j and <0 for the other. Then for $i \cdot j$ $\mathfrak{r}$ may be >0, <0, or 0 and the same holds for $i \vee j$, independently of $i \cdot j$; that is to say, all nine combinations are possible.

d. Let $\mathfrak{r} = 0$ for both i and j. Then either $\mathfrak{r} = 0$ for both $i \cdot j$ and $i \vee j$, or $\mathfrak{r} > 0$ for one and $\mathfrak{r} < 0$ for the other; in the latter case, the one $\mathfrak{r}$-value is the opposite of the other. (From T68-1a.)
(All items for which no references to other theorems are given can easily be established by scanning the list T1a; exact proofs are based on T68-3.)

From T2 we derive the analogous theorem T3. While the former deals with the three signs of $\mathfrak{r}$, the latter deals with the three corresponding relevance properties, viz., positive relevance, negative relevance, and irrelevance. From the point of view of application, the latter concepts and hence the theorem T3 dealing with them may perhaps be more interesting. However, T3 cannot be as simple as T2 but must contain restricting conditions at certain points, because the relevance properties do not always correspond to the sign of $\mathfrak{r}$. We require in T3 that (A) $e \cdot i$ is not almost L-false, and (B) $e \cdot j$ is not almost L-false. (A) means that either $e \cdot i$ is L-false or $\mathfrak{m}(e \cdot i) > 0$; (B) means that either $e \cdot j$ is L-false or $\mathfrak{m}(e \cdot j) > 0$. It follows from (A) and (B) that $e \cdot (i \vee j)$ is either L-false or its $\mathfrak{m} > 0$; in other words that (C) $e \cdot (i \vee j)$ is not almost L-false.

Proof. Let $e \cdot (i \vee j)$ be not L-false. It is L-equivalent to $(e \cdot i) \vee (e \cdot j)$. Hence at least one of the sentences $e \cdot i$ and $e \cdot j$ is not L-false (T20-2q). Therefore at least one of their $\mathfrak{m}$-values is >0. (From (A), (B).) Hence $\mathfrak{m} > 0$ for their disjunction (T57-1j) and hence for $e \cdot (i \vee j)$.

The conditions (A), (B), and (C) are needed for the use of T67-9 in the proofs (in particular, (C) for the application of T67-9d to $i \vee j$ in the proof of T3a(3)).

+**T69-3.** Let e, h, i, and j be sentences in $\mathfrak{L}$. For $\mathfrak{L}_\infty$ it is assumed that none of the following sentences is almost L-false: (A) $e \cdot i$, (B) $e \cdot j$, and hence (C) $e \cdot (i \vee j)$. Relevance and irrelevance are here always meant to h on e.

a. Let i and j be either both positive, or one of them positive and the other irrelevant. Then the following holds.

(1) Lemma. Either both $\mathfrak{r}(i,h,e)$ and $\mathfrak{r}(j,h,e)$ are >0, or one of them is >0 and the other 0. (From T67-9a, T67-8d.)

(2) At least one of the sentences $i \cdot j$ and $i \vee j$ is positive. (From (1), T2a(1), T67-8a.)

(3) If $i \cdot j$ is positive and $\mathfrak{m}(e \cdot i \cdot j) > 0$, then for $i \vee j$ all three cases are possible, that is to say, it may be positive, negative, or irrelevant.

Proof. For $i \cdot j$ $\mathfrak{r} > 0$ (T67-9a, since $\mathfrak{m}(e \cdot i \cdot j) > 0$). Hence for $i \vee j$ $\mathfrak{r}$ may be >0, <0, or 0 ((1), T2a(2)). Hence the assertion by T67-8a and b, T67-9d.

(4) If $i \vee j$ is positive and $\mathfrak{m}(e \cdot i \cdot j) > 0$, then for $i \cdot j$ all three cases are possible. (From T67-9a, (1), T2a(3), T67-8a and b, T67-9d; in analogy to (3).)

(5) Let $\mathfrak{m}(e \cdot i \cdot j) = 0$. [This holds in particular if $e \cdot i \cdot j$ is L-false, hence $\vdash e \supset \sim(i \cdot j)$; in this case, $i \cdot j$ is irrelevant.] Then $i \vee j$ is positive. (From (1), T2a(4), T67-8a.)

(6) Let $\mathfrak{m}(e \cdot \sim i \cdot \sim j) = 0$. [This holds in particular if $e \cdot \sim i \cdot \sim j$ and hence $e \cdot \sim(i \vee j)$ is L-false, hence $\vdash e \supset i \vee j$; in this case, $i \vee j$ is irrelevant.] Then $i \cdot j$ is positive. (From (1), T2a(5), T67-8a.)

b. Let i and j be either both negative, or one of them negative and the other irrelevant. Then the following holds.

(1) Lemma. Either both $\mathfrak{r}(i,h,e)$ and $\mathfrak{r}(j,h,e)$ are <0, or one is <0 and the other 0. (From T67-9b, T67-8d.)

(2) At least one of the sentences $i \cdot j$ and $i \vee j$ is negative. (From (1), T2b(1), T67-8b.)

(3) If $i \cdot j$ is negative and $\mathfrak{m}(e \cdot i \cdot j) > 0$, then for $i \vee j$ all three cases are possible. (From T67-9b, (1), T2b(2), T67-8a and b, T67-9d; in analogy to (a)(3).)

(4) If $i \vee j$ is negative and $\mathfrak{m}(e \cdot i \cdot j) > 0$, then for $i \cdot j$ all three cases are possible. (From T67-9b, (1), T2b(3), T67-8a, b, T67-9d.)

(5) Let $\mathfrak{m}(e \cdot i \cdot j) = 0$. [See remark in (a)(5).] Then $i \vee j$ is negative. (From (1), T2b(4), T67-8b.)

(6) Let $\mathfrak{m}(e \cdot \sim i \cdot \sim j) = 0$. [See remark in (a)(6).] Then $i \cdot j$ is negative. (From (1), T2b(5), T67-8b.)

c. Let one of the sentences i and j be positive and the other negative. Then for $i \cdot j$ all three cases are possible, and the same holds for $i \vee j$ independently of $i \cdot j$; that is to say, all nine combinations are possible. (From T67-8a and b, T2c, T67-9d.)

d. Let both i and j be irrelevant and $\mathfrak{m}(e \cdot i \cdot j) > 0$. Then $i \cdot j$ and $i \vee j$ are either both irrelevant or one is positive and the other negative. (From T67-8d, T2d, T67-9d, T67-8a and b.)

T3 gives account of all possible relevance situations described in terms of the relevance concepts: positive and negative relevance and irrelevance. We shall now study four cases whose possibility seems surprising at first. The cases 1a and 2a here are the cases 1 and 2 mentioned earlier (see the discussion preceding T68-1). We shall explain under what conditions they occur and illustrate them by simple examples with numerical values. Relevance and irrelevance is always meant to h on e.

1a. It is possible that *each of two sentences is positive* and nevertheless their *conjunction is negative.* For i and j, this occurs only in the case No. 9A in table T1a. The following is an example of $\mathfrak{r}$-values for this case: the values for (1) to (4) are $-r$, $2r$, $2r$, $-3r$, respectively; hence (5) and (6), that is, i and j, have both the value r. (This is like the example given above for No. 6E, but with opposite signs.) Generally speaking, any case constructed in the following way is of this kind. For given e and h, we take any three sentences (1), (2), and (3) satisfying the following conditions: they are L-exclusive in pairs with respect to e; (1) is negative (to h on e), its $\mathfrak{r}$-value being $-r$; both (2) and (3) are positive such that the $\mathfrak{r}$-value of each is greater than r. When we have found any three sentences of this kind, we take as i the disjunction of (1) and (2), and as j that of (1) and (3). Then for both i and j $\mathfrak{r} > 0$, and hence they are positive; but $i \cdot j$, which is (1), is negative.

1b. It is possible that *each of two sentences is negative* while their *conjunction is positive.* This occurs only in No. 6E. Cases of this kind can be constructed like those for (1a) but with opposite $\mathfrak{r}$-values.

Example for 1a. Let the prior evidence e contain the following information. Ten chess players participate in a chess tournament in New York City; some of them are local people, some from out of town; some are junior players, some seniors; some are men (M), some women (W). Their distribution is known to be as follows (see diagram); among the local juniors there is 1 M, 2 W; among

	i Local Players	i' Strangers
j Juniors	M, W, W	M, M
j' Seniors	M, M	W, W, W

the local seniors 2 M, no W; among the stranger juniors 2 M, no W; among the stranger seniors no M, 3 W. It is known that one and only one of the ten players will be the winner. Furthermore, the evidence e is supposed to be such that on its basis each of the ten players has an equal chance of becoming the winner, hence 1/10. (For this assumption we do not presuppose the principle of indifference; it may be that e contains reports about previous achievements of the players; all that is assumed is that, for the chosen $\mathfrak{c}$, each of the ten possibilities has the $\mathfrak{c}$-value 1/10 on e. Any additional evidence considered in this and the subsequent examples supplies the information that some of the ten players cannot win. It is assumed that in each case, on the basis of the increased evidence, the remaining players have equal chances of winning.) An observer X, who has this prior evidence e, considers the hypothesis h: 'A man wins'. (We take this neutral, tenseless formulation instead of the customary 'a man will win' because the same sentence will later be considered at other time points. The same holds for the formulations of i and j.) Consider the five sentences each of which predicts the winning of one of the five men. These sentences are L-exclusive in pairs with respect to e; and for each of them $\mathfrak{c} = 1/10$. h is the disjunction of these five sentences. Therefore $\mathfrak{c}(h,e) = 5/10 = 1/2$ (T59-1m). Now suppose that X receives during the course of the tournament the following report i: 'A local player wins'. The man who reports this to X may have seen on the scoreboard that, on the basis of the games finished so far, all strangers are out, that is, can no longer become the winner; in other words, only local people are still in. (The sentences (1) to (4) in our previous discussion and in the table T1a are here as follows: (1): 'a local junior wins'; (2): 'a local senior wins'; (3): 'a stranger junior wins'; and (4): 'a stranger senior wins'; i is L-equivalent (with respect to e) to the disjunction of (1) and (2).) On the basis of the increased evidence $e \cdot i$, the chance of winning is the same for each of the five local players, hence 1/5. There are 3 M among the five local players. Therefore, $\mathfrak{c}(h,e \cdot i) = 3/5$. Thus the $\mathfrak{c}$ of the prediction h has been increased by the addition of the new information i from 1/2 to 3/5. Hence i is positive to h on e. Suppose now that X receives instead of i the following report j: 'A junior wins'. There are 3 M among the five juniors. Therefore $\mathfrak{c}(h,e \cdot j) = 3/5$. Thus the addition of j to e leads likewise to an increase in the $\mathfrak{c}$ of h from 1/2 to 3/5. Hence j too is positive. However, if X receives both reports i and j, then he learns from them that a local junior wins. There are three local juniors, among them one man. Therefore $\mathfrak{c}(h,e \cdot i \cdot j) = 1/3$. Thus by the addition of $i \cdot j$ to e the $\mathfrak{c}$ of h has been decreased from 1/2 to 1/3. Hence $i \cdot j$ is negative to h on e.

Example for 1b. Let e, i, and j be as in the previous example. We take here the prediction h': 'A woman wins'. Thus $\vdash e \supset (h' \equiv \sim h)$. Therefore $\mathfrak{c}(h',e) = 1 - \mathfrak{c}(h,e)$, and the same holds for the other evidences containing e. Thus we find that $\mathfrak{c}(h',e) = 1/2$; $\mathfrak{c}(h',e \cdot i) = \mathfrak{c}(h',e \cdot j) = 2/5$. Hence both i and j are negative to h' on e. On the other hand, $\mathfrak{c}(h',e \cdot i \cdot j) = 2/3$. Hence $i \cdot j$ is positive to h' on e.

Results in the Examples 1a and 1b

Evidence	$\mathfrak{c}$ for h	Example 1a	$\mathfrak{c}$ for h'	Example 1b
e	0.5		0.5	
$e \cdot i$	0.6	i is positive	0.4	i is negative
$e \cdot j$	0.6	j is positive	0.4	j is negative
$e \cdot i \cdot j$	0.33	$i \cdot j$ is negative	0.67	$i \cdot j$ is positive

2a. It is possible that *each of two sentences is positive* and nevertheless their *disjunction is negative.* For i and j, this occurs only in case No. 6A in the table T1a. For this case we have given earlier (in the explanations preceding T1a) the following example of r-values: if the values for (1) to (4) are $3r$, $-2r$, $-2r$, and r, respectively, then (5) and (6), that is, i and j, have both the value r. Generally speaking, any case constructed in the following way is of this kind. For given e and h, we take any three sentences (1), (2), and (3) satisfying the following conditions: they are L-exclusive in pairs with respect to e; (2) and (3) are negative (to h on e), their r-values being $-r_2$ and $-r_3$, respectively; (1) is positive such that its r-value is greater than r_2 and greater than r_3 but less than $r_2 + r_3$; the latter condition is required in order to assure that for (4) $\mathfrak{r} > 0$ and hence for (7) $\mathfrak{r} < 0$. We take again as i the disjunction of (1) and (2), and as j that of (1) and (3). Then for both i and j $\mathfrak{r} > 0$, hence they are positive; but $i \vee j$, which is (7), is negative.

2b. It is possible that *each of two sentences is negative* while their *disjunction is positive.* This occurs only in No. 9E. Cases of this kind can be constructed like those for (2a) but with opposite r-values.

Example for 2a. We take e as before, and h' as in the example for 1b: 'A woman wins'. Hence $\mathfrak{c}(h',e) = 1/2$. Let i' be: 'A stranger wins'; this is L-equivalent to $\sim i$ with respect to e. Among the five strangers are 3 W. Hence $\mathfrak{c}(h',e \,.\, i') = 3/5 > 1/2$. Thus i' is positive to h' on e. Let j' be: 'A senior wins'; this is L-equivalent to $\sim j$ with respect to e. Among the five seniors there are again 3 W. Hence $\mathfrak{c}(h',e \,.\, j') = 3/5$. Thus j' too is positive. $i' \vee j'$ says that a stranger or a senior wins. Among the seven players who are strangers or seniors (including stranger seniors) there are 3 W. Hence $\mathfrak{c}(h',e \,.\, (i' \vee j')) = 3/7 < 1/2$. Thus $i' \vee j'$ is negative to h' on e.

Example for 2b. We take e, i', and j' as in 2a, but h as in 1a. h is L-equivalent to $\sim h'$ with respect to e; therefore the c-values here are the complements of those in 2a with respect to 1. $\mathfrak{c}(h,e) = 1/2$. $\mathfrak{c}(h,e \,.\, i') = \mathfrak{c}(h,e \,.\, j') = 2/5 < 1/2$. Hence both i' and j' are negative to h on e. $\mathfrak{c}(h,e \,.\, (i' \vee j')) = 4/7 > 1/2$. Hence $i' \vee j'$ is positive to h on e.

Results in the Examples 2a and 2b

Evidence	$\mathfrak{c}$ for h'	Example 2a	$\mathfrak{c}$ for h	Example 2b
e	0.5		0.5	
$e \,.\, i'$	0.6	i' is positive	0.4	i' is negative
$e \,.\, j'$	0.6	j' is positive	0.4	j' is negative
$e \,.\, (i' \vee j')$	0.43	$i' \vee j'$ is negative	0.57	$i' \vee j'$ is positive

Let us now investigate the case where j follows either from i alone or from i together with e. Our problem is whether in this case we can infer from the relevance of i (to h on e) something about the relevance of j, and vice versa. The following theorem T5 dealing with this situation is based on the earlier theorem on $\mathfrak{r}$-values in cases of deductive relations (T68-4).

T69-5. Let $\vdash e \,.\, i \supset j$, hence $e \,.\, i \,.\, \sim j$ is L-false. (This holds too if $\vdash i \supset j$, hence $i \,.\, \sim j$ is L-false.)

a. $\mathfrak{r}(j,h,e) = \mathfrak{r}(i,h,e) + \mathfrak{r}(\sim i \,.\, j,h,e)$. (From T68-4b(3) and (4).)

b. (1) $\mathfrak{r}(i,h,e) = \mathfrak{r}(j,h,e) - \mathfrak{r}(\sim i \,.\, j,h,e)$. (From (a).)

(2) $\qquad = \mathfrak{r}(j,h,e) + \mathfrak{r}(i \vee \sim j,h,e)$. (From (1), T67-5a, T21-5f(3).)

We see from T5 that neither $\mathfrak{r}$ for j is determined by $\mathfrak{r}$ for i nor vice versa; in each case another sentence is also to be taken into consideration, and its influence may change the sign of $\mathfrak{r}$. Thus, if $\mathfrak{r}$ for i is >0, $\mathfrak{r}$ for j may be >0, <0, or 0; and likewise if $\mathfrak{r}$ for i is <0, or is 0; and conversely, if $\mathfrak{r}$ for j has any sign, for i all three cases are still possible. In other words, in spite of the deductive relation holding, there are still all nine combinations possible for i and j. This is shown by *the following table.*

The Nine Combinations in the Case that $e \,.\, i$ L-implies j

	Signs of $\mathfrak{r}$		Case No.	Examples of Values for $\mathfrak{r}$				
				(1), (5)	(2)	(3)	(4)	(6)
For T69-5:	i	j	in T1a	i				j
For T71-5:	h	k	in T1b	h				k
			21	r	0	r	$-2r$	$2r$
	+	+	23	$2r$	0	$-r$	$-r$	r
			45	r	0	0	$-r$	r
	+	−	22	r	0	$-2r$	r	$-r$
	+	0	47	r	0	$-r$	0	0
	−	+	25	$-r$	0	$2r$	$-r$	r
			24	$-2r$	0	r	r	$-r$
	−	−	26	$-r$	0	$-r$	$2r$	$-2r$
			46	$-r$	0	0	r	$-r$
	−	0	48	$-r$	0	r	0	0
	0	+	39	0	0	r	$-r$	r
	0	−	40	0	0	$-r$	r	$-r$
	0	0	51	0	0	0	0	0

In the first two columns for i and j the nine combinations are listed. The next column cites for each combination at least one case from the list T1a. The following columns (1) to (4) and (6) correspond to the columns in T1a for the cases in question. Here, however, we give not only the signs of $\mathfrak{r}$ as in T1a but examples of $\mathfrak{r}$-values in accord with those signs; r is here some positive real number. Since $\vdash e \,.\, i \supset j$, the $\mathfrak{r}$-value for (2) is always 0 (T68-4b(1)); the cases here listed are all those from T1a where this holds. The r-value for (5), that is, i, is always the sum of the values for (1) and (2) (T68-3b), hence here it is the same as that for (1); the value for (6), that is, j, is the sum of those for (1) and (3) (T68-3c).

Simple cases where L-implication holds between two sentences and nevertheless the one is positive and the other negative can easily be found in the following way as special cases of the kinds 1a, 1b, 2a, and 2b earlier discussed.

1a. It is possible that i is positive (to h on e) but $i \cdot j$, although it L-implies i, is negative. See the former case 1a and the example for it.

1b. It is possible that i is negative but $i \cdot j$ is positive. See the former case 1b and the example for it.

2a. It is possible that i is positive but $i \vee j$, although L-implied by i, is negative. See the former case 2a and the example for it.

2b. It is possible that i is negative but $i \vee j$ is positive. See the former case 2b and the example for it.

These results are important because they show that certain opinions which seem to have been held sometimes are untenable. One is the view that, if i is positive (to h on e), then every sentence L-implied by i is likewise positive. The other is the view that, if i is positive, then every sentence L-implying i is likewise positive.

§ 70. Relevance Measures for Two Hypotheses and Their Connections

In this and the next section we investigate the case of two hypotheses h and k, and in particular the relations between the r-values of i to h and to k (on e), on the one hand, and the r-values of i to certain connections of h and k, especially $h \vee k$ and $h \cdot k$, on the other. Thus this section is analogous to § 68, which dealt with two evidences i and j. And, indeed, every theorem of § 68 can be transformed into an analogous one here concerning two hypotheses, because of the commutativity of r. Thus we find here two new theorems of additivity for r: (1) if h and k are L-exclusive with respect to e, then the r-value for i to $h \vee k$ (on e) is the sum of the r-values for i to h and to k (T1b); (2) if h and k are L-disjunct with respect to e, then the r-value for i to $h \cdot k$ (on e) is the sum of the r-values for i to h and to k (T2b).

If the r-values for i to each of the hypotheses $h \cdot k$, $h \cdot \sim k$, $\sim h \cdot k$, and $\sim h \cdot \sim k$ (on e) are given, then the r-values for i to h, k, and $h \vee k$ (on e) can be obtained as sums of one, two, or three of those four r-values. This is done first generally (T3) and then for all possible cases of deductive relations between h and k on the evidence e (T4).

We have discussed in § 68 the relation between the relevance measures of two evidences i and j, for instance, observation sentences, to a certain hypothesis h on the basis of a prior evidence e and the relevance measures of certain connections, especially $i \vee j$ and $i \cdot j$, to h on e. Because of the commutativity of r, every result we have found there can likewise be applied to the case of two hypotheses, say, h and k, and their connections. Suppose, for example, that we have found that under certain conditions for i and j $\mathfrak{r}(i \vee j,h,e) > 0$ and hence $i \vee j$ is positive to h on e. Then, by commutation (T67-3), we obtain the result that under the same conditions $\mathfrak{r}(h,i \vee j,e) > 0$. Here, simultaneous substitution of 'i', 'h', and 'k' for 'h', 'i', and 'j', respectively, yields this: if h and k satisfy certain conditions, namely, those stipulated in the first case for i and j, then $\mathfrak{r}(i,h \vee k,e) > 0$, hence i is positive to $h \vee k$ on e. In this way we reach theorems concerning the relevance of a given new evidence i to disjunctions or conjunctions of two hypotheses.

From a merely theoretical point of view there would not be much purpose in stating the new theorems, since they derive from the former ones merely by commutation and substitution. However, the practical situations to which the new theorems are applicable are quite different from those for the earlier theorems. There we had the case of an observer X who considers the relevance of two possible observations he might make and of their connections, while all the time it is only one hypothesis, say, a law or a singular prediction, for which the relevance is meant. Here, on the other hand, X considers the relevance of one observation, actually made or expected as possible, to two different hypotheses, for example, two predictions concerning different features of tomorrow's weather, and to their connections, especially their disjunction and their conjunction. For this reason, which concerns more the methodology of application than the system of inductive logic itself, it seems convenient to have the theorems which will be stated here in addition to the previous ones.

In most cases it will be unnecessary to give proofs. It will be sufficient to indicate for each theorem here that earlier theorem to which it is analogous and from which it is derivable in the way indicated above or in a similar simple manner.

The following two theorems of additivity are the analogues to T68-1 and 2, respectively.

T70-1. *Additivity for disjunctions of hypotheses.*

a. $\mathfrak{r}(i,h \vee k,e) = \mathfrak{r}(i,h,e) + \mathfrak{r}(i,k,e) - \mathfrak{r}(i,h \cdot k,e)$. (From T68-1a, T67-3.)

+b. Let $\mathfrak{m}(e \cdot h \cdot k) = 0$. (This is the case in particular if $e \cdot h \cdot k$ is L-false, in other words, if h and k are *L-exclusive* with respect to e.) Then $\mathfrak{r}(i,h \vee k,e) = \mathfrak{r}(i,h,e) + \mathfrak{r}(i,k,e)$. (From T68-1b.)

c. Let h be a disjunction with n ($\geqq 2$) components: $h_1 \vee h_2 \vee \ldots \vee h_n$. For any two distinct components h_m and h_p, let $\mathfrak{m}(e \cdot h_m \cdot h_p) = 0$.

(This is the case if $h_1, \ldots, h_n$ are L-exclusive in pairs with respect to e.) Then $\mathfrak{r}(i,h,e) = \sum_{p=1}^{n} \mathfrak{r}(i,h_p,e)$. (From T68-1c.)

T70-2. *Additivity for conjunctions of hypotheses.*

a. $\mathfrak{r}(i,h\,.\,k,e) = \mathfrak{r}(i,h,e) + \mathfrak{r}(i,k,e) - \mathfrak{r}(i,h \vee k,e)$. (From T68-2a.)

b. Let $\mathfrak{m}(e\,.\,\sim h\,.\,\sim k) = 0$. (This is the case if $\vdash e \supset h \vee k$, in other words, if h and k are *L-disjunct* with respect to e.) Then $\mathfrak{r}(i,h\,.\,k,e) = \mathfrak{r}(i,h,e) + \mathfrak{r}(i,k,e)$. (From T68-2b.)

c. Let h be a conjunction with n ($\geqq 2$) components: $h_1\,.\,h_2\,.\,\ldots\,.\,h_n$. For any two distinct components h_m and h_p, let $\mathfrak{m}(e\,.\,\sim h_m\,.\,\sim h_p) = 0$. (This is the case if h_m and h_p are L-disjunct with respect to e, i.e., $\vdash e \supset h_m \vee h_p$.) Then $\mathfrak{r}(i,h,e) = \sum_{p=1}^{n} \mathfrak{r}(i,h_p,e)$. (From T68-2c.)

Suppose two hypotheses h and k are given. We consider the four sentences $h\,.\,k$, $h\,.\,\sim k$, $\sim h\,.\,k$, and $\sim h\,.\,\sim k$. These sentences form a convenient basis for studying the r-values for any connections of h and k, because any such value can be determined as sum of the r-values of some of those four sentences. This leads to T3 as an analogue to T68-3.

In this section and the next one, we shall use the symbols '$\mathfrak{r}_1$', etc., for four r-values as follows. (Note that these symbols will no longer have the meanings they had in the two preceding sections; the r-values here denoted by them are analogous to but not identical with the earlier ones.)

$$\mathfrak{r}_1 = \mathfrak{r}(i,h\,.\,k,e),$$
$$\mathfrak{r}_2 = \mathfrak{r}(i,h\,.\,\sim k,e),$$
$$\mathfrak{r}_3 = \mathfrak{r}(i,\sim h\,.\,k,e),$$
$$\mathfrak{r}_4 = \mathfrak{r}(i,\sim h\,.\,\sim k,e).$$

T70-3. Let e, h, k, and i be sentences in $\mathfrak{L}$.

a. $\mathfrak{r}_1 + \mathfrak{r}_2 + \mathfrak{r}_3 + \mathfrak{r}_4 = 0$. (From T68-3a.)

b. $\mathfrak{r}(i,h,e) = \mathfrak{r}_1 + \mathfrak{r}_2$. (From T68-3b.)

c. $\mathfrak{r}(i,k,e) = \mathfrak{r}_1 + \mathfrak{r}_3$. (From T68-3c.)

d. (1) $\mathfrak{r}(i,h \vee k,e) = \mathfrak{r}_1 + \mathfrak{r}_2 + \mathfrak{r}_3$;
(2) $\qquad = -\mathfrak{r}_4$.
(From T68-3d.)

If any deductive relations hold between h and k, then one or two or three of the four sentences are L-false and hence have the r-value 0. These and related cases are dealt with in T4, which is analogous to T68-4.

T70-4.

a. Let $\mathfrak{m}(e\,.\,h\,.\,k) = 0$. (This is the case in particular if $e\,.\,h\,.\,k$ is

L-false, in other words, $\vdash e \,.\, h \supset \sim k$, h and k are L-exclusive with respect to e.) Then the following holds.

(1) $\mathfrak{r}_1 = 0$.

(2) $\mathfrak{r}_2 + \mathfrak{r}_3 + \mathfrak{r}_4 = 0$.

(3) $\mathfrak{r}(i,h,e) = \mathfrak{r}_2$.

(4) $\mathfrak{r}(i,k,e) = \mathfrak{r}_3$.

(5) $\mathfrak{r}(i,h \vee k,e) = \mathfrak{r}_2 + \mathfrak{r}_3 = -\mathfrak{r}_4$.

(From T68-4a.)

b. Let $\mathfrak{m}(e \,.\, h \,.\, \sim k) = 0$. (This is the case if $e \,.\, h \,.\, \sim k$ is L-false; hence $\vdash e \,.\, h \supset k$.)

(1) $\mathfrak{r}_2 = 0$.

(2) $\mathfrak{r}_1 + \mathfrak{r}_3 + \mathfrak{r}_4 = 0$.

(3) $\mathfrak{r}(i,h,e) = \mathfrak{r}_1$.

(4) $\mathfrak{r}(i,k,e) = \mathfrak{r}(i,h \vee k,e) = \mathfrak{r}_1 + \mathfrak{r}_3 = -\mathfrak{r}_4$.

(From T68-4b.)

c. Let $\mathfrak{m}(e \,.\, \sim h \,.\, k) = 0$. (This is the case if $e \,.\, \sim h \,.\, k$ is L-false; hence $\vdash e \,.\, k \supset h$.)

(1) $\mathfrak{r}_3 = 0$.

(2) $\mathfrak{r}_1 + \mathfrak{r}_2 + \mathfrak{r}_4 = 0$.

(3) $\mathfrak{r}(i,k,e) = \mathfrak{r}_1$.

(4) $\mathfrak{r}(i,h,e) = \mathfrak{r}(i,h \vee k,e) = \mathfrak{r}_1 + \mathfrak{r}_2 = -\mathfrak{r}_4$.

(From T68-4c.)

d. Let $\mathfrak{m}(e \,.\, \sim h \,.\, \sim k) = 0$. (This is the case if $e \,.\, \sim h \,.\, \sim k$ is L-false; in other words, $\vdash e \supset h \vee k$, h and k are L-disjunct with respect to e.)

(1) $\mathfrak{r}_4 = 0$.

(2) $\mathfrak{r}_1 + \mathfrak{r}_2 + \mathfrak{r}_3 = 0$.

(3) $\mathfrak{r}(i,h,e) = \mathfrak{r}_1 + \mathfrak{r}_2 = -\mathfrak{r}_3$.

(4) $\mathfrak{r}(i,k,e) = \mathfrak{r}_1 + \mathfrak{r}_3 = -\mathfrak{r}_2$.

(5) $\mathfrak{r}(i,h \vee k,e) = 0$.

(From T68-4d.)

e. Let $\mathfrak{m}(e \,.\, h \,.\, k) = \mathfrak{m}(e \,.\, h \,.\, \sim k) = 0$; in other words, $\mathfrak{m}(e \,.\, h) = 0$. (This is the case if $e \,.\, h$ is L-false; hence $\vdash e \supset \sim h$.)

(1) $\mathfrak{r}_1 = \mathfrak{r}_2 = 0$.

(2) $\mathfrak{r}_3 + \mathfrak{r}_4 = 0$.

(3) $\mathfrak{r}(i,h,e) = 0$.

(4) $\mathfrak{r}(i,k,e) = \mathfrak{r}(i,h \vee k,e) = \mathfrak{r}_3 = -\mathfrak{r}_4$.

(From T68-4e.)

f. Let $\mathfrak{m}(e \,.\, h \,.\, k) = \mathfrak{m}(e \,.\, \sim h \,.\, k) = 0$; in other words, $\mathfrak{m}(e \,.\, k) = 0$. (This is the case if $e \,.\, k$ is L-false; hence $\vdash e \supset \sim k$.)

(1) $\mathfrak{r}_1 = \mathfrak{r}_3 = 0$.

(2) $\mathfrak{r}_2 + \mathfrak{r}_4 = 0$.
(3) $\mathfrak{r}(i,k,e) = 0$.
(4) $\mathfrak{r}(i,h,e) = \mathfrak{r}(i,h \vee k,e) = \mathfrak{r}_2 = -\mathfrak{r}_4$.
(From T68-4f.)

g. Let $\mathfrak{m}(e \centerdot h \centerdot k) = \mathfrak{m}(e \centerdot \sim h \centerdot \sim k) = 0$; in other words, $\mathfrak{m}(e \centerdot (h \equiv k)) = 0$. (This is the case if $e \centerdot (h \equiv k)$ is L-false; hence $\vdash e \supset (h \equiv \sim k)$.)
(1) $\mathfrak{r}_1 = \mathfrak{r}_4 = 0$.
(2) $\mathfrak{r}_2 + \mathfrak{r}_3 = 0$.
(3) $\mathfrak{r}(i,h,e) = \mathfrak{r}_2 = -\mathfrak{r}_3$.
(4) $\mathfrak{r}(i,k,e) = \mathfrak{r}_3 = -\mathfrak{r}_2 = -\mathfrak{r}(i,h,e)$.
(5) $\mathfrak{r}(i,h \vee k,e) = 0$.
(From T68-4g.)

h. Let $\mathfrak{m}(e \centerdot h \centerdot \sim k) = \mathfrak{m}(e \centerdot \sim h \centerdot k) = 0$; in other words, $\mathfrak{m}(e \centerdot \sim (h \equiv k)) = 0$. (This is the case if $e \centerdot \sim (h \equiv k)$ is L-false; hence $\vdash e \supset (h \equiv k)$, h and k are L-equivalent with respect to e.)
(1) $\mathfrak{r}_2 = \mathfrak{r}_3 = 0$.
(2) $\mathfrak{r}_1 + \mathfrak{r}_4 = 0$.
(3) $\mathfrak{r}(i,h,e) = \mathfrak{r}(i,k,e) = \mathfrak{r}(i,h \vee k,e) = \mathfrak{r}_1 = -\mathfrak{r}_4$.
(From T68-4h.)

i. Let $\mathfrak{m}(e \centerdot h \centerdot \sim k) = \mathfrak{m}(e \centerdot \sim h \centerdot \sim k) = 0$; in other words, $\mathfrak{m}(e \centerdot \sim k) = 0$. (This is the case if $e \centerdot \sim k$ is L-false; hence $\vdash e \supset k$.)
(1) $\mathfrak{r}_2 = \mathfrak{r}_4 = 0$.
(2) $\mathfrak{r}_1 + \mathfrak{r}_3 = 0$.
(3) $\mathfrak{r}(i,h,e) = \mathfrak{r}_1 = -\mathfrak{r}_3$.
(4) $\mathfrak{r}(i,k,e) = \mathfrak{r}(i,h \vee k,e) = 0$.
(From T68-4i.)

j. Let $\mathfrak{m}(e \centerdot \sim h \centerdot k) = \mathfrak{m}(e \centerdot \sim h \centerdot \sim k) = 0$; in other words, $\mathfrak{m}(e \centerdot \sim h) = 0$. (This is the case if $e \centerdot \sim h$ is L-false; hence $\vdash e \supset h$.)
(1) $\mathfrak{r}_3 = \mathfrak{r}_4 = 0$.
(2) $\mathfrak{r}_1 + \mathfrak{r}_2 = 0$.
(3) $\mathfrak{r}(i,h,e) = \mathfrak{r}(i,h \vee k,e) = 0$.
(4) $\mathfrak{r}(i,k,e) = \mathfrak{r}_1 = -\mathfrak{r}_2$.
(From T68-4j.)

k. Let any three of the four sentences $h \centerdot k$, $h \centerdot \sim k$, $\sim h \centerdot k$, and $\sim h \centerdot \sim k$ be selected. Let $\mathfrak{m} = 0$ for the three conjunctions of e with each of the selected sentences. (This is the case if these three conjunctions are L-false, and hence e L-implies the one sentence among the four which has not been selected.)
(1) $\mathfrak{r}_1 = \mathfrak{r}_2 = \mathfrak{r}_3 = \mathfrak{r}_4 = 0$.

(2) r for i is 0 to each of the sentences h, k, $h \vee k$, and $h . k$ (on e). (From T68-4k.)

1. Let $\mathfrak{m}(e . h . k) = \mathfrak{m}(e . h . \sim k) = \mathfrak{m}(e . \sim h . k) = \mathfrak{m}(e . \sim h . \sim k) = 0$; in other words, $\mathfrak{m}(e) = 0$. (This holds if e is L-false.)
(1) $\mathfrak{r}_1 = \mathfrak{r}_2 = \mathfrak{r}_3 = \mathfrak{r}_4 = 0$.
(2) r for i is 0 to each of the sentences h, k, $h \vee k$, $h . k$ (on e). (From T68-4l.)

T4 deals with all possible cases of deductive relations between h and k on the evidence e. If the r-value of i is given for each of the four L-exclusive hypotheses $h . k$, $h . \sim k$, $\sim h . k$, and $\sim h . \sim k$, then T3 and T4 state the values for h, k, and $h \vee k$, and enable us to determine easily the values for any other connections of h and k. T3 does this in general, and T4 for all cases of deductive relations.

§ 71. The Possible Relevance Situations for Two Hypotheses and Their Connections

The possible relevance situations for i to two hypotheses h and k and their connections are investigated, as characterized by the signs of r. Thus this section is analogous to § 69. A complete list of the possible relevance situations is given by another interpretation of the earlier table (T69-1b). With the help of this table, general theorems about possible relevance situations are derived, first in terms of signs of r (T2), and then in terms of the relevance concepts (T3). Four kinds of relevance situations, whose possibility seems surprising at first glance, are studied more in detail; among them are the following: (3a) i is positive (on e) to both h and k, but negative to $h . k$; (4a) i is positive (on e) to both h and k, but negative to $h \vee k$. These possibilities are illustrated by examples with numerical values. Finally, a general theorem and examples show the following: if it is known that k is L-implied either by h alone or by $e . h$, then from the relevance of i to h (on e) nothing can be inferred concerning the relevance of i to k, or vice versa.

We have earlier constructed, on the basis of T68-4, the table T69-1a which lists all possible relevance situations with respect to i, j, and their connections. Each relevance situation is here characterized, not by the numerical values of r for the sentences involved, but merely by what we have called the *sign of* r, that is to say, a statement saying whether r is >0, <0, or 0. Now on the basis of T70-4, we can construct a completely analogous table. This table represents another but analogous class of possible relevance situations, namely, those for the sentence i, which remains the same throughout, but with respect to several hypotheses, viz., (1) $h . k$, (2) $h . \sim k$, (3) $\sim h . k$, (4) $\sim h . \sim k$, (5) h, (6) k, and (7) $h \vee k$. As previously, the relevance situations are characterized by the signs of r.

It is however not necessary to write an entirely new table; we take now as **Table T69-1b** simply the earlier table but with the seven sentences just mentioned at the heads of the seven columns, as indicated there on the line **b**. This simple procedure is possible because of the perfect analogy between T70-4 and T68-4; but we can also derive T69-1b directly from T69-1a, without the use of T70-4, by commutation and substitution, as explained in the preceding section.

As the table T69-1a led us to T69-2, so now the table T69-1b may lead us to the following analogous theorem T2; the latter can, however, be derived more simply from T69-2 directly by commutation. T2 states in general terms which combinations of signs of $\mathfrak{r}$ are possible for i to h, k, $h \,.\, k$, and $h \vee k$.

T71-2. Let four sentences e, h, k, and i in $\mathfrak{L}$ be given. (a), (b), (c), and (d) deal with four cases concerning the signs of $\mathfrak{r}$ for i to the hypotheses h and k on e. It is easily seen that for any four sentences exactly one of these cases (a) to (d) applies. $\mathfrak{r}$ is here always meant for i on e; thus only the hypothesis (i.e., the second argument of $\mathfrak{r}$) is explicitly referred to in each case.

a. Let $\mathfrak{r}$ either be >0 to both h and k (i.e., $\mathfrak{r}(i,h,e)$ and $\mathfrak{r}(i,k,e) > 0$), or >0 to one of them and 0 to the other. Then the following holds.
(1) $\mathfrak{r} > 0$ to at least one of the hypotheses $h \,.\, k$ and $h \vee k$.
(2) If $\mathfrak{r} > 0$ to $h \,.\, k$, then it may be >0, <0, or 0 to $h \vee k$.
(3) If $\mathfrak{r} > 0$ to $h \vee k$, then it may be >0, <0, or 0 to $h \,.\, k$.
(4) Let $\mathfrak{m}(e \,.\, h \,.\, k) = 0$. (This is the case in particular if $e \,.\, h \,.\, k$ is L-false; in other words, h and k are L-exclusive with respect to e.) Then $\mathfrak{r} = 0$ to $h \,.\, k$, and $\mathfrak{r} > 0$ to $h \vee k$.
(5) Let $\mathfrak{m}(e \,.\, \sim h \,.\, \sim k) = 0$. (This is the case if $e \,.\, \sim h \,.\, \sim k$ is L-false; hence $\vdash e \supset h \vee k$.) Then $\mathfrak{r} = 0$ to $h \vee k$, and $\mathfrak{r} > 0$ to $h \,.\, k$.
(From T69-2a.)

b. Let $\mathfrak{r}$ either be <0 to both h and k, or <0 to one of them and 0 to the other. Then the following holds.
(1) $\mathfrak{r} < 0$ to at least one of the hypotheses $h \,.\, k$ and $h \vee k$.
(2) If $\mathfrak{r} < 0$ to $h \,.\, k$, then $\mathfrak{r}$ may be >0, <0, or 0 to $h \vee k$.
(3) If $\mathfrak{r} < 0$ to $h \vee k$, then $\mathfrak{r}$ may be >0, <0, or 0 to $h \,.\, k$.
(4) Let $\mathfrak{m}(e \,.\, h \,.\, k) = 0$. Then $\mathfrak{r} = 0$ to $h \,.\, k$, and $\mathfrak{r} < 0$ to $h \vee k$.
(5) Let $\mathfrak{m}(e \,.\, \sim h \,.\, \sim k) = 0$. Then $\mathfrak{r} = 0$ to $h \vee k$, and $\mathfrak{r} < 0$ to $h \,.\, k$.
(From T69-2b.)

c. Let $\mathfrak{r}$ be >0 to one of the hypotheses h and k, and <0 to the other. Then $\mathfrak{r}$ may be >0, <0, or 0 to $h \,.\, k$, and it may also be >0, <0, or 0 to $h \vee k$, independently of $h \,.\, k$; that is to say, all nine combinations are possible. (From T69-2c.)

d. Let r = 0 to both h and k. Then either r = 0 to both $h \,.\, k$ and $h \vee k$, or r > 0 to the one and r < 0 to the other; in the latter case, the one r-value is the opposite of the other. (From T69-2d.)

While T2 is in terms of the three signs of r, the similar theorem T3 uses instead the three corresponding relevance concepts, viz., positive relevance, negative relevance, and irrelevance. We require in T3 that $e \,.\, i$ is not almost L-false. This assures that the correspondence between the three r-signs and the three relevance concepts holds here throughout (as seen from T67-8 and T67-9). [With respect to this restricting condition, the analogy between T69-3 and T3 does not hold. In T69-3 it was necessary to require that neither $e \,.\, i$ nor $e \,.\, j$ is almost L-false. The analogous condition here would be that neither $e \,.\, h$ nor $e \,.\, k$ is almost L-false. However, it is here sufficient to require instead that $e \,.\, i$ is not almost L-false. We do not prove T3 simply with the help of T69-3 by commutation, because the symmetry of the relevance concepts (T65-6) has earlier been proved only on the basis of assumptions which were stronger than the condition just mentioned. We shall instead base the proof on the theorem T2 concerning r-signs and the earlier theorems (T67-8 and T67-9) stating the correspondence between r-signs and relevance concepts.]

+T71-3. Let e, h, k, and i be sentences in $\mathfrak{L}$. For $\mathfrak{L}_\infty$ it is assumed that $e \,.\, i$ is not almost L-false. Relevance and irrelevance are here always meant on evidence e.

a. Let i be either positive to both h and k, or positive to one of them and irrelevant to the other. Then the following holds.

(1) i is positive to at least one of the hypotheses $h \,.\, k$ and $h \vee k$.

(2) If i is positive to $h \,.\, k$, then for $h \vee k$ all three cases are possible, that is to say, i may be positive, negative, or irrelevant to $h \vee k$.

(3) If i is positive to $h \vee k$, then for $h \,.\, k$ all three cases are possible.

(4) Let $\mathfrak{m}(e \,.\, h \,.\, k) = 0$. (This is the case if $e \,.\, h \,.\, k$ is L-false.) Then i is irrelevant to $h \,.\, k$ and positive to $h \vee k$.

(5) Let $\mathfrak{m}(e \,.\, {\sim}h \,.\, {\sim}k) = 0$. (This is the case if $e \,.\, {\sim}h \,.\, {\sim}k$ is L-false; hence $\vdash e \supset h \vee k$.) Then i is irrelevant to $h \vee k$, and positive to $h \,.\, k$.

b. Let i either be negative to both h and k, or negative to one of them and irrelevant to the other.

(1) i is negative to at least one of the hypotheses $h \,.\, k$ and $h \vee k$.

(2) If i is negative to $h \,.\, k$, then all three cases are possible for $h \vee k$.

(3) If i is negative to $h \vee k$, then all three cases are possible for $h \,.\, k$.

(4) Let $\mathfrak{m}(e \,.\, h \,.\, k) = 0$. Then i is irrelevant to $h \,.\, k$, and negative to $h \vee k$.

(5) Let $\mathfrak{m}(e \,.\, {\sim}h \,.\, {\sim}k) = 0$. Then i is irrelevant to $h \vee k$, and negative to $h \,.\, k$.

c. Let i be positive to one of the hypotheses h and k, and negative to to the other. Then i may have any of the three relevance relations to $h \,.\, k$, and, independently, any of the three to $h \vee k$; that is to say, all nine combinations are possible.

d. Let i be irrelevant to both h and k. Then i is either irrelevant to both $h \,.\, k$ and $h \vee k$, or it is positive to the one and negative to the other. (From T2, T67-8, T67-9.)

T3 states which relevance situations are possible in terms of the relevance concepts. Among these relevance situations there are some whose possibility seems surprising at first glance. We shall now describe and analyze four kinds of such cases, and then illustrate them by examples. The cases 3a, 3b, 4a, and 4b here are analogous to the cases 1a, 1b, 2a, and 2b, respectively, in § 69.

3a. It is possible that i is *positive to each of two hypotheses h* and k (on e) and nevertheless *negative to their conjunction*. This occurs only in the case No. 9A in table T69-1b. Example of $\mathfrak{r}$-values: for (1) to (4), $-r$, $2r$, $2r$, and $-3r$, respectively, hence r for (5) and for (6). In general, any case constructed by a procedure analogous to that described under (1a) in § 69 is of this kind (with h, k, and i for i, j, and h, respectively).

3b. It is possible that i is *negative to each of two hypotheses h* and k (on e) and nevertheless *positive to their conjunction*. This occurs only in No. 6E.

Example for 3a. This example is based on the previous example of the chess tournament given under (1a) in § 69. We take as prior evidence e the same as there. Here, however, the observer X is interested in two hypotheses h and k, which are predictions concerning the result of the tournament. h is: 'A local player wins'; and k: 'A junior wins'. Among the ten players five are local people; therefore $\mathfrak{c}(h,e) = 5/10 = 1/2$. The number of juniors is also five; hence likewise $\mathfrak{c}(k,e) = 1/2$. The conjunction $h \,.\, k$ says that a local junior wins. There are three local juniors; hence $\mathfrak{c}(h \,.\, k,e) = 3/10$. Now X receives the report i: 'A man wins'; it may be based on the result that all women are out. (The sentences h, k, and i here are the same as i, j, and h, respectively, in the example for (1a).) For the problems in inductive logic as to what is the $\mathfrak{c}$ of h, k, and their connections on the evidence $e \,.\, i$ and, consequently, what is the relevance of i to those hypotheses, it does not matter, of course, at which time point the report i is given to X, and what are the motives for the speaker to say no more than i; all that matters is that X acquires, in addition to e, the knowledge of i and nothing else. It may be, for instance, that the speaker himself knows only i; or, again, it may be that he knows that not only all women are out but also some of the men and that he does not care to specify the class of those who are still in beyond saying that all of them are men; finally, as an extreme case, it may be that the tournament is already finished and that the speaker knows who is the winner but says to X merely that he is a man. Among the five male players three are local; hence $\mathfrak{c}(h,e \cdot i) = 3/5$. Thus the addition of i to e increases the $\mathfrak{c}$ of h from $1/2$ to $3/5$. Hence i is positive to h (always on e). Among the five male players there are three juniors; hence $\mathfrak{c}(k,e \cdot i) = 3/5$. Thus the $\mathfrak{c}$ of k is likewise increased from $1/2$ to $3/5$. Hence i is positive also to k. On the other hand, there is only one local junior among the five men; hence $\mathfrak{c}(h \cdot k,e \cdot i) = 1/5$. Thus the $\mathfrak{c}$ of $h \cdot k$ is decreased from $3/10$ to $1/5$. Hence i is negative to $h \cdot k$.

Example for 3b. Let e, h, and k be as in the example just given for (3a). Hence the $\mathfrak{c}$-values on e are the same as there. However, instead of i we take here i': 'A woman wins'. (This is the same as h' in the earlier example for (1b) in § 69.) Among the five women, the number of local players is two, that of juniors is two, and that of local juniors is also two. (These are always the same two persons.) Hence $\mathfrak{c}(h,e \cdot i') = \mathfrak{c}(k,e \cdot i') = \mathfrak{c}(h \cdot k,e \cdot i') = 2/5$. Thus by the addition of i' to e, the $\mathfrak{c}$ of h is decreased from $1/2$ to $2/5$; and likewise the $\mathfrak{c}$ of k; but the $\mathfrak{c}$ of $h \cdot k$ is increased from $3/10$ to $2/5$. Hence i' is negative to h and to k (on e) but positive to $h \cdot k$.

Results in the Examples 3a and 3b

HYPOTHESIS	c		EXAMPLE 3a	c		EXAMPLE 3b
	on e	on $e \cdot i$		on e	on $e \cdot i'$	
h	0.5	0.6	i is positive	0.5	0.4	i' is negative
k	0.5	0.6	i is positive	0.5	0.4	i' is negative
$h \cdot k$	0.3	0.2	i is negative	0.3	0.4	i' is positive

4a. It is possible that i is *positive to each of two hypotheses* h and k (on e) and nevertheless *negative to their disjunction*. This occurs only in case No. 6A in the table T69-1b. Examples can be constructed as described under (2a) in § 69, but here with h, k, and i in the place of i, j, and h.

4b. It is possible that i is *negative to each of two hypotheses* h and k (on e) and nevertheless *positive to their disjunction*. This occurs only in No. 9E.

Example for 4a. (This example is analogous to that for (2a) in § 69; h', k', and i' here are the same as i', j', and h' there, respectively.) e is the same as in the previous examples. h' is: 'A stranger wins'; k': 'A senior wins'. Among the ten players the number of strangers is five, and that of seniors also five. Hence $\mathfrak{c}(h',e) = \mathfrak{c}(k',e) = 5/10 = 1/2$. $h' \vee k'$ says that the winner is a stranger or a senior (possibly a stranger senior). The number of those players who are strangers or seniors (not excluding stranger seniors) is seven. Hence $\mathfrak{c}(h' \vee k',e) = 7/10$. Let i' be: 'A woman wins'. The number of strangers among the five women is three, and likewise that of seniors, and likewise that of those who are strangers or seniors. (These are always the same three persons.) Hence $\mathfrak{c}(h',e \cdot i') = \mathfrak{c}(k',e \cdot i') = \mathfrak{c}(h' \vee k',e \cdot i') = 3/5$. Thus by the addition of i' to e the $\mathfrak{c}$ of h' is increased, and likewise the $\mathfrak{c}$ of k'. On the other hand, the $\mathfrak{c}$ of $h' \vee k'$ is decreased. Hence i' is positive to h' and to k' (on e), but negative to $h' \vee k'$.

Example for 4b. We take e, h', and k' as in (4a). Therefore the $\mathfrak{c}$-values on e are the same as in (4a). But instead of i' we take here i as in (3a): 'A man wins'. Among the five men the number of strangers is two, and likewise that of seniors; but the number of those who are strangers or seniors is 4. Hence $\mathfrak{c}(h',e \centerdot i) = \mathfrak{c}(k',e \centerdot i) = 2/5$; but $\mathfrak{c}(h' \vee k',e \centerdot i) = 4/5$. Thus i is negative to h' and to k' (on e), but positive to $h' \vee k'$.

Results in the Examples 4a and 4b

Hypothesis	$\mathfrak{c}$		Example 4a	$\mathfrak{c}$		Example 4b
	on e	on $e \centerdot i'$		on e	on $e \centerdot i$	
h'	0.5	0.6	i' is positive	0.5	0.4	i is negative
k'	0.5	0.6	i' is positive	0.5	0.4	i is negative
$h' \vee k'$	0.7	0.6	i' is negative	0.7	0.8	i is positive

The following theorem T5, which is analogous to T69-5, deals with the case where *one hypothesis*, either alone or together with e, *L-implies the other*. The theorem answers the question whether from the relevance of i to the one hypothesis something can be inferred about its relevance to the other. The answer is in the negative. T5 is based on the earlier theorem on $\mathfrak{r}$-values in cases of deductive relations (T70-4).

T71-5. Let $\vdash e \centerdot h \supset k$; hence $e \centerdot h \centerdot \sim k$ is L-false. (This holds too if $\vdash h \supset k$; hence $h \centerdot \sim k$ is L-false.)

a. $\mathfrak{r}(i,k,e) = \mathfrak{r}(i,h,e) + \mathfrak{r}(i,\sim h \centerdot k,e)$. (From T70-4b(3) and (4).)

b. (1) $\mathfrak{r}(i,h,e) = \mathfrak{r}(i,k,e) - \mathfrak{r}(i,\sim h \centerdot k,e)$. (From (a).)

(2) $= \mathfrak{r}(i,k,e) + \mathfrak{r}(i,h \vee \sim k,e)$. (From (1), T67-5b, T21-5f(3).)

T5 shows that neither the relevance of i to k is determined by that of i to h nor vice versa. In spite of the deductive relation holding between h and k, there are still all nine combinations of $\mathfrak{r}$-signs possible. This is shown by the *table* following T69-5, here interpreted as giving examples of $\mathfrak{r}$-values for i to h, k, and their connections, the numbers (1) to (6) referring to the table T69-1b.

Simple cases where L-implication holds between two hypotheses and nevertheless i is positive to the one and negative to the other can easily be found in the following way as special cases of the kinds 3a, 3b, 4a, and 4b discussed above.

3a. It is possible that *i* is positive to *h* (on *e*) but nevertheless negative to *h* . *k*, although the latter L-implies the former. See the previous case 3a and the example for it.

3b. It is possible that *i* is negative to *h* but positive to *h* . *k*. See the previous case 3b and the example for it.

4a. It is possible that *i* is positive to *h* but negative to $h \vee k$, although the latter is L-implied by the former. See the previous case 4a and the example for it.

4b. It is possible that *i* is negative to *h* but positive to $h \vee k$. See the previous case 4b and the example for it.

In our later discussion on the classificatory concept of confirmation $\mathfrak{C}$ we shall mention and examine certain principles stated by other authors (§ 87). One of these principles (called the Special Consequence Condition) says that, if *i* confirms *h* and $\vdash h \supset k$, then *i* confirms *k*. If we assume that the relation of confirming in this principle is meant in the sense of what we, following Keynes, have called positive relevance (either on a given evidence *e* or on the tautological evidence '*t*'), then the principle is refuted by the case (4a) just explained. Another principle (called the Converse Consequence Condition) that has been stated, though not together with the first, says that, if *i* confirms *k* and $\vdash h \supset k$, then *i* confirms *h*. If we interpret 'confirming' again as above, then this principle is refuted by the case (3a) just explained. Thus it seems important to become clearly aware of this result of our preceding discussions: if we know merely that *i* is positive to *h* on *e* (for example, if somebody tells us just this without, however, specifying the three sentences), then it is not possible for us to infer whether *i* is positive, negative, or irrelevant to a sentence L-implied by *h* or to a sentence L-implying *h*.

§ 72. Relevance Measures of State-Descriptions; First Method: Disjunctive Analysis

The first method for the relevance analysis of a sentence *i* in $\mathfrak{L}_N$ consists in analyzing *i* into its ultimate disjunctive components; these are the state-descriptions $\mathfrak{Z}$ in its range $\mathfrak{R}_i$. It is found that the relevance measure $\mathfrak{r}$ for *i* (to *h* on *e*) is the sum of the $\mathfrak{r}$-values for these $\mathfrak{Z}$ (T7b). Since for any $\mathfrak{Z}$ outside of $\mathfrak{R}_e$ $\mathfrak{r} = 0$ (T3c), the $\mathfrak{r}$ for *i* is the sum of the $\mathfrak{r}$-values for the $\mathfrak{Z}$ in $\mathfrak{R}(e \,.\, i)$ (T7d). This range consists of two parts, $\mathfrak{R}(e \,.\, i \,.\, h)$ and $\mathfrak{R}(e \,.\, i \,.\, \sim h)$, which we call $\mathfrak{R}_1$ and $\mathfrak{R}_2$, respectively. For every $\mathfrak{Z}$ in $\mathfrak{R}_1$ $\mathfrak{r} \geqq 0$, for every $\mathfrak{Z}$ in $\mathfrak{R}_2$ $\mathfrak{r} \leqq 0$ (T7c). A table is given (T8) which states, for all possible cases of deductive relations between *e*, *h*, and *i*, the sign and value of $\mathfrak{r}$ for *i* (to *h* on *e*) and the sign of $\mathfrak{r}$ for any $\mathfrak{Z}$ in $\mathfrak{R}_1$ and in $\mathfrak{R}_2$, and thereby the relevance of these sentences (to *h* on *e*).

We have seen that the relevance measure $\mathfrak{r}$ is additive with respect to a disjunction i with L-exclusive components (T68-1c), that is to say, the $\mathfrak{r}$-value of i to a given h on e is the sum of the values for the components. There are, of course, in general many ways of dividing a given i into L-exclusive disjunctive components. If one such disjunctive representation of i is known, then it will in general be possible to split its components again into further L-exclusive disjunctive components. Let us restrict the following discussion to sentences in a finite system $\mathfrak{L}_N$. Analyzing a sentence i into L-exclusive disjunctive components is the same as dividing its range $\mathfrak{R}_i$ into exclusive (i.e., nonoverlapping) parts. Thus it is clear that this procedure of further and further disjunctive analysis comes to an end when we have reached the smallest nonnull ranges, in other words, when we have reached state-descriptions $\mathfrak{Z}$ as disjunctive components. The range of $\mathfrak{Z}_i$ contains just $\mathfrak{Z}_i$ itself and nothing else. Therefore, we cannot divide $\mathfrak{R}(\mathfrak{Z}_i)$ into two nonempty parts. Hence it is not possible to transform $\mathfrak{Z}_i$ into a disjunction of two L-exclusive, non-L-false sentences in $\mathfrak{L}_N$. If this ultimate disjunctive analysis of i into certain $\mathfrak{Z}$ is carried out, then the $\mathfrak{r}$-value for i (to h on e) can be determined as the sum of the values for these $\mathfrak{Z}$. These latter values provide a more detailed characterization of the relevance situation for i than the mere $\mathfrak{r}$-value of i itself. They reveal how the latter value is, so to speak, built up out of its smallest parts. For example, the $\mathfrak{r}$-value 0 for i may emerge in two quite different situations: if $\mathfrak{r} = 0$ for every $\mathfrak{Z}$ in question, then $\mathfrak{r}$ must be 0 for i too; but $\mathfrak{r}$ for i is 0 also in the case where some of the $\mathfrak{Z}$ in question have positive $\mathfrak{r}$-values and others have negative ones, provided these values balance each other. Therefore, the $\mathfrak{r}$-values of the $\mathfrak{Z}$ involved furnish a good basis for a closer investigation of the relevance situation for i. This is what we call the first method; it will be developed in this section.

Since $\mathfrak{r}$ is additive also with respect to a conjunction with L-disjunctive components, there is another method for the investigation of the relevance situation. Here, i is analyzed into its smallest *conjunctive* parts. This second method, which uses likewise certain $\mathfrak{Z}$ but not the same as the first method, will be dealt with in the next section.

The basic ideas of the first method now to be developed are quite simple. Any non-L-false sentence i in $\mathfrak{L}_N$ is L-equivalent to the disjunction of the $\mathfrak{Z}$ in $\mathfrak{R}_i$ (T21-8c). These $\mathfrak{Z}$ are L-exclusive in pairs (T21-8a). Hence, according to the theorem of additivity for disjunctions (T68-1c), the $\mathfrak{r}$-value for i (always meant to a given h on e) is the sum of the $\mathfrak{r}$-values for the $\mathfrak{Z}$ in $\mathfrak{R}_i$. Now $\mathfrak{R}_i$ can be divided into two parts (one of which may be empty), $\mathfrak{R}(e \,.\, i)$ and $\mathfrak{R}(\sim e \,.\, i)$. If $\mathfrak{Z}_i$ is any $\mathfrak{Z}$ in the latter part, then e

does not hold in $\mathfrak{Z}_i$ and hence $\mathfrak{r}$ for $\mathfrak{Z}_i$ is 0, as we shall see. Thus the $\mathfrak{Z}$ in $\mathfrak{R}(\sim e \,.\, i)$ contribute nothing to the $\mathfrak{r}$ of *i*; hence the $\mathfrak{r}$ of *i* is the sum of the $\mathfrak{r}$-values for the $\mathfrak{Z}$ in $\mathfrak{R}(e \,.\, i)$. Now $\mathfrak{R}(e \,.\, i)$ can again be divided into two parts (possibly empty), $\mathfrak{R}(e \,.\, i \,.\, h)$ and $\mathfrak{R}(e \,.\, i \,.\, \sim h)$, which we shall call $\mathfrak{R}_1$ and $\mathfrak{R}_2$. We shall find that in general for all $\mathfrak{Z}$ in $\mathfrak{R}_1$ $\mathfrak{r} > 0$; if, however, *e* and *h* fulfil a certain special condition, then for all of those $\mathfrak{Z}$ $\mathfrak{r} = 0$; $\mathfrak{r} < 0$ cannot occur. On the other hand, for all $\mathfrak{Z}$ in $\mathfrak{R}_2$ in most cases $\mathfrak{r} < 0$; if *e* and *h* fulfil another special condition, then for all $\mathfrak{Z}$ in $\mathfrak{R}_2$ $\mathfrak{r} = 0$; $\mathfrak{r} > 0$ is not possible. We shall find theorems which state, for the different possibilities of deductive relations between the three sentences *e*, *h*, and *i*, the $\mathfrak{r}$-values for the $\mathfrak{Z}$ in the two ranges mentioned and the $\mathfrak{r}$-value for *i* based upon them.

It will be convenient for our discussions in the remainder of this chapter to use some abbreviations. We construct the truth-table for *e*, *i*, and *h*; then we use 'k_1', . . . , 'k_8' for the eight conjunctions representing the eight lines of the truth-table, as indicated in the following table. (For the

n	Truth-Table *e*	*i*	*h*	k_n	$\mathfrak{R}_n$			$\mathfrak{m}_n$
1	T	T	T	k_1: $e \,.\, i \,.\, h$	$\mathfrak{R}_1$	$\mathfrak{R}(e \,.\, i)$	$\mathfrak{R}(e)$	$\mathfrak{m}_1$
2	T	T	F	k_2: $e \,.\, i \,.\, \sim h$	$\mathfrak{R}_2$			$\mathfrak{m}_2$
3	T	F	T	k_3: $e \,.\, \sim i \,.\, h$	$\mathfrak{R}_3$	$\mathfrak{R}(e \,.\, \sim i)$		$\mathfrak{m}_3$
4	T	F	F	k_4: $e \,.\, \sim i \,.\, \sim h$	$\mathfrak{R}_4$			$\mathfrak{m}_4$
5	F	T	T	k_5: $\sim e \,.\, i \,.\, h$	$\mathfrak{R}_5$	$\mathfrak{R}(\sim e \,.\, i)$	$\mathfrak{R}(\sim e)$	$\mathfrak{m}_5$
6	F	T	F	k_6: $\sim e \,.\, i \,.\, \sim h$	$\mathfrak{R}_6$			$\mathfrak{m}_6$
7	F	F	T	k_7: $\sim e \,.\, \sim i \,.\, h$	$\mathfrak{R}_7$	$\mathfrak{R}(\sim e \,.\, \sim i)$		$\mathfrak{m}_7$
8	F	F	F	k_8: $\sim e \,.\, \sim i \,.\, \sim h$	$\mathfrak{R}_8$			$\mathfrak{m}_8$

logical properties of these eight conjunctions see § 21B.) For '$\mathfrak{R}(k_n)$' ($n = 1$ to 8), we write simply '$\mathfrak{R}_n$'; for '$\mathfrak{m}(k_n)$' '$\mathfrak{m}_n$'. (k_1 to k_4 and $\mathfrak{m}_1$ to $\mathfrak{m}_4$ are here the same as in § 65.)

For every *n* from 1 to 8, $\mathfrak{m}_n = 0$ if and only if k_n is L-false, hence if and only if $\mathfrak{R}_n$ is null. The eight *k*-sentences are L-exclusive in pairs (T21-7a). If *j* is any non-L-false molecular sentence constructed out of *e*, *i*, and *h*, then *j* is L-equivalent to a disjunction of some of the *k*-sentences (namely, those corresponding to the lines of the truth-table for which *j* has the truth-value T, T21-7d); hence $\mathfrak{R}_j$ is the class-sum of the ranges of these *k*-sentences, and $\mathfrak{m}(j)$ is the sum of the $\mathfrak{m}$-values for these *k*-sentences. (For example, $e \,.\, i$ is L-equivalent to $k_1 \vee k_2$; $\mathfrak{R}(e \,.\, i)$ consists of $\mathfrak{R}_1$ and $\mathfrak{R}_2$; $\mathfrak{m}(e \,.\, i) = \mathfrak{m}_1 + \mathfrak{m}_2$.)

The following theorem states the $\mathfrak{r}$-values for i, $\sim i$, and some of the k-sentences in terms of $\mathfrak{m}$-values.

T72-1. Let e, h, and i be any sentences in a finite or infinite system $\mathfrak{L}$ such that $\mathfrak{m}$ has values for the arguments involved (k_1, etc.).

a. $\mathfrak{r}(i,h,e) = \mathfrak{m}_1 \times \mathfrak{m}_4 - \mathfrak{m}_2 \times \mathfrak{m}_3$. (This is T67-1.)

b. $\mathfrak{r}(k_1,h,e) = \mathfrak{m}_1 \times (\mathfrak{m}_2 + \mathfrak{m}_4)$.

Proof. According to D67-1, $\mathfrak{r}(k_1,h,e) = \mathfrak{m}(e \cdot h \cdot e \cdot i \cdot h) \times \mathfrak{m}(e) - \mathfrak{m}(e \cdot h) \times \mathfrak{m}(e \cdot e \cdot i \cdot h) = \mathfrak{m}_1 \times \mathfrak{m}(e) - \mathfrak{m}(e \cdot h) \times \mathfrak{m}_1 = \mathfrak{m}_1 \times (\mathfrak{m}_2 + \mathfrak{m}_4)$ (T65-1e and c).

c. $\mathfrak{r}(k_2,h,e) = -\mathfrak{m}_2 \times (\mathfrak{m}_1 + \mathfrak{m}_3)$. (Analogous to (b).)

d. $\mathfrak{r}(i,h,e) = \mathfrak{r}(k_1,h,e) + \mathfrak{r}(k_2,h,e)$. (From (a), (b), (c).)

e. $\mathfrak{r}(k_3,h,e) = \mathfrak{m}_3 \times (\mathfrak{m}_2 + \mathfrak{m}_4)$. (Analogous to (b).)

f. $\mathfrak{r}(k_4,h,e) = -\mathfrak{m}_4 \times (\mathfrak{m}_1 + \mathfrak{m}_3)$. (Analogous to (b).)

g. $\mathfrak{r}(\sim i,h,e) = \mathfrak{m}_2 \times \mathfrak{m}_3 - \mathfrak{m}_1 \times \mathfrak{m}_4$. (From T67-5a, (a).)

h. $\mathfrak{r}(\sim i,h,e) = \mathfrak{r}(k_3,h,e) + \mathfrak{r}(k_4,h,e)$. (From (e), (f), (g).)

We shall now apply $\mathfrak{r}$ to $\mathfrak{Z}$. T2 is a lemma with whose help we determine the $\mathfrak{r}$-value of a $\mathfrak{Z}_i$ in each of the eight partial ranges (T3, T4, T5). The $\mathfrak{r}$-values for $\sim\mathfrak{Z}_i$ are stated also, because we shall need them later for the second method. These theorems and most of the subsequent ones are restricted to a finite system $\mathfrak{L}_N$ because only here do we have $\mathfrak{Z}$ as sentences. (In $\mathfrak{L}_\infty$, the $\mathfrak{Z}$ are infinite classes of sentences; $\mathfrak{m}$, $\mathfrak{c}$, the relevance concepts, and $\mathfrak{r}$ have been defined for sentences only.) Hence we can here use the theorem of the strict correspondence between relevance concepts and $\mathfrak{r}$-values (T67-10).

T72-2. Lemma. Let e, h, and i be any sentences in $\mathfrak{L}_N$, and $\mathfrak{Z}_i$ any $\mathfrak{Z}$ in $\mathfrak{L}_N$. Then $\mathfrak{r}(\mathfrak{Z}_i,h,e) = \mathfrak{m}(e \cdot h \cdot \mathfrak{Z}_i) \times \mathfrak{m}(e) - \mathfrak{m}(e \cdot h) \times \mathfrak{m}(e \cdot \mathfrak{Z}_i)$. (From D67-1.)

T72-3. Let $\mathfrak{Z}_i$ be any $\mathfrak{Z}$ (in $\mathfrak{L}_N$) in $\mathfrak{R}_5$, $\mathfrak{R}_6$, $\mathfrak{R}_7$, or $\mathfrak{R}_8$, hence in $\mathfrak{R}(\sim e)$; in other words, any $\mathfrak{Z}$ in which e does not hold. Then the following is the case.

a. (1) $\mathfrak{R}(\sim e)$ is not null.

(2) $\sim e$ is not L-false. (From (1).)

(3) e is not L-true. (From (2).)

b. $e \cdot \mathfrak{Z}_i$ is L-false; $\vdash e \supset \sim \mathfrak{Z}_i$.

Proof. $\sim e$ holds in $\mathfrak{Z}_i$ (T19-2); hence $\vdash \mathfrak{Z}_i \supset \sim e$ (T20-2t); hence the assertion.

c. $\mathfrak{r}(\mathfrak{Z}_i,h,e) = 0$. (From (b), T67-6d.)

d. $\mathfrak{r}(\sim \mathfrak{Z}_i,h,e) = 0$. (From (c), T67-5a.)

e. $\mathfrak{Z}_i$ and $\sim\mathfrak{Z}_i$ are irrelevant to h on e. (From (c), (d), T67-10d.)

T72-4. Let $\mathfrak{Z}_i$ be any $\mathfrak{Z}$ (in $\mathfrak{L}_N$) in $\mathfrak{R}_1$ or $\mathfrak{R}_3$, hence in $\mathfrak{R}(e \,.\, h)$; in other words, any $\mathfrak{Z}$ in which e and h hold.

a. (1) $\mathfrak{R}_1 \cup \mathfrak{R}_3$, that is, $\mathfrak{R}(e \,.\, h)$, is not null.
(2) $e \,.\, h$ is not L-false. (From (1).)
(3) $\mathfrak{m}_1 + \mathfrak{m}_3 > 0$. (From (1).)

b. (1) $\mathfrak{r}(\mathfrak{Z}_i,h,e) = \mathfrak{m}(e \,.\, \sim h) \times \mathfrak{m}(\mathfrak{Z}_i)$.
(2) $= (\mathfrak{m}_2 + \mathfrak{m}_4) \times \mathfrak{m}(\mathfrak{Z}_i)$.

Proof. 1. $\mathfrak{Z}_i$ L-implies $e \,.\, h$ and e (T20-2t). Therefore $\mathfrak{m}(\mathfrak{Z}_i \,.\, e \,.\, h) = \mathfrak{m}(\mathfrak{Z}_i \,.\, e) = \mathfrak{m}(\mathfrak{Z}_i)$ (T21-5i(1)). $\mathfrak{m}(e) - \mathfrak{m}(e \,.\, h) = \mathfrak{m}(e \,.\, \sim h)$ (T57-1r). Hence (1) by T2. 2. From (1), T65-1d.

c. (1) $\mathfrak{r}(\sim \mathfrak{Z}_i,h,e) = -\mathfrak{m}(e \,.\, \sim h) \times \mathfrak{m}(\mathfrak{Z}_i)$.
(2) $= -(\mathfrak{m}_2 + \mathfrak{m}_4) \times \mathfrak{m}(\mathfrak{Z}_i)$.
(From (b), T67-5a.)

d. Let $e \,.\, \sim h$ be L-false. Then the following holds.
(1) $\mathfrak{R}_2$ and $\mathfrak{R}_4$ are null.
(2) $\mathfrak{m}_2 = \mathfrak{m}_4 = 0$. (From (1).)
(3) $\mathfrak{r}(\mathfrak{Z}_i,h,e) = 0$. (From (d)(2), (b)(2).)
(4) $\mathfrak{r}(\sim \mathfrak{Z}_i,h,e) = 0$. (From (3), T67-5a.)
(5) $\mathfrak{Z}_i$ and $\sim\mathfrak{Z}_i$ are irrelevant to h on e. (From (3), (4), T67-10d.)

e. Let $e \,.\, \sim h$ not be L-false.
(1) $\mathfrak{R}_2 \cup \mathfrak{R}_4$ is not null.
(2) $\mathfrak{m}_2 + \mathfrak{m}_4 > 0$. (From (1).)
(3) $\mathfrak{r}(\mathfrak{Z}_i,h,e) > 0$. (From (e)(2), (b)(2).)
(4) $\mathfrak{Z}_i$ is positive to h on e. (From (3), T67-10a.)
(5) $\mathfrak{r}(\sim \mathfrak{Z}_i,h,e) < 0$. (From (3), T67-5a.)
(6) $\sim\mathfrak{Z}_i$ is negative to h on e. (From (5), T67-10b.)

T72-5. Let $\mathfrak{Z}_i$ be any $\mathfrak{Z}$ (in $\mathfrak{L}_N$) in $\mathfrak{R}_2$ or $\mathfrak{R}_4$, hence in $\mathfrak{R}(e \,.\, \sim h)$; in other words, any $\mathfrak{Z}$ in which e and $\sim h$ hold.

a. (1) $\mathfrak{R}_2 \cup \mathfrak{R}_4$, that is, $\mathfrak{R}(e \,.\, \sim h)$, is not null.
(2) $e \,.\, \sim h$ is not L-false. (From (1).)
(3) $\mathfrak{m}_2 + \mathfrak{m}_4 > 0$. (From (1).)

b. (1) $\mathfrak{r}(\mathfrak{Z}_i,h,e) = -\mathfrak{m}(e \,.\, h) \times \mathfrak{m}(\mathfrak{Z}_i)$.
(2) $= -(\mathfrak{m}_1 + \mathfrak{m}_3) \times \mathfrak{m}\mathfrak{Z}_i)$.

Proof. 1. $\vdash \mathfrak{Z}_i \supset \sim h$ (T20-2t), hence $\mathfrak{Z}_i \,.\, h$ is L-false, hence $\mathfrak{m}(e \,.\, h \,.\, \mathfrak{Z}_i) = 0$. Thus (1) by T2. 2. From (1), T65-1c.

c. (1) $\mathfrak{r}(\sim \mathfrak{Z}_i,h,e) = \mathfrak{m}(e \,.\, h) \times \mathfrak{m}(\mathfrak{Z}_i)$.
(2) $= (\mathfrak{m}_1 + \mathfrak{m}_3) \times \mathfrak{m}(\mathfrak{Z}_i)$.
(From (b), T67-5a.)

d. Let $e \,.\, h$ be L-false. Then the following holds.
(1) $\mathfrak{R}_1$ and $\mathfrak{R}_3$ are null.

(2) $\mathfrak{m}_1 = \mathfrak{m}_3 = 0$. (From (1).)
(3) $\mathfrak{r}(\mathfrak{Z}_i,h,e) = 0$. (From (d)(2), (b)(2).)
(4) $\mathfrak{r}(\sim \mathfrak{Z}_i,h,e) = 0$. (From (3), T67-5a.)
(5) $\mathfrak{Z}_i$ and $\sim\mathfrak{Z}_i$ are irrelevant to h on e. (From (3), (4), T67-10d.)

e. Let $e \,.\, h$ not be L-false.
(1) $\mathfrak{R}_1 \cup \mathfrak{R}_3$ is not null.
(2) $\mathfrak{m}_1 + \mathfrak{m}_3 > 0$. (From (1).)
(3) $\mathfrak{r}(\mathfrak{Z}_i,h,e) < 0$. (From (e)(2), (b)(2).)
(4) $\mathfrak{Z}_i$ is negative to h on e. (From (3), T67-10b.)
(5) $\mathfrak{r}(\sim \mathfrak{Z}_i,h,e) > 0$. (From (3), T67-5a.)
(6) $\sim\mathfrak{Z}_i$ is positive to h on e. (From (5), T67-10a.)

We shall now see how the $\mathfrak{r}$-value for i can be determined as the sum of the $\mathfrak{r}$-values for certain $\mathfrak{Z}$. T7 states this is general; T8 deals with cases where deductive relations hold. These two theorems give the chief results of what we have called the first method.

+**T72-7.** Let e, h, and i be any sentences in $\mathfrak{L}_N$.

a. Lemma. If i is not L-false, then i is L-equivalent to the disjunction of the $\mathfrak{Z}$ in $\mathfrak{R}_i$, hence in $\mathfrak{R}_1$, $\mathfrak{R}_2$, $\mathfrak{R}_5$, and $\mathfrak{R}_6$. (From T21-8c.)

b. $\mathfrak{r}(i,h,e) = \Sigma\mathfrak{r}(\mathfrak{Z}_i,h,e)$ for all $\mathfrak{Z}$ in $\mathfrak{R}_i$. (This and similar formulations later are always to be understood in the sense that, if the range in question, here $\mathfrak{R}_i$, is null, then $\mathfrak{r}(i,h,e) = 0$.)

Proof. 1. Let i be not L-false. Then $\mathfrak{R}_i$ is not null. The $\mathfrak{Z}$ are L-exclusive in pairs (T21-8a). Hence the assertion by (a), T68-1c. 2. Let i be L-false. Then $e \,.\, i$ is L-false; hence $\mathfrak{r} = 0$ (T67-6d).

c. Every $\mathfrak{Z}_i$ in $\mathfrak{R}_i$ belongs to $\mathfrak{R}_1$ or $\mathfrak{R}_2$ or $\mathfrak{R}_5$ or $\mathfrak{R}_6$.
(1) If it belongs to $\mathfrak{R}_1$, $\mathfrak{r}(\mathfrak{Z}_i,h,e) \geqq 0$. (From T4d(3) and e(3).)
(2) If it belongs to $\mathfrak{R}_2$, $\mathfrak{r}(\mathfrak{Z}_i,h,e) \leqq 0$. (From T5d(3) and e(3).)
(3) If it belongs to $\mathfrak{R}_5$ or $\mathfrak{R}_6$, $\mathfrak{r}(\mathfrak{Z}_i,h,e) = 0$. (From T3c.)

d. $\mathfrak{r}(i,h,e) = \Sigma\mathfrak{r}(\mathfrak{Z}_i,h,e)$ for all $\mathfrak{Z}$ in $\mathfrak{R}_1$ and $\mathfrak{R}_2$ (hence in $\mathfrak{R}(e \,.\, i)$). (From (b), (c)(3).)

On the basis of the preceding theorems we can now determine the sign and value of $\mathfrak{r}$ for i (to h on e) and for those $\mathfrak{Z}$ which influence the relevance of i for all cases. The results are shown in the *following table* T8. The possible cases are characterized by indicating (in columns (1) to (4)) which of the values $\mathfrak{m}_1$, $\mathfrak{m}_2$, $\mathfrak{m}_3$, and $\mathfrak{m}_4$ are 0 and which >0; this means here in $\mathfrak{L}_N$ the same as stating which of the four sentences k_1, k_2, k_3, and k_4 are L-false and which not. [The cases are in general listed in an order which is, so to speak, lexicographical with respect to the first four columns; only for Nos. 10 and 11 the inverse order is used because this simpli-

+**T72-8.** Let e, h, and i be any sentences in $\mathfrak{L}_N$. Then $\mathfrak{r}$ and relevance for i (to h on e) and for certain $\mathfrak{Z}$ or their negations are as follows. '+' means '>o'; '−' means '<o'.

No.	(1) $\mathfrak{m}_1$	(2) $\mathfrak{m}_2$	(3) $\mathfrak{m}_3$	(4) $\mathfrak{m}_4$	(5) $\mathfrak{m}$ of $e \cdot i$	(6) $\mathfrak{m}$ of $e \cdot h$	(7) $\mathfrak{m}$ of $e \cdot \sim h$	(8) $\mathfrak{r}(i,h,e)$		(9) Relevance of i to h on e	(10) $\mathfrak{r}(\mathfrak{Z}_i,h,e)$ in $\mathfrak{R}_1$	(11) $\mathfrak{r}(\mathfrak{Z}_i,h,e)$ in $\mathfrak{R}_2$	(12) $\mathfrak{r}(\sim\mathfrak{Z}_i,h,e)$ in $\mathfrak{R}_3$	(13) $\mathfrak{r}(\sim\mathfrak{Z}_i,h,e)$ in $\mathfrak{R}_4$	(14) Extreme and Complete Relevance of i to h on e
1	o	o	o	o	o	o	o		o	irrelevant (1–6)	none	none	none	none	extr. and compl. irrelevant (1–3)
2	o	o	o	+	o	o	+		o		none	none	none	o	
3	o	o	+	o	o	+	o		o		none	none	o	none	
4	o	o	+	+	o	+	+		o		none	none	−	+	extr. irrelevant
5	o	+	o	o	+	o	+		o		none	o	none	none	extr. and compl. irrelevant (5–6)
6	o	+	o	+	+	o	+		o		none	o	none	o	
7	o	+	+	o	+	+	+	$-\mathfrak{m}_2\times\mathfrak{m}_3$; (7–8)	−	negative (7–8)	none	−	−	none	extr. and compl. negative
8	o	+	+	+	+	+	+				none	−	−	+	extr. negative
9	+	o	o	o	+	+	o		o	irrelevant (9–10)	o	none	none	none	extr. and compl. irrelevant (9–10)
10	+	o	+	o	+	+	o		o		o	none	o	none	
11	+	o	o	+	+	+	+	$\mathfrak{m}_1\times\mathfrak{m}_4$; (11–12)	+	positive (11–12)	+	none	none	+	extr. and compl. positive
12	+	o	+	+	+	+	+				+	none	−	+	extr. positive
13	+	+	o	o	+	+	+		o	irrelevant	+	−	none	none	compl. irrelevant
14	+	+	o	+	+	+	+	$\mathfrak{m}_1\times\mathfrak{m}_4$;	+	positive	+	−	none	+	compl. positive
15	+	+	+	o	+	+	+	$-\mathfrak{m}_2\times\mathfrak{m}_3$;	−	negative	+	−	−	none	compl. negative
16 (A)	+	+	+	+	+	+	+	$\mathfrak{m}_1\times\mathfrak{m}_4-\mathfrak{m}_2\times\mathfrak{m}_3$;	+	positive	+	−	−	+	
16 (B)									−	negative					
16 (C)									o	irrelevant					

(A) $\mathfrak{m}_1\times\mathfrak{m}_4>\mathfrak{m}_2\times\mathfrak{m}_3$
(B) $\mathfrak{m}_1\times\mathfrak{m}_4<\mathfrak{m}_2\times\mathfrak{m}_3$
(C) $\mathfrak{m}_1\times\mathfrak{m}_4=\mathfrak{m}_2\times\mathfrak{m}_3$

Proof for columns (5) to (13). 5. $\mathfrak{m}(e \cdot i) = \mathfrak{m}_1 + \mathfrak{m}_2$ (T65-1a). 6. $\mathfrak{m}(e \cdot h) = \mathfrak{m}_1 + \mathfrak{m}_3$ (T65-1c). 7. $\mathfrak{m}(e \cdot \sim h) = \mathfrak{m}_2 + \mathfrak{m}_4$ (T65-1d). 8. From T1a. 9. From (8), T67-10. 10. 'None' means that in these cases (Nos. 1 to 8) there is no $\mathfrak{Z}$ in $\mathfrak{R}_1$; $\mathfrak{R}_1$ is null since $\mathfrak{m}_1 = 0$. For the other cases, the sign of $\mathfrak{r}$ for $\mathfrak{Z}_i$ is determined by T4d(3) or T4e(3). Which of these two applies depends upon column (7). 11. Analogously, from T5d(3) and e(3), with column (6). 12. Analogously, from T4d(4) and e(5), with column (7). 13. Analogously, from T5d(4) and e(5), with column (6).

fies the later columns.] It will be seen that in all cases except the last (No. 16), these indications concerning the $\mathfrak{m}$-values determine uniquely all indications in the other columns, among them the sign and value of $\mathfrak{r}$ for i and for the $\mathfrak{Z}$ in $\mathfrak{R}_1$ and $\mathfrak{R}_2$ and for the negations of the $\mathfrak{Z}$ in $\mathfrak{R}_3$ and $\mathfrak{R}_4$ (which will be used in the next section), and hence the relevance of all these sentences. No. 16, however, must be subdivided into three cases (A), (B), and (C), according to whether $\mathfrak{m}_1 \times \mathfrak{m}_4$ is greater, less, or equal to $\mathfrak{m}_2 \times \mathfrak{m}_3$. The last column (14) will be explained later (§§ 74–76).

The table T8 can be used in the following way. Suppose a statement is given saying that certain deductive relations hold between certain unspecified sentences e, i, and h, and that other deductive relations do not hold between them. Then this statement says, in other terms, that some of the sentences $k_1, k_2, \ldots, k_8$ are L-false and that some others are not; for still others it may be left open whether they are L-false or not. We need pay attention only to what is said about $k_1, \ldots, k_4$, because the status of the other four k-sentences does not influence the $\mathfrak{r}$ of i. k_n is L-false if and only if $\mathfrak{m}_n = 0$. Thus, on the basis of the given information concerning deductive relations, we can apply suitable lines of the table to the case in question, and thereby obtain results concerning the relevance of i and the $\mathfrak{r}$-value of i in terms of the $\mathfrak{m}$-values. More important, the table, since it gives an exhaustive list of all possible cases, serves to establish general theorems, e.g., T9 and some theorems in the following sections.

The following theorem can simply be read off from the table T8. It concerns the two parts of $\mathfrak{R}(e \,.\, i)$, viz., $\mathfrak{R}_1$ and $\mathfrak{R}_2$, whose $\mathfrak{Z}$ are used in the first method.

T72-9. Let e, h, and i be any sentences in $\mathfrak{L}_N$.

a. If both $\mathfrak{R}_1$ and $\mathfrak{R}_2$ are nonnull, then for every $\mathfrak{Z}$ in $\mathfrak{R}_1$ $\mathfrak{r} > 0$ (to h on e), and for every $\mathfrak{Z}$ in $\mathfrak{R}_2$ $\mathfrak{r} < 0$.

b. If for any (and hence for every) $\mathfrak{Z}$ in $\mathfrak{R}_1$ $\mathfrak{r} = 0$ to h on e, then $\mathfrak{R}_2$ is null.

c. If for any (and hence for every) $\mathfrak{Z}$ in $\mathfrak{R}_2$ $\mathfrak{r} = 0$ to h on e, then $\mathfrak{R}_1$ is null.

(From T8, columns (10) and (11).)

§ 73. Second Method: Conjunctive Analysis

The second method for the relevance analysis of a sentence i in $\mathfrak{L}_N$ consists in analyzing i into its weakest conjunctive components. These are the negations of the $\mathfrak{Z}$ in $\mathfrak{R}(\sim i)$; we call these negations the content-elements of i, and their class the content of i (D1). (It is explained, incidentally, that an alternative to the method which we have used earlier for the construction of deductive logic is possible; while our earlier method based deductive logic on the concept of range, the alternative method would use the concept of content instead.) It is found here, in analogy to the results of the first method, that the r-value for *i* (to *h* on *e*) is the sum of the values for the content-elements of *i* (T3b). Since for the negation of any $\mathfrak{Z}$ outside of $\mathfrak{R}_e$ $r = 0$, the r for *i* is the sum of the r-values for the negations of the $\mathfrak{Z}$ in $\mathfrak{R}(e \,.\, \sim i)$ (T3d). This range consists of two parts, $\mathfrak{R}(e \,.\, \sim i \,.\, h)$ and $\mathfrak{R}(e \,.\, \sim i \,.\, \sim h)$, which we call $\mathfrak{R}_3$ and $\mathfrak{R}_4$, respectively. For the negation of a $\mathfrak{Z}$ in $\mathfrak{R}_3$ $r \leqq 0$, in $\mathfrak{R}_4$ $r \geqq 0$. The signs of r for these content-elements of *i* for all possible cases of deductive relations between *i* and *h* on the evidence *e* are again listed in the earlier table (T72-8, columns (12) and (13)).

The first method of relevance analysis consisted in analyzing *i* into its ultimate disjunctive components, which are the $\mathfrak{Z}$ in $\mathfrak{R}_i$. Since these components are L-exclusive in pairs, the r-value of *i* (to *h* on *e*) is the sum of the values for the components.

Now we shall develop a *second method* for the same purpose of splitting up *i* into smallest parts in such a manner that the r-value for *i* is the sum of the values for the parts. Here, we represent *i* not as a disjunction but as a conjunction. The conjunctive analysis comes to an end when we come down to the weakest factual sentences in $\mathfrak{L}_N$. These are the negations of the state-descriptions in $\mathfrak{L}_N$. Let *i* be any non-L-true sentence. Let the $\mathfrak{Z}$ in which *i* does not hold, in other words, the $\mathfrak{Z}$ in $\mathfrak{R}(\sim i)$ be $\mathfrak{Z}_1, \mathfrak{Z}_2, \ldots, \mathfrak{Z}_n$. Then *i* is L-equivalent to $\sim\mathfrak{Z}_1 \,.\, \sim\mathfrak{Z}_2 \,.\, \ldots \,.\, \sim\mathfrak{Z}_n$. [This is T21-8f. It is easily seen as follows. $\sim i$ is L-equivalent to the disjunction of the $\mathfrak{Z}$ in its range, hence to $\mathfrak{Z}_1 \vee \mathfrak{Z}_2 \vee \ldots \vee \mathfrak{Z}_n$. Therefore, *i* is L-equivalent to the negation of this disjunction, hence to the conjunction with negated components. This result is also immediately plausible, because what *i* says is this: the universe is not in the state described by $\mathfrak{Z}_1$, nor in that described by $\mathfrak{Z}_2$, nor ..., nor in that described by $\mathfrak{Z}_n$.] The range of $\sim\mathfrak{Z}_i$ is the class of all $\mathfrak{Z}$ distinct from $\mathfrak{Z}_i$; thus it is a largest nonuniversal range. Therefore $\sim\mathfrak{Z}_i$ is a weakest sentence which is not yet L-true but still factual. In other words, $\sim\mathfrak{Z}_i$ cannot be divided into different (i.e., non-L-equivalent) factual conjunctive components. If $\mathfrak{Z}_i$ and $\mathfrak{Z}_j$ are any two distinct $\mathfrak{Z}$, then $\mathfrak{Z}_i \,.\, \mathfrak{Z}_j$ is L-false; hence $\vdash \sim\mathfrak{Z}_i \vee \sim\mathfrak{Z}_j$. Thus any two of the sentences $\sim\mathfrak{Z}_1, \ldots, \sim\mathfrak{Z}_n$ are L-disjunct. Therefore the simpler additivity theorem of r for conjunctions (T68-2c) can be applied to the conjunction of these sentences: $r(i,h,e) = r(\sim\mathfrak{Z}_1,h,e) + \ldots + r(\sim\mathfrak{Z}_n,h,e)$.

This situation makes it appear convenient to introduce a term for the class $\{\sim\mathfrak{Z}_1, \sim\mathfrak{Z}_2, \ldots, \sim\mathfrak{Z}_n\}$, that is, the class of the weakest conjunctive components into which *i* can be analyzed. We shall call it the L-content or, briefly, the *content* of *i*, and its elements the *content-elements* of *i*.

+D73-1. Let j be any sentence in $\mathfrak{L}_N$.

a. l is a ***content-element*** (in $\mathfrak{L}_N$) $=_{Df}$ l is the negation of a $\mathfrak{Z}$ (in $\mathfrak{L}_N$).

b. l is a *content-element of* j (in $\mathfrak{L}_N$) $=_{Df}$ l is the negation of a $\mathfrak{Z}$ in which j does not hold (in other words, the negation of a $\mathfrak{Z}$ in $\mathfrak{R}(\sim j)$).

c. The ***content*** of j (in $\mathfrak{L}_N$) $=_{Df}$ the class of the content-elements of j.

The following theorem follows simply from these definitions. It states the relations between content and the L-concepts.

+T73-1. Let j and k be any sentences in $\mathfrak{L}_N$.

a. The content of j is universal, that is, it contains all content-elements in $\mathfrak{L}_N$, if and only if $\mathfrak{R}_j$ is null, hence if and only if j is L-false.

b. The content of j is null if and only if $\mathfrak{R}_j$ is universal, hence if and only if j is L-true.

c. The content of j is included in (or, a subclass of) the content of k if and only if $\mathfrak{R}_k$ is included in $\mathfrak{R}_j$, hence if and only if k L-implies j.

d. j and k have the same content if and only if they have the same range, hence if and only if they are L-equivalent.

We see from this theorem that the class we call 'content of j' is the more comprehensive the stronger j is, or the more is asserted by j. Thus this class serves well to represent the assertive strength of j. This becomes still more clear when we remember that the assertive power of a sentence consists in its excluding certain possible cases; this has been pointed out by Karl Popper ([Logik], p. 67). Therefore the use of the term 'content' seems justified.

Remark for readers of [*Semantics*]. The definition for 'content' given here in D1c differs from the various tentative definitions for 'L-content' in [Semantics] (D23-B1, D23-F1, and D23-G1), which were meant as explications for the same explicandum. However, the present definition fulfils the earlier two Postulates for L-content ([Semantics] P23-1 and 2), which, if restricted to sentences, state that the L-content of j is included in that of i if and only if $\vdash i \supset j$; this is the present theorem T1c. Therefore, the new concept fulfils likewise the theorems which were based on those two postulates, among them especially the following two: (1) the L-content of j is included in that of i if and only if the L-range of i is included in that of j ([Semantics] T23-20; now T1c); (2) the L-contents of i and j are identical if and only if their ranges are identical ([Semantics] T23-21; now T1d).

My previous reference to Wittgenstein in this context ([Semantics], p. 151) was due to an error of memory; it should have been instead to Popper, as above.

Seeing the connection, expressed in T1, between content and L-concepts, we can easily imagine a method for the construction of deductive logic alternative to the method previously used (in chap. iii). While the earlier method used the concept of range, the alternative would use the concept of content. Instead of beginning with state-descriptions, this method would begin with the content-elements. (Instead of giving them the form of negations of conjunctions of basic sentences, as in D1a, the simpler form of disjunctions of basic sentences might then be taken.) Instead of the rules of ranges (D18-4), which determine for every sentence in which of the $\mathfrak{Z}$ it holds, we should here lay down analogous rules of contents determining for every sentence its content-elements. The content of a sentence would then be defined as the class of its content-elements. Then the definitions for the L-concepts would be laid down in terms of contents, in analogy to their definitions in terms of ranges in the earlier method (D20-1); the sufficient and necessary conditions for some L-concepts in terms of contents which we have stated in T1 would be taken as the defining conditions in this alternative method.

It would, of course, be possible to use both the concepts of range and of content in the system of deductive logic. In order not to complicate our construction of the system (in chap. iii) too much, we have decided to use only one of the two concepts. If it were only a question of constructing deductive logic, I think there would not be any difference between the two procedures from the point of view of simplicity and convenience. However, for inductive logic, the theory of degree of confirmation, it seems to me to be more convenient to take the concept of range as fundamental. The $\mathfrak{m}$- and $\mathfrak{c}$-functions are, as we have seen, additive with respect to disjunction but not with respect to conjunction (see the explanations in § 68). Therefore the concept of range, which is based on disjunctive analysis, is more suitable for the theory of those functions than the concept of content, which is based on conjunctive analysis. This is the reason why we have chosen the concept of range and not that of content also for our system of deductive logic, since this system was to be used as a foundation for inductive logic.

In the present special branch of inductive logic, the theory of the relevance measure $\mathfrak{r}$, the situation is again different. Since $\mathfrak{r}$ is additive with respect to both conjunction and disjunction (under certain conditions), the concept of content is here just as useful as the concept of range, and in the second method of relevance analysis it is even the more useful of the two concepts since this method is based on conjunctive analysis. That is the reason why we have introduced here the concept of content. However, we shall use this concept here chiefly in an auxiliary function, for the purpose of facilitating the understanding of the general nature of the second method. For the technical work, we shall still have to use the concept of range too, because the whole of the preceding theory, which we have to use for the proofs of our theorems here, is framed in terms of ranges.

The result of our previous discussion of the second method (in the beginning of this section) can now be formulated in terms of content as follows: *the* $\mathfrak{r}$*-value for* i (to h on e) *is the sum of the values for the content-elements of* i.

In the preceding section we have determined the $\mathfrak{r}$-values (always to a given h on e) for all content-elements in $\mathfrak{L}_N$, that is, for all sentences of the form $\sim\mathfrak{Z}_i$, where $\mathfrak{Z}_i$ belongs to any of the ranges $\mathfrak{R}_1$ to $\mathfrak{R}_8$ (for $\mathfrak{R}_5$, $\mathfrak{R}_6$, $\mathfrak{R}_7$, and $\mathfrak{R}_8$, this was done in T72-3d; for $\mathfrak{R}_1$ and $\mathfrak{R}_3$, in T72-4c, d(4), and e(5); for $\mathfrak{R}_2$ and $\mathfrak{R}_4$, in T72-5c, d(4), and e(5)). The range of $\sim i$ consists of $\mathfrak{R}_3$, $\mathfrak{R}_4$, $\mathfrak{R}_7$, and $\mathfrak{R}_8$. Therefore, the content of i consists of the negations of the $\mathfrak{Z}$ in $\mathfrak{R}_3$, $\mathfrak{R}_4$, $\mathfrak{R}_7$, and $\mathfrak{R}_8$. The $\mathfrak{r}$-value of i is the sum of the values for these negations. However, we may omit here $\mathfrak{R}_7$ and $\mathfrak{R}_8$, because we have found that, for any $\mathfrak{Z}_i$ in these ranges, $\mathfrak{r}(\sim\mathfrak{Z}_i,h,e) = 0$ (T72-3d); thus it is sufficient to consider the $\mathfrak{Z}$ in $\mathfrak{R}_3$ and $\mathfrak{R}_4$. In other words, in studying $\mathfrak{R}(\sim i)$, we may omit its part $\mathfrak{R}(\sim e \,.\, \sim i)$; we need only consider the remainder, that is $\mathfrak{R}(e \,.\, \sim i)$.

In accordance with the basic ideas of the second method so far explained informally, we shall now develop this method technically in the following theorems. T3 is analogous to T72-7; it is the fundamental theorem of the second method.

+**T73-3.** Let e, h, and i be any sentences in $\mathfrak{L}_N$.

a. Lemma. If i is not L-true, then i is L-equivalent to the conjunction of the content-elements of i, i.e., the conjunction of the negations of the $\mathfrak{Z}$ in $\mathfrak{R}(\sim i)$, hence in $\mathfrak{R}_3$, $\mathfrak{R}_4$, $\mathfrak{R}_7$, and $\mathfrak{R}_8$. (From T21-8f.)

b. $\mathfrak{r}(i,h,e) = \Sigma\mathfrak{r}(\sim\mathfrak{Z}_i,h,e)$ for all content-elements of i, that is, for the negations of all $\mathfrak{Z}$ in $\mathfrak{R}(\sim i)$. (If $\mathfrak{R}(\sim i)$ is null, $\mathfrak{r} = 0$.)

Proof. 1. Let $\mathfrak{R}(\sim i)$ be not null. Negations of distinct $\mathfrak{Z}$ are L-disjunct (T21-8g). Hence the assertion by (a), T68-2c. 2. Let $\mathfrak{R}(\sim i)$ be null. Then $\mathfrak{m}(e \,.\, \sim i) = 0$; hence $\mathfrak{r} = 0$ (T67-6e).

c. Every $\mathfrak{Z}_i$ in $\mathfrak{R}(\sim i)$ belongs to $\mathfrak{R}_3$ or $\mathfrak{R}_4$ or $\mathfrak{R}_7$ or $\mathfrak{R}_8$.

(1) If $\mathfrak{Z}_i$ belongs to $\mathfrak{R}_3$, $\mathfrak{r}(\sim\mathfrak{Z}_i,h,e) \leqq 0$. (From T72-4d(4) and e(5).)

(2) If $\mathfrak{Z}_i$ belongs to $\mathfrak{R}_4$, $\mathfrak{r}(\sim\mathfrak{Z}_i,h,e) \geqq 0$. (From T72-5d(4) and e(5).)

(3) If $\mathfrak{Z}_i$ belongs to $\mathfrak{R}_7$ or $\mathfrak{R}_8$, $\mathfrak{r}(\sim\mathfrak{Z}_i,h,e) = 0$. (From T72-3d.)

d. $\mathfrak{r}(i,h,e) = \Sigma\mathfrak{r}(\sim\mathfrak{Z}_i,h,e)$ for the negations of all $\mathfrak{Z}$ in $\mathfrak{R}_3$ and $\mathfrak{R}_4$ (hence in $\mathfrak{R}(e \,.\, \sim i)$). (From (b), (c)(3).)

We have earlier stated the signs of $\mathfrak{r}$ for the content-elements of i mentioned in T3d, viz., the negations of the $\mathfrak{Z}$ in $\mathfrak{R}_3$ and $\mathfrak{R}_4$, for all the possible cases of deductive relations between i and h with respect to e (see columns (12) and (13) of table T72-8). The following theorem follows from these columns; it is the analogue to T72-9. More important consequences will be drawn from these columns later (§ 75).

T73-4. Let e, h, and i be any sentences in $\mathfrak{L}_N$.

a. If both $\mathfrak{R}_3$ and $\mathfrak{R}_4$ are nonnull, then for the negation of every $\mathfrak{Z}$ in $\mathfrak{R}_3$ $\mathfrak{r} < 0$ (to h on e); and for the negation of every $\mathfrak{Z}$ in $\mathfrak{R}_4$ $\mathfrak{r} > 0$.

b. If for the negation of any (and hence of every) $\mathfrak{Z}$ in $\mathfrak{R}_3$ $\mathfrak{r} = 0$ (to h on e), then $\mathfrak{R}_4$ is null.

c. If for the negation of any (and hence of every) $\mathfrak{Z}$ in $\mathfrak{R}_4$ $\mathfrak{r} = 0$ (to h on e), then $\mathfrak{R}_3$ is null. (From T72-8, columns (12) and (13).)

On the basis of the second method, the r-value of i (to h on e) and the relevance of i are, of course, the same as before, as stated in columns (8) and (9) of the table T72-8; because the second method is merely a different way to the same aim. What is different here is only the relevance-elements, so to speak, out of which the relevance of i is composed. In the first method we split up the r of i into the values for the $\mathfrak{Z}$ in the range of i, and, more particularly, in $\mathfrak{R}_1$ and $\mathfrak{R}_2$, as stated in columns (10) and (11). Here, in the second method, we split up the same r-value of i in a different manner, into the values for the content-elements of i, and, more particularly, for the negations of the $\mathfrak{Z}$ in $\mathfrak{R}_3$ and $\mathfrak{R}_4$, as stated in columns (12) and (13).

§ 74. Extreme Relevance

We call i extremely positive (to h on e) if i is positive and no stronger sentence j (i.e., such that $\vdash e \,.\, j \supset i$) is negative (D1a). In this case, in $\mathfrak{L}_N$, by the addition of i to e, the $\mathfrak{c}$ of h is increased to the maximum value 1 (T1i). Extreme negative relevance is defined analogously (D1b); here, $\mathfrak{c}$ is diminished to the minimum value 0 (T2i). i is called extremely irrelevant if i is irrelevant and no stronger sentence is relevant (D1d). This concept occurs only in certain trivial cases (T3d). These concepts are here studied with the help of the first method (§ 72), the analysis of i as disjunction of the $\mathfrak{Z}$ in its range.

In this and the next sections we shall discuss some special cases of relevance. If i is positive to h on e, then the situation is in general such that among the disjunctive parts into which we divide i by what we have called the first method some are positive and others are negative and maybe still others irrelevant. However, it may occur that none of the parts is negative. This case is of special interest, and we shall introduce a new concept for it. Likewise, it may occur that none of the conjunctive parts into which we analyze i by the second method is negative; this leads to another new concept which will be introduced in the next section. Both concepts may hold simultaneously, but this is not always the case.

We begin with the first method as explained in § 72. Here i is analyzed into its ultimate disjunctive parts, namely, the $\mathfrak{Z}$ in its range. As we have seen (T72-7), $\mathfrak{R}_i$ consists of $\mathfrak{R}_1$, $\mathfrak{R}_2$, $\mathfrak{R}_5$, and $\mathfrak{R}_6$; however, for every $\mathfrak{Z}$ in the latter two ranges $\mathfrak{r} = 0$, while for those in $\mathfrak{R}_1$ $\mathfrak{r} \geqq 0$, and for those in $\mathfrak{R}_2$ $\mathfrak{r} \leqq 0$. The special case in which we are now interested is the case where for i $\mathfrak{r} > 0$ and for no disjunctive part of it $\mathfrak{r} < 0$; this means that for at least one, and hence for every, $\mathfrak{Z}$ in $\mathfrak{R}_1$ $\mathfrak{r} > 0$ and for no $\mathfrak{Z}$ in $\mathfrak{R}_2$ $\mathfrak{r} < 0$. The table T72-8 will help us to study this and similar other cases; we see easily from the columns (10) and (11) that the situation just described holds in the cases Nos. 11 and 12 and in no others. If the conditions described are fulfilled, we shall say that i is extremely positively relevant or, briefly, ***extremely positive*** to h on e. We shall however not use for the definition the condition as just formulated because this analysis of relevance in terms of $\mathfrak{Z}$ applies only to $\mathfrak{L}_N$. In order to make the definition applicable to all finite and infinite systems, we have to refer not to the $\mathfrak{Z}$ but generally to any disjunctive part of i, in other words, to any sentence j L-implying i (if i is L-equivalent to $j \vee k$, then j L-implies i). We shall even go one step further and require that any sentence j which either alone or together with e L-implies i is not negative (D1a); in fact, it makes no difference whether we add "either alone or together with e" or not. The term '***extremely negative***' will then be defined in an analogous way (D1b). We shall see that at least in $\mathfrak{L}_N$ the following holds: i is extremely positive to h on e if and only if the addition of i to e increases the $\mathfrak{c}$ of h to the maximum value 1; and i is extremely negative to h on e if and only if the addition of i to e decreases the $\mathfrak{c}$ of h to the minimum value 0. This is the reason for the choice of the term 'extremely'. Finally we shall say that i is ***extremely irrelevant*** to h on e if i is irrelevant and no disjunctive part of it or, more exactly, no sentence which either alone or together with e L-implies i, is relevant (D1c). (In this case the term 'extremely' is used only for the sake of analogy with the two other concepts.) This concept of extreme irrelevance is not very important because it holds only in certain trivial cases.

D74-1. Let e, h, and i be any sentences in a finite or infinite system $\mathfrak{L}$. Let $\mathfrak{c}$ be a regular $\mathfrak{c}$-function in $\mathfrak{L}$; the relevance concepts ('positive', etc.) are meant with respect to $\mathfrak{c}$ in $\mathfrak{L}$.

+a. i is ***extremely positive*** to h on e (with respect to $\mathfrak{c}$ in $\mathfrak{L}$) $=_{Df}$ (1) i is positive to h on e, and (2) for every sentence j in $\mathfrak{L}$, if $\vdash e \,.\, j \supset i$ then j is not negative to h on e.

+**b.** i is ***extremely negative*** to h on e (with respect to $\mathfrak{c}$ in $\mathfrak{L}$) $=_{\text{Df}}$ (1) i is negative to h on e, and (2) for every j, if $\vdash e \,.\, j \supset i$ then j is not positive to h on e.

c. i is ***extremely relevant*** to h on e (with respect to $\mathfrak{c}$ in $\mathfrak{L}$) $=_{\text{Df}}$ i is either extremely positive or extremely negative to h on e.

d. i is ***extremely irrelevant*** to h on e (with respect to $\mathfrak{c}$ in $\mathfrak{L}$) $=_{\text{Df}}$ (1) i is irrelevant to h on e, and (2) for every j, if $\vdash e \,.\, j \supset i$ then j is not relevant to h on e.

One might perhaps think of replacing the condition D1a(2) by a stronger one requiring that j be positive. This would lead, however, to undesirable consequences; see the later remark concerning an analogous change in D75-1.

For the sake of simplicity, the following theorems refer again to finite systems $\mathfrak{L}_N$ only. Here the relations stated hold without exceptions; and they can easily be proved with the help of the theorems of § 72 concerning $\mathfrak{Z}$, and especially the table T72-8. The theorems of the present section, as far as they do not refer to $\mathfrak{Z}$, hold likewise for nongeneral sentences in $\mathfrak{L}_\infty$; but for general sentences in $\mathfrak{L}_\infty$ they hold only under certain restricting conditions.

T1 gives various conditions which are logically equivalent to extreme positive relevance; T2 does the same for extreme negative relevance, and T3 for extreme irrelevance.

T74-1. Let e, h, and i be sentences in $\mathfrak{L}_N$. Each of the following conditions (a) to (i) is sufficient and necessary for i to be *extremely positive* to h on e.

+**a.** i is positive to h on e, and for no $\mathfrak{Z}$ in $\mathfrak{R}_i$ $\mathfrak{r} < 0$.

Proof. 1. Let i be extremely positive. If $\mathfrak{Z}_i$ is in $\mathfrak{R}_i$, then $\vdash \mathfrak{Z}_i \supset i$. Therefore $\mathfrak{Z}_i$ is not negative (D1a(2)), hence its $\mathfrak{r}$ is not <0 (T67-10b). 2. Let i be positive and let $\mathfrak{r}$ for no $\mathfrak{Z}$ in $\mathfrak{R}_i$ be <0. Let j be any sentence such that $\vdash e \,.\, j \supset i$. Then $\mathfrak{R}(e \,.\, j) \subset \mathfrak{R}_i$. Hence for no $\mathfrak{Z}$ in $\mathfrak{R}(e \,.\, j)$ $\mathfrak{r} < 0$. Therefore $\mathfrak{r}$ for j is not <0 (T72-7d); hence j is not negative (T67-10b). Since this holds for every j i is extremely positive.

b. Of the cases in the table T72-8 either No. 11 or No. 12 holds for e, h, and i. (From (a), with T72-8, columns (9), (10), and (11).)

+**c.** $\mathfrak{m}_2 = 0$, $\mathfrak{m}_1 > 0$, and $\mathfrak{m}_4 > 0$. (From (b), T72-8, columns (1), (2), (4).)

d. $e \,.\, i \,.\, \sim h$ is L-false (hence $\vdash e \,.\, i \supset h$); $e \,.\, i$ and $e \,.\, \sim h$ are not L-false (hence not $\vdash e \supset \sim i$ and not $\vdash e \supset h$). (From (c).)

e. $\mathfrak{m}_2 = 0$, and $\mathfrak{r}(i,h,e) = \mathfrak{m}_1 \times \mathfrak{m}_4$. (From (b), T72-8, column (8).)

f. $\mathfrak{m}_2 = 0$, and $\mathfrak{r}(i,h,e) > 0$. (From (b), T72-8, column (8).)

+**g.** i is positive, and $e \,.\, i \,.\, \sim h$ is L-false (hence $\vdash e \,.\, i \supset h$). (From (b), T72-8, columns (9) and (2).)

+**h.** i is positive, and $\mathfrak{c}(h,e \cdot i) = 1$. (From (g), T59-1b, T59-5b.)

+**i.** $\mathfrak{c}(h,e \cdot i) = 1$, and $\mathfrak{c}(h,e) < 1$. (From (h), D65-1a.)

T74-2. Let e, h, and i be sentences in $\mathfrak{L}_N$. Each of the following conditions (a) to (i) is sufficient and necessary for i to be *extremely negative* to h on e.

+**a.** i is negative to h on e, and for no $\mathfrak{Z}$ in $\mathfrak{R}_i$ $\mathfrak{r} > 0$. (From D1b, T67-10a, T72-7d, in analogy to T1a.)

b. Of the cases in the table T72-8 either No. 7 or No. 8 holds for e, h, and i. (From (a), with T72-8, columns (9), (10), and (11).)

+**c.** $\mathfrak{m}_1 = 0$, $\mathfrak{m}_2 > 0$, and $\mathfrak{m}_3 > 0$. (From (b), T72-8(1), (2), (3).)

d. $e \cdot i \cdot h$ is L-false (hence $\vdash e \cdot i \supset \sim h$, i and h are L-exclusive with respect to e); $e \cdot i$ and $e \cdot h$ are not L-false (hence not $\vdash e \supset \sim i$ and not $\vdash e \supset \sim h$). (From (c).)

e. $\mathfrak{m}_1 = 0$, and $\mathfrak{r}(i,h,e) = -\mathfrak{m}_2 \times \mathfrak{m}_3$. (From (b), T72-8(8).)

f. $\mathfrak{m}_1 = 0$, and $\mathfrak{r}(i,h,e) < 0$. (From (b), T72-8(8).)

+**g.** i is negative, and $e \cdot i \cdot h$ is L-false (hence $\vdash e \cdot i \supset \sim h$). (From (b), T72-8(9) and (1).)

+**h.** i is negative, and $\mathfrak{c}(h,e \cdot i) = 0$. (From (g), T59-1e, T59-5c.)

+**i.** $\mathfrak{c}(h,e \cdot i) = 0$, and $\mathfrak{c}(h,e) > 0$. (From (h), D65-1b.)

T74-3. Let e, h, and i be sentences in $\mathfrak{L}_N$. Each of the following conditions (a) to (h) is sufficient and necessary for i to be *extremely irrelevant* to h on e.

+**a.** i is irrelevant to h on e, and for every $\mathfrak{Z}$ in $\mathfrak{R}_i$ $\mathfrak{r} = 0$.

Proof. 1. Let i be extremely irrelevant. If $\mathfrak{Z}_i$ is in $\mathfrak{R}_i$, then $\vdash \mathfrak{Z}_i \supset i$. Therefore $\mathfrak{Z}_i$ is not relevant (D1c(2)), hence its $\mathfrak{r}$ is 0 (T67-10c). 2. Let i be irrelevant, and let $\mathfrak{r} = 0$ for every $\mathfrak{Z}$ in $\mathfrak{R}_i$. Let j be any sentence such that $\vdash e \cdot j \supset i$. Then $\mathfrak{R}(e \cdot j) \subset \mathfrak{R}_i$. Hence for every $\mathfrak{Z}$ in $\mathfrak{R}(e \cdot j)$ $\mathfrak{r} = 0$. Therefore $\mathfrak{r}$ for j is 0 (T72-7d), and hence j is not relevant (T67-10c). Since this holds for every j, i is extremely irrelevant.

b. One of the cases Nos. 1 to 6, 9, and 10 in the table T72-8 holds for e, h, and i. (From (a), T72-8(9), (10), and (11).)

c. Either all four values $\mathfrak{m}_1$, $\mathfrak{m}_2$, $\mathfrak{m}_3$, and $\mathfrak{m}_4$ are 0, or any three of them are 0, or $\mathfrak{m}_1$ and $\mathfrak{m}_2$ are 0, or $\mathfrak{m}_1$ and $\mathfrak{m}_3$ are 0, or $\mathfrak{m}_2$ and $\mathfrak{m}_4$ are 0. (From (b), T72-8(1) to (4).)

+**d.** At least one of the sentences $e \cdot i$, $e \cdot h$, and $e \cdot \sim h$ is L-false. (From (b), T72-8(5), (6), (7).)

e. i is irrelevant to h on e, and either $\mathfrak{m}_1 = 0$ or $\mathfrak{m}_2 = 0$. (From (b), T72-8(9), (1), and (2).)

f. Either $e \cdot i$ is L-false, or $\mathfrak{c}(h,e)$ is either 0 or 1. (From (d), T59-1b and e, T59-5b and c.)

+**g.** Either $e \cdot i$ is L-false, or $\mathfrak{c}(h,e)$ and $\mathfrak{c}(h,e \cdot i)$ are both 0 or both 1. (From (d), T59-1b and e, T59-5b and c.)

The results of T1b, T2b, and T3b, based on columns (9), (10), and (11) of Table T72-8, are now entered in column (14).

T3d shows that extreme irrelevance is not a very useful concept since it holds, at least in $\mathfrak{L}_N$, only in the following two trivial cases for *i* to *h* on *e:* (1) *e* L-implies *h* or $\sim h$; (2) $e \cdot i$ is L-false. In the case (1), the prior evidence *e* decides already completely about the hypothesis *h* either affirmatively or negatively; in this case *every* sentence is irrelevant and, moreover, extremely irrelevant to *h* on *e*. In the case (2), the sentence *i* describes an event which on the evidence *e* is no longer possible; hence *i* cannot occur as additional evidence to *e*. Nevertheless it is interesting to see that the defining condition in D1d does not hold in any other cases but the trivial ones described in T3d.

The following theorem shows that for any $\mathfrak{Z}$, relevance or irrelevance is always extreme.

T74-4. Let *e* and *h* be sentences in $\mathfrak{L}_N$, and $\mathfrak{Z}_i$ be any $\mathfrak{Z}$ in $\mathfrak{L}_N$.

a. If $\mathfrak{Z}_i$ is positive to *h* on *e*, then it is extremely positive.

Proof. $\mathfrak{Z}_i$ is the only $\mathfrak{Z}$ in $\mathfrak{R}(\mathfrak{Z}_i)$ (T19-6). For $\mathfrak{Z}_i$ $\mathfrak{r} > 0$ (T67-10a). Hence the assertion by T1a.

b. If $\mathfrak{Z}_i$ is negative to *h* on *e*, then it is extremely negative. (From T2a, in analogy to (a).)

c. If $\mathfrak{Z}_i$ is irrelevant to *h* on *e*, then it is extremely irrelevant. (From T3a, in analogy to (a).)

d. $\mathfrak{Z}_i$ is either extremely positive to *h* on *e*, or extremely negative, or extremely irrelevant. (From T65-4g, (a), (b), (c).)

+**T74-6.** Let *e, h, i,* and *j* be sentences in $\mathfrak{L}_N$ such that $\vdash e \cdot j \supset i$. Then the following holds.

a. If *i* is extremely positive to *h* on *e* and $e \cdot j$ is not L-false, then *j* is likewise extremely positive.

Proof. $\vdash e \cdot i \supset h$ (T1d). $\vdash e \cdot j \supset e \cdot i$, hence $\vdash e \cdot j \supset h$. Hence the assertion with T1d.

b. If *i* is extremely negative to *h* on *e*, and $e \cdot j$ is not L-false, then *j* is likewise extremely negative. (From T2d, in analogy to (a).)

c. If *i* is extremely irrelevant to *h* on *e*, then *j* is likewise.

Proof. 1. Let $e \cdot i$ be L-false. Since $\vdash e \cdot j \supset e \cdot i$, $e \cdot j$ is also L-false. Hence the assertion by T3d. 2. Let $e \cdot i$ be not L-false. Then either $e \cdot h$ or $e \cdot \sim h$ is L-false (T3d). Then *every* sentence is extremely irrelevant (T3d), hence also *j*.

T6 shows that extreme positive or negative relevance or irrelevance are transmitted from i to any stronger sentence j not excluded by e.

The simple relevance concepts are dependent upon the particular c-function chosen and hence upon the underlying m-function. For instance, i may be positive to h on e with respect to one regular c-function and negative with respect to another. On the other hand, the extreme relevance concepts are independent of the particular c-function chosen. For instance, if i is extremely positive to h on e with respect to any one regular c-function, then it is likewise with respect to every other one. This is stated by the following theorem.

T74-7. Let c and c′ be any regular c-functions for $\mathfrak{L}_N$, and h, e, and i any sentences in $\mathfrak{L}_N$.

a. If i is extremely positive to h on e with respect to c, then likewise with respect to c′. (From T1d.)

b. If i is extremely negative to h on e with respect to c, then likewise with respect to c′. (From T2d.)

c. If i is extremely relevant to h on e with respect to c, then likewise with respect to c′. (From (a), (b).)

d. If i is extremely irrelevant to h on e with respect to c, then likewise with respect to c′. (From T3d.)

§ 75. Complete Relevance

We call i completely positive to h on e if i is positive and no weaker sentence (or, more exactly, no sentence L-implied by $e \cdot i$) is negative (D1a). This holds, in $\mathfrak{L}_N$, if i is positive and no content-element of i is negative (T1a). Thus this concept is the counterpart to that of extreme positive relevance; while the latter is based on the first method, the present concept is based on the second. Analogous definitions are laid down for complete negative relevance and complete irrelevance. The latter concept occurs only in certain trivial cases. The same holds for Keynes's concept of irrelevance in the strict sense, which is similar to complete irrelevance.

The concepts to be introduced here are analogous to those in the preceding section. There we considered the special case of the positive relevance of i, where no *disjunctive* part of i is negative. Here we shall consider the case where no *conjunctive* part of i is negative.

Thus we apply here the second method of relevance analysis as explained in § 73. It consists in analyzing i into its ultimate conjunctive parts, the content-elements of i. These content-elements are the negations of the $\mathfrak{Z}$ in $\mathfrak{R}(\sim i)$ (D73-1b), hence in $\mathfrak{R}_3$, $\mathfrak{R}_4$, $\mathfrak{R}_7$, and $\mathfrak{R}_8$. However, as we have seen (T73-3c), for the negations of the $\mathfrak{Z}$ in $\mathfrak{R}_7$ and $\mathfrak{R}_8$ $\mathfrak{r} = 0$, while for those in $\mathfrak{R}_3$ $\mathfrak{r} \leqq 0$, and for those in $\mathfrak{R}_4$ $\mathfrak{r} \geqq 0$. The special case to be here considered is the case where for i $\mathfrak{r} > 0$ and for no content-element of i $\mathfrak{r} < 0$; it obviously holds if and only if for the negation of at least one, and hence of every, $\mathfrak{Z}$ in $\mathfrak{R}_4$ $\mathfrak{r} > 0$ and for none in $\mathfrak{R}_3$ $\mathfrak{r} < 0$. In the table T72-8 we find easily that this situation holds in the cases Nos. 11 and 14 and in no others. If the situation described holds, we shall say that i is completely positively relevant or, briefly, ***completely positive*** to h on e. However, here again we shall formulate the definition not in terms of $\mathfrak{Z}$ but in a manner applicable to $\mathfrak{L}_\infty$ too. We shall require in the definition that i is positive and that none of those sentences j is negative whose content is included in that of i or even in that of $e \,.\, i$, in other words, those which are L-implied either by i alone or by i together with e (D1a). (It makes no difference in the resulting concept whether we add 'either alone or together with e' or not.) The terms 'completely negative' and 'completely irrelevant' will be defined analogously (D1b and d). The latter concept is again not very important.

D75-1. Let e, h, and i be any sentences in a finite or infinite system $\mathfrak{L}$. Let $\mathfrak{c}$ be a regular $\mathfrak{c}$-function in $\mathfrak{L}$; the relevance concepts ('positive', etc.) are meant with respect to $\mathfrak{c}$ in $\mathfrak{L}$.

+**a.** i is ***completely positive*** to h on e (with respect to $\mathfrak{c}$ in $\mathfrak{L}$) $=_{Df}$ (1) i is positive to h on e, and (2) for every sentence j in $\mathfrak{L}$, if $\vdash e \,.\, i \supset j$ then j is not negative to h on e.

+**b.** i is ***completely negative*** to h on e (with respect to $\mathfrak{c}$ in $\mathfrak{L}$) $=_{Df}$ (1) i is negative to h on e, and (2) for every j, if $\vdash e \,.\, i \supset j$ then j is not positive to h on e.

c. i is ***completely relevant*** to h on e (with respect to $\mathfrak{c}$ in $\mathfrak{L}$) $=_{Df}$ i is either completely positive or completely negative to h on e.

d. i is ***completely irrelevant*** to h on e $=_{Df}$ (1) i is irrelevant to h on e, and (2) for every j, if $\vdash e \,.\, i \supset j$ then j is not relevant to h on e.

One might perhaps consider an alternative definition D′ formed from D1a by replacing the condition (2) by the stronger condition that every sentence L-implied by $e \,.\, i$ be positive. This change, however, would not lead to a suitable concept. It is certainly convenient to define all concepts of relevance or irrelevance in such a manner that they make no difference between two sentences i and i' which are L-equivalent with respect to e. This requirement is fulfilled by all concepts defined in this chapter, but it would not be fulfilled by D′. In order to show this, let i be completely positive to h on e in the stronger sense of D′, and let e be factual. Now we take as i' the conjunction $i \,.\, \sim\mathfrak{Z}_i$, where $\mathfrak{Z}_i$ is any $\mathfrak{Z}$ in $\mathfrak{R}(\sim e)$. (There must be such $\mathfrak{Z}$ because e is not L-true.) Then it can be shown that (1) i and i' are L-equivalent with respect to e, and (2) nevertheless, i' does not satisfy the definition D′. [*Proof.* 1. $\vdash \mathfrak{Z}_i \supset \sim e$ (T20-2t), hence $\vdash e \supset \sim\mathfrak{Z}_i$. Therefore $e \,.\, i$ L-implies $\sim\mathfrak{Z}_i$, and also i, hence their conjunction i'. On the other hand, i' and hence $e \,.\, i'$ L-implies i. Hence the assertion (1). 2. $\sim\mathfrak{Z}_i$ is L-implied by i' and hence by $e \,.\, i'$. Nevertheless, $\sim\mathfrak{Z}_i$ is not positive to h on e but irrelevant (T72-3e). Hence the assertion (2).]

The following theorems are restricted to $\mathfrak{L}_N$ for the same reason as those in the preceding section. T1 gives various conditions which are logically equivalent to complete positive relevance; T2 does the same for complete negative relevance, and T3 for complete irrelevance.

T75-1. Let e, h, and i be sentences in $\mathfrak{L}_N$. Each of the following conditions (a) to (h) is sufficient and necessary for i to be *completely positive* to h on e.

+a. i is positive to h on e, and for no content-element of i $\mathfrak{r} < 0$.

Proof. 1. Let i be completely positive. Let $\sim\mathfrak{Z}_i$ be a content-element of i, in other words, let $\mathfrak{Z}_i$ be in $\mathfrak{R}(\sim i)$. Then $\vdash \mathfrak{Z}_i \supset \sim i$, hence $\vdash i \supset \sim \mathfrak{Z}_i$. Therefore $\sim\mathfrak{Z}_i$ is not negative (D1a(2)), hence its $\mathfrak{r}$ is not <0 (T67-10b). 2. Let i be positive, and let $\mathfrak{r}$ for no content-element of i be <0. Let j be any sentence such that $\vdash e \centerdot i \supset j$. Then $\vdash \sim j \supset \sim (e \centerdot i)$; and hence $\mathfrak{R}(\sim j) \subset \mathfrak{R}(\sim(e \centerdot i))$. If j is L-true, its $\mathfrak{r}$ is 0 and hence j is not negative. Now suppose that j is not L-true; then $\sim j$ is not L-false, and hence $\mathfrak{R}(\sim j)$ is not null. Let $\sim\mathfrak{Z}_j$ be a content-element of j; in other words, let $\mathfrak{Z}_j$ be in $\mathfrak{R}(\sim j)$. Then $\mathfrak{Z}_j$ is in $\mathfrak{R}(\sim(e \centerdot i))$, hence in one of the ranges $\mathfrak{R}_3, \mathfrak{R}_4, \ldots, \mathfrak{R}_8$. If $\mathfrak{Z}_j$ is in one of the ranges $\mathfrak{R}_5, \ldots, \mathfrak{R}_8$, then for $\sim\mathfrak{Z}_j$ $\mathfrak{r} = 0$ (T72-3d). If $\mathfrak{Z}_j$ is in $\mathfrak{R}_3$ or in $\mathfrak{R}_4$, then it is in $\mathfrak{R}(\sim i)$; therefore $\sim\mathfrak{Z}_j$ is a content-element of i and hence, according to our assumption, its $\mathfrak{r}$ is not <0. Thus for no content-element of j $\mathfrak{r} > 0$. Therefore $\mathfrak{r}$ for j is not <0 (T73-3b); hence j is not negative (T67-10b). Since this holds for every j, i is completely positive.

b. Of the cases in the table T72-8 either No. 11 or No. 14 holds for e, h, and i. (From (a), T72-8(9), (12), and (13).)

+c. $\mathfrak{m}_3 = 0$, $\mathfrak{m}_1 > 0$, and $\mathfrak{m}_4 > 0$. (From (b), T72-8(1), (3), (4).)

d. $e \centerdot \sim i \centerdot h$ is L-false (hence $\vdash e \centerdot h \supset i$); $e \centerdot \sim i$ and $e \centerdot h$ are not L-false (hence not $\vdash e \supset i$ and not $\vdash e \supset \sim h$). (From (c).)

e. $\mathfrak{m}_3 = 0$, and $\mathfrak{r}(i,h,e) = \mathfrak{m}_1 \times \mathfrak{m}_4$. (From (b), T72-8(8).)

f. $\mathfrak{m}_3 = 0$, and $\mathfrak{r}(i,h,e) > 0$. (From (b), T72-8(8).)

+g. i is positive, and $e \centerdot \sim i \centerdot h$ is L-false (hence $\vdash e \centerdot h \supset i$). (From (b), T72-8(9) and (3).)

+h. i is positive, and $\mathfrak{c}(i,e \centerdot h) = 1$. (From (g), T59-1b, T59-5b.)

The condition which (g) and (h) add to the positive relevance of i may be formulated as follows in terms previously used (§ 61): the *likelihood* of i is 1, hence i is *predictable* by h on e.

T75-2. Let e, h, and i be sentences in $\mathfrak{L}_N$. Each of the following conditions (a) to (g) is sufficient and necessary for i to be *completely negative* to h on e.

+a. i is negative to h on e, and for no content-element of i $\mathfrak{r} > 0$. (Analogous to T1a.)

b. Of the cases in the table T72-8 either No. 7 or No. 15 holds for e, h, and i. (From (a), T72-8(9), (12), and (13).)

+**c.** $\mathfrak{m}_4 = 0$; $\mathfrak{m}_2 > 0$, and $\mathfrak{m}_3 > 0$. (From (b), T72-8 (2), (3), (4).)

d. $e \cdot \sim i \cdot \sim h$ is L-false (hence $\vdash e \cdot \sim h \supset i$; $\vdash e \supset i \vee h$; i and h are L-disjunct with respect to e); $e \cdot \sim i$ and $e \cdot \sim h$ are not L-false (hence not $\vdash e \supset i$ and not $\vdash e \supset h$). (From (c).)

e. $\mathfrak{m}_4 = 0$, and $\mathfrak{r}(i,h,e) = -\mathfrak{m}_2 \times \mathfrak{m}_3$. (From (b), T72-8(8).)

f. $\mathfrak{m}_4 = 0$, and $\mathfrak{r}(i,h,e) < 0$. (From (b), T72-8(8).)

+**g.** i is negative, and $e \cdot \sim i \cdot \sim h$ is L-false. (From (b), T72-8(9) and (4).)

T75-3. Let e, h, and i be sentences in $\mathfrak{L}_N$. Each of the following conditions (a) to (f) is sufficient and necessary for i to be *completely irrelevant* to h on e.

+**a.** i is irrelevant to h on e, and for every content-element of i $\mathfrak{r} = 0$.

Proof. 1. Let i be completely irrelevant. Let $\sim \mathfrak{Z}_i$ be a content-element of i. Then $\vdash i \supset \sim \mathfrak{Z}_i$. Therefore $\sim \mathfrak{Z}_i$ is not relevant (D1c(2)); hence its $\mathfrak{r}$ is 0 (T67-10c). 2. Let i be irrelevant, and let $\mathfrak{r} = 0$ for every content-element of i. Let j be any sentence such that $\vdash e \cdot i \supset j$. Then $\mathfrak{r}$ for j is 0 (in analogy to the proof of T1a(2)). Hence j is not relevant (T67-10c). Since this holds for every j, i is completely irrelevant.

b. One of the cases Nos. 1, 2, 3, 5, 6, 9, 10, and 13 in the table T72-8 holds for e, h, and i. (From (a), T72-8(9), (12), and (13).)

c. Either all four values $\mathfrak{m}_1$, $\mathfrak{m}_2$, $\mathfrak{m}_3$, and $\mathfrak{m}_4$ are 0, or any three of them are 0, or $\mathfrak{m}_1$ and $\mathfrak{m}_3$ are 0, or $\mathfrak{m}_2$ and $\mathfrak{m}_4$ are 0, or $\mathfrak{m}_3$ and $\mathfrak{m}_4$ are 0. (From (b), T72-8(1) to (4).)

+**d.** At least one of the sentences $e \cdot \sim i$, $e \cdot h$, and $e \cdot \sim h$ is L-false.

Proof. $e \cdot \sim i$ is L-false if and only if $\mathfrak{m}_3 = \mathfrak{m}_4 = 0$ (T65-1b). This is the case in Nos. 1, 5, 9, and 13 in T72-8. $e \cdot h$ or $e \cdot \sim h$ or both are L-false in Nos. 1, 2, 3, 5, 6, 9, and 10 (T72-8(6) and (7)). Hence the assertion by (b).

e. i is irrelevant to h on e, and either $\mathfrak{m}_3 = 0$ or $\mathfrak{m}_4 = 0$. (From (b), T72-8(9), (3), and (4).)

f. Either $e \cdot \sim i$ is L-false (hence $\vdash e \supset i$), or $\mathfrak{c}(h,e)$ is either 0 or 1. (From (d), T59-1b and e, T59-5b and c.)

The results of T1b, T2b, and T3b, based on columns (9), (12), and (13) of Table T72-8, are listed in column (14).

The following theorem shows that for any content-element, relevance and irrelevance is always complete.

T75-4. Let e and h be sentences in $\mathfrak{L}_N$, and $\mathfrak{Z}_i$ be any $\mathfrak{Z}$ in $\mathfrak{L}_N$.

a. If $\sim \mathfrak{Z}_i$ is positive to h on e, then it is completely positive.

Proof. The content-elements of $\sim \mathfrak{Z}_i$ are the negations of the $\mathfrak{Z}$ in $\mathfrak{R}(\sim\sim \mathfrak{Z}_i)$ (D73-1b), that is, $\mathfrak{R}(\mathfrak{Z}_i)$. $\mathfrak{Z}_i$ is the only $\mathfrak{Z}$ in $\mathfrak{R}(\mathfrak{Z}_i)$ (T19-6). Hence the only content-element of $\sim \mathfrak{Z}_i$ is $\sim \mathfrak{Z}_i$ itself. For $\sim \mathfrak{Z}_i$ $\mathfrak{r} > 0$ (T67-10a). Hence the assertion by T1a.

b. If $\sim\mathfrak{Z}_i$ is negative to h on e, then it is completely negative. (From T2a, in analogy to (a).)

c. If $\sim\mathfrak{Z}_i$ is irrelevant to h on e, then it is completely irrelevant. (From T3a, in analogy to (a).)

d. $\sim\mathfrak{Z}_i$ is either completely positive to h on e, or completely negative, or completely irrelevant. (From T65-4g, (a), (b), (c).)

+T75-6. Let e, h, i, and j be sentences in $\mathfrak{L}_N$ such that $\vdash e \,.\, i \supset j$. Then the following holds.

a. If i is completely positive to h on e, and not $\vdash e \supset j$, then j is likewise completely positive.

Proof. $\vdash e \,.\, h \supset i$ (T1d). Hence $\vdash e \,.\, h \supset e \,.\, i$ hence $\vdash e \,.\, h \supset j$. Hence the assertion with T1d.

b. If i is completely negative to h on e and not $\vdash e \supset j$, then j is likewise completely negative. (From T2d, in analogy to (a).)

c. If i is completely irrelevant to h on e, then j is likewise.

Proof. 1. Let $e \,.\, \sim i$ be L-false. Since $\vdash e \,.\, i \supset j$, $\vdash e \,.\, \sim j \supset \sim i$ (T21-5h(6)), hence $\vdash e \,.\, \sim j \supset e \,.\, \sim i$; therefore $e \,.\, \sim j$ is L-false too. Hence the assertion by T3d. 2. Let $e \,.\, \sim i$ be not L-false. Then either $e \,.\, h$ or $e \,.\, \sim h$ is L-false (T3d). Therefore *every* sentence is completely irrelevant (T3d), hence also j.

T6 shows that complete positive or negative relevance and complete irrelevance are transmitted from i to any weaker sentence j not L-implied by e.

The complete relevance concepts are, like the extreme relevance concepts (T74-7), independent of the particular c-function chosen. This is stated by the following theorem.

T75-7. Let $\mathfrak{c}$ and $\mathfrak{c}'$ be any regular c-functions for $\mathfrak{L}_N$, and h, e, and i any sentences in $\mathfrak{L}_N$.

a. If i is completely positive to h on e with respect to $\mathfrak{c}$, then likewise with respect to $\mathfrak{c}'$. (From T1d.)

b. If i is completely negative to h on e with respect to $\mathfrak{c}$, then likewise with respect to $\mathfrak{c}'$. (From T2d.)

c. If i is completely relevant to h on e with respect to $\mathfrak{c}$, then likewise with respect to $\mathfrak{c}'$. (From (a), (b).)

d. If i is completely irrelevant to h on e with respect to $\mathfrak{c}$, then likewise with respect to $\mathfrak{c}'$. (From T3d.)

Complete irrelevance is, like extreme irrelevance, not a very useful concept. At least in $\mathfrak{L}_N$, it occurs only in the following two trivial cases, as we see from T3d: (1) e L-implies h or $\sim h$; (2) e L-implies i. In the case (1), the prior evidence e decides already entirely about the hypothesis h by either L-implying or excluding it; thus no additional evidence can have any relevance; in this case *every* sentence is irrelevant to h on e and, moreover, extremely and completely irrelevant. In the case (2), i does not add any new evidence to e. Nevertheless, in analogy to the situation with extreme irrelevance, it is of interest to notice that the defining condition in D1d does only hold in the trivial cases just described.

Keynes has given definitions for the concepts of irrelevance and relevance which we have adopted (except for the somewhat wider sense which we have given to 'irrelevance' in D65-1d). He believes, however, that another, stronger concept of irrelevance would be theoretically preferable ([Probab.], p. 55). His definition for it, expressed in our terminology, is as follows: i is irrelevant in the strict sense to h on evidence $e =_{Df}$ there is no j such that $c(j,e \,.\, i) = 1$, $c(j,e) \neq 1$, and $c(h,e \,.\, j) \neq c(h,e)$. For the sake of simplicity, let us restrict the following discussion to a finite system $\mathfrak{L}_N$ (Keynes's axioms and definitions hold only for a finite system, since he identifies logical implication with probability 1; see above, § 62). Then the definiens just given can be formulated in this way: (1) $e \,.\, i$ is not L-false, and (2) there is no j such that $\vdash e \,.\, i \supset j$ but not $\vdash e \supset j$ and that j is relevant to h on e (in the simple sense of D65-1c). (The condition (1) is implicitly contained in the statement of a probability value with the evidence $e \,.\, i$.) Keynes points out, correctly, that "it would sometimes occur that a part of evidence would be relevant, which taken as a whole was irrelevant" (p. 55). He believes that "we must regard evidence as relevant, part of which is favourable [i.e., positive] and part unfavourable [i.e., negative], even if, taken as a whole, it leaves the probability unchanged" (p. 72). These considerations may seem quite plausible at first. As an example, let us take a case of the singular predictive inference. Let h be '*Pc*', where '*P*' is a primitive predicate. Let e describe a sample of $s = 2n$ individuals, to which c does not belong, to the effect that n of these individuals are P and the other n are not-P. Then for many c-functions (among them our function c* to be introduced later) $c(h,e) = 1/2$, independently of s. Let i be '$Pa \,.\, \sim Pb$', where 'a' and 'b' do not occur in e. Then the sample described in $e \,.\, i$ does again contain equal numbers of P and not-P; thus again $c(h,e \,.\, i) = 1/2$. Therefore i is irrelevant (in the simple sense) to h on e. Let j_1 be 'Pa', j_2 '$\sim Pb$'; hence i is $j_1 \,.\, j_2$. Now in $e \,.\, j_1$ the number of P is larger than that of not-P, while in $e \,.\, j_2$ the inverse holds. Therefore, for many c-functions (among them c* and presumably all adequate explicata) the following is the case: $c(h,e \,.\, j_1) > 1/2$, $c(h,e \,.\, j_2) < 1/2$. Thus j_1 is positive to h on e, and j_2 negative. i is irrelevant as a whole but consists of positive and negative parts. Keynes presumably intended to exclude cases of this kind when he suggested the stronger concept of irrelevance. In the example just given, i is irrelevant to h on e in the simple sense but not in the strict sense. The problem is whether under normal conditions any cases can be found where the latter concept applies. Keynes himself has not given any example for his concept. If we analyze his concept for a finite system $\mathfrak{L}_N$ with the help of our second method, we find that it is essentially the same as our concept of complete irrelevance with the condition added that $e \,.\, i$ not be L-false.

Proof. Condition (2) in the above formulation of Keynes's definition can be transformed as follows. It says that no j such that $\vdash e \,.\, i \supset j$ but not $\vdash e \supset j$ is relevant to h on e. $\vdash e \,.\, i \supset j$ if and only if $\vdash \sim j \supset \sim (e \,.\, i)$, hence if and only if $\mathfrak{R}(\sim j)$ is included in $\mathfrak{R}(\sim (e \,.\, i))$, hence in the class-sum of $\mathfrak{R}_3, \mathfrak{R}_4, \ldots, \mathfrak{R}_8$. $\vdash e \supset j$ if and only if $\vdash \sim j \supset \sim e$, hence if and only if $\mathfrak{R}(\sim j)$ is included in $\mathfrak{R}(\sim e)$, hence in the class-sum of $\mathfrak{R}_5, \ldots, \mathfrak{R}_8$. Thus (2) means the following: no j is relevant if it is such that every content-element of it is the negation of a $\mathfrak{Z}$ in one of the ranges $\mathfrak{R}_3, \ldots, \mathfrak{R}_8$, and at least one is the negation of a $\mathfrak{Z}$ in $\mathfrak{R}_3$ or $\mathfrak{R}_4$. In other words, (2) means that no negation of any $\mathfrak{Z}$ in one of the ranges $\mathfrak{R}_3, \ldots, \mathfrak{R}_8$ is relevant. (This shows, incidentally, that the condition 'not $\vdash e \supset j$' in Keynes's definition can be omitted without changing the result.) Thus (2) means that no content-element of i is relevant. And this is indeed what Keynes intended; because he required that no part of i be relevant, and by 'part' he meant content-part, i.e., conjunctive part. Now we see that this is the same as complete irrelevance of i (T3a). Thus, i is irrelevant to h on e (in $\mathfrak{L}_N$) in Keynes's strict sense if and only if (1) $e \,.\, i$ is not L-false, and (2) i is completely irrelevant to h on e. Among the cases in the table T72-8, (2) holds in Nos. 1, 2, 3 5, 6, 9, 10, and 13 (T3b); (1) holds in Nos. 5 to 16 (T72-8(5)); thus Keynes's concept holds in Nos. 5, 6, 9, 10, and 13.

We see that i is irrelevant in the strict sense to h on e (in $\mathfrak{L}_N$) if and only if (1) $e \,.\, i$ is not L-false, and (2) at least one of the sentences $e \,.\, \sim i$, $e \,.\, h$, and $e \,.\, \sim h$ is L-false (T3d). This shows that for any e and h (in $\mathfrak{L}_N$) such that neither h nor $\sim h$ follows from e, there cannot be any sentence i which says anything new in comparison with e (i.e., which is not L-implied by e) and which is irrelevant to h on e in the strict sense as defined by Keynes. [Suppose that not $\vdash e \supset i$. Then $e \,.\, \sim i$ is not L-false, and hence its range is not null. If $\mathfrak{Z}_i$ is any $\mathfrak{Z}$ in this range, hence in $\mathfrak{R}_3$ or $\mathfrak{R}_4$, then $\sim \mathfrak{Z}_i$ is a counterexample to Keynes's definition; it is L-implied by $e \,.\, i$ but not by e, and it is relevant to h on e (T72-4e(6), T72-5e(6)).] In other words, under ordinary conditions there are always content-elements of i which are relevant to h on e. Therefore, the concept of irrelevance in the strict sense, like that of complete irrelevance, is not preferable to the simple concept of irrelevance; it cannot take its place but is useful, if at all, only as a special or, so to speak, degenerate case of the latter concept.

§ 76. Relations between Extreme and Complete Relevance

Theorems are stated which deal with extreme and complete relevance and irrelevance. Four kinds of positive relevance are distinguished (neither extreme nor complete, extreme but not complete, complete but not extreme, extreme and complete); and for each of them a sufficient and necessary condition is given (T1). The same is done for negative relevance (T2) and for irrelevance (T3). Finally it is examined how each of the concepts of extreme or complete, positive or negative, relevance or irrelevance is transformed by negating i or h or both or by exchanging i and h (T5). Thus it is found, for example, that the following conditions are logically equivalent (T5a): (1) i is extremely positive to h on e; (2) $\sim i$ is completely negative to h on e; (3) i is extremely negative to $\sim h$ on e; (4) h is completely positive to i on e.

The theorems of this section make use of the concepts of extreme relevance and of complete relevance. T1 deals with the four possible cases of positive relevance for a finite system $\mathfrak{L}_N$; T2 does the same for negative relevance, and T3 for irrelevance. The results in these theorems are easily found with the help of the table T72-8, which gives a complete survey of all possible cases.

T76-1. Let i be *positive* to h on e in $\mathfrak{L}_N$. Then the following holds. (It is easily seen that for any given sentences e, h, and i exactly one of the four conditions is fulfilled.)

a. i is neither extremely nor completely positive if and only if the case No. 16A in the table T72-8 holds; hence if and only if k_1, k_2, k_3, and k_4 are not L-false (hence there are no deductive relations between i and h with respect to e) and $\mathfrak{m}_1 \times \mathfrak{m}_4 > \mathfrak{m}_2 \times \mathfrak{m}_3$ (where all four $\mathfrak{m}$-values are >0).

b. i is extremely but not completely positive if and only if No. 12 holds; hence if and only if k_2 is L-false (hence $\vdash e \,.\, i \supset h$) but k_1, k_3, and k_4 are not.

c. i is completely but not extremely positive if and only if No. 14 holds; hence if and only if k_3 is L-false (hence $\vdash e \,.\, h \supset i$) but k_1, k_2, and k_4 are not.

d. i is extremely and completely positive if and only if No. 11 holds; hence if and only if k_2 and k_3 are L-false (in other words, $\vdash e \supset (i \equiv h)$, i and h are L-equivalent with respect to e) but k_1 and k_4 are not L-false (in other words, i and h are neither L-exclusive nor L-disjunct with respect to e; it follows from this that e L-implies none of the sentences i, $\sim i$, h, and $\sim h$).

(From T72-8.)

T76-2. Let i be *negative* to h on e in $\mathfrak{L}_N$. Then the following holds. (It is easily seen that for any e, h, and i exactly one of the four conditions is fulfilled.)

a. i is neither extremely nor completely negative if and only if the case No. 16B in the table T72-8 holds; hence if and only if k_1, k_2, k_3, and k_4 are not L-false (hence there are no deductive relations between i and h with respect to e) and $\mathfrak{m}_1 \times \mathfrak{m}_4 < \mathfrak{m}_2 \times \mathfrak{m}_3$ (where all four $\mathfrak{m}$-values are >0).

b. i is extremely but not completely negative if and only if No. 8 holds; hence if and only if k_1 is L-false (hence i and h are L-exclusive with respect to e) but k_2, k_3, and k_4 are not.

c. i is completely but not extremely negative if and only if No. 15 holds; hence if and only if k_4 is L-false (hence $\vdash e \supset i \vee h$, i and h are L-disjunct with respect to e) but k_1, k_2, and k_3 are not.

d. i is extremely and completely negative if and only if No. 7 holds; hence if and only if k_1 and k_4 are L-false (in other words, $\vdash e \supset (i \equiv \sim h)$, i and h are L-exclusive and L-disjunct with respect to e, i is L-equivalent to $\sim h$ with respect to e) but k_2 and k_3 are not L-false (in other words, neither $\vdash e \,.\, i \supset h$ nor $\vdash e \,.\, h \supset i$; it follows from this that e L-implies none of the sentences i, $\sim i$, h, and $\sim h$).

(From T72-8.)

T76-3. Let i be *irrelevant* to h on e in $\mathfrak{L}_N$. Then the following holds. (It is easily seen that for any e, h, and i exactly one of the four conditions is fulfilled.)

a. i is neither extremely nor completely irrelevant if and only if the case No. 16C in the table T72-8 holds; hence, if and only if k_1, k_2, k_3, and k_4 are not L-false (hence there are no deductive relations between i and h with respect to e) and $\mathfrak{m}_1 \times \mathfrak{m}_4 = \mathfrak{m}_2 \times \mathfrak{m}_3$ (where all four $\mathfrak{m}$-values are >0).

b. i is extremely but not completely irrelevant if and only if No. 4 holds; hence if and only if k_1 and k_2 are L-false (in other words, $e \,.\, i$ is L-false) but k_3 and k_4 are not L-false (in other words, $e \,.\, \sim i$ L-implies neither h nor $\sim h$).

c. i is completely but not extremely irrelevant if and only if No. 13 holds; hence if and only if k_3 and k_4 are L-false (in other words, $e \,.\, \sim i$ is L-false, $\vdash e \supset i$) but k_1 and k_2 are not L-false (in other words, $e \,.\, i$ L-implies neither h nor $\sim h$).

d. i is extremely and completely irrelevant if and only if one of the cases Nos. 1, 2, 3, 5, 6, 9, 10 holds; hence if and only if one, two, or three of the sentences $e \cdot i$, $e \cdot h$, and $e \cdot {\sim}h$ are L-false but not $e \cdot i$ alone. Here we may distinguish two kinds of cases:

(1) One of the cases Nos. 1, 2, 3 holds if and only if k_1, k_2, and at least one of the sentences k_3 and k_4 are L-false (in other words, $e \cdot i$ and at least one of the sentences $e \cdot h$ and $e \cdot {\sim}h$ are L-false).

(2) One of the cases Nos. 5, 6, 9, 10 holds if and only if either k_1 and k_3 are L-false but not k_2, or k_2 and k_4 are L-false but not k_1 (in other words, exactly one of the sentences $e \cdot h$ and $e \cdot {\sim}h$ is L-false but $e \cdot i$ is not).

(From T72-8.)

It is interesting to notice that in each of the three theorems T1, T2, and T3, only part (a) is dependent upon the choice of a particular $\mathfrak{m}$-function. These are the cases No. 16A, B, and C, where no deductive relations hold between i and h with respect to e. All other parts of these theorems hold alike for all regular $\mathfrak{m}$-functions; they depend merely upon deductive relations or, more specifically, upon the L-falsity of some of the sentences $k_1, \ldots, k_4$. Thus, as we found earlier (T74-7, T75-7), all the concepts of extreme or complete relevance or irrelevance with respect to finite systems $\mathfrak{L}_N$ are independent of the $\mathfrak{m}$-functions.

In general the transition from one $\mathfrak{c}$-function to another changes the relevance situation. However, there are special cases where one and the same of the four relevance concepts holds with respect to *every* regular $\mathfrak{c}$-function. The following theorem says that in any case of this kind either the extreme or the complete concept holds.

T76-4. Let h, e, and i be sentences in $\mathfrak{L}_N$.

a. i is *positive* to h on e with respect to *every* regular $\mathfrak{c}$-function in $\mathfrak{L}_N$ if and only if i is either extremely positive to h on e with respect to every regular $\mathfrak{c}$ or completely positive to h on e with respect to every regular $\mathfrak{c}$, or both.

Proof. Let i be positive to h on e with respect to every regular $\mathfrak{c}$. Then, for every regular $\mathfrak{m}$, (1) $\mathfrak{m}_1 \times \mathfrak{m}_4 > \mathfrak{m}_2 \times \mathfrak{m}_3$ (T65-4c(2).) Therefore, for every regular $\mathfrak{m}$, (2) $\mathfrak{m}_1 > 0$ and $\mathfrak{m}_4 > 0$, and (3) $\mathfrak{m}_2 \times \mathfrak{m}_3 = 0$. [(3) is seen as follows. If for some $\mathfrak{m}$ (3) did not hold, $\mathfrak{m}_2$ and $\mathfrak{m}_3$ and hence all four $\mathfrak{m}$-values would be > 0. Since the four k-sentences are L-exclusive in pairs and their disjunction is L-equivalent to e, we could in this case choose another $\mathfrak{m}$-function $\mathfrak{m}'$ such that $\mathfrak{m}'_1 = \mathfrak{m}'_2 = \mathfrak{m}'_3 = \mathfrak{m}'_4 = \mathfrak{m}'(e)/4$; hence (1) would not hold for $\mathfrak{m}'$.] From (3): for any $\mathfrak{m}$, either $\mathfrak{m}_2$ or $\mathfrak{m}_3$ or both are 0. Hence either i is extremely positive with respect to the given $\mathfrak{c}$ ((2), T74-1c) and hence with respect to every $\mathfrak{c}$ (T74-7a), or i is completely positive with respect to every $\mathfrak{c}$ ((2), T75-1c, T75-7a) or both. The converse follows from D74-1a(1) and D75-1a(1).

b. i is *negative* to h on e with respect to *every* regular c-function in $\mathfrak{L}_N$ if and only if i is either extremely negative to h on e with respect to every regular c or completely negative to h on e with respect to every regular c, or both. (From T65-4d(2), T74-2c, T74-7b, T75-2c, T75-7b, D74-1b(1), D75-1b(1), in analogy to (a).)

c. i is *relevant* to h on e with respect to *every* regular c-function in $\mathfrak{L}_N$ if and only if at least one of the following four conditions is fulfilled: (i) i is extremely positive to h on e with respect to every regular c; (ii) i is completely positive to h on e with respect to every regular c; (iii) i is extremely negative to h on e with respect to every regular c; (iv) i is completely negative to h on e with respect to every regular c. (From T65-5c, (a,) (b).)

d. i is *relevant* to h on e with respect to *every* regular c-function in $\mathfrak{L}_N$ if and only if i is either extremely relevant to h on e with respect to every regular c or completely relevant to h on e with respect to every regular c, or both. (From (c), D74-1c, D75-1c.)

e. If i is *irrelevant* to h on e with respect to *every* regular c-function in $\mathfrak{L}_N$, then i is either extremely irrelevant to h on e with respect to every regular c or completely irrelevant to h on e with respect to every regular c, or both.

Proof. Let the condition be fulfilled. Then, for every regular m, (1) $m_1 \times m_4 = m_2 \times m_3$ (T65-4f(2)). Therefore, for every regular m, (2) $m_1 \times m_4 = m_2 \times m_3 = 0$. [This is seen as follows. If for some m (2) were not fulfilled, then both products and hence all four m-values would be >0. Then, however, we could easily construct another function m′ which would not satisfy (1) (for instance, by taking $m'_1 = m'_4 = m(e)/3$ and $m'_2 = m'_3 = m(e)/6$).] From (2): for any m, in each of the two products at least one factor must be 0. Hence, for any m, at least one of the following four conditions is fulfilled: (i) $m_1 = m_2 = 0$; (ii) $m_1 = m_3 = 0$; (iii) $m_2 = m_4 = 0$; (iv) $m_3 = m_4 = 0$. If one of the first three conditions is fulfilled, i is extremely irrelevant with respect to the c in question (T74-3c) and hence with respect to every c (T74-7d). If one of the last three conditions is fulfilled, i is completely irrelevant with respect to every c (T75-3c, T75-7d).

We have earlier seen (§ 65) how positive or negative relevance or irrelevance is changed or remains unchanged when i or h are negated or when i and h exchange their places. Now we shall investigate what happens to extreme or complete relevance or irrelevance under such conditions. T5 gives the answers to these questions.

T76-5. Let e, h, and i be any sentences in $\mathfrak{L}_N$. On each of the lines (a) to (f) in the following table, the condition in column (1) is logically equiva-

	(1) i to h on e	(2) $\sim i$ to h on e	(3) i to $\sim h$ on e	(4) $\sim i$ to $\sim h$ on e	(5) h to i on e
a.	extr. pos.	compl. neg.	extr. neg.	compl. pos.	compl. pos.
b.	extr. neg.	compl. pos.	extr. pos.	compl. neg.	extr. neg.
c.	extr. irrel.	compl. irrel.	extr. irrel.	compl. irrel.	(extr. or compl. irrel.)
d.	compl. pos.	extr. neg.	compl. neg.	extr. pos.	extr. pos.
e.	compl. neg.	extr. pos.	compl. pos.	extr. neg.	compl. neg.
f.	compl. irrel.	extr. irrel.	compl. irrel.	extr. irrel.	(extr. or compl. irrel.)

lent to each of the conditions in columns (2) to (5) (except for (c)(5) and (f)(5)); hence any two of the latter conditions are likewise logically equivalent. (Thus, for instance, (a)(1)(2) says this: i is extremely positive to h on e if and only if $\sim i$ is completely negative to h on e.) We write 'extr.', 'compl.', 'pos.', 'neg.', and 'irrel.' as short for 'extremely', 'completely', 'positive', 'negative', and 'irrelevant', respectively.

Proof. If i or h are negated or i and h are exchanged, then each of the sentences k_1, k_2, k_3, and k_4 (as explained in § 72) is transformed into another one as follows.

(1) i, h, e	k_1	k_2	k_3	k_4
(2) $\sim i, h, e$	k_3	k_4	k_1	k_2
(3) $i, \sim h, e$	k_2	k_1	k_4	k_3
(4) $\sim i, \sim h, e$	k_4	k_3	k_2	k_1
(5) h, i, e	k_1	k_3	k_2	k_4

Thus each of the cases Nos. 1 to 16 in the table T72-8 is transformed into another of these cases as indicated in the following table:

No.	(1) i, h, e	(2) $\sim i, h, e$	(3) $i, \sim h, e$	(4) $\sim i, \sim h, e$	(5) h, i, e
1	extr. and compl. irrel. (1–3)	1	1	1	1
2		5	3	9	2
3		9	2	5	5
4	extr. irrel.	13	4	13	6
5	extr. and compl. irrel. (5–6)	2	9	3	3
6		6	10	10	4
7	extr. and compl. neg.	11	11	7	7
8	extr. neg.	14	12	15	8
9	extr. and compl. irrel. (9–10)	3	5	2	9
10		10	6	6	13
11	extr. and compl. pos.	7	7	11	11
12	extr. pos.	15	8	14	14
13	compl. irrel.	4	13	4	10
14	compl. pos.	8	15	12	12
15	compl. neg.	12	14	8	15
16		16	16	16	16

For example, the table says that No. 2 for *i,h,e* is transformed for *∼i,h,e* into No. 5. This is seen as follows. No. 2 is the case where $\mathfrak{m}_1 = \mathfrak{m}_2 = \mathfrak{m}_3 = 0$, $\mathfrak{m}_4 > 0$ (T72-8, columns (1) to (4)), hence where k_1, k_2, and k_3 are L-false but k_4 not. Now, according to line (2) of the previous table in this proof, k_1, k_2, k_3, and k_4 are transformed for *∼i,h,e* into k_3, k_4, k_1, and k_2, respectively. Therefore, case No. 2 is transformed into the case where k_3, k_4, and k_1 are L-false but k_2 is not, hence where $\mathfrak{m}_3$, $\mathfrak{m}_4$, and $\mathfrak{m}_1$ are 0 but $\mathfrak{m}_2 > 0$; and this is No. 5.

In column (1) of the last table, indications of extreme and complete relevance or irrelevance are given for each case, taken from column (14) of T72-8. This makes it easy to prove each item of T5. It will be sufficient to explain here one instance, say the item (a)(1)(2). It says that *i* is extr. pos. to *h* on *e* if and only if *∼i* is compl. neg. to *h* on *e*. This is proved by the above table as follows. We see in column (1) that *i* is extr. pos. to *h* on *e* in the cases Nos. 11 and 12 and no others. We see in column (2) that for *∼i* to *h* on *e* these two cases are transformed into the cases Nos. 7 and 15. And then we find (by going back to column (1)) that Nos. 7 and 15 are the only cases in which compl. neg. holds. This and the other items can also be proved directly (i.e., without the use of the last table) with the help of T74-1c, T74-2c, T74-3c, T75-1c, T75-2c, T75-3c, and the first table.

The procedure for all other items in T5 is analogous, except for (c)(5) and (f)(5). In these two points there is no sufficient and necessary condition. For example, (c)(1)(5) says merely that, if (but not only if) *i* is extr. irrel. to *h* on *e*, then *h* is either extr. irrel. or compl. irrel. (or both) to *i* on *e*. This is seen as follows. We find in the last table that *i* is extr. irrel. to *h* on *e* in Nos. 1 to 6, 9, and 10, and in no others. We see in column (5) that these cases are transformed for *h,i,e* into Nos. 1, 2, 5, 6, 3, 4, 9, and 13. These cases, however, do not represent just one kind of irrel.; some are extr. irrel., but No. 13 is not; some are compl. irrel., but No. 4 is not; and No. 10 is not among them although it is extr. and compl. irrel. Thus here only the weak statement given above can be made.

Now let us see what is stated by T5. First let us look only whether pos., neg., or irrel. holds in a given case, leaving aside the questions of extr. and compl. We find that negating *i* alone or *h* alone turns pos. into neg. and vice versa; that negating both *i* and *h* or exchanging *i* and *h* leaves pos. and neg. unchanged; and that irrel. remains unchanged under any of these transformations. All this was already known (T65-3).

The new results in T5 concern the transformation of extr. and compl. We see that by negating *h* alone extr. becomes again extr., and compl. again compl. Negating *i* (no matter whether *i* alone or both *i* and *h*, since negating *h* has no effect in this point, as we have just seen) turns extr. into compl., and vice versa. Now let us inspect the relation between columns (1) and (5), the effect of exchanging *i* and *h*. For irrel., we have here only weak statements as explained previously (see the end of the proof). The results for pos. and neg. may seem surprising at first: for pos., extr. is turned into compl. and vice versa; for neg., however, extr. and compl. remain unchanged. The following considerations may make these results plausible. Extr. neg. means that *i* and *h* are L-exclusive with respect to e ($\vdash e \supset \sim(i \,.\, h)$, T74-2d); this relation remains, of course, unchanged when i and h are exchanged. The same holds for compl. neg., because this means that i and h are L-disjunct with respect to e ($\vdash e \supset i \vee h$, T75-2d). On the other hand, extr. pos. involves an implicative relation between i and h ($\vdash e \supset (i \supset h)$, T74-1d) while compl. pos. involves the converse implicative relation ($\vdash e \supset (h \supset i)$, T75-1d). Therefore, the exchange of i and h cannot leave these relations unchanged but transforms each into the other.

This concludes the theory of relevance dealt with in this chapter, and also the general theory of regular c-functions discussed in the last two chapters, which constitutes the first and fundamental part of quantitative inductive logic. The next chapter (vii) does not belong to quantitative inductive logic but gives an outline of the foundations of comparative inductive logic. The construction of quantitative inductive logic will be continued in the chapters after the next.

CHAPTER VII

COMPARATIVE INDUCTIVE LOGIC

In this chapter a system of comparative inductive logic is constructed. Its basis is a comparative concept of confirmation $\mathfrak{MC}$. '$\mathfrak{MC}(h,e,h',e')$' is intended as explicatum for 'the hypothesis *h* is confirmed by the evidence *e* equally strongly or more strongly than *h'* by *e'*' (§ 79). Thus its meaning corresponds in some sense to the quantitative statement '$\mathfrak{c}(e,h) \geqq \mathfrak{c}(e',h')$' (§ 80). However, the definition of $\mathfrak{MC}$ (D81-1) uses only L-concepts, no quantitative concepts. Nevertheless, it is shown that the required correspondence between $\mathfrak{MC}$ and the quantitative $\mathfrak{c}$-functions holds (§ 81).

In the same way, '$\mathfrak{Gr}(h,e,h',e')$' corresponds to '$\mathfrak{c}(e,h) > \mathfrak{c}(e',h')$', '$\mathfrak{Eq}(h,e,h',e')$' to '$\mathfrak{c}(e,h) = \mathfrak{c}(e',h')$' (§ 82), '$\mathfrak{Max}(h,e)$' to '$\mathfrak{c}(h,e) = 1$', and '$\mathfrak{Min}(h,e)$' to '$\mathfrak{c}(h,e) = 0$' (§ 84). All these concepts are defined, directly or indirectly, on the basis of L-concepts without use of quantitative concepts like $\mathfrak{c}$-functions. Therefore they are called purely comparative (i.e., nonquantitative) concepts.

Some of the theorems of this chapter involving these comparative concepts (§ 85) correspond to certain theorems concerning $\mathfrak{c}$-functions stated in a preceding chapter.

Although we shall try in later chapters to construct a quantitative system of inductive logic, at the present time the question whether a comprehensive and adequate quantitative system is at all possible is still controversial. This fact is the chief reason for the importance of a comparative system of inductive logic. However, even if a quantitative system is possible, it is still interesting to see which results can be obtained with more restricted means.

In the last three sections (§§ 86–88) the classificatory concept of confirmation is investigated: '*i* is confirming evidence for the hypothesis *h* (on the evidence *e*)', in symbols '$\mathfrak{C}(h,i,e)$'. It is related to our earlier concept of positive relevance (§ 65), which was defined in quantitative terms. The problem of an explicatum for the classificatory concept defined in nonquantitative terms is discussed but remains unsolved. Several explicata of this kind are examined but are found to be too narrow.

§ 79. The Problem of a Comparative Concept of Confirmation

Our problem is to find an adequate definition for a comparative concept of confirmation $\mathfrak{MC}$. '$\mathfrak{MC}(h,e,h',e')$' is to be an explicatum for the following explicandum: 'The hypothesis *h* is confirmed by the evidence *e* equally strongly or more strongly than *h'* by *e'*'. The task of this explication is important because some authors believe that only a comparative concept of confirmation is possible, not a quantitative one.

In this chapter the basis of a comparative inductive logic will be constructed by laying down a definition of a comparative concept of confirmation and stating some theorems based on this and some other definitions.

We explained earlier the nature of comparative concepts in general, in contradistinction to classificatory and quantitative concepts (§ 4), and the role of comparative concepts as explicata (§ 5). Then we discussed the comparative concept of confirmation as an explicandum (§ 8). For reasons explained earlier, we use the following form for this concept (see end of § 4, there called the second kind of comparative concept): 'the hypothesis *h* is confirmed by the evidence *e* equally strongly or more strongly than *h*′ by *e*′'. Our task will now be to find an adequate explicatum for this concept. We shall use the symbol '𝔐𝔆' for the explicatum to be defined; hence we shall write '𝔐𝔆(*h*,*e*,*h*′,*e*′)' as explicatum for the sentence mentioned. It is to be noticed that '𝔐𝔆' is not a symbol of our symbolic object-languages 𝔏, but belongs to the metalanguage like the other German letters used (§ 14). While a quantitative concept of confirmation, i.e., any one of the c-functions which have been discussed in the two preceding chapters, assigns a number to a pair of sentences, the comparative concept 𝔐𝔆 is a relation between four sentences (*h*, *e*, *h*′, *e*′ in the above example); we shall sometimes regard it as a dyadic relation between two pairs of sentences (the pair *h*,*e* and the pair *h*′,*e*′).

An investigation of the possibilities for defining a comparative concept of confirmation, in other words, a comparative explicatum for probability$_1$, is the more important, since some authors believe that no adequate, entirely quantitative explicatum for probability$_1$ can be found and that therefore any explicatum must be at least partly comparative. Thus Kries, Keynes, and Koopman in their theories of probability$_1$ restrict the possibility for numerical values to a narrow class of special cases; and Nagel likewise expresses serious doubts in this direction.

We have mentioned Kries's arguments against the possibility of numerical values (§ 46). Let us now briefly look at the reasons given by Keynes. He admits that the generally accepted opinion is that the assignment of numerical values for probability$_1$ is at least theoretically possible, no matter whether the actual determination of the values in given cases is practically possible or not ([Probab.], p. 20); and he quotes W. F. Donkin and De Morgan to this effect. But as an argument for his own, more skeptical view he points out the fact that probability$_1$ is often based on similarity. Thus the probability$_1$ of the hypothesis that a certain picture was made by a certain painter may depend upon its similarity to other known paintings by the same artist. "We can say that one thing is more like a second object than it is like a third; but there will very seldom be any meaning in saying that it is twice as like. Probability is, so far as measurement is concerned, closely analogous to similarity" (p. 28).

Keynes goes even further and argues that the task of arranging probabilities$_1$ without numerical values in a mere order of magnitude—so that we might say that one probability$_1$ is greater than another without saying how much greater—is often unsolvable (p. 29). Consider a general hypothesis *h* judged on the basis of different reports *e* and *e'* concerning the results of different sets of experiments. "If we have *more* grounds than before," that is, if *e'* L-implies *e* without being L-equivalent to it, "comparison is possible; but if the grounds in the two cases are quite different" (which presumably means that *e* and *e'* are L-independent, i.e., L-implication does not hold between either of them and the other or its negation) "even a comparison of more and less, let alone numerical measurement, may be impossible" (p. 30).

Similarly, Nagel says: "It does not seem possible to assign a quantitative value to the degree of confirmation of a theory" ([Principles], p. 68). One of his arguments is based on the principle of the variety of instances (see above, § 47E, and below, § 110 I). Nagel believes that in some cases a nonnumerical comparison in terms of more or less is possible, while in general not even this is possible so that two degrees are in this case incomparable.

The comparative concept 𝔐𝔆 which we shall define will be in agreement with the conceptions of Kries, Keynes, Nagel, and Koopman in the following respect. It does not give a comparison in all cases of four sentences. Not even with respect to a given fixed evidence *e* does it arrange all hypotheses in a linear order; in general, two hypotheses *h* and *h'* will turn out to be incomparable on the evidence *e*. Likewise, with respect to a given hypothesis *h*, comparison will be possible only in certain cases while in general two evidences *e* and *e'* are incomparable with respect to *h*. Moreover we shall find that 𝔐𝔆 fulfils all the axioms in Koopman's axiom system (§ 83B).

§ 80. Requirements of Adequacy

In view of the explicandum mentioned in § 79, a relation between sentences *h*, *e*, *h'*, *e'* may be said to be in accord with a given regular c-function c if for all of its instances the following holds: $\mathfrak{c}(h,e) \geqq \mathfrak{c}(h',e')$. We lay down two requirements which a relation must fulfil in order to be an adequate explicatum for our explicandum: (1) it must be in accord with *all* regular c-functions (R1); (2) it must be the most comprehensive relation of this kind (R2). The task is to construct a purely comparative, i.e., nonquantitative definition such that those two quantitative requirements are fulfilled. In preparation for this task, the relations between the ranges of the sentences involved are analyzed.

In order to prepare the way for the later construction of a definition of the comparative concept of confirmation 𝔐𝔆, we shall discuss here the question which requirements a concept must fulfil in order to be acceptable as an adequate explicatum for our explicandum. We remember that the explicandum was as follows:

(1) h is confirmed by e equally strongly or more strongly than h' by e'.

Although our aim is to construct a purely comparative definition of $\mathfrak{MC}$, that is, one not containing any quantitative concepts, it will, nevertheless, be helpful to study, merely for heuristic purposes, the relation between $\mathfrak{MC}$ and the quantitative concepts of confirmation, in other words, the regular $\mathfrak{c}$-functions defined earlier (D55-4). The following analysis refers to the finite language systems $\mathfrak{L}_N$.

Suppose somebody has chosen a certain regular $\mathfrak{c}$-function $\mathfrak{c}$ as his concept of degree of confirmation. Then, to the comparative explicandum (1) mentioned above, the following quantitative formulation (2) corresponds in some sense:

(2) $$\mathfrak{c}(h,e) \geqq \mathfrak{c}(h',e') \,.$$

If he now wants to choose a comparative relation of confirmation, say T, he would make sure that T is ***in accord with*** his concept $\mathfrak{c}$ in this sense: any sentences h, e, h', e' for which T holds fulfil the condition (2).

Which way of finding an adequate concept $\mathfrak{MC}$ is suggested by these considerations? It would not do, first to select a suitable $\mathfrak{c}$-function and then to look for a relation $\mathfrak{MC}$ which is in accord with it. The task of selecting an adequate concept among the infinitely many $\mathfrak{c}$-functions involves very serious problems and difficulties. On the other hand, the general concept of regular $\mathfrak{c}$-functions is simple and relatively unproblematic. As we have seen earlier (§§ 52 f.), this concept is based on conventions which seem very plausible and widely accepted. The properties which the regular $\mathfrak{c}$-functions have in common are those which nearly all authors who have worked on probability$_1$ have attributed to this concept (§ 62). Our aim is to find a comparative relation $\mathfrak{MC}$ which grasps those logical relations between sentences which are, so to speak, prior to the introduction of any particular $\mathfrak{m}$-function for the ranges and any particular $\mathfrak{c}$-function; in other words, those logical relations with respect to which all the various $\mathfrak{c}$-functions agree. This suggests the stipulation that the relation $\mathfrak{MC}$ be defined in such a way that it is in accord with *all* regular $\mathfrak{c}$-functions. This is formulated in the following requirement, to which we shall later add a second one.

R80-1. ***First Requirement*** for $\mathfrak{MC}$ (with respect to $\mathfrak{L}_N$). For any sentences h, e, h', e', if $\mathfrak{MC}(h,e,h',e')$ then, for every regular $\mathfrak{c}$-function $\mathfrak{c}$, $\mathfrak{c}(h,e) \geqq \mathfrak{c}(h',e')$.

It is quite easy to find relations which, taken as 𝔐𝔈, fulfil this requirement. It is clear that these relations can hold only in cases where e and e' are not L-false, because otherwise the c-functions are not applicable (T55-2b). We shall presuppose for all examples of the following discussion that this condition is fulfilled, without mentioning it explicitly in the definiens of T_1, etc.

First let us see whether we can find quadruples of sentences h, e, h', e' which satisfy the following condition (3) occurring in R1:

(3) For every regular c-function c, $c(h,e) \geqq c(h',e')$.

This condition (3) is, among other cases, always satisfied if $\vdash e \supset h$, because then $c(h,e) = 1$ (T59-1b); likewise if $\vdash e' \supset \sim h'$, because then $c(h',e') = 0$ (T59-1e). (Here the fact is used that any c-value is $\leqq 1$ and $\geqq 0$ (T59-1a).) Thus, if we define '$T_1(h,e,h'e') =_{\mathrm{Df}} \vdash e \supset h$', then T_1, taken as 𝔐𝔈, fulfils the first requirement R1. The same holds for the relation T_2 defined by '$\vdash e' \supset \sim h'$'; and also for the disjunction of T_1 and T_2. However, it is obvious that these relations are not adequate for our purpose, although they fulfil R1. They are too narrow because they are restricted to two rather trivial kinds of cases. As an example of a non-trivial case in which condition (3) is satisfied, consider the following, where 'M' is any molecular predicate: h and h' are '$(x)(Mx)$'; e is '$Ma \,.\, Mb$'; e' is 'Ma'. h and h' are here the same sentence, a simple universal law. e' gives just one confirming instance for the law; e gives two, among them the one of e'. It seems plausible that the law is confirmed by the two instances at least as strongly as by the one, in other words, that the example satisfies condition (3). And this can indeed easily be proved (with the help of T61-3e). More generally, let T_3 be defined as follows: '$T_3(h,e,h',e') =_{\mathrm{Df}}$ h' is the same as h, and there is a sentence i such that e is $e' \,.\, i$, and $\vdash e' \,.\, h \supset i$'. The example just discussed represents a special case of T_3. It can then be shown (again with the help of T61-3e) that T_3 satisfies the first requirement. Further, let T_4 be defined by the following conditions: e' is the same as e, and $\vdash h' \supset h$. Here, the evidences in the two pairs are the same, and the second hypothesis L-implies the first and hence is at least as strong as the first. Therefore it seems plausible that the second hypothesis is confirmed by the common evidence at most as strongly as the first, and hence that T_4 satisfies the first requirement. And this can indeed be proved (with the help of T59-2d). Every case, i.e., quadruple of sentences, in which one of the relations T_1, T_2, T_3, T_4 holds, satisfies condition (3). Therefore, also, the disjunction T_5 of these four relations fulfils the first requirement. Shall we then take T_5 as 𝔐𝔈? The objection of triviality mentioned earlier against the disjunction of T_1 and T_2 would not hold here because the cases of T_3 and T_4 are not trivial. The reason why we would hesitate to take T_5 is rather the fact that it seems arbitrary to stop here. There might be still other cases likewise satisfying condition (3). If somebody then defines a relation including, in addition to our cases, some new cases of this kind, then his concept is more comprehensive than T_5 and therefore a more satisfactory explicatum for the comparative concept of confirmation. And a further relation may be still more comprehensive and hence still more satisfactory. Thus the problem is: how can we know when we have exhausted all possible cases? If we can, then a relation comprehending all these cases would be the most satisfactory solution. Therefore we shall lay down as the second requirement that the relation should have the *maximum extension* among all relations fulfilling the first requirement; in other words, it should hold in all cases satisfying condition (3). This leads to the following formulation:

R80-2. ***Second Requirement*** for $\mathfrak{MC}$ (with respect to $\mathfrak{L}_N$). For any sentences h, e, h', e', if $\mathfrak{c}(h,e) \geqq \mathfrak{c}(h',e')$ for every regular $\mathfrak{c}$, then $\mathfrak{MC}(h,e,h',e')$.

The two requirements R1 and R2 together stipulate that $\mathfrak{MC}$ is to be defined in such a manner that the following condition (4) is fulfilled:

(4) For any sentences h, e, h', e' (in $\mathfrak{L}_N$), $\mathfrak{MC}(h,e,h',e')$ if and only if, for every regular $\mathfrak{c}$, $\mathfrak{c}(h,e) \geqq \mathfrak{c}(h',e')$.

It is clear that this condition (4) determines uniquely a relation $\mathfrak{MC}$. (4) says in effect that this relation is the most comprehensive relation which is in accord with all regular $\mathfrak{c}$-functions.

We could take (4) itself as definition for $\mathfrak{MC}$. But this is not the form of definition we are looking for. We intend to give a purely comparative definition, that is to say, one not referring to any quantitative concepts. (4) however refers to the quantitative $\mathfrak{c}$-functions and thereby implicitly to the measure functions $\mathfrak{m}$ for the ranges of the sentences involved. A purely comparative definition may only refer to those relations between ranges which are independent of any particular $\mathfrak{m}$-function for the ranges, hence to the inclusion relations between ranges. Inclusion between the ranges of two sentences means the same as L-implication between the sentences (D20-1c). Therefore, we aim at a definition of $\mathfrak{MC}$ in terms of L-implication (or other L-concepts related to L-implication, like L-truth and L-falsity). A definition of this kind will be given later (D81-1). Then it will be shown that the concept $\mathfrak{MC}$, although defined in a purely comparative way, satisfies the requirements R1 and R2, which are formulated in quantitative terms.

Statement (4) says that (3) is a sufficient and necessary condition for $\mathfrak{MC}$. In order to construct a purely comparative definition, we have to find a sufficient and necessary condition for $\mathfrak{MC}$ in comparative terms. To prepare the way to this goal, we shall now investigate what the condition (3) means in terms of $\mathfrak{m}$-functions and ranges. $\mathfrak{c}$-values (for $\mathfrak{L}_N$) are defined as certain quotients of $\mathfrak{m}$-values (D55-4 and 3). (3) means, accordingly, that for every regular $\mathfrak{m}$-function $\mathfrak{m}$ (with respect to $\mathfrak{L}_N$) the following condition is fulfilled:

(5) $$\frac{\mathfrak{m}(e \,.\, h)}{\mathfrak{m}(e)} \geqq \frac{\mathfrak{m}(e' \,.\, h')}{\mathfrak{m}(e')} ,$$

where $\mathfrak{m}(e) > 0$ and $\mathfrak{m}(e') > 0$, and hence e and e' are not L-false. Since $\mathfrak{m}(e)$ and $\mathfrak{m}(e')$ are positive, (5) can be transformed into

(6) $$\mathfrak{m}(e \,.\, h) \times \mathfrak{m}(e') \geqq \mathfrak{m}(e' \,.\, h') \times \mathfrak{m}(e) .$$

e' is L-equivalent to $(e' \,.\, h') \vee (e' \,.\, \sim h')$ (T21-5j(2)); therefore $\mathfrak{m}(e') = \mathfrak{m}(e' \,.\, h') + \mathfrak{m}(e' \,.\, \sim h')$ (T57-1m). Analogously, $\mathfrak{m}(e) = \mathfrak{m}(e \,.\, h) + \mathfrak{m}(e \,.\, \sim h)$. By substituting these values in (6) and simplifying, we obtain:

(7) $$\mathfrak{m}(e \,.\, h) \times \mathfrak{m}(e' \,.\, \sim h') \geqq \mathfrak{m}(e' \,.\, h') \times \mathfrak{m}(e \,.\, \sim h) .$$

This is obviously satisfied if at least one of the two $\mathfrak{m}$-values on the right side is 0. $\mathfrak{m}(e \,.\, \sim h)$ is 0 if and only if

(8) $$\vdash e \supset h ;$$

$\mathfrak{m}(e' \,.\, h')$ is 0 if and only if

(9) $$\vdash e' \supset \sim h'$$

(according to T58-1b). These are the two trivial kinds of cases mentioned earlier as T_1 and T_2, respectively. Now let us suppose that both $\mathfrak{m}$-values on the right side of (7) are positive. Which relations must then hold between the ranges of the sentences involved in order to assure that (7) holds for every regular $\mathfrak{m}$?

The $\mathfrak{m}$-value for any sentence j has been defined (D55-2) as the sum of the $\mathfrak{m}$-values for those $\mathfrak{Z}$ (state-descriptions) which belong to $\mathfrak{R}(j)$ (the range of j). $\mathfrak{m}$-values for all $\mathfrak{Z}$ may be chosen arbitrarily as any positive numbers whose sum is 1 (D55-1). Now we shall see that (7) holds for every regular $\mathfrak{m}$ only if the ranges of the following three sentences are null: $e' \,.\, h' \,.\, \sim e$, $e' \,.\, h' \,.\, e \,.\, \sim h$, $e \,.\, \sim h \,.\, \sim e'$; let us call them $\mathfrak{R}_1$, $\mathfrak{R}_2$, and $\mathfrak{R}_3$, respectively. $\mathfrak{R}_1$ is included in $\mathfrak{R}(e' \,.\, h')$, while it has no elements in common with the following three ranges: $\mathfrak{R}(e \,.\, h)$, $\mathfrak{R}(e' \,.\, \sim h')$, and

$\mathfrak{R}(e \,.\, \sim h)$. Therefore, if $\mathfrak{R}_1$ is not null, we can find a regular m-function whose value for $\mathfrak{R}_1$ and thereby for $e' \,.\, h'$ is arbitrarily high, that is, as close to 1 as we want, while the other three values in (7) are small and equal to one another; hence (7) is in this case not satisfied. $\mathfrak{R}_2$ is included in $\mathfrak{R}(e' \,.\, h')$ and in $\mathfrak{R}(e \,.\, \sim h)$, while it has no elements in common with $\mathfrak{R}(e \,.\, h)$ and with $\mathfrak{R}(e' \,.\, \sim h')$. Therefore, if $\mathfrak{R}_2$ is not null, we can choose an m-function such that its two values on the right side of (7) are close to 1, while the two values on the left side are very small, and hence (7) is violated. Finally, $\mathfrak{R}_3$ is included in $\mathfrak{R}(e \,.\, \sim h)$, while it has no element in common with the ranges of the other three sentences in (7). Here, a consideration analogous to that concerning $\mathfrak{R}_1$ shows that, if $\mathfrak{R}_3$ is not null, there is an m-function violating (7). Thus it is a necessary condition for the general validity of (7) that $\mathfrak{R}_1$, $\mathfrak{R}_2$, and $\mathfrak{R}_3$ are null. Let us now formulate this condition in L-terms. That $\mathfrak{R}_1$ is null means that $\mathfrak{R}(e' \,.\, h') \subset \mathfrak{R}(e)$, hence that $\vdash e' \,.\, h' \supset e$. That $\mathfrak{R}_2$ is null means that $\mathfrak{R}(e' \,.\, h' \,.\, e) \subset \mathfrak{R}(h)$, hence that $\vdash e' \,.\, h' \,.\, e \supset h$. The two results combined say that $\vdash e' \,.\, h' \supset e \,.\, h$. $\mathfrak{R}_3$ is $\mathfrak{R}(e \,.\, \sim(h \vee e'))$; that this range is null means that $\vdash e \supset h \vee e'$. Thus the following is a necessary condition for the general validity of (7):

(10) $\vdash e' \,.\, h' \supset e \,.\, h$ and simultaneously $\vdash e \supset h \vee e'$.

It can easily be shown that T_3 and T_4 as earlier discussed are special cases of (10) and that (10) is much more general. However, we have not shown that it is general enough. Let us tentatively assume that it is; in other words, that the disjunction of (8), (9), and (10) is a sufficient and necessary condition for the general validity of (7), and hence for (5), and hence for (3). That is to say, we shall choose this disjunction for constructing a tentative definition of $\mathfrak{MC}$ in the next section (D81-1). Then we shall prove that the assumption just made is correct, in other words, that the relation thus defined fulfils the two requirements of adequacy earlier stated.

§ 81. Definition of the Comparative Concept of Confirmation $\mathfrak{MC}$

Suggested by the considerations in the preceding section, a definition for $\mathfrak{MC}$ based on L-concepts is laid down (D1). Then it is shown that $\mathfrak{MC}$ fulfils the two requirements stated earlier, for any finite system $\mathfrak{L}_N$ (T1). For $\mathfrak{L}_\infty$, a similar but somewhat restricted result is found (T2).

We shall now lay down a definition (D1) for $\mathfrak{MC}$, the comparative concept of confirmation. This definition is suggested by the considerations in the preceding section. The conditions (a) and (b) in D1 have been mentioned at the beginning of § 80; they are obviously required because we apply the concept of confirmation only to non-L-false evidences. (c_1) and (c_2) in D1 correspond to (8) and (9) in § 80; these are the two trivial cases where $\mathfrak{c}(h,e) = 1$ or $\mathfrak{c}(h',e') = 0$, respectively. (c_3) corresponds to (10) in § 80; this condition applies to the nontrivial cases. The preliminary considerations in § 80 were restricted to finite systems $\mathfrak{L}_N$, but the definition D1 is laid down in a general form for any finite or infinite system $\mathfrak{L}$.

+D81-1. $\mathfrak{MC}(h,e,h',e')$ (with respect to a system $\mathfrak{L}$) $=_{Df}$ the following three conditions are fulfilled (in $\mathfrak{L}$):

a. e is not L-false.

b. e' is not L-false.

c. Either (c_1) $\vdash e \supset h$,

or (c_2) $\vdash e' \supset \sim h'$,

or (c_3) $\vdash e' \,.\, h' \supset e \,.\, h$ and simultaneously $\vdash e \supset h \vee e'$.

(The three conditions under (c) are meant in a nonexclusive sense: two or all three of them may be fulfilled.)

Now we have to show that the relation $\mathfrak{MC}$ defined by the purely comparative definition D1 nevertheless fulfils the quantitative requirements of adequacy discussed earlier and hence is an adequate explicatum for the comparative explicandum (as formulated, e.g., by (1) in § 80). The first requirement (R80-1) demands that $\mathfrak{MC}$ be in accord with every regular $\mathfrak{c}$-function. The second requirement (R80-2) demands that $\mathfrak{MC}$ be the most comprehensive relation fulfilling the first requirement. The following considerations—which, although somewhat lengthy, are quite elementary—prove that both requirements are fulfilled. This result will be formulated in T1. The following considerations and T1 apply to any finite system $\mathfrak{L}_N$. The question of $\mathfrak{L}_\infty$ will be dealt with later, in T2.

Let h, e, h', and e' be any sentences in $\mathfrak{L}_N$ such that e and e' are not L-false. Our aim is to show that if these sentences satisfy the following condition (1) then they satisfy also (2), and vice versa:

(1) $$\mathfrak{MC}(h,e,h',e')\,,$$

(2) For every regular $\mathfrak{c}$-function $\mathfrak{c}$, $\mathfrak{c}(h,e) \geqq \mathfrak{c}(h',e')$.

In what follows we shall transform condition (2) step for step into other forms. Each step here made is a reversible logical transformation, that is to say, the conditions which will be stated are not only logical consequences of (2) but logically equivalent to (2), in other words, each is a sufficient and necessary condition for (2). In this way, (2) will be transformed in turn into (3), (4), (5), (6), (7), (8), (9), (10), (11), and thereby into (1). Thus the aim will be reached.

We form certain conjunctions out of the given four sentences and their negations and denote them by 'j_1', . . . , 'j_9' as follows:

j_1 is $e \,.\, e' \,.\, h \,.\, h'$,
j_2 is $e \,.\, e' \,.\, h \,.\, \sim h'$,
j_3 is $e \,.\, e' \,.\, \sim h \,.\, h'$,
j_4 is $e \,.\, e' \,.\, \sim h \,.\, \sim h'$,
j_5 is $e \,.\, \sim e' \,.\, h$,
j_6 is $e \,.\, \sim e' \,.\, \sim h$,
j_7 is $\sim e \,.\, e' \,.\, h'$,
j_8 is $\sim e \,.\, e' \,.\, \sim h'$,
j_9 is $\sim e \,.\, \sim e'$.

These nine j-sentences are L-exclusive in pairs and L-disjunct. [This can be shown as follows. The j-sentences may be regarded as formed in the following way. Consider the truth-table for the four sentences e, e', h, and h' as explained in § 21B, and let $k_1, \ldots, k_{16}$ be the sixteen conjunctions corresponding to the lines of the truth-table. Then each of the sentences j_1, j_2, j_3, and j_4 is one of these k-sentences; each of j_5, j_6, j_7, and j_8 is L-equivalent to a disjunction of two k-sentences; and j_9 is L-equivalent to a disjunction of four k-sentences. Each k-sentence occurs here in exactly one j-sentence. Hence the assertion (from T21-7a,b).] Therefore the ranges of the j-sentences constitute an exhaustive and nonoverlapping division for the state-descriptions $\mathfrak{Z}$ in $\mathfrak{L}_N$. [Incidentally, the j-sentences are to some extent analogous to the $\mathfrak{Z}$ themselves, which are conjunctions of atomic sentences and their negations. However, there is one important difference. The atomic sentences are assumed to be logically independent of one another, and therefore all $\mathfrak{Z}$ are factual. On the other hand, among the sentences h, e, h', and e', some L-relations (e.g., L-implication) may hold; then some of the j-sentences will be L-false. We shall soon discuss cases of this kind.] We can easily see that the following L-equivalences hold (in analogy to T21-7d):

$\vdash e \equiv j_1 \vee j_2 \vee j_3 \vee j_4 \vee j_5 \vee j_6$,
$\vdash e' \equiv j_1 \vee j_2 \vee j_3 \vee j_4 \vee j_7 \vee j_8$,
$\vdash e \,.\, h \equiv j_1 \vee j_2 \vee j_5$,
$\vdash e' \,.\, h' \equiv j_1 \vee j_3 \vee j_7$.

For any regular $\mathfrak{m}$-function $\mathfrak{m}$, its value for each of these disjunctions is the sum of the values for the components, since these are L-exclusive in pairs (T57-1n). Writing '$\mathfrak{m}_n$' for '$\mathfrak{m}(j_n)$' ($n = 1, \ldots, 9$), we obtain:

$\mathfrak{m}(e) = \mathfrak{m}_1 + \mathfrak{m}_2 + \mathfrak{m}_3 + \mathfrak{m}_4 + \mathfrak{m}_5 + \mathfrak{m}_6$,
$\mathfrak{m}(e') = \mathfrak{m}_1 + \mathfrak{m}_2 + \mathfrak{m}_3 + \mathfrak{m}_4 + \mathfrak{m}_7 + \mathfrak{m}_8$,

$$\mathfrak{m}(e \,.\, h) = \mathfrak{m}_1 + \mathfrak{m}_2 + \mathfrak{m}_5,$$
$$\mathfrak{m}(e' \,.\, h') = \mathfrak{m}_1 + \mathfrak{m}_3 + \mathfrak{m}_7.$$

Condition (2) can be expressed in terms of $\mathfrak{m}$-functions (see (5) and (6) in § 80) as follows:

(3) For every regular $\mathfrak{m}$-function $\mathfrak{m}$,
$$\mathfrak{m}(e \,.\, h) \times \mathfrak{m}(e') \geqq \mathfrak{m}(e' \,.\, h') \times \mathfrak{m}(e)\,.$$

Substituting here the $\mathfrak{m}$-values just found and multiplying out, we obtain on either side a sum whose terms are products of two $\mathfrak{m}_n$-values each. If equal terms on both sides are omitted, the remaining terms can be combined as follows:

(4) For every regular $\mathfrak{m}$,
$$(\mathfrak{m}_1 + \mathfrak{m}_2 + \mathfrak{m}_5) \times (\mathfrak{m}_2 + \mathfrak{m}_8) + (\mathfrak{m}_2 + \mathfrak{m}_5) \times \mathfrak{m}_4 \geqq$$
$$(\mathfrak{m}_1 + \mathfrak{m}_3 + \mathfrak{m}_7) \times (\mathfrak{m}_3 + \mathfrak{m}_6) + (\mathfrak{m}_3 + \mathfrak{m}_7) \times \mathfrak{m}_4\,.$$

Let us write '$\mathfrak{R}_n$' as short for '$\mathfrak{R}(j_n)$' ($n = 1, \ldots, 9$). These nine ranges form, as mentioned above, a complete division for the $\mathfrak{Z}$. Therefore, if we choose an arbitrary sequence of nine nonnegative real numbers r_1, r_2, $\ldots$, r_9 such that (a) $r_n = 0$ if and only if j_n is L-false, and (b) $r_1 + r_2 + \ldots + r_9 = 1$, then we can find a regular $\mathfrak{m}$ such that, for every n from 1 to 9, $\mathfrak{m}(j_n) = r_n$. (This follows for any L-false j_n from (a) and D55-2a; for any other j_n from (b) and T58-1l.)

Now we shall show that (4) holds if and only if the right-hand side in (4) equals 0, that is:

(5) For every regular $\mathfrak{m}$,
$$(\mathfrak{m}_1 + \mathfrak{m}_3 + \mathfrak{m}_7) \times (\mathfrak{m}_3 + \mathfrak{m}_6) + (\mathfrak{m}_3 + \mathfrak{m}_7) \times \mathfrak{m}_4 = 0\,.$$

Proof. (a) If the sentences h, e, h', e' are such that (5) is satisfied, then obviously (4) is also satisfied, because $\mathfrak{m}$-values are always nonnegative. (b) Now the converse must be shown. Suppose that (5) is not satisfied. This means that there is an $\mathfrak{m}$-function, say $\mathfrak{m}'$, such that the left side of the equation in (5) is > 0, hence also the right side in (4). Now we take another $\mathfrak{m}$-function $\mathfrak{m}''$ which has the following values. For $n = 1, 3, 4, 6$, and 7, $\mathfrak{m}_n'' = \mathfrak{m}_n'$; $\mathfrak{m}_2'' = \frac{1}{2}\mathfrak{m}_3'$; $\mathfrak{m}_5'' = \frac{1}{2}\mathfrak{m}_7'$; $\mathfrak{m}_8'' = \frac{1}{2}\mathfrak{m}_6'$. Let us abbreviate (4) for $\mathfrak{m}''$ by '$q_1 + q_2 \geqq q_3 + q_4$', where the q-symbols stand for the four products occurring. Then we easily see from the defined values of $\mathfrak{m}''$ that $q_1 \leqq q_3$ and $q_2 \leqq q_4$; moreover, since $q_3 + q_4 > 0$, either q_3 or q_4 (or both) > 0, and hence either $q_1 < q_3$ or $q_2 < q_4$ (or both). Hence, $q_1 + q_2 < q_3 + q_4$. Thus $\mathfrak{m}''$ does not satisfy (4). Therefore, if (4) is satisfied then so is (5).

Since $\mathfrak{m}$-values are nonnegative, the sum in (5) is 0 if and only if both terms of the sum are 0. A product is 0 if and only if at least one factor is 0. A sum of certain $\mathfrak{m}$-values is 0 if and only if all these $\mathfrak{m}$-values are 0. Therefore (5) holds if and only if (6) holds:

(6) For every regular $\mathfrak{m}$,

(a) either $\mathfrak{m}_1 = \mathfrak{m}_3 = \mathfrak{m}_7 = 0$ or $\mathfrak{m}_3 = \mathfrak{m}_6 = 0$;

and (b) either $\mathfrak{m}_3 = \mathfrak{m}_7 = 0$ or $\mathfrak{m}_4 = 0$.

('Either–or' is here always understood in the nonexclusive sense.) Combining each of the two cases in (a) with each in (b), we obtain:

(7) For every regular $\mathfrak{m}$,

either (a) $\mathfrak{m}_1 = \mathfrak{m}_3 = \mathfrak{m}_7 = 0$,
or (b) $\mathfrak{m}_1 = \mathfrak{m}_3 = \mathfrak{m}_7 = \mathfrak{m}_4 = 0$,
or (c) $\mathfrak{m}_3 = \mathfrak{m}_6 = \mathfrak{m}_7 = 0$,
or (d) $\mathfrak{m}_3 = \mathfrak{m}_4 = \mathfrak{m}_6 = 0$.

Here we may omit (b) because (a) follows from it. ('*A* or (*A* and *B*)' means the same as '*A*', T21-5p(1)). The $\mathfrak{m}$-values here are those of the *j*-sentences with the same subscripts. $\mathfrak{m}(j_n) = 0$ if and only if j_n is L-false (T58-1b, see also T58-1h). Several sentences are L-false if and only if their disjunction is L-false (T20-2q). Hence we obtain (in the order (7)(d), (a), (c)):

(8) Either (a) $j_3 \vee j_4 \vee j_6$ is L-false ,
or (b) $j_1 \vee j_3 \vee j_7$ is L-false ,
or (c) $j_7 \vee j_3$ is L-false, and j_6 is L-false .

Now we eliminate the *j*-abbreviations. (For (b), we use the last of the four L-equivalences mentioned earlier.)

(9) Either (a) $(e \,.\, e' \,.\, \sim h \,.\, h') \vee (e \,.\, e' \,.\, \sim h \,.\, \sim h') \vee (e \,.\, \sim e' \,.\, \sim h)$ is L-false ,
or (b) $e' \,.\, h'$ is L-false ,
or (c) $(\sim e \,.\, e' \,.\, h') \vee (e \,.\, e' \,.\, \sim h \,.\, h')$ is L-false and $e \,.\, \sim e' \,.\, \sim h$ is L-false .

We transform this as follows (for (a): T21-5j(2); for (c): T21-5f(1)):

(10) Either (a) $e \,.\, \sim h$ is L-false ,
or (b) $e' \,.\, h'$ is L-false ,
or (c) $e' \,.\, h' \,.\, [\sim e \vee (e \,.\, \sim h)]$ is L-false and $e \,.\, \sim(e' \vee h)$ is L-false .

$\sim e \vee (e \,.\, \sim h)$ is L-equivalent to $\sim e \vee \sim h$ (T21-5m(4), T21-3c, T21-5s(1)), and hence to $\sim(e \,.\, h)$ (T21-5f(3)). Now we transform in terms of L-truth (T20-1a, T21-5g(1)):

(11) Either (a) $\vdash e \supset h$,
or (b) $\vdash e' \supset \sim h'$,
or (c) $\vdash e' \,.\, h' \supset e \,.\, h$ and $\vdash e \supset (e' \vee h)$.

Since we have presupposed that e and e' are not L-false, we see from D1 that (11) holds if and only if

$$(12) \qquad \mathfrak{MC}(h,e,h',e') \; .$$

Thus we have shown that (2) holds if and only if (12) holds. This result is stated in the following theorem.

+T81-1. Let h, e, h', e' be any sentences in $\mathfrak{L}_N$. Let e and e' be non-L-false in $\mathfrak{L}_N$.

a. If $\mathfrak{MC}(h,e,h',e')$ (in $\mathfrak{L}_N$), then for every regular $\mathfrak{c}$ (with respect to $\mathfrak{L}_N$), $\mathfrak{c}(h,e) \geqq \mathfrak{c}(h',e')$.

b. (The converse of (a)). If for every regular $\mathfrak{c}$ (with respect to $\mathfrak{L}_N$) $\mathfrak{c}(h,e) \geqq \mathfrak{c}(h',e')$, then $\mathfrak{MC}(h,e,h',e')$.

T1 shows that $\mathfrak{MC}$, as defined by D1, fulfils the requirements R80-1 and 2 which we have laid down for an adequate comparative concept of confirmation. Moreover, $\mathfrak{MC}$ is the only relation fulfilling both requirements, because, as we have seen earlier, these requirements determine uniquely one relation; nevertheless, definitions for $\mathfrak{MC}$ differing from D1 considerably in their formulations while stating logically equivalent conditions are of course possible. In the terminology of § 80, T1a says that $\mathfrak{MC}$ is in accord with every regular $\mathfrak{c}$-function, and it, together with T1b, says that $\mathfrak{MC}$ is the most comprehensive relation for which this holds.

The definition D1 of $\mathfrak{MC}$ has been formulated in a general way for any finite or infinite system $\mathfrak{L}$. T1, however, refers only to the finite systems $\mathfrak{L}_N$. Now we shall see how the results can be transferred to $\mathfrak{L}_\infty$. In the following theorem T2, (a) corresponds to T1a, and (b) to T1b. However, we restrict T2b to nongeneral sentences. The reason for this is the fact, which we found earlier, that in $\mathfrak{L}_\infty$ the relations between $\mathfrak{m}$- and $\mathfrak{c}$-values, on the one hand, and L-concepts, on the other hand, are simple only for nongeneral sentences but rather complicated for general sentences (see the discussion in § 58, and T59-5).

+T81-2. Let h, e, h', and e' be sentences in $\mathfrak{L}_\infty$. Let e and e' be non-L-false in every system $\mathfrak{L}$ in which they occur.

a. If $\mathfrak{MC}(h,e,h',e')$ in $\mathfrak{L}_\infty$ and ${}_\infty\mathfrak{c}$ is any regular $\mathfrak{c}$-function for $\mathfrak{L}_\infty$ possessing values for the pairs h,e and h',e', then ${}_\infty\mathfrak{c}(h,e) \geqq {}_\infty\mathfrak{c}(h',e')$.

Proof. Let the conditions be fulfilled. Then D1c is fulfilled in $\mathfrak{L}_\infty$ and hence likewise in every system $\mathfrak{L}_N$ of a final segment of the sequence of finite systems (T20-11). It follows from the assumptions stated that D1a and b are fulfilled in every system $\mathfrak{L}$ in which e and e' occur. Thus in every system of a final segment all conditions in D1 are fulfilled and hence $\mathfrak{MC}(h,e,h',e')$. Let ${}_N\mathfrak{c}$ be the $\mathfrak{c}$-sequence on which the given ${}_\infty\mathfrak{c}$ is based. Then in the final segment ${}_N\mathfrak{c}(h,e) \geqq {}_N\mathfrak{c}(h',e')$ (T1a). Therefore (T40-21f) ${}_\infty\mathfrak{c}(h,e) \geqq {}_\infty\mathfrak{c}(h',e')$.

b. Let h, e, h', and e' be *nongeneral* (hence every regular $_\infty\mathfrak{c}$ has values for the pairs h,e and h',e'). If for every regular $_\infty\mathfrak{c}$ in $\mathfrak{L}_\infty$ $_\infty\mathfrak{c}(h,e) \geqq {}_\infty\mathfrak{c}(h',e')$, then $\mathfrak{MC}(h,e,h',e')$ in $\mathfrak{L}_\infty$.

Proof. Let the conditions be fulfilled. Let $\mathfrak{L}_N$ be any of those finite systems in which all four sentences occur. These systems form a final segment. Then for every regular c-function $_N\mathfrak{c}$ for $\mathfrak{L}_N$ $_N\mathfrak{c}(h,e) \geqq {}_N\mathfrak{c}(h',e')$ (T57-6c). Therefore $\mathfrak{MC}(h,e,h',e')$ in $\mathfrak{L}_N$ (T1b) and hence also in $\mathfrak{L}_\infty$ (T20-10).

Examples. 𝔐ℭ holds in the following three examples. They belong to the nontrivial kind D1c3.

First example. e and e' are 'P_1a'; h is '$P_2a \vee P_3a$'; h' is 'P_2a'. We see easily that $\vdash e' \supset e$, $\vdash h' \supset h$, $\vdash e \supset e'$; hence D1c3 is fulfilled. In this simple case it is also rather obvious that the explicandum holds, that is to say, that h is confirmed by the common evidence at least as strongly as h', because h is weaker than h' (i.e., $\vdash h' \supset h$ but not $\vdash h \supset h'$).

Second example. e is '$(P_1b \vee P_2b) \cdot (P_2b \vee P_3b)$'; e' is 'P_1b'; h and h' are 'P_2b'. We see easily that $\vdash e' \cdot h' \supset e$, $\vdash h' \supset h$, and $\vdash e \supset h \vee e'$. Thus D1c3 is fulfilled. This case is not quite as simple as (1), although the hypotheses are the same; there is no simple logical relation between e and e'. Therefore we cannot see immediately that the explicandum holds. However, the following method can be used for an examination of this example; it is analogous to the method which led above to T1 but much more simple because of the simplicity of the example. We regard the sentences e, h, e', and h' as sentences of $\mathfrak{L}_1^3$ (§ 31), and hence transform them into disjunctions of Q-sentences (D31-1d) with 'Q_1', . . . , 'Q_8'. These Q-sentences are the $\mathfrak{Z}$ in this system because $N = 1$ (D34-1a). Then we can easily show that for any regular $\mathfrak{m}$ and $\mathfrak{c}$, the conditions (6), and hence (5), and hence (2) in § 80 are fulfilled.

Third example. We combine the sentences of the preceding examples by taking as e here the conjunction of the sentences e in the first and the second examples, and likewise with h, e', and h'. Thus e is here '$P_1a \cdot (P_1b \vee P_2b) \cdot (P_2b \vee P_3b)$'; h is '$(P_2a \vee P_3a) \cdot P_2b$'; e' is '$P_1a \cdot P_1b$'; h' is '$P_2a \cdot P_2b$'. Here, neither the evidences are L-equivalent nor the hypotheses. But we see easily that $\vdash e' \cdot h' \supset e$, $\vdash h' \supset h$, $\vdash e \supset h \vee e'$, and hence D1c3 is fulfilled.

§ 82. Some Concepts Based on 𝔐ℭ

On the basis of 𝔐ℭ, three other comparative concepts are defined. As 𝔐ℭ corresponds to the relation $\geqq$ between c-values, 𝔈𝔮 is defined (D1) in such a way that it corresponds to the relation = (T1a), and 𝔊𝔯 (D2) corresponds to > (T1b). Finally, two pairs of sentences are called comparable if the relation 𝔐ℭ holds between the first and the second or between the second and the first (D3). Some theorems are given which state sufficient and necessary conditions for the concepts defined in terms of L-concepts.

We shall define here four concepts on the basis of the comparative concept of confirmation 𝔐ℭ. These four concepts are, like 𝔐ℭ, tetradic relations between sentences in any system 𝔏. Here, as in the case of 𝔐ℭ, it is convenient to regard the concepts as relations between two pairs of sentences. In this sense, we use the term 'the converse of 𝔐ℭ' (without a special symbol) for that relation which holds between two pairs h',e'

and *h*,*e* if and only if $\mathfrak{MC}$ holds between the pairs *h*,*e* and *h'*,*e'*, that is, between the same pairs in the opposite direction.

The relation $\mathfrak{Eq}$ will be defined in such a way that it holds between two pairs of sentences if and only if both $\mathfrak{MC}$ and its converse hold between them (D1). The symbol '$\mathfrak{Eq}$' is intended to suggest 'equal'; this is justified by T1a. The relation $\mathfrak{Gr}$ is to hold if $\mathfrak{MC}$ holds but not the converse of $\mathfrak{MC}$ (D2). The symbol '$\mathfrak{Gr}$' is to suggest 'greater than'; it is, however, to be noticed that, if $\mathfrak{Gr}$ holds between two pairs of sentences, the first pair does not necessarily have a greater $\mathfrak{c}$-value than the second for every regular $\mathfrak{c}$; in general, only a somewhat weaker statement holds (T1b). We shall say that two pairs of sentences *h*,*e* and *h'*,*e'* are ***comparable*** if the relation $\mathfrak{MC}$ holds between these pairs in at least one direction (D3). Otherwise the pairs are said to be ***incomparable.*** In the latter case, no purely comparative relation holds between the pairs in the sense that no general relation between their $\mathfrak{c}$-values holds for all regular $\mathfrak{c}$-functions; some $\mathfrak{c}$-functions rate the one pair higher and other $\mathfrak{c}$-functions the other pair (T1d).

+**D82-1.** $\mathfrak{Eq}(h,e,h',e')$ (in a finite or infinite system $\mathfrak{L}$) $=_{\text{Df}}$ $\mathfrak{MC}(h,e,h',e')$ and $\mathfrak{MC}(h',e',h,e)$.

+**D82-2.** $\mathfrak{Gr}(h,e,h',e')$ (in $\mathfrak{L}$) $=_{\text{Df}}$ $\mathfrak{MC}(h,e,h',e')$ and not $\mathfrak{MC}(h',e',h,e)$.

+**D82-3.** The pairs of sentences *h*,*e* and *h'*,*e'* are ***comparable*** (in $\mathfrak{L}$) $=_{\text{Df}}$ $\mathfrak{MC}(h,e,h',e')$ or $\mathfrak{MC}(h',e',h,e)$ (or both).

The following theorem T1 states relations between the comparative concepts just defined and the quantitative concepts, that is, the regular $\mathfrak{c}$-functions. This theorem is restricted to finite systems $\mathfrak{L}_N$ for the reasons mentioned earlier in connection with T81-1. However, if the four sentences involved are nongeneral and *e* and *e'* are non-L-false in every system in which they occur, then the assertions of this theorem hold likewise for $\mathfrak{L}_\infty$ (see T81-2).

+**T82-1.** Let *h*, *e*, *h'*, and *e'* be sentences in $\mathfrak{L}_N$. Let *e* and *e'* be non-L-false in $\mathfrak{L}_N$.

- **a.** $\mathfrak{Eq}(h,e,h',e')$ if and only if, for every regular $\mathfrak{c}$ with respect to $\mathfrak{L}_N$, $\mathfrak{c}(h,e) = \mathfrak{c}(h',e')$. (From D1, T81-1.)
- **b.** $\mathfrak{Gr}(h,e,h',e')$ if and only if, for every regular $\mathfrak{c}$ with respect to $\mathfrak{L}_N$, $\mathfrak{c}(h,e) \geqq \mathfrak{c}(h',e')$ and, for at least one such $\mathfrak{c}$, $\mathfrak{c}(h,e) > \mathfrak{c}(h',e')$. (From D2, T81-1.)
- **c.** The pairs *h*,*e* and *h'*,*e'* are *comparable* if and only if either, for every regular $\mathfrak{c}$ with respect to $\mathfrak{L}_N$, $\mathfrak{c}(h,e) \geqq \mathfrak{c}(h',e')$ or, for every such $\mathfrak{c}$, $\mathfrak{c}(h',e') \geqq \mathfrak{c}(h,e)$. (From D3, T81-1.)

d. The pairs h,e and h',e' are *incomparable* if and only if there are two regular $\mathfrak{c}$-functions $\mathfrak{c}$ and $\mathfrak{c}'$ with respect to $\mathfrak{L}_N$, such that $\mathfrak{c}(h,e) > \mathfrak{c}(h',e')$ and $\mathfrak{c}'(h',e') > \mathfrak{c}'(h,e)$. (From (c).)

The remaining theorems of this section and the next one do not involve quantitative concepts, that is, $\mathfrak{c}$-functions, but state relations between the defined comparative concepts and the original L-concepts. All these theorems hold for any finite or infinite system $\mathfrak{L}$ which contains the sentences in question.

The following theorem T3, which follows immediately from D81-1, states a sufficient and necessary condition for the converse of $\mathfrak{MC}$. It serves merely as a lemma for some later theorems.

T82-3. Lemma. $\mathfrak{MC}(h',e',h,e)$ if and only if the following three conditions are fulfilled:

a. e' is not L-false.

b. e is not L-false.

c. Either (c_1) $\vdash e' \supset h'$,
or (c_2) $\vdash e \supset \sim h$,
or (c_3) $\vdash e \,.\, h \supset e' \,.\, h'$ and $\vdash e' \supset h' \vee e$.

The following theorems T4 to T7 state sufficient and necessary conditions for the concepts introduced in this section. They refer not to $\mathfrak{MC}$ but directly to the original L-concepts. (They could be taken as alternative definitions for the new concepts on the basis of L-concepts.)

+T82-4. $\mathfrak{Eq}(h,e,h',e')$ if and only if e and e' are non-L-false and, in addition, at least one of the following three conditions is fulfilled:

Either **a.** $\vdash e \supset h$ and $\vdash e' \supset h'$;
or **b.** $\vdash e \supset \sim h$ and $\vdash e' \supset \sim h'$;
or **c.** $\vdash e \equiv e'$ and $\vdash e \,.\, h \equiv e' \,.\, h'$.

Proof. 1. Suppose that $\mathfrak{Eq}(h,e,h',e')$. Then (D1) both $\mathfrak{MC}$ and its converse hold; hence the conditions both in D81-1 and in T3 are fulfilled. According to D81-1a and b, which are the same as T3b and a, e and e' are non-L-false. Further, the conditions under (c) in D81-1 and in T3 are fulfilled. Let us denote the three items under (c) in D81-1 by 'c_1', 'c_2', and 'c_3', and those in T3 by 'c_1'', 'c_2'', and 'c_3''. Thus the following holds: (c_1 or c_2 or c_3) and (c_1' or c_2' or c_3'). This can be transformed by distribution (T21-5m(3)) as follows: (c_1 and c_1') or (c_1 and c_2') or (c_1 and c_3') or (c_2 and c_1') or (c_2 and c_2') or (c_2 and c_3') or (c_3 and c_1') or (c_3 and c_2') or (c_3 and c_3'). Now we shall examine each of these nine disjunctive components. We must show for each of them either that one of the three conditions in our theorem follows from it, or that the component cannot hold under the assumption here made. (c_1 and c_1') is the condition (a) in this theorem. (c_1 and c_2') says that $\vdash e \supset h \,.\, \sim h$ (T21-5m(8)); hence e would be L-false, which is impossible on our assumption. (c_1 and c_3') says that $\vdash e \supset h$ and $\vdash e \,.\, h \supset e' \,.\, h'$ and $\vdash e' \supset h' \vee e$; from this it follows that $\vdash e' \supset h' \vee (e \,.\, h)$ (T21-5i(1)), hence $\vdash e' \supset h' \vee h'$, hence $\vdash e' \supset h'$, hence (a). (c_2 and c_1') says that $\vdash e' \supset \sim h' \,.\, h'$; thus e' would be L-false, which is not possible. (c_2 and c_2') is (b) in this theorem. (c_2 and c_3') says that (1) $\vdash e' \supset \sim h'$ and (2) $\vdash e \,.\, h \supset e' \,.\, h'$ and a third item; it follows from (1) that $\vdash \sim(e' \,.\, h')$ (T21-5f(3)); from this and (2) that $\vdash \sim(e \,.\, h)$ (T21-4h), hence $\vdash e \supset \sim h$; thus (b) in this theorem follows. (c_3 and c_1') says that $\vdash e' \,.\, h' \supset e \,.\, h$ and $\vdash e \supset h \vee e'$ and $\vdash e' \supset h'$; hence it follows that $\vdash e \supset h \vee (e' \,.\, h')$ (T21-5i(1)); hence $\vdash e \supset h \vee h$, hence $\vdash e \supset h$; thus (a) follows. (c_3 and c_2') says that $\vdash e' \,.\, h' \supset e \,.\, h$ and $\vdash e \supset h \vee e'$ and $\vdash e \supset \sim h$; hence $\vdash e' \,.\, h' \supset \sim h \,.\, h$, hence $e' \,.\, h'$ is L-false, hence $\vdash e' \supset \sim h'$; thus (b) follows. Finally, (c_3 and c_3') says that (1) $\vdash e' \,.\, h' \supset e \,.\, h$, (2) $\vdash e \supset h \vee e'$, (3) $\vdash e \,.\, h \supset e' \,.\, h'$, and (4) $\vdash e' \supset h' \vee e$; from (2) it follows that $\vdash e \supset (e \,.\, h) \vee e'$, hence with (3) $\vdash e \supset e' \vee e'$, hence $\vdash e \supset e'$; and analogously from (4) and (1) that $\vdash e' \supset e$; therefore $\vdash e \equiv e'$; from this and (3) and (1), (c) in this theorem follows. 2. The converse says that, if the conditions stated in the theorem are fulfilled, $\mathfrak{Eq}$ holds, that is, that the conditions in both D81-1 and T3 are fulfilled. The conditions D81-1a and b and T3a and b, namely that e and e' are non-L-false, are stated explicitly in the present theorem. Thus it remains to be shown that the conditions under (c) in D81-1 and T3 are fulfilled. They may be abbreviated as above. If (a) in this theorem holds, then c_1 and c_1' hold, hence D81-1c and T3c hold. If (b) here holds, then c_2 and c_2' hold, hence again D81-1c and T3c hold. If (c) in this theorem holds, then c_3 and c_3' hold, thus again D81-1c and T3c hold.

+T82-5. $\mathfrak{Gr}(h,e,h',e')$ if and only if the following four conditions are simultaneously fulfilled:

a. Not $\vdash e \supset \sim h$. (Hence e is not L-false.)

b. Not $\vdash e' \supset h'$. (Hence e' is not L-false.)

c. Either (c_1) $\vdash e \supset h$,
or (c_2) $\vdash e' \supset \sim h'$,
or (c_3) $\vdash e' \,.\, h' \supset e \,.\, h$ and $\vdash e \supset h \vee e'$.

d. Either (d_1) not $\vdash e \,.\, h \supset e' \,.\, h'$,
or (d_2) not $\vdash e' \supset h' \vee e$.

Proof. 1. Suppose that $\mathfrak{Gr}(h,e,h',e')$. Then (D2) $\mathfrak{MC}$ holds but not the converse of $\mathfrak{MC}$. Therefore the conditions of D81-1 are fulfilled but not those of T3. We have to show that the above conditions (a) to (d) are fulfilled. a. $\vdash e \supset \sim h$ cannot hold because otherwise it would follow with D81-1c, that $\vdash e \supset \sim h \,.\, h$; hence e would be L-false, contrary to D81-1a. b. Analogously, $\vdash e' \supset h'$ cannot hold because of D81-1c_2 and D81-1b. c. From D81-1c. d. Suppose that (d) did not hold. Then its negation would hold, which is the same as T3c_3; hence T3c would hold. From (a) and (b), which we have just derived, it follows that e and e' are not L-false; hence T3a and b hold. Thus the conditions of T3 would be fulfilled, contrary to our assumption. Therefore (d) must hold. 2. Suppose that the four conditions (a) to (d) are fulfilled. We have to show that $\mathfrak{MC}$ holds but not its converse, in other words, that all conditions of D81-1 are fulfilled but not all conditions of T3. D81-1a and b follow from (a) and (b) here. D81-1c is the same as (c) here. Now we shall show that T3c is not fulfilled. This means that the three conditions (c_1), (c_2), and (c_3) in T3 are all violated. For (c_1), this follows from (b) here; for (c_2), from (a) here; for (c_3), from (d) here.

Examples for T5. 𝔊r holds in the three examples given at the end of § 81. There we have seen that D81-1c_3 is fulfilled, and this is the same as T5c_3 here. We can further easily see that T5a, b, and d_1 are fulfilled in these examples. In the first example, $\vdash e \supset e'$, but not $\vdash e \,.\, h \supset h'$. In the second example, $\vdash h \supset h'$, but not $\vdash e \,.\, h \supset e'$. In the third example, neither $\vdash e \,.\, h \supset e'$ nor $\vdash e \,.\, h \supset h'$. Thus d_1 is always fulfilled.

T82-6. The pairs *h,e* and *h′,e′* are *comparable* if and only if *e* and *e′* are not-L-false and, in addition, at least one of the following six conditions is fulfilled:

Either **a.** $\vdash e \supset h$;
or **b.** $\vdash e' \supset \sim h'$;
or **c.** $\vdash e' \,.\, h' \supset e \,.\, h$ and $\vdash e \supset h \vee e'$;
or **d.** $\vdash e' \supset h'$;
or **e.** $\vdash e \supset \sim h$;
or **f.** $\vdash e \,.\, h \supset e' \,.\, h'$ and $\vdash e' \supset h' \vee e$.

(From D3, D81-1, T3.)

+**T82-7.** The pairs *h,e* and *h′,e′* are *incomparable* if either *e* is L-false or *e′* is L-false or the following six conditions are fulfilled simultaneously:

a. Not $\vdash e \supset h$.
b. Not $\vdash e' \supset \sim h'$.
c. Either not $\vdash e' \,.\, h' \supset e \,.\, h$, or not $\vdash e \supset h \vee e'$.
d. Not $\vdash e' \supset h'$.
e. Not $\vdash e \supset \sim h$.
f. Either not $\vdash e \,.\, h \supset e' \,.\, h'$, or not $\vdash e' \supset h' \vee e$.

(From T6.)

§ 83. Further Theorems on Comparative Concepts

A. Some further theorems are given concerning the concepts 𝔐𝔆, 𝔈q, 𝔊r, and comparability, defined in the two preceding sections. *B.* It is shown that all axioms of B. O. Koopman's axiom system for "intuitive probability" are here provable as theorems on 𝔐𝔆.

A. *Theorems*

This section contains some further theorems concerning 𝔐𝔆 and the three other comparative concepts introduced in the preceding section. Most of these theorems, like those in the preceding section, connect these concepts with L-concepts; thus they build a bridge between comparative inductive logic and deductive logic. Other theorems attribute to the comparative concepts (as relations between pairs of sentences) relational characteristics like reflexivity or transitivity. All theorems of this section hold for any finite or infinite system 𝔏.

T83-1. Let $\vdash e \supset e'$. $\mathfrak{MC}(h,e,h',e')$ if and only if e is non-L-false and either $\vdash e \supset h$ or $\vdash e' \,.\, h' \supset e \,.\, h$.

Proof. From D81-1. Of the conditions in this definition, only (a), (c_1), and the first part of (c_3) are here stated explicitly. (b) and the second part of (c_3) are here omitted (T21-5p(2)) because they follow from the assumption that $\vdash e \supset e'$ and (a). (c_2) is omitted (T21-5p(1)) because the stated first part of (c_3) follows from it (T21-5g(1)).

The following theorem states the invariance of $\mathfrak{MC}$ with respect to replacements of arguments by any L-equivalent ones. The same holds obviously for $\mathfrak{Eq}$ and $\mathfrak{Gr}$ since they are defined in terms of $\mathfrak{MC}$ (D82-1 and 2).

T83-2. Let h_1 be L-equivalent to h_2, likewise e_1 to e_2, h'_1 to h'_2, and e'_1 to e'_2. Then $\mathfrak{MC}(h_1,e_1,h'_1,e'_1)$ if and only if $\mathfrak{MC}(h_2,e_2,h'_2,e'_2)$. (From D81-1.)

T83-3. Let h be L-equivalent to h', and likewise e to e', and e be non-L-false.

a. $\mathfrak{MC}(h,e,h',e')$. (From D81-1, since (c_3) is fulfilled.)

b. $\mathfrak{Eq}(h,e,h',e')$. (From (a).)

The following theorem says that $\mathfrak{MC}$ and $\mathfrak{Eq}$ are reflexive relations (between pairs of sentences).

T83-4. Let e be non-L-false, and h be any sentence.

a. $\mathfrak{MC}(h,e,h,e)$. (From T3.)

b. $\mathfrak{Eq}(h,e,h,e)$. (From (a).)

It seems that scientists use comparative concepts of confirmation mostly in cases of two special kinds: (1) two hypotheses are compared on the same evidence, or (2) two evidences are compared with respect to the same hypothesis. Therefore we shall now state some theorems (T6 to T13) for the case that the same evidence occurs in both pairs. Because of T2, analogous theorems hold, of course, when different but L-equivalent evidences e and e' occur. Later theorems will deal with the case that the same hypothesis occurs in both pairs.

+T83-6. $\mathfrak{MC}(h,e,h',e)$ if and only if the following two conditions are fulfilled.

a. e is not L-false.

b. $\vdash e \,.\, h' \supset h$.

Proof. 1. Suppose that $\mathfrak{MC}(h,e,h',e)$. Then (a) follows from D81-1a, and (b) from D81-1c_3. 2. Let (a) and (b) be fulfilled. We have to show that the conditions in D81-1 are fulfilled with 'e' for 'e''. D81-1a and b correspond to (a) here. (b) here yields $\vdash e \,.\, h' \supset e \,.\, h$; further $\vdash e \supset h \lor e$ (T21-4a); thus D81-1c_3 follows, hence D81-1c.

The following theorem T7 is analogous to T6 but deals with the converse of $\mathfrak{MC}$. It is merely a lemma for subsequent theorems.

T83-7. Lemma. $\mathfrak{MC}(h',e,h,e)$ if and only if the following two conditions are fulfilled.

a. e is not L-false.

b. $\vdash e \,.\, h \supset h'$.

(From T6.)

The following is a corollary to T6.

T83-8. Let e be non-L-false, h and i arbitrary.

a. $\mathfrak{MC}(h,e,h \,.\, i,e)$.

b. $\mathfrak{MC}(h \vee i,e,h,e)$.

(From T6.)

(a) says that if we join a conjunctive component to a given hypothesis, then the confirmation is at most as high as before. (b) says that if we join a disjunctive component to a hypothesis, the confirmation is at least as high as before.

+T83-9. $\mathfrak{Eq}(h,e,h',e)$ if and only if the following three conditions are fulfilled.

a. e is not L-false.

b. $\vdash e \,.\, h' \supset h$.

c. $\vdash e \,.\, h \supset h'$. ((b) and (c) may be combined as follows: $\vdash e \supset (h \equiv h')$).

(From T6, T7.)

The following is a corollary to T9.

T83-10. If e is non-L-false and $\vdash e \,.\, h \supset i$, then $\mathfrak{Eq}(h \,.\, i,e,h,e)$. (From T9.)

+T83-11 $\mathfrak{Gr}(h,e,h',e)$ if and only if the following two conditions are fulfilled.

a. $\vdash e \,.\, h' \supset h$.

b. Not $\vdash e \,.\, h \supset h'$. (Hence $e \,.\, h$ and e are not L-false.) (From T6, T7.)

Example (previously mentioned in § 81). e is 'P_1a'; h is '$P_2a \vee P_3a$'; h' is 'P_2a'. According to T8b, $\mathfrak{MC}(h,e,h',e)$. According to T11, $\mathfrak{Gr}(h,e,h',e)$.

T83-12. The pairs h,e and h',e are comparable if and only if the following two conditions are fulfilled.

a. e is not L-false.

b. Either $\vdash e \,.\, h' \supset h$ or $\vdash e \,.\, h \supset h'$.

(From T6, T7.)

T83-13. The pairs h,e and h',e are incomparable if and only if either e is L-false or the following two conditions are fulfilled simultaneously:

a. Not $\vdash e \,.\, h' \supset h$.

b. Not $\vdash e \,.\, h \supset h'$.

(From T12.)

T12 and T13 say in effect that on the basis of a given (non-L-false) evidence, two hypotheses can be compared only if one of them follows from the other together with the evidence. This seems quite plausible; because otherwise the ranges of $e \,.\, h$ and of $e \,.\, h'$ have nonoverlapping parts, and therefore we can, by the choice of suitable measure functions, give at will a greater measure either to the one or to the other.

The following theorems T15 to T18 deal with the case that the same hypothesis occurs in both pairs. Analogous theorems hold, of course, when different but L-equivalent hypotheses h and h' occur.

+**T83-15.** $\mathfrak{MC}(h,e,h,e')$ if and only if e and e' are non-L-false and, in addition, at least one of the following three conditions is fulfilled:

Either **a.** $\vdash e \supset h$;

or **b.** $\vdash e' \supset \sim h$;

or **c.** $\vdash e' \,.\, h \supset e$ and $\vdash e \supset h \vee e'$.

(From D81-1.)

The condition (c) says the following about the three sentences h, e', and $\sim e$: both their disjunction and the disjunction of their negations are L-true; in other words, it is logically necessary that at least one of the three sentences is true and at least one is false.

We found earlier (T7) that, on the basis of the same evidence, a stronger hypothesis is confirmed at most as much as a weaker one, e.g., $h \,.\, i$ in comparison to h (T8a) or h in comparison to $h \vee i$ (T8b). There are no simple analogues for the comparison of two evidences with respect to the same hypothesis. $e \,.\, i$ may give either more or less support to h than e, depending on whether the additional evidence i is positively or negatively relevant to h.

T83-16. $\mathfrak{Eq}(h,e,h,e')$ if and only if e and e' are non-L-false and, in addition, at least one of the following three conditions is fulfilled:

Either **a.** $\vdash e \supset h$ and $\vdash e' \supset h$;

or **b.** $\vdash e \supset \sim h$ and $\vdash e' \supset \sim h$;

or **c.** $\vdash e \equiv e'$.

(From T82-4.)

T83-17. $\mathfrak{Gr}(h,e,h,e')$ if and only if the following four conditions are fulfilled simultaneously.

a. Not $\vdash e \supset \sim h$. (Hence e is not L-false.)
b. Not $\vdash e' \supset h$. (Hence e' is not L-false.)
c. Either (c_1) $\vdash e \supset h$,
or (c_2) $\vdash e' \supset \sim h$,
or (c_3) $\vdash e' . h \supset e$ and $\vdash e \supset h \vee e'$.
d. Either (d_1) not $\vdash e . h \supset e'$,
or (d_2) not $\vdash e' \supset h \vee e$.
(From T82-5.)

(The condition (c_3) here is the same as T15c; see the remark made there.)

As an *example* for T17, see the second of the three examples given at the end of § 81.

T83-18. The pairs h,e and h,e' are comparable if and only if e and e' are non-L-false and, in addition, at least one of the following six conditions is fulfilled:
Either **a.** $\vdash e \supset h$;
or **b.** $\vdash e' \supset \sim h$;
or **c.** $\vdash e' . h \supset e$ and $\vdash e \supset h \vee e'$;
or **d.** $\vdash e' \supset h$;
or **e.** $\vdash e \supset \sim h$;
or **f.** $\vdash e . h \supset e'$ and $\vdash e' \supset h \vee e$.
(From T82-6.)

The customary concepts of the logic of relations usually applied to dyadic relations (see D25-2) may be applied to our present comparative concepts if we regard the latter as dyadic relations between pairs of sentences, as earlier explained. In this sense, $\mathfrak{MC}$ is *reflexive* (T4a) and *transitive* (T22). This seems plausible since $\mathfrak{MC}$ is analogous to the relation $\geqq$.

T83-22. If $\mathfrak{MC}(h,e,h',e')$ and $\mathfrak{MC}(h',e',h'',e'')$, then $\mathfrak{MC}(h,e,h'',e'')$.

Proof. This theorem can easily be proved by two applications of T81-1a and one of T81-1b, referring to $\mathfrak{c}$-functions. However, we shall give here a proof which is based directly on D81-1 and does not involve any quantitative concept but stays within the boundaries of comparative inductive logic. Let the two conditions be fulfilled; we call them (1) and (2). Then e and e'' are not L-false (D81-1a and b). We have moreover to prove that the condition D81-1c is fulfilled for the assertion, that is, that either (c_1) $\vdash e \supset h$, or (c_2) $\vdash e'' \supset \sim h''$, or ($c_3$) $\vdash e'' . h'' \supset e . h$ and $\vdash e \supset h \vee e''$. Suppose that ($c_1$) and ($c_2$) are not fulfilled; we have to show that then (c_3) is fulfilled. It follows from condition (1), according to D81-1c, that either (1A) $\vdash e \supset h$ or (1B) $\vdash e' \supset \sim h'$ or (1C) both ($1C_1$) $\vdash e' . h' \supset e . h$ and ($1C_2$) $\vdash e \supset h \vee e'$. Likewise, it follows from (2) that either (2A) $\vdash e' \supset h'$ or (2B) $\vdash e'' \supset \sim h''$ or (2C) both ($2C_1$) $\vdash e'' . h'' \supset e' . h'$ and ($2C_2$) $\vdash e' \supset h' \vee e''$. (1A) is the same as ($c_1$) and hence is not fulfilled, according to our assumption; likewise (2B) since it is the same as (c_2). Therefore the following holds: (1′) either (1B) or (1C); and (2′) either (2A) or (2C); hence also (3′) either (2A) or ($2C_1$). Now it can be shown that (1B) is not fulfilled. For if it were, it would hold, according to (3′), either together with (2A) or together with ($2C_1$). However, in the first case, e' would be L-false, which it is not. And in the second case, $\vdash \sim(e' \,.\, h')$ (T21-5f(3)), hence with ($2C_1$) $\vdash \sim(e'' \,.\, h'')$ (T21-5h(1)), hence $\vdash e'' \supset \sim h''$, which is not the case since, according to our assumption, (c_2) is not fulfilled. Thus from (1′) we obtain (1C), i.e., both ($1C_1$) and ($1C_2$). It can further be shown that (2A) is not fulfilled. For, from this together with ($1C_1$) it would follow that $\vdash e' \supset h$ (T21-5i(1)), and hence with ($1C_2$) $\vdash e \supset h$, which is not the case since (c_1) is not fulfilled. Thus from (2′) we obtain (2C), i.e., both ($2C_1$) and ($2C_2$). Hence our result is: ($1C_1$) and ($1C_2$) and ($2C_1$) and ($2C_2$). It follows from ($2C_1$) and ($1C_1$) that $\vdash e'' \,.\, h'' \supset e \,.\, h$; this is the first part of the condition (c_3) mentioned above. From ($1C_1$) it follows that $\vdash h' \,.\, e' \supset h$; from ($2C_2$) that $\vdash e' \supset (h' \,.\, e') \vee e''$. From these two results we see that $\vdash e' \supset h \vee e''$. From this and ($1C_2$) we find that $\vdash e \supset h \vee (h \vee e'')$, hence $\vdash e \supset h \vee e''$. This is the second part of (c_3). Thus it has been proved that (c_3) is fulfilled.

𝔈q, again with respect to pairs of sentences as members, is *reflexive* (T4b), *symmetrical* (T23), and *transitive* (T24). Thus it has the structural properties of an equality relation. This seems plausible since 𝔈q corresponds in a certain sense to equality of confirmation, as we have seen earlier (T82-1a).

T83-23. If 𝔈q(h,e,h',e'), then 𝔈q(h',e',h,e). (From D82-1.)

T83-24. If 𝔈q(h,e,h',e') and 𝔈q(h',e',h'',e''), then 𝔈q(h,e,h'',e''). (From D82-1, T22.)

The relation 𝔊r is *asymmetrical* (T26), *irreflexive* (T27), and *transitive* (T29). This is plausible since 𝔊r is in a certain sense analogous to the relation >.

T83-26. If 𝔊r(h,e,h',e'), then not 𝔊r(h',e',h,e). (From D82-2.)

T83-27. Not 𝔊r(h,e,h,e). (From T26.)

T83-28.

a. If 𝔊r(h,e,h',e') and 𝔐𝔈(h',e',h'',e''), then 𝔊r(h,e,h'',e'').

b. If 𝔐𝔈(h,e,h',e') and 𝔊r(h',e',h'',e''), then 𝔊r(h,e,h'',e'').

(From D82-2, T22.)

T83-29. If 𝔊r(h,e,h',e') and 𝔊r(h',e',h'',e''), then 𝔊r(h,e,h'',e''). (From D82-2, T28a.)

B. *Koopman's Axiom System*

B. O. Koopman [Axioms] has constructed an axiom system with one primitive concept, which is explained as follows: "*a* on the presumption that *h* is true is equally or less probable than *b* on the presumption that *k* is true". This relation is obviously the converse of that which we have taken as explicandum (see (1) in § 80) and for which we have proposed the concept $\mathfrak{MC}$ as an explicatum. Therefore it is interesting to examine whether the converse of $\mathfrak{MC}$ fulfils Koopman's axioms. The following theorems together with two earlier ones show that this is indeed the case. Koopman's axiom V, if reformulated by taking instead of his primitive relation the converse of $\mathfrak{MC}$, is our subsequent theorem T31; likewise, his axiom I is T32; axiom R is T4a; T is T22; A is T33; C_1 is T34; C_2 is T35; D is T36; P is T37b; axiom S is a special case of T38c for special arguments *h* and *e*.

T83-31. Let *e* and *e'* be non-L-false. Then for any *h'* $\mathfrak{MC}(e,e,h',e')$. (From D81-1a, b, c_1.)

T83-32. If $\mathfrak{MC}(h,e,e',e')$, then $\vdash e \supset h$.

Proof. Let the condition be fulfilled. Then (D81-1) either (c_1) $\vdash e \supset h$, or (c_2) $\vdash e' \supset \sim e'$, or ($c_3$): (1) $\vdash e' \supset e \cdot h$ and (2) $\vdash e \supset h \vee e'$. ($c_1$) is the assertion. ($c_2$) is impossible because e' would be L-false, in contradiction to D81-1b. In the case (c_3), $\vdash e' \supset h$ (1) and hence $\vdash e' \equiv e' \cdot h$ (T20-2l); therefore $\vdash e \supset h \vee (e' \cdot h)$ (2); hence $\vdash e \supset h$ (T21-5p(1)).

T83-33. If $\mathfrak{MC}(h,e,h',e')$, then $\mathfrak{MC}(\sim h',e',\sim h,e)$.

Proof. Let the condition be fulfilled. Then (D81-1c) either (c_1) $\vdash e \supset h$, or (c_2) $\vdash e' \supset \sim h'$, or ($c_3$): (1) $\vdash e' \cdot h' \supset e \cdot h$ (2) $\vdash e \supset h \vee e'$. In the case ($c_1$) the assertion holds (D81-1c_2); likewise in the case (c_2) (D81-1c_1). In the case (c_3), the following assertions (3), (4), (5), and (6) hold. (3) $\vdash e \cdot \sim h \supset e'$ (from (2), T21-5h(7)). From (1): $\vdash e \cdot h' \supset h$; hence (4) $\vdash e \cdot \sim h \supset \sim h'$ (T21-5h(6)). From (3) and (4): (5) $\vdash e \cdot \sim h \supset e' \cdot \sim h'$ (T21-5m(8)). From (1): $\vdash e' \cdot h' \supset e$, hence (6) $\vdash e' \supset \sim h' \vee e$ (T21-5h(8)). Therefore the assertion holds (from (5), (6), D81-1c_3).

T83-34. Let $e \cdot h \cdot j$ and $e' \cdot h' \cdot j'$ be non-L-false. If (1) $\mathfrak{MC}(h,e,h',e')$ and (2) $\mathfrak{MC}(j,e \cdot h,j',e' \cdot h')$, then $\mathfrak{MC}(h \cdot j,e,h' \cdot j',e')$.

Proof. Let the conditions be fulfilled. Condition (1) says (D81-1c) that either (1a) $\vdash e \supset h$, or (1b) $\vdash e' \supset \sim h'$, or (1c) both (1$c_1$) $\vdash e' \cdot h' \supset e \cdot h$ and (1c_2) $\vdash e \supset h \vee e'$. Condition (2) says that either (2a) $\vdash e \cdot h \supset j$, or (2b) $\vdash e' \cdot h' \supset \sim j'$, or (2c) both (2$c_1$) $\vdash e' \cdot h' \cdot j' \supset e \cdot h \cdot j$ and (2c_2) $\vdash e \cdot h \supset j \vee (e' \cdot h')$. (1b) is impossible because $e' \cdot h'$ would be L-false, and hence $e' \cdot h' \cdot j'$ too; similarly, (2b) is impossible. Thus there remain four combinations of a case (1) with a case (2). The assertion says that either (A1) $\vdash e \supset h \cdot j$, or (A2) $\vdash e' \supset \sim(h' \cdot j')$ (which is impossible), or (A3) both (A3a) $\vdash e' \cdot h' \cdot j' \supset e \cdot h \cdot j$ and (A3b) $\vdash e \supset (h \cdot j) \vee e'$. We have to show that in each of the four cases either (A1) or (A3) holds. I: From (1a) and (2a), (A1) follows. II: (1a) and (2c). (2c_1) is (A3a). (A3b) follows from (2c_2) and (1a). III: (1c) and (2a). (A3a) follows from (1c_1) and (2a). (A3b) follows from (1c_2) and (2a). IV: (1c) and (2c). (2c_1) is (A3a). (A3b) follows from (1c_2) and (2c_2). Thus the assertion is proved.

T83-35. Let $e \cdot h \cdot j$ and $e' \cdot h' \cdot j'$ be non-L-false. If (1) $\mathfrak{MC}(j, e \cdot h, h', e')$ and (2) $\mathfrak{MC}(h, e, j', e' \cdot h')$, then $\mathfrak{MC}(h \cdot j, e, h' \cdot j', e')$.

Proof, similar to the preceding theorem. (1) says that either (1a) $\vdash e \cdot h \supset j$, or (1b) $\vdash e' \supset \sim h'$, or (1c) both ($1c_1$) $\vdash e' \cdot h' \supset e \cdot h \cdot j$ and ($1c_2$) $\vdash e \cdot h \supset j \vee e'$. (2) says that either (2a) $\vdash e \supset h$, or (2b) $\vdash e' \cdot h' \supset \sim j'$, or (2c) both ($2c_1$) $\vdash e' \cdot h' \cdot j' \supset e \cdot h$ and ($2c_2$) $\vdash e \supset h \vee (e' \cdot h')$. (1b) and (2b) are impossible. Thus four combinations remain. The assertion is the same as in T34; see there for (A1), etc. I: From (1a) and (2a), (A1) follows. II: (1a) and (2a). Here (A3a) follows from ($2c_1$) and (1a); (A3b) follows from ($2c_2$) and (1a). III: (1c) and (2a). Here (A3a) follows from ($1c_1$); (A3b) follows from (2a) and ($1c_2$). IV: (1c) and (2c). Here (A3a) follows from ($1c_1$); (A3b) follows from ($2c_2$) and ($1c_2$).

T83-36. Let $e \cdot h \cdot j$ and $e' \cdot h' \cdot j'$ be non-L-false, and let $\mathfrak{MC}(h \cdot j, e, h' \cdot j', e')$. Consider the following two pairs of sentences:

(i) h', e'; $j', e' \cdot h'$;
(ii) h, e; $j, e \cdot h$.

If $\mathfrak{MC}$ holds between either pair in (i) and either pair in (ii), then $\mathfrak{MC}$ holds likewise between the remaining pair in (ii) and the remaining pair in (i).

Proof. This theorem is a combination of four statements. We shall give the proof for one; the proofs for the three others are similar. The one statement is this: 'If (2) $\mathfrak{MC}(h', e', h, e)$, then (A) $\mathfrak{MC}(j, e \cdot h, j', e' \cdot h')$'. Let (1) be the $\mathfrak{MC}$-condition mentioned in the first sentence of the theorem; it says that either (1a) $\vdash e \supset h \cdot j$, or (1b) $\vdash e' \supset \sim(h' \cdot j')$, or (1c) both ($1c_1$) $\vdash e' \cdot h' \cdot j' \supset e \cdot h \cdot j$ and ($1c_2$) $\vdash e \supset (h \cdot j) \vee e'$. (2) says that either (2a) $\vdash e' \supset h'$, or (2b) $\vdash e \supset \sim h$, or (2c) both ($2c_1$) $\vdash e \cdot h \supset e' \cdot h'$ and ($2c_2$) $\vdash e' \supset h' \vee e$. (1b) and (2b) are impossible. The assertion (A) says that either (A1) $\vdash e \cdot h \supset j$, or (A2) $\vdash e' \cdot h' \supset \sim j'$ (which is impossible), or (A3) both (A3a) $\vdash e' \cdot h' \cdot j' \supset e \cdot h \cdot j$ and (A3b) $\vdash e \cdot h \supset j \vee (e' \cdot h')$. I: From (1a), (A1) follows. II: (1c) and (2a). (A3a) is the same as ($1c_1$); (A3b) follows from ($1c_2$) and (2a); hence (A3) follows. III: (1c) and (2c). (A3a) is ($1c_1$); (A3b) follows from ($2c_1$).

T83-37. Let $\mathfrak{MC}(h, e, h', e' \cdot i)$.

a. If $\mathfrak{MC}(h, e, h', e' \cdot j)$, then $\mathfrak{MC}(h, e, h', e' \cdot (i \vee j))$.

Proof. Let the initial assumption be (1), the condition in (a) be (2), and the assertion in (a) be (A). (1) says that either (1a) $\vdash e \supset h$, or (1b) $\vdash e' \cdot i \supset \sim h'$, or (1c) both ($1c_1$) $\vdash e' \cdot h' \cdot i \supset e \cdot h$ and ($1c_2$) $\vdash e \supset h \vee (e' \cdot i)$. (2) says that either (2a) $\vdash e \supset h$, or (2b) $\vdash e' \cdot j \supset \sim h'$, or (2c) both ($2c_1$) $\vdash e' \cdot h' \cdot j \supset e \cdot h$ and ($2c_2$) $\vdash e \supset h \vee (e' \cdot j)$. (A) says that (A1) $\vdash e \supset h$, or (A2) $\vdash e' \cdot (i \vee j) \supset \sim h'$, or (A3) both (A3a) $\vdash e' \cdot h' \cdot (i \vee j) \supset e \cdot h$ and (A3b) $\vdash e \supset h \vee (e' \cdot (i \vee j))$. (A2) says that both (A2a) $\vdash e' \cdot i \supset \sim h'$ and (A2b) $\vdash e' \cdot j \supset \sim h'$ (T21-5n(3)). (A3a) says that both ($A3a_1$) $\vdash e' \cdot h' \cdot i \supset e \cdot h$ and ($A3a_2$) $\vdash e' \cdot h' \cdot j \supset e \cdot h$ (T21-5n(3)). (1a), (2a), and (A1) are the same. Thus four cases remain. I: (1b) and (2b). They are the same as (A2a) and (A2b) respectively; hence (A2) follows. II: (1b) and (2c). ($A3a_1$) follows from (1b). ($A3a_2$) is ($2c_1$). (A3b) follows from ($2c_2$). Hence (A3) follows. III: (1c) and (2b). ($A3a_1$) is ($1c_1$). ($A3a_2$) follows from (2b). (A3b) follows from ($1c_2$). Hence (A3) follows. IV: (1c) and (2c). ($A3a_1$) is ($1c_1$). ($A3a_2$) is ($2c_1$). (A3b) follows from ($1c_2$). Hence (A3) follows.

b. If $\mathfrak{MC}(h,e,h',e' \,.\, \sim i)$, then $\mathfrak{MC}(h,e,h',e')$.
(From (a), with '$\sim i$' for 'j'.)

T83-38. Let $j_1, \ldots, j_n$ ($n \geqq 2$) fulfil the following conditions. (1) These sentences are L-exclusive in pairs. (2) j, that is, $j_1 \vee \ldots \vee j_n$, is non-L-false (hence $j_1, \ldots, j_n$ are non-L-false). (3) For every p from 1 to $n-1$, $\mathfrak{MC}(j_{p+1},j,j_p,j)$. Then the following holds.

a. For every p from 1 to $n-1$, $\vdash j_p \supset j_n$.

Proof. For every p, the following holds. $\vdash j \,.\, j_p \supset j_{p+1}$ (from (3), T83-6b). $j \,.\, j_p$ is L-equivalent to $(j_1 \vee \ldots \vee j_n) \,.\, j_p$, hence to $(j_1 \,.\, j_p) \vee \ldots \vee (j_n \,.\, j_p)$, hence to $j_p \,.\, j_p$, because all other conjunctions in this disjunction are L-false (from (1), T21-5r(2)); hence to j_p. Therefore $\vdash j_p \supset j_{p+1}$. Hence the assertion (with T20-2b, by mathematical induction).

b. $\vdash j \supset j_n$.

Proof. For every p from 1 to n, $\vdash j_p \supset j_n$ (from (a) and $\vdash j_n \supset j_n$). Therefore $\vdash j_1 \vee \ldots \vee j_n \supset j_n$ (T21-5n(4)); this is the assertion.

c. For any h and non-L-false e, $\mathfrak{MC}(j_n,j,h,e)$. (From (b), D81-1c_1.)

Since Koopman's axioms hold in the present system of comparative confirmation, the theorems which he derives from the axioms hold likewise. However, with respect to the nature and function of the theory, there are some differences between the conception presented here and that of Koopman. He believes that the theory can only supply conditional statements concerning the comparative concept of confirmation; direct comparative statements of the form 'h is confirmed by e at least as strongly as h' by e'' are not supplied by his theory. Statements of this kind cannot, in his opinion, be obtained with the help of any general principle, be it a principle of probability, of logic, or of experimental science; they can be obtained only by intuition. The results of this special kind of intuition seem to be regarded as not subject to rational examination (except for questions of consistency) and therefore not capable of rational reconstruction. This view is similar to, and probably influenced by, Keynes's conception of probability as undefinable and based on intuition. In contrast to Koopman's view, I am convinced that it is possible to give a rational reconstruction or explication for the comparative concept of confirmation, and I believe, moreover, that it is possible to define an explicatum without using any other terms than those of deductive logic, hence, of semantics. The concept $\mathfrak{MC}$ is here proposed merely as a tentative explicatum. If it is found not to be quite adequate, it will be replaced by a more adequate explicatum. But I fail to see at present any reasons for the view that it should be impossible in principle to construct an adequate explicatum.

§ 84. Maximum and Minimum Confirmation

Two more concepts are introduced into comparative inductive logic, expressing maximum and minimum confirmation, respectively. '$\mathfrak{Max}(h,e)$' is the comparative analogue to the quantitative statement '$\mathfrak{c}(h,e) = 1$' (for all c-functions); '$\mathfrak{Min}(h,e)$' is the analogue to '$\mathfrak{c}(h,e) = 0$'. The definitions of these two concepts (D1, D2) do not, however, refer to c-functions but only to L-concepts.

We shall here introduce two more concepts into comparative inductive logic. They are L-semantical concepts like $\mathfrak{MC}$ and the other concepts earlier defined; in distinction to those concepts, they are relations between two sentences, not four. They are intended to express maximum and minimum confirmation, respectively, of a hypothesis *h* on an evidence *e*. More exactly speaking, their connection with the quantitative c-concepts is intended to be as follows. We shall say that *h* has the maximum confirmation on evidence *e*, in symbols of the metalanguage: '$\mathfrak{Max}(h,e)$', if and only if, for *every* regular c, $\mathfrak{c}(h,e)$ has the maximum value, that is, 1. Analogously, we shall say that *h* has the minimum confirmation on evidence *e*, in symbols '$\mathfrak{Min}(h,e)$', if and only if, for *every* regular c, $\mathfrak{c}(h,e)$ has the minimum value, that is, 0. The reference to *all* regular c-functions here is analogous to that in the requirements R80-1 and 2 for $\mathfrak{MC}$. Here, as there, these conditions referring to quantitative concepts are merely meant as requirements of adequacy but are not taken as definitions. The definitions will here again be purely comparative; it will then be shown later that these comparative concepts fulfil the quantitative requirements just stated (T4).

In terms of $\mathfrak{MC}$, the two new concepts are intended to fulfil the following requirements, which obviously correspond to the quantitative requirements stated above. $\mathfrak{Max}(h,e)$ is to hold if and only if the pair of sentences *h*,*e* bears the relation $\mathfrak{MC}$ to every pair *h'*,*e'* (where *e'* is not L-false). Analogously, $\mathfrak{Min}(h,e)$ is to hold if and only if every pair *h'*,*e'* (where *e'* is not L-false) bears the relation $\mathfrak{MC}$ to *h*,*e*. Since these conditions are in purely comparative terms, we could take them as comparative definitions for '$\mathfrak{Max}$' and '$\mathfrak{Min}$'. Instead, we shall define these two predicates, as we did with '$\mathfrak{MC}$', directly on the basis of the old L-concepts (D1, D2); these definitions hold for both finite and infinite systems $\mathfrak{L}$. It will then be shown that the two concepts thus defined fulfil the requirements just stated in terms of $\mathfrak{MC}$ (T2, T3).

+D84-1. $\mathfrak{Max}(h,e)$ (with respect to a system $\mathfrak{L}$) $=_{Df}$ the following two conditions are fulfilled (in $\mathfrak{L}$):

a. *e* is not L-false.

b. $\vdash e \supset h$.

+D84-2. $\mathfrak{Min}(h,e)$ (with respect to a system $\mathfrak{L}$) $=_{\text{Df}}$ the following two conditions are fulfilled (in $\mathfrak{L}$):

a. e is not L-false.

b. $\vdash e \supset \sim h$.

The following theorems T1 to T3 hold for any finite or infinite system $\mathfrak{L}$.

T84-1. Lemma.

a. $\mathfrak{Max}(h,e)$ does not hold if and only if either e is L-false or not $\vdash e \supset h$. (From D1.)

b. $\mathfrak{Min}(h,e)$ does not hold if and only if either e is L-false or not $\vdash e \supset \sim h$. (From D2.)

c. Neither $\mathfrak{Max}(h,e)$ nor $\mathfrak{Min}(h,e)$ if and only if either e is L-false, or neither $\vdash e \supset h$ nor $\vdash e \supset \sim h$. (From (a), (b).)

+T84-2. $\mathfrak{Max}(h,e)$ if and only if, for all sentences h' and e' (in the system $\mathfrak{L}$ in question), where e' is not L-false, $\mathfrak{MC}(h,e,h',e')$.

Proof. 1. Suppose that $\mathfrak{Max}(h,e)$ and that e' is not L-false. Then $\mathfrak{MC}(h,e,h',e')$ (D1, D81-1c_1.) 2. Suppose that $\mathfrak{MC}(h,e,h',e')$ for every h' and e', where e' is not L-false. Then e is not L-false (D81-1a). Now we take for both e' and h' the tautological sentence 't'. Then in D81-1 (c_2) is impossible; hence either (c_1) or (c_3) holds. The first part of (c_3) says that $\vdash t \supset e \,.\, h$, hence $\vdash h$, hence $\vdash e \supset h$. This is likewise stated by (c_1); therefore it must hold. Hence $\mathfrak{Max}(h,e)$ (D1).

+T84-3. $\mathfrak{Min}(h',e')$ if and only if, for all sentences h and e (in $\mathfrak{L}$), where e is not L-false, $\mathfrak{MC}(h,e,h',e')$.

Proof. Suppose that $\mathfrak{Min}(h',e')$ and that e is not L-false. Then $\mathfrak{MC}(h,e,h',e')$ (D2, D81-1c_2). 2. Suppose that $\mathfrak{MC}(h,e,h',e')$ for every h and e, where e is not L-false. Then e' is not L-false (D81-1b). Now we take for 'h' '$\sim t$', and for 'e' 't'. Then in D81-1 (c_1) is impossible; hence either (c_2) or (c_3) holds. From the first part of (c_3) it follows that $\vdash e' \,.\, h' \supset \sim t$, hence $\vdash e' \supset \sim h'$. This is likewise stated by (c_2); therefore it must hold. Hence $\mathfrak{Min}(h',e')$ (D2).

The following theorems T4a and b state the connections between the two new concepts and the $\mathfrak{c}$-functions. They show that the new concepts fulfil the quantitative requirements laid down earlier.

+T84-4. Let h and e be any sentences in a finite system $\mathfrak{L}_N$ or nongeneral sentences in $\mathfrak{L}_\infty$.

a. $\mathfrak{Max}(h,e)$ if and only if, for every regular $\mathfrak{c}$, $\mathfrak{c}(h,e) = 1$. (From D1, T59-1b; T59-5b.)

b. $\mathfrak{Min}(h,e)$ if and only if, for every regular $\mathfrak{c}$, $\mathfrak{c}(h,e) = 0$. (From D2, T59-1e; T59-5c.)

Both (a) and (b) hold likewise with 'for some' instead of 'for every'.

§ 85. Correspondence between Comparative and Quantitative Theorems

Further theorems concerning the comparative concepts are stated. Some theorems in this and earlier sections of this chapter correspond to certain theorems on regular c-functions in the sense that 𝔐ℭ, 𝔊𝔯, and 𝔈𝔮 correspond to the relations ≧, >, and =, respectively, between c-values, and 𝔐𝔞𝔵 and 𝔐𝔦𝔫 correspond to the c-values 1 and 0, respectively.

Some further purely comparative theorems will here be stated. They involve the comparative concepts (𝔐ℭ, 𝔈𝔮, 𝔊𝔯, comparability, 𝔐𝔞𝔵, 𝔐𝔦𝔫) but no c-functions or other quantitative concepts. These theorems hold for any finite or infinite system 𝔏.

The theorems on regular c-functions which have been stated in chapter v are of two different kinds. For some of them it is essential that the c-functions are quantitative, that is to say, that they have numerical values. This holds for all those theorems which refer to an arithmetical function (sum, difference, product, quotient, and the like) of values of c-functions (e.g., T59-1k, l, m, n, p, T59-2a, b, g, k, T59-3a, T60-1, T60-2, T60-3, T60-5, T60-6, T61-1b, c, d, T61-3a, b, c, d, T61-5a, b, T61-6a, b, f, T61-7). However, there are other theorems which treat of c-functions in a comparative way, so to speak. They say, for instance, that a certain c-value is equal to another or that it is greater than another. To this kind belong also those theorems which ascribe the c-value 1 (because this is the same as saying that the c-value in question is higher than or equal to every c-value) or the c-value 0. To some of these quantitative theorems with a merely comparative content we find corresponding theorems here in comparative inductive logic. It seems plausible that to the relations ≧, >, and = between c-values, the comparative relations 𝔐ℭ, 𝔊𝔯, and 𝔈𝔮, respectively, correspond; to a statement ascribing the c-value 1 or 0, there is here a corresponding statement attributing the relation 𝔐𝔞𝔵 or 𝔐𝔦𝔫, respectively. The following are examples of this correspondence between some theorems of § 59 and certain items (theorems or definitions) of the present chapter (earlier sections or this section): as a comparative analogue to the quantitative T59-1b and 5b we find here D84-1; to T59-1c —T85-2a; to T59-1e and 5c—D84-2; to T59-1f—T85-2b; to T59-1h and i —T83-3b; to T59-2d—T83-6; to T59-2e—T83-8a; to T59-2f—T83-8b; to T59-2h—T83-10; to T59-2j—T83-9. The analogues of theorems in § 61 (confirmation of a hypothesis by a predictable observation) are especially interesting; they will occur in this section, the correspondence being indicated by remarks in square brackets.

It is to be noted that this correspondence between some quantitative and comparative theorems is not always a simple translation. Often a comparative theorem is weaker than the quantitative theorem to which it corresponds. Consider, for instance, a quantitative theorem of the form:

(1) 'For every regular $\mathfrak{c}$, if $\mathfrak{c}(\mathfrak{P}_1) \geqq \mathfrak{c}(\mathfrak{P}_2)$, then $\mathfrak{c}(\mathfrak{P}_3) \geqq \mathfrak{c}(\mathfrak{P}_4)$',

where $\mathfrak{P}_1$, $\mathfrak{P}_2$, $\mathfrak{P}_3$, and $\mathfrak{P}_4$ are four pairs of sentences for which certain logical relations hold. The corresponding comparative theorem will then be:

(2) 'If $\mathfrak{MC}(\mathfrak{P}_1,\mathfrak{P}_2)$, then $\mathfrak{MC}(\mathfrak{P}_3,\mathfrak{P}_4)$'.

If (2) is translated in terms of $\mathfrak{c}$-functions (according to T81-1), it says merely this:

(3) 'If, for every regular $\mathfrak{c}$, $\mathfrak{c}(\mathfrak{P}_1) \geqq \mathfrak{c}(\mathfrak{P}_2)$, then, for every regular $\mathfrak{c}$, $\mathfrak{c}(\mathfrak{P}_3) \geqq \mathfrak{c}(\mathfrak{P}_4)$.'

That this is weaker than the quantitative theorem (1) is easily seen by the following consideration. Suppose we find a certain regular $\mathfrak{c}$-function such that $\mathfrak{c}(\mathfrak{P}_1) \geqq \mathfrak{c}(\mathfrak{P}_2)$, whereas for other $\mathfrak{c}$-functions this does not hold. Then we can apply the quantitative theorem (1); it yields the result that for the given $\mathfrak{c}$, $\mathfrak{c}(\mathfrak{P}_3) \geqq \mathfrak{c}(\mathfrak{P}_4)$. On the other hand, (3) does not say anything about this case.

The correspondence described is more complicated for theorems concerning $\mathfrak{Gr}$ than for those concerning $\mathfrak{MC}$ or $\mathfrak{Eq}$. This is seen from T82-1b in comparison with T81-1 and T82-1a.

Some of our comparative theorems correspond to quantitative theorems which have already been stated in the classical theory of probability or in modern systems by other authors. Among them are the interesting theorems stated by Hosiasson as Theorems (f_1), (f_2), (f_3), and (f_4) in [Confirmation]. It is noteworthy that our corresponding comparative theorems (T85-4c, 5c, 10b, and 11d) are proved within a purely comparative theory or, in other words, simply in L-semantics, while Hosiasson's theorems are proved on the basis of her quantitative axioms.

T85-1.

a. If $\mathfrak{Max}(h,e)$ and $\mathfrak{Max}(h',e')$, then $\mathfrak{Eq}(h,e,h',e')$. (From T84-2.)

b. If $\mathfrak{Min}(h,e)$ and $\mathfrak{Min}(h',e')$, then $\mathfrak{Eq}(h,e,h',e')$. (From T84-3.)

T85-2. Let e be not L-false.

a. If h is L-true, then $\mathfrak{Max}(h,e)$. (From D84-1.) [This theorem corresponds to the quantitative theorem T59-1c in the sense explained above.]

b. If h is L-false, then $\mathfrak{Min}(h,e)$. (From D84-2.) [Corresponds to T59-1f.]

T85-3. Let $\mathfrak{MC}(h,e,h',e')$.

a. If $\mathfrak{Max}(h',e')$, then $\mathfrak{Max}(h,e)$.

Proof. The condition implies that $\vdash e' \supset h'$ (D84-1). Because $\mathfrak{MC}$ holds, according to D81-1 either (c_1) $\vdash e \supset h$; or (c_3) $\vdash e' \cdot h' \supset e \cdot h$ and $\vdash e \supset h \vee e'$, hence with the former result $\vdash e \supset h \vee (e' \cdot h')$, hence $\vdash e \supset h \vee h$, hence $\vdash e \supset h$. The case (c_2) in D81-1 is here impossible; for it would imply that $\vdash e' \supset \sim h'$, hence, since $\vdash e' \supset h'$, e' would be L-false, in contradiction to D81-1b. Thus in any case $\vdash e \supset h$. From this together with D81-1a, it follows that $\mathfrak{Max}(h,e)$.

b. If $\mathfrak{Min}(h,e)$, then $\mathfrak{Min}(h',e')$.

Proof. The condition implies that $\vdash e \supset \sim h$. Since $\mathfrak{MC}$ holds, according to D81-1 either (c_2) $\vdash e' \supset \sim h'$; or ($c_3$) $\vdash e' \cdot h' \supset e \cdot h$, hence, since $\vdash e \supset \sim h$, $\vdash e' \cdot h' \supset \sim h \cdot h$, hence $\vdash e' \supset \sim h'$. The case ($c_1$) in D81-1 is here impossible; for it would imply that $\vdash e \supset h$, hence, since $\vdash e \supset \sim h$, e would be L-false, in contradiction to D81-1a. Thus in any case $\vdash e' \supset \sim h'$. Hence, with D81-1b, $\mathfrak{Min}(h',e')$.

T85-4.

a. If $\mathfrak{Max}(h \cdot i,e)$, then $\mathfrak{Max}(h,e)$.

b. If $\mathfrak{Max}(h,e)$, then $\mathfrak{Max}(h \vee i,e)$.

c. Let $e \cdot i$ be non-L-false. If $\mathfrak{Max}(h,e)$, then $\mathfrak{Max}(h,e \cdot i)$. [Corresponds to T61-3k.]

(From D84-1.)

T85-5.

a. If $\mathfrak{Min}(h,e)$, then $\mathfrak{Min}(h \cdot i,e)$.

b. If $\mathfrak{Min}(h \vee i,e)$, then $\mathfrak{Min}(h,e)$.

c. Let $e \cdot i$ be non-L-false. If $\mathfrak{Min}(h,e)$, then $\mathfrak{Min}(h,e \cdot i)$. [Corresponds to T61-3l.]

(From D84-2.)

T85-6. Let $e \cdot i$ not be L-false. If either $\mathfrak{Max}(h,e)$ or $\mathfrak{Min}(h,e)$, then $\mathfrak{Eq}(h,e,h,e \cdot i)$. [Corresponds to T65-7 and 8.] (From T4c, T1a; T5c, T1b.)

The following theorems are chiefly of interest when applied to a situation like that described in § 61: h is a hypothesis which may be a deterministic or a statistical law; i is a sentence reporting (or predicting) an observation; e is the prior evidence, that is, the knowledge available before the observation i is made. The following assumptions will occur in the theorems:

A. $\vdash e \cdot h \supset i$; in other words, $\mathfrak{Max}(i,e \cdot h)$. In § 61, we called this the assumption of the *predictability* of the observation i.

B. $e \cdot h$ is not L-false; in other words, not $\vdash e \supset \sim h$; hence, not $\mathfrak{Min}(h,e)$.

C. $e \cdot i$ is not L-false; in other words, not $\vdash e \supset \sim i$; hence, not $\mathfrak{Min}(i,e)$. (B) and (C) serve merely to exclude trivial cases.

The following theorem exhibits a connection between these assumptions.

T85-8. Lemma. If (A) and (B) hold, then (C) holds.

Proof, indirect. Suppose that (C) does not hold. Then $\vdash e \supset \sim i$, and $\vdash e \cdot h \supset \sim i$. Hence, if (A) holds, $e \cdot h$ is L-false, in contradiction to (B).

T85-9. Let assumption (A) hold. If $\mathfrak{Min}(h,e \cdot i)$, then $\mathfrak{Min}(h,e)$.

Proof. The condition implies that (1) $e \cdot i$ is not L-false (D84-2a), hence e is not L-false; (2) $\vdash e \cdot i \supset \sim h$ (D84-2b), hence $\vdash e \cdot h \supset \sim i$, hence, because of (A), $e \cdot h$ is L-false, hence $\vdash e \supset \sim h$. Therefore, $\mathfrak{Min}(h,e)$ (D84-2).

T9 says in effect that, if the hypothesis is impossible after the predictable observation, then it was so before.

T85-10. Let the conditions (A) and (B) be fulfilled; hence (C) holds too (T8).

a. $\mathfrak{MC}(h,e \cdot i,h,e)$. (From T83-15c.) (Here (A) and (C) would suffice.) [This theorem corresponds to T61-3e.]

b. $\mathfrak{Eq}(h,e \cdot i,h,e)$ if and only if $\mathfrak{Max}(i,e)$. [Corresponds to T61-3f and g.]

Proof. 1. Suppose that $\mathfrak{Eq}(h,e \cdot i,h,e)$. Then (T83-16) either (a) $\vdash e \supset h$, hence because of (A) $\vdash e \supset i$; or (c) $\vdash e \supset e \cdot i$, hence $\vdash e \supset i$. The case (b) in T83-16 is excluded by (B). Thus in any case $\vdash e \supset i$, hence $\mathfrak{Max}(i,e)$. 2. Suppose that $\mathfrak{Max}(i,e)$. Then $\vdash e \supset i$, hence $\vdash e \equiv e \cdot i$ (T21-5i(1)), hence $\mathfrak{Eq}$ holds (T83-16c).

c. $\mathfrak{Gr}(h,e \cdot i,h,e)$ if and only if not $\mathfrak{Max}(i,e)$. [Corresponds to T61-3h.]

Proof. 1. Let the condition with $\mathfrak{Gr}$ be fulfilled. Suppose that $\mathfrak{Max}(i,e)$, hence $\vdash e \supset i$, hence $\vdash e \supset e \cdot i$. Thus in T83-17 both ($d_1$) and ($d_2$) would be violated, hence also (d), in contradiction to the assumption concerning $\mathfrak{Gr}$. Therefore the supposition made cannot hold. 2. Let $\mathfrak{Max}(i,e)$ not hold. Then not $\vdash e \supset i$, hence not $\vdash e \supset e \cdot i$. Suppose now that $\mathfrak{MC}(h,e,h,e \cdot i)$ were to hold. Then, according to T83-15, one of the following three cases would hold: either (a) $\vdash e \supset h$, hence because of (A) $\vdash e \supset i$, in contradiction to the above result; or (b) $\vdash e \cdot i \supset \sim h$, hence $\vdash e \cdot h \supset \sim i$ (T21-5h), hence because of (A) $e \cdot h$ would be L-false, in contradiction to (B); or (c) $\vdash e \supset h \vee (e \cdot i)$, hence $\vdash e \supset (e \cdot h) \vee i$, hence because of (A) $\vdash e \supset i$, in contradiction to the initial assumption. Therefore the supposition concerning $\mathfrak{MC}$ cannot hold. From this and T10a the condition with $\mathfrak{Gr}$ follows (D82-2).

T10c says in effect that the confirmation of the hypothesis is increased by the predictable observation i, in other words, i is positively relevant to h on e, if and only if i was neither entailed nor excluded by the prior evidence e.

The following theorem makes a comparison between two observations i_1 and i_2, both predictable by the hypothesis h.

T85-11. Let (A) and (B), and hence (C) too, hold for both i_1 and i_2. Let not $\mathfrak{Min}(h,e \cdot i_2)$.

a. If $\mathfrak{MC}(h,e \cdot i_1,h,e \cdot i_2)$, then $\mathfrak{MC}(i_2,e,i_1, e)$.

Proof. Let the condition be fulfilled. Then one of the three cases (a), (b), (c) in T83-15 must hold. In case (a), $\vdash e \cdot i_1 \supset h$, hence $\vdash e \cdot i_1 \supset e \cdot h$, hence, because of (A) for i_2, $\vdash e \cdot i_1 \supset i_2$. Case (b) is impossible, for here $\vdash e \cdot i_2 \supset \sim h$, hence $\vdash e \cdot h \supset \sim i_2$, hence, because of (A) for i_2, $e \cdot h$ would be L-false, in contradiction to (B). In case (c), $\vdash e \cdot i_1 \supset h \vee (e \cdot i_2)$, hence $\vdash e \cdot i_1 \supset (e \cdot h) \vee i_2$, hence, because of (A) for i_2, $\vdash e \cdot i_1 \supset i_2$. Thus the latter holds in any case. Therefore $\mathfrak{MC}(i_2,e,i_1,e)$ (T83-6).

b. The converse of (a). If $\mathfrak{MC}(i_2,e,i_1,e)$, then $\mathfrak{MC}(h,e \cdot i_1,h,e \cdot i_2)$.

Proof. Let the condition be fulfilled. Then $\vdash e \cdot i_1 \supset i_2$ (T83-6b), hence $\vdash e \cdot i_1 \supset h \vee (e \cdot i_2)$; this is the second part of T83-15c for the assertion. The first part, viz., $\vdash e \cdot i_2 \cdot h \supset e \cdot i_1$, follows from (A) for i_1. Hence (T83-15c) the assertion.

c. If $\mathfrak{Gr}(h,e \cdot i_1,h,e \cdot i_2)$, then $\mathfrak{Gr}(i_2,e,i_1,e)$. [Corresponds to T61-5c.]

Proof. The condition entails (D82-2) that $\mathfrak{MC}(h,e \cdot i_1,h,e \cdot i_2)$ and not $\mathfrak{MC}(h,e \cdot i_2,h,e \cdot i_1)$. Therefore $\mathfrak{MC}(i_2,e,i_1,e)$ (from (a)) and not $\mathfrak{MC}(i_1,e,i_2,e)$ (from (b)). Hence $\mathfrak{Gr}(i_2,e,i_1,e)$ (D82-2).

d. The converse of (c). If $\mathfrak{Gr}(i_2,e,i_1,e)$, then $\mathfrak{Gr}(h,e \cdot i_1,h,e \cdot i_2)$. (From (b) and (a).) [Corresponds to T61-5d.]

e. If $\mathfrak{Eq}(h,e \cdot i_1,h,e \cdot i_2)$, then $\mathfrak{Eq}(i_2,e,i_1,e)$. (From (a) and (b).) [Corresponds to T61-5e.]

f. The converse of (e). If $\mathfrak{Eq}(i_2,e,i_1,e)$, then $\mathfrak{Eq}(h,e \cdot i_1,h,e \cdot i_2)$. (From (b) and (a).) [Corresponds to T61-5f.]

T11c and d say in effect this. The posterior confirmation of the hypothesis h after the observation i_1 is higher than that after the observation i_2 if and only if the expectedness of i_1, that is, its confirmation on the prior evidence e, is smaller than that of i_2. In other words, the more improbable the occurrence of a predictable event, the more does its observation increase the confirmation of the hypothesis. The corresponding result concerning $\mathfrak{c}$-functions has been discussed earlier (see remark (iii) on T60-1c).

The following theorem makes a comparison between two hypotheses h_1 and h_2, by each of which the observation i is predictable.

T85-12. Let (A) and (B), and hence (C) too, hold for both h_1 and h_2.

a. If $\mathfrak{MC}(h_1,e \cdot i,h_2,e \cdot i)$, then $\mathfrak{MC}(h_1,e,h_2,e)$.

Proof. Let the condition be fulfilled. Then $e \cdot i$ is not L-false (T83-6a), hence e is not. Further (T83-6b) $\vdash e \cdot i \cdot h_2 \supset h_1$. (A) for h_2 says that $\vdash e \cdot h_2 \supset i$, hence $\vdash e \cdot h_2 \supset i \cdot e \cdot h_2$, hence with the former result $\vdash e \cdot h_2 \supset h_1$. This yields the assertion (T83-6).

b. The converse of (a). If $\mathfrak{MC}(h_1,e,h_2,e)$, then $\mathfrak{MC}(h_1,e \cdot i,h_2,e \cdot i)$.

Proof. The condition implies (T83-6b) that $\vdash e \cdot h_2 \supset h_1$, hence $\vdash e \cdot i \cdot h_2 \supset h_1$. Thus T83-6b for the assertion is fulfilled; likewise T83-6a because of (C).

c. If $\mathfrak{Gr}(h_1,e \cdot i,h_2,e \cdot i)$, then $\mathfrak{Gr}(h_1,e,h_2,e)$. (From (a) and (b); the proof is analogous to that of T11c.)

d. The converse of (c). If $\mathfrak{Gr}(h_1,e,h_2,e)$, then $\mathfrak{Gr}(h_1,e \cdot i,h_2,e \cdot i)$. (From (b) and (a).) [(c) and (d) correspond to T61-6c.]

e. If $\mathfrak{Eq}(h_1,e \cdot i,h_2,e \cdot i)$, then $\mathfrak{Eq}(h_1,e,h_2,e)$. (From (a) and (b).) [Corresponds to T61-6d.]

f. The converse of (e). If $\mathfrak{Eq}(h_1,e,h_2,e)$, then $\mathfrak{Eq}(h_1,e \cdot i,h_2,e \cdot i)$. (From (b) and (a).) [Corresponds to T61-6e.]

T12f and e say in effect this. If the two hypotheses have equal prior confirmation (i.e., on evidence e alone), then they have also equal posterior confirmation (i.e., on evidence $e \cdot i$), and vice versa. T12d and c say this. If the prior confirmation of one hypothesis is higher than that of the other hypothesis, then its posterior confirmation is likewise higher than that of the other, and vice versa. The corresponding results for c-functions have been discussed earlier (in § 61).

This concludes our outline of a system of comparative inductive logic. The system deals with comparative concepts of confirmation, $\mathfrak{MC}$ and other concepts. These concepts are purely comparative, nonquantitative, in the sense that they do not presuppose any confirmation concepts with numerical values (c-functions). Instead, they are defined on the basis of the simple L-concepts (L-implication, etc.). Since the latter concepts constitute the basis of deductive logic, comparative inductive logic may be regarded as a simple extension of deductive logic. Comparative inductive relations between sentences are not identical with the ordinary deductive relations between them (e.g., L-implication), but they are uniquely determined by the latter. This may be illustrated by the following simple example. A hypothesis h is more strongly confirmed (in the comparative sense, as expressed by '$\mathfrak{Gr}$') than h' by the evidence e if and only if the following deductive relations hold: $e \cdot h'$ L-implies h, and $e \cdot h$ does not L-imply h' (T83-11).

The present outline may suffice to show in general what kinds of results are obtainable on a purely comparative basis. We shall not pursue this course further, because we believe in the possibility of a quantitative inductive logic. For those, however, who regard a quantitative inductive logic either as entirely impossible or, like Kries and Keynes, as possible only within certain very narrow limits, the construction of a more comprehensive comparative system on the basis here supplied or a similar one might be an important task.

§ 86. The Concept of Confirming Evidence

Of the three semantical concepts of confirmation (§ 8), we have so far discussed the quantitative (degree of confirmation $\mathfrak{c}$) and the comparative ($\mathfrak{MC}$). In the last three sections of this chapter we shall discuss the problem of explicating the *classificatory concept* of confirmation: 'i is *confirming evidence* for the hypothesis h on the basis of e', in symbols: '$\mathfrak{C}(h,i,e)$'. This means in terms of $\mathfrak{c}$ that the $\mathfrak{c}$ of h is increased by adding the new evidence i to the prior evidence e; in other words, i is positively relevant to h on e (§ 65). We define a relation $\mathfrak{C}'$ (8); the essential condition for $\mathfrak{C}'(h,i,e)$ is that either $\vdash e \cdot h \supset i$ or $\vdash e \cdot i \supset h$. It is found that $\mathfrak{C}'$ holds if and only if the condition in terms of $\mathfrak{c}$ mentioned above is fulfilled for every regular $\mathfrak{c}$ (11). However, it is found that $\mathfrak{C}'$ is too narrow as an explicatum. A definition for a relation $\mathfrak{C}^*$ is indicated (5) such that the above condition is fulfilled for our $\mathfrak{c}$-function $\mathfrak{c}^*$ to be introduced later; this is a definition in quantitative terms. We leave the question open whether an adequate explicatum can be found that is defined in nonquantitative terms (like $\mathfrak{C}'$ and $\mathfrak{MC}$).

We have earlier (§ 8) distinguished three semantical concepts of confirmation: (i) the classificatory concept of confirmation, the concept of confirming evidence, (ii) the comparative concept ('more or equally confirmed'), and (iii) the quantitative concept, the concept of degree of confirmation. The first of these three concepts is the simplest; the second is more complicated but also more efficient; the third is still more efficient, provided an adequate explicatum of this kind can be found. Our discussions do not take up the problems of these three concepts in the order just mentioned, which is the order of increasing complexity, but rather in the opposite order. We have first dealt with the regular $\mathfrak{c}$-functions (in the two preceding chapters); they—or rather, some of them—come into consideration as explicata for the quantitative concept of confirmation. Only afterward, in the preceding sections of this chapter, did we study the problem of the comparative concept and propose the relation $\mathfrak{MC}$ as an explicatum for it. The discussion of this problem was postponed for the following reason. Although the definition itself of the concept $\mathfrak{MC}$ is in purely comparative, nonquantitative terms, that is, it does not refer to the $\mathfrak{c}$-functions, nevertheless the conditions of adequacy for the comparative concept do refer to the $\mathfrak{c}$-functions. Therefore it seemed advisable, from the heuristic point of view, to take up the study of the problem of the comparative concept only after a theory of the regular $\mathfrak{c}$-functions had been constructed. For the same reason the discussion of the simplest concept, the classificatory concept, was postponed.

We distinguish two forms of the classificatory concept of confirming evidence. The general form is relative to some evidence *e*. '*i* confirms *h* on the basis of *e*' is understood in the following sense: *i* is an additional item of evidence which, if added to the prior evidence *e*, contributes positively to the confirmation of the hypothesis *h*. In particular, the concept is applicable to the following situation: *e* represents the prior evidence (in the sense of § 60, that is, the evidence available before the results *i* are found); *i* describes new observational results, for instance, results of experiments made in order to test the hypothesis *h*. We shall use the symbol '$\mathfrak{C}$' for any explicatum of this classificatory concept that might be considered. Thus an explicatum of the above statement will be symbolized by '$\mathfrak{C}(h,i,e)$' ('*h is confirmed by i on the basis e*'). The second form of the concept means simply that *i* is confirming evidence for *h* so to speak absolutely; that is, without reference to any prior factual evidence *e*. More exactly speaking, it refers to that special case of the first concept, where no prior factual evidence is available, in other words, where *e* is the tautology '*t*'. We might say in this case that *i* is *initially* (or a priori) *confirming evidence* for *h*. For an explicatum of this second concept we shall use the symbol '$\mathfrak{C}_0$', in analogy to '$\mathfrak{c}_0$' (D57-1), which likewise refers to the evidence '*t*'. Thus, if a function $\mathfrak{C}$ is given, we define:

(1) $$\mathfrak{C}_0(h,i) =_{\mathrm{Df}} \mathfrak{C}(h,i,t) \, .$$

('$\mathfrak{C}$' and '$\mathfrak{C}_0$' are not symbols of the object-languages $\mathfrak{L}$, but predicates in the metalanguage like '$\mathfrak{MC}$', '$\mathfrak{Gr}$', etc.)

We began the study of the problem of an explication for the comparative concept by investigating the relation which must hold between any adequate explicatum $\mathfrak{MC}$ and the regular $\mathfrak{c}$-functions (§ 80). We shall now do the same for the classificatory concept. Suppose we had a regular $\mathfrak{c}$-function $\mathfrak{c}$ which we regarded as an adequate explicatum of the quantitative concept. How could we express with its help the classificatory concept of confirming evidence? This concept means that the degree of confirmation of *h* is increased by the addition of *i* to *e*; hence it is expressible in terms of $\mathfrak{c}$ as follows:

(2) $$\mathfrak{c}(h,e \,.\, i) > \mathfrak{c}(h,e) \, .$$

(This condition implies that *e* and *e* . *i* are non-L-false, because otherwise $\mathfrak{c}$ would not have values for the sentences in question.) Therefore we shall say that a triadic relation R among sentences, considered as an explicatum for the classificatory concept, is *in accord with* a given c-function $\mathfrak{c}$ under the following condition:

(3) R is *in accord with* $\mathfrak{c} =_{\mathrm{Df}}$ for any sentences h, i, and e, if $R(h,i,e)$, then

$$\mathfrak{c}(h,e \,.\, i) > \mathfrak{c}(h,e) \,,$$

in other words (D65-1a), i is *positively relevant* to h on e with respect to $\mathfrak{c}$.

For $\mathfrak{C}_0$, 't' takes the place of e. Thus here the condition (2) is replaced by:

(4) $$\mathfrak{c}(h,i) > \mathfrak{c}(h,t) \,,$$

in other words (D65-2a), i is initially positive to h.

We shall later introduce a particular c-function $\mathfrak{c}^*$ as our explicatum for the quantitative concept (§ 110A). On the basis of this function we might then introduce a concept of confirming evidence $\mathfrak{C}^*$ and a concept of initially confirming evidence $\mathfrak{C}_0^*$ by explicit definitions in terms of $\mathfrak{c}^*$ as follows:

(5) $$\mathfrak{C}^*(h,i,e) =_{\mathrm{Df}} \mathfrak{c}^*(h,e \,.\, i) > \mathfrak{c}^*(h,e) \,;$$

(6) $$\mathfrak{C}_0^*(h,i) =_{\mathrm{Df}} \mathfrak{c}^*(h,i) > \mathfrak{c}^*(h,t) \,.$$

An analogous procedure is possible on the basis of any other function $\mathfrak{c}$ chosen as explicatum. However, definitions of this kind would not yield purely classificatory concepts but only classificatory concepts quantitatively defined. The concepts $\mathfrak{C}^*$ and $\mathfrak{C}_0^*$ may be useful; they represent indeed positive relevance and initial positive relevance, respectively, with respect to $\mathfrak{c}^*$. If, however, we are looking for purely classificatory concepts, then these definitions do not supply a solution.

A purely classificatory concept $\mathfrak{C}$ would be a concept adequate as an explicatum for the classificatory explicandum and defined without the use of any quantitative concepts like c-functions; it might instead be defined, like $\mathfrak{MC}$ (D81-1), in terms of L-concepts. We shall not give a solution of this problem but only indicate, in these last three sections of this chapter, some considerations relevant for the problem and discuss a few concepts which might be considered as explicata.

Instead of basing the classificatory concept $\mathfrak{C}$ on one particular c-function, one might think of requiring that it be in accord with *all* regular c-functions. If, moreover, $\mathfrak{C}$ is required to be the most comprehensive relation fulfilling the first requirement, then the following would be a necessary and sufficient condition for $\mathfrak{C}$:

(7) for every regular $\mathfrak{c}$, $\mathfrak{c}(h,e \,.\, i) > \mathfrak{c}(h,e)$.

This procedure would be analogous to the earlier one concerning $\mathfrak{MC}$. There we laid down a necessary and sufficient condition referring to all c-functions (§ 80, (4)). Then we defined the relation $\mathfrak{MC}$ in terms of L-concepts (D81-1) and showed that it fulfilled the requirement (for $\mathfrak{L}_N$, T81-1). We can now proceed here similarly. We shall define the relation $\mathfrak{C}'$ in terms of L-concepts, hence in a nonquantitative way; then we shall show that it satisfies the quantitative requirement stated above. The concept $\mathfrak{C}'$ is here merely offered for discussion but not proposed as an explicatum. We shall later indicate some reasons which make its adequacy appear doubtful. The definition of $\mathfrak{C}'$ is as follows:

(8) $\mathfrak{C}'(h,i,e) =_{\mathrm{Df}}$ the following three conditions are fulfilled :
  a. $e \cdot i \cdot h$ is not L-false;
  b. $e \cdot \sim i \cdot \sim h$ is not L-false;
  c. Either $\vdash e \cdot h \supset i$ or $\vdash e \cdot i \supset h$ or both.

We shall now develop several sufficient and necessary conditions for $\mathfrak{C}'$. This will lead to the result that $\mathfrak{C}'$ satisfies the quantitative requirement. We restrict this consideration to finite systems; all the results hold likewise for nongeneral sentences in the infinite system (compare T81-1 and 2).

For sentences in a finite system, $\mathfrak{C}'$ can be expressed in terms of relevance concepts as follows.

(9) For any triple of sentences h,i,e in $\mathfrak{L}_N$, $\mathfrak{C}'(h,i,e)$ if and only if i is either extremely positive to h on e (D74-1a) with respect to every regular c-function or completely positive to h on e (D75-1a) with respect to every regular c-function.

Proof. 1. Suppose that $\mathfrak{C}'(h,i,e)$. Then k_2 and k_3 are L-false but k_1 and k_4 are not (from (8); for k_1, etc., and $\mathfrak{m}_1$, etc., see the explanations preceding T65-1). Therefore, for every regular $\mathfrak{m}$, $\mathfrak{m}_2$ and $\mathfrak{m}_3$ are 0 but $\mathfrak{m}_1$ and $\mathfrak{m}_4$ are not. Therefore, i is either extremely positive (T74-1c) with respect to every $\mathfrak{c}$ (T74-7a) or completely positive (T75-1c) with respect to every $\mathfrak{c}$ (T75-7a). 2. Let i be extremely positive to h on e. Then $\mathfrak{m}_1$ and $\mathfrak{m}_4$ are > 0 (T74-1c), hence k_1 and k_4 are not L-false; and $\vdash e \cdot i \supset h$ (T74-1d). Hence $\mathfrak{C}'(h,i,e)$. 3. Let i be completely positive to h on e. Then k_1 and k_4 are not L-false (T75-1c); and $\vdash e \cdot h \supset i$ (T75-1d). Hence $\mathfrak{C}'(h,i,e)$.

(10) For any triple of sentences h,i,e in $\mathfrak{L}_N$, $\mathfrak{C}'(h,i,e)$ if and only if i is positive to h on e with respect to every regular c-function. (From (9), T76-4a.)

(11) For any triple of sentences h,i,e in $\mathfrak{L}_N$, $\mathfrak{C}'(h,i,e)$ if and only if, for every regular c-function $\mathfrak{c}$, $\mathfrak{c}(h,e \cdot i) > \mathfrak{c}(h,e)$. (From (10), D65-1a.)

(11) says that the condition (7) is sufficient and necessary for $\mathfrak{C}'$. Thus $\mathfrak{C}'$, as defined by (8), satisfies our quantitative requirement: $\mathfrak{C}'$ is in accord with *every* regular c-function and it is the most comprehensive relation fulfilling this condition. [We see from (11) that the sentence '$\mathfrak{C}'(h,i,e)$' means something similar to '$\mathfrak{Gr}(h,e \cdot i,h,e)$'. However, there is the follow-

ing difference. $\mathfrak{Gr}(h,e\,.\,i,h,e)$ if and only if '$\geqq$' holds between $\mathfrak{c}(h,e\,.\,i)$ and $\mathfrak{c}(h,e)$ for every $\mathfrak{c}$ and '$>$' holds for *at least one* $\mathfrak{c}$ (T82-1b). On the other hand, $\mathfrak{C}'(h,i,e)$ if and only if '$>$' (and hence '$\geqq$') holds for *every* $\mathfrak{c}$. Therefore, if $\mathfrak{C}'(h,i,e)$, then $\mathfrak{Gr}(h,e\,.\,i,h,e)$; but the converse does not always hold.]

Now we have to study the question of adequacy. Suppose that a relation R among sentences is considered as a possible explicatum for the concept of confirming evidence as explicandum. Since the explicandum is vague, there will be no general agreement for all cases whether it holds or not; but there are certain cases for which there is practical agreement that the explicandum holds, other cases for which there is practical agreement that it does not hold, while in still other cases there is no agreement. Now we might say that R is *clearly too wide* if we find cases in which R holds but the explicandum clearly (i.e., with practically general agreement) does not hold. And we might say that R is *clearly too narrow* if we find cases in which R does not hold but the explicandum clearly holds. It is possible that R is clearly too wide in one direction and clearly too narrow in another.

Let us examine the question whether $\mathfrak{C}'$ may be regarded as an adequate explicatum for the classificatory concept of confirmation. $\mathfrak{C}'$ is certainly not too wide. Whenever $\mathfrak{C}'(h,i,e)$ holds, everybody will agree that i is confirming evidence for h on e because, no matter which particular $\mathfrak{c}$-function he has chosen, he will find that the $\mathfrak{c}$ of h is increased by the addition of i to e; this is seen from (11). The question remains whether $\mathfrak{C}'$ is not too narrow. The definition of $\mathfrak{C}'$ requires that either $\vdash e\,.\,i \supset h$ or $\vdash e\,.\,h \supset i$. In the first case h follows from e together with i; this means that, after the additional observation i, the hypothesis h is certain. In the second case, i follows from e together with h; i is a predictable observation in our earlier sense (§ 61). These two cases together are far from covering all instances in which the explicandum clearly holds, that is to say, all those instances in which, according to customary inductive thinking, i would be regarded as confirming evidence for h with respect to e. This is shown by the following examples. Thus $\mathfrak{C}'$ is *clearly too narrow.*

Counterexamples to $\mathfrak{C}'$.

1. Let h be a simple *law* of conditional form (§ 38), say '$(x)(Mx \supset M'x)$' ('all swans are white') for a finite domain of individuals ($N > 1$). Let e be the tautology 't'. Let i be '$Mb\,.\,M'b$' ('b is a swan and b is white'). i would generally be regarded as a confirming instance for h even without any prior evidence. However, neither $\vdash h \supset i$ nor $\vdash i \supset h$; hence $\mathfrak{C}'$ does not hold.

2. Let 'P' be a primitive predicate. Let e be '$Pa_1\,.\,\sim Pa_2$'. Let i be '$Pa_3\,.\,Pa_4\,.\,\ldots\,.\,Pa_{12}$', a conjunction of ten full sentences of 'P'. Let h be the

singular prediction 'Pa_{13}'. According to customary inductive thinking, h is regarded as more probable after the observations reported in i than before; in other words, i is regarded as confirming evidence for h on e. However, neither $\vdash e \cdot h \supset i$ nor $\vdash e \cdot i \supset h$; hence $\mathfrak{C}'$ does not hold.

The definition of $\mathfrak{C}'$ is constructed in such a way that $\mathfrak{C}'$ satisfies the requirement that it be in accord with *all* regular c-functions. We have found that $\mathfrak{C}'$ is too narrow. The reason is that the requirement mentioned is too strong. The definition can be made wider and thereby more adequate if we require only that $\mathfrak{C}$ be in accord with *some* regular c-functions. It is not difficult to find more restricted classes of c-functions for which it seems still plausible that they contain all adequate quantitative explicata for probability$_1$. We might, for instance, take the class of all those c-functions which fulfil the condition of symmetry which will be discussed in the next chapter (D91-1); we might also add further conditions which seem plausible (for instance, symmetry with respect to basic matrices (§ 28), and other conditions to be discussed in later chapters). However, if we choose any such class of c-functions and then require that $\mathfrak{C}$ be the most comprehensive relation which is in accord with just these c-functions, then it appears rather doubtful whether it is possible to construct a definition for this $\mathfrak{C}$ of not too complicated structure in terms of L-concepts, like the definitions of $\mathfrak{MC}$ and $\mathfrak{C}'$.

Incidentally, it would be of interest to investigate the possibility of applying the method just outlined also to the problem of explicating the *comparative* concept; that is to say, the possibility of an explicatum which is wider than $\mathfrak{MC}$ because based on a narrower class of c-functions. However, in this case likewise it seems doubtful whether a simple definition in L-terms can be found.

We shall not try here to find an adequate explicatum defined in nonquantitative terms for the classificatory concept either by the method just indicated or by any other method. For our system of inductive logic the theory of confirming evidence is represented first by the general theory of relevance for regular c-functions as developed in the preceding chapter, and second by the theory of $\mathfrak{C}^*$ or, in other words, of positive relevance with respect to c* to be developed later. It is true that these theories are quantitative, but from our point of view this fact is not necessarily a disadvantage. The task of finding an adequate explicatum for the classificatory concept of confirmation defined in purely classificatory, that is, nonquantitative terms is certainly an interesting problem; but it is chiefly of importance for those who do not believe that an adequate explicatum for the quantitative concept of confirmation can be found.

§ 87. Hempel's Analysis of the Concept of Confirming Evidence

Some interesting investigations by Hempel concerning the concept of confirming evidence are here discussed. Hempel shows correctly that two widespread conceptions are too narrow: Nicod's criterion (the law 'all swans are white' is confirmed by observations of white swans and only by these) and the prediction-criterion (a hypothesis is confirmed by given evidence if and only if one part of this evidence can be deduced from the other part with the help of the hypothesis). Hempel lays down some general conditions which, in his view, a concept must fulfil in order to be an adequate explicatum of the concept of confirming evidence. It is shown that some of these conditions are not valid, that is to say, no adequate explicatum can fulfil them.

In this and the next sections we shall discuss investigations made by Carl G. Hempel concerning confirmation in general and especially the classificatory concept. The following discussion is chiefly based on an article of his published in two parts in *Mind* 1945 ([Studies]; references in the following are to this article); some of his technical results had been published previously ([Syntactical], 1943). The first-mentioned article gives a clear and illuminating exposition of the whole problem situation concerning confirmation and the distinction between the classificatory, the comparative, and the quantitative concepts of confirmation. A number of points in this problem complex are here clarified for the first time. For instance, Hempel's distinction between the pragmatical concept of the confirmation of a hypothesis by an observer and the logical (semantical) concept of the confirmation of a hypothesis on the basis of an evidence sentence is important; likewise his distinction of the three phases in the procedure of testing a given hypothesis (*op. cit.*, p. 114): making observations, confronting the hypothesis with the observation report, accepting or rejecting the hypothesis. These distinctions are valuable tools for clarifying the situation for many discussions and controversies at the present time concerning confirmation, the foundations of empiricism, verifiability, and related problems.

The main part of Hempel's article concerns the problem of an explication for the classificatory concept of confirmation. We shall now discuss his views in detail. His explicandum is as follows: a sentence (or a class of sentences, or perhaps an individual) represents confirming (corroborating, favorable) evidence or constitutes a confirming instance for a given hypothesis. In his general discussion and in the examples, no reference is made to any *prior* evidence. Thus Hempel's explicandum corresponds to our dyadic relation $\mathfrak{C}_0(h,i)$ ('h is confirmed by i') rather than to the triadic relation $\mathfrak{C}(h,i,e)$ ('h is confirmed by i on the basis of the prior evidence e'). Therefore we shall in the following compare the explicata discussed by Hempel with $\mathfrak{C}_0$.

Hempel starts with a critical discussion of an explicatum which seems widely accepted (*op. cit.*, pp. 9 ff.); he quotes the following passages by Jean *Nicod* as a clear formulation for it: "Consider the formula or the law: *A entails B*. How can a particular proposition, or more briefly, a fact, affect its probability? If this fact consists of the presence of *B* in a case of *A*, it is favourable to the law '*A entails B*'; on the contrary, if it consists of the absence of *B* in a case of *A*, it is unfavourable to this law. It is conceivable that we have here the only two direct modes in which a fact can influence the probability of a law. . . . Thus, the entire influence of particular truths or facts on the probability of universal propositions or laws would operate by means of these two elementary relations which we shall call *confirmation* and *invalidation*" ([Induction], p. 219). Hempel refers here also to R. M. Eaton's discussion on "Confirmation and Infirmation" ([Logic], chap. iii), which is based on Nicod's conception. Thus, according to Nicod's criterion, the fact that the individual b is both M and M', or the sentence '$Mb \,.\, M'b$' describing this fact, is confirming evidence for the law '$(x)(Mx \supset M'x)$'. Hempel discusses this criterion in detail, and I agree entirely with his views. As he points out, the criterion is applicable only to a quite special, though important, form of hypothesis. But even if restricted to this form, the criterion does not constitute a necessary condition; in other words, it is clearly too narrow (in the sense of § 86). Hempel shows that it is not in accord with the Equivalence Condition for Hypotheses (see below, H8.22). For instance, '$Mb \,.\, M'b$' is confirming evidence, according to Nicod's criterion, for the law stated above, but not for the L-equivalent law '$(x)(\sim M'x \supset \sim Mx)$'. This is an instance of what Hempel calls the *paradox of confirmation*. He discusses this paradox in detail and reveals its main sources (*op. cit.*, pp. 13–21). [We have briefly indicated this paradox earlier (§ 46) and we shall discuss it later (in Vol. II) in connection with the universal inductive inference; we shall try to throw some light on the problem from the point of view of our inductive logic; our results will essentially be in agreement with Hempel's views.] Nicod's criterion may be taken as a sufficient condition for the concept of confirming evidence if it is restricted to laws of the form mentioned with only *one* variable. That in the case of laws with several variables it is not even sufficient is shown by Hempel with the help of the following counterexample (*op. cit.*, p. 13 n.), which is interesting and quite surprising. Let the hypothesis be the law '$(x)(y)[\sim(Rxy \,.\, Ryx) \supset (Rxy \,.\, \sim Ryx)]$'. [Incidentally, by an unfortunate misprint in the footnote mentioned, the second conjunctive component in the antecedent was omitted.] Now the fact described by '$Rab \,.\, \sim Rba$' fulfils both the antecedent and the consequent in the law; hence this fact should be taken as a confirming case according to Nicod's criterion. However, since the law stated is L-equivalent to '$(x)(y)Rxy$', the fact mentioned is actually disconfirming.

Hempel proposes (p. 22) to take the concept of confirming evidence not, like Nicod, as a relation between an object or fact and a sentence, but as a semantical relation—or, alternatively, a syntactical (i.e., purely formal) relation—between two sentences, as we do with $\mathfrak{C}_0$ (and $\mathfrak{c}$). A language system L is presupposed. The primitive predicates in L designate directly observable properties or relations. An observation sentence is a basic sentence (atomic sentence or negation, D16-6b) in L. An observation report in the narrower sense is a class or conjunction of a finite number of observation sentences (*op. cit.*, p. 23); an observation report in the wider sense is any nongeneral sentence. We shall henceforth use the term in the wider sense. [Hempel uses the wider sense in the more technical paper [Syntactical], p. 126. In the text of [Studies] he uses the narrower sense, but he mentions the wider sense in footnotes (pp. 108, 111) and declares that the narrower sense was used in the text only for greater convenience of exposition and that all results, definitions, and theorems remain applicable if the wider sense is adopted. Thus our use of the wider sense is justified; it will facilitate the construction of some examples.] Hempel admits also contradictory sentences as observation reports (p. 103, footnote 1); however, we shall exclude them, in accord with our general requirement that the evidence referred to by any confirmation concept be non-L-false. (This requirement was later accepted by Hempel [Degree], p. 102; our exclusion here will not affect the results of the subsequent discussion of Hempel's views.) Hempel restricts the evidence e referred to by the concept of confirmation to observation reports, but the hypothesis h may be any sentence of the language L. The structure of L is similar to that of our systems $\mathfrak{L}$ except that L does not contain a sign of identity.

Hempel makes (*op. cit.*, pp. 97 ff.) a critical examination of another explicatum of the concept of confirming evidence, which is often used at least implicitly and which at first glance appears as quite plausible. This explicatum, which Hempel calls the *prediction-criterion* of confirmation, is based on the consideration that it is customary to regard a hypothesis as confirmed if a prediction made with its help is borne out by the facts. This consideration suggests the following definition: An observation report $\mathfrak{K}_i$ confirms the hypothesis $h =_{Df}$ $\mathfrak{K}_i$ can be divided into two mutually exclusive subclasses $\mathfrak{K}_{i1}$ and $\mathfrak{K}_{i2}$ such that $\mathfrak{K}_{i2}$ is not empty, and every sentence of $\mathfrak{K}_{i2}$ can be logically deduced from (i.e., is L-implied by) $\mathfrak{K}_{i1}$ together with h but not from $\mathfrak{K}_{i1}$ alone. Hempel shows that this concept is indeed a sufficient condition for the explicatum sought, but not a necessary condition; in other words, it is not too wide, but it is clearly too narrow. The chief reason is the obvious fact that most scientific hypotheses do not simply express a conditional connection between observable properties but have a more general and often more complex form. This is illustrated by the simple example of the sentence '$(x)[(y)R_1xy \supset (\exists z)R_2xz]$' in an infinite universe, where R_1 and R_2 are observable relations. If we take any instance of this universal sentence, say with '*b*' for '*x*', then we see that the antecedent (i.e., '$(y)R_1by$') is not L-implied by any finite class of observation sentences, and that the consequent (i.e., '$(\exists z)R_2bz$') does not L-imply any observation sentence. This shows that it is "a considerable over-simplification to say that scientific hypotheses and theories enable us to derive predictions of future experiences from descriptions of past ones" (p. 100). The logical connection which a scientific hypothesis establishes between observation reports is in general not merely of a deductive kind; it is rather a combination of deductive and nondeductive steps. The latter are inductive in one wide sense of this word; Hempel calls them 'quasi-inductive'.

After these discussions of Nicod's criterion and the prediction-criterion resulting in the rejection of both explicata as too narrow, Hempel proceeds to the positive part of his discussion. He states a number of general conditions for the adequacy of any explicatum for the concept of confirming evidence (pp. 102 ff.); we shall discuss them in the present section. Then he defines his own explicatum and shows that it fulfils the conditions of adequacy; this will be discussed in the next section. Hempel's *conditions of adequacy* are as follows ('H' is here attached to his numbers); the evidence *e* is always an observation report as explained earlier, while the hypothesis *h* may be any sentence of the language *L*.

(H8.1) *Entailment Condition:* If *h* is entailed by *e* (i.e., $\vdash e \supset h$), then *e* confirms *h*.

(H8.2) *Consequence Condition:* If *e* confirms every sentence of the class $\mathfrak{K}_i$ and *h* is a consequence of (i.e., L-implied by) $\mathfrak{K}_i$, then *e* confirms *h*.

The following two more special conditions follow from H8.2.

(H8.21) *Special Consequence Condition:* If *e* confirms *h*, then it also confirms every consequence of *h* (i.e., sentence L-implied by *h*).

(H8.22) *Equivalence Condition for Hypotheses:* If *h* and *h'* are L-equivalent and *e* confirms *h* then *e* confirms *h'*.

(H8.3) *Consistency Condition:* The class whose elements are e and all the hypotheses confirmed by e is consistent (i.e., not L-false).

The following two more special conditions follow from H8.3.

(H8.31) If e and h are incompatible (i.e., L-exclusive, $e \cdot h$ is L-false), then e does not confirm h.

(H8.32) If h and h' are incompatible (i.e., L-exclusive), then e does not confirm both h and h'.

(H8.4) *Equivalence Condition for Observation Reports* (*op. cit.*, p. 110 n.): If e and e' are L-equivalent and e confirms h, then e' confirms h.

Now we shall examine these conditions of adequacy stated by Hempel. We interpret these conditions as referring to the concept of initial confirming evidence as explicandum; we shall soon come back to the question whether Hempel has not sometimes a different explicandum in mind. Thus we shall apply the conditions to $\mathfrak{C}_0$; but when we accept one of them, we shall state not only a condition (b) for $\mathfrak{C}_0$, but first a more general condition (a) for $\mathfrak{C}$; (b) is then a special case of (a) with 't' for 'e'. It is presupposed for (a) that $e \cdot i$ is non-L-false, because otherwise $\mathfrak{c}(h,e \cdot i)$ would have no value and hence the subsequent condition (2) could not be applied; and it is presupposed for (b) that e is not L-false. Our statements of conditions will have the same numbers as Hempel's but with 'C' instead of 'H'. For this discussion we remember that we found that $\mathfrak{C}$ is the same as positive relevance and $\mathfrak{C}_0$ the same as initial positive relevance; therefore we shall make use of the results concerning relevance concepts stated in the preceding chapter. Our examination will be based on the view that any adequate explicatum for the classificatory concept of confirmation must be in accord with at least one adequate explicatum for the quantitative concept of confirmation; in other words, a relation $\mathfrak{C}_0$ proposed as explicatum cannot be accepted as adequate unless there is at least one $\mathfrak{c}$-function $\mathfrak{c}$, which is an adequate explicatum for probability$_1$, such that, if $\mathfrak{C}_0(h,i)$ then

(1) $$\mathfrak{c}(h,i) > \mathfrak{c}(h,t)\ .$$

Analogously, it is necessary for the adequacy of a proposed explicatum $\mathfrak{C}$ that there is at least one adequate $\mathfrak{c}$ such that, if $\mathfrak{C}(h,i,e)$, then

(2) $$\mathfrak{c}(h,e \cdot i) > \mathfrak{c}(h,e)\ .$$

In examining Hempel's statements of conditions of adequacy or our subsequent statements, we shall regard such a statement as valid if there is at least one explicatum $\mathfrak{C}_0$ (or $\mathfrak{C}$) which is adequate in the sense just explained, i.e., in accord with an adequate c-function, and which satisfies the statement generally, i.e., for any sentences as arguments.

The *entailment condition* H8.1 may appear at first glance as quite plausible. And it is indeed valid in ordinary cases. However, it does not hold in some special cases as we shall see by the subsequent counterexamples. Therefore we restate it in the following qualified form.

(C8.1) *Entailment Condition.* Let h be either a sentence in a finite system or a nongeneral sentence in the infinite system.

a. If $\vdash e \cdot i \supset h$ and not $\vdash e \supset h$, then $\mathfrak{C}(h,i,e)$.

b. If $\vdash i \supset h$ and h is not L-true, then $\mathfrak{C}_0(h,i)$.

The following theorem shows that the entailment condition in the modified form C8.1 is valid.

T87-1.

a. Any instance of the relation $\mathfrak{C}$ which is required by C8.1a is in accord with every regular c-function.

Proof. Let $\vdash e \cdot i \supset h$ and not $\vdash e \supset h$. It was presupposed that $e \cdot i$ is not L-false. Therefore, for every regular c, $c(h,e \cdot i) = 1$ (T59-1b) and $c(h,e) < 1$ (T59-5a). Thus this instance of $\mathfrak{C}$ is in accord with c ((3) in § 86).

b. Any instance of $\mathfrak{C}_0$ required by C8.1b is in accord with every regular c-function. (From (a), with '*t*' for *e*.)

In C8.1a, we have excluded the case that $\vdash e \supset h$. This restriction is necessary, because in this case $c(h,e) = 1 = c(h,e \cdot i)$; hence c is not increased. For the same reason, the case that h is L-true must be excluded in C8.1b.

For the sake of simplicity, we have stated C8.1 only for the case that h is a sentence in a finite system or a nongeneral sentence in the infinite system. However, C8.1 is valid also if h is a general sentence in the infinite system except in the case where h is almost L-implied by e (D58-1c) with respect to any of the c-functions on which $\mathfrak{C}$ is based. In the latter case, $c(h,e) = 1$ although not $\vdash e \supset h$; thus here again c is not increased and hence i is not positively relevant. (This holds if positive relevance is defined by D65-1a; see, however, the subsequent remark concerning the alternative definition D′.)

We considered in § 65 the following *example* in the infinite system: h is '$(\exists x)Px$', i is 'Pb', '*t*' is taken as e. We mentioned that, for certain c-functions, e.g., c^*, h is almost L-true. Although in every finite system the c of h on '*t*' is increased by the addition of i, in the infinite system $c(h,t)$ is already 1 and hence is not increased by the addition of i. Therefore i is here irrelevant to h; i is not confirming evidence for h.

Cases of the kind of this example suggested the alternative definition (D′)

for positive relevance indicated in § 65. If this alternative definition is chosen, then in cases like the above example i is called positive to h and hence is regarded as confirming evidence for h. Then the restriction of h to nongeneral sentences in the infinite system in C8.1 can be omitted. (But the restricting conditions in (a) that not $\vdash e \supset h$ and in (b) that h is not L-true remain.)

The *equivalence conditions* for hypotheses (H8.22) and for observation reports (H8.4) are obviously valid, because the corresponding principles hold for all regular c-functions (T59-1i and h). For $\mathfrak{C}$, the former condition can be generalized; the hypotheses h and h' need only be L-equivalent with respect to e, i.e., $\vdash e \supset (h \equiv h')$ (cf. T59-2j).

The *consequence condition* H8.2 and the special consequence condition H8.21 are not valid, as we shall see. In his discussion of H8.21, Hempel refers (p. 105, n. 1) to William Barrett ([Dewey], p. 312), whose view that "not every observation which confirms a sentence need also confirm all its consequences" is obviously in contradiction to the consequence condition. Barrett supports his view by pointing to "the simplest case: the sentence '*C*' is an abbreviation of '*A* . *B*', and the observation *O* confirms '*A*', and so '*C*', but is irrelevant to '*B*', which is a consequence of '*C*' ". This situation can indeed occur, as we shall see; thus Barrett is right in rejecting the consequence condition. Now Hempel points out that Barrett, in the phrase "and so '*C*' " just quoted, seems to presuppose tacitly the *converse consequence condition:* if e confirms h, then it confirms also any sentence of which h is a consequence. Hempel shows correctly that a simultaneous requirement of both the consequence condition and the converse consequence condition would immediately lead to the absurd result that any observation report e confirms any hypothesis h (because e confirms e, hence $e \,.\, h$, hence h). Since he accepts the consequence condition, he rejects the converse consequence condition. On the other hand, Barrett, accepting the latter, rejects the former. Each of the two incompatible conditions has a certain superficial plausibility. Which of them is valid? The answer is, neither.

In our investigation of the possible relevance situations for two hypotheses (§§ 70, 71) we found the following results, which hold for all regular c-functions. It is possible that, on the same evidence e, which may be factual or tautological, i is positive to h but negative to $h \vee k$, although the latter is L-implied by the former. This is possible not only if i is negative to k but also if i is irrelevant or even positive to k (§ 71, case 4a). We have indicated there a general procedure for constructing cases of this kind, and given a numerical example (§ 71, example for 4a). This shows that *the consequence condition is not valid*, that is, not in accord with any regular c-function. We have further found that it is possible that i is positive to h but negative to $h \cdot k$, although the latter L-implies the former. This is possible even if i is positive to k (§ 71, case 3a). Here likewise a general construction procedure has been indicated and a numerical example given (§ 71, example for 3a). This shows that *the converse consequence condition is not valid.*

A remark made by Hempel in his discussion of Barrett is interesting because it throws some light on the reasoning which led Hempel to the consequence condition. Hempel quotes Barrett's statement that "the degree of confirmation for the consequence of a sentence cannot be less than that of the sentence itself". This statement is correct; it does indeed hold for every regular c-function (T59-2d). Hempel agrees with this principle but regards it as incompatible with a renunciation of the special consequence condition, "since the latter may be considered simply as the correlate, for the non-gradated [i.e., classificatory] relation of confirmation, of the former principle which is adapted to the concept of degree of confirmation". This seems to show that here Hempel has in mind as explicandum the following relation: 'the degree of confirmation of h on i is greater than r', where r is a fixed value, perhaps 0 or 1/2. This interpretation seems indicated also by another remark which Hempel makes in support of the consequence condition: "An observation report which confirms certain hypotheses would invariably be qualified as confirming any consequence of those hypotheses. Indeed: any such consequence is but an assertion of all or part of the combined content of the original hypotheses and has therefore to be regarded as confirmed by any evidence which confirms the original hypotheses" (p. 103). This reasoning may appear at first glance quite plausible; but this is due, I think, only to the inadvertent transition to the explicandum mentioned above. This relation, however, is not the same as our original explicandum, the classificatory concept of confirmation as used, for instance, by a scientist when he says something like this: 'The result of the experiment just made supplies confirming evidence for my hypothesis'. Hempel's general discussions give the impression that he too is originally thinking of this explicandum, when he refers to favorable and unfavorable data, both of which are regarded as relevant and distinguished from irrelevant data, and when he speaks of given evidence as strengthening or weakening a given hypothesis. The difference between the two explicanda is easily seen as follows. Let r be a fixed value. The result that the degree of confirmation of h after the observation i is $q > r$ does not by itself show that i furnishes a positive contribution to the confirmation of h; for it may be that the prior degree of confirmation of h (i.e., before the observation i) was already q, in which case i is irrelevant; or it may have been even greater than q, in which case i is negative. [Example. Let h be '$P_1b \vee P_2b$', and i 'P_3a'. Take $r = 1/2$. For many $\mathfrak{c}$-functions $\mathfrak{c}(h,i) = \mathfrak{c}(h,t) = 3/4$. Therefore i is (initially) irrelevant to h, although $\mathfrak{c}(h,i) > 1/2$.] And, the other way round, the result that the posterior degree of confirmation of h is higher than the prior one does not necessarily make it higher than r (unless $r = 0$). Thus we see that the essential criterion for the concept of confirming evidence must take into account not simply the posterior degree of confirmation but rather a comparison between this and the prior one.

The consistency condition H8.3 is not valid; it seems to me not even plausible. The special condition H8.31, requiring compatibility of the hypothesis with the evidence, is certainly valid. We restate it here in the general form as Compatibility Condition:

(C8.31) *Compatibility Condition.*

a. If i and h are L-exclusive with respect to e, that is, if $e \centerdot i \centerdot h$ is L-false, then not $\mathfrak{C}(h,i,e)$.

b. If i and h are L-exclusive, that is, if $i \centerdot h$ is L-false, then not $\mathfrak{C}_0(h,i)$.

The following theorem shows that C8.31 is valid, no matter on which $\mathfrak{c}$-function or class of $\mathfrak{c}$-functions $\mathfrak{C}$ is based.

T87-2.

a. If a relation $\mathfrak{C}$ holds in any instance excluded by C8.31a, then it is not in accord with any regular $\mathfrak{c}$-function.

Proof. Let $e \centerdot i \centerdot h$ be L-false. Then, for every regular $\mathfrak{c}$, $\mathfrak{c}(h,e \centerdot i) = 0$ (T59-1e), hence not $> \mathfrak{c}(h,e)$.

b. If a relation $\mathfrak{C}_0$ holds in any instance excluded by C8.31b, then it is not in accord with any regular $\mathfrak{c}$-function. (From (a), with 't' for e.)

On the other hand, the second special condition H8.32 seems to me invalid. Hempel himself shows that a set of physical measurements may confirm several quantitative hypotheses which are incompatible with each other (p. 106). This seems to me a clear refutation of H8.32. Hempel discusses possibilities of weakening or omitting this requirement, but he decides at the end to maintain it unchanged, without saying how he intends to overcome the difficulty which he has pointed out himself. Perhaps he thinks that he may leave aside this difficulty because the results of physical measurements cannot be formulated in the simple language L to which his analysis applies. However, it seems to me that there are similar but simpler counterexamples which can be formulated in our systems $\mathfrak{L}$ and in Hempel's system L. For instance, let i describe the frequency of a property M in a finite population, and h and h' state two distinct values m and m' for the frequency of M in a sample of s individuals belonging to the population, such that the relative frequencies m/s and m'/s are both near to the relative frequency of M in the population as stated in i. Then i confirms both h and h', although they are incompatible with each other.

Example. Let i be a statistical distribution (D26-6c) for M and non-M with respect to 10,000 individuals with the cardinal number 8,000 for M. Let h be a statistical distribution with respect to 100 of these individuals with the cardinal number 80 for M, and similarly h' with respect to the same individuals and with the cardinal number 79. Note that a statistical distribution for a finite class has the form of a disjunction of conjunctions and does not contain variables or the sign of identity; therefore it occurs also in L and it is an observation report (in the wider sense). Let e be either the tautology 't' or a factual sentence irrelevant to h and to h' (on 't' and on i). Then for many c-functions (presumably including all adequate ones) $\mathfrak{c}(h,e \,.\, i) > \mathfrak{c}(h,e)$ and $\mathfrak{c}(h',e \,.\, i) > \mathfrak{c}(h',e)$. (These are cases of the direct inductive inference, see § 94.) Thus i is positively relevant and hence constitutes confirming evidence for both h and h'.

Hempel mentions in this context still another condition, which might be called the *Conjunction Condition:* if e confirms each of two hypotheses, then it also confirms their conjunction (p. 106). Hempel seems to accept this condition; he regards any violation of it as "intuitively rather awkward". However, this condition is not valid for our explicandum; we have found earlier that i may be positive both to h and to k but negative to $h \,.\, k$ (see § 71, case 3a and the example for it; this was mentioned above as a refutation of the converse consequence condition). And it is not valid for the second explicandum either, no matter which value we choose for r.

This is seen as follows. Let r be any real number such that $0 \leqq r < 1$. Let q be $(1 - r)/2$; hence $q > 0$. Let i say that in a given finite population the relative frequencies are as follows: for '$P_1 \,.\, P_2$', r; for '$P_1 \,.\, \sim P_2$', q; for '$P_2 \,.\, \sim P_1$', q; hence for '$\sim P_1 \,.\, \sim P_2$', 0; for 'P_1', $r + q$; for 'P_2', $r + q$. Let h be '$P_1 b$' and h' '$P_2 b$', where b belongs to the population. Then (as we shall see later, T94-1e) for every symmetrical c-function and hence for every adequate one, the following holds. $\mathfrak{c}(h,i) = \mathfrak{c}(h',i) = r + q > r$; on the other hand, $\mathfrak{c}(h \,.\, h',i) = r$.

What may be the reasons which have led Hempel to the consistency conditions H8.32 and H8.3? He regards it as a great advantage of any explicatum satisfying H8.3 "that it sets a limit, so to speak, to the strength of the hypotheses which can be confirmed by given evidence", as was pointed out to him by Nelson Goodman. This argument does not seem to have any plausibility for *our* explicandum, because a weak additional evidence can cause an increase, though a small one, in the confirmation even of a very strong hypothesis. But it is plausible for the second explicandum mentioned earlier: the degree of confirmation exceeding a fixed value r. Therefore we may perhaps assume that Hempel's acceptance of the consistency condition is due again to an inadvertent shift to the second explicandum. This assumption seems corroborated by the following result. Although H8.32 is not valid for our explicandum, it is valid for the second explicandum if we take for r 1/2 or any greater value (<1). For if h and h' are L-exclusive, then it is impossible that $\mathfrak{c}(h,i)$ and $\mathfrak{c}(h',i)$ both exceed 1/2, because the sum of those two $\mathfrak{c}$-values is $\mathfrak{c}(h \vee h',i)$ (according to the special addition theorem, T59-1l), and hence cannot exceed 1.

§ 88. Hempel's Definition of Confirming Evidence

Hempel defines a concept *Cf* as an explicatum for confirming evidence, and he shows that *Cf* fulfils his conditions of adequacy, which we discussed in the preceding section. It is found that *Cf* is too narrow as an explicatum for the general concept of confirming evidence, but it seems adequate as an explicatum for the special case where the evidence shows that *all* observed individuals have the property referred to in the hypothesis.

This concludes the discussion of the concept of confirming evidence.

On the basis of his analysis of the problem of an explication of the concept of confirming evidence, Hempel proceeds to construct the definition of a dyadic relation *Cf* between sentences, which he proposes as an explicatum. (His construction is given in technical details in [Syntactical], pp. 130–42, and briefly outlined in [Studies], p. 109.) We shall briefly state the series of definitions, using our terminology and notation and omitting minor details not relevant for our discussion. We add again 'H' to the numbers in the latter article and call the first definition 'H9.0'. e is any molecular sentence, h any sentence of Hempel's language system L earlier indicated (similar to $\mathfrak{L}$ but without a sign of identity).

(H9.0) The *development* of h for a finite class C of individual constants $=_{Df}$ the sentence formed from h by the following transformations: (1) every universal matrix $(\mathfrak{i}_k)(\mathfrak{M}_k)$ is replaced by the conjunction of the substitution instances of its scope $\mathfrak{M}_k$ for all $\mathfrak{in}$ in C; (2) every existential matrix $(\exists \mathfrak{i}_k)(\mathfrak{M}_k)$ is replaced by the disjunction of the substitution instances of its scope $\mathfrak{M}_k$ for all $\mathfrak{in}$ in C. (If h contains no variables, then its development is h itself.)

(H9.1) $Cfd(e,h)$, *e directly confirms h* $=_{Df}$ e L-implies the development of h for the class of those $\mathfrak{in}$ which occur essentially in e (i.e., which occur in every sentence L-equivalent to e).

(H9.2) $Cf(e,h)$, *e confirms h* $=_{Df}$ h is L-implied by a class of sentences each of which is directly confirmed by e.

Example. Let e be '$Pa_1 \,.\, Pa_2 \,.\, \ldots \,.\, Pa_{10}$', l '$(x)Px$', and h 'Pa_{12}'. Then $Cfd(e,l)$; and, since $\vdash l \supset h$, $Cf(e,h)$; but not $Cfd(e,h)$.

(H9.3) *e disconfirms h* $=_{\text{Df}}$ *e* confirms non-*h*.

(H9.4) *e* is *neutral* with respect to *h* $=_{\text{Df}}$ *e* neither confirms nor disconfirms *h*.

Now let us see whether the concept *Cf* defined by H9.2 seems adequate as an explicatum for our explicandum, the concept of confirming evidence. Hempel shows that *Cf* satisfies all his conditions of adequacy earlier stated. While he takes this fact as an indication of adequacy, it will make us doubtful, since we found that some of the requirements are invalid.

It follows from our refutation of the special consequence condition H8.21 and the special consistency condition H8.32 that no *R* can possibly fulfil all of the following four conditions:

(i) *R* is not clearly too wide (in the sense of § 86),
(ii) *R* is not clearly too narrow,
(iii) *R* satisfies H8.21,
(iv) *R* satisfies H8.32.

For if (ii) and (iii) are fulfilled, then our counterexamples to H8.21 lead to cases where *R* holds but the explicandum does clearly not hold; hence (i) is not fulfilled. And if (i) and (iv) are fulfilled, then our counterexamples to H8.32 lead to cases which are excluded by H8.32 but in which the explicandum clearly holds; hence (ii) is not fulfilled.

Since Hempel has shown that his explicatum *Cf* satisfies all his requirements, among them H8.21 and H8.32, *Cf* must be either clearly too wide or clearly too narrow or both. I am not aware of any cases in which *Cf* holds but the explicandum does clearly not hold. Thus we may assume, unless and until somebody finds counterinstances, that *Cf* is not clearly too wide. However, it is clearly too narrow; we shall see, indeed, that *Cf* is limited to some quite special kinds of cases of the explicandum. The result that a proposed explicatum is found too narrow constitutes a much less serious objection than the result that it is too wide. In the former case the proposed concept may still be useful; it may be an adequate explicatum for a subkind of the explicandum within a limited field. It seems that this is the case with *Cf*.

We shall now consider the four most important kinds of inductive reasoning as explained earlier (§ 44B) and examine, for each of them, under what conditions *Cf* holds. In the following discussion the population is assumed to be finite. Individuals not referred to in the evidence *e* are called new individuals. 'rf' means relative frequency. (In (1) and (2) we restrict the present discussion, for the sake of simplicity, to a hypothesis *h* concerning one individual.)

1. *Direct inference.* e is a statistical distribution (D26-6c) to the effect that the rf of a property in the population, say, the primitive property P, has the value r; h is 'Pb', where b belongs to the population.

1a. Let r be 1; that is, all individuals in the population are known to be P. Then Cf holds, but this case is trivial because e L-implies h.

1b. Let $0 < r < 1$. Cf does *not* hold. However, if r is close to 1, most people would regard e as confirming evidence for h. This holds even for both explicanda: (i) $\mathfrak{c}$ is increased by adding e to 't'; (ii) $\mathfrak{c}(h,e)$ exceeds the fixed value q, say 1/2. (We shall see later (T94-1e) that for every symmetrical $\mathfrak{c}$, and hence for every adequate $\mathfrak{c}$, $\mathfrak{c}(h,e) = r$.)

2. *Predictive inference.* e is a statistical distribution to the effect that the rf of a property, say, P, in a given sample is r; h is the singular prediction 'Pd', where d is a new individual.

2a. Let r be 1; that is, all individuals in the observed sample have been found to be P. Then Cf holds (see the above example following H9.2).

2b. Let $0 < r < 1$. Cf does *not* hold. However, if r is close to 1, most people would regard e as confirming evidence for h, in the sense of either explicandum (as in 1b). (For any adequate $\mathfrak{c}$-function, in the case of a sufficiently large sample $\mathfrak{c}(h,e)$ is close or equal to r.)

Example. Let e and h be as in the earlier example following (H9.2) and i '$\sim Pa_{11}$'. (i is negative to h on e.) Then not $Cf(e \,.\, i,h)$.

2c. Let the evidence contain, in addition to e with $r = 1$, irrelevant data on additional individuals. Then Cf does *not* hold.

Example. Let e and h be as above, and i' be 'P_2a_{11}'. (i' is irrelevant to h on e.) Then not $Cf(e \,.\, i',h)$. However, for every adequate $\mathfrak{c}$, $\mathfrak{c}(h,e \,.\, i') = \mathfrak{c}(h,e)$. Therefore, since e is regarded as confirming evidence for h, $e \,.\, i'$ will usually be regarded so too.

3. *Inverse inference.* e is a statistical distribution to the effect that the rf of P in a given sample of a population is r; h is a statistical distribution saying that the rf of P in the population is r'.

3a. Let r and r' be 1, that is, all individuals in the sample and in the population are stated to be P. Here $Cf(e,h)$ holds, and even $Cfd(e,h)$ (see $Cfd(e,l)$ in the example following H9.2).

3b. Let $0 < r < 1$. Then Cf holds for *no* value of r'. However, for r' equal or near to r, many people, though not all, would regard e as confirming evidence for h.

4. *Universal inductive inference.* Let h be a universal sentence, say '$(x)Mx$', and e be a conjunction of sentences concerning the individuals of a given sample not containing negative instances. (If 'b' occurs essentially in e, it is called a positive instance for h if e L-implies 'Mb', a negative instance if e L-implies '$\sim Mb$', and a neutral instance if it is neither a positive nor a negative instance.)

4a. Let e contain only positive instances. Then *Cf* and even *Cfd* hold. (This case is the same as 3a.)

4b. Let e contain both positive and neutral instances. Then *Cf* does *not* hold.

Example. Let l, e, and i' be as previously. Then not $Cf(e \,.\, i',l)$. However, many will regard i' as irrelevant to l on e, that is, $\mathfrak{c}(l,e \,.\, i') = \mathfrak{c}(l,e)$. Since now e is regarded as confirming l, that is, $\mathfrak{c}(h,e) > \mathfrak{c}(h,t)$, $\mathfrak{c}(h,e \,.\, i')$ is likewise $> \mathfrak{c}(h,t)$. Hence $e \,.\, i'$ will be regarded as confirming h.

Thus we see that in each of the kinds of inductive inference just discussed *Cf* holds only in the special case where the evidence ascribes to *all* individuals essentially occurring in it the property in question. Although this case is of great importance, it is very limited. In the great majority of the cases in which scientists speak of confirming evidence, the rf in e is not 1 or 0 but has an intermediate value. These cases are not covered by *Cf*. However, *Cf* can presumably be regarded as an adequate explicatum for the concept of confirming evidence in the special case described.

Hempel's investigations of the problem of confirming evidence supplied the first thoroughgoing and clear analysis of the whole problem complex. As such they remain valuable independently of his attempted solution of the particular problem of finding a nonquantitative explicatum for the concept of confirming evidence. The latter problem is today no longer as important as it was at the time Hempel made his investigations. He himself has defined, in the meantime, in collaboration with others, an interesting concept *dc*, proposed as an explicatum for degree of confirmation (see Hempel and Oppenheim [Degree], and Helmer and Oppenheim [Degree]); this will be discussed in a later chapter (in Vol. II). Some years ago those who worked on these problems expected that, if and when a definition of degree of confirmation were to be constructed, it would be based on a definition of a nonquantitative concept of confirming evidence. However, today it is seen that this is not the case either for Hempel's definition of *dc* nor for my definition of $\mathfrak{c}^*$, and it is not regarded as probable that it will be the case for other definitions which will be proposed. It appears at present more promising to proceed in the opposite direction, that is, to define a quantitative form of the concept of confirming evidence on the basis of an explicatum for degree of confirmation, for instance, $\mathfrak{C}^*$ (or $\mathfrak{C}_0^*$) based on $\mathfrak{c}^*$ (see (5) and (6) in § 86) or analogous concepts based on Hempel's *dc* or on other explicata for degree of confirmation.

This concludes the discussion of the classificatory concept of confirming evidence. We have not found an adequate explicatum defined in nonquantitative terms. The concepts which were considered as possible explicata were found to be too narrow. However, we have a theory of confirming evidence in quantitative terms. The general part of this theory, which refers to all regular c-functions, was constructed in the preceding chapter as the theory of relevance. Later we shall find specific results concerning relevance with respect to the function c*.

CHAPTER VIII

THE SYMMETRICAL c-FUNCTIONS

In this chapter we return to quantitative inductive logic. A special kind of regular c-functions is introduced, called symmetrical c-functions. The definition is as follows. An m-function is called symmetrical (D90-1) if it has the same value for any state-descriptions which are isomorphic (D26-3a), i.e., such that one is constructed from the other by replacing individual constants with others. Then a c-function is called symmetrical (D91-1) if it is based upon a symmetrical m-function. It is shown (T91-2) that any symmetrical c-function fulfils the requirement of invariance, that is to say, its value for two sentences is not changed if the individual constants occurring in the sentences are replaced with other ones. It seems generally, though tacitly, agreed that any adequate explicatum for probability$_1$, i.e., degree of confirmation, must fulfil this requirement and hence be symmetrical. Theorems concerning symmetrical c-functions are developed (§§ 92–96), among them theorems concerning the direct inductive inference, that is, the inference from the frequency of a property in a population to its frequency in a sample (§ 94). (The other inductive inferences will be dealt with only in later chapters, because they presuppose the choice of a particular c-function.) The classical formulas of the binomial law (§ 95) and of Bernoulli's theorem (§ 96) are here construed as approximations for special cases of the direct inference.

This chapter presupposes §§ 25–27 of the earlier chapter on deductive logic.

§ 90. Symmetrical m-Functions

It seems plausible to require that an adequate concept of degree of confirmation should treat all individuals on a par. Those c-functions which fulfil this requirement will later (§ 91) be called symmetrical. As a preliminary step toward this concept we define here (D1) symmetrical m-functions as those regular m-functions which ascribe to any two isomorphic (D26-3a) state-descriptions the same value.

In the preceding chapter we have discussed the two nonquantitative concepts of confirmation, viz., the comparative concept 𝔐ℭ and the classificatory concept ℭ. Now we return to the investigation of the quantitative concept, the concept of degree of confirmation. This investigation was begun in chapter v. There we introduced the general concept of regular c-functions and stated theorems which hold indiscriminately for *all* c-functions, no matter whether or not they are adequate explicata for our explicandum, the quantitative concept of probability$_1$ or degree of confirmation. In the present chapter we strengthen the assumptions underlying our system of inductive logic. Our final aim will be to choose one particular c-function as our explicatum. This will be done in a later chapter (in Vol. II); there we shall define the function c* and take it as the basis of our system of quantitative inductive logic. In the present chapter we shall take only an intermediary step; we shall select a certain kind of regular c-functions, which we call the symmetrical c-functions. This kind, although considerably narrower than the general class of regular c-functions, still comprehends an infinite number of c-functions with greatly varying characters. It seems to me that the property of symmetry characterizing this class is very plausible and has indeed been tacitly presupposed by all authors on probability$_1$.

In this chapter we shall make use of some more of the material explained in *chapter iii on deductive logic*. As indicated at the beginning of that chapter, §§ 14–20 were already presupposed for chapters iv–vii, while §§ 21–24 list well-known theorems not for reading but for the purpose of later references. In the present chapter we shall, in addition, use the content of §§ 25–27. Especially the following concepts explained in those sections will often be used: *division* (D25-4), *isomorphism* of sentences (D26-3) and especially of state-descriptions $\mathfrak{Z}$ (§ 27), *individual* and *statistical distributions* (D26-6), *structure* (§ 27) and *structure-description* ($\mathfrak{S}$tr, D27-1).

The following consideration will lead us to the concept of symmetrical c-functions. Suppose *X* has found by observation that the individuals *a* and *b* are *P;* the individuals may be physical objects and *P* may be an observable property. Let *e* be the sentence expressing these results: '*Pa* . *Pb*'. *X* considers two hypotheses *h* and *h'; h* is the prediction that another object *c* is likewise *P* ('*Pc*'), and *h'* says the same for still another object *d* ('*Pd*'). If *X* has chosen a concept c of degree of confirmation, he will ascribe a certain value to c(*h*,*e*). We cannot determine this value generally because it depends upon the choice of c. Different functions c, even if each of them appears as not implausible, may yield different numerical values for the given case. However, we shall expect that if *X* ascribes a certain value to c(*h*,*e*), no matter which value this may be, he will ascribe the same value to c(*h'*,*e*). We should find it entirely implausible if he were to ascribe different values here; that is to say, we should not regard such a function c as an adequate explicatum. The reason is that the logical relation between *e* and *h* is just the same as that between *e* and *h'*. Although the individuals *c* and *d* may, of course, be very different in their empirical properties, their logical status cannot be different. The evidence *e* does not say anything about either *c* or *d;* therefore, if *e* is all the relevant evidence available to *X*, he has no rational reasons to expect *h* more than

h' or vice versa. If we consider a case where the same individual constant occurs both in the evidence and in the hypothesis, the result will be fundamentally the same; but we have, of course, to take care that the individual constant is replaced in the same way in both sentences. Thus, for example, we shall require that $\mathfrak{c}(Pc,Pc \vee Pa)$ and $\mathfrak{c}(Pd,Pd \vee Pa)$ have the same value. To put it in very general terms, we require that logic should not discriminate between the individuals but treat all of them on a par; although we know that individuals are not alike, they ought to be given equal rights before the tribunal of logic. This is never questioned in deductive logic, although it is seldom stated explicitly. For example, since 'Pc' L-implies '$Pc \vee Pa$', 'Pd' L-implies '$Pd \vee Pa$'. This important character of deductive logic is stated in general terms in the theorem of the invariance of the L-concepts (T26-2). What we require here is that inductive logic should have the same character. However, this requirement is not fulfilled by all regular $\mathfrak{c}$-functions. We shall call those regular $\mathfrak{c}$-functions which fulfil the requirement of nondiscrimination among individuals ***symmetrical*** $\mathfrak{c}$***-functions***. For reasons of technical expediency, we shall not define this concept directly by the characteristic just indicated. Instead, we shall first define the concept of symmetrical $\mathfrak{m}$-functions by an analogous characteristic (D1). Later we shall define the symmetrical $\mathfrak{c}$-functions as those based on symmetrical $\mathfrak{m}$-functions (D91-1); and then we shall show that they fulfil our requirement (theorem of invariance, T91-2).

Before we come to the definition, we state here a simple theorem concerning the $\mathfrak{m}$ of a structure-description.

T90-1. Let $\mathfrak{m}$ be a regular $\mathfrak{m}$-function with respect to $\mathfrak{L}_N$. Let $\mathfrak{Str}_j$ be any $\mathfrak{Str}$ in $\mathfrak{L}_N$, and $\mathfrak{Z}_i$ be any $\mathfrak{Z}$ belonging to $\mathfrak{Str}_j$ (D27-1a). Then $\mathfrak{m}(\mathfrak{Str}_j)$ is the sum of the $\mathfrak{m}$-values for all those $\mathfrak{Z}$ which belong to $\mathfrak{Str}_j$, in other words, for all those $\mathfrak{Z}$ which are isomorphic to $\mathfrak{Z}_i$. (From D55-2b, T27-2f.)

Our intention is to characterize the symmetrical $\mathfrak{m}$-functions as those which treat all individuals on a par. Now, two isomorphic $\mathfrak{Z}$ differ only in their references to different individuals (§ 27); exactly the same properties and relations which the one attributes to a, b, c, etc., the other attributes to, say, d, b, a, etc. Thus, to treat all individuals on a par amounts to treating isomorphic $\mathfrak{Z}$ on a par. This leads us to the following definition; it refers only to finite systems $\mathfrak{L}_N$; the extension to $\mathfrak{L}_\infty$ will be made later (D91-3).

+D90-1. $\mathfrak{m}$ is a ***symmetrical measure function*** (or briefly, a symmetrical $\mathfrak{m}$-function) for the $\mathfrak{Z}$ in $\mathfrak{L}_N =_{Df}$ $\mathfrak{m}$ is a regular $\mathfrak{m}$-function for the $\mathfrak{Z}$ in $\mathfrak{L}_N$ (D55-1), and $\mathfrak{m}$ has for isomorphic $\mathfrak{Z}$ the same value (i.e., if $\mathfrak{Z}_i$ is isomorphic to $\mathfrak{Z}_j$, then $\mathfrak{m}(\mathfrak{Z}_i) = \mathfrak{m}(\mathfrak{Z}_j)$).

The following definitions D2, D3, and D4 are analogous to the corresponding definitions concerning regular m-functions: D55-2, D57-3, and D57-4, respectively.

+**D90-2.** Let m be a symmetrical m-function for the 3 in $\mathfrak{L}_N$. We extend m to a *symmetrical* m*-function for the sentences* in $\mathfrak{L}_N$ in the following way.

a. For any L-false sentence j in $\mathfrak{L}_N$, m(j) $=_{\text{Df}}$ 0.

b. For any non-L-false sentence j in $\mathfrak{L}_N$, m(j) $=_{\text{Df}}$ the sum of the values of m for the 3 in $\mathfrak{R}_j$ (the range of j).

D90-3. A sequence of functions $_1$m, $_2$m, $_3$m, etc., is a fitting symmetrical sequence of m-functions for 3 or, briefly, a ***fitting symmetrical*** m***-sequence*** for 3 $=_{\text{Df}}$ the sequence is a fitting m-sequence for 3 (D57-3), and, for every N, the function $_N$m in the sequence is a symmetrical m-function for the 3 in $\mathfrak{L}_N$ (D1).

D90-4. A sequence of functions $_1$m, $_2$m, $_3$m, etc., is a fitting symmetrical sequence of m-functions for sentences or, briefly, a *fitting symmetrical* m*-sequence for sentences* $=_{\text{Df}}$ the sequence is a fitting m-sequence for sentences (D57-4), and, for every N, the function $_N$m in the sequence is a symmetrical m-function for the sentences in $\mathfrak{L}_N$ (D2).

§ 91. Symmetrical c-Functions

The symmetrical c-functions are defined (D1) as those which are based upon symmetrical m-functions. The value of a symmetrical m- or c-function in $\mathfrak{L}_\infty$ is defined (D3, D4) as the limit of the values in the finite systems $\mathfrak{L}_N$, as previously (§ 56). Then it is shown (theorem of invariance T2) that the value of a symmetrical m- or c-function remains unchanged if the individual constants involved are replaced by any other ones. Thus the symmetrical functions fulfil the requirement stated in the preceding section. It seems that all authors on probability$_1$ tacitly accept that requirement.

We have earlier (D55-3) said of a function c that it is based upon a function m, if c(h,e) is always m$(e \,.\, h)$/m(e). It seems natural, in analogy to our earlier procedure (D55-4), to define the symmetrical c-functions as those based upon symmetrical m-functions (D1). The first items in this section will be restricted to $\mathfrak{L}_N$; the concepts for $\mathfrak{L}_\infty$ will be defined later (D3, D4).

+**D91-1.** c is a ***symmetrical confirmation function*** or, briefly, a symmetrical c-function, for $\mathfrak{L}_N$ $=_{\text{Df}}$ c is based upon a symmetrical m-function for the sentences in $\mathfrak{L}_N$.

From this definition the following theorem follows which is analogous to T55-2.

T91-1. Let $\mathfrak{c}$ be a symmetrical $\mathfrak{c}$-function for $\mathfrak{L}_N$. Then there is a symmetrical $\mathfrak{m}$ for the sentences of $\mathfrak{L}_N$ (namely that upon which $\mathfrak{c}$ is based) such that the following holds.

a. For any pair of sentences h,e in $\mathfrak{L}_N$, where $\mathfrak{m}(e) \neq 0$, $\mathfrak{c}(h,e) = \frac{\mathfrak{m}(e \,.\, h)}{\mathfrak{m}(e)}$. (From D1, D55-3.)

b. $\mathfrak{c}$ has a value for a pair of sentences h,e in $\mathfrak{L}_N$ if and only if $\mathfrak{m}(e) \neq 0$, hence if and only if e is not L-false in $\mathfrak{L}_N$. (From D1, D55-3, D90-2.)

The following definition is analogous to D57-5.

D91-2. A sequence of functions ${}_1\mathfrak{c}$, ${}_2\mathfrak{c}$, ${}_3\mathfrak{c}$, etc., is a fitting symmetrical sequence of confirmation functions or, briefly, a ***fitting symmetrical*** $\mathfrak{c}$-***sequence*** $=_{Df}$ there is a fitting symmetrical $\mathfrak{m}$-sequence for sentences (D90-4) ${}_1\mathfrak{m}$, ${}_2\mathfrak{m}$, etc., such that, for every N, ${}_N\mathfrak{c}$ is the symmetrical $\mathfrak{c}$-function based upon ${}_N\mathfrak{m}$.

We define the values of symmetrical $\mathfrak{m}$- and $\mathfrak{c}$-functions for the infinite system $\mathfrak{L}_\infty$ as limits of their values for finite systems (D3 and D4). This is analogous to our earlier procedure for regular functions (D56-1 and 2). Here, as previously, 'lim (. .)' is meant as short for '$\lim_{N\to\infty}$ (. .)', unless otherwise indicated.

+**D91-3.** Let ${}_1\mathfrak{m}$, ${}_2\mathfrak{m}$, etc., be a sequence of symmetrical $\mathfrak{m}$-functions for the sentences in $\mathfrak{L}_1$, $\mathfrak{L}_2$, etc. $\mathfrak{m}$ is the *symmetrical* $\mathfrak{m}$-*function for the sentences in* $\mathfrak{L}_\infty$ corresponding to this sequence $=_{Df}$ for every sentence j in $\mathfrak{L}_\infty$ for which the limit exists, $\mathfrak{m}(j) = \lim {}_N\mathfrak{m}(j)$; if the limit does not exist, $\mathfrak{m}(j)$ has no value.

D91-4. Let ${}_1\mathfrak{c}$, ${}_2\mathfrak{c}$, etc., be a sequence of symmetrical $\mathfrak{c}$-functions for $\mathfrak{L}_1$, $\mathfrak{L}_2$, etc. $\mathfrak{c}$ is the *symmetrical* $\mathfrak{c}$-*function for* $\mathfrak{L}_\infty$ corresponding to this sequence $=_{Df}$ for any pair of sentences h,e in $\mathfrak{L}_\infty$ for which the limit exists, $\mathfrak{c}(h,e) = \lim {}_N\mathfrak{c}(h,e)$; if the limit does not exist, $\mathfrak{c}(h,e)$ has no value.

Since the symmetrical $\mathfrak{m}$-functions form a subclass of the regular $\mathfrak{m}$-functions, all theorems concerning the latter hold also for the former. Likewise, all theorems concerning regular $\mathfrak{c}$-functions hold also for the symmetrical $\mathfrak{c}$-functions. Thus we may here apply all the theorems of chapters v and vi; especially those of §§ 55, 57, and 59 will here be used. Further there are theorems which hold for the symmetrical functions but not for all regular functions. Some of them will here be stated.

T91-2. ***Invariance of symmetrical functions*** with respect to in-correlations. Let ${}_1\mathfrak{m}$, ${}_2\mathfrak{m}$, etc., be a fitting symmetrical $\mathfrak{m}$-sequence for sentences, and ${}_\infty\mathfrak{m}$ be the symmetrical $\mathfrak{m}$-function for the sentences in $\mathfrak{L}_\infty$ corresponding to this sequence (D3); $\mathfrak{m}$ may be either ${}_N\mathfrak{m}$ for any N or ${}_\infty\mathfrak{m}$.

Let $_1\mathfrak{c}$, $_2\mathfrak{c}$, etc., be the sequence of those c-functions which are based upon the given m-functions and hence are symmetrical c-functions; and let $_\infty\mathfrak{c}$ be the symmetrical c-function for $\mathfrak{L}_\infty$ corresponding to this sequence (D4); c may be either $_N\mathfrak{c}$ for any N or $_\infty\mathfrak{c}$. Let $\mathfrak{L}$ be any finite or infinite system. Let C be an in-correlation in $\mathfrak{L}$ (D26-1). Let i, h, and e be sentences in $\mathfrak{L}$, and let e not be L-false in $\mathfrak{L}$. Let i' be the C-correlate of i (D26-2b), h' that of h, and e' that of e. (Hence e' is likewise not L-false (T26-2c).) Then the following holds.

a. $\mathfrak{m}(i') = \mathfrak{m}(i)$.

Proof. I. For $_N\mathfrak{m}$. 1. Let i be L-false. Then i' too is L-false (T26-2c). Therefore both m-values are 0 (D90-2a). 2. Let i not be L-false. Then i' too is not L-false (T26-2c). Therefore the ranges of these two sentences, $\mathfrak{R}(i)$ and $\mathfrak{R}(i')$, are not null. $\mathfrak{R}(i')$ is the class of those $\mathfrak{Z}$ in $\mathfrak{L}_N$ which are constructed from the $\mathfrak{Z}$ in $\mathfrak{R}(i)$ by C (T26-2a). Thus there is a one-one correlation between the $\mathfrak{Z}$ in $\mathfrak{R}(i)$ and those in $\mathfrak{R}(i')$ such that any two correlated $\mathfrak{Z}$ are isomorphic (D26-4b, D26-3a) and hence have the same m-value (D90-1). Hence the assertion (D90-2b). II. For $_\infty\mathfrak{m}$. From (I), with D3 and T40-21e.

+b. $\mathfrak{c}(h',e') = \mathfrak{c}(h,e)$. (For $_N\mathfrak{c}$, from T1a, (a). For $_\infty\mathfrak{c}$, from D4, T40-21e.)

c. Let h and e have no in in common; likewise h' and e. Then $\mathfrak{c}(h',e) = \mathfrak{c}(h,e)$.

Proof. We take a correlation C' which, like C, correlates the in in h' with those in h, but which correlates every in in e with itself. Then the assertion follows from (b).

T2b is especially important. It says in effect that values of symmetrical c-functions are invariant with respect to a transformation of the sentences by any in-correlation (where, of course, for both sentences the same in-correlation must be taken). This shows that our definition of symmetrical c-functions does fulfil its purpose; it characterizes those c-functions which treat all individuals on a par. T2 is the analogue in inductive logic to the theorem of invariance in deductive logic (T26-2), because the latter states the invariance of the L-concepts, the fundamental concepts of deductive logic, with respect to the transformations described.

The principle of invariance seems to have been accepted by all authors on probability$_1$, both classical and modern, although it has hardly ever been expressed explicitly. All authors would, for instance, raise and answer questions of the following kind: Suppose that among s observed objects there have been found s_1 with the property M and $s_2 = s - s_1$ with non-M; what is, on this evidence, the probability that another object has the property M? Although nobody says so in so many words, it would presumably appear absurd to everybody to assume that the value of the probability on the evidence described depended also on the question *which* particular *s* individuals were observed and *which* particular other individual was concerned in the prediction. For classical authors, this would appear simply as a consequence of the principle of indifference; but also those modern authors who reject the latter principle seem to take it for granted that in questions of the kind mentioned only the statement of the numbers but not a specification of the individuals is relevant for the probability. To put it in our terminology, there seems to be general agreement among authors on probability$_1$ that no concept can be regarded as an adequate explicatum for probability$_1$ unless it possesses the characteristic of symmetry.

As *examples* for an application of T2 we may take those mentioned in § 90. If c is a symmetrical c-function, then the requirements there stated are fulfilled; (1) $\mathfrak{c}(Pc,Pa \cdot Pb) = \mathfrak{c}(Pd,Pa \cdot Pb)$, and (2) $\mathfrak{c}(Pc,Pc \vee Pa) = \mathfrak{c}(Pd,Pd \vee Pa)$. Both hold on the basis of the correlation $\binom{a\ b\ c\ d}{a\ b\ d\ c}$.

T91-3. Let m be a symmetrical m-function for the sentences in $\mathfrak{L}_N$, and c be based upon m, hence a symmetrical c-function. Let $\mathfrak{Z}_i$ be an arbitrary $\mathfrak{Z}$ in $\mathfrak{L}_N$, and $\mathfrak{Str}_j$ be the structure-description corresponding to $\mathfrak{Z}_i$ (D27-1a). Let ζ_i be the number of those $\mathfrak{Z}$ in $\mathfrak{L}_N$ which are isomorphic to $\mathfrak{Z}_i$ and hence belong to $\mathfrak{Str}_j$. Then the following holds.

a. $\mathfrak{m}(\mathfrak{Str}_j) = \zeta_i \times \mathfrak{m}(\mathfrak{Z}_i)$. (From D90-1, T90-1.)

b. $\mathfrak{c}(\mathfrak{Z}_i,\mathfrak{Str}_j) = 1/\zeta_i$.

Proof. $\vdash \mathfrak{Z}_i \supset \mathfrak{Str}_j$ (T27-2a), hence $\vdash \mathfrak{Str}_j \cdot \mathfrak{Z}_i \equiv \mathfrak{Z}_i$ (T21-5i(1)) .Therefore $\mathfrak{m}(\mathfrak{Str}_j \cdot \mathfrak{Z}_i) = \mathfrak{m}(\mathfrak{Z}_i)$; and $\mathfrak{c}(\mathfrak{Z}_i,\mathfrak{Str}_j) = \mathfrak{m}(\mathfrak{Z}_i)/\mathfrak{m}(\mathfrak{Str}_j)$ (D55-3). Hence, with (a), the assertion.

§ 92. Theorems on Symmetrical c-Functions

Some general theorems concerning symmetrical c-functions are stated. These theorems will later be used for the theory of inductive inferences.

The theorems of this section will later be used in the theory of inductive inferences. They hold for any finite or infinite system $\mathfrak{L}$, provided the conditions (A) and (B) stated at the beginning of § 59 (and a condition for m-expressions analogous to (B)) are fulfilled.

T1a is analogous to a previous theorem concerning $\mathfrak{Z}$ (T35-4); it will later be used for the predictive inference.

T92-1. Let the *p* predicates 'M_1', 'M_2', . . . , 'M_p' form a division (D25-4). Let *i* and *i'* be isomorphic individual distributions (D26-6a) for *n* given individual constants with respect to the given division, and let *j* be the corresponding statistical distribution (D26-6b). (Hence *i* and *i'* are disjunctive components in *j*.) Let n_m ($m = 1$ to p) be the number of full sentences of 'M_m' in i (and hence likewise in every other disjunctive component of j). Let d be the number of disjunctive components in j (in other words, the number of individual distributions isomorphic to i). Let h and e be any sentences not containing any of the individual constants occurring in j, and let e be not L-false. Let m and c be symmetrical functions as in T91-2. Then the following holds. (Some of the indications for proofs refer only to a finite system; in this case the same assertions for the infinite system follow with the help of T57-5 or T57-6, respectively.)

a. $d = \frac{n!}{n_1!\, n_2! \ldots n_p!}$. (From T40-32b.)

b. $\mathfrak{m}(i') = \mathfrak{m}(i)$. (From T91-2a.)

c. $\mathfrak{m}(j) = d \times \mathfrak{m}(i)$. (From T26-5b, T57-1n, (b).) (c) is analogous to T91-3, but it holds also for the infinite system because, also in this system, i and j refer only to a finite number n of individuals.

d. $\mathfrak{m}(h \,.\, i) = \mathfrak{m}(h \,.\, i')$.

Proof. The two conjunctions are isomorphic, because the second is constructed out of the first by that correlation which leads from i to i' and leaves all in not occurring in i unchanged. Hence the assertion (T91-2a).

e. $\mathfrak{m}(h \,.\, j) = d \times \mathfrak{m}(h \,.\, i)$.

Proof. Let j be $i_1 \vee i_2 \vee \ldots \vee i_d$. Then $h \,.\, j$ is L-equivalent (by distribution, T21-5m(2)) to $(h \,.\, i_1) \vee (h \,.\, i_2) \vee \ldots \vee (h \,.\, i_d)$. The components in the latter disjunction are L-exclusive in pairs (T26-5b) and have the same m-value (d). Hence the assertion (T57-1n), in analogy to (c).

f. $\mathfrak{c}(i,e) = \mathfrak{c}(i',e)$. (From (d).)

g. $\mathfrak{c}(j,e) = d \times \mathfrak{c}(i,e)$. (From (e).)

h. $\mathfrak{c}(h,i) = \mathfrak{c}(h,i')$. (From (b), (d).)

+i. $\mathfrak{c}(h,j) = \mathfrak{c}(h,i)$. (From (c), (e).)

j. $\mathfrak{m}(j) = \frac{n!}{n_1!\, n_2! \ldots n_p!} \times \mathfrak{m}(i)$. (From (c), (a).)

+k. Let e be not L-false and not contain any in occurring in i. Then $\mathfrak{c}(j,e) = \frac{n!}{n_1!\, n_2! \ldots n_p!} \times \mathfrak{c}(i,e)$. (From (g), (a).)

(i) is of special importance. It shows that for a symmetrical c of a hypothesis referring to other individuals than the evidence it makes no difference whether the evidence is an individual distribution or merely a statistical distribution; in other words, even if the evidence specifies the individuals, only their numbers are relevant for c. ((i) may be regarded as a special case of the more general theorem T59-3c.)

T92-3. Let 'M_1', . . . , 'M_p' form a division. Let i be an individual distribution for s individual constants with respect to the given division with the cardinal numbers $s_1, s_2, \ldots, s_p$; likewise i' for s' individual constants, which do not occur in i, with the cardinal numbers $s'_1, s'_2, \ldots, s'_p$. Let j be the statistical distribution corresponding to i, and j' that corresponding to i'. It is clear that $i \cdot i'$ differs at most in the order of the conjunctive components from an individual distribution for the $s + s'$ in with respect to the given division with the cardinal numbers $s_1 + s'_1, \ldots, s_p + s'_p$; let e be the corresponding statistical distribution. Then the following holds. (Here again, the assertion for $\mathfrak{L}_\infty$ can be proved with the help of T57-5 or 6.)

a. Lemma. The number of disjunctive components in j is $\frac{s!}{s_1!\, s_2! \ldots s_p!}$, in j' $\frac{s'!}{s'_1!\, s'_2! \ldots s'_p!}$, in e $\frac{(s+s')!}{(s_1+s'_1)!(s_2+s'_2)!\ldots(s_p+s'_p)!}$. (From T1a.)

b. $\mathfrak{m}(e) = \frac{(s+s')!}{(s_1+s'_1)!(s_2+s'_2)!\ldots(s_p+s'_p)!} \times \mathfrak{m}(i \cdot i')$.

(From (a), in analogy to T1j.)

c. Lemma. $\vdash j \cdot j' \supset e$.

Proof. $j \cdot j'$ says that, for every m (from 1 to p), s_m of the first s individuals are M_m and s'_m of the second s' individuals are M_m. From this it follows that of the total of $s + s'$ individuals $s_m + s'_m$ are M_m. This is what e says.

d. Lemma. $\vdash e \cdot j \supset j'$.

Proof. e says that, for every m, of the total of $s + s'$ individuals $s_m + s'_m$ are M_m. j says that of the first s individuals s_m are M_m. Therefore $e \cdot j$ entails that of the second s' individuals, since they are distinct from the first ones, s'_m are M_m. This is what j' says.

e. Lemma. $\vdash e \cdot j \equiv j \cdot j'$. (From (c), (d).)

f. Lemma. $\vdash e \cdot i \equiv i \cdot j'$.

Proof. 1. $\vdash i \supset j$ (T26-5c). Therefore, with (d), $\vdash e \cdot i \supset i \cdot j'$. 2. Since $\vdash i \supset j$, $\vdash i \cdot j' \supset j \cdot j'$. Hence, with (c), $\vdash i \cdot j' \supset e \cdot i$.

g. Lemma. $\mathfrak{m}(e \cdot i) = \mathfrak{m}(i \cdot j') = \frac{s'!}{s'_1!\, s'_2! \ldots s'_p!} \times \mathfrak{m}(i \cdot i')$.

Proof. The first equation follows from (f). Since i and j' have no in in common, the second equation follows from T1e (with 'i' for 'h', 'j'' for 'j', and 'i'' for 'i') and (a).

h. (1) $\mathfrak{m}(j \cdot j') = \frac{s!}{s_1!\, s_2! \ldots s_p!} \times \mathfrak{m}(i \cdot j')$,

(2) $= \frac{s!}{s_1!\, s_2! \ldots s_p!} \times \frac{s'!}{s'_1!\, s'_2! \ldots s'_p!} \times \mathfrak{m}(i \cdot i')$.

Proof. Since j and j' have no in in common, (1) follows from T1e (with 'j'' for 'h') and (a). (2) from (g).

+i. (1) $\mathfrak{c}(i,e) = \frac{s'!}{s'_1!\, s'_2! \ldots s'_p!} \times \frac{(s_1+s'_1)!(s_2+s'_2)!\ldots(s_p+s'_p)!}{(s+s')!}$. (From (g), (b).)

(2) $= \frac{\left[{s_1+s'_1 \atop s_1}\right]\left[{s_2+s'_2 \atop s_2}\right]\cdots\left[{s_p+s'_p \atop s_p}\right]}{\left[{s+s' \atop s}\right]}$. (From (1), D40-3.)

+j. (1) $\mathfrak{c}(j,e) = \frac{s!}{s_1!\, s_2! \ldots s_p!} \times \frac{s'!}{s'_1!\, s'_2! \ldots s'_p!} \times \frac{(s_1+s'_1)!(s_2+s'_2)!\ldots(s_p+s'_p)!}{(s+s')!}$.

Proof. $\mathfrak{m}(e \,.\, j) = \mathfrak{m}(j \,.\, j')$ (from (e)). Therefore $\mathfrak{c}(j,e) = \mathfrak{m}(j \,.\, j')/\mathfrak{m}(e)$. Hence, with (h)(2) and (b), the assertion.

(2) $$= \frac{s!}{s_1!\, s_2! \ldots s_p!} \times \mathfrak{c}(i,e). \text{ (From (1), (i)(1).)}$$

(3) $$= \frac{\binom{s_1+s_1'}{s_1}\binom{s_2+s_2'}{s_2}\cdots\binom{s_p+s_p'}{s_p}}{\binom{s+s'}{s}}. \text{ (From (1).)}$$

(We shall often state the value of a function in several forms, marked by figures under the same letter. The difference between them is often (as here with (1) and (2) under (i) and (1) and (3) under (j)) merely one of mathematical notation. Listing of various forms is often convenient for reference in proofs of later theorems.)

T3i and j are the first theorems in our theory which state values of c (except for the trivial values 0 and 1) absolutely, so to speak, that is to say, not only in relation to other c-values but in such a manner that they show how actually to compute the values for given sentences. Theorems of this kind are possible at the present stage of our construction, i.e., in the theory of symmetrical c-functions, only for those particular cases where the individuals referred to in the hypothesis occur already in the evidence, as is the case in T3i and j. T3 will be used in § 94 for the direct inductive inference.

Comparing the values T3i(2) and j(3), we find a striking similarity. This is the first example of a relationship which we shall find in many theorems later: if *i* is an individual distribution and *j* the corresponding statistical distribution, then often $\mathfrak{c}(i,e)$ is entirely expressed in terms of the [ ]-function and $\mathfrak{c}(j,e)$ in terms of the ( )-function with the same arguments. This was our reason for the choice of the notation with '[ ]' in analogy to the customary notation with '( )'.

§ 94. The Direct Inductive Inference

The direct inference is that from the population to a sample. *e* states the *absolute frequency* (*af*) n_i of a property *M* in a population of *n* individuals; hence the *relative frequency* (*rf*) is $r_i = n_i/n$. The hypothesis h_{st} states the rf of *M* in a sample. It is found that the c of h_{st} has its greatest value when the rf of *M* in the sample is equal, or as near as possible, to the rf in the population. If the hypothesis says that a certain individual of the population is *M*, then its c is r_i. This shows a close connection between c (probability$_1$) and the rf in the population (probability$_2$). The results here, in distinction to our later results concerning other kinds of inductive inference, are in agreement with those of the classical theory of probability.

The remainder of this chapter deals with the direct inference, which is one of the principal kinds of inductive inference (§ 44B). This part of inductive logic is located in this chapter because, in distinction to the theories of the other kinds of inductive inference, it does not require the choice of a particular c-function but holds for all symmetrical c-functions.

The ***direct*** (or internal or downward) ***inference*** is the inference from the population to a sample. Example: the evidence *e* says that among the three million inhabitants of Chicago 80 per cent are born in America. A sample of fifty persons is given; nothing is known about these persons except that they are inhabitants of Chicago. The hypothesis *h* may say that among these fifty persons forty (or forty-three, or between thirty-seven and forty-three, or less than thirty) will be found to be born in America. c(*h*,*e*) is to be determined.

We shall now formulate this kind of inference in general terms. We consider a population of n individuals. This population is supposed to be given by enumeration, that is, by a list of n in. A division consisting of p properties $M_1, M_2, \ldots, M_p$ is given. Let the evidence *e* say that of these n individuals n_1 have the property M_1, n_2 have $M_2, \ldots, n_p$ have M_p. For any i (from 1 to p), n_i is called the *absolute frequency* (*af*) of M_i in the population. The *relative frequency* (*rf*) of M_i in the population is $r_i = n_i/n$. *e* states only these frequencies of M_i without specifying *which* n_i individuals are M_i. Thus *e* is not an individual distribution but a statistical distribution. Our problem of the direct inference refers to a sample from the population containing s individuals. The given evidence *e* says nothing about their properties; the individuals are merely given by a list of individual constants, and from that it is seen that they belong to the population. The hypothesis *h* says that s_1 specified individuals of this sample are M_1, s_2 are $M_2, \ldots, s_p$ are M_p. Thus, *h* is an individual distribution. Furthermore, we consider the corresponding statistical hypothesis h_{st} which states for each M_i the same frequency s_i as *h* but does not specify which s_i individuals are M_i. The problem of the direct inference is that of determining the c-values of *h* and especially h_{st} on *e*. The solution of this problem for all symmetrical c-functions is given by the subsequent theorem T1 which is a simple consequence of earlier results (§ 92).

We understand here and further on by a *sample* simply a subclass of the population without any qualification. It is customary in the statistical theory of samples to regard a statistical inference with respect to a given sample as valid only if this sample is a *random sample*. A sample is called a random sample if it has been selected from the population by a procedure of such a kind that all individuals of the population have the same probability$_2$ of being selected, that is, such that in a prolonged application of the procedure all individuals will be selected with equal frequencies. (For original formulations of the definition see Venn [Logic], chap. v, and C. S. Peirce [Theory], p. 454; for a modern formulation, e.g., Cramér [Statistics], p. 324.) The fact that this theory uses the concept of probability$_2$ instead of probability$_1$ has the effect that we can hardly ever know whether a sample that we have selected from a population is a random sample in the defined sense. This was correctly pointed out by Keynes ([Probab.], pp. 290 ff.). The validity of any inductive inference, even in practical application, does not depend on the actual state of affairs, and certainly not on any unknown frequencies; it depends merely on the given knowledge situation or, more exactly speaking, on the logical relations between the given evidence and the hypothesis. The individuals of the sample must not be *known* to have any common property beyond what is said about them in the evidence, or at least not any property that is relevant for the hypothesis in question. This requirement, however, need not be mentioned in any theorem of inductive logic as a qualifying condition. It concerns not the theorem but its practical application to given knowledge situations; for this purpose, however, it is already implied by our requirement of total evidence (§ 45B): the evidence must state all observational knowledge that is actually available; in other words, a theorem is not directly applicable to a knowledge situation in which the available observational knowledge contains more than the evidence described in the theorem. The main difficulty in the practical application of inductive theorems consists in the fact that actual knowledge situations contain much more than any of the simple evidences referred to in theorems. A theorem can nevertheless be applied indirectly, provided the additional knowledge is, at least approximately, irrelevant for the hypothesis in question. The requirement that a random method be chosen for the selection of the sample is not a rule of inductive logic but a methodological rule (§ 44A) intended to assure the irrelevance of the known common property of the individuals of the sample for the hypothesis in question. The procedure used for selecting the sample usually determines such a common property. For example, suppose that the hypothesis concerns the distribution of political opinions among the students at a certain university. If we take as sample those students who major in history, then this fact constitutes a common property which, taken together with previous experiences concerning political opinions of history students, is *not* irrelevant for the hypothesis in question. If, on the other hand, the sample is selected by a blind drawing of lots, then the common property of being selected by this procedure is irrelevant. Irrelevance is here meant, of course, not in the frequency sense but in the inductive sense as discussed earlier (§ 65).

Although theorems like T1 do not involve the concept of randomness, this concept is nevertheless of great importance for inductive logic, especially in application to random distributions and random order. Randomness in this sense is the opposite to uniformity. Both concepts will be discussed in Volume II.

+T94-1. Let $\mathfrak{L}$ be any finite or infinite system. Let the predicates 'M_i' (i = 1 to p) form a division. Let e be a statistical distribution for n given in (in $\mathfrak{L}$) with respect to the division, with the cardinal number n_i for 'M_i'. Let $r_i = n_i/n$. Let h be an individual distribution for s of the n in in e (hence $s \leqq n$) with the cardinal number s_i for 'M_i'. Let $s_i \leqq n_i$, because otherwise obviously $\vdash e \supset \sim h$ and hence $\mathfrak{c}(h,e) = 0$. Let h_{st} be the statistical distribution corresponding to h. Let $\mathfrak{c}$ be any symmetrical c-function for $\mathfrak{L}$. Then the following holds.

a. (1) $\mathfrak{c}(h,e) = \frac{(n-s)!}{(n_1-s_1)!(n_2-s_2)!\dots(n_p-s_p)!} \times \frac{n_1!n_2!\dots n_p!}{n!}$;

(2) $= \frac{\left[{n_1 \atop s_1}\right]\left[{n_2 \atop s_2}\right]\dots\left[{n_p \atop s_p}\right]}{\left[{n \atop s}\right]}$.

Proof. From T92-3i by substituting 'h' for 'i', '$n - s$' for 's'', '$n_i - s_i$' for 's_i''. (This means that we apply the sentence i in the earlier theorem to the sample and i' to the remainder of the population.)

b. (1) $\mathfrak{c}(h_{st},e) = \frac{s!}{s_1!s_2!\dots s_p!} \times \mathfrak{c}(h,e)$;

(2) $= \frac{\binom{n_1}{s_1}\binom{n_2}{s_2}\dots\binom{n_p}{s_p}}{\binom{n}{s}}$.

Proof. From T92-3j, by the same substitutions as for (a), and 'h_{st}' for 'j'.

c. Let $p = 2$; hence the division consists simply of M_1 and M_2 (which is non-M_1). We consider the values of $\mathfrak{c}(h_{st},e)$ for constant s when s_1 runs through those values from 0 to s which are possible on evidence e (that is, $s_1 \leqq n_1$ and, if $n_2 < s$, $s_1 \geqq s - n_2$). Let 'q' be short for '$(s+1)(n_1+1)/(n+2)$'. Then the following holds.

(1) If the interval from $q - 1$ to q contains only one integer which is a possible value of s_1, say s^*, then $\mathfrak{c}(h_{st},e)$ has its only maximum for $s_1 = s^*$.

(2) If both q and $q - 1$ are integers and possible values of s_1, then $\mathfrak{c}(h_{st},e)$ has two equal maxima for $s_1 = q$ and $s_1 = q - 1$.

(3) If sr_1 is an integer, then $\mathfrak{c}(h_{st},e)$ has its only maximum for $s_1 = sr_1$.

Proof. Let h'_{st} be like h_{st} but with the cardinal number $s_1 - 1$ instead of s_1 for 'M' and hence $s_2 + 1$ instead of s_2 for '$\sim M$'. Then (b(2)):

(A) $\mathfrak{c}(h_{st},e)/\mathfrak{c}(h'_{st},e) = (s_2+1)(n_1-s_1+1)/s_1(n_2-s_2)$.

This value decreases with increasing s_1. It is 1 for $s_1 = q$. 1. If q is not an integer, let q' be the greatest integer smaller than q. Then the quotient (A) for $s_1 = q' + 1$ is < 1 because $q' + 1 > q$. Therefore the c for $s_1 = q' + 1$ is smaller than for $s_1 = q'$; and likewise the c for any $s_1 > q' + 1$. On the other hand, the quotient (A) for $s_1 = q'$ is > 1 because $q' < q$. Therefore the c for $s_1 = q' - 1$, and likewise for any smaller s_1, is smaller than for $s_1 = q'$. Thus c has its only maximum for $s_1 = q'$. 2. If q is an integer and q and $q - 1$ are possible values of s_1, then c is equal for these values because (A) is 1 for $s_1 = q$, and has its maxima for them. 3. It can easily be seen that $q - 1 < r_1 s < q$. Hence the assertion (3) from (1).

d. Let $p = 2$. For any m (from 0 to s), let h_m be the statistical distribution h_{st} with $s_1 = m$ and $s_2 = s - m$; s remains unchanged. Then $\sum_{m=0}^{s} [m \times c(h_m,e)] = sr_1$. (For $m = 0$, the product is 0; for those values of s_1 which are not possible on e, $c = 0$. Therefore, the sum may be restricted to the positive possible values of s_1.)

Proof. According to b(2) for $p = 2$, the sum mentioned is $\sum_{m=1}^{s} [m\binom{n_1}{m}\binom{n_2}{s-m}]/\binom{n}{s}$. Since $m\binom{n_1}{m} = n_1 \binom{n_1-1}{m-1}$ (T40-8e), the numerator is, with $l = m - 1$: $n_1 \sum_{l=0}^{s-1} [\binom{n_1-1}{l}\binom{n_2}{s-1-l}]$, $= n_1 \binom{n-1}{s-1}$ (T40-9c). Therefore the quotient is $n_1(n-1)!\, s!\, (n-s)!/(s-1)!(n-s)!n!$ (D40-2a), $= sn_1/n = sr_1$.

e. Corollary. Let $p = 2$, $s = s_1 = 1$, $s_2 = 0$; hence h_{st} is the same as h. Then $c(h,e) = n_1/n = r_1$. (From (a(2)), T40-13a and b.)

T1a(2) and b(2) show again the analogy explained at the end of § 92. *T1c* says that the c for h_{st} has a maximum if the rf (relative frequency) of M in the sample is equal, or as near as possible, to the rf in the population. Note that this holds only for the statistical distribution h_{st}, not for the individual distribution h; this will be explained in connection with the subsequent examples (§ 95).

We shall explain later (§ 99) that the estimate of a magnitude (in the sense of the c-mean estimate) is the sum of its possible values each multiplied with the c for the hypothesis stating that value. Therefore the estimate of the af (absolute frequency) s_1 of M in the sample, with respect to the evidence e stating the rf of M in the population as r_1, is given by the sum mentioned in *T1d*. Thus we see from T1d that the estimate of s_1 on e is sr_1. Therefore *the estimate of the rf in the sample is sr_1/s, that is, r_1, hence equal to the rf in the population*. We have seen (T1c) that the most probable value of s_1 (i.e., that with the maximum c) is either sr_1 or, if this is not an integer, it is an integer nearest to sr_1. The estimate of s_1, however, is always exactly sr_1 even if this is not an integer. (The estimate of a magnitude need not be one of its possible values; this will be explained later.)

T1e says that, for the hypothesis that a given individual belonging to the population is M, $\mathfrak{c}$ is r_1, that is, the rf of M in the population. For example, if the evidence e says that four-fifths of the inhabitants of Chicago are M, then the $\mathfrak{c}$ or, in other words, the probability that an inhabitant of Chicago taken at random is M is four-fifths. Many, especially those accustomed to the frequency conception of probability, will perhaps be tempted to say that this statement is quite trivial because by the probability of a Chicagoan being M we mean just the rf of M among Chicagoans. However, this judgment about the theorem is based upon a confusion of the two concepts of probability; and the theorem is, in fact, very important and far from trivial. It is true that the probability$_2$ of a Chicagoan being M means the rf of M among Chicagoans. The theorem T1e, however, does not speak about probability$_2$ but probability$_1$, that is, $\mathfrak{c}$. It says, applied to the present example, that the probability$_1$ of a Chicagoan being M with respect to a given evidence e is equal (not, as the probability$_2$, to the actual rf, irrespective of whether anybody knows it or not, but) to that value of the rf which is stated in the evidence e (irrespective of whether this is the actual value or not). Thus we see that, in the situation of the direct inference, there is a very close connection between the rf of M in the population as stated in e and the $\mathfrak{c}$ for a full sentence of M, in other words, between a known value of probability$_2$ and the value of probability$_1$. It was earlier mentioned (§ 42A (1)), that this connection makes the historical shift in the meaning of the word 'probability' understandable; this word had first only the sense of probability$_1$ and later was used in certain contexts in the sense of probability$_2$.

There can be no doubt that the direct inference is genuinely inductive in our sense, that is, nondeductive; it is obviously impossible to deduce the frequency in the sample from that in the population. (The fact that some authors call it a deductive probability inference is due, it seems to me, not to a difference in opinion, but merely to a difference in terminology.) Nevertheless, the direct inference is fundamentally different from the other inductive inferences in this point: all the individuals to which the hypothesis refers occur already in the evidence. In consequence of this, the direct inference is in certain respects more similar to the deductive inference than the other inductive inferences. First, the direct inference holds for all symmetrical $\mathfrak{c}$-functions alike. Thus it presupposes only that all individuals are treated on a par, but it is independent of the choice of a particular measure function. Further, it is independent of that characteristic of the property M which we call its logical width (§ 32). We shall later see that for all the other kinds of inductive inference the value of $\mathfrak{c}$

depends upon the choice of the c-function and hence of the underlying m, and that for at least some c-functions, among them our function c*, the value depends also upon the logical width of *M*. The theory of the other inferences cannot be developed in a general form. Therefore, we postpone it after the definition of c*, and then we shall construct it for this function.

The results stated in T1 are in agreement with those given in the traditional calculus of probability based upon the classical conception, although the results are usually interpreted in a different way. This agreement is a consequence of the fact that these results are independent of the m-function and independent of the width of *M*. (We shall see later that the results to which our system of inductive logic leads in the case of all other inductive inferences differ from the traditional results; the latter are valid only in certain special cases, for instance, as approximations in the case of sufficiently large samples or for certain kinds of properties.)

For the direct inference and for most of the other inductive inferences with the exception of the universal inference, the values of c are independent of the total number *N* of individuals in the universe (though not of the number *n* of individuals in the population, which is here regarded as part of the universe). Therefore, the results hold for any finite or infinite system 𝔏.

A numerical example for T1 will be given at the end of the next section.

§ 95. The Binomial Law

From the earlier theorem on the direct inference the binomial law in its classical form can be derived. It holds as an approximation for a large finite population. It holds further exactly either as limiting value for an infinite sequence of increasing populations or for an infinite population. Some traditional uses of it are not admissible. Numerical examples for the theorems in this and the preceding sections are given.

Because of the agreement between our theory of symmetrical c-functions and the traditional method, as far as the direct inference is concerned, we may follow the traditional method for some further steps, which are of a purely mathematical nature. These steps lead to certain results which hold as approximations for a sufficiently large population. These results are stated in the theorems of this and the next sections, leading to the famous Bernoulli theorem.

+T95-1.

Let 𝔏, 'M_i' ($i =$ 1 to p), e, n, n_i, r_i, h, s, s_i, h_{st}, and c be as in T94-1. Then the subsequent results hold in the following two senses (A) and (B).

A. If n is very large in relation to s, and likewise n_i to s_i for every i, then the results hold *approximately*.

B. If for $n \to \infty$, for every i, the rf n_i/n approaches to a limit r_i, then the c-values stated are the limits to which c approaches.

a. $c(h,e) = r_1^{s_1} r_2^{s_2} \ldots r_p^{s_p}$. (From T94-1a(2), T40-17a(3).)

b. $c(h_{st},e) = \frac{s!}{s_1!\, s_2! \ldots s_p!} r_1^{s_1} r_2^{s_2} \ldots r_p^{s_p}$. (From T94-1b(1), (a).)

+**c.** ***Binomial Law.*** For $p = 2$:

$c(h_{st},e) = \binom{s}{s_1} r_1^{s_1} r_2^{s_2}$. (From (b).)

d. As T94-1c, but with $q = (s + 1)r_1$. (From T94-1c, for $n \to \infty$.)

(d) says here, as in the earlier theorem, that $c(h_{st},e)$ has its maximum when s_1 is equal, or the nearest integer, to sr_1, hence when the rf of M in the sample is equal, or as close as possible, to that in the population.

The ***binomial law*** of probability bears this name because of its relationship to the binomial theorem (T40-10a). Our formulation of it (T1c) as a special case of the general law T1b refers to an evidence stating the rf r_1 of a property M in a population to which the sample in question belongs. The traditional formulation does not refer to this rf; it speaks of r_1 rather as the probability of an individual's being M; a restricting condition is usually added to the effect that r_1 must be the probability of M for each individual in the sample or each trial in the series of experiments, "independently" of the other individuals. This independence is meant in the sense that, even after some of the individuals have been observed, the probability for any other one is still r_1. As Keynes has pointed out correctly ([Probab.], pp. 342 f.), this condition is very seldom fulfilled. If we deal with a fixed population which is finite but very large, then the condition cannot be fulfilled exactly; and, although it is fulfilled with good approximation as long as the sample is small in relation to the population, it is in general not even approximately fulfilled for large samples. The condition is exactly fulfilled and therefore the theorem holds exactly for any sample size s, if the population is infinite (see below) or if, after each observation of an event, the situation is rearranged so as to be like the original one. In this case, we have to do, strictly speaking, with a series of similar populations instead of one population. Consider the familiar example of an urn containing n balls of which n_1 are known to have the color M and n_2 non-M. A ball is drawn at random; its property is observed; then *the ball is replaced*, the content of the urn is mixed, and then again a ball is drawn, etc. The situation before the second drawing is similar to that before the first in this essential point: we know again that there is a population of n individuals of which n_1 are M and n_2 are non-M. Therefore, the probability (c) for the second drawing yielding a ball that is M

is again $n_1/n = r_1$; thus the condition for the binomial theorem is exactly fulfilled. Strictly speaking, the population for the second drawing is not the same as that for the first. What we usually call the same ball a_k at the first and at the second time-point are, strictly speaking, two different individuals a_{k1} and a_{k2} which stand in that relation which we may call 'genidentity' (Kurt Lewin); this is an empirical relation established by a continuity of observation. We know from experience that under usual circumstances two genidentical ball-moments have the same color; and therefore we assume that the frequency of *M* at the second time-point is the same as at the first. However, this is obviously an inductive result from many previous experiences. In order to be independent of these earlier observations and to obtain a pure case for the binomial theorem, we ought to count the number of balls with *M* and non-*M* again after replacing the ball. This shows that the experiment described with replacement of each ball drawn is not essentially different from an experiment in which we take each time a new urn with new balls but such that the same numbers n, n_1, and n_2 hold for each urn. The experiment with replacement is, strictly speaking, likewise an experiment with a series of populations; the procedure of replacement is merely a convenient technical device to assure the constancy of the frequencies without the need of new balls and repeated countings.

The theorem T1 is formulated only for finite populations (even (B) refers only to an infinite sequence of finite populations, not to an infinite population). But it holds likewise for an *infinite population* K_∞, that is, for the class of all individuals in $\mathfrak{L}_\infty$ or an infinite subclass of it. In this case, r_i is to be defined, not as a quotient, but as the limit of n_i/n for $n \rightarrow \infty$ with respect to a given serial order of the elements of K_∞. In our language system $\mathfrak{L}_\infty$ there is no sentence *e* saying that the limit of rf is r_i; therefore, we had to formulate our theorems for finite populations. [In the metalanguage, however, variables for natural numbers and real numbers are available and hence the limit concept is expressible; we use it often in definitions (e.g., for $_\infty\mathfrak{c}$ in D56-2) and theorems (e.g., here T1(B)).] If a stronger language system is chosen which contains natural number variables (for instance, the system $\mathfrak{L}'$ described in § 15B), then the limit statement can be formulated in it (it is usually formulated with real number variables, but natural number variables are sufficient). The definition of symmetrical c-functions can easily be adapted to this stronger system (see the indications given in § 15B concerning form I of an extended inductive logic). Then the binomial law and Bernoulli's theorem can be proved with respect to an evidence *e* which says that in the infinite population the limit of the rf of M_i is r_i (in the case of $\mathfrak{L}'$, with respect to the basic order of the individuals). In this case, the c-value stated by the binomial law holds exactly.

However, in the case of an infinite population the binomial law—and the same holds for Bernoulli's theorem—involves a certain difficulty concerning not its theoretical validity but rather the possibility of its application. We have seen that *if* e says that the limit of rf of M is r_1, then c has the value given by the theorem. Now, in order to apply any inductive theorem to a given knowledge situation, e must represent the knowledge available. Let us leave aside here the difficulty connected with the requirement of total evidence (§ 45B), because this difficulty is not specific to the present problem but is found in all applications of inductive logic. In other words, let us assume that all observational results about other things which the observer X may have are irrelevant for h_{st} and hence may be omitted. Then the question remains as to how X can ever possess evidence stating the exact value of the limit of rf of M. The question I am raising here is not meant in the sense of the assertion that statements concerning infinite sequences of events are meaningless because it is not possible to know anything about an infinite sequence and, least of all, about a limiting value for it. This assertion has sometimes been made as an objection against the frequency theory of probability, because this theory explicates probability$_2$ by the limit of the rf in an infinite sequence. I agree with the frequentists in the view that the assertion is too strong. If we were to require for knowledge absolute certainty, then we would have to give up all claim to knowledge in science. If, consequently, we admit also knowledge short of certainty, then we may admit hypotheses concerning limits of rf just as well as other hypotheses with the same degree of logical complexity (cf. [Testability] §§ 25 f.); and then we may try to confirm hypotheses of this kind by observations. A statement concerning the limit of rf is a confirmable hypothesis and hence empirically meaningful. However this does not solve our present difficulty. Although the limit statement can be indirectly confirmed by observational evidence, it is hardly possible to imagine a situation in which the limit statement itself formulates the observational evidence available to an observer X. Thus the binomial theorem for an infinite population, although theoretically valid, can hardly ever be applied directly to a given knowledge situation. Indirect application may still be possible, as for any other inductive theorem; that means it may help in establishing other theorems which in turn are directly applicable.

The binomial theorem has, since classical times, often been applied to situations of the following kind, which are fundamentally different from those referred to in our formulation T1c. The latter presupposes that r_1, the rf of *M* in the population, is given in the evidence *e*. Now the traditional way of reasoning is as follows: if the rf of *M* in the population is not known, then we may take instead the rf of *M* in a past series of observations. For example, suppose that we want to determine the probability for the hypothesis h_{st} that in the next hundred throws with this die there will be twenty aces. We do, of course, not know the rf of aces in any population of which the next hundred throws constitute a sample. But suppose we have earlier made two hundred throws and found among them twenty-four aces, hence an rf of 0.12. Then the traditional procedure consists in taking this value as the 'probability' r_1 to be used in the binomial law and hence to give as c for h_{st}: $\binom{100}{20} \times (0.12)^{20} \times (0.88)^{80}$. This procedure is not admitted by the above formulation of the binomial law (T1c), and I think it is incorrect. Inductive logic must, of course, also provide a solution for this problem where the evidence states statistical results concerning past events while the hypothesis states the rf for a series of future events. Since the class described in *e* does not comprehend the class described in *h*, this inductive inference is not from the population to a sample but from one sample to another not overlapping with the first. Therefore, it is not a case of direct inference but rather of predictive inference. In a later chapter (in Vol. II) we shall deal with this kind of inference and then give also a solution to the above problem (cf. § 110C in this volume). We shall see that here the binomial formula does not in general hold but only as an approximation under certain restricting conditions which are even stronger than those for T1 and which are not fulfilled in the example mentioned.

Numerical Examples for the Direct Inference.

First Example, for T94-1, with $p = 2$, '*M*' and '$\sim$*M*'. We consider a sample with $s = 7$ from a *small population:* $n = 14$, $n_1 = 10$; hence $n_2 = 4$, $r_1 = 5/7$, $r_2 = 2/7$. We consider all possible values for s_1. Since the population contains 4 individuals with non-*M*, the sample cannot contain more; hence $s_2 \leqq 4$, $s_1 \geqq 3$.

Let the population contain the individuals $a_1, a_2, \ldots, a_{14}$, and the sample the individuals $a_1, \ldots, a_7$. *h* is the prediction that s_1 specified individuals of the sample, say $a_1, \ldots, a_{s_1}$, are *M* and the others non-*M*. h_{st} is the weaker prediction that exactly s_1 of the seven mentioned individuals of the sample are *M*, no matter which they are. According to T94-1a(1), $c(h,e) = 7!10!4!/(10 - s_1)!(s_1 - 3)!14!$; according to T94-1b(1), $c(h_{st},e) = \binom{7}{s_1} \times c(h,e)$. This yields the values stated in the subsequent table. We see that, in accordance with T94-1c(3), c for h_{st} has its only maximum for $s_1 = sr_1 = 5$, that is, for the case in which the rf of *M* in the sample is the same as that in the population.

Second Example, for T95-1. We take $p = 2$ and $s = 7$, as in the first example. We make no specific assumption concerning the size of the population;

we presuppose merely that it is very large in relation to the sample (say, at least $n = 500$). We take, as in the first example, $r_1 = 5/7$. If the population is infinite, this means that the limit of the rf of M with respect to a given serial order of the individuals is $5/7$; in this case, the computed values for c hold exactly. If the population has a finite size n, it means that the rf of M (n_1/n) is $5/7$; in this case the values of c hold approximately. According to T95-1a, $c(h,e) = (5/7)^{s_1} \times (2/7)^{7-s_1}$. In this example, in distinction to the first, all values of s_1 from 0 to 7 are possible. The results are shown in the following table. According to T95-1c, the c-values for h_{st} are again found by multiplying with $\binom{7}{s_1}$. These values are shown in the last column of the table.

s_1	FIRST EXAMPLE: $n=14$		SECOND EXAMPLE: LARGE n	
	$c(h,e)$	$c(h_{st},e)$	$c(h,e)$	(Binomial Law) $c(h_{st},e)$
0	0	0	0.000155	0.000155
1	0	0	0.000388	0.00272
2	0	0	0.000971	0.0204
3	0.00100	0.0350	0.00243	0.0850
4	0.00700	0.245	0.00607	0.212
5	0.0210	*0.441*	0.0152	*0.319*
6	0.0350	0.245	0.0380	0.266
7	0.0350	0.0350	0.0948	0.0948
		1.001		1.000

In the second example we find again, in accordance with T94-1d, that c for h_{st} has its maximum for $s_1 = sr_1 = 5$. Note that this holds only for the statistical distribution h_{st}, not for the individual distribution h. For the latter, in the case $p = 2$, c increases always with increasing s_1 and has its maximum when all individuals in the sample are M. This holds always if $r_1 > 1/2$; if $r_1 < 1/2$, the maximum holds for $s_1 = 0$; if $r_1 = 1/2$, c is the same for all values of s_1. These results are plausible. If we take $s_1 + 1$ instead of s_1 and hence $s_2 - 1$ instead of s_2, then the new value of $c(h,e)$ (T95-1a with $p = 2$) is r_1/r_2 times the earlier one; and this ratio is >1 if $r_1 > 1/2$. In the second example, $r_1/r_2 = 5/2$. And this is indeed the ratio of each value in the column for $c(h,e)$ to the preceding value. (In the first example the situation is not so simple because of the small size of the population. When six individuals have been found to be M, then we see from e that among the remaining eight there are four with M and four with non-M. Therefore it is equally probable for the seventh individual to be M or non-M. This is the reason why $c(h,e)$ has the same value for $s_1 = 6$ and $s_1 = 7$).

§ 96. Bernoulli's Theorem

Bernoulli's theorem in its classical form holds as an approximation for the direct inference, if the sample is large and the population still much larger or even infinite. Bernoulli's limit theorem says that the c for the assumption that the relative frequency of a property M in a sample lies within a fixed interval, however small, around its relative frequency in the population can be brought as close to 1 as required by making the sample sufficiently large.

We shall now follow still further the classical method as far as the mathematical transformations are concerned, though not necessarily in the interpretation. These transformations, due to Jacob Bernoulli and Laplace, lead to the famous and important results stated in the following theorem T1, which often are collectively called Bernoulli's theorem (sometimes even including the binomial law); sometimes this name is applied in a more specific sense to T1e. Our interpretation of these results and the details of our formulations in T1 are determined by the fact that we locate the results into the framework of the theory of symmetrical c-functions as special cases of the direct inference. (We omit here the details of the mathematical transformations, because they have no bearing on the interpretation and can be found in most textbooks on probability.)

+T96-1. ***Bernoulli's Theorem.*** Let $\mathfrak{L}$, 'M' (for 'M_1', with '$\sim M$' for 'M_2'), e, n, n_1, n_2, r_1, r_2, s, s_1, s_2, h_{st}, and c be as in T94-1 but with $p = 2$. For abbreviation, let $\sigma = \sqrt{sr_1r_2}$ (this is the *standard deviation;* cf. remarks on T105-1); $\delta = s_1 - sr_1$ (this is the deviation of s_1 from its estimate sr_1). Let h be a disjunction of sentences of the form h_{st} but with different values of s_1, running from $s_{1,1}$ to $s_{1,2}$ ($s_{1,1} < s_{1,2}$). Let $\delta_1 = s_{1,1} - sr_1$, and $\delta_2 = s_{1,2} - sr_1$. Then the following approximations hold, provided that the sample size s and even sr_1r_2 is sufficiently large and the population size n is very large in relation to s (and n_1 to s_1, and n_2 to s_2).

a. The ***normal law***, concerning a *single frequency.*

$\mathfrak{c}(h_{st},e) \cong \frac{1}{\sigma\sqrt{2\pi}}\,\mathrm{e}^{-\delta^2/2\sigma^2} = \frac{1}{\sigma}\,\phi\left(\frac{\delta}{\sigma}\right)$. (The constants '$\pi$' and 'e' have here their usual mathematical meaning, while the variable 'e' refers to the evidence. For the normal function ϕ see D40-4a and the table T40-20.)

Proof. From the binomial law (T95-1c) with the help of Stirling's formula (T40-4). The proof is given in the textbooks on probability or statistics.

b. Concerning any *frequency interval.* Let s_1 in h run through all values (integers) from $s_{1,1}$ to $s_{1,2}$, both included. Hence the disjunction h says that s_1 belongs to the closed interval ($s_{1,1}$, $s_{1,2}$). Then the following holds.

(1) $\mathfrak{c}(h,e) \cong \frac{1}{\sigma}\sum_{\delta=\delta_1}^{\delta_2} \phi\left(\frac{\delta}{\sigma}\right)$.

(2) Rougher approximation:

$\mathfrak{c}(h,e) \cong \int_{u_1}^{u_2} \phi(t)dt = \Phi(u_2) - \Phi(u_1)$, where $u_1 = (\delta_1 - \frac{1}{2})/\sigma$; $u_2 = (\delta_2 + \frac{1}{2})/\sigma$. '$\Phi$' denotes the probability integral, see D40-4b and the table T40-20.

(3) Still rougher approximation:
as (2), but with $u_1 = \delta_1/\sigma$, $u_2 = \delta_2/\sigma$.

((1) from (a); (2) from (1) by an approximative transformation which replaces a sum with a sufficient number of terms by an integral; (3) holds as an approximation for (2), if the size of the interval, i.e., $s_{1,2} - s_{1,1}$, is sufficiently large.)

c. Concerning a *symmetrical frequency interval.* Let s_1 in h run from $sr_1 - \delta$ (or the integer nearest to it) to $sr_1 + \delta$. Hence h says that s_1 does not deviate from sr_1 by more than δ to either side.

(1) $\mathfrak{c}(h,e) \cong 2\Phi(u) - 1$, where $u = (\delta + \frac{1}{2})/\sigma$. (From (b)(2).)

(2) Rougher approximation: as (1), but with $u = \delta/\sigma$. (From (b)(3).)

(3) Alternative formulation for (2). Let h say that the rf of M in the sample is within the closed interval $r_1 \pm q$, where $q = \delta/s$. Then $\mathfrak{c}$ is as in (1), but with $u = q\sqrt{s/r_1 r_2}$. (From (2).)

d. Let s_1 in h run through all possible values (from 0 to s) which deviate from sr_1 by δ *or more* to either side.

(1) $\mathfrak{c}(h,e) \cong 2(1 - \Phi(u))$, where $u = (\delta - \frac{1}{2})/\sigma$. (From (c)(1).)

(2) Rougher approximation: as (1), but with $u = \delta/\sigma$. (From (c)(2).)

(3) Alternative formulation for (2). Let h say that the rf of M in the sample deviates from r_1 by q *or more* to either side. Then $\mathfrak{c}$ is as in (1), but with $u = q\sqrt{s/r_1 r_2}$. (From (2).)

Sometimes a table is given directly for the function $2(1 - \Phi(u))$; see, e.g., Fry [Probab.], pp. 453–55, Cramér [Statistics], p. 558.

e. ***Bernoulli's Limit Theorem.*** For a given r_1 and arbitrary positive real numbers q and ϵ, there is a number s' such that for every $s \geqq s'$ $\mathfrak{c}(h,e) > 1 - \epsilon$, where h says (as in (c)(3)) that the rf of M in the sample of size s is within the interval $r_1 \pm q$. In other words, if an interval, however small, around r_1 is chosen for the rf of M in a sample, $\mathfrak{c}(h,e)$ can be brought as close to 1 as desired by making the sample sufficiently large. (From (c)(3).)

The approximative results stated in these theorems are independent of the size of the population; it is presupposed only that the population is very large in comparison to the sample. Only r_1, the rf of M in the population, is relevant for the results; it enters through $\sigma = \sqrt{(sr_1(1 - r_1))}$. The theorems are here formulated only for finite populations, for the reasons explained in the preceding section. The results hold likewise for an infinite population with r_1 as the limit of rf. But even in this case the results are only approximations, in distinction to the binomial theorem. The accuracy of the approximations increases with increasing sample size s; the requirement that not only s but also sr_1r_2 must be sufficiently large was stated by Keynes ([Probab.], p. 339). Formulas with closer approximations have been stated by Laplace and later authors; they are given in textbooks on probability.

In the *normal law* (T1a), sr_1 (or the integer nearest to it) is that value of the af (absolute frequency) of M in the sample for which c has its maximum (T94-1c(3)). sr_1 is also the estimate of the af of M in the sample. Therefore $s_1 - sr_1$ is the difference between that value of s_1 which is stated in the hypothesis h_{st} and the most probable value of s_1 (or the estimate of s_1). The normal law states c as dependent merely upon the square of this difference and thus as equal for positive and negative deviations from sr_1. Thus the approximation given in the normal law gives a distribution of c which is symmetrical at both sides of the maximum, while the exact function (given for a finite population by T94-1b and for an infinite population by the binomial law T95-1c) is not symmetrical. However, the error made by the symmetrical function is small as long as s_1 is not too far away from sr_1 (cf. Keynes, pp. 338 f., 358–61).

T1 deals with the case that the rf of M in the population is known as r_1. It is presupposed that the sample size s is large and that the population is even much larger still. T1a answers questions of the form: what is the c for the assumption that s_1, the af of M in the sample, has such and such a *single value?* The theorem gives this value of c as a function of the difference between s_1 and its most probable value sr_1. On the other hand, T1b, c, and d answer questions, not concerning a single value of s_1, but *intervals* of such values. For large samples these questions concerning intervals are more important than those concerning single values. The content of the theorems is best seen from some numerical examples.

Example. Let us consider a sample of $s = 2400$ persons taken from the population of Chicago with $n = 3{,}000{,}000$. Let us suppose that it has been found in the census that the rf of a certain property M in this population is $r_1 = 0.6$; hence $r_2 = 0.4$. Thus, $sr_1r_2 = 576$; this is sufficiently large, as required. $\sigma = \sqrt{(sr_1r_2)} = 24$. The estimate and the most probable value of the rf in the sample is the same as in the population: $r_1 = 0.6$; and the estimate and the most probable value of the af s_1 in the sample is $sr_1 = 1440$.

Example for T1a. Let h_{st} say that $s_1 = 1452$; hence $\delta = 12$; $\delta/\sigma = 0.5$. Then T1a says that c for this hypothesis is $(1/\sigma)\phi(0.5)$. With the help of the table T40-20 we find that this is $0.352/24 = 0.0147$. The same c-value holds for $s_1 = 1428$.

T1b refers to any interval for s_1. If the interval contains only few values of s_1, we can determine c according to (1) by a sum extending over the possible cases. If, however, the interval is not small, this procedure becomes too cumbersome, and the use of the probability integral is much more convenient. The form (2) gives a good approximation even for small intervals. If the interval is sufficiently large, the simpler form (3) may be used.

Example for T1b. We take s, n, r_1, r_2, and σ as above. Let $\delta_1 = -12$, $\delta_2 = 24$; hence the interval for s_1 is (1428, 1464). This interval contains 37 values. Therefore the use of T1b(1) would be very cumbersome. Let us first use (2). $u_1 = -12.5/24 = -0.52$. $\Phi(u_1) = 1 - \Phi(0.52)$ (T40-19h), $= 1 - 0.698$ (table T40-20) $= 0.302$. $u_2 = 24.5/24 = 1.02$. $\Phi(u_2) = 0.846$. Hence $\mathfrak{c} = 0.544$. According to the rougher approximation (3), $u_1 = -12/24 = -0.5$. $\Phi(u_1) = 1 - 0.691 = 0.309$. $u_2 = 1$; $\Phi(u_2) = 0.841$. Hence $\mathfrak{c} = 0.532$. This value deviates from that obtained by (2) by about 2 per cent.

T1c is usually called *Bernoulli's theorem*, and we shall follow this usage. This is actually the form in which the theorem was formulated and proved by Laplace ([Théorie], in 1812) while Jacob Bernoulli himself ([Ars], published in 1713) stated the limit theorem (T1e). T1c deals with an interval for the af of M, i.e., s_1, which extends equally on both sides of sr_1 (forms (1) and (2)), or with an interval for the rf of M around r_1 (form (3)).

Example for T1c. Let us take $\delta = 24$. Thus h says that s_1 is somewhere in the interval 1440 ± 24 (that is, between 1416 and 1464). According to (1), $u = 24.5/24 = 1.02$; $\Phi(u) = 0.846$; $\mathfrak{c} = 0.692$. According to the rougher approximation (2), $u = 1$; $\Phi(u) = 0.841$; $\mathfrak{c} = 0.682$, which deviates from the value under (1) by 1.5 per cent. (3) leads, of course, to the same value as (2): $q = 0.01$; $s/r_1r_2 = 10{,}000$; $\sqrt{\ } = 100$; $u = 1$.

In *T1d*, h refers to the opposite case of T1c; it says that s_1 is *outside* a given symmetrical interval around sr_1. This theorem is often used when the statement e concerning the rf of M in the population is not actually known but either believed or merely considered and a sample is found which shows a surprisingly large deviation δ from the most probable value of the af (i.e., sr_1). Then the following question is raised: suppose we knew that the rf in the population were r_1, how probable would it be for a sample to have the observed deviation δ or a larger one to either side? T1d gives the answer to this question. For example, we make a long series of throws with a coin which has not been previously examined. We observe heads in considerably more than half of the throws. Shall we take this as an indication that the coin is loaded? Or could the coin be symmetrical and the surprising outcome merely a strange accident? In order to judge the latter case, we might be interested in determining the probability that a coin which is symmetrical and hence yields heads in one-half of all throws would give a result like the one observed or deviating even more from the most probable result. This probability is determined by T1d. This theorem is often used, in particular, by those statisticians who have no general concept of probability$_1$ and reject the inverse inductive inference but admit the direct inference and thereby Bernoulli's theorem. For what we call the rf in the population they use the term 'probability' in the sense of probability$_2$. Their theory does not admit the question: 'How probable is it, on the basis of the observed sample, that the rf in the population is $1/2$, in other words, that the coin is symmetrical?' Nevertheless they wish, of course, to make an inductive judgment on the hypothesis of the symmetry of the coin on the basis of the observed sample of throws. As a substitute for the rejected question, they judge the hypothesis by the probability determined by T1d. If the probability of a result like the one observed or still further away from the expected rf $1/2$ is very small, then they reject the hypothesis of symmetry. If this probability is large, the hypothesis may be accepted until further notice but need not be accepted. If the probability is neither very small nor large, judgment on the hypothesis is postponed until more observational results are available. This use of T1d is thus a weaker inductive method used as a substitute for those purposes for which a full inductive logic applies the inverse inference. [See the later remarks (§ 98) on the methods of testing hypotheses developed by Fisher, Neyman, and others.]

Example for T1d. Let us take $\delta = 72$. This means that we ask for the probability that s_1 lies *outside* the interval 1440 ± 71. Since this interval is large, we may use rhe rougher approximation (2). $u = 72/24 = 3$; $\Phi(u) = 0.99865$; $c = 0.00260$. This means that there is only a chance of about one-fourth of 1 per cent for a sample having an s_1 which deviates from 1440 by 72 or more. The method mentioned above might use this result in the following way. If a sample with $s_1 = 1512$ and hence $\delta = 72$ is found, the hypothesis that this is a random sample from a population with $r_1 = 0.6$ is rejected. (For instance, if someone draws 2400 balls from a large bag containing 60 per cent white balls and 40 per cent black balls and he finds 1512 white balls among the 2400 drawn, the assumption that this result is merely due to chance is rejected.)

Now let us go back to *T1c*, the theorem for symmetrical intervals, and compare the c-values determined by it for *two samples;* this will lead to an important general result. For this comparison we do not need any specific knowledge about the values of Φ and c but only the fact, obvious from the definition of Φ, that $\Phi(u)$ increases with increasing u and hence c increases with increasing δ. Within a population, where the rf of M is r_1, we consider a first sample of size s and a second, larger sample of size $s' = sm^2$ with $m > 1$. In both samples we consider intervals for s_1 around the most probable value of s_1; let the interval size be $\pm\delta$ in the first sample and $\pm\delta'$ in the second. We assume that both intervals are large enough so that we can use the rougher approximation T1c(2). In the first sample

$\sigma = \sqrt{(sr_1r_2)}$; in the second sample, $\sigma' = \sqrt{(s'r_1r_2)} = m\sigma$. If now we choose the interval in the second sample m times as large as that in the first, that is, with $\delta' = m\delta$, then $\delta'/\sigma' = \delta/\sigma$; hence $\mathfrak{c}$ has the same value in both samples. Thus we find the following results:

(i) If the size of the interval for af in the second sample is m times that in the first, $\mathfrak{c}$ remains unchanged.

(ii) If the interval size increases by less than m, $\mathfrak{c}$ decreases. This is the case in particular if the interval size for af remains the same.

(iii) If the interval size for af increases by more than m, $\mathfrak{c}$ increases. This is the case in particular if the interval for af increases by m^2, hence in proportion to the sample, and therefore the interval for rf remains the same. This is the most important result: $\mathfrak{c}$ for the same rf-interval increases with increasing sample.

Example. We considered previously, in the example for T1c, a sample with $s = 2400$, and within it the interval 1440 ± 24 for the af of *M;* in other words, the interval 0.6 ± 0.01 for the rf of *M*. Now we take a second sample with $s' = 9600$; $m^2 = 4$; that is, this sample has four times the size of the first. The most probable value for af (s_1) is here $s'r_1 = 5760$. $\sigma' = \sqrt{(s'r_1r_2)} = 48 = 2\sigma$. We shall now examine three different intervals within this sample:

(1) $\delta' = 24 = \delta$. The interval for af is 5760 ± 24; therefore the interval for rf is 0.6 ± 0.0025.

(2) $\delta' = 48 = 2\delta$. The interval for af is 5760 ± 48, that for rf is 0.6 ± 0.005.

(3) $\delta' = 96 = 4\delta$. The interval for af is 5760 ± 96; its size is four times the earlier one, for a sample which has four times the earlier size; thus the interval has increased in proportion to the sample. The interval for rf is 0.6 ± 0.01; this interval is the same as that considered for the first sample.

Now let us compare the $\mathfrak{c}$-value for the interval chosen in the first sample with that for the interval (2) in the second sample. Here we have $\delta' = 2\delta$. We found earlier that $\sigma' = 2\sigma$. Hence $\delta'/\sigma' = \delta/\sigma$. Therefore, according to T1c(2), $\mathfrak{c}$ has the same value in these two cases. Since interval (1) is smaller than (2), $\mathfrak{c}$ for (1) is smaller than for (2), and hence smaller than in the first sample. Since interval (3) is larger than (2), $\mathfrak{c}$ for (3) is greater than for (2), and hence greater than in the first sample.

Let us now compute the $\mathfrak{c}$-values, according to T1c(2), although they are not required for the comparative results just found. Since $\sigma' = 48$, for the interval (1) $\delta'/\sigma' = 0.5$; $\Phi = 0.691$; $\mathfrak{c} = 0.382$. For the interval (2), $\delta'/\sigma' = 1$; $\Phi = 0.841$; $\mathfrak{c} = 0.682$. For the interval (3), $\delta'/\sigma' = 2$; $\Phi = 0.9773$; $\mathfrak{c} = 0.9546$.

The last result we found under (iii) was this: If we take a fixed interval, however small, for rf around the most probable value r_1, say, the interval $r_1 \pm q$, and go to larger and larger samples, then the $\mathfrak{c}$ for the assumption that the rf of *M* in the sample lies in this interval grows more and more. Now *Bernoulli's Limit Theorem T1e* says that we can bring this $\mathfrak{c}$ as close to 1 as we want to by taking a sufficiently large sample; in other words, that, with increasing s, $\mathfrak{c}$ converges toward the limit 1. (Note that the theorem, even in the latter formulation in terms of a limit, speaks about an infinite sequence of larger and larger *finite* samples, not about an infinite sample.)

Example for the limit theorem *T1e*. We take $r_1 = 0.6$ as in the earlier examples so that the earlier results hold for the samples there considered. However, we do not fix the size of the population beforehand. r_1 is either the limit of rf for M in an infinite population or the rf in a finite population of size n provided that n is large enough to accommodate the sample size s which we shall determine. Let us consider a small interval around r_1, say, 0.6 ± 0.0025. We wish to determine how probable the assumption is that the rf of M in samples of various sizes lies within this interval. We found earlier (second sample, interval (1)) that, if the sample size s is 9600, c for our assumption is 0.382. This is not a large probability; that is not surprising, since we chose a rather small interval for rf. Now the limit theorem says that, in spite of the smallness of the interval chosen, we can bring c as close to 1 as we want to if only we take sufficiently large samples. Suppose we want c for our assumption to be $\geqq 0.999$. Bernoulli's theorem in its formulation for an rf-interval (T1c(3)) says this: if the interval for rf is $r_1 \pm q$, then $c = 2\Phi(q\sqrt{(s/r_1r_2)}) - 1$. In order to make $c = 2\Phi - 1 \geqq 0.999$, we must have $2\Phi \geqq 1.999$, $\Phi \geqq 0.9995$. We find in the table for Φ (T40-20) that $\Phi(3.3) = 0.9995$; and Φ increases with increasing argument. Therefore, we must have $q\sqrt{(s/r_1r_2)} \geqq 3.3$. Since $q = 0.0025$ and $r_1r_2 = 0.24$, s must be $\geqq 418{,}280$. This means that for a sample of size 418,280, $c = 0.999$; and for any larger sample, $c > 0.999$. For instance, for a sample containing 500,000 individuals we find $c = 0.99968$; for one million individuals, $c > 0.999999$. (The population of three million considered originally is not large in relation to these samples; the results here obtained presuppose a much larger population.)

This concludes our discussion of the direct inductive inference. The general theorems concerning this inference have first been given (§ 94), and then the classical formulas of the binomial law (§ 95) and of Bernoulli's theorems (§ 96). The latter two are here construed as approximations for special cases of the direct inference. The other kinds of inductive inference will be dealt with in later chapters in Volume II (see the summary in § 110).

CHAPTER IX

ESTIMATION

Besides the determination of the degree of confirmation, perhaps the most important task of inductive logic is that of estimation, that is, of determining an estimate of the unknown value of a magnitude on the basis of given evidence. We propose to explicate the estimate as a mean of the possible values of the magnitude; not simply the arithmetic mean but rather a weighted mean with degree of confirmation as weight (§§ 98, 99). Consequently, we define the c-mean estimate of a magnitude on the basis of the evidence *e* as the sum of the possible values of the magnitude, each value multiplied with the degree of confirmation for its occurrence (§ 100A). If an estimate (now always understood in the sense of c-mean estimate) for a magnitude on evidence *e* has been determined, the question arises how reliable it is, that is to say, how probable it is that its error, i.e., the difference between the estimated value of the magnitude and its actual value, is small. We take as measure of the reliability (or, rather, unreliability) of the first estimate another estimate, viz., the estimate of the square of the error of the first estimate (§§ 102, 103). The discussions so far, constituting the first part of the chapter, deal with the problem of the estimation of any magnitude in general. These considerations apply to any language containing quantitative concepts, provided a concept of degree of confirmation for that language is available.

The second part of the chapter refers to the language systems $\mathfrak{L}$ to which the theory of degree of confirmation developed in this book applies. The general concept of (c-mean) estimation, discussed in the first part in general terms, is here applied to the two chief quantitative magnitudes expressible in the systems $\mathfrak{L}$, viz., absolute and relative frequency. This may be either the frequency of truth in a class of sentences or the frequency of a given property *M* in a class *K* of individuals (§ 104). In analogy to the earlier distinction between various kinds of inductive inference (§ 44B), we distinguish now the corresponding kinds of estimation. The direct and the predictive estimation of frequencies are dealt with in particular. The direct estimation applies to the case where the evidence *e* gives the frequency of *M* in a population and the estimate is made for its frequency in a sample taken from the population (§ 105). In the case of the predictive estimation, *e* states the frequency of *M* in one sample and the estimate is made for its frequency in a second sample not overlapping with the first (§§ 106, 107).

§ 98. The Problem of Estimation

The procedure of estimating the unknown value of a magnitude is an inductive procedure. Therefore, we shall try (in the subsequent sections) to base this procedure on the concept of degree of confirmation as the fundamental concept of inductive logic. Contemporary statisticians (especially R. A. Fisher, Neyman, Pearson, Wald) have developed methods of estimation independent of the concept of degree of confirmation; but there is no agreement as to the logical foundations and the validity of these methods. After rejecting the classical methods based on the principle of indifference, the statisticians seem to have given up the hope of finding an adequate explicatum for probability$_1$; this was probably their chief reason for constructing independent methods of estimation.

We have seen earlier (§§ 49–51) that the concept of an estimate of an unknown value of a magnitude plays an important role in the application of inductive logic for the rational determination of decisions. We also briefly indicated a way for defining the concept of estimate in terms of probability$_1$ (§ 41D (3)), without, however, discussing the technical details. This led to a clearer understanding of the meaning of the logical concept of probability$_1$ and its relation to the statistical concept of probability$_2$. We found that probability$_1$ may, in certain cases, be interpreted as an estimate of probability$_2$ (§ 41D). In the present chapter we shall again take up the general problem of estimation and analyze it with the technical means developed in the intermediate chapters. We shall state in more exact terms the definition of a general estimate-function, called the c-mean estimate-function $\mathfrak{e}$, taking as the basis not the concept of probability$_1$ but that of a regular c-function as an explicatum of probability$_1$. Then we shall discuss, on the basis of this definition, various problems of estimation. In particular, we shall develop the theory of estimates of frequencies with respect to our systems $\mathfrak{L}$.

Both in everyday life and in the practice of science, estimates are made of the unknown values of magnitudes. The treasury makes an estimate of the income to be expected from a new tax, a hostess makes a guess as to the number of guests who will come, a general estimates the strength of the forces the enemy has now or will have tomorrow at a certain place, a physicist tries to find the best value for the velocity of light on the basis of several measurements which have yielded slightly different values. An estimate we make cannot be asserted with certainty. Strictly speaking, it is a guess. That does not mean that it is necessarily an arbitrary guess, that "any guess is as good as any other". Sometimes it is a "good guess", that is to say, the estimate is made by a careful procedure; but even for the most careful estimation there is no guarantee of success. To make a careful estimate means to utilize all relevant knowledge available and to reason well in deriving the estimate from this knowledge. Since the procedure of estimation cannot lead to certainty, it is not a deductive but an inductive procedure. In an ordinary inductive procedure we reason from given knowledge, the evidence *e*, to an unknown event, expressed in the hypothesis *h;* for instance, from our knowledge about the present weather situation and earlier meteorological observations to the prediction that it will rain tomorrow. The procedure of estimation is similar to this ordinary inductive procedure, but with this difference: the question is no longer how probable it is that it will rain tomorrow but, rather, *how much* will it presumably rain tomorrow.

Since estimation is an inductive procedure, it is the task of inductive logic to provide a method for it. We regard the concept of degree of confirmation as the fundamental concept of inductive logic. Accordingly, we shall show how the concept of an estimate can be based on that of degree of confirmation. Although scientists make estimations all the time and elaborate methods of estimation have been developed in mathematical statistics, there is at present no agreement as to the nature and definition of the concept of estimate and as to its relation to the concept of probability$_1$ or degree of confirmation. As was mentioned earlier, many scientists are skeptical with respect to the possibility of constructing an adequate quantitative explicatum for probability$_1$. Therefore, some statisticians have developed independent methods of estimation, that is to say, methods not based on probability$_1$. However, the present situation in the theory of estimation as dealt with in treatises on probability and statistics gives a startling spectacle of unsolved controversies and mutual misunderstandings, all the more disturbing when we compare it with the exactness, clarity, and possibility of coming to a general agreement in other fields of mathematics. A typical example of this situation is the problem, famous and much discussed since classical times, of estimating simultaneously the mean and the variance (mean square deviation, square of the standard deviation) of the distribution of a magnitude in the whole population on the basis of the mean and the variance found in an observed sample of n individuals. It was originally customary to take in this case as estimate for the variance in the population simply the variance found in the sample. Then the mathematician Carl Friedrich Gauss (in 1823) and the astronomer Bessel suggested a modified estimate containing the corrective factor $n/(n - 1)$. [Concerning the historical origin of this correction see Wolfenden [Statistics], p. 164.] It seems that the majority of statisticians since that time have regarded the modified value as a more adequate estimate. However, this is not a matter of refutation of one result and proof of another result but rather a matter of plausibility. This is shown by the fact that even today some statisticians, and among them prominent men in the field, still regard in certain cases the original value of the estimate as adequate. [For instance, R. A. Fisher's method of maximum likelihood yields the original value; see Wolfenden [Statistics], pp. 39 f.; Cramér [Statistics], p. 504.] Some statisticians declare frankly that any assertion of the validity of either value would be purely dogmatic and that this and similar controversial questions of estimation are ultimately matters of taste.

R. A. Fisher has carried out a systematic investigation of methods of estimation, which led to many fruitful results. He examined estimate-functions with respect to their "efficiency" and other properties. In spite of the great advance which the theory of estimation has made in recent decades due to the work of Fisher and other statisticians, it is understandable that many statisticians even today regard the situation in this field as rather unsatisfactory. This is not merely due to the fact that any procedure of estimation depends upon a choice, which is a matter of practical decision and not uniquely determined by purely theoretical, logico-mathematical considerations. There are many points in the procedure of science which involve a choice; for instance, the choice of a system of geometry as a theory of physical space or, alternatively, the choice of an operational definition for equality of distances. Also for the method which we shall propose here, which bases the concept of estimate upon that of degree of confirmation, there remains still the necessity of a choice, viz., the choice of a concept of degree of confirmation as an adequate explicatum for probability$_1$. But the advantage of this method is this: only one fundamental decision is required. As soon as anybody makes this decision, that is to say, chooses a concept of degree of confirmation which seems to him adequate, then he is in the possession of a general method which makes it possible to deal with all the various problems of inductive logic in a coherent and systematic way, including the problems of estimation. Thus this method helps to overcome what seems to me the greatest weakness in the contemporary statistical theory of estimation, namely, the lack of a general method. There is in general (with the exception of Fisher's method, see below) no unique set of rules, say, in the form of a postulate system, let alone an explicit definition for the concept of estimate. Instead, for every new problem of estimation, new considerations of plausibility are made which may lead to the choice of a particular procedure for that particular problem. Consequently, any proposed solution of a problem of estimation is more or less isolated and often not well in accord with accepted solutions of other problems. For instance, nobody can say today whether Gauss's solution of the problem of the estimation of variance and mean may be regarded as definitive or whether somebody might not come tomorrow with similar plausibility considerations and show us that it seems advisable to take still another value as the estimate.

While it is true that the work of most of the contemporary statisticians in problems of estimation is not based upon a general method, there is one partial exception to this statement. R. A. Fisher's method of maximum likelihood is a general method at least for a large class of problems of estimation, including those most frequently dealt with in modern statistics. This method applies to those cases in which the estimation concerns the value of a parameter in the distribution of some magnitudes in the whole population and the evidence describes the distribution of the same magnitudes in a given sample. The maximum likelihood estimate is that value among the possible values of the parameter for which the likelihood (that is, the probability on the basis of a given parameter value) of the observed sample is a maximum. ('Probability' is to be understood here in the sense of probability$_2$; it is equal to the probability$_1$ for the description of the given sample as hypothesis and the statement of any value of the parameter as evidence.) The validity of this method is today still controversial. It seems that the majority of statisticians are not willing to accept it as a *general* method (which would, for instance, imply the rejection of Gauss's correction in some cases, see above) although they apply it frequently in certain kinds of problems. In a later chapter (in Vol. II) we shall discuss in greater detail that part of the method of maximum likelihood which applies to those problems of estimation which occur in the limited domain of our system of inductive logic, especially problems of estimation of relative frequency. It will then be shown that there are serious reasons for doubting the adequacy of the values to which this method leads in many cases on the basis of small samples. But even if the method cannot be regarded as generally valid, the estimates which result from it are in many cases practically acceptable as approximations, especially when the sample which serves as basis is sufficiently large; and in these cases the use of the method is often very convenient.

An incidental remark apropos the concept of an approximate estimate may be made here. It is sometimes said that all estimates are approximations. This formulation seems to me misleading. What is presumably meant is that we have no certainty that our estimate of a magnitude is equal to or even close to its true value; and this is, of course, correct. But it would be better not to use the term 'approximation' for this fact. The term in its original and generally accepted sense is needed in order to distinguish between an exact estimate and an approximate estimate. When somebody has chosen a method of estimation, he may use it in a given case either exactly or with some convenient simplification in order to find in a shorter time a somewhat deviating value. Suppose, for example, that a rule of estimation which he has accepted says that in certain cases the arithmetic mean of the observed values of a magnitude is to be taken as the estimate. Suppose further that in a given case of this kind the observed values are 79.852 and 82.176. Then he might, if he is in a hurry or lazy, reason as follows: the first value is somewhat less than 80, the second is somewhat more than 82; hence let's take 81 as an estimate good enough for the practical purposes at hand. In this case, 81 is an approximate estimate; 81.014 is the exact estimate. This means merely that 81.014 is exactly that value to which the method leads on the basis of the two given values. It does not, of course, mean that this is the true value.

The most influential school in contemporary mathematical statistics and especially in the theory of statistical inference and estimation, besides that of Fisher, is the school founded by J. Neyman and E. S. Pearson. These authors do not, like Fisher, base their work on one particular method. Instead they make very fruitful and interesting *general* investigations concerning methods of testing statistical hypotheses. A method of determining an estimate u' for a parameter in the population on the basis of an observed sample as evidence is a special case of this kind; in this case the hypothesis asserts that the actual value u of the parameter is u'. Since these authors, like Fisher, do not believe in the possibility of an inverse inductive inference based on a quantitative explicatum for probability$_1$, they regard it as the task of an observer X merely to decide whether he should reject or accept the hypothesis in question, but not to determine its degree of confirmation. X's decision is based upon the evidence concerning the sample he has observed. A test method for the determination of this decision may be given by characterizing a class of possible samples (called 'the critical region in the sample space'); if the observed sample belongs to this class, the hypothesis is to be rejected. The resulting decision may be wrong in either of two different ways: (1) X may reject the hypothesis although it is true; in the example of the estimate: X assumes that $u \neq u'$ although in fact $u = u'$; this is called an error of type I; or (2) X may accept the hypothesis although it is false; in the example: X assumes that $u = u'$ although in fact $u \neq u'$; this is called an error of type II. The aim is to control the errors of the first kind on a fixed level of probability$_2$ and then to diminish the probability$_2$ of occurrences of errors of the second kind as much as possible.

Another method developed by Neyman is the method of making an interval estimate for the unknown value u of a parameter characterizing the population on the basis of a given sample. For a fixed value r, say 0.99, called the confidence coefficient, the method determines an interval (u_1,u_2), called the confidence interval. Then the estimate-assumption is made that the actual value u of the parameter lies within the interval (u_1,u_2). The theory states that the probability for obtaining correct statements of this kind in a series of repeated drawings of samples of equal size from the same population is r. It is to be noted that 'probability' is here meant in the sense of probability$_2$; the term 'confidence coefficient' must not be understood in the sense of probability$_1$ or degree of confirmation. Let e be the description of the observed sample and h_e the statement that the actual value u lies within the confidence interval determined on the basis of e. The above statement of the probability value r cannot be interpreted as saying that $\mathfrak{c}(h_e,e) = r$; any question concerning the probability of a parameter value in the population with respect to given evidence concerning an observed sample is regarded as meaningless in this theory, as generally in contemporary mathematical statistics. This follows from the clear explanations given by Neyman himself ([Outline], pp. 347 ff.) as well as from those by other authors (see Wald [Principles], pp. 25 ff., Wilks [Statistics], pp. 122 ff., Cramér [Statistics], pp. 512 ff.). The probability$_2$-value r, like any probability$_2$-value, is indeed equal to a value of probability$_1$ or $\mathfrak{c}$. This holds, however, only for the $\mathfrak{c}$ in a direct inference (as mentioned in § 94), not in an inverse inference. Thus, if j is the assumption that the actual value of the parameter is u, then, for any e describing any sample, the $\mathfrak{c}$ of h_e with respect to j, not to e, equals r.

The ideas of Neyman and Pearson have been further developed by A. Wald ([Contributions], [Principles], [Risk]). He investigates decision functions (e.g., estimate-functions which determine an estimate u' of the value of a parameter u in the population as a function of an observed sample as evidence) from the point of view of the risk functions associated with them (the risk function states the expectation value of the loss suffered by X if he chooses a particular estimate-function, as a function of the actual value u of the parameter). Wald ([Risk]) considers, in particular, the so-called minimax-rule for the choice of a decision function, e.g., an estimate function: X determines for every decision function the risk as a function of u, and then the maximum risk for varying u; then the rule tells him to choose that decision function for which this maximum risk is a minimum. For any given observed sample as evidence, the chosen decision function will then determine the decision to be taken. This rule leads in general to decisions different from those determined by our rules R_4 (§ 50E) and R_5 (§ 51A). Our rules prescribe to minimize, not the maximum risk, as Wald's rule does, but the probability$_1$-weighted risk (R_4 considers the risk with respect to the monetary gain, R_5 with respect to the utility). The probability$_1$-weighted risk will be explicated in this chapter as the c-weighted mean of the loss. We shall later discuss Wald's rule and compare it with our rule (in Vol. II).

Why did statisticians spend so much effort in developing independent methods of estimation, i.e., methods not based on a concept of probability$_1$? One gets the impression that the strongest motive was not a positive one, say, the attraction of convincing and fruitful methods of a new kind. It seems clear that even for Gauss and still more for contemporary statisticians the main reason was purely negative; it was the dissatisfaction with the classical approach, in particular with the principle of indifference (or insufficient reason). This principle enters the problems of estimation for parameters of the population by way of the Bayes-Laplace theorem. Since this principle leads sometimes to quite absurd results and in its strongest form even to contradictions, it must indeed be rejected. The classical theory of probability was essentially based on this principle, and there was no other general theory of probability$_1$ avoiding this principle. Therefore, it is psychologically understandable that statisticians believed themselves compelled to look for independent methods of estimation as the only solution. By developing these methods, modern statisticians made important progress in comparison with the uncritical methods which were still in almost general use throughout the nineteenth century. Thus, it is due to their work that the statistical practice today is sounder and leads to more reliable values of estimates and to a more efficient design of experiments than was previously the case.

However, today it is necessary to re-examine the question of the necessity of independent methods. *If* we have to come to the conclusion that there is no adequate quantitative explicatum for probability$_1$, then the methods developed by Fisher, Neyman, Pearson, and Wald or new methods of a similar nature are presumably the best instruments for estimating parameter values and testing hypotheses. They are ingenious devices for achieving these ends without making use of any general explicatum for probability$_1$, as far as the ends *can* be achieved under this restricting condition. *If*, on the other hand, we should find it possible to define a concept of degree of confirmation which does not lead to the inacceptable consequences of the principle of indifference, then the main reason for developing independent methods of estimation and testing would vanish. Then it would seem more natural to take the degree of confirmation as the basic concept for all of inductive statistics. This would lead to simpler and more effective procedures. In testing a given hypothesis concerning the population or an unobserved sample, we could take its degree of confirmation with respect to the observed sample as a measure of its acceptability. All problems of estimation could then be answered by one general estimate-function to be defined on the basis of degree of confirmation. The latter definition can easily be constructed in analogy to customary conceptions, as we shall soon see.

The fundamental problem of the possibility of an adequate explicatum for probability$_1$ is at present still an open question. Only the first steps toward an affirmative answer have been made: in this volume the theory of regular and symmetrical $\mathfrak{c}$-functions has been developed, and the theory of the function $\mathfrak{c}^*$ will be given in the second volume. However, these parts of inductive logic apply only to our simple language $\mathfrak{L}$. It remains a task for the future to extend the theory to more comprehensive languages, first to a co-ordinate language which makes it possible to take into account the temporal order of events (see the explanations in § 15B), and finally to the full quantitative language of physics. It is true that these extensions, especially the latter one, involve serious difficulties which certainly should not be underestimated. But it seems to me that the situation, as we see it today, gives no reason for regarding the difficulties as insuperable. Some ways which might lead to an adequate extended theory will be discussed later (in Vol. II).

In the foregoing discussion we have looked at methods of estimation from the point of view of their logical form, distinguishing between those based on degree of confirmation and the independent ones. However, the goodness of a method is to be judged primarily, not by its form, but by its results. Therefore, a method of estimation must be judged primarily, not by simply asking whether or not it is independent, but rather by examining the estimates to which it leads. Later (in Vol. II) we shall compare the function $\mathfrak{c}^*$, which is our explicatum for probability$_1$ (see § 110A), with other explicata with respect to the adequacy of the values of degree of confirmation for given cases of a hypothesis *h* and an evidence *e*. Then we shall also make comparisons of various methods of estimation. We shall see in the next section how any concept of degree of confirmation leads to a general estimate-function based upon it. Therefore, we shall later compare the method of estimation based on the various concepts of confirmation, $\mathfrak{c}^*$ and others, but also independent methods of estimation proposed or discussed in modern statistics. The comparison will have the purpose of judging the goodness of the various methods irrespective of their logical form. Therefore, we shall have to judge the adequacy of the values of estimates furnished by the various methods for given cases.

The comparison will chiefly concern estimates of the relative frequency of a property in the whole population on the basis of an observed sample, because the problem of this kind of estimate belongs to the most important problems of estimation, and it can be dealt with in our system of inductive logic, as we shall soon see (§§ 104 ff.). In certain cases all methods under consideration supply equal estimates (for instance, in the example of the lottery mentioned in the next section); in others the estimates will be close together. But there will also be cases where some of the methods lead to very different estimates. In some cases a discussion of these different values will show that one of them is adequate and the other inadequate, or at least that one is more adequate than the other. In this way we shall try to judge the adequacy of the methods.

§ 99. A General Estimate-Function

Suppose that, on the basis of given evidence *e*, several values of a certain magnitude are possible with various degrees of confirmation. Then it seems natural to take as the estimate of the magnitude the weighted mean of the possible values with the degrees of confirmation as weights. This is called the c-mean estimate.

We shall now study the question as to how a general method of estimation can be defined in terms of degree of confirmation. We imagine a scientist *X* who is in possession of a concept of degree of confirmation, say c, which he regards as adequate, in application to the sentences of his scientific language. We leave aside the question how the concept c is defined and for what reasons *X* has chosen this particular concept. We are only interested in the problem how he can use the chosen concept c in order to construct a method of estimation, a general method that will supply estimates for all kinds of magnitudes expressible in his language. The general discussion in this and the following sections will not be restricted to our language systems $\mathfrak{L}$ but will refer to any language containing quantitative concepts. This may, for instance, be a language of physics containing numerical functions like length, mass, temperature, etc., or a language of economics containing, in addition to physical concepts, economic quantitative concepts like price, wage, demand, etc. We suppose that the concept c is applicable to the sentences of this language. Since the c-functions of our inductive logic apply only to the simple languages $\mathfrak{L}$ and no adequate concept of degree of confirmation for more comprehensive languages of the kinds just mentioned have been constructed so far, the assumption of the concept c is made in anticipation of the future development of inductive logic.

Suppose that X wants to make an estimate of the unknown value of the function f for the argument u (e.g., the temperature at the space-time point u, or the cardinal number of the class u of the hydrogen molecules in a given vessel). Although X does not know the value $f(u)$, he knows other data related to it. Let e be the evidence available to him on the basis of which he attempts to find an estimate of $f(u)$. Let us assume that there is only a finite number of possible values for $f(u)$, say $r_1, r_2, \ldots, r_n$, and that X is aware of this fact on the basis either of the definitions of f and u, or of the evidence e. This assumption serves to simplify the following discussion; the result can later be extended to the more general case. Let h_p ($p = 1, \ldots, n$) be the hypothesis that $f(u) = r_p$. Then the assumption mentioned means that $h_1 \vee h_2 \vee \ldots \vee h_n$ is either L-true or at least L-implied by e:

(1) $$\vdash e \supset h_1 \vee \ldots \vee h_n .$$

[For example, X wants to make an estimation as to how many of a hundred given objects have the property M. Here $n = 101$; the possible values are the cardinal numbers 0, 1, . . . , 100.] We presuppose further that f (either by definition or on the basis of e) is a univalued function, that is to say, only one of the values can occur; hence

(2) $h_1, \ldots, h_n$ are L-exclusive in pairs (D20-2d) with respect to e.

How should X proceed in order to obtain an estimate on the basis of the possible values $r_1, \ldots, r_n$? He might perhaps consider taking simply an average of these values, for instance, the arithmetic mean or the median. However, this procedure would seem very crude and unsatisfactory, because it does not utilize all the relevant information contained in e. If we see from e that there is more reason to expect some of the possible values than the others, then it would be wrong to treat all values alike. It would seem more appropriate to take a weighted average than a simple average. The concept of a weighted mean is generally defined in this way: if weights w_p are assigned to the values r_p, the weighted mean is

(3) $$\sum_p [r_p \times w_p] / \sum_p w_p .$$

What should we take as weights of the values r_p for the purpose of an estimation? It seems natural to give to a value r_p the more weight the more probable its occurrence is. Hence we shall take as weight of r_p $\mathfrak{c}(h_p,e)$; the resulting $\mathfrak{c}$-weighted mean will be called, for short, the ***$\mathfrak{c}$-mean.*** Let D be the denominator in (3); that is,

(4) $$D = \sum_p \mathfrak{c}(h_p,e) .$$

Therefore (from (2), with T59-1m):

(5) $$D = \mathfrak{c}(h_1 \vee \ldots \vee h_n, e) .$$

Hence (from (1), with T59-1b):

(6) $$D = 1 .$$

Thus the denominator in (3) can be omitted. Hence the c-mean is equal to the numerator in (3), that is, the sum of the possible values r_p, each multiplied with the c for its occurrence:

(7) $$\sum_{p=1}^{n} [r_p \times \mathfrak{c}(h_p, e)] .$$

This we shall use for our definition of the c-mean estimate-function in the next section (D100-1).

Example. Suppose that *X* has a ticket in a lottery and wants to make an estimate of his gain. His evidence *e* contains the following facts: for one hundred tickets there is one prize of \$10 and fifteen prizes of \$2 each; eighty-four tickets will not win anything; the ordinary procedure is applied so that every ticket has an equal chance for each of the prizes. Thus, the possible values are: $r_1 = 10$, $r_2 = 2$, $r_3 = 0$. Suppose that the chosen c-function c, as seems plausible, is such that its value for r_1 is 0.01, for r_2 0.15, for r_3 0.84. Then the c-mean, according to (7), is $10 \times 0.01 + 2 \times 0.15 + 0 \times 0.84 = 0.4$. What is the meaning of accepting this value as the estimate? It does not mean that a gain of 0.4 is the most probable outcome. The most probable outcome is rather 0, because c is highest for this value. And 0.4 is not even a possible outcome; the possible values are only 10, 2, and 0. The estimate 0.4 has been determined as the probability-weighted mean. It means that for *X*, on the basis of the chosen c and in view of the available evidence *e*, 0.4 is the reasonable valuation for his ticket. If *X* is motivated only by a sober examination of his chances and not by the gambler's urge for excitement, he will not buy a ticket in this lottery for more than 40 cents or sell it for less.

We shall use the symbol 'e' for the c-mean taken as an estimate-function. We shall write 'e(f,u,e)' as abbreviation for 'the c-mean estimate of the value of the function *f* for the argument *u* with respect to the evidence *e*'. Thus 'e' is a functor in the semantical metalanguage, like 'm', 'c', etc., not a symbol of the object language, which may here be the language of physics. For example, if 'temp(*a*)' means 'the temperature at the space-time point *a*', then we write 'e(temp,*a*,*e*)' for 'the c-mean estimate of the temperature at *a* on the evidence *e*'.

Note that we must write here 'temp' and 'a' as two separate argument expressions, not 'temp(a)' as one. For the c-mean depends upon (i.e., is a function of) the function f (here, temperature) and the argument u (here, the point a) and not simply of the number $f(u)$ (here, temp(a)). Note further that the simple use in 'e(temp,a,e) of the symbols 'temp' and 'a' of the object language instead of their names is a simplification of the notation permitted by Convention 14-2, case (b).

Several methods are known in statistics for defining a kind of average or central tendency for a given frequency distribution (called probability distribution, in the sense of probability$_2$). The three most customary concepts of this kind are the mean, the mode, and the median. These concepts can be transferred to a c-distribution; the resulting concepts of inductive logic, for which we may use the terms 'c-mean', 'c-mode', and 'c-median', have the same analogy to the three statistical concepts as probability$_1$ has to probability$_2$; the general character of this analogy will be discussed later (§ 100B). The c-mean has been defined above. A *c-mode* is any of the possible values for which c has its maximum. If r is such that it is just as probable that the actual value is below r as that it is above r, then r is a *c-median* (more generally speaking, r is a c-median if either (1) $c = 1/2$ for the hypothesis that the actual value $f(u) \leqq r$, or (2) $c < 1/2$ for the assumption that $f(u) < r$ and $c > 1/2$ for the assumption that $f(u) \leqq r$). The question might be raised why just the c-mean should be chosen as the estimate-function rather than the c-mode or the c-median. Theoretically either of the latter two or any other definition of a central value might be used as an estimate-function. However, the estimates are here meant to serve as guides for practical decisions in the sense discussed earlier: X is advised to act in certain respects as if he knew that the unknown value were equal or near to the estimate for it (R_3, § 50D), or it is recommended to him to maximize the estimate of his gain (R_4, § 50E) or its utility (R_5, § 51A). With regard to this purpose of estimation, it seems doubtful whether the c-mode or the c-median could be regarded as adequate estimate-functions. In the above example of a lottery, the c-mode of X's gain is 0, because its c is the maximum; the same holds for most of the actual commercial lotteries. It is obvious that this value 0 is unsuitable as a basis for X's decision (see the earlier discussion of rule R_2 in § 50C). In the same example, the c-median is likewise 0; this holds for most lotteries, namely, whenever it is more probable to win nothing than to win something. To take another example, suppose that there is an odd number $2n - 1$ of possible values, all of which have the same c; then the c-median is the nth value in the order of increasing magnitude. Thus, if the equiprobable values are 3, 4, and 5, the c-median is 4. This seems plausible;

4 is also the c-mean. But for the values 3, 4, and 500, the c-median is likewise 4, while the c-mean is $507/3 = 169$. (There is no c-mode in these two cases.) Generally speaking, the c-median, in contradistinction to the c-mean, is insensitive to certain changes in the situation (namely, to any change, however large, in a possible value provided only that it remains on the same side of the original c-median). On the other hand, the decision of X should be influenced by such changes. For example, if the equiprobable gains in a game are 3, 4, 500, then X should be willing to pay more for the right of participation than if they were 3, 4, 5. Thus the c-mean seems the most suitable among the customary concepts of a central value to be chosen as an estimate function.

It is important to distinguish clearly between an ***estimate-function*** and the ***estimates*** which it supplies in given cases, that is, the values of the estimate-function for given arguments. Instead of the term 'estimate-function' the term 'estimator' is sometimes used (Kendall [Statistics], II, 2, following E. J. G. Pitman). An estimate-function may be defined in such a way that it is applicable only to one particular kind of magnitude, say, the relative frequency of a property in a class or the mean or the variance of a magnitude within a class; in this case we call it a *special estimate-function*. (An example is the straight rule for estimating relative frequency, which will be mentioned later.) A *general estimate-function*, on the other hand, is one applicable to different kinds of magnitude, possibly to all magnitudes expressible in the given object language. Fisher's maximum likelihood estimate-function mentioned in the preceding section is general in this sense; and the c-mean estimate-function e, which was discussed in this section and will be defined in the next one, is general to a still greater extent.

§ 100. Definition of the c-Mean Estimate-Function

A. The Definition. If any regular c-function c is given, the c-mean estimate-function e is defined as follows. The estimate e of a magnitude with respect to given evidence e is the sum of the possible values of the magnitude, each multiplied by the degree of confirmation c for its occurrence on evidence e. If the magnitude has a continuous scale of values, an integral takes the place of the sum. From now on the term 'estimate' is to be understood in the sense of 'c-mean estimate' as just defined.

Some simple theorems concerning estimation are given, among them the following (T5): if the function f is defined as a certain linear function of f_1, f_2, etc., then the estimate of f is the same linear function of the estimates of f_1, f_2, etc.

B. Terminological Remarks. Our concept of c-mean estimate is essentially the same as the concept of mathematical expectation in the classical sense of this term. In modern statistics, however, the term 'mathematical expectation' has changed from the earlier inductive, logical sense to a statistical, empirical sense; this change is analogous to, and caused by, the change in the meaning of the word 'probability' from probability$_1$ to probability$_2$.

C. The Paradox of Estimation. It is found that in general the estimate of f^2 is different from the square of the estimate of f, and similarly with other nonlinear functions. Each of these two values seems to be a good basis for a rational expectation concerning f^2 and a practical decision based on this expectation. However, since the two values are different, they seem to lead to incompatible expectations and decisions. This paradox is solved with the help of earlier considerations (§§ 50, 51): the decision is ultimately determined by the estimate of only one magnitude, the utility.

A. *Definition of the c-Mean Estimate-Function*

Our discussion in the preceding section suggests the following definition D1. This definition does not introduce one estimate-function but rather a general form which, if any regular c-function is chosen, determines one general estimate-function based upon it ('general' in the sense of 'applicable to any function f'). As earlier on every m-function a c-function was based (D55-3), thus here on every c-function an e-function is based. Later (in Vol. II), after introducing our particular c-function c*, we shall deal with the e-function e* based upon it; in the present chapter, however, we deal with e-functions in general. The object language is not specified in the definition; it need not necessarily be one of our systems $\mathfrak{L}$ but may be any system, provided the concept of regular c-functions is defined for that system in analogy to our earlier definition.

+D100-1. (For any language system, not necessarily $\mathfrak{L}$.) e is ***the* c-*mean estimate-function*** (e-function) *based upon the confirmation-function* (c-function) c $=_{Df}$ if f is any function, u an argument of f, e any non-L-false sentence, $r_1, \ldots, r_n$ the possible values of $f(u)$ with respect to e, and $h_1, \ldots, h_n$ the hypotheses stating these values, such that the conditions (1) and (2) in § 99 are fulfilled, then

$$\mathfrak{e}(f,u,e) = \sum_{p=1}^{n} [r_p \times \mathfrak{c}(h_p,e)] .$$

What is here called the c-mean estimate of a magnitude is essentially the same as what often is called the mathematical expectation. (Compare, however, the terminological remarks below.) The term 'estimate' will be used in this chapter, unless otherwise indicated, in the sense of 'c-mean estimate', that is, in the sense of the function e defined by D1.

The following theorem T1 follows directly from D1. (It is, so to speak, merely a reformulation of D1, stated for the convenience of later application.)

T100-1. (For any language system, not necessarily $\mathfrak{L}$.) Let $\mathfrak{c}$ be a c-function, $\mathfrak{e}$ be based upon $\mathfrak{c}$, f be any function, u an argument of f, e be any non-L-false sentence, $r_1, \ldots, r_n$ be (or include) the possible values of $f(u)$ with respect to e, and $h_1, \ldots, h_n$ be hypotheses stating these values, such that (1) $\vdash e \supset h_1 \vee \ldots \vee h_n$ and (2) $h_1, \ldots, h_n$ are L-exclusive in pairs with respect to e. Then

$$\mathfrak{e}(f,u,e) = \sum_{p=1}^{n} [r_p \times \mathfrak{c}(h_p,e)] .$$

For the sake of simplicity we have restricted our discussion and the definition to cases in which the number of possible values of $f(u)$ is finite. This condition is always fulfilled for the estimate of the absolute or relative frequency of a property within a given finite class, and it is usually fulfilled for the estimate of the gain in a game of chance (see the example of a lottery in the preceding section). However, in estimations in physics there is usually a *continuum of possible values*, for instance, the totality of real numbers or an interval in it. In cases of this kind the probability distribution for the infinitely many possible values cannot be described simply by $\mathfrak{c}$; because the $\mathfrak{c}$ for any single value is in general 0. Other methods must instead be used. It is clear that both the determination of degree of confirmation and that of estimates for magnitudes with a continuous scale of values require a more complex system of inductive logic. The development of such a system remains a task for the future.

In our subsequent discussions we shall mostly deal with cases in which the number of possible values is finite. A few remarks may here be made concerning methods for cases with a continuum of possible values.

1. In many cases of this kind, though not in all, a *c-density function* corresponding to $\mathfrak{c}$ can be used, say $\mathfrak{c}'(r,e)$. It may be defined for all real numbers r, but its value is 0 for those numbers which are not possible values of $f(u)$ on e. The connection between $\mathfrak{c}'$ and $\mathfrak{c}$ is then as follows. If, for any values r_1 and r_2, h_{12} is the hypothesis that $f(u)$ lies in the interval between r_1 and r_2, then

$$\mathfrak{c}(h_{12},e) = \int_{r_1}^{r_2} \mathfrak{c}'(r,e)\, dr .$$

In the definition of the estimate, we have now an integral instead of the sum mentioned in D1:

$$\mathfrak{e}(f,u,e) = \int_{-\infty}^{+\infty} r\, \mathfrak{c}'(r,e)\, dr .$$

Let K be the set of all values r of $f(u)$ which are possible on e; usually K is an interval of real numbers, but it may be any other (integrable) subset. Then it is sufficient to extend the integral just mentioned over K, because outside of K $\mathfrak{c}' = 0$.

2. A more general method consists in using a *cumulative c-distribution function* (analogous to a cumulative frequency function in statistics), say $\mathfrak{c}_c$, defined for all real numbers r. Its meaning is as follows. Let h_r be the hypothesis that $f(u) \leq r$. Then $\mathfrak{c}(h_r,e) = \mathfrak{c}_c(r,e)$. Thus $\mathfrak{c}_c(r,e)$ is the degree of confirmation on e for the assumption that the unknown value of the magnitude in question

does not exceed r. (If $\mathfrak{c}_c$ is differentiable throughout, its derivative $d\mathfrak{c}_c(r,e)/dr$ defines the density function $\mathfrak{c}'(r,e)$. Thus in this case method (1) is applicable. If $\mathfrak{c}'$ is taken as primitive, $\mathfrak{c}_c(r,e)$ can be defined as its integral from $-\infty$ to r.) Suppose that the function $\mathfrak{c}_c(r,e)$ is given, and that h_{12} is the hypothesis that $r_1 < f(u) \leqq r_2$ (in other words, that the unknown value in question lies within the interval (r_1,r_2) closed at the right end). Then $\mathfrak{c}(h_{12},e) = \mathfrak{c}_c(r_2,e) - \mathfrak{c}_c(r_1,e)$. The estimate function is, in this method, to be defined by a so-called Stieltjes integral (see, e.g., Cramér [Statistics], chap. 7):

$$\mathfrak{e}(f,u,e) = \int_{-\infty}^{+\infty} r \, d\mathfrak{c}_c$$

(Cramér, pp. 170 f.).

We shall now state some elementary theorems concerning estimates. They are simple consequences from T1 and hence from D1. In these theorems it is tacitly presupposed that $\mathfrak{e}$ is any $\mathfrak{e}$-function based upon a regular $\mathfrak{c}$-function, that f, f', f_1, etc., are functions with numerical values, that u is an argument of these functions, and e is a non-L-false sentence. The proofs, like D1, refer only to the case that the possible values are finite in number; therefore they use finite sums. The proofs for the more general case are analogous but use integrals instead of finite sums.

T2 says that the *estimate for the sum of two magnitudes* is equal to the sum of the estimates of the two magnitudes.

T100-2. $\mathfrak{e}(f+f',u,e) = \mathfrak{e}(f,u,e) + \mathfrak{e}(f',u,e)$.

Proof. Let the possible values of $f(u)$ be $r_1, \ldots, r_m$, and those of $f'(u)$ $r'_1, \ldots, r'_{m'}$. Let the sentences stating these values be $h_1, \ldots, h_m, h'_1, \ldots, h'_{m'}$, respectively. Then, according to T1: (a) $\mathfrak{e}(f,u,e) = \sum_{p=1}^{m} [r_p \times \mathfrak{c}(h_p,e)]$; (b) $\mathfrak{e}(f',u,e) = \sum_{p'=1}^{m'} [r'_{p'} \times \mathfrak{c}(h'_{p'},e)]$; (c) $\mathfrak{e}(f+f',u\ e) = \sum_{p=1}^{m} \sum_{p'=1}^{m'} [(r_p + r'_{p'}) \times \mathfrak{c}(h_p \cdot h'_{p'},e)] = \sum_{p} \sum_{p'} [r_p \times \mathfrak{c}(\ldots)] + \sum_{p} \sum_{p'} [r'_{p'} \times \mathfrak{c}(\ldots)]$. Let this be $q_1 + q_2$. $q_1 = \sum_{p} [r_p \times \sum_{p'} \mathfrak{c}(\ldots)]$. Herein $\sum_{p'} = \mathfrak{c}(h_p \cdot h'_1,e) + \ldots + \mathfrak{c}(h_p \cdot h'_{m'},e)$; hence, since the m' conjunctions are L-exclusive in pairs (§ 99, condition (2)), according to T59-1m: $\sum_{p'} = \mathfrak{c}[(h_p \cdot h'_1) \vee \ldots \vee (h_p \cdot h'_{m'}),e] = \mathfrak{c}[h_p \cdot (h'_1 \vee \ldots \vee h'_{m'}),e] = \mathfrak{c}(h_p,e)$ (§ 99(1), T59-2h). Therefore $q_1 = \sum_{p} [r_p \times \mathfrak{c}(h_p,e)] = \mathfrak{e}(f,u,e)$, (a). It is found analogously that $q_2 = \mathfrak{e}(f',u,e)$. Hence the assertion.

The following theorem says that, for any fixed number q, the estimate of q times f is equal to q times the estimate of f.

T100-3. For any real number q, $\mathfrak{e}(q \times f,u,e) = q \times \mathfrak{e}(f,u,e)$.

Proof. Let r_p and h_p ($p = 1, \ldots, m$) be as in T1. Then (T1): $\mathfrak{e}(q \times f,u,e) = \sum_{p} [q \times r_p \times \mathfrak{c}(h_p,e)] = q \times \sum_{p} [r_p \times \mathfrak{c}(h_p,e)] = q \times \mathfrak{e}(f,u,e)$.

The following theorem refers analogously to the addition of a fixed number q.

T100-4. For any real number q, $\mathfrak{e}(f+q,u,e) = \mathfrak{e}(f,u,e) + q$. (Proof analogous to T3.)

The following is the most important of these theorems. It says that the *estimate for any linear function* of the values of given functions is equal to the same linear function of the estimates for the given functions.

$+$**T100-5.** Let f be defined in terms of given functions $f_1, \ldots, f_n$ as follows: $f(u) = q_0 + q_1 \times f_1(u) + \ldots + q_n \times f_n(u)$, where $q_0, \ldots, q_n$ are any fixed real numbers. Then $\mathfrak{e}(f,u,e) = q_0 + q_1 \times \mathfrak{e}(f_1,u,e) + \ldots + q_n \times \mathfrak{e}(f_n,u,e)$. (From T3, T2, T4.)

B. *Some Terminological Remarks*

The nature of the concepts defined or indicated in this section may perhaps be clarified by comparing and contrasting them with certain concepts in modern mathematical statistics which are analogous to our concepts but different from them. The fundamental difference consists in the fact that our concepts are based upon probability$_1$ and hence are concepts of inductive logic, while the corresponding concepts in statistics are based upon probability$_2$, that is, relative frequency in the whole population, and hence are empirically determined magnitudes. We have earlier (§ 9) mentioned the fact that there are two contemporary schools who use the word 'probability' in the sense of 'probability$_2$': (1) the probability theories of Mises and Reichenbach, who define 'probability' as 'limit of relative frequency in an infinite sequence', and (2) modern mathematical statistics, where 'probability' is likewise understood as 'relative frequency in an infinite population', but is used as an undefined term not involving the concept of limit. We have further discussed (§ 42A) the historical fact that nearly all authors in these two schools seem to be unaware of the fact that their meaning of the term 'probability' (viz., probability$_2$) is fundamentally different from the meaning which the same word has for the classical authors and their followers (viz., probability$_1$). Consequently they have taken over from the earlier authors a number of definitions of other terms based on the term 'probability'; and here again they seem not to realize that they merely copy the words of the old definitions but thereby assign to the defined terms meanings quite different from the original ones. This holds in the first place for the term '*mathematical expectation*'. This and similar terms ('mathematical hope', etc.) have been used in the classical theory of probability, especially with respect to games of chance, either for the product of a possible gain and its probability or for the sum of all these products for all possible cases ('espérance totale', 'total expectation'). Thus our concept of the estimate of a magnitude is essentially the same as the classical concept of mathematical expectation. It seems that the classical meaning of the term 'mathematical expectation' remained in use throughout the last century and likewise with those authors of our time who deal with probability$_1$ (e.g., Keynes [Probab.], pp. 311 ff., Jeffreys [Probab.], p. 42). However, when we come to the authors in modern statistics, we find that the meaning of the term changes radically. Terms like 'mathematical expectation', 'expected value', 'mean value' are defined in an apparently similar way as previously, that is, as a sum (or integral) of the products of the possible values and their probabilities (see, for instance, Wilks [Statistics], p. 29, Wolfenden [Statistics], p. 12, Cramér [Statistics], p. 170). Since, however, 'probability' means now probability$_2$, the concept defined is no longer a concept of inductive logic, dependent upon evidence, but rather a function whose values are determined by observation. It is descriptive of certain facts irrespective of anybody's knowledge about them. It is therefore without any inductive significance for presumption or expectation. Although the new concept may be interesting and fruitful and hence acceptable in its own right, both the terms 'mathematical' and 'expectation' seem strange misnomers, especially the latter. The fact that the authors use the term 'expectation' for the new concept can be explained only by their erroneous belief that in adopting this term they follow the traditional usage. Let us use (only in the present discussion) the term 'expectation$_1$' for the inductive concept based on probability$_1$, and 'expectation$_2$' for the statistical concept based on probability$_2$. In order to clarify the difference between these two concepts, let us go back to the example of the lottery in the preceding section. Here both the expectation$_1$ and the expectation$_2$ of *X*'s gain have the same numerical value 0.4; but nevertheless the meanings are different. The statement

(1) 'The expectation$_1$ of *X*'s gain with respect to *e* is 0.4',

where *e* is the evidence described earlier, is analytic. Suppose that *e* is false and that actually there are not one hundred but two hundred tickets. Then the statement mentioned is still true, and the value 0.4 of the expectation$_1$ is still valid (with respect to the erroneous evidence *e*). On the other hand, the statement

(2) 'The expectation$_2$ of *X*'s gain is 0.4'

is of an entirely different nature. It is factual and empirical. It does not contain any reference to *e*, but it can be inferred from *e* (which is itself factual). Suppose again that *e* is false, that there are two hundred tickets but that the numbers and amounts of positive prizes are as stated in *e*. Then the statement (2) is false; the expectation$_2$ is not 0.4 but 0.2. If *X*'s beliefs based on his observations are formulated in *e*, then his presumption of gain is determined (if he is a rational man) by the value 0.4 of the expectation$_1$; it is not influenced by the expectation$_2$. This is especially clear in the second case mentioned, where *X*'s belief is erroneous and the expectation$_2$ is actually 0.2; since this value is, in this case, not known to *X*, it cannot influence his presumption. This shows that the term 'expectation' when used in the statistical sense of 'expectation$_2$' is a misnomer.

The situation with respect to the concept of a c-*density function* (mentioned above in the passage in small print) is similar. I might have taken the term 'probability density function' were it not for the fact that this term is used in modern statistics in the sense of probability$_2$ density. The latter concept is again an empirically determined function descriptive of an actual physical distribution of the values of a magnitude in an infinite population irrespective of any knowledge or evidence of an observer.

The term '*probable error*' has undergone a similar change in meaning. For the classical authors and those modern authors who deal with probability$_1$ it means "the amount, which the difference between the actual value of the quantity and its most probable value is as likely as not to exceed" (Keynes [Probab.], p. 74); and we shall use it in a similar sense (§ 102). Contemporary statisticians, on the other hand, use the same term for the corresponding statistical concept; this is the amount δ such that, in the actual distribution of the magnitude in question in the population, irrespective of whether anybody knows it or not, one half of the cases lie within the interval $m \pm \delta$, where m is the mean value of the magnitude in the population. Keynes complains that statisticians often mix both uses of the term 'probable error' and generally slip somewhat easily from descriptive-statistical to inductive statements (*op. cit.*, pp. 327 ff.). I think that statisticians today are more careful in their formulations in this point than the earlier authors whom Keynes criticized. But they avoid the previous ambiguity chiefly by restricting themselves in most cases to the use of statistical concepts, sometimes to the neglect of inductive concepts, which are equally important for their problems.

C. *The Paradox of Estimation*

We found (T5) that, if f is defined in terms of f_1, f_2, etc., in the form of a linear function, then it makes no difference whether we determine the estimate for f directly or whether we first determine the estimates for f_1, f_2, etc., and then apply the linear function to them. It is important to notice that the same does not in general hold for a nonlinear function. This is shown by the following counterexample.

Let the possible values of $f(u)$ be 1, 2, 3. Let c have equal values, hence 1/3, for these three cases. Therefore, the estimate is 2, the mean of the three values. [$e(f,u,e) = 1 \times 1/3 + 2 \times 1/3 + 3 \times 1/3 = 2$.] Hence $e^2 = 4$. On the other hand, the possible values for f^2 are 1, 4, 9. c is again equal for them; hence the estimate for $f^2(u)$ is their mean, that is, 14/3. [$e(f^2,u,e) = 1 \times 1/3 + 4 \times 1/3 + 9 \times 1/3 = 14/3$.] This, however, is different from 4, the square of the estimate for f.

As the example shows, in general *the square of an estimate is not the same as the estimate of the square*. Likewise, the estimate of the product $f \times g$ is in general not the same as the product of the estimates of f and of g. And analogously with other nonlinear functions. This fact raises a serious problem for the application of the method of estimation. Suppose that the observer X has chosen a certain c-function c, which determines a certain e-function e. He possesses a certain amount of evidence e. He has to make practical decisions and he wants to base them on the estimates with respect to the evidence e. Suppose a particular decision depends upon what he presumes the value of $f^2(u)$ to be. Let us assume that the conditions of the above example hold. Then there are two possible ways for X to determine that value of $f^2(u)$ which he may rationally expect on the basis of his evidence e and therefore take as basis for his practical decision. (1) He finds that the estimate for $f(u)$ on e is 2; therefore he decides to act as though he knew that $f(u)$ is 2 and hence $f^2(u)$ is 4. (2) As an alternative, he applies the procedure of estimation directly to f^2; he finds that the estimate of $f^2(u)$ on e is 14/3; therefore he thinks he ought to act as though he knew that $f^2(u)$ is 14/3. However, these two decisions are incompatible. Two incompatible expectations for $f^2(u)$ are obtained on the basis of the same evidence e and with the help of the same estimation function e by two procedures which apparently are both correct. We propose to call this situation the *paradox of estimation*.

If a system of inductive logic for languages containing quantitative magnitudes is to be constructed, which is not intended in this book, and if rules for the application of this inductive logic to given knowledge situations are to be laid down, then this paradox must be eliminated.

One way of achieving this would consist in choosing the c-median instead of the c-mean as the estimate-function. The square of the c-median of the possible values (if these are nonnegative) is the same as the c-median of their squares; in the above example, the c-median of the equiprobable values 1, 2, 3 is 2, and the c-median of their squares, 2, 4, 9, is 4. The same holds for any other monotonic increasing function. However, it seems to me that this advantage of the c-median as an estimate-function is far outweighed by its serious disadvantages, above all its insensitivity to certain practically relevant changes in the situation, as explained earlier (near the end of § 99).

It seems to me that the paradox can be solved without abandoning the c-mean as the estimate-function. Let us first look at the situation from a purely theoretical point of view, leaving aside the problem of practical decisions. Then it must be said that each of the two estimation procedures is correct. Their results do not contradict each other because they are answers to two distinct questions. In the above example the two answers are:

'The estimate of f is 2; hence the square of the estimate of f is 4'

and

'The estimate of f^2 is 14/3'.

These two statements appear as incompatible only if the estimates are interpreted, incorrectly, as the most reasonable expectations. However, an estimate must not be understood as a prediction but only as a weighted mean. This is especially clear in those cases (as in the example of the lottery in § 99) where the estimate is not a possible value. If the estimate statements are interpreted correctly, there is no contradiction and hence no paradox.

The paradox appears as more serious when we turn from the theoretical to the practical question. X asks for advice as to which decision he ought to take. He will not be satisfied if we tell him that, from one point of view, he should act as if he knew that $f = 2$, in other words, that $f^2 = 4$, but, from another point of view, he should act as if he knew that $f^2 = 14/3$. He can take only one decision. Although the two answers to the theoretical questions of estimation are not incompatible, the two suggestions for a practical decision are indeed incompatible. The solution is found with the help of our earlier analysis of rules for the application of inductive logic and, in particular, of estimates for the determination of practical decisions (§§ 50, 51). We saw that the customary rule: 'Act as if you knew that the unknown value of the magnitude in question were equal or near to the estimate' (Rule R_3, § 50D) deserves its widespread acceptance to a certain extent, because it is not only simple and convenient but also in many cases adequate, that is, leading to a reasonable decision. However, we found that it is not adequate in all cases. In order to come to generally adequate results, another rule must be applied which tells X to take that decision for which the estimate of his gain, expressed on a monetary scale, is a maximum (Rule R_4, § 50E); if the possible gains and losses are not small in relation to *X*'s present fortune, then a still further refined rule must be applied which prescribes the maximization of the estimate of the utility, that is, the amount of satisfaction which *X* derives from the gain (Rule R_5, § 51A). If *X* follows either of the two last-mentioned rules, the paradox of estimation disappears because *X* will apply the procedure of estimation to the values of only one magnitude.

§ 102. The Problem of the Reliability of an Estimate

Some estimates are more reliable than others, that is to say, there is more reason for the expectation that the error of the estimate, that is, the difference between it and the actual value of the magnitude in question will turn out to be small. The problem is to explicate this concept of reliability. Several methods of explication are discussed.

Suppose that the observer *X* has chosen a function $\mathfrak{c}$ and, based upon it, an estimate-function $\mathfrak{e}$. Suppose further that he has calculated the estimate $\mathfrak{e}(f,u,e)$ for $f(u)$ with respect to his evidence *e*. Then it will be of interest to him to determine the precision or *reliability of this estimate*. It is clear that estimates may vary greatly in their reliability, that is, the probability that the actual value of $f(u)$ (in the terminology of statisticians, the "true value") is close to the estimated value. For instance, we shall obviously have much more confidence in the estimate of the relative frequency of red-haired people among the inhabitants of Chicago based upon an observed sample of 10,000 persons than in an estimate based on a sample of only 100 persons. Thus we know practically, though inexactly, what we mean when we regard one estimate as more reliable than another. Our task is now to find an exact explicatum for the inexact concept of reliability as an explicandum. There are several possible methods for an explication. We shall discuss three of them which are related to customary conceptions and which seem promising; we shall then adopt a form of the third method. In order to explain the three methods, let us take the following example. On the basis of the description *e* of a certain sample, *X* has found as estimate for the rf (relative frequency) of the property *M* in a given population the value $\mathfrak{e} = 0.27$. Let us suppose that the whole population is infinite, and rf is taken as the limit of the relative frequency with respect to a fixed serial order of the individuals (cf. § 95). In this case the possible values of rf form a continuous scale. If the population is finite but sufficiently large (e.g., the inhabitants of Chicago), the possible values of rf, although finite in number, lie so close to each other that dealing with them as if they formed a continuous scale is a good approximation.

1. X considers an interval $\mathfrak{e} \pm \delta$ around his estimate $\mathfrak{e}(f,u,e)$ (for example, with $\delta = 0.02$, the interval between 0.25 and 0.29). Then he determines the value of $\mathfrak{c}$, on his evidence e, for the hypothesis h_δ that rf lies within this interval: $\mathfrak{c}_\delta = \mathfrak{c}(h_\delta,e)$. If he finds that $\mathfrak{c}_\delta$ is large, then he knows that it is very probable that the actual value of rf is close to the estimate $\mathfrak{e}$; hence $\mathfrak{c}_\delta$ measures the reliability of this estimate. However, X must clearly take into consideration not $\mathfrak{c}_\delta$ alone but $\mathfrak{c}_\delta$ in relation to the size 2δ of the interval (in our case, 0.04). For if the interval size 2δ is increased, $\mathfrak{c}_\delta$ will in general be increased too. Therefore X might consider taking the quotient $\mathfrak{c}_\delta/2\delta$. But since this again varies with δ, it seems more appropriate to take the limit toward which this quotient converges when smaller and smaller intervals are taken, provided this limit exists. Thus we may define the reliability of the estimate as

$$\lim_{\delta \to 0} (\mathfrak{c}_\delta/2\delta) .$$

[This is the same as the confirmation density $\mathfrak{c}'$ for the value $\mathfrak{e}(f,u,e)$ (§ 100A).]

2. The second method proceeds as follows. We have seen that for any interval $\mathfrak{e} \pm \delta$ around the estimate $\mathfrak{e}$ there is a value $\mathfrak{c}_\delta$ for the $\mathfrak{c}$ of the hypothesis that the actual value $f(u)$ lies in this interval. If the interval is very small, $\mathfrak{c}_\delta$ is small; if the interval covers all possible values of $f(u)$, $\mathfrak{c}_\delta$ is 1. For intermediate intervals, $\mathfrak{c}_\delta$ will have intermediate values. Instead of choosing an interval and then determining its $\mathfrak{c}_\delta$, as in the first method, X may choose once for all a fixed value between 0 and 1, and then determine the interval $\mathfrak{e} \pm \delta$ for which $\mathfrak{c}_\delta$ has this value. Suppose he chooses $\mathfrak{c}_\delta = 1/2$; then the corresponding interval $\mathfrak{e} \pm \delta$ has the characteristic property that it is, on the evidence e, just as probable for the actual value of $f(u)$ to lie within this interval as without. Let us call the value δ defined in this way the *probable error* of the estimate $\mathfrak{e}$. The smaller the probable error, the more reliable is the estimate. The concept here defined is essentially the same as that for which the term 'probable error' was originally used in the theory of probability; in modern statistics, however, the same term is used, not for this inductive concept but for an analogous statistical concept (see § 100B). [In many cases the confirmation density $\mathfrak{c}'$ is not symmetrical on both sides of the value $\mathfrak{e}$. In cases of this kind a better characterization of the reliability of the estimate is given by distinguishing between the lower probable error δ_1 and the upper probable error δ_2. They are defined in such a manner that the $\mathfrak{c}$ both for the interval between $\mathfrak{e} - \delta_1$ and $\mathfrak{e}$ and for that between $\mathfrak{e}$ and $\mathfrak{e} + \delta_2$ is

1/4; hence the $\mathfrak{c}$ for the whole interval around $\mathfrak{e}$ is here again 1/2, but $\mathfrak{e}$ is here not necessarily in the middle of the interval.]

3. The third method seems to be the most adequate of the three. The first two methods take into consideration only the $\mathfrak{c}$ for those of the possible values of f which lie in the neighborhood of the estimate $\mathfrak{e}$ of f. Often $\mathfrak{c}$ is rather low for the more remote values of f (especially if e describes not a sample but the whole population, as in the direct inference, §§ 94–96). However, in other cases $\mathfrak{c}$ may be relatively high even for remote values; and in these cases the third method may give a more adequate characterization of the nature of the estimate. Instead of asking: 'Is it very probable that the actual value of f is near to the estimate we have calculated, in other words, that the error we have made by our estimate is small?' we shall now ask: '*How* small is this error presumably; in other words, what is the estimate for the error of our estimate for f?' This method can be applied also if the number of possible values of f is finite and even very small. We assume in the following that it is a finite number n. Analogous definitions can be constructed for a continuous scale of values, on the basis of the methods indicated earlier (§ 100A).

By the *error* of the estimate for $f(u)$ we mean the difference between the estimated value and the actual value of $f(u)$:

D102-1. *The* ***error*** *of the estimate* $\mathfrak{e}(f,u,e)$:

$$\mathfrak{v}(f,u,e) =_{\text{Df}} \mathfrak{e}(f,u,e) - f(u) \,.$$

Let $r_1, \ldots, r_n$, as previously (§ 99), be the possible values of $f(u)$ on e, and $h_1, \ldots, h_n$ be the hypotheses stating these values. Suppose X has calculated the estimate of $f(u)$ on his evidence e and has found the value r':

$$(1) \qquad \mathfrak{e}(f,u,e) = \sum_p [r_p \times \mathfrak{c}(h_p,e)] = r' \,.$$

The actual value r of $f(u)$ is either r_1 or r_2 or ... or r_n. If $r = r_p$, then the error of X's estimate r' is

$$(2) \qquad \mathfrak{v}_p =_{\text{Df}} r' - r_p \,.$$

This error is positive if the estimate r' is too high; it is negative if the estimate is too low. The actual error $\mathfrak{v}$ of the estimate, that is, the difference between the estimated value r' and the actual value r of $f(u)$, is, of course, unknown to X, since the actual value r of $f(u)$ is not known. But just as he can determine the estimate r' for the unknown r, so he can apply the same general method of estimation in order to determine the estimate for $\mathfrak{v}$ or for simple functions of $\mathfrak{v}$. We shall study: (A) the estimate for $\mathfrak{v}$ itself;

(B) that for $|\,\mathfrak{v}\,|$, that is, the absolute value of $\mathfrak{v}$ (irrespective of sign), and (C) the estimate for $\mathfrak{v}^2$.

A. We write '$\mathfrak{c}_p$' as short for '$\mathfrak{c}(h_p,e)$'; this is the $\mathfrak{c}$ for the case in which $f(u)$ has the value r_p and hence the error $\mathfrak{v}$ is $\mathfrak{v}_p = r' - r_p$. Hence the *estimate of the error* $\mathfrak{v}$ of the estimate r' for $f(u)$ is:

$$\text{(3)} \qquad \mathfrak{e}(\mathfrak{v},f,u,e) = \sum_{p=1}^{n} [\mathfrak{v}_p \times \mathfrak{c}_p] \,.$$

We find easily the following result.

T102-1. $\mathfrak{e}(\mathfrak{v},f,u,e) = 0$.

Proof. According to (2), the sum in (3) is $\Sigma[(r' - r_p) \times \mathfrak{c}_p]$, hence $r' \times \Sigma\mathfrak{c}_p - \Sigma[r_p \times \mathfrak{c}_p]$. Of the two sums here occurring, the first is 1, the second r' (1). Hence the result is $r' - r' = 0$.

T1 says that the estimate of the error itself of any estimate is 0. This means that the estimate of any function f is such that the possible positive errors and the possible negative errors, each weighted with its $\mathfrak{c}$, cancel each other out. This result is interesting because it states an important characteristic of the estimate-function $\mathfrak{e}$; but it shows that the estimate of $\mathfrak{v}$ cannot be used for measuring the reliability of the estimate for f.

B. The estimate for the absolute value $|\,\mathfrak{v}\,|$ of the error $\mathfrak{v}$ is

$$\text{(4)} \qquad \mathfrak{e}(|\,\mathfrak{v}\,|,f,u,e) = \sum_{p} [|\, r' - r_p \,| \times \mathfrak{c}_p] \,.$$

Now we divide the possible values of $f(u)$, viz., $r_1, \ldots, r_n$, into two classes: the first contains those values r_p for which $r_p \leqq r'$, and hence $\mathfrak{v}_p \geqq 0$ and $|\,\mathfrak{v}_p\,| = \mathfrak{v}_p$; the second contains those for which $r_p > r'$, hence $\mathfrak{v}_p < 0$, and $|\,\mathfrak{v}_p\,| = -\mathfrak{v}_p$. In the following theorem, 'Σ_1' is meant to extend over the first class and 'Σ_2' over the second.

T102-2. $\mathfrak{e}(|\,\mathfrak{v}\,|,f,u,e) = \mathfrak{e}(f,u,e)[\Sigma_1\mathfrak{c}_p - \Sigma_2\mathfrak{c}_p] - \Sigma_1[r_p \times \mathfrak{c}_p] + \Sigma_2[r_p \times \mathfrak{c}_p]$.

Proof. The sum in (4) is

$$\Sigma_1[(r' - r_p)\mathfrak{c}_p] + \Sigma_2[(r_p - r')\mathfrak{c}_p] = r' \times \Sigma_1\mathfrak{c}_p - \Sigma_1[r_p \times \mathfrak{c}_p] + \Sigma_2[r_p \times \mathfrak{c}_p] - r' \times \Sigma_2\mathfrak{c}_p \,.$$

Hence the assertion.

C. The *estimate of the square error* $\mathfrak{v}^2$ is:

$$\text{(5)} \qquad \mathfrak{e}(\mathfrak{v}^2,f,u,e) = \sum_{p} [(r' - r_p)^2 \times \mathfrak{c}_p] \,.$$

We shall adopt this method as our explication of the reliability of an estimate. It will be discussed in the next section.

§ 103. The Estimated Square Error of an Estimate

The last of the methods explained in the preceding section is adopted for explicating the reliability of an estimate. It consists in applying the general method of $\mathfrak{e}$-mean estimation (§ 99) to the square of the error.

The development of the statistical theory of errors since Gauss has shown that, at least in all those cases in which the distribution is known or assumed to be normal, the square error is a more fruitful concept than the error itself or its absolute value. Therefore the last of the methods discussed in the preceding section seems especially suitable as an explicatum for reliability. We now adopt it as our explicatum; that is to say, if an estimate r' of f has been determined, then we take as measure of its reliability the estimate of its square error. (Both estimates are, of course, meant as $\mathfrak{e}$-mean estimates, in the sense of the function $\mathfrak{e}$.) The square root of this estimate of the square error serves, of course, just as well. The latter concept is the inductive analogue to, but more general than, the statistical concept usually called the standard deviation σ (square root of the variance); we shall call it the estimated standard error and designate it by '$\mathfrak{f}$'; hence the estimated square error is $\mathfrak{f}^2$.

+D103-1.

a. The ***estimated square error*** of $\mathfrak{e}(f,u,e)$, in symbols: $\mathfrak{f}^2(f,u,e)$, $=_{Df}$ $\mathfrak{e}(\mathfrak{v}^2,f,u,e)$.

b. The ***estimated standard error*** of $\mathfrak{e}(f,u,e)$, in symbols: $\mathfrak{f}(f,u,e)$, $=_{Df}$ $\sqrt{\mathfrak{e}(\mathfrak{v}^2,f,u,e)}$.

The following theorem shows how $\mathfrak{f}^2$ can be determined from $\mathfrak{e}(f)$ and $\mathfrak{e}(f^2)$ without the use of $\mathfrak{v}$.

+T103-1.

a. $\mathfrak{f}^2(f,u,e) = \mathfrak{e}(f^2,u,e) - \mathfrak{e}^2(f,u,e)$.

Proof. Let us first determine the estimate of the square of the difference between an arbitrarily chosen fixed number q (instead of r') and r, i.e., $f(u)$. Later we shall substitute r' for q. The estimate mentioned is $\Sigma[(q - r_p)^2 \times \mathfrak{c}_p] = \Sigma[(q^2 - 2qr_p + r_p^2) \times \mathfrak{c}_p] = q^2 \times \Sigma\mathfrak{c}_p - 2q \times \Sigma[r_p \times \mathfrak{c}_p] + \Sigma[r_p^2 \times \mathfrak{c}_p]$. The first of the latter three sums is 1, the second is r'; hence the whole is

(1) $$q^2 - 2qr' + \Sigma[r_p^2 \times \mathfrak{c}_p]\,.$$

This will be used later. Now we substitute r', that is, $\mathfrak{e}(f)$, for q; the first two terms become $r'^2 - 2r'^2 = -r'^2$. The third term in (1) is the estimate for r^2, hence $\mathfrak{e}(f^2)$. Hence the assertion.

b. $\mathfrak{f}(f,u,e) = \sqrt{\mathfrak{e}(f^2,u,e) - \mathfrak{e}^2(f,u,e)}$. (From (a).)

It was remarked earlier that we should clearly distinguish between the estimate of f^2 and the square of the estimate of f. We see now that (except for the trivial case that there is only one possible value of f) the first of these two values is always greater than the second and that their difference is the estimated square error.

The following theorem says that the estimate $\mathfrak{e}(f)$ has this characteristic property: the estimate of the square of the difference between any fixed number q and $f(u)$ has its smallest value if we take $\mathfrak{e}(f)$ as q.

T103-2. $\mathfrak{e}[(q - f(u))^2, e]$ varies with q in such a way that it is a minimum for $q = \mathfrak{e}(f,u,e)$.

Proof. The estimate mentioned has been determined above as (1). By differentiating (1) partially with respect to q we obtain $2q - 2r'$. This is 0 only for $q = r'$. The second differential coefficient is 2, hence positive. Therefore (1) has a minimum for $q = r'$.

Examples. 1. The earlier example (beginning of § 101): $r_p = 1, 2, 3$ with equal values $\mathfrak{c}_p = 1/3$. We find, as previously, $\mathfrak{e}(f) = 2$, hence $\mathfrak{e}^2(f) = 4$;

	$p =$			Sum
	1	2	3	
r_p	1	2	3	
$\mathfrak{c}_p$	1/3	1/3	1/3	
$r_p\mathfrak{c}_p$	1/3	2/3	3/3	2; this is $\mathfrak{e}(f)$.
r_p^2	1	4	9	
$r_p^2\mathfrak{c}_p$	1/3	4/3	9/3	14/3; this is $\mathfrak{e}(f^2)$.
$\mathfrak{v}_p$	−1	0	1	
$\mathfrak{v}_p^2$	1	0	1	
$\mathfrak{v}_p^2\mathfrak{c}_p$	1/3	0	1/3	2/3; this is $\mathfrak{e}(\mathfrak{v}^2)$.

$\mathfrak{e}(f^2) = 14/3$. Further, $\mathfrak{f}^2 = \mathfrak{e}(\mathfrak{v}^2) = 2/3$; this is indeed $= \mathfrak{e}(f^2) - \mathfrak{e}^2(f)$, in accordance with T1a. The estimated standard error $\mathfrak{f}$ is $\sqrt{2/3} = 0.82$.

2. We take the same r_p-values, but with $\mathfrak{c}_p = 1/5, 3/5, 1/5$; thus the outside values are *less* probable than the middle value. (We omit in the table those lines which are as above.) We find, as in the first example, $\mathfrak{e}(f) = 2$, hence

	$p =$			Sum
	1	2	3	
$\mathfrak{c}_p$	1/5	3/5	1/5	
$r_p\mathfrak{c}_p$	1/5	6/5	3/5	2; this is $\mathfrak{e}(f)$.
$r_p^2\mathfrak{c}_p$	1/5	12/5	9/5	22/5; this is $\mathfrak{e}(f^2)$.
$\mathfrak{v}_p^2\mathfrak{c}_p$	1/5	0	1/5	2/5; this is $\mathfrak{e}(\mathfrak{v}^2)$.

$\mathfrak{e}^2(f) = 4$. $\mathfrak{e}(f^2) = 22/5$. $\mathfrak{f}^2 = \mathfrak{e}(\mathfrak{v}^2) = 2/5$; this is again $= \mathfrak{e}(f^2) - \mathfrak{e}^2(f)$. $\mathfrak{f} = 0.63$. $\mathfrak{f}$ is here smaller than in the first case. Thus the estimate of f, although it has the same value 2, is here more reliable than in the first case. This is plausible because the probability for the outside values and thus for a discrepancy between the actual and the estimated value of f is here smaller than in the first case.

3. Finally, we take the same r_p-values with $\mathfrak{c}_p = 2/5, 1/5, 2/5$; thus the outside values are here *more* probable than the middle value. We find, as in

	$p =$			Sum
	1	2	3	
$\mathfrak{c}_p$	2/5	1/5	2/5	
$r_p \mathfrak{c}_p$	2/5	2/5	6/5	2; this is $\mathfrak{e}(f)$.
$r_p^2 \mathfrak{c}_p$	2/5	4/5	18/5	24/5; this is $\mathfrak{e}(f^2)$.
$\mathfrak{v}_p^2 \mathfrak{c}_p$	2/5	0	2/5	4/5; this is $\mathfrak{e}(\mathfrak{v}^2)$.

the other examples, $\mathfrak{e}(f) = 2$, hence $\mathfrak{e}^2(f) = 4$. $\mathfrak{e}(f^2) = 24/5$. $\mathfrak{s}^2 = \mathfrak{e}(\mathfrak{v}^2) = 4/5$; $\mathfrak{s} = 0.89$. This is here greater than in the first case. Thus the same estimate of f is here less reliable. This is plausible because the outside values are here more probable than in the other cases.

The judgment that a given estimate $\mathfrak{e}(f)$ is highly reliable is explicated in our method by the statement that its estimated square error $\mathfrak{s}^2(f)$ is small. It is important to see clearly that this judgment of reliability itself is again an inductive judgment. It says something about the *probable* relation between the estimated value r' and the actual value r of f. A judgment on the *actual* relation between these two values cannot be given by inductive logic; it presupposes a determination of the actual value r, which can be made only by empirical investigations going beyond e. Furthermore, the judgment on the reliability of an estimate $\mathfrak{e}(f)$ of f is itself an estimation $\mathfrak{e}(\mathfrak{v}^2)$ of the square error; and the $\mathfrak{e}$-function used in the latter estimation is the same as that used for $\mathfrak{e}(f)$. Therefore, this determination of the reliability of estimates is, so to speak, an internal affair within one system of inductive logic based upon a chosen function $\mathfrak{c}$; it cannot be used as a method for obtaining an external, objective judgment on the goodness of a system of inductive logic. Suppose that X chooses the $\mathfrak{c}$-function $\mathfrak{c}_1$, and the estimate-function $\mathfrak{e}_1$ based upon $\mathfrak{c}_1$ and $\mathfrak{s}_1$ based upon $\mathfrak{e}_1$. Suppose he finds as estimate for $f(u)$ $\mathfrak{e}_1(f) = 0.6$ with $\mathfrak{s}_1(f) = 0.1$. Similarly, X_2 chooses $\mathfrak{c}_2$ and, based upon it, $\mathfrak{e}_2$ and $\mathfrak{s}_2$, and finds, for the same $f(u)$, on the same evidence, $\mathfrak{e}_2(f) = 0.7$ with $\mathfrak{s}_2(f) = 0.01$. X_2 might perhaps be tempted to conclude from these results that 0.7 is a much more reliable estimate of $f(u)$ than 0.6, because his estimated standard error is much smaller than that found for $\mathfrak{e}_1(f)$; and if similar results would be obtained for other magnitudes, he might claim that his estimate-function $\mathfrak{e}_2$ were generally more reliable than $\mathfrak{e}_1$. However, these conclusions would constitute a disastrous fallacy. If $\mathfrak{c}_2$ happens to be an inadequate explicatum for probability$_1$, then not only are the $\mathfrak{c}_2$-values and the $\mathfrak{e}_2$-values unreliable but also the estimated standard error 0.01, since this is determined by the same function $\mathfrak{c}_2$; hence in this case nothing can be inferred from the smallness of the value 0.01. What then is the use of determining the estimated standard error? It is not a method of comparing two functions $\mathfrak{c}_1$ and $\mathfrak{c}_2$. It is useful only if we have other reasons for regarding a chosen function $\mathfrak{c}$ as adequate. (Such reasons may, for instance, consist in the fact that in many actual or imagined knowledge situations the values of $\mathfrak{c}$ are sufficiently in agreement with the inductive thinking of a careful scientist.) If $\mathfrak{c}$ is adequate, then the method of the estimated standard error may be used for comparing the reliability of estimates made on the basis of different evidences but with the same function $\mathfrak{c}$.

This concludes the general discussion of estimation. In the following sections we shall deal with those special cases of estimation which arise with respect to our language systems $\mathfrak{L}$.

§ 104. Estimation of Frequencies

In the remainder of this chapter the general method of estimation previously developed, that is, the $\mathfrak{c}$-mean estimate-function $\mathfrak{e}$, is applied to our systems $\mathfrak{L}$, and in particular to absolute and relative frequencies, which can be expressed in $\mathfrak{L}$. First, the frequency of true sentences in a class of given sentences is studied. It is found that the estimate of the relative frequency of truth among given sentences of any kind is equal to the arithmetic mean of the degree of confirmation of these sentences (T2b). This important result justifies our earlier explanation of probability$_1$ as an explicandum in terms of an estimate of relative truth-frequency (§ 41D). Secondly, the estimate of the frequency of a given property among given individuals is discussed. In analogy to our earlier distinction between direct and predictive inferences, we distinguish now between direct and predictive estimations. The estimation of the frequency in a sample is called direct, if the given frequency on which the estimation is based is that in the population; it is called predictive, if the given frequency refers to another sample.

In the foregoing sections of this chapter we have discussed the general features of a method of estimation for any languages, especially languages containing quantitative magnitudes like those of physics. This method consists in the use of the $\mathfrak{c}$-mean estimate-function $\mathfrak{e}$. In the remainder of this chapter we shall discuss the results to which this method leads if it is applied to our simple language systems $\mathfrak{L}$.

The systems $\mathfrak{L}$ do not contain any quantitative magnitudes in the ordinary sense like length, mass, temperature, and the like. Nevertheless certain numerical functions based, not on measurement, but on counting, can be expressed in the systems $\mathfrak{L}$. The two most important of these functions are the absolute and the relative frequency of a property within a given class. In the following our method of estimation will be applied to these two functions only.

We shall first discuss the frequency of truth among given sentences, and later the frequency of any molecular property among given individuals. We shall find that the first application of frequency is the most general case expressible in our language systems and that the second can be obtained as a specialization of the first.

Suppose a finite class $\mathfrak{K}_i$ of s sentences is given by enumeration: $\{i_1, i_2, \ldots, i_s\}$. By the *absolute truth-frequency* or, briefly, *truth-frequency* in $\mathfrak{K}_i$, in signs of the metalanguage: '$\text{tf}(\mathfrak{K}_i)$', we mean the number of true sentences in $\mathfrak{K}_i$. By the *relative truth-frequency* in $\mathfrak{K}_i$, in signs: '$\text{rtf}(\mathfrak{K}_i)$', we mean the quotient $\text{tf}(\mathfrak{K}_i)/s$.

For example, let $\mathfrak{K}_1$ be the class $\{i_1, i_2, i_3\}$, where i_1, i_2, and i_3 are given sentences of any form of a given system $\mathfrak{L}$. That the cardinal number s of $\mathfrak{K}_1$ is three is seen from the definition of $\mathfrak{K}_1$; it is obviously not dependent on the facts referred to by the three sentences of $\mathfrak{K}_1$ or any other facts. On the other hand, the sentence

(1) $$\text{'tf}(\mathfrak{K}_1) = 2\text{'}$$

is a factual, empirical sentence (of the metalanguage); it says that, among the three sentences of $\mathfrak{K}_1$, there are exactly two which are true. Since we know from the definition of $\mathfrak{K}_1$ that $s = 3$, we can deduce from (1) the sentence

(2) $$\text{'rtf}(\mathfrak{K}_1) = 2/3\text{'}$$

and vice versa. Hence (1) and (2) are logically equivalent; they express the same factual content in different conceptual forms. Both sentences belong to the metalanguage, not to $\mathfrak{L}$. $\mathfrak{L}$ contains neither functors like 'tf' or 'rtf', nor numerical expressions like '2' or '2/3'. Nevertheless, the common factual content of (1) and (2) is expressible in $\mathfrak{L}$, in a still different form. The term 'truth' is here understood in the semantical sense (see § 17). The statement 'i is true' has the same factual content as the statement i in $\mathfrak{L}$ and can therefore be translated into i. Likewise, the statement 'i is false' is translatable into $\sim i$. (1) says that two of the three i-sentences are true and one is false. There are three possibilities in which this is the case. Each of these possibilities is expressible by a conjunction in $\mathfrak{L}$, and hence the whole by the disjunction of these conjunctions, viz. $(i_1 . i_2 . \sim i_3) \vee (i_1 . \sim i_2 . i_3) \vee (\sim i_1 . i_2 . i_3)$. Let this be h_2. Thus this disjunction h_2 in $\mathfrak{L}$ may serve as a translation of (1), and simultaneously as a translation of (2), because the latter is logically equivalent to (1).

In general terms, let $\mathfrak{K}_i$ be a class of s given sentences, $\{i_1, i_2, \ldots, i_s\}$. We shall now explain a few terms to be used only in the present discussion and in the proof of T2a. The following sentences are called the k-sentences for the given class (as in T21-7; their number is 2^s): first the conjunction $i_1 . i_2 . \ldots . i_s$, and furthermore all conjunctions formed from this one by negating some or all of the components. A k-sentence obtained by negating $s - m$ ($m = 0, \ldots, s$) of the s components in the original conjunction is called a k^m-sentence. (The number of the k^m-sentences is $\binom{s}{m}$.) For every m, let h_m be the disjunction of all k^m-sentences (in the lexicographical order). There is only one k^s-sentence, viz., the conjunction of the i-sentences; thus h_s is this conjunction itself. There is likewise only one k^0-sentence, viz., the conjunction of the negations of the i-sentences; thus h_0 is this conjunction. For all other values of m, the number of k^m-sentences is $\geqq 2$, and h_m is their disjunction. For any particular value m, the sentence (in the metalanguage) '$\text{tf}(\mathfrak{K}_i) = m$' is true if and only if one of the k^m-sentences is true; hence it is translatable into their disjunction, that is, h_m. This leads to the following theorem.

T104-1. Let $\mathfrak{L}$ be any finite or infinite system, $\mathfrak{c}$ a regular $\mathfrak{c}$-function in $\mathfrak{L}$, $\mathfrak{e}$ based upon $\mathfrak{c}$ (D100-1), e any non-L-false sentence in $\mathfrak{L}$, and $\mathfrak{K}_i$ a class of s given sentences in $\mathfrak{L}$. For any m ($m = 0, 1, \ldots, s$), let h_m be as explained above. Then the *estimate of truth-frequency* for $\mathfrak{K}_i$ on e is determined as follows:

$$\mathfrak{e}(\text{tf}, \mathfrak{K}_i, e) = \sum_{m=0}^{s} [m \times \mathfrak{c}(h_m, e)] .$$

(From T100-1. The value $m = 0$, although possible, need not be included in the sum because the term of the sum for this value is 0.)

We shall now proceed to prove a theorem (T2) which is of great importance for the foundation of inductive logic, since it justifies the interpretation of probability$_1$ as an estimate of relative truth-frequency. We have used this interpretation in our earlier discussion of the meaning of probability$_1$ as an explicandum (§ 41D). The theorem is of great generality. It holds for all regular $\mathfrak{c}$-functions. It holds for any given sentences, irrespective of inductive or even deductive dependencies among them. One such sentence may, for instance, L-imply another one or even be L-equivalent to it. In the latter case, the same proposition would be expressed by two or more of the given sentences, and hence their truth-values would necessarily be the same. Nevertheless the theorem of the estimate of truth-frequency holds in this case just as if the sentences were logically independent of each other.

+**T104-2.** Let $\mathfrak{K}$, c, e, e, $\mathfrak{K}_i$, and s be as in T1. Let the sentences of $\mathfrak{K}_i$ be $i_1, i_2, \ldots, i_s$. Then the following holds.

a. $\mathfrak{e}(\text{tf},\mathfrak{K}_i,e) = \sum_{n=1}^{s} \mathfrak{c}(i_n,e)$.

Proof. Concerning k-sentences, k^m-sentences, and the hypotheses h_m (m = 0 to s), see the explanations preceding T1. For any n (from 1 to s), the nth conjunctive component in some of the k-sentences (indeed in half of them) is i_n; let $\mathfrak{K}_n$ be the class of these k-sentences. In the other k-sentences it is $\sim i_n$. The sentence i_n is L-equivalent to the disjunction of the sentences of $\mathfrak{K}_n$ (T21-7d). Therefore, since the k-sentences are L-exclusive in pairs (T21-7a), $\mathfrak{c}(i_n,e) = \sum_k \mathfrak{c}(k,e)$ where k runs through the k-sentences in $\mathfrak{K}_n$ (T59-1m). Hence,

$$\sum_{n=1}^{s} \mathfrak{c}(i_n,e) = \sum_{n=1}^{s} \sum_k \mathfrak{c}(k,e), \quad (4)$$

where for every n, the second sum covers the k-sentences in $\mathfrak{K}_n$. The c-value of any k^m-sentence appears m times in the double sum in (4). (Consider, as an example, the k-sentence k' which contains i_2, i_4, i_5, and the negations of the other i-sentences as conjunctive components. k' is a k^3-sentence. Its c-value occurs in the double sum in (4) three times: first for n = 2, because k' contains i_2 and hence belongs to $\mathfrak{K}_2$; then for n = 4 because of i_4; and finally for n = 5 because of i_5.) Therefore the double sum is equal to $\sum_k [m \times \mathfrak{c}(k,e)]$, where the sum covers all k-sentences, and the c-value of any k^m-sentence (m = 0 to s) is multiplied by m. This sum is now transformed into another double sum by grouping together the k-sentences with equal m: $\sum_{m=0}^{s} [m \times \sum_k \mathfrak{c}(k,e)]$, where for any m, the second sum covers all k^m-sentences. Now the value of this second sum is equal to $\mathfrak{c}(h_m,e)$ (T59-1m), because h_m is the disjunction of the k^m-sentences and these sentences are L-exclusive in pairs. Thus we obtain from (4):

$$\sum_{n=1}^{s} \mathfrak{c}(i_n,e) = \sum_{m=0}^{s} [m \times \mathfrak{c}(h_m,e)]. \quad (5)$$

The right-hand side here is the estimate of tf (T1); hence the theorem.

b. $\mathfrak{e}(\text{rtf},\mathfrak{K}_i,e) = \frac{1}{s} \sum_{n=1}^{s} \mathfrak{c}(i_n,e)$; that is, the estimate of the relative truth-frequency in $\mathfrak{K}_i$ is the arithmetic mean of the c-values of the sentences in $\mathfrak{K}_i$. (From (a), T100-3.)

c. (Corollary.) If all i-sentences have the same c-value on e, then $\mathfrak{e}(\text{rtf},\mathfrak{K}_i,e)$ is equal to this value. (From (b).)

T2c can be used in the clarification of probability$_1$ as an explicandum. Suppose a person X has an idea of what he means by the estimate (or expectation-value, in the classical sense of this term) of a magnitude; this idea is an explicandum, that is to say, it is clear enough to him for practical purposes on a pre-systematic level, although he may not yet have a systematic explicatum for it. Suppose further that the idea of probability$_1$ as a quantitative concept which takes a numerical value for any given hypothesis with respect to any given evidence is less clear to *X*. (A psychological situation of this kind is by no means fictitious. Many authors, among them perhaps a majority of contemporary statisticians, reject the logical concept of probability$_1$ or admit it only in a nonquantitative form. On the other hand, practically all statisticians either apply methods of estimation or are at least in search of satisfactory methods, which shows that they admit the concept of estimation at least as an explicandum.) The result T2c shows the following way of explaining to *X* the meaning of probability$_1$ in terms of estimation. If you ascribe the same value, say, 0.3, to several, say, one hundred, hypotheses on the basis of the same evidence *e*, then thereby you show that you estimate, on the evidence *e*, the number of true ones among the one hundred hypotheses as thirty. Or, the other way round: suppose that on the basis of your total observational knowledge expressed by *e*, you have equal confidence in each of one hundred hypotheses but do not know how to measure this confidence quantitatively, but you are able to make estimations and you estimate the number of true ones among the hundred hypotheses as thirty, then take 0.3 as a measure of rational confidence, that is, ascribe the value 0.3 to each of the hypotheses as its probability$_1$ on *e*. T2b can be used analogously, but in a more general way. Here the values of probability$_1$ need not be equal; if they differ, still their arithmetic mean expresses the estimate of the relative truth-frequency. In our earlier discussions on the meaning of probability$_1$ as an explicandum, we have equated the value of probability$_1$ with the estimate of rtf (§ 41D). This procedure is now justified by T2c. (This theorem itself refers to the concepts of estimate and of degree of confirmation as explicata. But it holds generally for all regular c-functions. Therefore it shows that we shall not involve ourselves in contradictions when we explain the concept of an estimate as an explicandum in terms of probability$_1$ and then again explain probability$_1$ in terms of an estimate of rtf.)

Now we proceed to another application of the frequency concepts, viz., the frequency of a given property among the individuals of a given class. These explanations will be perfectly analogous to the former ones on truth-frequency. Here again, we formulate these concepts first in the metalanguage. Let *M* be a property expressible by a molecular predicate in $\mathfrak{L}$, say, 'M'. Let K be a finite class of s individuals defined by enumeration: $K =_{\text{Df}} \{a_1, a_2, \ldots, a_s\}$. By the *absolute frequency* of M in K, in signs of the metalanguage: 'af(M,K)', we mean the number of those individuals in K which have the property M. The *relative frequency* of M in K is $\text{rf}(M,K) =_{\text{Df}} \text{af}(M,K)/s$.

To take a concrete example, let us define: $K =_{\text{Df}} \{a,b,c\}$. It follows from this definition that the cardinal number of K is three. On the other hand,

(6) $$\text{'af}(M,K) = 2\text{'}$$

is a factual, empirical sentence. From (6) we can deduce

(7) $$\text{'rf}(M,K) = 2/3\text{'}\,.$$

Hence (6) and (7) are logically equivalent. The following sentence (8) is a translation of (6) into $\mathfrak{L}$; it serves simultaneously as a translation of (7):

(8) $$\text{'}(Ma\,.\,Mb\,.\,{\sim}Mc) \lor (Ma\,.\,{\sim}Mb\,.\,Mc) \lor ({\sim}Ma\,.\,Mb\,.\,Mc)\text{'}\,.$$

This sentence is a special case of our former h_2 for $s = 3$, with full sentences of 'M' as i-sentences. It is a statistical distribution (D26-6c) for the division 'M', '${\sim}M$' with respect to the three individuals of K. The three disjunctive components in (8) are isomorphic individual distributions (D26-6a, D26-3).

The subsequent theorem T3 is analogous to T1. It determines the estimate of af in terms of the $\mathfrak{c}$-values for hypotheses which state the possible values of af. These values are the cardinal numbers 0, 1, . . . , s (or those of them which are not excluded by e). Therefore the hypotheses stating these values are statistical distributions, like the example sentence (8) (for $s = 3$, af $= 2$).

T104-3. Let $\mathfrak{L}$, $\mathfrak{c}$, $\mathfrak{e}$, and e be as in T1. Let K be a class of s individuals in $\mathfrak{L}$ ($s > 0$), 'M' a molecular predicate in $\mathfrak{L}$, h_m ($m = 0, 1, \ldots, s$) the statistical distribution for 'M' and '${\sim}M$' with respect to the s individuals in K with the cardinal number m for 'M'. Then

$$\mathfrak{e}(\text{af},M,K,e) = \sum_{m=1}^{s} [m \times \mathfrak{c}(h_m,e)]\,.\ \text{(From T1.)}$$

The following theorem states the simple relation between the estimates of rf and af.

T104-4. Let $\mathfrak{L}$, $\mathfrak{c}$, $\mathfrak{e}$, and e be as in T1. Let K, s, and 'M' be as in T3. Then the following holds.

a. $\mathfrak{e}(\text{rf},M,K,e) = \mathfrak{e}(\text{af},M,K,e)/s$. (From T100-3.)

b. $\mathfrak{e}(\text{rf}^2,M,K,e) = \mathfrak{e}(\text{af}^2,M,K,e)/s^2$. (Likewise.)

c. $\mathfrak{f}^2(\text{rf},M,K,e) = \mathfrak{f}^2(\text{af},M,K,e)/s^2$. (From T103-1a, (a), (b).)

d. $\mathfrak{f}(\text{rf},M,K,e) = \mathfrak{f}(\text{af},M,K,e)/s$. (From (c).)
e. $\mathfrak{f}(\text{rf})/\mathfrak{e}(\text{rf}) = \mathfrak{f}(\text{af})/\mathfrak{e}(\text{af})$. (From (d), (a).)

T4a compares the estimates for rf and af themselves. T4c compares $\mathfrak{f}^2$, i.e., $\mathfrak{e}(\mathfrak{v}^2)$ (D103-1a), the estimated square errors of those estimates of rf and af. T4d compares the estimated standard errors $\mathfrak{f}$. T4e says that the estimated *relative errors*, that is, the quotients $\mathfrak{f}/\mathfrak{e}$, are the same for rf and af. (The relative error in this sense is the inductive analogue to the statistical concept of coefficient of variation.) These relations will be used in the following.

Let K_1 be the class of individuals described in e and K_2 that described in h. The two chief cases to be distinguished here are the following. (1) K_2 is contained in K_1; (2) K_2 is outside of K_1. In the first case, we have earlier called K_1 the population and K_2 a sample from the population; and the determination of $\mathfrak{c}(h,e)$ was called the direct (or internal) inference. In the second case, K_1 is one sample and K_2 is another, nonoverlapping sample; the determination of $\mathfrak{c}$ in this case was called the predictive (or external) inference. Now an estimate of af or rf of M in K_2 with respect to e is based on $\mathfrak{c}(h,e)$. Hence this estimate is made in the first case with the help of direct inferences, in the second case with the help of predictive inferences. Therefore we shall speak in the first case of a ***direct*** (or internal) ***estimate,*** and in the second case of a ***predictive*** (or external) ***estimate.***

The direct estimation of frequencies will be discussed in the next section, and the predictive estimation later.

§ 105. Direct Estimation of Frequencies

The direct estimation of frequencies is here discussed, that is to say, the frequency of a property M in a population is given, and on this basis an estimate of the frequency in a sample is to be made. Theorems are given which determine the values of these estimates and their estimated square errors (T1). The most important result is this (T1h): the estimate of the relative frequency in the sample is equal to the given relative frequency in the population. The theorems on direct estimation hold for all symmetrical $\mathfrak{c}$-functions, like the theorems on the direct inference from which they are derived.

In this section we shall deal with *direct estimation*, that is, with the estimates of af and rf in a sample based on the given frequency in the population. We found earlier that it was possible in the case of the direct inference, in distinction to all other kinds of inductive inference, to prove theorems determining the $\mathfrak{c}$-values without specifying a particular $\mathfrak{c}$-function, because these values are the same for all symmetrical $\mathfrak{c}$-functions (§§ 94–96). We can now use the earlier results concerning $\mathfrak{c}$ for deriving results concerning direct estimation, which likewise hold for all symmetrical 𝔠-functions.

As in the earlier theorem stating the exact 𝔠-values for the direct inference (T94-1), we consider a population of n individuals. We take here $p = 2$, that is, a division consisting of only two properties, M and non-M. The evidence e is a statistical distribution stating that the af of M in the population is n_1 and that of non-M $n_2 = n - n_1$; hence the rf of M is $n_1/n = r_1$ and that of non-M is $n_2/n = r_2$. K is a sample of s individuals taken from the population. The earlier theorem (T94-1b(2)) gives the 𝔠-value for any s_1, that is, for any possible value of af of M in the sample. This enables us now to determine the estimate of af in the sample, and then that of rf.

+T105-1. ***Direct estimates of frequencies.*** Let $\mathfrak{L}$, 'M' (for 'M_1'), e, n, n_1, n_2, r_1, r_2 be as in T94-1, but with $p = 2$. Let K be a class of s individuals belonging to the n individuals referred to in e. Let h_m ($m = 0, \ldots, s$) be as in T104-3. Let 𝔠 be a symmetrical 𝔠-function and 𝔢 be based on 𝔠. Then the following holds.

a. $\mathfrak{e}(\text{af},M,K,e) = sr_1$. (From T104-3, T94-1d).

b. That value of m, that is, af, for which $\mathfrak{c}(h_m,e)$ has its maximum either coincides with 𝔢(af), if the latter is an integer, or is an integer close to 𝔢(af). (From (a), T94-1c.)

c. (1) $\mathfrak{e}(\text{af}^2,M,K,e) = \frac{sn_1}{n(n-1)}\,[s(n_1 - 1) + n_2]$;

(2) $= s\,\frac{n_1}{n}\left[s\,\frac{n_1 - 1}{n - 1} + \frac{n_2}{n - 1}\right]$.

Proof. $\mathfrak{e}(\text{af}^2) = \sum_{m=1}^{s} [m^2 \times \mathfrak{c}(h_m,e)]$ in analogy to T104-3, $= \sum_m \left[m^2\binom{n_1}{m}\binom{n_2}{s-m}\right] / \binom{n}{s}$ (T94-1b(2)). $m^2\binom{n_1}{m} = mn_1\binom{n_1-1}{m-1}$ (T40-8e). Hence the sum is (with $l = m - 1$) $n_1 \sum_{l=0}^{s-1} \left[(l + 1)\binom{n_1-1}{l}\binom{n_2}{s-1-l}\right]$. The latter sum is $\sum_{l=0}^{s-1} \left[l\binom{n_1-1}{l}\binom{n_2}{s-1-l}\right] + \sum_{l=0}^{s-1} \left[\binom{n_1-1}{l}\binom{n_2}{s-1-l}\right]$. The first of these two sums becomes (with T40-8e, and $k = l - 1$) $(n_1 - 1) \sum_{k=0}^{s-2} \left[\binom{n_1-2}{k}\binom{n_2}{s-2-k}\right]$, hence $(n_1 - 1)\binom{n-2}{s-2}$ (T40-9c). The second of the above two sums is $\binom{n-1}{s-1}$ (T40-9c). Hence, with some simple transformations (using D40-2a), the assertion.

d. Approximation for the case that n_1 (and hence n) is large in relation to 1 (it need not be large in relation to s):
$\mathfrak{e}(\text{af}^2,M,K,e) \cong sr_1(sr_1 + r_2)$. (From (c)(2).)

e. $\mathfrak{f}^2(\text{af},M,K,e) = s\,\frac{n_1 n_2}{n(n-1)}\left(1 - \frac{s}{n}\right)$. (From T103-1a, (c)(2), (a).)

f. Approximation for the case that n is large in relation to 1:
$\mathfrak{f}^2(\text{af},M,K,e) \cong sr_1r_2\left(1 - \frac{s}{n}\right)$. (From (e).)

g. Approximation for the case that n is, moreover, large in relation to s:
$\mathfrak{f}^2(\text{af},M,K,e) \cong sr_1r_2$; hence $\mathfrak{f} = \sqrt{sr_1r_2}$. (From (f).)

h. $\mathfrak{e}(\text{rf},M,K,e) = r_1$. (From T104-4a, (a).)

i. $\mathfrak{f}^2(\text{rf},M,K,e) = \frac{n_1 n_2}{sn(n-1)}\left(1 - \frac{s}{n}\right)$. (From T104-4c, (e).)

j. Approximation for the case that n is large in relation to 1:
$\mathfrak{f}^2(\text{rf},M,K,e) \cong \frac{r_1 r_2}{s}\left(1 - \frac{s}{n}\right)$. (From T104-4c, (f).)

k. Approximation for the case that n is, moreover, large in relation to s:
$\mathfrak{f}^2(\text{rf},M,K,e) \cong r_1 r_2/s$; hence $\mathfrak{f}(\text{rf}) = \sqrt{r_1 r_2/s}$. (From T104-4c, (g).)

l. Approximation for the case that n is large in relation to s:
$\mathfrak{f}(\text{rf})/\mathfrak{e}(\text{rf}) = \mathfrak{f}(\text{af})/\mathfrak{e}(\text{af}) \cong \sqrt{r_2/sr_1}$. (From (h), (k); T104-4e.)

The most important results are T1a: $\mathfrak{e}(\text{af}) = sr_1$, and T1h: $\mathfrak{e}(\text{rf}) = r_1$. Thus, if the rf of M in the population is known to be r_1, then the estimate of rf in any sample is likewise r_1. Note that this result holds exactly for any n and s, even if the population is not large and the sample constitutes a considerable part of the population. (The proof of T1a is based, not on the binomial law (T95-1), but on the unrestricted theorem for the direct inference (T94-1).)

T1b says that the estimate of af and the most probable value of af are either equal or close together.

The values found for $\mathfrak{e}(\text{af}^2)$ (T1c and d) are chiefly used for determining $\mathfrak{f}^2$ (T1e, f, g), that is, the estimated square error by which we measure the reliability of the estimate made for the af in the sample. The value T1g can be derived also from the binomial law. For the case where the sample is not a small part of the population, T1f gives a convenient approximation more exact than T1g. The estimated square error for the estimate of the rf in the sample, which is r_1 (T1h), is stated in T1i, j, and k. The approximation T1k can be derived also from the binomial law. When the sample size s increases, $\mathfrak{f}^2(\text{af})$ increases and is approximately proportional to s; but $\mathfrak{f}^2(\text{rf})$ decreases and is approximately proportional to $1/s$. T1l states the relative error, i.e., $\mathfrak{f}/\mathfrak{e}$, which is the same for rf and af (T104-4e).

T1 is formulated for a finite population size n. Now it was mentioned earlier (§ 95) that the values of $\mathfrak{c}$ for the direct inference stated in the binomial law (T95-1) hold exactly if the population is infinite and r_1 is the limit of rf with respect to a fixed serial order of the individuals. Under these conditions the values stated in T1a, d, g, h, k, and l hold likewise exactly, because they can be derived from the binomial law.

The customary methods in statistics regard the rf in the population, for which they use the term 'probability', as given or hypothetically assumed; therefore they correspond to what we call the direct inference and the direct estimation. Hence our direct estimate of af corresponds to what is called in statistics the expected value of af; $\mathfrak{s}^2(\text{af})$ corresponds to the mean square deviation (or the second moment about the mean); $\mathfrak{s}(\text{af})$ to the standard deviation σ. Thus, leaving aside the difference in interpretation—which is here again the difference between inductive and statistical concepts—we can compare the values stated in T1 with the customary values given in statistics. We find that the values given in T1a, d, and g agree with the traditional values in statistics. However, the latter values are usually derived from the binomial law. If the population is infinite, this law and hence the values mentioned hold exactly. On the other hand, in the case of a finite population the binomial law holds only approximately. In order to find the exact values in this case, derivations independent of the restrictions of the binomial law must be used, as was done in the proofs of T1a, c, and e above. It is interesting to see how in this case the exact values (T1c, e) differ from the customary values (T1d, g); and it is likewise interesting to see that the value for $\mathfrak{e}(\text{af})$ (T1a) holds unchanged. In comparison with our general method for the estimation of af, the customary method may be characterized as dealing with the special case in which (1) the estimation is direct, that is, the frequency in the population is given, and (2) the population is infinite.

Examples, for direct estimates of frequencies (T1). We take the numerical values of the two examples for direct inference given in § 95.

First Example. Small population: $n = 14$. $n_1 = 10$; hence $n_2 = 4$, $r_1 = 5/7$. $r_2 = 2/7$. We consider a sample K with $s = 7$. We find (T1a): $\mathfrak{e}(\text{af}) = sr_1 = 5$, Since this is an integer, it must be the most probable value of af, i.e., that value of s_1 for which $\mathfrak{c}(h_{st},e)$ has its maximum (T1b); the table in § 95 shows that this is indeed the case. T1e: $\mathfrak{s}^2(\text{af}) = 10/13 = 0.769$; hence $\mathfrak{s}(\text{af}) = 0.877$. $\mathfrak{s}(\text{af})/\mathfrak{e}(\text{af}) = 0.175$. [The conditions for the approximations T1f and g are here not fulfilled. In particular, T1g cannot be applied because the sample is one half of the population; T1g would give for $\mathfrak{s}^2$ the value $10/7 = 1.43$, which is nearly double the correct value. T1f would give $10/14 = 0.714$ instead of $10/13 = 0.769$; here the deviation is much smaller than in T1g.] T1h: $\mathfrak{e}(\text{rf}) = r_1 = 5/7 = 0.714$. Since $\mathfrak{s}^2(\text{af})$ has been determined, it is simpler to determine $\mathfrak{s}^2(\text{rf})$ by T104-4c than by T1i: $\mathfrak{s}^2(\text{rf}) = \mathfrak{s}^2(\text{af})/s^2 = 0.0157$. Hence (or with T104-4d): $\mathfrak{s}(\text{rf}) = 0.125$. $\mathfrak{s}(\text{rf})/\mathfrak{e}(\text{rf}) = 0.175$; the relative error is here the same as for af, in accordance with T104-4e.

Second Example. Large population, size not specified; either infinite or a large finite n. $r_1 = 5/7$; hence $r_2 = 2/7$. Sample K with $s = 7$. T1a: $\mathfrak{e}(\text{af}) = sr_1 = 5$, as in the first case; here it is again the most probable value of af. In the present case T1g can be applied: $\mathfrak{s}^2(\text{af}) = 10/7 = 1.429$. Hence $\mathfrak{s}(\text{af}) = 1.195$. This is considerably greater than in the first case. An estimate from a smaller population is generally more reliable than from a larger one; this can be seen from T1e. $\mathfrak{s}(\text{af})/\mathfrak{e}(\text{af}) = 0.239$. T1h: $\mathfrak{e}(\text{rf}) = r_1 = 5/7 = 0.714$, as in the first case. Here we may apply T1k; but it is again simpler to use T104-4c: $\mathfrak{s}^2(\text{rf}) = \mathfrak{s}^2(\text{af})/s^2 = 0.0292$. Analogously, with T104-4d: $\mathfrak{s}(\text{rf}) = \mathfrak{s}(\text{af})/s = 0.171$. $\mathfrak{s}(\text{rf})/\mathfrak{e}(\text{rf}) = 0.239$, as for af.

§ 106. Predictive Estimation of Frequencies

The last two sections of this chapter deal with predictive estimation of frequencies. The evidence describes an observed sample, and the estimate is made for the frequency of a property *M* in a second sample *K* not overlapping with the first. The values of predictive estimates cannot be stated generally, because they vary with the c-function chosen; but general theorems concerning relations between such estimates can be stated. *A*. It is found that the estimate of the relative frequency of *M* in *K* is equal to the degree of confirmation for any singular prediction '*Mb*' (T1c). Therefore this estimate is the same for any finite class *K*, independently of the number and choice of the individuals in *K* (T1d). The same estimate holds also for an infinite class. *B*. It is shown that the concept of the limit of the estimate of rf in an infinite sequence does not involve any of the problems and difficulties which are connected with the limit of rf itself. *C*. The problem of the *reliability* of a value of degree of confirmation is discussed. A tentative solution is indicated in terms of the estimated standard error of an estimate of the relative truth-frequency.

A. *Theorems on Predictive Estimation of Frequencies*

We shall now study the predictive estimation of frequencies in a class of individuals. It was mentioned earlier (§ 94) that the predictive inference, in distinction to the direct inference, depends upon the choice of a c-function. That is to say, theorems determining the c-values for the predictive inference cannot be stated, like those for the direct inference, in a general form for all symmetrical c-functions, but only for a particular c-function; this will be done later for our function c* (in Vol. II; cf. § 110C). For the same reason it is not possible to state theorems giving e-values for the predictive estimation in the general form as we did for the direct estimation in the preceding section; these theorems will likewise be stated later for e*, based upon c*. Nevertheless, it will be possible here to state general theorems on the predictive estimation which do not give the e-values themselves but relations between them.

In the case of the predictive estimation, the evidence *e* refers to one sample and the estimate is to be made for a second sample *K* not overlapping with the first. If the estimate concerns the frequency of a property *M* in *K*, then the case that *e* is an individual or statistical distribution giving the frequency of *M* in the first sample is of special interest. For the following discussion we shall, however, not restrict the form of *e*. With respect to a given *e*, we call any individual constant not occurring in *e* *new*, and likewise any individual named by a new constant. In application to a knowledge situation, *e* may report the observational results with respect to the individuals of a given sample. *K* is a class of individuals which have not yet been observed but which we perhaps expect to observe in the future. *K* may, for instance, be a second sample chosen from the population, or it may be the remainder of the whole population. An estimate for this latter case is often of especial interest.

We shall now apply our earlier result on truth-frequency (T104-2) to the predictive estimation of the frequency of M in an unobserved sample K. If we take as the former class $\mathfrak{K}_i$ of sentences the class of full sentences of 'M' for the individuals in K, then the truth-frequency in $\mathfrak{K}_i$ is obviously the same as the absolute frequency of M in K. Thus we obtain the following results.

T106-1. Let $\mathfrak{L}$ be any finite or infinite system, $\mathfrak{c}$ a regular $\mathfrak{c}$-function, $\mathfrak{e}$ based upon $\mathfrak{c}$, K a class of s new individuals in $\mathfrak{L}$ ($s > 0$), 'M' a molecular predicate in $\mathfrak{L}$, $i_1, i_2, \ldots, i_s$ the full sentences of 'M' for the individuals in K, e a non-L-false sentence in $\mathfrak{L}$. Then the following holds.

a. $\mathfrak{e}(\text{af},M,K,e) = \sum_{n=1}^{s} \mathfrak{c}(i_n,e)$.

Proof. This follows from T104-2a. If we take as $\mathfrak{K}_i$ the class of the s i-sentences, then tf ($\mathfrak{K}_i$) is the same as af(M,K).

b. $\mathfrak{e}(\text{rf},M,K,e) = \frac{1}{s}\sum_{n=1}^{s} \mathfrak{c}(i_n,e)$. (From (a), T100-3.)

+c. If $\mathfrak{c}$ is a symmetrical $\mathfrak{c}$-function and i is a full sentence of 'M' with any new in in $\mathfrak{L}$, then

$$\mathfrak{e}(\text{rf},M,K,e) = \mathfrak{c}(i,e)\ .$$

Proof. Since the individuals in K are new, i.e., their in do not occur in e, for every i_n ($n = 1, \ldots, s$), $\mathfrak{c}(i_n,e) = \mathfrak{c}(i,e)$ (T91-2c). Hence the theorem, with (b).

d. Let $\mathfrak{c}$ be a symmetrical $\mathfrak{c}$-function. Let K' be any class of s' new individuals in $\mathfrak{L}$ ($s' > 0$). (It is irrelevant whether K' does or does not overlap with K.) Then

$$\mathfrak{e}(\text{rf},M,K') = \mathfrak{e}(\text{rf},M,K).\ \text{(From (c).)}$$

For T1c and d we need the assumption that $\mathfrak{c}$ has the same value for all new individuals. Therefore these theorems are restricted to symmetrical $\mathfrak{c}$-functions.

The theorem T1c is of great importance. It concerns *the predictive estimate of the relative frequency* of a property M in any finite or infinite class based on any symmetrical $\mathfrak{c}$-function. The theorem says that this estimate *is equal to the confirmation of a singular prediction* for M. Therefore the $\mathfrak{c}$-value for a singular prediction may be interpreted as an estimate of the relative frequency of M and thus as determining a fair betting quotient. This interpretation has been used earlier for explaining probability$_1$ as an explicandum (§ 41D).

B. *The Limit of Relative Frequency in an Infinite Class*

It was explained earlier that the concept of rf of M in an infinite (denumerable) class K_∞ must be based on a fixed serial order O of the elements of K_∞; rf(M,K_∞,O) can then be defined as the limit of rf(M,K_n), where K_n is the class of the first n individuals with respect to the order O. Therefore the estimate of rf of M in K_∞ is the limit of the estimate of rf(M,K_n). Now, according to T1d, the latter estimate has a constant value, which is independent of the number n and of the choice of individuals in K_n. Therefore the estimate of rf(M,K_∞,O) is this same constant value and hence is independent of O.

It should be noticed that the *question of the existence of the limit* for e(rf) is quite different from that for rf. In the latter case, this question involves serious difficulties. For an infinite (denumerable) class K_∞ the concept of the relative frequency of M has no direct meaning (unless either af(M,K_∞) or af($\sim M$,K_∞) is finite, in which case rf(M,K_∞) = 0 or 1, respectively). A meaning to rf is given as a limit with respect to an order O, as just mentioned. It is essential that the order O be specified because the result depends upon its choice. For the same class K_∞, the choice of one order may lead to a different value of the limit and hence of rf as defined than the choice of another order, and for a third order there may be no limit. The problems here involved are of great importance and have been much discussed because rf(M,K_∞,O) as just defined is taken as explicatum for probability$_2$ in the frequency theories of probability proposed by Mises and by Reichenbach (§ 9). The question of the choice of an order may be answered in many cases by taking the temporal order of the events or observations in question. The question of the existence of the limit for a specified sequence of events cannot be decided empirically by any finite number of observations. Some philosophers have thought that therefore these limit statements and hence all probability$_2$ statements, if explicated as limit statements, are meaningless. However, I think, like Mises and Reichenbach, that this objection is based upon a too narrow conception of the requirement of verifiability. It is possible to state the existence and the value of the limit for a given sequence of events as a hypothetical assumption. Then inductive relations between this limit statement and observational reports can be established, for instance, with the help of the binomial law or Bernoulli's theorem. [A few incidental remarks may here be made concerning the role of the concept of rf and its limit in mathematical statistics. There seems to be practical agreement that the problems raised by the use of the limit in this context are very serious and deserve careful and thoroughgoing examination; and they have indeed been amply discussed from various points of view by Mises, Reichenbach, their followers, and their critics. It seems all the more surprising that some authors in modern mathematical statistics declare simply that they intend to use the term 'probability' for the relative frequency in an infinite population K_∞ of actual or possible events. No reference to a limit is made, the question of the choice of an order is neither answered nor even raised; the term 'relative frequency in an infinite class' is innocently used as if it had as clear and unique a meaning as for a finite class. Other statisticians use formulations which are more cautious and unobjectionable. For instance, S. S. Wilks ([Statistics], p. 3) says that the empirically found cumulative distribution function F_n (which shows the absolute and thereby the relative frequencies) with increasing n "appears to approach a limit F_∞"; this appearance within long finite sequences is then taken as suggesting the construction of a mathematical model for the infinite sequence. Similarly, Cramér ([Statistics], pp. 148 f.) says that it is found by an "empirical study of the behavior of frequency ratios" that the rf of a certain kind of event in a sequence of n repetitions of a random experiment "shows a tendency to become constant as n increases". This leads to the "conjecture that for large n the frequency ratio would with practical certainty be approximately equal to some assignable number P." Accordingly, a number P is introduced into the axiomatic theory of probability (as a primitive idea) and is called the probability of the kind of event in question. The axioms ascribe to these probability numbers "the fundamental properties of frequency ratios . . . in an idealized form", just as the axioms of geometry ascribe to lines those properties in an idealized form which we find empirically with lines made by chalk. Still other statisticians define probability explicitly as a limit.]

Now it is important to realize that the use of the concept of limit in defining the predictive *estimate* of rf in K_∞ does not involve any problems or difficulties analogous to those we have just mentioned in connection with the definition of rf itself in K_∞. $\mathfrak{e}$(rf) in K_∞ is independent of the order of the elements of K_∞. If we change the order, then other individuals take the first s positions and hence the rf for the first s individuals may change its value. On the other hand, $\mathfrak{e}$(rf) for s new individuals does not change if we take s other individuals; for, although those other individuals may have different empirical properties, they have the same logical status, and this is all that matters for $\mathfrak{e}$(rf), if it is based on a symmetrical $\mathfrak{c}$. Further, there is no problem of the existence of the limit for $\mathfrak{e}$(rf) as there is for rf. While rf changes with s and the course of its values is determined empirically, not logically, the course of values of $\mathfrak{e}$(rf) with increasing s is logically given. As we have seen (T1d) it follows from the definition of $\mathfrak{e}$(rf) that its value remains constant. Therefore there is always a limit; and this limit is equal to the value for any finite s.

C. *The Problem of the Reliability of a Value of Degree of Confirmation*

The possibility of regarding a $\mathfrak{c}$-value as an estimate of relative frequency points also a way to at least a tentative solution of the problem whether and how *the reliability of a value of probability$_1$ or degree of confirmation* could be measured. This problem has been discussed by only a few authors. Keynes gives a detailed discussion ([Probab.], chap. vi) but does not find a satisfactory solution. He remarks that with increasing relevant evidence the probability itself may either decrease or increase; "but *something* seems to have increased in either case,—we have a more substantial basis upon which to rest our conclusion" (p. 71). This he proposes to call 'the weight of an argument'. He refers to only two previous authors who have touched the problem, namely, Meinong ([Kries]) and Nitsche ([Dimensionen], esp. pp. 70–74). However, C. S. Peirce had indicated the same concept at a still earlier time: "Now, as the whole utility of probability is to insure us in the long run, and as that insurance depends, not merely on the value of the chance, but also on the accuracy of the evaluation, it follows that we ought not to have the same feeling of belief in reference to all events of which the chance is even. In short, to express the proper state of our belief, not *one* number but *two* are requisite, the first depending on the inferred probability, the second on the amount of knowledge on which that probability is based"; here Peirce adds a footnote: "Strictly we should need an infinite series of numbers each depending on the probable error of the last" ([Probab.] 1878, see [Papers], II, 421). Recently, C. I. Lewis discussed the problem without giving a solution ([Analysis], pp. 292–303).

Let us now approach the problem on the basis of our results. Suppose a symmetrical $\mathfrak{c}$ has been chosen, and $\mathfrak{e}$ is based upon it. For any given e and M, we can then determine the predictive estimate $\mathfrak{e}(\text{rf},M,K,e)$, which holds for any nonnull class K of new individuals; suppose we find the value r'. We can further determine, for this estimate $\mathfrak{e}(\text{rf}) = r'$, the estimated standard error $\mathfrak{f}(\text{rf},M,K,e)$ (D103-1b). This, however, is in general not, like $\mathfrak{e}$(rf), independent of the cardinal number s of K. The value of $\mathfrak{f}$ for the infinite class K_∞ (for which $\mathfrak{e}(\text{rf},M,K_\infty,e)$ has the same value r') is the limit (for $s \rightarrow \infty$) of the $\mathfrak{f}$-values for finite classes; let this value be $\mathfrak{f}(\text{rf},M,K_\infty,e) = q$. (This value is independent of any order of the elements of K_∞, since $\mathfrak{f}$(rf) for a finite class K is, although dependent upon s, not dependent upon the choice of individuals in K.) q is the estimated standard error; it measures the reliability of the estimate $\mathfrak{e}(\mathrm{rf}) = r'$. According to T1c, $\mathfrak{c}(h,e)$, where h is a singular prediction for M with a new individual, has always the same value as $\mathfrak{e}(\mathrm{rf})$; hence here $\mathfrak{c}(h,e) = r'$. This suggests the idea of transferring the estimated standard error q, which was determined for the estimate $\mathfrak{e}(\mathrm{rf}) = r'$, to the result $\mathfrak{c}(h,e) = r'$. It is true that here the value q cannot be regarded as an estimated standard error in the literal sense of the word 'error'. For $\mathfrak{c}$ is a logical function, and hence the determination of its value r' cannot lead to an error (except in the sense of a miscalculation). But q may perhaps still be regarded in some sense as a measure for the reliability of the value r' for $\mathfrak{c}(h,e)$. This seems rather plausible in view of the fact that $\mathfrak{c}(h,e)$ claims to state a fair betting quotient for h on e (see § 41B), which is essentially the same as stating a predictive estimate of the rf of M on e. Thus, if the value $\mathfrak{c}(h,e) = r'$ has been determined, the question may be raised whether betting according to this $\mathfrak{c}$-value will in the long run probably be successful; or, in other words, whether the estimate of rf will probably be accurate. It is this question that is answered by the determination of the value q as the 'estimated standard error' for $\mathfrak{c}(h,e)$. The direct analogy with $\mathfrak{e}(\mathrm{rf})$ helps in determining and interpreting the value q for $\mathfrak{c}(h,e)$ only in the case where h is a singular prediction. In order to find a more general concept of the estimated standard error of $\mathfrak{c}$, the following procedure might be considered, which is applicable to any form of h. Let any h in $\mathfrak{L}$ be given; let the number of different new in in h be n. Let $\mathfrak{K}_h$ be the class of all sentences obtained from h by replacing these n new in by n likewise new in in $\mathfrak{L}$. [In technical terms, $\mathfrak{K}_h$ is the class of correlates of h with respect to all those in-correlations which correlate the in occurring in e with themselves. If the number of different in in e is m, and the number of different new in in h is n, then in $\mathfrak{L}_N$ the number of sentences in $\mathfrak{K}_h$ is $(N-m)!/(N-m-n)!$ (T40-32h).] Let us assume that $\mathfrak{c}$ is symmetrical. Then all sentences in $\mathfrak{K}_h$ have the same $\mathfrak{c}$-value on e (T91-2b, e' is e). Therefore $\mathfrak{c}(h,e) = \mathfrak{e}(\mathrm{rtf},\mathfrak{K}_h,e)$ (T104-2c). Since here the $\mathfrak{c}$ for h is again equal to an estimate, we may again measure the reliability of $\mathfrak{c}(h,e)$ by (the smallness of) the estimated standard error of this estimate, that is, $\mathfrak{f}(\mathrm{rtf},\mathfrak{K}_h,e)$. This tentative explication seems well in accord with the explicandum indicated by Peirce.

§ 107. Further Theorems on Predictive Estimation of Relative Frequency

A. A theorem is proved concerning the estimate of the rf of Q-properties (i.e., the strongest factual properties expressible in the system) on the null evidence. *B*. The problem of the admissibility of the null evidence as a basis of confirmation or estimation is discussed. *C*. Further theorems on the predictive estimation of relative frequency are derived from earlier theorems on degree of confirmation. One of these theorems (T3l) says that if '*Mb*' is a factual sentence, the estimate of the relative frequency of *M* is neither 0 nor 1. This leads to a criticism of the so-called straight rule of estimation. *D*. The inverse estimation is the estimation of the frequency in a population based on an observed sample. The inverse estimate can be derived from the predictive estimate.

A. *Frequencies of Q-Properties*

The following theorem T1 refers to those systems $\mathfrak{L}$ which contain primitive predicates for properties only, not for relations. Systems of this kind were called systems $\mathfrak{L}^\pi$, where π is the number of the primitive predicates (see §§ 31, 32). The *Q*-properties are the strongest factual properties expressible in the system; they are designated by the *Q*-predicates 'Q_1', etc. (A31-1, D31-1b); their number is $\kappa = 2^\pi$ (D31-2, T31-1). A molecular predicate is said to have the (logical) width w if it is L-equivalent to a disjunction of w *Q*-predicates; w/κ is called its relative width (D32-1).

+T107-1. Let $\mathfrak{m}$ be an $\mathfrak{m}$-function in a system $\mathfrak{L}^\pi$ such that (1) $\mathfrak{m}$ is symmetrical, and (2) any two *Q*-sentences with the same in have the same $\mathfrak{m}$-value. Let $\mathfrak{c}$ be based upon $\mathfrak{m}$, and $\mathfrak{e}$ be based upon $\mathfrak{c}$. Let *K* be any nonnull class of individuals.

a. For any *Q*-predicate '*Q*', $\mathfrak{e}(\text{rf},Q,K,t) = 1/\kappa$.

Proof. $\mathfrak{e}(\ldots) = \mathfrak{c}(Qa,t)$ (T106-1c), $= \mathfrak{m}(Qa)$ (T57-3). Consider the sentences 'Q_1a', . . . , '$Q_\kappa a$', one of which is '*Qa*'. According to condition (2), these sentences have equal $\mathfrak{m}$-values. They are L-exclusive in pairs (T31-2a). Let *j* be their disjunction. Then $\mathfrak{m}(j)$ is the sum of the $\mathfrak{m}$-values of the κ sentences (T57-1v), which is $\kappa \times \mathfrak{m}(Qa)$. But *j* is L-true (T31-2b); hence $\mathfrak{m}(j) = 1$. Therefore $\mathfrak{m}(Qa) = 1/\kappa$. Hence the assertion.

b. If '*M*' is a molecular predicate with the width w, $\mathfrak{e}(\text{rf},M,K,t) = w/\kappa$.

Proof. 1. Let $w = 0$. Then '*M*' is L-empty (T32-2a). Hence 0 is the only possible value for af(*M*,*K*). Therefore $\mathfrak{e}(\text{af}) = 0$, and $\mathfrak{e}(\text{rf}) = 0$ (T104-4a). 2. Let $w > 0$. Then '*M*' is L-equivalent to a disjunction of w *Q*-predicates (D32-1a). The latter are L-exclusive in pairs (T31-2a). Therefore af(*M*) is the sum of the af of the w *Q*'s. Hence likewise for rf and for $\mathfrak{e}(\text{rf})$ (T99-2). Hence the theorem with (a).

These results can be made plausible by the following consideration. Consider first T1a. The evidence is the tautology '*t*'; that means that empirically nothing is known about the property *Q*. However, the logical character of *Q* is known; in particular, it is a *Q*-property. The rf of *Q* in a given class *K* is, of course, an empirical matter and hence unknown as long as no empirical evidence is available. And the same holds for the rf-values of the other Q-properties. However, one thing is known about the rf-values of the Q-properties in K: their arithmetic mean is $1/\kappa$. This is not a factual matter but a logical necessity. Since the κ Q-properties form a division (T31-2d), the sum of their rf-values is 1; hence the mean is $1/\kappa$. Thus the situation is this: empirically nothing is known about Q; but it is logically known that Q belongs to a certain class of properties of the same logical nature for which the mean rf is $1/\kappa$. Therefore it seems not implausible that the estimate of the rf of Q is this mean value $1/\kappa$.

T1b says that the estimate of the rf of M on the null evidence is equal to the relative width of M. This result follows from T1a. But it can be made plausible also directly. Although the number of those molecular predicate expressions in a system $\mathfrak{L}^\pi$ which have a given width w is infinite, the number of properties expressed by them is finite, if we regard L-equivalent expressions as expressing the same property. [The properties of width w correspond to the possible selections of w among the κ Q-properties; therefore (T40-32d) their number is $\binom{\kappa}{w}$.] It can easily be shown that the mean rf of the properties with the width w is w/κ. This holds always (technically speaking, it holds in every $\mathfrak{Z}$). Here again it seems plausible that the estimate of the rf of M is this mean value of rf.

B. *The Problem of the Null Evidence*

The results just stated (T1) and discussed refer to the null evidence. Now some philosophers reject all inductive procedures based on the null evidence. They believe that nothing can be said about the $\mathfrak{c}$ of a hypothesis or the estimate of a function as long as no empirical evidence is available. I think that in this extreme form the view is certainly wrong; it seems to me clear that at least comparative inductive judgments can be made with respect to the null evidence. I regard also numerical inductive judgments as possible; but I admit that their possibility is problematic. That is to say, if somebody believes that there is no adequate quantitative explicatum for probability$_1$, then he can maintain this belief consistently, and we cannot compel him to change his view in the same sense in which we can compel any consistent thinker to accept a *deductive* result. But if somebody accepts a quantitative concept $\mathfrak{c}$ for factual evidence, then there seem to be no good reasons for the rejection of the null evidence. To take an example, suppose that 'M' is a molecular predicate with the relative width 1/8 (for instance, '$P_1 \cdot P_2 \cdot P_3$'), and that nothing is known about the distribution of M. Thus the rf of M in a given population may have any value between 0 and 1 (both included), and the same holds for the rf of non-M. If the rf of M is r, that of non-M is $1 - r$. Can we say anything more about the two values? It seems to me clear that we have more reason to expect that the rf of *M* is below that of non-*M* than to expect the converse, although either case is possible and neither is certain. And therefore, for any individual *a*, it seems to me clear that there is more reason to expect that *a* is non-*M* than that it is *M*. If we are willing to admit inductive reasoning at all, although its success cannot be deductively demonstrated, then we can hardly reject these comparative judgments.

Now let us examine the question of numerical values for confirmation and estimation. For the sake of this discussion, let us assume the skeptical view (as held by Kries, Keynes, Nagel, and others) that in most cases comparative judgments at best are possible and that numerical values can be stated only in a special kind of case. Let us consider a case of this special kind. The following evidence *e* is given: a bag contains 80 balls of which 10 are white, and the ball *b* is now drawn at random from the bag. Let *h* be the hypothesis that *b* is white. I presume that this is a case where even most of the skeptics will admit not only the comparative judgment that the $\mathfrak{c}$ for *h* on *e* is less than for non-*h*, but also the quantitative judgment that $\mathfrak{c}(h,e) = 1/8$. However, does the skeptic have any means to compel the ultra-skeptic, who admits even in this case only the comparative judgment, to change his mind and to accept also the numerical judgment? He is certainly unable to do so; but he can show that the numerical judgment is plausible and in accord with customary inductive thinking. Now consider again the predicate '*M*' with the relative width 1/8. With respect to the numerical judgment that $\mathfrak{c}$ for '*Ma*' on the null evidence is 1/8 and that the estimate for the rf of *M* on the null evidence is 1/8, my relation to the skeptic who rejects numerical judgments on the null evidence is the same as the relation of the skeptic to the ultra-skeptic in the example of the ball. I cannot compel the skeptic, but I can give plausibility reasons which seem just as good as the reasons the skeptic gives to the ultra-skeptic. Since the mean rf of those properties which have the same width as *M* is 1/8 and that for non-*M* is 7/8, it seems plausible to say not only that the estimate for the rf of *M* must be smaller than that of non-*M* but also that it must be exactly one-seventh of it and hence must be 1/8. For the same reason, the only fair betting quotient on '*Ma*' is 1/8, and hence the probability$_1$ of '*Ma*' should be regarded as 1/8.

When we say that, in our example, the estimate for the rf of *M* on the null evidence is 1/8, we do not mean to say that this is a *good* estimate. It means merely that this is the best estimate that can be made by an observer *X* who has no factual evidence. But the best in this case is still not good. It must be admitted that this estimate is very unreliable because it has only very little support. If X had observed a very large sample in which M had the rf 1/8, he might perhaps find as estimate of the rf of M in any unobserved class again 1/8; the same value of the estimate would in this case have much more support and hence be more reliable. However, the fact that the estimate in the first case, on the null evidence, has only a low reliability, does not nullify the inductive validity of that estimate.

C. *Further Theorems on the Estimate of Relative Frequency*

Since the estimate of rf is equal to a certain value of $\mathfrak{c}$ (T106-1c), we can derive further theorems on $\mathfrak{e}$(rf) from earlier theorems on $\mathfrak{c}$ (mostly from § 59).

T107-3. Let $\mathfrak{L}$, $\mathfrak{e}$, e, and K be as in T106-1. Let $\mathfrak{c}$ be a symmetrical $\mathfrak{c}$-function. Let 'M' and 'M'' be molecular predicates in $\mathfrak{L}$, and 'b' any new in in $\mathfrak{L}$. Then the following holds.

a. If $\vdash e \supset Mb$ (hence, in particular, if 'M' is L-universal (D25-1a)), $\mathfrak{e}(\text{rf},M,K,e) = 1$. (From T106-1c, T59-1b.)

b. If $\vdash e \supset \sim Mb$ (hence, in particular, if 'M' is L-empty (D25-1b)), $\mathfrak{e}(\text{rf},M,K,e) = 0$. (From T106-1c, T59-1e.)

c. *General addition theorem.*
$\mathfrak{e}(\text{rf},M \vee M',K,e) = \mathfrak{e}(\text{rf},M,K,e) + \mathfrak{e}(\text{rf},M',K,e) - \mathfrak{e}(\text{rf},M \,.\, M',K,e)$. (From T106-1c, T59-1k.)

+d. *Special addition theorem.* If 'M' and 'M'' are L-exclusive with respect to e (D25-3b), then
$\mathfrak{e}(\text{rf},M \vee M',K,e) = \mathfrak{e}(\text{rf},M,K,e) + \mathfrak{e}(\text{rf},M',K,e)$. (From (c), (b); analogous to T59-1l.)

e. $\mathfrak{e}(\text{rf},M \,.\, M',K,e) = \mathfrak{e}(\text{rf},M,K,e) + \mathfrak{e}(\text{rf},M',K,e) - \mathfrak{e}(\text{rf},M \vee M',K,e)$. (From (c); analogous to T59-1q.)

f. If $\vdash e \supset Mb \vee M'b$ (hence, in particular, if 'M' and 'M'' are L-disjunct, in other words, '$M \vee M'$' is L-universal), then
$\mathfrak{e}(\text{rf},M \,.\, M',K,e) = \mathfrak{e}(\text{rf},M,K,e) + \mathfrak{e}(\text{rf},M',K,e) - 1$. (From (e), (a).)

+g. *Special multiplication theorem.* If 'Mb' is irrelevant to '$M'b$' on evidence e (D65-1d), then
$\mathfrak{e}(\text{rf},M \,.\, M',K,e) = \mathfrak{e}(\text{rf},M,K,e) \times \mathfrak{e}(\text{rf},M',K,e)$.

Proof. If the condition is fulfilled, $\mathfrak{c}(Mb \,.\, M'b,e) = \mathfrak{c}(Mb,e) \times \mathfrak{c}(M'b,e)$ (T65-6l, the special multiplication theorem for $\mathfrak{c}$). Hence the assertion with T106-1c.

+h. $\mathfrak{e}(\text{rf},\sim M,K,e) = 1 - \mathfrak{e}(\text{rf},M,K,e)$. (From T106-1c, T59-1p.)

i. If 'M' L-implies 'M'', then $\mathfrak{e}(\text{rf},M,K,e) \leq \mathfrak{e}(\text{rf},M',K,e)$. (From T106-1c, T59-2d.)

j. $\mathfrak{e}(\mathrm{rf}, M \cdot M', K, e) \leqq \mathfrak{e}(\mathrm{rf}, M, K, e)$. (From (i); analogous to T59-2e.)

k. $\mathfrak{e}(\mathrm{rf}, M, K, e) \leqq \mathfrak{e}(\mathrm{rf}, M \vee M', K, e)$. (From (i); analogous to T59-2f.)

+l. If '*M*' is a factual predicate (D25-1c), in other words, '*Mb*' is a factual sentence (T25-1c), then (1) neither '*Mb*' nor '$\sim$*Mb*' is L-implied by *e*, and (2) if $\mathfrak{K}$ is finite or *e* is nongeneral, then $0 < \mathfrak{e}(\mathrm{rf}, M, K, e) < 1$.

Proof. 1. '$\sim$*Mb*' is also factual (T20-6a). *e* is either L-true or factual. If *e* is L-true, it cannot L-imply either of the two factual sentences (T20-2c). If *e* is factual, (1) follows from T21-11c. 2. $\mathfrak{c}(Mb,e)$ is >0 (from (1), T59-5d) and <1 (from (1), T59-5a). Hence the assertion (2) with T106-1c.

In most applications of predictive inference and predictive estimation the property *M* in question is factual, that is, neither L-universal nor L-empty (D25-1c); hence '*Mb*' is a factual sentence. T3l says that in this case the predictive estimate of rf cannot be either 0 or 1. This is quite plausible. Even if the finite sample described in *e* is very large and none of its individuals has been found to be *M*, the case that a finite class *K* of new individuals contains at least one element which is *M* is certainly not impossible although it may be highly improbable. Therefore the probability$_1$ of this case, although small, cannot be 0, because it is a possible case in a finite domain. Therefore the estimate of af, that is, the probability$_1$-weighted mean, must be positive, and hence likewise the estimate of rf. A frequently used method of predictive estimation of frequencies is based on what might be called the *straight rule of estimation;* this rule determines the predictive estimate of rf as equal to the observed rf. Thus, if the observed sample does not contain any individual with *M* and hence the observed rf of *M* is 0, the rule says that $\mathfrak{e}(\mathrm{rf}) = 0$; and if the observed rf is 1, the rule says that $\mathfrak{e}(\mathrm{rf}) = 1$. T3l shows that these results are not in agreement with any $\mathfrak{c}$-mean estimate-function based on any symmetrical $\mathfrak{c}$-function. For this and other reasons it seems to me that the straight rule violates principles which seem to be generally accepted explicitly or implicitly in the customary ways of inductive thinking. A detailed critical analysis of the straight rule and related inductive methods will be given in a later chapter (in Vol. II).

D. *The Inverse Estimation of Frequency*

The inductive inference from a sample to the population was called inverse (or upward) inference (§ 44B). Similarly we shall call the estimation of a frequency in the population based on an observed sample ***inverse*** (or upward) ***estimation***. It is easily seen that the inverse estimate of af for a finite population can be derived from the predictive estimate. In this case we take as K not a limited second sample but the whole remainder, that is, the class of all individuals in the population not belonging to the first sample described in e. The af in the population is, of course, the sum of the af in the first sample and that in the remainder. The inverse estimate of rf is likewise determined by the given rf in the sample and the predictive estimate of rf in the remainder (since the cardinal numbers of the sample and the remainder are given by the definitions of the sample and the population). As explained earlier, the concept of rf, and hence also $\mathfrak{e}$(rf), can also be applied to an infinite class K_∞, provided a fixed serial order for the individuals is established. In many statistical problems the population is either infinite or very large in comparison with the first sample; in cases of this kind the rf in the population is either exactly or approximately equal to that in the remainder.

The inverse estimate of rf plays an important role in many theories of induction or statistics. For instance, Reichenbach's rule of induction, if interpreted as a rule of estimation (cf. § 41E), applies only to this special case of estimation, and his whole theory of induction is based upon this rule. In mathematical statistics various methods have been developed for estimating the values of parameters characterizing a distribution of properties or quantitative magnitudes in a population; and one of the simplest and most fundamental of these parameters is the rf of a property. The rf of a property in the whole population, especially in the case of an infinite population, is called 'probability' both by Mises and Reichenbach and by contemporary statisticians. This is the second meaning of the term 'probability' (in our terminology, probability$_2$). The suitability of the use of the word in this sense might be debated, but the fact that a simple term has been chosen is a clear indication for the importance of the concept. The inverse estimate of rf is thus the estimate of probability$_2$; in our method, this estimate is based upon probability$_1$.

Theorems on predictive and inverse estimation of rf, stating not only relations between values but the values themselves, will later (in Vol. II) be given on the basis of our functions $\mathfrak{c}^*$ and $\mathfrak{e}^*$.

APPENDIX

§ 110. Outline of a Quantitative System of Inductive Logic

This appendix gives a brief summary of the system of quantitative inductive logic to be constructed in Volume II. This system is the theory of a certain function c* which is proposed as a quantitative explicatum of probability$_1$. The definition of c* is here given, but, for the sake of brevity, not the reasons for its choice. Furthermore, a few theorems are stated without proofs. m* is defined in such a way that it is symmetrical and has equal values for all structure-descriptions. c* is the c-function based upon m* (A). Theorems concerning c* are stated for the principal kinds of inductive inference earlier explained (§ 44 B): the direct inference (B), the predictive inference (C), the inference by analogy (D), the inverse inference (E), and the universal inference (F). The latter concerns universal laws. In connection with it, the concept of the instance confirmation of a law is introduced as an explicatum for what a scientist or an engineer means when he says that a given law of physics is "reliable" or "well-founded" (G). It is shown that for predicting a future event on the basis of observations made, it is not necessary to make use of laws; the prediction can be inductively inferred directly from the observations (H). The requirement of the variety of instances in testing a law is briefly discussed (I). The system of inductive logic here outlined is meant as a rational reconstruction and systematization of customary inductive reasoning (J).

A. *The Function* c*

In Volume II a quantitative system of inductive logic will be constructed, based upon an explicit definition of a particular c-function c* and containing theorems concerning the various kinds of inductive inference and especially of statistical inference in terms of c*. In the present appendix we shall indicate the definition of c* and briefly mention a few of the theorems on c*, omitting proofs and technical details.

Space does here not permit an explanation of the reasons for choosing just the function c* out of an infinite number of c-functions. The reasons are chiefly negative, in the following sense. A critical examination of various quantitative inductive methods which have been proposed from the classical period to our time will be given in Volume II. These methods include both those for the calculation of numerical values of probability$_1$ and those for the calculation of estimates of parameters characterizing a population (inverse estimation) or a second sample (predictive estimation) on the basis of a given sample, especially estimates of relative frequency. The examination will refer only to those methods which are not merely constructed for a special kind of case but have a general character. It will be shown that the general methods to be examined, from Laplace's rule of succession down to R. A. Fisher's method of maximum likelihood, show certain disadvantages. Each of these methods leads in certain cases to numerical values which are not in accord with the implicit principles of customary inductive thinking as represented by the judgments of good scientists or careful, rational bettors. This result does not exclude the possibility that any of these methods may be adequate and useful within an extensive field; this is certainly the case, e.g., with Fisher's method mentioned above. Now the chief arguments in favor of the function $\mathfrak{c}^*$, though there are also a few others of a more positive nature, will consist in showing that this function is free of the inadequacies found in the other methods. It may then still be inadequate in other respects. It will not be claimed that $\mathfrak{c}^*$ is a perfectly adequate explicatum for probability$_1$, let alone that it is the only adequate one. For the time being it would be sufficient that $\mathfrak{c}^*$ be a better explicatum than the previous methods (*if* indeed it is); in the future still better explicata may be found.

From the preceding remarks it seems clear that a criticism of the system based on $\mathfrak{c}^*$ would hardly be useful at the present time, that is, before the publication of the full explanation of this system, if it would merely raise the objection that the basis of the system seems arbitrary, that is to say, that the reasons for the choice of $\mathfrak{c}^*$ as an explicatum are not clear. On the other hand, if it could be shown that another method, for instance, a new definition for degree of confirmation, leads in certain cases to numerical values more adequate than those furnished by $\mathfrak{c}^*$, that would constitute an important criticism. Or, if someone, even without offering an explicatum, were to show that any adequate explicatum must fulfil a certain requirement and that $\mathfrak{c}^*$ does not fulfil it, it might be a helpful first step toward a better solution.

We take as the basis of our system of inductive logic that $\mathfrak{m}$-function $\mathfrak{m}^*$ which fulfils the following two conditions:

(1) **a.** $\mathfrak{m}^*$ is a symmetrical $\mathfrak{m}$-function (D90-1 and 2).

b. $\mathfrak{m}^*$ has the same value for all $\mathfrak{Str}$ (structure-descriptions, D27-1) in $\mathfrak{L}_N$.

It is easily seen that there is exactly one $\mathfrak{m}$-function for $\mathfrak{L}_N$ which fulfils these two conditions and that it is the function $\mathfrak{m}^*$ defined as follows:

(2) Let $\mathfrak{Z}_i$ be any $\mathfrak{Z}$ (state-description, D18-1a) in $\mathfrak{L}_N$. Let τ be the number of $\mathfrak{Str}$ in $\mathfrak{L}_N$ and ζ_i the number of those $\mathfrak{Z}$ in $\mathfrak{L}_N$ which are isomorphic to $\mathfrak{Z}_i$ (§§ 26 f.). Then we define:

$$\mathfrak{m}^*(\mathfrak{Z}_i) =_{\mathrm{Df}} 1/\tau\zeta_i \, .$$

This defines $\mathfrak{m}^*$ as an $\mathfrak{m}$-function for the $\mathfrak{Z}$ in $\mathfrak{L}_N$. We extend it to the sentences of $\mathfrak{L}_N$ by our earlier procedure (D55-2).

The function $\mathfrak{m}^*$ thus defined does indeed fulfil the conditions (1)(a) and (b).

Proof. It follows from (2) that all $\mathfrak{Z}$ isomorphic to $\mathfrak{Z}_i$ have the same $\mathfrak{m}^*$-value; hence (1)(a) is fulfilled. Let $\mathfrak{Str}_j$ be the $\mathfrak{Str}$ corresponding to $\mathfrak{Z}_i$ (D27-1a). Then $\mathfrak{R}(\mathfrak{Str}_j)$ is the class of those $\mathfrak{Z}$ which are isomorphic to $\mathfrak{Z}_i$ (T27-2f). Therefore $\mathfrak{m}^*(\mathfrak{Str}_j) = \zeta_i \mathfrak{m}^*(\mathfrak{Z}_i) = 1/\tau$. Since this holds for every $\mathfrak{Str}$, (1)(b) is fulfilled.

$\mathfrak{c}^*$ is then defined as the $\mathfrak{c}$-function based upon $\mathfrak{m}^*$ (D55-3). All these definitions refer to $\mathfrak{L}_N$. The functions $\mathfrak{m}^*$ and $\mathfrak{c}^*$ for $\mathfrak{L}_\infty$ are then defined by our earlier limit-procedure (D56-1 and 2). $\mathfrak{c}^*$ is our concept of degree of confirmation, that is, the concept which we propose as a quantitative explicatum for probability$_1$ in application to our systems $\mathfrak{L}$. Our system of inductive logic is the theory of $\mathfrak{c}^*$.

It seems to me that there are good and even compelling reasons for the stipulation (1)(a), i.e., the choice of a symmetrical function. The proposal of any nonsymmetrical $\mathfrak{c}$-function as degree of confirmation could hardly be regarded as acceptable; this was shown by earlier explanations (§ 90). The same cannot be said, however, for the stipulation (1)(b). No doubt, to the way of thinking which was customary in the classical period of the theory of probability, (1)(b) would appear as validated, like (1)(a), by the principle of indifference. However, to modern, more critical thought, this mode of reasoning appears as invalid because the structure-descriptions (in contradistinction to the individual constants) are by no means alike in their logical features but show very conspicuous differences. The definition of $\mathfrak{c}^*$ shows a great simplicity in comparison with other functions which might be taken into consideration. Although this fact may influence our decision to choose $\mathfrak{c}^*$, it cannot, of course, be regarded as a sufficient reason for this choice. It seems to me that the choice of $\mathfrak{c}^*$ cannot be justified by any features of the definition which are immediately recognizable, but only by studying the consequences to which the definition leads and especially by comparing them with the consequences of other definitions. This will be done in Volume II.

There is another $\mathfrak{c}$-function $\mathfrak{c}^\dagger$ which at first glance appears not less plausible than $\mathfrak{c}^*$. The choice of this function may be suggested by the following consideration. Prior to experience, there seems to be no reason to regard one $\mathfrak{Z}$ as less probable than another. Accordingly, it might seem natural to assign equal $\mathfrak{m}$-values to the $\mathfrak{Z}$ instead of to the $\mathfrak{Str}$. This is done in the following definition of $\mathfrak{m}^\dagger$ for the $\mathfrak{Z}$:

(3) $$\mathfrak{m}^\dagger(\mathfrak{Z}_i) = 1/\zeta\,,$$

where ζ is the number of the $\mathfrak{Z}$ in $\mathfrak{L}_N$. This is still simpler than the definition (2) for $\mathfrak{m}^*$. The measures ascribed to the ranges are here simply taken as proportional to the cardinal numbers of the ranges. $\mathfrak{m}\dagger$ is then extended to sentences as before, and $\mathfrak{c}\dagger$ is defined as the $\mathfrak{c}$-function based upon $\mathfrak{m}\dagger$. Earlier authors have often discussed the problem whether the principle of indifference should be applied to individual distributions (often called 'constitutions') or to statistical distributions (frequencies), in other words, whether the former should be regarded as a priori equiprobable or the latter. It will be shown in Volume II that both sides were wrong. The principle of the equiprobability of individual distributions, if applied to the whole universe, would lead to the equiprobability of all $\mathfrak{Z}$, and hence to $\mathfrak{m}\dagger$ and $\mathfrak{c}\dagger$. This principle has been accepted by some prominent writers, among them C. S. Peirce ([Theory], see [Papers], II, 470 f.), Keynes ([Probab.], pp. 56 f.), Wittgenstein ([Tractatus] *5.15). However, in spite of its apparent plausibility, the functon $\mathfrak{c}\dagger$ can easily be seen to be entirely inadequate as a concept of degree of confirmation. As an example, consider the system $\mathfrak{L}_{101}$ with 'P' as the only $\mathfrak{pr}$. Let e be the conjunction '$Pa_1 \centerdot Pa_2 \centerdot Pa_3 \centerdot \ldots \centerdot Pa_{100}$' and let h be 'Pa_{101}'. Then $e \centerdot h$ is a $\mathfrak{Z}$ and hence $\mathfrak{m}\dagger(e \centerdot h) = 1/\zeta$. e holds only in the two $\mathfrak{Z}$, $e \centerdot h$ and $e \centerdot \sim h$; hence $\mathfrak{m}\dagger(e) = 2/\zeta$. Therefore $\mathfrak{c}\dagger(h,e) = 1/2$. If e' is formed from e by replacing some or even all of the atomic sentences with their negations, we obtain likewise $\mathfrak{c}\dagger(h,e') = 1/2$. Thus the $\mathfrak{c}\dagger$-value for the prediction that a_{101} is P is always the same, no matter whether among the hundred observed individuals the number of those which have been found to be P is 100 or 50 or 0 or any other number. Thus the choice of $\mathfrak{c}\dagger$ as the degree of confirmation would be tantamount to the principle never to let our past experiences influence our expectations for the future. This would obviously be in striking contradiction to the basic principle of all inductive reasoning.

The second of the two controversial principles, which declares statistical distributions as equiprobable, is likewise wrong. In the general form in which it is usually stated it leads to contradictions. It is, however, consistent if it is applied only to the Q-division. In this case it asserts the equiprobability of the $\mathfrak{Str}$, which correspond to the statistical distributions for the Q-division (T34-6), and thus leads to $\mathfrak{m}^*$ and $\mathfrak{c}^*$.

The preceding considerations show that the following argument, admittedly not a strong one, can be offered in favor of $\mathfrak{m}^*$. Of the two $\mathfrak{m}$-functions which are most simple and suggest themselves as the most natural ones, $\mathfrak{m}^*$ is the only one which is not entirely inadequate.

The definitions of $\mathfrak{m}^*$ and $\mathfrak{c}^*$ indicated above are formulated in a general way so as to apply to all our systems $\mathfrak{L}$. But the greater part of our system of inductive logic, including all theorems mentioned in the remainder of this section, will be restricted to the systems $\mathfrak{L}^\pi$ which contain only $\mathfrak{pr}$ of degree one (§ 31). This restriction to properties is customary in theories on probability$_1$. An extension of this part of inductive logic to relations would require certain results in the deductive logic of relations, results which this discipline, although widely developed in other respects, has not yet reached (for example, an answer to the apparently simple question as to the number of structures in a given finite language system). We shall make use of the following concepts earlier explained in connection with the systems $\mathfrak{L}^\pi$: the Q-properties (§ 31); the number π of the $\mathfrak{pr}$; the number κ of the Q-properties, which is 2^π (T31-1); the width w of a property and its relative width w/κ (D32-1); the Q-numbers (§ 34). Here for $\mathfrak{L}_N^\pi$—in contradistinction to systems containing relations—it is easy to state explicit functions for τ (T35-1d) and ζ_i for a $\mathfrak{Z}_i$ with the Q-numbers N_1, $N_2, \ldots, N_\kappa$ (T35-4). Substituting in (2) the values given by the theorems just mentioned, we obtain:

(4) $$\mathfrak{m}^*(\mathfrak{Z}_i) = \frac{N_1!N_2!\ldots N_\kappa!(\kappa - 1)!}{(N + \kappa - 1)!}.$$

This result serves as a basis for all further theorems.

Let j be a nongeneral sentence in $\mathfrak{L}_N^\pi$. The application of (4) to all $\mathfrak{Z}$ in $\mathfrak{R}_j$ furnishes an effective procedure for the computation of $\mathfrak{m}^*(j)$. However, since the number of $\mathfrak{Z}$ becomes very large even for small systems (see T35-2), this procedure, although effective, is impracticable, that is, too lengthy for practical purposes. Another procedure for the computation of $\mathfrak{m}^*(j)$ which is practicable if the number of $\mathfrak{in}$ in j is not too large will be explained in Volume II.

$\mathfrak{m}^*(i)$ in $\mathfrak{L}_\infty$ is defined by a limit (D56-1). The question arises under what conditions this limit exists. We have to distinguish two cases. (i) Suppose that i is nongeneral. Here the situation is simple; it can be shown that in this case $\mathfrak{m}^*(i)$ is the same in all finite systems in which i occurs; hence it has the same value also in $\mathfrak{L}_\infty$. (ii) Let i be general. Here the situation is quite different. For a given $\mathfrak{L}_N$, i can of course easily be transformed into an L-equivalent sentence i'_N without variables (T22-3). The values of $\mathfrak{m}^*(i'_N)$ are in general different for each N; and although the simplified procedure mentioned above is available for the computation of these values, this procedure becomes impracticable even for moderate N. Thus for general sentences the problem of the existence and the practical computability of the limit becomes serious. It can be shown that for every general sentence the limit exists; hence $\mathfrak{m}^*$ has a value for all sentences in $\mathfrak{L}_\infty$. Moreover, an effective procedure for the computation of $\mathfrak{m}^*(i)$ for any sentence i in $\mathfrak{L}_\infty$ has been constructed. This is based on a procedure for transforming any given general sentence i into a nongeneral sentence i' such that i and i', although not necessarily L-equivalent, have the same $\mathfrak{m}^*$-value in $\mathfrak{L}_\infty$ and i' does not contain more in than i; this procedure is not only effective but also practicable for sentences of customary length. Thus, the computation of $\mathfrak{m}^*(i)$ for a general sentence i is in fact much simpler for $\mathfrak{L}_\infty$ than for a finite system $\mathfrak{L}_N$ with a large N.

With the help of the procedure mentioned, the following theorem is obtained:

(5) If i is a purely general sentence (D16-6g) in $\mathfrak{L}_\infty^\pi$, then $\mathfrak{m}^*(i)$ is either 0 or 1.

For a sentence of the form '$(x)(Mx)$', where 'M' is a factual molecular predicate, $\mathfrak{m}^*$ is 0. This leads to the later result (12).

B. *The Direct Inference*

One of the most important tasks of inductive logic is to furnish general theorems on the degree of confirmation in the various cases called kinds of inductive inference which were earlier explained (§ 44B). We shall now indicate some results of this kind concerning $\mathfrak{c}^*$. Inductive inferences are of special importance when they become statistical inferences, that is to say, when e or h or both give statistical information, e.g., concerning the absolute or relative frequencies of given properties in a population or a sample. Most of the subsequent theorems are of this kind.

The direct inference is the inference from the population to a sample. Here it is not necessary to state special theorems on $\mathfrak{c}^*$ because the theorems stated earlier for all symmetrical $\mathfrak{c}$-functions (§§ 94–96) hold, of course, for $\mathfrak{c}^*$ too. We have seen that these theorems state the same values as classical theorems, including the binomial law (§ 95) and the various parts of Bernoulli's theorem (§ 96), although the restricting conditions and the interpretations are somewhat different in some cases.

C. *The Predictive Inference*

The predictive inference is the inference from one sample to another. Let the properties M_i (i = 1 to p) form a division (D25-4). Let e be an individual distribution (D26-6a) saying that in a first sample of s individuals s_i specified ones are M_i (i = 1 to p); let e' be the statistical distribution corresponding to e (D26-6b); let h be a statistical distribution (D26-6c) for the same division, but for a second sample of s' other individuals with the cardinal numbers s'_i; let the width of M_i be w_i. Then the following holds:

$$(6) \qquad \mathfrak{c}^*(h,e) = \mathfrak{c}^*(h,e') = \frac{\prod_{i=1}^{p} \binom{s_i + s_i' + w_i - 1}{s_i'}}{\binom{s + s' + \kappa - 1}{s'}} .$$

The predictive inference is the most important kind of inductive inference. The other kinds which will be discussed here may be construed as special cases of the predictive inference. Therefore the further theorems in this section can be derived from (6).

The most important special case of the predictive inference is the *singular predictive inference*. Here *h* is a singular prediction '*Mc*' (with '*M*' for 'M_1'), where '*c*' is an in not occurring in *e*. *e* and *e'* are as before. In this case

$$(7) \qquad \mathfrak{c}^*(h,e) = \mathfrak{c}^*(h,e') = \frac{s_1 + w_1}{s + \kappa} .$$

Laplace's much-debated rule of succession gives in this case simply the value $\frac{s_1+1}{s+2}$ for any property whatever; this, however, if applied to different properties, leads to contradictions. Other authors state the value s_1/s, that is, they take simply the observed relative frequency as the probability for the prediction that an unobserved individual has the property in question. We call this the *straight rule*. This rule, however, leads to quite implausible results. If $s_1 = s$, e.g., if three individuals have been observed and all of them have been found to be *M*, the last-mentioned rule gives the probability for the next individual being *M* as 1, which seems hardly acceptable (see § 47 A). According to (7), $\mathfrak{c}^*$ is influenced by the following two factors (though not uniquely determined by them):

(i) w_1/κ, the relative width of *M*;
(ii) s_1/s, the relative frequency of *M* in the observed sample.

The factor (i) is purely logical; it is determined by the semantical rules. (ii) is empirical; it is determined by observing and counting the individuals in the sample. The value of $\mathfrak{c}^*$ always lies between those of (i) and (ii). Before any individual has been observed, $\mathfrak{c}^*$ is equal to the logical factor (i). As we first begin to observe a sample, $\mathfrak{c}^*$ is influenced more by this factor than by (ii). As the sample is increased by observing more and more individuals (but not including the one mentioned in *h*), the empirical factor (ii) gains more and more influence upon $\mathfrak{c}^*$. Let us assume that, as the sample increases, the relative frequency of *M* continues to have the same value $r = s_1/s$. In this case $\mathfrak{c}^*$ moves slowly toward this value *r*, which it approaches as a limit; when the sample is sufficiently large, $\mathfrak{c}^*$ is practically equal to *r*. This result seems more adequate than the value $\mathfrak{c} = s_1/s$ of the straight rule; but the latter is acceptable as an approximation in the case of sufficiently large samples.

According to our previous analysis of estimation (T106-1c), the value of c* stated in (7) is likewise the estimate of the relative frequency of M within any unobserved class.

D. *The Inference by Analogy*

Here the situation is as follows. The evidence known to us is the fact that individuals b and c agree in certain properties and, in addition, that b has a further property; thereupon we consider the hypothesis that c too has this property. Logicians have always felt that a peculiar difficulty is here involved. It seems plausible to assume that the probability of the hypothesis is the higher the more properties b and c are known to have in common; on the other hand, it is felt that these common properties should not simply be counted but weighed in some way. This becomes possible with the help of the concept of width. Let M_1 be the conjunction of all properties which b and c are known to have in common. The known similarity between b and c is the greater the stronger the property M_1, hence the smaller its width. Let M_2 be the conjunction of all properties which b is known to have. Let the width of M_1 be w_1, and that of M_2, w_2. According to the above description of the situation, we presuppose that M_2 L-implies M_1 but is not L-equivalent to M_1; hence $w_1 > w_2$. Now we take as evidence the conjunction $e \,.\, j$; e says that b is M_2, and j says that c is M_1. The hypothesis h says that c has not only the properties ascribed to it in the evidence but also the one (or several) ascribed in the evidence to b only, in other words, that c has all known properties of b, or briefly that c is M_2. Then

$$(8) \qquad c^*(h, e \,.\, j) = \frac{w_2 + 1}{w_1 + 1} \,.$$

j and h speak only about c; e introduces the other individual b which serves to connect the known properties of c expressed by j with its unknown properties expressed by h. The chief question is whether the degree of confirmation of h is increased by the analogy between c and b, in other words, by the addition of e to our knowledge j. An affirmative answer to this question can be derived from (8). However, the increase of c* is under ordinary conditions rather small; this is in agreement with the general conception according to which reasoning by analogy, although admissible, can usually yield only rather weak results.

Neither the classical theory nor modern theories of probability have been able to give a satisfactory account of and justification for the inference by analogy. This fact is not surprising since the degree of confirmation depends here not on relative frequencies but entirely on the widths of the properties involved, thus on magnitudes neglected by both classical and modern theories.

E. *The Inverse Inference*

The inverse inference is the inference from a sample to the whole population. This inference can be regarded as a special case of the predictive inference with the second sample covering the whole remainder of the population. Let M_i, e, s, s_i, e', and w_i be as under (C). Let h be a statistical distribution which says that in the whole population of n individuals, of which the sample described in e is a part, there are n_i individuals with M_i ($i = 1$ to p). Then

$$(9) \qquad \mathfrak{c}^*(h,e) = \mathfrak{c}^*(h,e') = \frac{\prod_{i=1}^{p} \binom{n_i + w_i - 1}{s_i + w_i - 1}}{\binom{n + \kappa - 1}{n - s}}.$$

This theorem shows that in the inverse inference, in distinction to the direct inference, $\mathfrak{c}^*$ is dependent not only upon the frequencies but also upon the widths of the properties.

F. *The Universal Inference*

The universal inference is the inference from an observed sample to a hypothesis of universal form. Let l be a factual sentence of the form '$(x)(Mx \supset M'x)$', where 'M' and 'M'' are factual molecular predicates. Hence l is an unrestricted simple law (D37-2a). As an example, let 'M' designate the property Swan and 'M'' White; hence l says that all swans are white. Let us take 'M_1' as an abbreviation for '$M \cdot \sim M'$' (Non-White Swan), and let the width of 'M_1' be w_1. Then l is L-equivalent to '$(x)(\sim M_1 x)$' ('there are no non-white swans') (T21-5g(1)) and hence is a law with the strength w_1 (T37-3a). Let e be a conjunction of s full sentences of '$\sim M_1$' with s different in. Thus e describes a sample of s individuals none of which violates the law l. Then, for any finite system $\mathfrak{L}_N^\pi$,

$$(10) \qquad \mathfrak{c}^*(l,e) = \frac{\binom{s + \kappa - 1}{w_1}}{\binom{N + \kappa - 1}{w_1}}.$$

In the special case of a system containing 'M_1' as the only pr, we have $w_1 = 1$ and $\kappa = 2$, and hence $\mathfrak{c}^*(l,e) = (s + 1)/(N + 1)$. The latter value is given by some authors as holding generally (see Jeffreys [Probab.], p. 106 (16)). However, it seems plausible that the degree of confirmation must be smaller for a stronger law and hence depend upon w_1.

If s is very large in relation to κ, the following approximation holds:

$$\text{(11)} \qquad \mathfrak{c}^*(l,e) \cong \left(\frac{s}{N}\right)^{w_1}.$$

For $\mathfrak{L}^\pi_\infty$,

$$\text{(12)} \qquad \mathfrak{c}^*(l,e) = 0.$$

These theorems show that for finite systems the confirmation of the law l decreases with increasing N. This seems plausible because, the larger N is, the more is asserted by l. If N is very large, $\mathfrak{c}^*$ becomes very small; and for the infinite system it is 0. The latter result may seem surprising; it seems not in accord with the fact that scientists often say of a law that it is "well-confirmed"; this problem will be discussed under (G).

Let us now consider the case where also negative instances are observed. Let e' be an individual distribution for 'M_1' and '$\sim M_1$' with s in with the cardinal numbers s_1 and $s - s_1$. Thus e' says that the observed sample of s individuals contains s_1 negative instances (non-white swans). Obviously, in this case there is no point in taking as hypothesis the law in its original form l, because e' and l are L-exclusive. We take instead the corresponding restricted law (D37-2b) l' which says that all individuals not belonging to the sample described in e' have the property $\sim M_1$ ('all unobserved swans are white'). Then for $\mathfrak{L}^\pi_N$:

$$\text{(13)} \qquad \mathfrak{c}^*(l',e') \cong \frac{\binom{s+\kappa-1}{s_1+w_1}}{\binom{N+\kappa-1}{s_1+w_1}}.$$

This shows that $\mathfrak{c}^*(l',e')$ decreases with an increase of N and even more with an increase in the number s_1 of violating cases. It can be shown that, under ordinary circumstances with large N, $\mathfrak{c}^*$ increases moderately when a new individual is observed which satisfies the original law l. On the other hand, if the new individual violates l, $\mathfrak{c}^*$ decreases very much, its value becoming a small fraction of its previous value. This seems in good agreement with the general conception.

For the infinite system, $\mathfrak{c}^*$ is again 0, as in the previous case.

G. *The Instance Confirmation of a Law*

Suppose we ask an engineer who is building a bridge why he has chosen the particular design. He will refer to certain physical laws and tell us that he regards them as "very reliable", "well founded", "amply confirmed by numerous experiences". What do these phrases mean? It is clear that they are intended to say something about probability$_1$ or degree of confirmation. Hence, what is meant could be formulated more explicitly in a statement of the form '$\mathfrak{c}(h,e)$ is high' or the like. Here the evidence *e* is obviously the relevant observational knowledge. But what is to serve as the hypothesis *h*? One might perhaps think at first that *h* is the law in question, hence a universal sentence *l* of the form: 'For every space-time point *x*, if such and such conditions are fulfilled at *x*, then such and such is the case at *x*'. I think, however, that the engineer is chiefly interested not in this sentence *l*, which speaks about an immense number, perhaps an infinite number, of instances dispersed through all time and space, but rather in one instance of *l* or a relatively small number of instances. When he says that the law is very reliable, he does not mean to say that he is willing to bet that among the billion of billions, or an infinite number, of instances to which the law applies there is not one counterinstance, but merely that this bridge will not be a counterinstance, or that among all bridges which he will construct during his lifetime there will be no counterinstance. Thus *h* is not the law *l* itself but only a prediction concerning one instance or a relatively small number of instances. Therefore, what is vaguely called the reliability of a law is measured not by the degree of confirmation of the law itself but by that of one or several instances. This suggests the subsequent definitions. They refer, for the sake of simplicity, to just one instance; the case of several, say, one hundred, instances can then easily be judged likewise. Let *e* be any non-L-false, nongeneral sentence. Let *l* be a simple law (D37-1) of the form $(\mathfrak{i}_k)(\mathfrak{M}_i)$. Then we understand by the ***instance confirmation*** of *l* on the evidence *e*, in symbols '$\mathfrak{c}_i^*(l,e)$', the degree of confirmation, on the evidence *e*, of the hypothesis that a new individual not mentioned in *e* fulfils the law *l*:

$$(14) \qquad \mathfrak{c}_i^*(l,e) =_{Df} \mathfrak{c}^*(h,e) \,,$$

where *h* is an instance of $\mathfrak{M}_i$ formed by substituting for $\mathfrak{i}_k$ an in not occurring in *e*.

The second concept, now to be defined, seems in many cases to represent still more accurately what is vaguely meant by the reliability of a law *l*. We suppose here that *l* has the frequently used conditional form mentioned earlier: '$(x)(Mx \supset M'x)$' (e.g., 'all swans are white'). By the ***qualified-instance confirmation*** of the law that all swans are white we mean the degree of confirmation for the hypothesis *h'* that the next swan to be observed will likewise be white. The difference between the hypothesis h used previously for the instance confirmation and the hypothesis h' just described consists in the fact that the latter concerns an individual which is already qualified as fulfilling the condition M. That is the reason why we speak here of the qualified-instance confirmation, in symbols '$\mathfrak{c}^*_{qi}$':

$$(15) \qquad \mathfrak{c}^*_{qi}(M,M',e) =_{Df} \mathfrak{c}^*(h',e\,.\,j)\ ,$$

where j is a full sentence of 'M' with an in not occurring in e, and h' is the full sentence of 'M'' with the same in.

We shall now give two theorems concerning the concepts just defined. Let l be '$(x)(Mx \supset M'x)$'. Let 'M_1' be defined, as earlier, by '$M\,.\sim M'$' (Non-White Swan) and 'M_2' by '$M\,.\,M'$' (White Swan). Let the widths of 'M_1' and 'M_2' be w_1 and w_2, respectively. Let e be a report about s observed individuals saying that s_1 of them are M_1 (negative cases) and s_2 are M_2, while the remaining ones are $\sim M$ (Non-Swan) and hence neither M_1 nor M_2. Then the following holds:

$$(16) \qquad \mathfrak{c}^*_{i}(l,e) = 1 - \frac{s_1 + w_1}{s + \kappa}\ .$$

$$(17) \qquad \mathfrak{c}^*_{qi}(M,M',e) = 1 - \frac{s_1 + w_1}{s_1 + w_1 + s_2 + w_2}\ .$$

The values of the two functions stated by these theorems are independent of N and hold therefore for all finite and infinite systems. The values for the case that the observed sample does not contain any individuals violating the law l can easily be obtained from the values stated by taking $s_1 = 0$.

It can be shown that, if the number s_1 of observed negative cases is either 0 or a fixed small number, then, with the increase of the sample size s, both $\mathfrak{c}^*_i$ and $\mathfrak{c}^*_{qi}$ grow close to 1, in contradistinction to $\mathfrak{c}^*$ for the law itself. This justifies the customary manner of speaking of "very reliable" or "well-founded" or "well-confirmed" laws, provided we interpret these phrases as referring to a high value of either of our two concepts just introduced. Understood in this sense, the phrases are not in contradiction to the previous results that the $\mathfrak{c}^*$ of a law is very small in a large system and 0 in the infinite system.

These concepts will also be of help in situations of the following kind. Suppose an observer X has observed certain events and finds two L-exclusive laws, each of which would explain the observed events satisfactorily. Which of them should he prefer? With respect to a finite system, he may take the law with the higher $\mathfrak{c}$. With respect to the infinite system, however, this method of comparison fails, because for either law $\mathfrak{c} = 0$ (in the case of $\mathfrak{c}^*$ and similar functions). Here the concept of instance confirmation (or that of qualified-instance confirmation) will help. If it has a higher value for one of the two laws, then this law will be preferable, if no reasons of another nature are against it.

H. *Are Laws Needed for Making Predictions?*

The expectations of future events which people actually entertain are influenced not only by rational factors but also by irrational ones like wishful thinking or fear. In a rational procedure, expectations should somehow be "founded upon" or "inductively inferred from" past experiences, in some sense of those phrases. In order to see more clearly how this is to be done and, in particular, which part in this procedure is played by laws, let us consider the following simplified schema. Suppose that X wants to determine, either for practical purposes of everyday life or for theoretical purposes of science, whether it would be reasonable for him to expect that a given individual c is M' in view of his earlier experiences. Let h be this prediction '$M'c$'. Suppose that his relevant observational results are as follows: (1) Many other things were M and all of them were also M'; let this be formulated in the sentence e; (2) c is M; let this be j. Thus he knows e and j by observation. How does he proceed from these premises to the desired conclusion h? It is clear that this cannot be done by deduction; an inductive procedure must be applied. What is this inductive procedure? It is usually explained in the following way. From the evidence e, X infers inductively the law l which says that all M are M'; this inference is supposed to be inductively valid because e contains many positive and no negative instances of the law l; then he infers h ('c is white') from l ('all swans are white') and j ('c is a swan') deductively. Now let us see how the procedure appears from the point of view of our inductive logic. One might perhaps be tempted to transcribe the usual description of the procedure just given into technical terms as follows. X infers l from e inductively because $\mathfrak{c}(l,e)$ is high; since $l \,.\, j$ L-implies h, $\mathfrak{c}(h,e \,.\, j)$ is likewise high; thus h may be inductively inferred from $e \,.\, j$. However, this way of reasoning would not be correct, because, under ordinary conditions, $\mathfrak{c}(l,e)$ (at least for $\mathfrak{c}^*$ and similar functions) is not high but very low, and even 0 if the number of individuals is infinite. The difficulty disappears when we realize, on the basis of our previous discussions, that X does not need a high $\mathfrak{c}^*$ for l in order to obtain the desired high $\mathfrak{c}^*$ for h; all he needs is a high $\mathfrak{c}^*_{qi}$ for l; and this he has by knowing e and j. Thus we see that X need not take the roundabout way through the law l at all, as is usually believed; he can instead go from his observational knowledge $e \cdot j$ directly to the singular prediction h. That is to say, our inductive logic makes it possible to determine $\mathfrak{c}^*(h, e \cdot j)$ directly and to find that it has a high value, without making use of any law. Customary thinking in everyday life likewise often takes this short cut, which is now justified by inductive logic. For instance, suppose somebody asks X what he expects to be the color of the next swan he will see. Then X may reason like this: he has seen many white swans and no non-white swans; therefore he presumes, admittedly not with certainty, that the next swan will likewise be white; and he is willing to bet on it. Perhaps he does not even consider the question whether all swans in the universe without a single exception are white; and, if he did, he would not be willing to bet on the affirmative answer.

We see that the use of laws is not indispensable for making predictions. Nevertheless it is expedient, of course, to state universal laws in books on physics, biology, psychology, etc. Although these laws stated by scientists do not have a high degree of confirmation, they have a high qualified-instance confirmation and thus serve as efficient instruments for finding those highly confirmed singular predictions which are needed in practical life.

I. *The Variety of Instances*

A generally accepted rule of scientific method says that for testing a given law we should choose a variety of specimens as great as possible (§ 47E). Suppose that one physicist tests the law l by making experiments with one hundred specimens, all of the same kind, and finds all results positive. Suppose that another physicist does the same with one hundred specimens taken from various kinds and finds likewise positive results. Let e_1 express the common prior knowledge of both physicists and the results of the hundred experiments of the first physicist; let e_2 be the corresponding statement for the second physicist. Then we should say that the second physicist has made a more thoroughgoing examination of the law and therefore has more reason than the first to believe in the law l or in the prediction h of a future instance of the law. Therefore, we should require of an adequate explicatum $\mathfrak{c}$ that its value for l or for h be higher on e_2 than on e_1. Ernest Nagel ([Principles], pp. 68–71) has discussed this problem in detail and explained the difficulties involved in finding a concept of degree of confirmation that would satisfy the requirement; he expresses doubts as to whether such a concept can be found at all. However, it can be shown that $\mathfrak{c}^*$ satisfies the requirement (see [Inductive] § 15).

J. *Inductive Logic as a Rational Reconstruction*

Sometimes a theory is offered as a "rational reconstruction" of a body of generally accepted but more-or-less vague beliefs. This means that the theory introduces explicata for the concepts involved in those beliefs and that the content of the beliefs is represented in a more exact and more systematic form by statements of the theory. The demand for a justification of a theory proposed as a rational reconstruction may be understood in two different ways. (1) The first, more modest task is to validate the claim that the new theory is a satisfactory reconstruction of the beliefs in question. It must be shown that the statements of the theory are in sufficient agreement with those beliefs; this comparison is possible only on those points where the beliefs are sufficiently precise. The question whether the given beliefs are true or false is here not even raised. (2) The second task is to show the validity of the new theory and thereby of the given beliefs. This is a much deeper-going and often much more difficult problem.

For example, Euclid's axiom system of geometry was a rational reconstruction of the beliefs concerning spatial relations which were generally held, based on experience and intuition, and applied in the practices of measuring, surveying, building, etc. Euclid's axiom system was accepted because it was in sufficient agreement with those beliefs and gave a more exact and consistent formulation for them. In other words, it was a rational reconstruction and systematization. A critical investigation of the validity, the factual truth, of the axioms and the beliefs was not made until more than two thousand years later by Gauss and Einstein.

The system of inductive logic here proposed, that is, the theory of $\mathfrak{c}^*$ based on the definition of this function, is intended as a reconstruction restricted to a simple language form, of inductive thinking as customarily applied in everyday life and in science. However, it is meant not merely as an uncritical representation of customary ways of thinking with all their defects and inconsistencies, but rather as a rational, critically corrected reconstruction. It is intended to lead to results which are more systematized, more consistent, and in certain points more correct than customary ways of thinking. One method of inductive thinking is regarded as more correct or more reasonable than another one if it is in better accord with the basic principle of inductive reasoning, which says that expectations for the future should be guided by the experiences of the past. More specifically: what has been observed more frequently should, under otherwise equal conditions, be regarded as more probable for the future.

Since the implicit rules of customary inductive thinking are rather vague, any rational reconstruction contains statements which are neither supported nor rejected by the ways of customary thinking. Therefore, a comparison is possible only on those points where the procedures of customary inductive thinking are precise enough. It seems to me that on these points the theory of $\mathfrak{c}^*$ is sufficiently in agreement with customary inductive thinking to be regarded as an adequate reconstruction. This agreement is found in many theorems, of which a few have been indicated in this appendix. And it seems further that in the points where there is a divergence, the theory of $\mathfrak{c}^*$ is more correct than customary thinking in the sense just explained.

GLOSSARY

Brief explanations are given for the main terms used in this volume. The exact definitions are stated in the body of the book (sometimes here referred to by their number or section); here we give only rough indications to help the reader's memory. Sometimes two explanations are given separated by a solidus '/'; in such cases the first holds for the explicandum, the second for the explicatum proposed in this book.

* A starred word is explained elsewhere in this glossary.

A

Absolute frequency (af) of the property M in the class K: the number of those elements of K which have the property M (D104-1a).

Additional evidence: If to the available *evidence e an additional evidence i is added, with regard to a *hypothesis h, then we call e the **prior evidence,** $e \cdot i$ the **posterior evidence,** $\mathfrak{c}(h,e)$ the **prior confirmation** of h, $\mathfrak{c}(h,e \cdot i)$ the **posterior confirmation** of h, $\mathfrak{c}(i,e)$ the **expectedness** of i, $\mathfrak{c}(i,e \cdot h)$ the **likelihood** of i (§ 60). i is said to be **predictable** if it follows from $e \cdot h$ (§ 61); $\mathfrak{c}(h,e \cdot i)/\mathfrak{c}(h,e)$ is called the **relevance quotient** (D66-1a).

Almost L-false sentence i: i is not *L-false, but $\mathfrak{m}(i) = 0$ (D58-1b, T58-3a).

Almost L-true sentence i: i is not *L-true, but $\mathfrak{m}(i) = 1$ (D58-1a).

Atomic sentence: consisting of a *primitive predicate and one or more *individual constants (D16-6a).

Attribute: property or relation.

B

($\mathfrak{c}$ is) **based upon** $\mathfrak{m}$: $\mathfrak{c}(h,e) = \mathfrak{m}(e \cdot h)/\mathfrak{m}(e)$ (D55-3).

Basic pair: consisting of an *atomic sentence and its *negation (D16-6c).

Basic sentence: *atomic sentence or *negation of such (D16-6b).

Biconditional: $i \equiv j$; i if and only if j (§ 15A).

C

$\mathfrak{c}$-function: any numerical function considered as an *explicatum for *probability$_1$.

$\mathfrak{c}$-mean estimate of an unknown magnitude: the weighted mean of the possible values of the magnitude with *degree of confirmation as weight (i.e., the sum of the possible values each multiplied with the *degree of confirmation for its occurrence) (§§ 99, 100A).

Classificatory concept: a property or relation of a simple kind, neither *comparative nor *quantitative (§ 4).

Classificatory concept of confirmation: ($\mathfrak{C}(h,i,e)$): the *additional evidence i is confirming evidence for the *hypothesis h (on the basis of the *prior evidence e) (§§ 8, 86).

Comparative concept: a relation characterizing a thing in comparison with another thing in terms of 'more' (or 'more or equal') without using numerical values (e.g., 'x is warmer than y') (§ 4).

Comparative concept of confirmation ($\mathfrak{MC}(h,e,h',e')$): the *hypothesis h is confirmed by the *evidence e more strongly or equally strongly as h' by e' (§§ 8, 79, 81).

Concept: property, relation, or function (§ 3).

Conditional: $i \supset j$; if i then j (§ 15A).

Conjunction: $i \cdot j$; i and j (§ 15A).
Connectives: the following signs: '$\sim$' (*negation), '$\vee$' (*disjunction), '$\cdot$' (*conjunction), '$\supset$' (*conditional), '$\equiv$' (*biconditional) (§ 15A).
Correlation of the in: a one-one relation among all *individual constants (D26-1).

D

Deductive inference: inference based upon *L-implication.
Deductive logic: the theory of logical deduction / the theory of *L-implication, *L-truth, etc. (§§ 20, 43B).
Degree of confirmation ($\mathfrak{c}(h,e)$): a *quantitative concept representing the degree to which the assumption of the *hypothesis h is supported by the *evidence e (§§ 8 to 10A).
Direct inference: the *inductive inference from the *population to a *sample (§ 44B).
Disjunction: $i \vee j$; i or j (or both) (§ 15A).
Division: an exhaustive and nonoverlapping set of properties (or *predicates designating them) (D25-4).

E

Empty class = *Null class.
Empty property M (or *predicate 'M'): not holding for any *individual (D25-1b).
Estimate; *see* $\mathfrak{c}$-mean estimate.
Evidence: (a sentence expressing) the knowledge (usually results of observations) available to the observer and used by him as a basis for determining the *degree of confirmation of a *hypothesis or an *estimate (§§ 8, 10A).
Existential quantifier: '$(\exists x)$', 'there is an *individual x such that . . .' (§ 15A).
Existential sentence: consisting of an *existential quantifier and a *matrix as its *scope (e.g., '$(\exists x) Px$') (§§ 15A, 16).
Expectedness; *see* Additional evidence.
Explication: the introduction of a new, exact *concept (the **explicatum**) to take the place of a given inexact *concept (the **explicandum**) (§ 2).
Expression: a finite sequence of *signs (§ 14).

F

F-false sentence: *factual and false (§ 20).
F-true sentence: *factual and true (§ 20).
Factual predicate 'M' (or property M): 'Ma' is a *factual sentence (§ 25).
Factual sentence: contingent, synthetic / neither *L-true nor *L-false (§ 20).
Frequency; *see* Absolute frequency; Relative frequency.
Frequency concept of probability; *see* Probability$_2$.
Full matrix of 'M': a *matrix consisting of 'M' and *individual signs, e.g., 'Mx' (§ 25).
Full sentence of 'M': a sentence consisting of 'M' and *individual constants, e.g., 'Ma' (§ 25).

G

General sentence: containing *variables (D16-6f).

H

Hypothesis: a sentence concerning unknown facts (e.g., a prediction or a law) which is judged on the basis of given *evidence (§§ 8, 10A).

I

Identity sentence: '$a = b$', 'a is the same *individual as b' (§ 15A).
in: *individual constant.

Individual constants (in): names of *individuals, '*a*', '*b*', etc. (§ 15A).

Individual distribution for a given *division and *n* given *individual constants: a sentence specifying for each of the *n* *individuals to which kind in the *division it belongs / a *conjunction of *n* *full sentences of the *predicates of the *division with one each of the given *individual constants (D26-6a).

Individual sign: *individual constant or *individual variable.

Individual variables: the variables '*x*', '*y*', etc., whose values are the *individuals; they are used in *quantifiers (§ 15A).

Individuals: the things or events or positions which constitute the universe of discourse (§ 15A).

Inductive inference: an inference which is nondeductive, nondemonstrative / determination of the *degree of confirmation c(h,e) (in particular, when e *L-implies neither h nor $\sim h$) (§ 44B).

Inductive logic: theory of the (*classificatory, *comparative, or *quantitative) concept of confirmation (§§ 8, 10A, 43).

Inference; *see* Deductive inference; Inductive inference.

Initial confirmation = *Null confirmation.

Initially relevant: *relevant with respect to the *tautologous evidence (D65-2).

Inverse inference: the *inductive inference from a *sample to the *population (§ 44B).

i is **irrelevant** to h on e: the *degree of confirmation of h remains unchanged when i is added to e (D65-1d).

Isomorphic sentences i, j: j is formed from i by replacing each *individual constant occurring in i by its correlate with respect to a *correlation of the in (D26-3a).

L

L-disjunct sentences i, j: the *disjunction $i \vee j$ is *L-true (§ 20).

L-equivalent sentences i, j: i and j have the same content; they entail each other logically / i and j have the same *range (§ 20).

L-exclusive sentences i, j: i is logically incompatible with j / the *conjunction $i \,.\, j$ is *L-false (§ 20).

L-false sentence i: i is logically false, self-contradictory / the *range of i is *empty, i holds in no *state-description (§ 20).

i **L-implies** j: i logically implies j; j follows logically from i / the *range of i is contained in that of j (§ 20).

L-true sentence i ($\vdash i$): i is logically true, analytic / i has the universal *range, i holds in every *state-description (§ 20).

Law; *see* Simple law and § 37.

Likelihood; *see* Additional evidence.

Logic; *see* Deductive logic; Inductive logic.

Logical width; *see* Width.

M

m-function: a measure function assigning numerical values first to the *state-descriptions, then to all sentences, representing an *explicatum for *probability$_1$ a priori (§ 55A).

Matrix, sentential: sentence or sentence-like expression with free *variables, e.g., '$\sim Px \vee Rax$' (§ 15A).

Metalanguage: the language in which we make statements about the symbolic *object language; the metalanguage used in this book is the English word-language supplemented with some technical signs (e.g., 'm', 'c', 'pr', '*i*', '*j*', etc.) (§ 14).

Molecular predicate: a *predicate introduced as an abbreviation for a *molecular predicate expression (§ 25).

Molecular predicate expression: consisting of *primitive predicates and *connectives, e.g., '$\sim P_1 \vee P_2$' (§ 25).

Molecular property: designated by a *molecular predicate expression (§ 25).
Molecular sentence: consisting of *atomic sentences and *connectives (D16-6e).

N

Negation: $\sim i$; not-*i* (§ 15A).
i is **negatively relevant** (or **negative**) to *h* on *e:* the *degree of confirmation of *h* is decreased when *i* is added to *e* (D65-1b).
Nongeneral sentence: not containing *variables (D16-6g).
Null class: class to which no element belongs.
Null confirmation: *degree of confirmation before any *factual *evidence is available / $\mathfrak{c}(h,t)$, where '*t*' is *tautologous (§ 57B).

O

Object language: the language investigated (not used) in a certain context; in this book, the symbolic systems $\mathfrak{L}$.

P

Population: the class of *individuals studied in a given investigation (§ 44B).
i is **positively relevant** (or **positive**) to *h* on *e:* the *degree of confirmation of *h* is increased by the addition of *i* to *e* (D65-1a).
Posterior confirmation, Posterior evidence; *see* Additional evidence.
$\mathfrak{pr}$: *primitive predicate.
Predicate: a *sign designating an *attribute, e.g., '*P*', '*M*' (§ 15A).
Predicate expression: an *expression designating an *attribute (§ 25).
Predictable; *see* Additional evidence.
Predictive inference: the *inductive inference from one *sample to another *sample (§ 44B).
Primitive predicates: the undefined *predicates of a language system, e.g., 'P_1', 'P_2', etc., 'R_1', etc. (§ 15A).
Prior confirmation, Prior evidence; *see* Additional evidence.
Probability$_1$: the logical concept of probability, *degree of confirmation (§ 9).
Probability$_2$: the statistical concept of probability, *relative frequency in the long run (§ 9).
Psychologism: wrong interpretation of logical problems in psychological terms (§§ 11, 12).

Q

Q-predicates: the *predicates designating *Q-properties, 'Q_1', 'Q_2', etc. (§ 31).
Q-properties: the strongest *factual properties in a language system (§ 31).
Quantifier; *see* Existential quantifier; Universal quantifier.
Quantitative concept: function with numerical values (§ 4).
Quantitative concept of confirmation: *degree of confirmation with numerical values (§ 8).

R

Range of a sentence *i:* the class of *state descriptions in which *i* holds (§ 18D).
Regular $\mathfrak{c}$-function: any *$\mathfrak{c}$-function fulfilling certain plausible conventions (§ 53) / a *$\mathfrak{c}$-function *based on a *regular $\mathfrak{m}$-function (D55-4).
Regular $\mathfrak{m}$-function: any *$\mathfrak{m}$-function fulfilling certain plausible conventions (§ 53) / any *$\mathfrak{m}$-function whose values for *state-descriptions are positive numbers whose sum is 1 (§ 55A).
Relative frequency of the property *M* in the class *K:* the *absolute frequency of *M* in *K* divided by the cardinal number of *K* (D104-1b).
Relative width of '*M*': the *width of '*M*' divided by the number of the *Q-predicates (κ) (D32-1b).

Relevance quotient; *see* Additional evidence.
Relevant: either *positively relevant or *negatively relevant (D65-1c).

S

Sample: a subclass (usually described in the *evidence) of the *population (§ 44B).
Scope of a *quantifier: the *matrix following it.
Semantics: the analytic theory of meaning (designation), truth, logical deduction (*L-implication), etc. (§ 8).
Signs: the smallest units of which the *expressions of the *object language consist, e.g., '*P*', '*x*', '$\vee$', etc. (D16-1).
Simple law: a *universal sentence whose *scope contains no *quantifier (e.g., '$(x)(P_1x \supset P_2x)$') (D37-1).
Singular sentence, hypothesis: concerning one *individual (D16-6i).
Singular predictive inference: *predictive inference with a *singular hypothesis (§ 44B).
State-description ($\mathfrak{Z}$): a sentence (or class of sentences) describing completely a possible state of affairs of the universe of discourse / a *conjunction (or class of sentences) containing as components (or elements) one sentence out of each *basic pair (D18-1).
Statistical distribution for a given *division and *n* given *individual constants: a sentence which states how many (but not, which) of the *n* given *individuals belong to each of the kinds in the *division / a *disjunction of all *individual distributions which are *isomorphic to a given one (D26-6c).
Statistical inference: *inductive inference involving *frequencies (§ 44B).
Structure-description ($\mathfrak{Str}$): a sentence which states for each *Q-property how many (but not, which) of the *individuals belong to it / a *disjunction of all *state-descriptions which are *isomorphic to a given one (D27-1).
Symmetrical $\mathfrak{c}$-function: a *$\mathfrak{c}$-function treating all *individuals on a par / a *$\mathfrak{c}$-function *based upon a *symmetrical $\mathfrak{m}$-function (§§ 90, 91).
Symmetrical $\mathfrak{m}$-function: an *$\mathfrak{m}$-function treating all *individuals on a par / an *$\mathfrak{m}$-function which has equal values for *isomorphic *state-descriptions (§ 90).

T

Tautologous: *L-true (in propositional logic), e.g., '$Pa \vee \sim Pa$'.

U

Universal inference: the *inductive inference from a *sample to a *universal sentence as *hypothesis (§ 44B).
Universal property *M* (or predicate '*M*'): holding for every *individual (D25-1a).
Universal quantifier: '(x)', 'for every *individual *x*, . . .' (§ 15A).
Universal sentence: consisting of a *universal quantifier and a *matrix as its *scope (e.g., '$(x)(P_1x \supset P_2x)$') (§§ 15A, 16).

V

Variable: all variables in our systems are *individual variables.

W

Width of the *molecular predicate '*M*' is *w*: *M* is a *disjunction of *w* *Q-properties (D32-1a).

Z

$\mathfrak{Z}$: *state-description.

SELECTED BIBLIOGRAPHY

The present bibliography gives only a limited selection from the large number of publications on problems of probability and induction. The publications here listed are chiefly those which are mentioned in the discussions in this book or are related to these discussions. Of the period up to 1920 only a few works are listed; a comprehensive bibliography for this time is given by Keynes. For more recent publications see the bibliography in Wright [Induction]. I am planning to give a more comprehensive bibliography in Volume II.

From the very extensive literature on mathematical statistics only a few works are listed here, chiefly those which discuss the logical foundations of statistical inference and the nature of the concept of probability. More titles will be given in Volume II (which will contain a more detailed discussion of the relations between mathematical statistics and inductive logic) but still only a small part of the large field. For comprehensive bibliographies on mathematical statistics see Cramér [Statistics], Kendall [Statistics], Vol. II, H. M. Walker [History], Wilks [Statistics], Wolfenden [Statistics].

The *abbreviated titles in square brackets* are used in citations throughout this book.

An *angle* '⟨' preceding the title of a publication indicates that it does not deal with problems of probability and induction. Most of the publications of this kind deal with deductive logic; they are listed because they are referred to in chapter iii.

In the *names of periodicals* the following abbreviations are used in addition to obvious ones:

Arist.: Aristotelian
C.R.: Comptes Rendus
Ges.: Gesellschaft
Int.: International
J.: Journal
Jber.: Jahresberichte
N.S.: New Series
Phen.: Phenomenological
Phil.: Philosophy
Res.: Research
Sc.: Science
Scient.: Scientific
Sitz.: Sitzungsberichte
Stat.: Statistics
Trans.: Transactions
Wiss.: Wissenschaft
ZS: Zeitschrift

Ackoff, R. L.; *see* CHURCHMAN

Ambrose, Alice

The problem of justifying inductive inference, *J. Phil.*, 44 (1947), 253–72.

Bachelier, Louis

Calcul des probabilités, Tome I. Paris, 1912.

Barrett, William

[Induction] The present state of the problem of induction, *Theoria*, 6 (1940), 150–57.

[Dewey] On Dewey's logic, *Phil. Review*, 50 (1941), 305–15.

Bayes, Thomas

[Essay] An essay towards solving a problem in the doctrine of chances (with an introductory letter, footnotes, and an appendix by Richard Price), *Phil. Trans. Royal Soc.*, 53 (1763), 370–418. (Reprinted in [Facsimiles].)

[Facsimiles] *Facsimiles of two papers by Bayes.* Ed. W. Edwards Deming. With comments by Edward C. Molina. Washington, D.C., 1940. (Contains [Essay].)

[Demonstration] A demonstration of the second rule in the essay . . . , *Phil. Trans. Royal Soc.*, 54 (1764), 296–325. (Partly due to R. Price.)

[Wahrsch.] (German transl. of [Essay] and [Demonstration]) *Versuch zur Lösung eines Problems der Wahrscheinlichkeitsrechnung.* Hsgg. H. E. Timerding. (Ostwalds Klassiker, Bd. 169.) Leipzig, 1908.

Bergmann, Gustav
The logic of probability, *Amer. J. Phys.*, 9 (1941), 263–72.
Frequencies, probabilities, and positivism, *Phil. Phen. Res.*, 6 (1946), 26–44.
Some comments on Carnap's logic of induction, *Phil. of Sc.*, 13 (1946), 71–78.

Berlin, Isaiah
Induction and hypothesis, *Proc. Arist. Soc.*, Suppl. Vol. 16 (1937), 63–102.

Bernays, Paul; *see* HILBERT

Bernoulli, Daniel
[Specimen] Specimen theoriae novae de mensura sortis, *Commentarii Acad. Sc. Imperialis Petropolitanae* (for 1730 and 1731), 5 (1738), 175–92.
[Grundlage] (German transl.) *Die Grundlage der modernen Wertlehre. Versuch einer neuen Theorie der Wertbestimmung von Glücksfällen.* Übersetzt und mit Erläuterungen von Alfred Pringsheim. Mit einer Einleitung von Ludwig Frick. Leipzig, 1896.

Bernoulli, Jacob
[Ars] *Ars conjectandi.* Basileae, 1713.
[Wahrsch.] (German transl.) *Wahrscheinlichkeitsrechnung.* (Transl. by R. Haussner, 2 vols.; Ostwalds Klassiker.) Leipzig, 1899.

Bertrand, Joseph
Calcul des probabilités. Paris, 1889; 2d ed., 1907.

Birge; *see* DEMING

Blume, Johannes
[Axiom.] *Zur axiomatischen Grundlegung der Wahrscheinlichkeitsrechnung.* Bochum, 1934. (Diss. Münster i.W.)
[Finite] Mathematische Begründung und Entwicklung einer Wahrscheinlichkeitsrechnung mit finiten Kollektiven, *ZS Phys.*, 92 (1934), 232–52.
[Anwendung] Zur Anwendung der Wahrscheinlichkeitsrechnung finiter Kollektive, *ibid.*, 94 (1935), 192–203.

Boole, George
[Laws] *An investigation of the laws of thought, on which are founded the mathematical theories of logic and probabilities.* London, 1854. (= Collected Logical Works, Vol. 2; ed. P. E. B. Jourdain. Chicago and London, 1916.)

Borel, Émile
[Traité] (Editor) *Traité du calcul des probabilités et de ses applications.* 4 vols. Paris, 1925 ff.
[Valeur] *Valeur pratique et philosophie des probabilités.* (= [Traité] Tome IV, Fasc. 3.) Paris, 1939.

Boring, E. G.
Statistical frequencies as dynamic equilibria, *Psych. Review*, 48 (1941), 279–301.

Bortkiewicz, Ladislaus von
Das Gesetz der kleinen Zahlen. Leipzig, 1898.
Anwendungen der Wahrscheinlichkeitsrechnung auf Statistik. In: *Enzykl. Math. Wiss.*, Band I, Teil 2, D4a (1901), 821–51.

Broad, C. D.
On the relation between induction and probability, *Mind*, 27 (1918), 389–404; 29 (1920), 11–45.
The principles of problematic induction, *Proc. Arist. Soc.*, 28 (1927–28), 1–46.
The principles of demonstrative induction, *Mind*, 39 (1930), 302–17, 426–39.
[Mises] Review of: Mises [Statistik], *Mind*, 46 (1937), 478–91.

[Wright] Hr. von Wright on the logic of induction, *Mind,* 53 (1944), 1–24, 97–119, 193–214.

Bruns, H.

Wahrscheinlichkeitsrechnung und Kollektivmasslehre. Leipzig, 1906.

Brunswik, Egon

Probability as a determiner of rat behavior, *J. Exper. Psych.*, 25 (1939), 175–97.

Organismic achievement and environmental probability, *Psych. Review,* 50 (1943), 255–72.

Bures, Charles E.

The concept of probability, *Phil. of Sc.*, 5 (1938), 1–20.

Burks, Arthur W.

Peirce's theory of abduction, *Phil. of Sc.*, 13 (1946), 301–6.

Carnap, Rudolf

⟨[Syntax] *Logical syntax of language.* London, 1937.

⟨[Testability] Testability and meaning, *Phil. of Sc.*, 3 (1936), 419–71, and 4 (1937), 1–40.

⟨[Foundations] *Foundations of logic and mathematics.* (Int. Encycl. of Unified Sc., Vol. I, No. 3.) Chicago, 1939.

⟨[Semantics] *Introduction to semantics.* (Studies in semantics, Vol. I.) Cambridge, Mass., 1942.

⟨[Formalization] *Formalization of logic.* (Studies in semantics, Vol. II.) Cambridge, Mass., 1943.

[Inductive] On inductive logic, *Phil. of Sc.*, 12 (1945), 72–97.

[Concepts] The two concepts of probability, *Phil. Phen. Res.*, 5 (1945), 513–32. Reprinted in: Feigl [Readings].

[Remarks] Remarks on induction and truth, *Phil. Phen. Res.*, 6 (1946), 590–602.

Rejoinder to Mr. Kaufmann's reply, *ibid.*, 609–11.

⟨[Modalities] Modalities and quantification, *J. Symbolic Logic,* 11 (1946), 33–64.

Theory and prediction in science, *Science,* 104 (1946), 520–21.

Probability as a guide in life, *J. Phil.*, 44 (1947), 141–48.

⟨[Meaning] *Meaning and necessity: a study in semantics and modal logic.* Chicago, 1947.

[Application] On the application of inductive logic, *Phil. Phen. Res.*, 8 (1947–48), 133–48.

Reply to Nelson Goodman, *ibid.*, 461–62.

[Truth] Truth and confirmation. (Adapted from an earlier paper (1936) and [Remarks].) In: Feigl [Readings].

Cavaillès, Jean

Du collectif au pari. A propos de quelques théories récentes sur les probabilités, *Revue métaphysique et morale,* 47 (1940), 139–63.

Church, Alonzo

⟨[Dictionary] Articles in: *Dictionary of philosophy,* ed. D. D. Runes. New York, 1942.

Churchman, C. West

Probability theory, *Phil. of Sc.*, 12 (1945), 147–73.

Theory of experimental inference. New York, 1948.

Statistics, pragmatics, induction, *Phil. of Sc.*, 15 (1948), 249–68. See discussion notes by J. E. Freund and T. A. Cowan, and reply by Churchman, *ibid.*, 16 (1949), 142–53.

Churchman, C. West, and **Ackoff, Russell L.**

Ethics and science, *Phil. of Sc.*, 14 (1947), 269–71.

Clopper, C. J., and **Pearson, E. S.**
The use of confidence or fiducial limits illustrated in the case of the binomial, *Biometrika*, 26 (1934), 404–13.

Colloque
Colloque consacré au calcul des probabilités. Act. Scient. Nos. 734–40, 766. Paris, 1938.

Coolidge, Julian L.
An introduction to mathematical probability. Oxford and New York, 1925.

Copeland, Arthur H.
Predictions and probabilities (mit deutscher Inhaltsangabe), *Erkenntnis*, 6 (1936–37), 189–203.
Consistency of the conditions determining kollektivs, *Trans. Amer. Math. Soc.*, 42 (1937), 333–57.
The role of observations in a formal theory of probability, *J. Unified Sc.*, 9 (1940), 159–63.
[Postulates] Postulates for the theory of probability, *Amer. J. Math.*, 63 (1941), 741–62.
[Fundamental] Fundamental concepts of the theory of probability, *Amer. Math. Monthly*, 48 (1941), 522–30.
The teaching of the calculus of probability. In: *Notre Dame Math. Lect.* No. 4 (1944), 31–43.

Cournot, Augustin
[Exposition] *Exposition de la théorie des chances et des probabilités.* Paris, 1843.

Couturat, Louis
La logique de Leibniz d'après des documents inédits. Paris, 1901.
La logique algorithmique et le calcul des probabilités, *Revue métaphysique et morale*, 24 (1917), 291–313.

Cox, R. T.
Probability, frequency, and reasonable expectation, *Amer. J. Phys.*, 14 (1946), 1–13.

Cramér, Harald
Random variables and probability distributions. Cambridge, Eng., 1937.
[Statistics] *Mathematical methods of statistics.* Princeton, 1946.

Creed, Isabel P.
[Justification] The justification of the habit of induction, *J. Phil.*, 37 (1940), 85–97. (On Reichenbach.)

Czuber, Emanuel
Die Entwicklung der Wahrscheinlichkeitstheorie und ihrer Anwendungen. Leipzig, 1899.
[Wahrsch.] *Wahrscheinlichkeitsrechnung und ihre Anwendung auf Fehlerausgleichung, Statistik und Lebensversicherung.* Leipzig, 1903. Later editions, 2 vols.
Wahrscheinlichkeitsrechnung. In: *Enzykl. Math. Wiss.*, Band I, Teil 2, D1 (1900–1904), 734–67.
[Grundlagen] *Die philosophischen Grundlagen der Wahrscheinlichkeitsrechnung.* Leipzig, 1923.

Dalkey, Norman
The limits of meaning, *Phil. Phen. Res.*, 4 (1944), 401–9.

Darwin, Charles G.
Logic and probability in physics, *Phil. of Sc.*, 6 (1939), 48–64.

De Finetti, Bruno
Sul significato soggettivo della probabilità, *Fundamenta Math.*, 17 (1931), 298–329.

La logique de la probabilité, *Actes Congrès Int. de Phil. Scient.* (Paris, 1935). Paris, 1936.

La prévision: ses lois logiques, ses sources subjectives, *Ann. Inst. H. Poincaré*, 7 (1937), 1–68.

Deming, W. Edwards, and **Birge, Raymond T.**

On the statistical theory of errors. (Reprinted from: *Reviews of Modern Physics*, 6 (1934), 119–61, with additional notes 1937 and 1938.) Washington, D.C., 1938.

See also BAYES [Facsimiles] and NEYMAN [Lectures]

De Moivre, Abraham

The doctrine of chances, or a method of calculating the probabilities of events in play. London, 1718. 3d ed., 1756.

De Morgan, Augustus

Essay on probabilities and on their application to life contingencies and insurance offices. London, 1838.

[Logic] *Formal logic: or the calculus of inference, necessary and probable.* London, 1847.

Diskussion

Diskussion über Wahrscheinlichkeit (Prague, Sept., 1929), *Erkenntnis*, 1 (1930–31), 260–85. (This discussion follows papers read by Reichenbach, Mises, Hertz, Waismann, Feigl; it consists of short remarks made by Zilsel, Reichenbach, Dubislav, Härlen, Carnap, Mises, Neurath, Tornier, Grelling, Hostinsky.)

Dörge, Karl

Zu der von R. von Mises gegebenen Begründung der Wahrscheinlichkeitsrechnung. I: Theorie des Glücksspiels, *Math. ZS*, 32 (1930), 232–58; II: Allgemeine Wahrscheinlichkeitstheorie, *ibid.*, 40 (1935), 161–93.

[Axiomatisierung] Eine Axiomatisierung der von Misesschen Wahrscheinlichkeitstheorie, *Jber. Deutsche Math. Vereinigung*, 43 (1933), 39–47.

Doob, J. L.

Probability and statistics, *Trans. Amer. Math. Soc.*, 36 (1934), 759–75.

Statistical estimation, *ibid.*, 39 (1936), 410–21.

Probability as measure, *Ann. Math. Stat.*, 12 (1941), 206–14.

Dotterer, Ray H.

Ignorance and equal probability, *Phil. of Sc.*, 8 (1941), 297–303.

Dubs, Homer H.

Rational induction. Chicago, 1930.

The principle of insufficient reason, *Phil. of Sc.*, 9 (1942), 123–31.

Ducasse, C. J.

Some observations concerning the nature of probability, *J. Phil.*, 38 (1941), 393–403.

Eaton, Ralph M.

[Logic] *General logic. An introductory survey.* New York, 1931. (Part IV: Induction.)

Edgeworth, F. Y.

Philosophy of chance, *Mind*, 9 (1884), 222–35.

Metretike: or the method of measuring probability and utility. 1887.

Applications of probabilities to economics, *Econ. J.*, 20 (1910), 284–304, 441–65.

Edwards, Paul

Russell's doubts about induction, *Mind*, 58 (1949), 141–63.

Ellis, R. Leslie

[Foundations] On the foundations of the theory of probabilities, *Trans. Cambridge Phil. Soc.*, 8 (1844), 1–6. (Paper read, February, 1842.) Reprinted in [Writings].

Remarks on the fundamental principle of the theory of probabilities (1854), *ibid.*, 9 (1856). Reprinted in [Writings].
[Writings] *The mathematical and other writings.* Cambridge, Eng., 1863.

Evans, H. P., and **Kleene, S. C.**
[Probab.] A postulational basis for probability, *Amer. Math. Monthly*, 46 (1939), 141–48.

Feibleman, James
Pragmatism and inverse probability, *Phil. Phen. Res.*, 5 (1945), 309–19.

Feigl, Herbert
Wahrscheinlichkeit und Erfahrung, *Erkenntnis*, 1 (1930–31), 249–59.
[Induction] The logical character of the principle of induction, *Phil. of Sc.*, 1 (1934), 20–29 (and 484–86). Reprinted in [Readings].

Feigl, Herbert, and **Sellars, Wilfrid** (eds.).
[Readings] *Readings in philosophical analysis.* New York, 1949. (Contains articles on probability by Reichenbach, Feigl, and Carnap.)

Fisher, Arne
The mathematical theory of probabilities and its application to frequency curves and statistical methods, Vol. I. New York, 1915; 2d ed., 1923.

Fisher, Ronald Aylmer
[Foundations] On the mathematical foundations of theoretical statistics, *Phil. Trans. Royal Soc.*, Series A, Vol. 222 (1922), 309–68.
Theory of statistical estimation, *Proc. Cambridge Phil. Soc.*, 22 (1923–25), 700–725.
Statistical methods for research workers. Edinburgh and London, 1925; and later editions.
Inverse probability, *Proc. Cambridge Phil. Soc.*, 26 (1930), 528–35.
Inverse probability and the use of likelihood, *ibid.*, 28 (1932), 257–61.
The concepts of inverse probability and fiducial probability referring to unknown parameters, *Proc. Royal Soc.*, Section A, 139 (1933), 343–48.
The logic of inductive inference, *J. Royal Stat. Soc.*, 98 (1935), 39–82.
The design of experiments. Edinburgh and London, 1935; and later editions.
Conclusions fiduciaires, *Ann. Inst. H. Poincaré*, 10 (1948), 191–213.

Fréchet, Maurice
Recherches théoriques modernes sur la théorie des probabilités. (Avec une note de Paul Lévy.) (=Borel [Traité], Tome I, Fasc. III.) Premier livre: Généralités sur les probabilités. Variables aléatoires. Paris, 1937. Second livre: Méthode des fonctions arbitraires. Théorie des événements en chaîne dans le cas d'un nombre fini d'états possibles. Paris, 1938.
The diverse definitions of probability, *J. Unified Sc.*, 8 (1939–40), 7–23.

Fréchet, Maurice, and **Halbwachs, Maurice**
Le calcul des probabilités à la portée de tous. Paris, 1924.

Freudenthal, Hans
Is there a specific problem of application for probability? *Mind*, 50 (1941), 367–73.

Frick, Ludwig
[Einleitung] Einleitung zu: Daniel Bernoulli [Grundlage], 1896, 1–20.

Fries, Jacob Fr.
Versuch einer Kritik der Prinzipien der Wahrscheinlichkeitsrechnung. Braunschweig, 1842.

Fry, Thornton C.
Probability and its engineering uses. New York, 1928.

Geiringer, Hilda
[Hypothesen] Über die Wahrscheinlichkeit von Hypothesen, *J. Unified Sc.*, 8 (1939), 151-76, 352-53. (On Reichenbach.)
"Falsification" and theory of errors, *Synthese*, 5 (1946), 86-89. (Written 1939.)

Goldschmidt, L.
Die Wahrscheinlichkeitsrechnung. Versuch einer Kritik. Hamburg und Leipzig, 1897.

Goodman, Nelson
A query on confirmation, *J. Phil.*, 43 (1946), 383-85.
On infirmities of confirmation-theory, *Phil. Phen. Res.*, 8 (1947-48), 149-51. (On Carnap [Application].)

Goodstein, R. L.
On von Mises' theory of probability, *Mind*, 49 (1940), 58-62.

Goudge, Thomas A.
Peirce's treatment of induction, *Phil. of Sc.*, 7 (1940), 56-68.

Grelling, Kurt
Die philosophischen Grundlagen der Wahrscheinlichkeitsrechnung, *Abhandlungen der Fries'schen Schule*, 3 (1910), 439-78.

Hailperin, Theodore
Foundations of probability in mathematical logic, *Phil. of Sc.*, 4 (1937), 125-50.

Halbwachs; *see* FRÉCHET

Halmos, Paul R.
The foundations of probability, *Amer. Math. Monthly*, 51 (1944), 493-510.

Hawkins, David
[Probab.] Existential and epistemic probability, *Phil. of Sc.*, 10 (1943), 255-61.

Helmer, Olaf, and **Oppenheim, Paul.**
[Degree] A syntactical definition of probability and of degree of confirmation, *J. Symbolic Logic*, 10 (1945), 25-60.

Hempel, Carl G.
Beiträge zur logischen Analyse des Wahrscheinlichkeitsbegriffs. (Diss. Berlin, 1934.) Jena, 1934.
[Gehalt] Über den Gehalt von Wahrscheinlichkeitsaussagen, *Erkenntnis*, 5 (1935-36), 228-60.
[Vérité] Le problème de la vérité, *Theoria*, 3 (1937), 206-46.
On the logical form of probability-statements, *Erkenntnis*, 7 (1937-39), 154-60, 360-63.
[Syntactical] A purely syntactical definition of confirmation, *J. Symbolic Logic*, 8 (1943), 122-43.
[Studies] Studies in the logic of confirmation, *Mind*, 54 (1945), 1-26, 97-121. (See also *ibid.*, 55 (1946), 79-82.)

Hempel, Carl G., and **Oppenheim, Paul.**
[Degree] A definition of "degree of confirmation," *Phil. of Sc.*, 12 (1945), 98-115.
Studies in the logic of explanation, *ibid.*, 15 (1948), 135-75. (§ 9: Systematic power and logical probability of a theory.)

Hertz, Paul
[Reichenbach] Kritische Bemerkungen zu Reichenbachs Behandlung des Humeschen Problems, *Erkenntnis*, 6 (1936-37), 25-31.

Hilbert, David, and **Bernays, Paul**
⟨[Grundlagen] *Grundlagen der Mathematik.* Berlin, Vol. I, 1934; II, 1939. (Reprinted, Ann Arbor, Mich. 1944.)

Hohenemser, K.
Beitrag zu den Grundlagenproblemen in der Wahrscheinlichkeitsrechnung, *Erkenntnis*, 2 (1931), 354–64.

Hosiasson (-Lindenbaum), Janina
Why do we prefer probabilities relative to many data? *Mind*, 40 (1931), 23–36.
La théorie des probabilités est-elle une logique généralisée? *Actes Congrès Int. de Phil. Scient.* (Paris, 1935). Paris, 1936.
[Confirmation] On confirmation, *J. Symbolic Logic*, 5 (1940), 133–48.
[Induction] Induction et analogie: comparaison de leur fondement, *Mind*, 50 (1941), 351–65.

Hume, David
A treatise on human nature, being an attempt to introduce the experimental method of reasoning into moral subjects. London, 1739.
An enquiry concerning human understanding. London, 1748.

Huyghens, Christian
De ratiociniis in ludo aleae. (First published in: F. Schooten, *Exercitationum mathematicarum libri quinque*, 1657; reprinted as Part I of: Jacob Bernoulli [Ars]; German transl. is contained in that of the latter work; English transl. by W. Browne, London, 1714.)

Jeffreys, Harold
Scientific inference. Cambridge, Eng., 1931. 2d ed., 1937.
The problem of inference, *Mind*, 45 (1936), 324–33.
[Probab.] *Theory of probability.* Oxford, 1939.

Jevons, William Stanley
The principles of science. A treatise on logic and scientific method. 2 vols. London, 1874; and later editions.

Johnson, W. E.
Logic. 3 vols. Cambridge, Eng., 1921–24.
Probability, *Mind*, 41 (1932), 1–16, 281–96, 408–23.

Jordan, Charles
[Bernoulli] On Daniel Bernoulli's "moral expectation" and on a new conception of expectation, *Amer. Math. Monthly*, 31 (1924), 183–90.

Joseph, H. W. B.
An introduction to logic. Oxford, 1906; 2d ed., 1916.

Jourdain, P. E. B.
Causality, induction, and probability, *Mind*, 28 (1919), 162–79.

Kaila, Eino
Der Satz vom Ausgleich des Zufalls und das Kausalprinzip (=Annales Universitatis Fennicae Aboensis, Ser. B, Vol. 2, No. 2.) Turku (Finland), 1924.
Die Prinzipien der Wahrscheinlichkeitslogik. (=*Ibid.*, Vol. 4, No. 1.) Turku, 1926.

Kamke, Erich
Einführung in die Wahrscheinlichkeitstheorie. Leipzig, 1932. (Reprinted, Ann Arbor, Mich.)
Über neuere Begründungen der Wahrscheinlichkeitsrechnung, *Jber. Deutsche Math. Vereinigung*, 42 (1933), 14–27.

Kaufmann, Felix
The logical rules of scientific procedure, *Phil. Phen. Res.*, 2 (1942), 457–71.
Scientific procedure and probability, *ibid.*, 6 (1945–46), 47–66.
On the nature of inductive inference, *ibid.*, 602–9. (On Carnap [Remarks].)

Kemble, Edwin C.
The probability concept, *Phil. of Sc.*, 8 (1941), 204–32.
Is the frequency theory of probability adequate for all scientific purposes? *Amer. J. Phys.*, 10 (1942), 6–16.

Kendall, Maurice G.
[Statistics] *Advanced theory of statistics.* London, Vol. I, 1943. 2d ed., 1945; Vol. II, 1946.
See also YULE.

Keynes, John Maynard
[Probab.] *A treatise on probability.* London and New York, 1921; 2d ed. 1929.

Kleene, S. C.; *see* EVANS

Kneale, William
Probability and induction. Oxford, 1949.

Kolmogoroff, A.
[Wahrsch.] *Grundbegriffe der Wahrscheinlichkeitsrechnung.* Berlin, 1933. Reprinted, New York, 1946.

Koopman, B. O.
The bases of probability, *Bull. Amer. Math. Soc.*, 46 (1940), 763–74.
[Axioms] The axioms and algebra of intuitive probability, *Ann. Math.*, Ser. 2, 41 (1940), 269–92.
Intuitive probabilities and sequences, *ibid.*, 42 (1941), 169–87.
[Review] (Review of [Symposium]; *see below under* SYMPOSIUM), *Math. Reviews*, 7 (1946), 186–93, and 8 (1947), 245–47.

Kries, J. von
[Prinzipien] *Die Prinzipien der Wahrscheinlichkeitsrechnung. Eine logische Untersuchung.* Freiburg i.B., 1886. 2d ed., Tübingen, 1927.

Lalande, André
Les théories de l'induction et de l'expérimentation. Paris, 1929.

Laplace, Pierre Simon de
[Théorie] *Théorie analytique des probabilités.* Paris, 1812; 2d ed., 1814; 3d ed., 1820. (Reprinted in: *Œuvres complètes*, Vol. VII. Paris, 1847.)
[Essai] *Essai philosophique sur les probabilités.* (Originally printed as introduction to [Théorie] in 2d and later editions; reprinted in *Œuvres complètes*, Vol. VII; edition in 2 vols. (reprinted from 5th ed., 1825) Paris, 1921.) (German transl. by R. v. Mises, Leipzig, 1932; English transl. by Truscott and Emory, New York, 1902.)

Levy, Hyman
Probability laws—a methodological and historical survey, *Sc. and Soc.*, 1 (1937), 230–40.

Levy, Hyman, and **Roth, L.**
Elements of probability. Oxford, 1936.

Lévy, Paul
Calcul des probabilités. Paris, 1925.

Lewis, Clarence Irving
An analysis of knowledge and valuation. (Carus lectures, delivered December, 1945.) La Salle, Ill., 1946. (Chap. x: Probability; xi: Probable knowledge.)

Lewy, Casimir
On the 'justification' of induction, *Analysis*, 6 (1939), 87–90. (This paper is discussed by M. A. Cunningham, L. D. Sass, C. H. Whiteley, and H. W. Chapman, in *Analysis*, 7 (1940).)

Lindenbaum, Janina; *see* HOSIASSON

Lukasiewicz, Jan

Die logischen Grundlagen der Wahrscheinlichkeitsrechnung. Krakau, 1913.

Macdonald, Margaret

Induction and hypothesis, *Proc. Arist. Soc.*, Suppl. Vol. 16 (1937), 20–35.

Mally, Ernst

Wahrscheinlichkeit und Gesetz. Berlin, 1938.

Marbe, Karl

Die Gleichförmigkeit in der Welt. Untersuchungen zur Philosophie und positiven Wissenschaft. München, 1916.

Margenau, Henry

Probability, many-valued logics, and physics, *Phil. of Sc.*, 6 (1939), 65–87.

Probability and physics, *J. Unified Sc.*, 9 (1940), 63–69.

The role of definitions in physical science, with remarks on the frequency definition of probability, *Amer. J. Phys.*, 10 (1942), 224–32.

On the frequency theory of probability, *Phil. Phen. Res.*, 6 (1945–46), 11–25.

Mazurkiewicz, Stefan

[Axiomatik] Zur Axiomatik der Wahrscheinlichkeitsrechnung, *C.R. Soc. Sc. Varsovie*, Cl. III, 25 (1932), 1–4.

Über die Grundlagen der Wahrscheinlichkeitsrechnung. I, *Monatshefte Math. Phys.*, 41 (1934), 343–52.

Meinong, Alexius von

[Kries] Besprechung von Kries [Prinzipien], *Göttingische Gelehrte Anzeigen*, 2 (1890), 56–75.

Über Möglichkeit und Wahrscheinlichkeit. Beiträge zur Gegenstandstheorie und Erkenntnistheorie. Leipzig, 1915.

Menger, Karl

[Wertlehre] Das Unsicherheitsmoment in der Wertlehre. Betrachtungen im Anschluss an das sogenannte Petersburger Spiel, *ZS für Nationalökonomie*, 5 (1934), 459–85. (See also "Bemerkungen", *ibid.*, 6 (1935), 283–85.)

On the relation between calculus of probability and statistics. In: *Notre Dame Math. Lect.* No. 4 (1944), 44–53.

Mill, John Stuart

A system of logic, ratiocinative and inductive, being a connected view of the principles of evidence and the methods of scientific investigation. 2 vols. London, 1843. 8th ed., New York, 1930.

Miller, Dickinson S.

Professor Donald Williams versus Hume, *J. Phil.*, 44 (1947), 673–84.

Mises, Richard von

[Grundlagen] Grundlagen der Wahrscheinlichkeitsrechnung, *Math. ZS*, 5 (1919), 52–99.

[Statistik] *Wahrscheinlichkeit, Statistik und Wahrheit. Einführung in die neue Wahrscheinlichkeitslehre und ihre Anwendung*. Wien, 1928. 2d ed., 1936. (Compare: Broad [Mises].)

[Probab.] (Transl. of [Statistik].) *Probability, statistics, and truth*. New York, 1939.

Über kausale und statistische Gesetzmässigkeit in der Physik, *Erkenntnis*, 1 (1930–31), 189–210.

[Wahrsch.] *Wahrscheinlichkeitsrechnung und ihre Anwendung in der Statistik und theoretischen Physik*. Wien, 1931.

[Comments 1] Comments on Donald Williams' paper, *Phil. Phen. Res.*, 6 (1945–46), 45–46.
[Comments 2] Comments on Donald Williams' reply, *ibid.*, 611–13.

Molina, Edward C.
The theory of probability; some comments on Laplace's *Théorie analytique*, *Bull. Amer. Math. Soc.*, 36 (1930), 369–92.
Bayes' theorem; an expository presentation, *Ann. Math. Stat.*, 2 (1931), 23–37.
See also BAYES [Facsimiles]

Morgenstern, O.; *see* NEUMANN

Nagel, Ernest
A frequency theory of probability, *J. Phil.*, 30 (1933), 533–54.
[Reichenbach] Review of: Reichenbach [Wahrsch.], *Mind*, 45 (1936), 501–14.
The meaning of probability, *J. Amer. Stat. Assoc.*, 31 (1936), 10–26.
Probability and the theory of knowledge, *Phil. of Sc.*, 6 (1939), 212–53. (On Reichenbach [Experience].)
[Principles] *Principles of the theory of probability*. Int. Encycl. Unif. Sc., Vol. I, No. 6. Chicago, 1939.
Probability and non-demonstrative inference, *Phil. Phen. Res.*, 5 (1945), 485–507. (On Williams [Derivation].)
Is the Laplacean theory of probability tenable? *ibid.*, 6 (1946), 614–18. (On Williams.)
Review of: Williams [Induction], *J. Phil.*, 44 (1947), 685–93.

Nelson, Everett J.
[Reichenbach] Professor Reichenbach on induction, *J. Phil.*, 33 (1936), 577–80.
The external world and induction, *Phil. of Sc.*, 9 (1942), 261–67.

Neumann, John von, and **Morgenstern, Oskar**
[Games] *Theory of games and economic behavior*. Princeton, 1944; 2d ed., 1947.

Neyman, Jerzy
[Outline] Outline of a theory of statistical estimation based on the classical theory of probability, *Phil. Trans. Royal Soc.*, Series A, 236 (1937), 333–80.
[Lectures] *Lectures and conferences on mathematical statistics* (1937). Revised and supplemented by W. E. Deming. Washington, D.C., 1938.

Neyman, Jerzy, and **Pearson, E. S.**
On the problem of the most efficient tests of statistical hypotheses, *Phil. Trans. Royal Soc.*, Series A, 231 (1933), 289–337.
The testing of statistical hypotheses in relation to probabilities a priori, *Proc. Cambridge Phil. Soc.*, 29 (1933), 492–510.
Contributions to the theory of testing statistical hypotheses, *Stat. Res. Memoirs*, 1 (1936), 1–37; 2 (1938), 25–57.

Nicod, Jean
[Induction] *The logical problem of induction*. (Orig. Paris, 1923.) In: *Foundations of geometry and induction*. London and New York, 1930.

Nisbet, R. H.
The foundations of probability, *Mind*, 35 (1926), 1–27.

Nitsche, A.
[Dimensionen] Die Dimensionen der Wahrscheinlichkeit und die Evidenz der Ungewissheit, *Vierteljahrsschrift für wiss. Phil.*, 16 (1892), 20–35.

Northrop, F. S. C.
The philosophical significance of the concept of probability in quantum mechanics, *Phil. of Sc.*, 3 (1936), 215–32. (Reprinted in: *The logic of the sciences. . . .* 1947, chap. xi.)

Oppenheim, Paul; *see* HELMER; HEMPEL

Pearson, Egon S.; *see* CLOPPER; NEYMAN

Pearson, Karl

The grammar of science. London, 1892; and later editions.

On the influence of past experience on future expectation, *Phil. Magazine,* 13 (1907), 365–78.

The fundamental problem of practical statistics, *Biometrika,* 13 (1920), 1–16.

Peirce, Charles Sanders

[Probab.] The probability of induction. 1878. Reprinted in [Papers], Vol. II, 415–32.

[Theory] A theory of probable inference. 1883. Reprinted in [Papers], Vol. II, 433–77.

[Papers] *Collected papers.* Ed. Ch. Hartshorne and Paul Weiss. Cambridge, Mass. (Articles on probability and induction are mostly in Vol. II, 1932, and Vol. III, 1933.)

Picard, Jacques

Méthode inductive et raisonnement inductif, *Revue Phil.,* 114 (1932), 397–436.

Poincaré, Henri

Calcul des probabilités. Paris, 1896; and later editions.

Poirier, R.

Remarques sur les probabilités des inductions. Paris, 1931.

Poisson, S. D.

Recherches sur la probabilité des jugements en matière criminelle et en matière civile, précédées des règles générales du calcul des probabilités. Paris, 1837.

Pólya, G.

Heuristic reasoning and the theory of probability, *Amer. Math. Monthly,* 48 (1941), 450–65.

On patterns of plausible inference. In: *Courant anniversary volume* (1948), 277–88.

Popper, Karl

"Induktionslogik" und "Hypothesenwahrscheinlichkeit," *Erkenntnis,* 5 (1935) 170–72.

[Logik] *Logik der Forschung. Zur Erkenntnistheorie der modernen Naturwissenschaft.* Wien, 1935.

A set of independent axioms for probability, *Mind,* 47 (1938), 275–77.

Price, Richard; *see* BAYES [Essay] and [Demonstration]

Quetelet, Adolphe

Instructions populaires sur le calcul des probabilités. Bruxelles, 1828. (Engl. transl., 1839.)

Lettres sur la théorie des probabilités appliquée aux sciences morales et politiques. Bruxelles, 1846. (Engl. transl., 1849.)

Quine, Willard Van Orman

⟨[Math. Logic] *Mathematical logic.* New York, 1940.

Ramsey, Frank P.

[Truth] *Truth and probability.* 1926. Reprinted in [Foundations], 156–98.

[Considerations] *Further considerations.* 1928. (A. Reasonable degree of belief. B. Statistics. C. Chance.) Reprinted in [Foundations], 199–211.

[Foundations] *The foundations of mathematics and other logical essays.* London and New York, 1931.

Reach, Karl

The foundations of our knowledge, *Synthese,* 5 (1946), 83–86. (Written 1937.)

Reichenbach, Hans

[Begriff] *Der Begriff der Wahrscheinlichkeit für die mathematische Darstellung der Wirklichkeit.* (Diss. Erlangen, 1915.) Leipzig, 1916. (Also in: *ZS Phil. u. phil. Kritik*, 161 (1917) and 162 (1918).)

[Kausalität] Kausalität und Wahrscheinlichkeit, *Erkenntnis*, 1 (1930–31), 158–88.

[Axiomatik] Axiomatik der Wahrscheinlichkeitsrechnung, *Math. ZS*, 34 (1932), 568–619.

Die logischen Grundlagen des Wahrscheinlichkeitsbegriffs, *Erkenntnis*, 3 (1932–33), 401–25. Engl. transl.: The logical foundations of the concept of probability; in: Feigl [Readings].

[Wahrsch.] *Wahrscheinlichkeitslehre. Eine Untersuchung über die logischen und mathematischen Grundlagen der Wahrscheinlichkeitsrechnung.* Leiden, 1935. Engl. transl., with new additions: *The theory of probability.* Berkeley, 1949.

[Wahrscheinlichkeitslogik] Wahrscheinlichkeitslogik, *Erkenntnis*, 5 (1935–36), 37–43.

(Diskussionsbemerkungen), *ibid.*, 172–73, 177–78.

Bemerkungen zu Carl Hempel's Versuch einer finitistischen Deutung des Wahrscheinlichkeitsbegriffs, *ibid.*, 261–66. (On Hempel [Gehalt].)

Über Induktion und Wahrscheinlichkeit. Bemerkungen zu K. Popper [Logik], *ibid.*, 267–84.

Warum ist die Anwendung der Induktionsregel für uns die notwendige Bedingung zur Gewinnung von Voraussagen? *Erkenntnis*, 6 (1936–37), 32–40. (Reply to Hertz [Reichenbach].)

Les fondements logiques du calcul des probabilités, *Ann. Inst. H. Poincaré*, 7 (1937), 267–348.

On probability and induction, *Phil. of Sc.*, 5 (1938), 21–45. (Reply to Nagel [Reichenbach].)

(Without title; reply to Nelson [Reichenbach]), *J. Phil.*, 35 (1938), 127–30.

[Experience] *Experience and prediction. An analysis of the foundations and the structure of knowledge.* Chicago, 1938.

Über die semantische und die Objektauffassung von Wahrscheinlichkeitsaussagen, *J. Unified Sc.*, 8 (1939–40), 50–68.

Bemerkungen zur Hypothesenwahrscheinlichkeit, *ibid.*, 256–60. (Reply to Geiringer [Hypothesen].)

On the justification of induction, *J. Phil.*, 37 (1940), 97–103. Reprinted in: Feigl [Readings]. (Reply to Creed [Justification].)

Reply to Donald C. Williams' criticism of the frequency theory of probability, *Phil. Phen. Res.*, 5 (1945), 508–12. (On Williams [Derivation].)

Ritchie, A. D.

Scientific method. An inquiry into the character and validity of natural laws. London and New York, 1923.

Induction and probability, *Mind*, 35 (1926), 301–18.

Roth, L.; *see* LEVY

Russell, Bertrand

The problems of philosophy. London and New York, 1912. (Chap. vi: On induction.)

Philosophy. New York, 1927 (=*An outline of philosophy;* London, 1927.) (Chap. 25: The validity of inference.)

Physics and experience. (Lecture, 1945.) London and New York, 1946.

[Knowledge] *Human knowledge. Its scope and limits.* New York, 1948. (Chap. v: Probability; vi: Postulates of scientific inference.)

See also WHITEHEAD.

Ryle, G.

Induction and hypothesis, *Proc. Arist. Soc.*, Suppl. Vol. 16 (1937), 36–62.

Rynin, David

Probability and meaning, *J. Phil.*, 44 (1947), 589–97.

Schlick, Moritz

Gesetz und Wahrscheinlichkeit, *Actes Congrès Int. de Phil. Scient.* (Paris, 1935), Fasc. IV (=Actualités Scient., 391). Paris, 1936. (Reprinted in: *Gesammelte Aufsätze*, Wien, 1938, 323–36.)

Shewhart, Walter A.

Statistical method from the viewpoint of quality control. (Ed. W. E. Deming.) Washington, D.C., 1939.

Sterzinger, Othmar

Zur Logik und Naturphilosophie der Wahrscheinlichkeitslehre. Ein umfassender Lösungsversuch. Leipzig, 1911.

Strauss, Martin

Ungenauigkeit, Wahrscheinlichkeit und Unbestimmtheit, *Erkenntnis*, 6 (1936–37), 90–113.

Formal problems of probability theory in the light of quantum mechanics, *Unity of Sc. Forum* (Synthese) (1938), 35–40; (1939), 49–54 and 65–72.

Ist die Limes-Theorie der Wahrscheinlichkeit eine sinnvolle Idealisation? *Synthese*, 5 (1946), 90–91. (Written 1939.)

Struik, D. J.

On the foundations of the theory of probabilities, *Phil. of Sc.*, 1 (1934), 50–70.

Stumpf, K.

Über den Begriff der mathematischen Wahrscheinlichkeit, *Sitz. Bayr. Akad. München*, Phil. Kl. (1892) 37–120.

Symposium

[Symposium] Symposium on probability. Part I, *Phil. Phen. Res.*, 5 (1945); Parts II and III, *ibid.*, 6 (1946). (Contributions by Williams, Nagel, Reichenbach, Carnap, Margenau, Bergmann, Mises, Felix Kaufmann.) (*See* KOOPMAN [Review].)

Tarski, Alfred

⟨[Wahrheitsbegriff] Der Wahrheitsbegriff in den formalisierten Sprachen. (Orig., 1933.) *Studia Phil.*, 1 (1936), 261–405.

Wahrscheinlichkeitslehre und mehrwertige Logik, *Erkenntnis*, 5 (1935–36), 174–75. (On Reichenbach [Wahrscheinlichkeitslogik].)

Timerding, H. E.

[Bernoulli] Die Bernoullische Wertetheorie, *ZS Math. Phys.*, 47 (1902), 321–54. (On Daniel Bernoulli [Specimen].)

Die Analyse des Zufalls. Braunschweig, 1915.

See also BAYES [Wahrsch.].

Tintner, Gerhard

[Choice] The theory of choice under subjective risk and uncertainty, *Econometrica*, 9 (1941), 298–304.

[Contribution] A contribution to the non-static theory of choice, *Quarterly J. Econ.*, 56 (1942), 274–306.

Foundations of probability and statistical inference, *J. Royal Stat. Soc.*, Series A, 112, Part III (1949), 251–86. (On Carnap [Inductive].)

Todhunter, I.
[History] *A history of the mathematical theory of probability, from the time of Pascal to that of Laplace.* London, 1865. (Reprinted, New York, 1931.)

Tornier, Erhard
Grundlagen der Wahrscheinlichkeitsrechnung, *Acta Math.*, 60 (1933), 239–380.
Wahrscheinlichkeitsrechnung und allgemeine Integrationstheorie. Leipzig, 1936. (Reprinted, Ann Arbor, Mich.)

Uspensky, J. V.
Introduction to mathematical probability. New York, 1937.

Venn, John
[Logic] *The logic of chance. An essay on the foundations and province of the theory of probability, with especial reference to its logical bearings and its application to moral and social science and to statistics.* London and New York, 1866, and later editions.

Vietoris, L.
Über den Begriff der Wahrscheinlichkeit, *Monatsh. Math.*, 52 (1948) 55–85.

Waismann, Friedrich
[Wahrsch.] Logische Analyse des Wahrscheinlichkeitsbegriffs, *Erkenntnis*, 1 (1930–31), 228–48.

Wald, Abraham
[Kollektiv] Die Widerspruchsfreiheit des Kollektivbegriffs der Wahrscheinlichkeitsrechnung, *Ergebnisse math. Kolloquium*, 8 (1937), 38–72. (On Mises.)
[Contributions] Contributions to the theory of statistical estimation and testing hypotheses, *Ann. Math. Stat.*, 10 (1939), 299–326.
[Principles] *On the principles of statistical inference.* Notre Dame, 1942.
[Risk] Statistical decision functions which minimize the maximum risk, *Ann. Math.*, 46 (1945), 265–80.
[Sequential] *Sequential analysis.* New York and London, 1947.

Walker, Edwin Ruthven
Verification and probability, *J. Phil.*, 44 (1947), 97–104.

Walker, Helen M.
[History] *Studies in the history of statistical method.* Baltimore, 1929.

Wang, Hao
Notes on the justification of induction, *J. Phil.*, 44 (1947), 701–10.

White, Morton
Probability and confirmation, *J. Phil.*, 36 (1939), 323–28.

Whitehead, Alfred North, and **Russell, Bertrand**
⟨[Princ. Math.] *Principia mathematica.* 3 vols. Cambridge, Eng., 1910–12. 2d ed., 1925.

Whittaker, E. T.
On some disputed questions of probability, *Trans. Faculty Actuaries Scotland*, 8 (1920), 163–206.

Wilks, S. S.
[Statistics] *Mathematical statistics.* Princeton, 1943.

Will, Frederick L.
Is there a problem of induction? *J. Phil.*, 39 (1942), 505–13.
[Future] Will the future be like the past? *Mind*, 56 (1947), 332–47.
Donald Williams' theory of induction, *Phil. Review*, 57 (1948), 231–47. (On Williams [Induction].)

Williams, Donald
On the derivation of probabilities from frequencies, *Phil. Phen. Res.*, 5 (1945), 449–84.
The challenging situation in the philosophy of probability, *ibid.*, 6 (1945–46), 67–86.
The problem of probability, *ibid.*, 619–22.
[Induction] *The ground of induction.* Cambridge, Mass., 1947.
Induction and the future, *Mind*, 57 (1948), 226–29. (On Will [Future].)

Wittgenstein, Ludwig
[Tractatus] *Tractatus logico-philosophicus.* With introd. by B. Russell. London, 1922.

Wold, H.
[Time series] *Analysis of stationary time series.* Upsala, 1938 (Diss. Stockholm.)

Wolfenden, Hugh H.
[Statistics] *The fundamental principles of mathematical statistics with special reference to the requirements of actuaries and vital statisticians.* Toronto, 1942.

Wright, Georg Henrik von
On probability, *Mind*, 49 (1940), 265–83.
[Induction] *The logical problem of induction.* (=Acta Phil. Fennica, Fasc. 3.) Helsinki, 1941.
[Wahrsch.] *Über Wahrscheinlichkeit. Eine logische und philosophische Untersuchung.* (=Acta Soc. Scient. Fennicae, n.s.A, Vol. 3, No. 11.) Helsinki, 1945.

Yule, George Udny, and **Kendall, M. G.**
An introduction to the theory of statistics. London, 1911; and many later editions.

Zawirski, Zygmunt
Über das Verhältnis der mehrwertigen Logik zur Wahrscheinlichkeitsrechnung, *Studia Phil.*, 1 (1935), 407–42.

Zilsel, Edgar
Das Anwendungsproblem. Ein philosophischer Versuch über das Gesetz der grossen Zahlen und die Induktion. Leipzig, 1916.

SUPPLEMENTARY BIBLIOGRAPHY, 1962

This is a list of selected items on probability and inductive logic. (See the explanations on p. 583.) More comprehensive bibliographies are given in the books by Kyburg, Savage, and von Wright (1957).

Arrow, Kenneth J.

Alternative approaches to the theory of choice in risk-taking situations. *Econometrica*, 19 (1951), 404–37. (Reprinted: *Cowles Commission Paper* No. 51. Chicago, 1952.)

Bar-Hillel, Yehoshua

A note on state-descriptions. *Phil. Studies*, 2 (1951), 72–75.

A note on comparative inductive logic. *Brit. J. Phil. Sc.*, 3 (1953), 308–10.

An examination of information theory. *Phil. Sc.*, 22 (1955), 86–105.

Bar-Hillel, Yehoshua, and **Carnap, R.**

Semantic information. *Brit. J. Phil. Sc.*, 4 (1953), 147–57. (Also in: Jackson, Willie (ed.), *Communication theory*. London, 1953.)

Barker, S.

Induction and hypothesis. Ithaca, N.Y., 1957.

Barker, S., and **Achinstein, Peter**

On the new riddle of induction. *Phil. Rev.*, 69 (1960), 511–22.

Barnard, G. A.

Statistical inference. *J. Roy. Stat. Soc.*, Ser. B, 11 (1949), 115–39.

Bartlett, M. S.

The present position of mathematical statistics. *J. Roy. Stat. Soc.*, 103 (1940), 1–19.

Black, Max

The justification of induction. In: *Language and philosophy*, chap. iii. Ithaca, N.Y., 1949.

Problems of analysis. Ithaca, N.Y. 1954. (Part III: Induction.)

Blackwell, David, and **Girschick, M. A.**

Theory of games and statistical decisions. New York, 1954.

Braithwaite, Richard B.

Scientific explanation. Cambridge, 1953.

Burks, Arthur

Review of: R. Carnap [Prob.] *J. Phil.*, 48 (1951), 524–35.

The presupposition theory of induction. *Phil. Sc.*, 20 (1953), 177–97.

On the presuppositions of induction. *Rev. of Metaphysics*, 8 (1955), 574–611.

On the significance of Carnap's system of inductive logic for the philosophy of induction. To appear in: Schilpp.

Carnap, Rudolf

[Analysis] Science and analysis of language. (Fifth Int. Congress for the Unity of Science, Cambridge, Mass., 1939.) *J. Unified Science*, 9 (1940), 221–26.

[Prob.] *Logical foundations of probability*. Chicago, 1950. (The first edition of the present book.)

The nature and application of inductive logic. (Consisting of six sections (41–43, 49–51) from [Prob.].)
The problem of relations in inductive logic. *Phil. Studies*, 2 (1951–52), 75–80.
[Continuum] *The continuum of inductive methods.* Chicago, 1952.
[Postulates] Meaning postulates. *Phil. Studies*, 3 (1952), 65–73. (Reprinted in: *Meaning and necessity.* 2d ed., 1956.)
[Comparative] On the comparative concept of confirmation. *Brit. J. Phil. Sc.*, 3 (1953), 311–18.
[Science] Inductive logic and science. *Proc. Amer. Academy of Arts and Sciences*, 80 (1953), 189–97.
Remarks to Kemeny's paper. *Phil. Phen. Res.*, 13 (1953), 375–76.
[What] What is probability? *Scient. American*, 189 (1953), 128–38.
I. Statistical and inductive probability. (An extended version of [What].) *II. Inductive logic and science.* (Same as [Science].) Galois Inst. of Math. and Art, Brooklyn, N.Y., 1955.
[Aim] The aim of inductive logic. In: *Proc. Int. Congress for Logic and Methodology of Science* (Stanford, 1960), 113–28, Stanford, Calif., 1962.
Intellectual autobiography. To appear in: Schilpp. (§12: Probability and inductive logic.)
[Replies] Replies and systematic expositions. To appear in: Schilpp. (§ 25: My basic conceptions of probability and induction; § 26: An axiom system for inductive logic; §§ 27–31: Replies to Kemeny, Burks, Putnam, Nagel, and Popper, respectively.)
[Studies] Studies in probability and inductive logic. Ed. R. Carnap. (In preparation.)
Inductive logic and practical decisions. To appear in [Studies], Vol. I.
The basic system of inductive logic. To appear in [Studies], Vol. I.

Carnap, Rudolf, and **Bar-Hillel, Y.**

An outline of the theory of semantic information. Res. Lab. of Electronics, M.I.T., Report No. 247. Boston, 1952. (See also Bar-Hillel and Carnap.)

Carnap, Rudolf, and **Stegmüller, Wolfgang**

[Wahrsch.] *Induktive Logik und Wahrscheinlichkeit.* Wien, 1959.

Chernoff, Herman, and **Moses, Lincoln E.**

Elementary decision theory. New York, 1959.

Cox, Richard T.

The algebra of probable inference. Baltimore, 1961.

Császár, Ákos

Sur la structure des espaces de probabilité conditionelle. *Acta Math. Acad. Scient. Hungaricae*, 6 (1955), 337–61.

Davidson, Donald, and **Suppes, Patrick**

A finitistic axiomatization of subjective probability and utility. *Econometrica*, 24 (1956), 264–75.
Decision making: An experimental approach. Stanford and London, 1957.

Day, John Patrick

Inductive probability. London, 1961.

De Finetti, Bruno

Sur la condition d'équivalence partielle. In: *Colloque consacré à la théorie des probabilités* (Genève, 1937). (Part VI, 5–18.) (Act. Scient. 740.) Paris, 1938.

Sull'impostazione assiomatica del calcolo delle probabilità. *Annali Triestini*, Ser. 2, 19 (1949), 29–81.

Sulla preferibilità. *Giorn. degli economisti*, 11 (1952). Padova, 1952.

Expérience et théorie dans l'élaboration et dans l'application d'une doctrine scientifique. (Troisièmes Entretiens de Zürich, 1951.) *Revue de Métaphys.*, 60 (1955), 264–86.

Foundations of probability. In: Klibansky (ed.) *Philosophy in the mid-century*, Vol. I: Logic. Firenze, 1958.

La probabilità e la statistica nei rapporti con l'induzione, secondo i diversi punti da vista. In: *Induzione e statistica.* Istituto Matematico dell'Università. Roma, 1959.

Feigl, Herbert

Scientific method without metaphysical presuppositions. *Phil. Studies*, 5 (1954), 17–29.

Feigl, Herbert, and **Maxwell, Grover**

Current issues in the philosophy of science. New York, 1961.

Feller, William

An introduction to probability theory and its applications. 2d ed. New York and London, 1957.

Fisher, R. A.

Contributions to mathematical statistics. New York and London, 1950.

Statistical methods and scientific inference. New York and London, 1956.

Good, I. J.

Probability and the weighing of evidence. New York and London, 1950.

Rational decisions. *J. Roy. Stat. Soc.*, Ser. B, 14 (1952), 107–14.

Kinds of probability. *Science*, 129 (1959), 443–46.

Goodman, Nelson

Fact, fiction, and forecast. Cambridge, Mass., 1955.

Harrod, Roy

Foundations of inductive logic. New York and London, 1956.

Hempel, Carl G.

Inductive inconsistencies. *Synthese*, 12 (1960), 439–69.

Hermes, Hans

Über eine logische Begründung der Wahrscheinlichkeitstheorie. *Math.-Phys. Semesterberichte*, 5 (1957), 214–24.

Zum Einfachheitsprinzip in der Wahrscheinlichkeitsrechnung. *Dialectica*, 12 (1958), 317–31.

Jeffrey, Richard C.

Contributions to the theory of inductive probability. Ph.D. thesis, Princeton, 1957. (Typescript.)

Valuation and acceptance of scientific hypotheses. *Phil. Sc.*, 23 (1956), 237–46.

Jeffreys, Harold

Theory of probability. 2d ed. Oxford, 1948.

The present position in probability theory. *Brit. J. Phil. Sc.*, 5 (1955), 275–89.

Scientific inference. 2d ed. Cambridge and New York, 1957.

Kappos, Demetrios A.

Strukturtheorie der Wahrscheinlichkeitsfelder und -Räume. Berlin, 1960.

Kemeny, John G.

Carnap on probability (review of Carnap [Prob.]). *Rev. of Metaphys.*, 5 (1951), 145–56.

Extension of the methods of inductive logic. *Phil. Studies*, 3 (1952), 38–42.

A contribution to inductive logic. *Phil. Phen. Res.*, 13 (1953), 371–74.

The use of simplicity in induction. *Phil. Rev.*, 62 (1953), 391–408.

A logical measure function. *J.S.L.*, 18 (1953), 289–308.

Fair bets and inductive probabilities. *Ibid.*, 20 (1955), 263–73.

A philosopher looks at science. Princeton and London, 1959. (Chap. 4: Probability; chap. 6: Credibility and induction.)

Carnap's theory of probability and induction. To appear in: Schilpp.

Kemeny, John G., Mirkil, H., Snell, J. L., and **Thompson, G. L.**

Finite mathematical structures. Englewood Cliffs, N.J., 1959. (Chap. 3: Probability theory; Chap. 7: Continuous probability theory.)

Kemeny, John G., and **Oppenheim, Paul**

Degree of factual support. *Phil. Sc.*, 19 (1952), 307–24.

Kolmogoroff, A. N.

Foundations of the theory of probability. 2d ed. New York, 1956.

Kyburg, Henry E.

The justification of induction. *J. Phil.*, 53 (1956), 394–400.

Probability and the logic of rational belief. Middletown, Conn., 1961.

Laplace, P. S.

A philosophical essay on probabilities. New York, 1951.

Leblanc, Hugues

Statistical and inductive probabilities. (Forthcoming.)

Lehman, R. Sherman

On confirmation and rational betting. *J.S.L.*, 20 (1955), 251–262.

Lehmann, Erich L.

Testing statistical hypotheses. New York, 1959.

Lenz, J. W.

Carnap on defining "degree of confirmation." *Phil. Sc.*, 23 (1956), 230–35.

Lindley, Dennis V.

Statistical inference. *J. Roy. Stat. Soc.*, Ser. B, 15 (1953), 30–76.

Loève, M.

Probability theory. 2d ed. Princeton, N.J., 1960.

Madden, E. H. (ed.)

The structure of scientific thought. Boston, 1960. (Chap. 5: Probability; chap. 6: Induction.)

Mehlberg, Josephine J.

Is a unitary approach to foundations of probability possible? In: Feigl and Maxwell (eds.), *Current issues in the philosophy of science*, pp. 287–301. New York, 1961.

Mises, Richard V.

Probability, statistics, and truth. 2d rev. ed. New York, 1957.

Nagel, Ernest

Carnap's theory of induction. To appear in: Schilpp.

Neyman, Jerzy
Lectures and conferences on mathematical statistics and probability. 2d rev. ed. Washington, D.C., 1952.
The problem of inductive inference. *Communications on Pure and Applied Math.*, 8 (1955), 13–45.
"Inductive behavior" as a basic concept of philosophy of science. *Rev. of Int. Statist. Inst.*, 25 (1957), 7–22.

Parzen, Emanuel
Modern probability theory and its applications. New York, 1960.

Popper, Karl
Two autonomous axiom systems for the calculus of probabilities. *Brit. J. Phil. Sc.*, 6 (1955), 51–57.
Probability magic or knowledge out of ignorance. *Dialectica*, 11 (1957), 354–74.
The propensity interpretation of probability. *Brit. J. Phil. Sc.*, 10 (1959), 25–42.
[Logic] *The logic of scientific discovery*. (Translation of [Logik], 1953.) London and New York, 1959.
The demarcation between science and metaphysics. To appear in: Schilpp.

Putnam, Hilary
"Degree of confirmation" and inductive logic. To appear in: Schilpp.

Raiffa, Howard, and **Schlaifer, Robert**
Applied statistical decision theory. Cambridge, Mass., 1961.

Rényi, Alfréd
On a new axiomatic theory of probability. *Acta Math. Acad. Scient. Hungaricae.*, 6 (1955), 285–335.

Richter, Hans
Wahrscheinlichkeitstheorie. Berlin, 1956.

Salmon, W. C.
Regular rules of induction. *Phil. Rev.*, 65 (1956), 385–88.
Should we attempt to justify induction? *Phil. Studies*, 8 (1957), 33–48.
Vindication of induction. In: Feigl and Maxwell (eds.), *Current issues in the philosophy of science*, pp. 245–56. New York, 1961.

Savage, Leonard J.
The foundations of statistics. New York, 1954.
Subjective probability and statistical practice. Chicago, 1959.
Bayesian statistics. (Forthcoming.)

Schilpp, Paul A. (ed.)
The philosophy of Rudolf Carnap. (The Library of Living Philosophers.) La Salle, Ill. (Forthcoming.)

Schlaifer, Robert
Probability and statistics for business decisions. New York, 1959.

Schrödinger, Erwin
The foundation of the theory of probability. *Proc. Roy. Irish Acad.*, 51A (1947), 51-66, 141–46.

Shimony, Abner
Coherence and the axioms of confirmation. *J.S.L.*, 20 (1955), 1–28.

Stegmüller, Wolfgang
Bemerkungen zum Wahrscheinlichkeitsproblem. *Studium Generale*, 6 (1953), 563-93.
(See also Carnap and Stegmüller.)

Vietoris, L.
Häufigkeit und Wahrscheinlichkeit. *Studium Generale*, 9 (1956), 86-96.

Wald, Abraham
Statistical decision functions. New York, 1950.
Selected papers in statistics and probability. New York, 1955.

Watanabe, Satosi
Inference and information. (Chap. iv: Inductive inference.) (Forthcoming.)

Wright, G. H. von
A treatise on induction and probability. London, 1951.
Carnap's theory of probability. *Phil. Rev.*, 60 (1951), 362-74.
The logical problem of induction. 2d rev. ed. Oxford, 1957.

INDEX

[The numbers refer to pages. The most important references are indicated by boldface type. Starred terms (*) are explained in the Glossary (pp. 578 ff.).]

D

E